Jane's
URBAN TRANSPORT SYSTEMS

Edited by Tony Pattison
Cartography by Roger Carvell

Eighteenth Edition
1999-2000

Bookmark Jane's homepage on
http://www.janes.com

Jane's award-winning web site provides you with continuously updated news and information.
As well as extracts from our world renowned magazines, you can browse the online catalogue,
visit the Press Centre, discover the origins of Jane's, use the extensive glossary,
download our screen saver and much more.

Jane's now offers powerful electronic solutions to meet the rapid changes in your
information requirements. All our data, analysis and imagery is available on CD-ROM
or via a new secure web service – Jane's Online at www.janesonline.com.

Tailored electronic delivery can be provided through Jane's Data Services.
Contact an information consultant at any of our international offices,
find out how Jane's can change the way you work or e-mail us at

info.janes.co.uk *or* **info@janes.com**

ISBN 0 7106 1921 9
"Jane's" is a registered trade mark

Copyright © 1999 by Jane's Information Group Limited, Sentinel House, 163 Brighton Road, Coulsdon, Surrey CR5 2YH, UK

In the USA and its dependencies
Jane's Information Group Inc, 1340 Braddock Place, Suite 300, Alexandria, Virginia 22314-1651, USA

DPA
DIRECTORY & DATABASE
PUBLISHERS ASSOCIATION
MEMBER

British Library Cataloguing-in-Publication Data.
A catalogue record for this book is available from the British Library.

Printed and bound in Great Britain by Butler and Tanner Limited, Frome and London

SIEMENS

Ready to go!
Whatever leaves our test center
can deliver full performance
right from the start.

The challenge: How to use railway technology to full advantage and gain the edge on competitive modes of transportation – without having to compromise when it comes to trying and testing the reliability of new rail-based systems.

Our answer: Establish a new dimension in "tried and tested" railway products. Where rolling stock, components and entire systems undergo extreme trial operation and endurance testing at our Wegberg-Wildenrath Test Center until they attain production maturity. More quickly. More rigorously. More efficiently. Realistic conditions at the world's most modern test site allow us to develop and test innovative, economical railway equipment that offers full performance right from the start.

Proven design for low life cycle costs: This intensive testing guarantees mature products with high availability and low life cycle costs – from the leading supplier of railway systems.

The class 152 locomotive was put through its paces at our Wegberg-Wildenrath Test Center.

M o b i l i t y for a moving world.
Siemens Transportation Systems

Siemens AG, Transportation Systems Group,
Internet: www.siemens.de/vt

A19100–V700–Z555–X–7600 PUBLICIS MCD

Contents

ADMINISTRATION

Publisher, Law Enforcement and Transport: *Fabiana Angelini*
Managing Editor: *Mary Webb*
Database Manager/Data Administrator: *Ruth Simmance*
Editorial: *Janet Appleyard*
Diana Barrick

EDITORIAL OFFICE

Jane's Information Group Limited, Sentinel House, 163 Brighton Road,
Coulsdon, Surrey CR5 2YH, UK
Tel: (+44 181) 700 37 00 Fax: (+44 181) 700 37 88
Telex: 916907 Janes G
e-mail: juts@janes.co.uk

SALES OFFICES

Send UK/ROW enquiries to: *Karine Bach – Sales and Marketing Manager*
Jane's Information Group Limited, UK address as Editorial Office
Tel: (+44 181) 700 37 67 Fax: (+44 181) 700 37 15

Send USA enquiries to: *Robert Loughman – Vice-President Product Sales*
Jane's Information Group Inc, 1340 Braddock Place, Suite 300,
Alexandria, Virginia 22314-1651, USA
Tel: (+1 703) 683 37 00 Fax: (+1 703) 836 00 29 Telex: 6819193

Send Asia enquiries to: *David Fisher*
Jane's Information Group Asia, 60 Albert Street, #15-01 Albert Complex,
Singapore 189969
Tel: (+65) 336 64 11 Fax: (+65) 336 99 21

Send Australia/New Zealand enquiries to: *Pauline Roberts*
Jane's Information Group Australia, PO Box 3502, Rozelle, New South
Wales 2039, Australia
Tel: (+612) 85 87 79 00 Fax: (+612) 85 87 79 01

ADVERTISEMENT SALES OFFICES

Robert Sitch: Advertisement Sales Executive
Jane's Information Group, Sentinel House, 163 Brighton Road, Coulsdon,
Surrey CR5 2YH, UK
Tel: (+44 181) 700 37 41 Fax: (+44 181) 700 37 26
e-mail: robert.sitch@janes.co.uk

Annabel Chisholm: Senior Advertisement Sales Executive
Jane's Information Group, Sentinel House, 163 Brighton Road, Coulsdon,
Surrey CR5 2YH, UK
Tel: (+44 181) 700 39 09 Fax: (+44 181) 700 37 26
e-mail: annabel.chisholm@janes.co.uk

Australia: *Robert Sitch*

Austria: *Robert Sitch*

Benelux: *Robert Sitch*

Brazil: *Kristin Schulze*

China: *Robert Sitch*

CIS: *Robert Sitch*

Eastern Europe: *Robert Sitch*

Far East: *Robert Sitch*

France: *Robert Sitch*

Germany: *Robert Sitch*

Indian Subcontinent: *Robert Sitch*

Ireland: *Robert Sitch*

Israel: *Oreet Ben-Yaacov*
Oreet International Media, 15 Kinneret Street, IL-51201 Bene Berak
Tel: (+972 3) 570 65 27 Fax: (+972 3) 570 65 26
e-mail: oreet@netvision.net.il

Italy and Switzerland: Ediconsult Internazionale Srl
Piazza Fontane Marose 3, I-16123 Genova, Italy
Tel: (+39 010) 58 36 84 Fax: (+39 010) 56 65 78
e-mail: ediconsult@iol.it

Korea, South: *Young Seoh Chinn*
JES Media International, 2nd Floor ANA Building, 257 1, Myungil-dong,
Kangdong gu, Seoul 134-070, Korea
Tel: (+82 2) 481 34 11 Fax: (+82 2) 481 34 14
e-mail: jesmedia@unitel.co.kr

Middle East: *Robert Sitch*

New Zealand: *Robert Sitch*

Pakistan: *Robert Sitch*

Poland: *Robert Sitch*

Scandinavia: *Gillian Thompson*
The Falsten Partnership, 11 Chardmore Road, Stamford Hill,
London N16 6JA, UK
Tel: (+44 181) 806 23 01 Fax: (+ 44 181) 806 81 37
e-mail: falsten@dial.pipex.com

South Africa: *Robert Sitch*

Spain: *Michael Andrade*
Via Exclusivas SL, Viriato, 69 S-C, E-28010 Madrid
Tel: (+34 91) 448 76 22 Fax: (+34 91) 446 02 14
e-mail: via@varenga.com

Turkey: *Robert Sitch*

UK and ROW: *Robert Sitch*

USA, Mid Atlantic and Midwest; New England and Canada:
Ronald R Lichtinger – US Advertising Sales Director
Jane's Information Group Inc, 1340 Braddock Place, Suite 300,
Alexandria, Virginia 22314-1651, USA
Tel: (+1 703) 683 37 00 Fax: (+1 703) 836 55 37
e-mail: lichtinger@janes.com

Southern USA: *Kristin Schulze*
Jane's Information Group, 5370 East Bay Drive, Suite 104, Clearwater,
Florida 33764, USA
Tel: (+1 727) 524 77 41 Fax: (+1 727) 524 75 62
e-mail: kristin@intnet.net

Western USA and Canada: *Richard Ayer*
127 Avenida del Mar, Suite 2A, San Clemente, California 92672, USA
Tel: (+1 949) 366 84 55 Fax: (+1 949) 366 92 89
e-mail: ayercomm@earthlink.net

Administration:
USA and Canada: *Maureen Nute – Advertising Production Manager*
Jane's Information Group Inc, 1340 Braddock Place, Suite 300,
Alexandria, Virginia 22314-1651, USA
Tel: (+1 703) 683 37 00 Fax: (+1 703) 836 00 29
e-mail: nute@janes.com

UK and Rest of World: *Chris French*
Jane's Information Group Limited, Sentinel House, 163 Brighton Road,
Coulsdon, Surrey CR5 2YH, UK
Tel: (+44 181) 700 37 42 Fax: (+44 181) 700 38 59
e-mail: christopher.french@janes.co.uk

accessibility

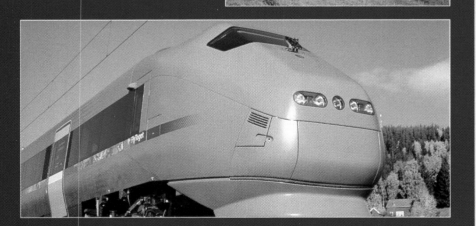
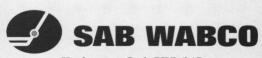

Users' Charter

This publication is brought to you by Jane's Information Group, a global company with more than 100 years of innovation and an unrivalled reputation for impartiality, accuracy and authority.

Our collection and output of information and images is not dictated by any political or commercial affiliation. Our reportage is undertaken without fear of, or favour from, any government, alliance, state or corporation.

We publish information that is collected overtly from unclassified sources, although much could be regarded as extremely sensitive or not publicly accessible.

Our validation and analysis aims to eradicate misinformation or disinformation as well as factual errors; our objective is always to produce the most accurate and authoritative data.

In the event of any significant inaccuracies, we undertake to draw these to the readers' attention to preserve the highly valued relationship of trust and credibility with our customers worldwide.

If you believe that these policies have been breached by this title, you are invited to contact the editor.

A copy of Jane's Information Group's Code of Conduct for its editorial teams is available from the publisher.

INVESTOR IN PEOPLE

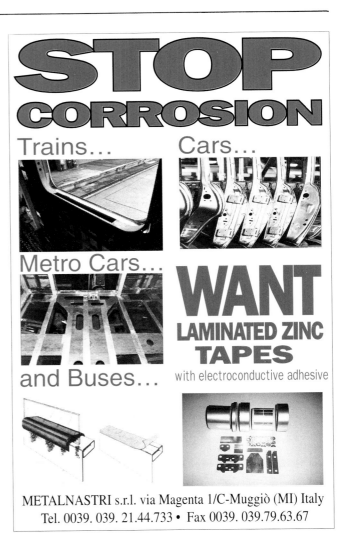

Alphabetical list of advertisers

Hong Kong's Tuen Mun light rail network serves the new town of Tuen Mun. It was opened in 1988 and is 31.8 km long with 28 km on reserved track. Seen here is one of the new Goninan LRVs on the network (T V Runnacles)

WE'RE

Now that may sound strange coming from a company in the mass transportation industry. After all, we've built our reputation on reliable products that move people efficiently. But here's the point. When we build or overhaul public transportation equipment, you can bet we'll be there to service it.

NOT

We've been in business for 45 years, and we plan on being around for a very long time to come. What's more, we are a U.S.-owned company with fabrication, overhaul and maintenance experience unmatched by other domestic companies in this industry. And our ISO-9001 Certification

GOING

demonstrates our commitment to quality and consistency. Find out more about how we serve the public transportation industry with expertise that can take you into the new millennium.

AAI
CORPORATION
A Subsidiary Of United Industrial Corporation
An ISO 9001–Certified Company

Call Jackson R. Bell at 410-683-6385. He'll be there.

ANYWHERE.

Foreword

One of the themes that runs through a great deal of public transport planning at present is 'getting more out of less'. Or, put another way, how to get more efficient use of the infrastructure and facilities we have, without having to create something entirely new.

More for less

In May 1998, former European Commissioner, Neil Kinnock referred to this more for less theory in Brussels at the retirement party for Dr Pierre Laconte as UITP Secretary General, and Robert Coleman, Director of the EC's Transport Directorate General VII, told the Chartered Institute of Transport in London in November that the emphasis was moving towards achieving improvements at less cost in the shorter term. This shift of emphasis away from large infrastructure is influenced by many factors: tightness of money supply, scepticism of lending authorities, the financial problems experienced with projects as diverse as the Los Angeles Metro and Sheffield Supertram, and the fragility of national economies which would rely heavily on imported equipment.

But some of the 'more for less' movement has been driven by the experience of major airports, which in many developed countries have faced environmental opposition to the expansion they need to cope with increasing passenger numbers. Amsterdam—Schiphol's proposal to create a new airport on an artificial island in the sea, London—Heathrow's long-running battle to get approval for its Terminal 5, and Hong Kong—Chek Lap Kok on reclaimed land are all examples of this pressure. Airports and airlines have therefore worked to improve efficiency to such effect that passengers handled have increased in some cases at twice the rate of air transport movements.

One result of this is that not only have airports increasingly looked to public transport to provide their ground links, but they themselves have become public transport nodes in their own right. And paradoxically airport links are likely to be one aspect of public transport which will continue to find a ready supply of capital, with the airport operators themselves as major contributors.

All this highlights the distinction, not always clearly understood, between public transport funding that is aimed simply at facilitating the movement of the masses, and that which is aimed at containing or reducing growth of car use by offering an attractive alternative. Policies adopted in Belgium, Brazil, Greece, Singapore and the United Kingdom are likely to reflect the differing levels of car ownership in those countries as well as the availability of land for expanded infrastructure.

But, wherever the driving force for investment comes from, there is a need to move car drivers on to public transport, but experience so far has in general shown that only rail-based solutions will be seen as sufficiently attractive. For the car driver, the bus often still has an unacceptably down-market image.

The UK 1999 Lex Report on Motoring says that 75 per cent of motorists who travel to work in their cars would still not use public transport even if fares were halved. Even if the frequency were improved 67 per cent said that they would still not use it. But in the report is the revelation that 43 per cent would use their cars less if public transport were improved.

An interesting point highlighted by the report is a lack of knowledge and problems with accessing information about public transport. This is of growing importance because of whole generations that have never used public transport.

It does not take a public transport expert to point out that, worldwide, motorists are wedded to their cars. The Lex Report says that doubling petrol prices would force 50 per cent of motorists to use their car less and a road tax of £500 a year would, according to the report, still make no difference to 41 per cent of motorists though 39 per cent said that they would give up owning a car.

Bus or rail light rapid transit systems

The rail solution, by very virtue of its infrastructure, offers a sense of permanence which suggests a high level of service.

To avoid the high cost of this infrastructure, various bus-based solutions continue to be offered. The bus has the advantage of low first cost, itself only possible because many major components are derived from truck manufacture with a market ten times that of buses. Systems with electronic or mechanical guidance, electric or other non-pollutant fuels have been tried or demonstrated in many places and with some success, though it is not easy to determine whether these are simply expanding the existing public transport user market or having any real effect in creating a modal shift from car use. An interesting figure has been quoted from experience gained in Plymouth by Citybus Managing Director Brian Fisher, who reports that introduction of accessible buses increases usage by around five per cent.

In terms of passenger movement, the bus systems developed in South American cities including São Paulo and Curitiba, Brazil, and Quito, Ecuador, have been some of the most notable, with articulated buses, busways and high-platform stations, giving a capacity comparable with light rail. In Europe and Australia busways (guided or non-guided) are gaining ground using medium-floor or low-floor buses, and, together with bus lanes and selective detection at traffic lights, are seen as a cheaper alternative to light rail.

The other main development to make buses more attractive and available to more people is the move to low floors. Now virtually unstoppable in Europe, this development is still viewed with unease

More for less — this newly introduced low-floor double-deck bus built by Plaxton Wigan, UK, on Volvo B7L chassis, carries around 80 seated and can take wheelchairs and buggies
***1999**/0043961*

in North America, with concerns being voiced about high levels of maintenance needing larger fleets, and added costs brought about by relocation of components from on-chassis positions. History is repeating itself here; twenty years ago United States engineers thought that watchmaker skills would be needed to cope with articulated vehicles and were surprised to find that they were maintained in quite conventional workshops in Germany and France.

One problem which can arise from rapid introduction of low-floor buses is that cascading of older vehicles becomes difficult. Renewals of franchises in London specifying low-floor buses, many of them double-deck, will render large numbers of relatively new high-floor vehicles difficult to sell, and so reduce their second-hand value. One advantage of low-floor vehicles is that they offer the potential of faster boarding times, which in turn can reduce dwell times at stops and, by speeding up the service, can enable more efficient use to be made of vehicles.

Changes in fare collection

A lot of this depends on the speed of fare collection. Contactless smartcards, now being tried or introduced in cities across the world, could offer a serious way forward, and the cost of introduction can be met over two or three years through savings and improved efficiency. This is being demonstrated by the London Transport (LT) Prestige project, where a consortium of suppliers is to provide an integrated smartcard ticketing system from August 2002 on buses, trams, light rail, underground and suburban railways. LT will make no capital contribution and the risk and a share of the profits will go to the consortium.

Smartcard ticketing also offers potential savings where public authorities fund concessions on the basis of estimates of journeys generated. With smartcard systems, precise number of those travelling can be determined and payments made on that basis. One area, however, which remains in debate is the security systems attached to new-generation ticketing. Electronic recognition of facial characteristics, fingerprints, voices and the pattern of the iris of the eye are all now possible. There is also an electronic pen which measures movements of the hand in making a signature. It remains to be seen which, if any, of these systems will have the speed and stamina to cope with public transport applications of high throughput, dust and vibration.

As the 1990s draw to their close it is pleasing to see that authorities and public transport operators are taking note not only of the developments of the past decade, but also of the mistakes. The headlong scramble to divide large public enterprises into profit centres has slowed down, and the 'Rail Summit' called in Britain in March by Deputy Prime Minister John Prescott serves as a warning to the various operating, infrastructure and leasing units that they have an overriding purpose to serve the public.

At the same time, urban road pricing seems set to become a serious option sooner rather than later in many parts of the world, ensuring that the road user pays something approximating to the real cost of a vehicle's journey. Moves to devote the proceeds of road pricing to improvements in public transport must be welcomed, but there is always a lurking danger that road pricing could instead be used to lay a tax on public transport by bus. Current plans in New Zealand to farm out the national road system to contractors, rather like eighteenth century turnpikes in Britain, will need to be watched with care.

Acknowledgements

My particular thanks go to Chris Bushell, Ken Harris and Ian Yearsley for invaluable support, help and advice. I would also like to express my gratitude to those involved with production of *Jane's Urban Transport Systems* at the Transport Division of *Jane's Information Group* and in particular to my Managing Editor Mary Webb, Copy Editor Diana Barrick and Typesetter Melanie Rovery. Diana has put in much effort to enhance the quality of *Jane's Urban Transport Systems*. I would like to thank Karine Bach, Suzanne Brockwell and Robert Stich for the help I have received from them in identifying manufacturers, discovering new products and collecting information for the book. Keith Faulkner and Belinda Cunningham have also put in major efforts to streamline the information flow for *Jane's Urban Transport Systems* and I have much appreciated their help with this edition. I would also like to thank John Sulman for his work on the index and Janet Appleyard and Ruth Simmance for their forebearance and help with flow of copy.

I am very grateful, too, to all the following for pictures and contributions:
Wilhelm Pflug (Germany and other sections), K K Gupta (India), Aare Olander (Russia and elsewhere), Andy Phipps (Japan), Mike Davis (Hong Kong, Guangzhou and other sections), Julian Wolinsky and Van Wilkins (USA), Doug Jack, Transport Resources International (Buses section), Andrew Jarosz (UK cities, photos throughout the book), Stephen Morris, Alan Yearsley (Consultants) and Tim Runnacles (Hong Kong and Almaty), Norman Griffiths (German tram operators), Mike Taplin (World List of LRT and Metro operators) and many others who prefer to remain anonymous.

I would also like to thank Roger Carvell who drew and amended the maps with great expertise.

Photo credits are due to John Bamforth, Roger Carvell, Bill Godwin, Norman and Su Griffiths, K K Gupta, Andrew Jarosz, Bill Luke, Steve Morgan, Itsuhiro Mori, Yozura Morimura, Peter Newman, Aare Olander, Andrew Phipps, D Trevor-Rowe, Marcel Vleugels, Milan Šrámek, Van Wilkins, Gordon Wiseman and Julian Wolinsky.

Tony Pattison
London, April 1999

Information Services & Solutions

for military, government and commercial organisations worldwide, in the fields of defence, geopolitics, transportation and law enforcement.

We are dedicated to providing the information our customers need, to the formats and frequency they require. Read on to find out how Jane's information in electronic format can provide you with the best way to access the information you require.

Jane's Online

Instant access to all of Jane's information and analysis via the Internet

Created for the professional seeking specific detailed information, this user-friendly service can be customised to suit your ever-changing information needs. Search across any combination of titles to retrieve the information you need quickly and easily. You set the query — Jane's Online finds the answer!

Key benefits of Jane's Online include:
- frequent updates
- you create your own custom library
- saves time — research can be carried out quickly and easily
- archives enable you to compare how specifics have changed over time
- accurate analysis at your fingertips
- site licences available
- user-friendly interface
- high-quality images linked to text

Check out this site today: www.janesonline.com

Jane's CD-ROM Libraries

Fast, accurate searching of Jane's databases

Choose from nine powerful CD-ROM libraries for quick and easy access to the defence, geopolitical, space, transportation and law enforcement information you need. Take full advantage of the information groupings and purchase the entire library.

Libraries available:
Jane's Air Systems Library
Jane's Defence Equipment Library
Jane's Defence Magazines Library
Jane's Geopolitical Library
Jane's Land and Systems Library
Jane's Market Intelligence Library
Jane's Police and Security Library
Jane's Sea and Systems Library
Jane's Transport Library

Key benefits of Jane's CD-ROM include:
- quick and easy access to Jane's information and graphics
- easy-to-use Windows interface with powerful search capabilities
- online glossary and synonym searching
- search across all the titles on each disc, even if you do not subscribe to them, to determine whether you would like to add them to your library
- export and print out text or graphics
- quarterly updates
- full networking capability
- supported by an experienced technical team

Jane's Data Services

Get Jane's information working for your entire organisation

Jane's Data Services brings together more than 200 sources of near-real time and technical reference information serving defence, intelligence, space, transportation and law enforcement professionals. By making Jane's data (HTML) and images (JPEG)

available for integration behind Intranet environments or closed networks, this unique service offers you a way to receive information that is updated frequently and works in tune with your organisation.
We can also offer a complete management service where Jane's hosts the information and server for you.

Jane's EIS

Jane's Electronic Information System (EIS)

This is a unique research tool developed to satisfy the technology requirements of many defence and military intelligence users. Jane's EIS is available in a convenient CD-ROM format that operates across a broad range of UNIX™ and Windows NT™ platforms (it will not work in Intranet).

Jane's EIS gives you immediate access to most Jane's defence, aerospace and geopolitical information. Please contact us if you would like more information about this service.

Jane's Consultancy

Whether it is research on your competitors' markets, in-depth analysis or customised content that you require, Jane's Consultancy can offer you a tailored, highly confidential personal service to help you achieve your objectives. However large or small your requirement, contact us in confidence for a free proposal and quotation.

Jane's Consultancy will bring you a variety of benefits:
- expert personnel in a wide variety of disciplines
- a global and well-established information network
- total confidentiality
- objective analysis
- Jane's reputation for accuracy, authority and impartiality

Receive only the information you require, delivered in a format to suit your needs.

URBAN TRANSPORT SYSTEMS

Statistical data in this section has been collected in co-operation with the International Union of Public Transport (UITP)
* Metro in operation † Metro under construction or in design

ALBANIA
Tirana 354

ALGERIA
Alger † 13

ARGENTINA
Buenos Aires * 65
Cordobá 88
Mendoza 219
Rosario 300
Tucumán 363

ARMENIA
Erevan * 106

AUSTRALIA
Adelaide 11
Brisbane 57
Canberra 72
Hobart 138
Melbourne 217
Perth 275
Sydney 344

AUSTRIA
Graz 120
Linz 182
Vienna * 373

AZERBAIJAN
Baku * 26

BANGLADESH
Dhaka 97

BELARUS
Minsk 227

BELGIUM
Antwerp 19
Brussels * 60
Charleroi 76
Ghent 115
Liège 180

BOLIVIA
La Paz 173

BRAZIL
Belo Horizonte * 38
Brasilia * 54
Curitiba 89
Fortaleza 108
Porto Alegre * 283
Recife * 290
Rio de Janeiro * 295
Salvador 305
Santos 316
São Paulo * 317

BULGARIA
Sofia * 332

CAMBODIA
Phnom Penh 278

CANADA
Calgary 71
Edmonton 105
Halifax 126
Hamilton 130
Mississauga 228
Montreal * 231
Ottawa 270
Quebec 289
Toronto * 360
Vancouver * 370
Winnipeg 381

CHILE
Santiago de Chile * 315
Valparaíso 369

CHINA, PEOPLE'S REPUBLIC
Anshan 18
Beijing * 34
Changchun 75
Chengdu 78
Chongqing 81
Dalian 91
Fushun 113
Guangzhou * 123
Hangzhou 130
Harbin 133
Hohhot 139
Hong Kong * 139
Jilin 152
Kunming 170
Nanjing 240
Shanghai * 326
Shenyang 329
Taiyuan 347
Tangshan 349
Tianjin * 352
Wuhan 382
Xi'an 383

COLOMBIA
Bogota 49
Medellín * 216

CONGO, DEMOCRATIC REPUBLIC
Kinshasa 163

COTE D'IVOIRE
Abidjan 9

CROATIA
Zagreb 386

CUBA
Havana 134

CYPRUS
Nicosia 254

CZECH REPUBLIC
Brno 60
Ostrava 270
Prague * 285

DENMARK
Aarhus 8
Copenhagen 87

ECUADOR
Quito 289

EGYPT
Alexandria † 12
Cairo * 68

ESTONIA
Tallinn 347

ETHIOPIA
Addis Ababa 10

FINLAND
Helsinki * 134

FRANCE
Bordeaux 52
Grenoble 120
Lille-Roubaix-Tourcoing * 180
Lyons * 202
Marseille * 215
Nancy 240

Nantes 241
Nice 254
Paris * 272
Rennes 291
Rouen 302
St Etienne 334
Strasbourg 341
Toulouse * 362

GEORGIA
Tbilisi 350

GERMANY
Aachen 8
Augsburg 24
Berlin * 39
Bielefeld 44
Bochum-Gelsenkirchen 48
Bonn 51
Bremen 56
Chemnitz 77
Cologne * 84
Dortmund 98
Dresden 99
Duisburg 101
Düsseldorf 103
Essen 106
Frankfurt am Main * 109
Halle 126
Hamburg * 127
Hannover 131
Karlsruhe 156
Krefeld 167
Leipzig 178
Magdeburg 206
Mannheim-Ludwigshafen 213
Mönchengladbach 228
Munich * 234
Nuremburg * 258
Rhein-Ruhr * 292
Stuttgart 342
Wuppertal 382

GHANA
Accra 10

GREECE
Athens * 21

HUNGARY
Budapest * 63

ICELAND
Reykjavik 292

INDIA
Ahmedabad 12
Bangalore 29
Bombay (Mumbai) 50
Calcutta * 69
Coimbatore 84
Delhi † 94
Hyderabad/Secunderabad 147
Jaipur 151
Kanpur 154
Lucknow 200
Madras (Chennai) † 203
Nagpur 239
Poona 280
Srinagar 334
Trivandrum 363

INDONESIA
Bandung 28
Jakarta 151
Semarang 323
Surabaya 343
Ujung Pandang 367

WORLD URBAN TRAM AND LIGHT RAIL SYSTEMS

(excluding museum, rural and purely interurban lines)

Some 350 light rail and tramway systems are operating in cities and towns worldwide, some serving urban areas too small to be covered in the following pages. Below is a comprehensive list of all urban LRT and tramway systems. We are indebted to *Tramways & Urban Transit* magazine and the Light Rail Transit Association for compilation of this list.

* indicates a system built new since 1978
† indicates a system extending or extended (including tunnel construction) recently
§ indicates operations suspended
(T) indicates a heritage tramway operated primarily for tourist purposes
(2) indicates two (or more) separate operations

Systems in italics are steel-wheeled, automated, fully segregated lines.

ARGENTINA
Buenos Aires*(2)
Mar del Plata (T)

ARMENIA
Yerevan

AUSTRALIA
Adelaide
Bendigo (T)
Melbourne†
Sydney*†

AUSTRIA
Gmunden†
Graz†
Innsbruck
Linz†
Vienna†

AZERBAIJAN
Baku
Sumgait

BELARUS
Minsk
Mosyr*
Novopolotsk*
Vitebsk

BELGIUM
Antwerp†
Brussels†
Charleroi†
Ghent†
Ostend

BOSNIA
Sarajevo

BRAZIL
Campos do Jordão
Rio de Janeiro* (also T)

BULGARIA
Sofia†

CANADA
Calgary*†
Edmonton*
Nelson (T)
Toronto†(2)
Vancouver†

CHINA
Anshan
Changchun
Dalian
Hong Kong*(2)

CROATIA
Osijek
Zagreb†

CZECH REPUBLIC
Brno†
Liberec
Most
Olomouc
Ostrava
Plzen†
Prague†

EGYPT
Alexandria
Cairo
Heliopolis
Helwan*

ESTONIA
Tallinn

FINLAND
Helsinki†

FRANCE
Grenoble*†
Lille
Marseille†
Nantes*†
Paris*†(2)
Rouen*†
St Etienne
Strasbourg*†

GEORGIA
Tbilisi

GERMANY
Augsburg†
Bad Schandau
Berlin†
Bielefeld†
Bochum-Gelsenkirchen†
Bonn†
Brandenburg
Braunschweig†
Bremen†
Chemnitz†
Cologne†
Cottbus
Darmstadt†
Dessau†
Dortmund†
Dresden
Düsseldorf†
Duisburg†
Erfurt†

Essen†
Frankfurt/Main†
Frankfurt/Oder
Freiburg/Breisgau†
Gera
Görlitz
Gotha
Halberstadt
Halle†
Hannover†
Heidelberg†
Jena†
Karlsruhe†
Kassel†
Krefeld†
Leipzig†
Ludwigshafen
Magdeburg†
Mainz†
Mannheim†
Mülheim/Ruhr†
Munich†
Naumburg§
Nordhausen
Nuremburg
Oberhausen*†
Plauen
Potsdam†
Rostock†
Saarbrücken*†
Schöneiche
Schwerin
Strausberg†
Stuttgart†
Ulm†
Woltersdorf
Würzburg†
Zwickau

HUNGARY
Budapest†
Debrecen
Miskolc
Szeged

INDIA
Calcutta

ITALY
Genoa*†
Milan†
Naples
Rome†
Trieste
Turin

JAPAN
Enoshima
Fukui
Gifu
Hakodate
Hiroshima
Kagoshima
Kitakyushu
Kochi
Kumamoto
Kyoto
Matsuyama
Nagasaki
Okayama
Osaka
Sapporo
Takaoka
Tokyo
Toyama
Toyohashi

KAZAKHSTAN
Almaty
Oskemen
Pavlodar
Temirtau

KOREA, DEMOCRATIC PEOPLE'S REPUBLIC
Pyongyang*(2)

LATVIA
Daugavpils
Liepaya
Riga

MALAYSIA
*Kuala Lumpur**

MEXICO
Guadalajara*
Mexico City
Monterrey*

NETHERLANDS
Amsterdam†
The Hague†
Rotterdam†
Utrecht*†

NEW ZEALAND
Christchurch*(T)

NORWAY
Oslo†
Trondheim†

PHILIPPINES
Manila*†

POLAND
Bydgoszcz
Czestochowa
Elblag
Gdansk
Gorzow
Grundziadz
Katowice†
Krakow†
Lódź
Poznan†
Szczecin
Torun
Warsaw†
Wrocław

PORTUGAL
Lisbon
Oporto (T)

ROMANIA
Arad
Botoşani*
Braila
Braşov*
Bucharest†
Cluj*
Constanta*
Craiova*
Galati
Iasi
Oradea
Ploiesti*
Reşiţa*
Sibiu
Timişoara†

RUSSIA
Achinsk
Angarsk
Arkhangelsk
Astrakhan
Barnaul
Biysk
Chelyabinsk
Cherepovets
Dzerzhinsk
Grozniy§
Irkutsk
Ivanovo
Izhevsk
Kaliningrad
Kazan
Kemerovo
Kharbarovsk
Kolomna
Komsomolsk-na-Amure
Krasnoarmeisk
Krasnodar
Krasnoturinsk
Krasnoyarsk
Kursk
Lipetsk
Magnitogorsk
Moscow
Naberezhnye Chelny

Nizhnikamsk
Nizhny Novgorod
Nizhniy-Tagil
Noginsk
Novocherkassk
Novokuznetsk
Novosibirsk
Novotroitsk
Omsk
Orel
Orsk
Osinniki
Perm
Prokopyevsk
Pyatigorsk
Rostov-on-Don
Ryazan
Salavat
Samara
Saratov
Shakhty
Smolensk
Stary Oskol*
St Petersburg
Taganrog
Tomsk
Tula
Tver
Ufa
Ulan-Ude
Ulyanovsk
Usolye-Sibirskoye
Ust-Ilimsk*
Ust-Katav
Vladikavkaz
Vladivostok
Volchansk
Volgograd(2)
Volzhskiy
Voronezh
Yaroslavl
Yekaterinburg
Zlatoust

SLOVAKIA
Bratislava
Kosice
Trencianska-Tepla

SPAIN
Barcelona (T)
La Coruna (T)
Soller
Valencia*†

SWEDEN
Gothenburg†
Lidingo
Norrköping
Stockholm† (also T)

SWITZERLAND
Basle
Berne
Bex
Geneva†
Lausanne*
Neuchâtel
Zürich†

TUNISIA
Tunis*†

TURKEY
Ankara*
Antalya*
Istanbul*(2) (also T)
Izmir*†
Konya*†

UKRAINE
Avdiyivka
Dniprodzerzhinsk
Dnipropetrovsk
Donetsk
Druzhkivka
Horlivka
Kharkov
Kiev†
Konotop

Kostyatinivka
Kramatorsk
Kriviy Rih (2*)
Lugansk
Lviv
Makiyivka
Mariupol
Molochne*
Nikolayiv
Odessa
Stakhanov
Vinnitsya
Yenakiyeve
Yevpatoriya
Zaporizhzhya
Zhitomir

UNITED KINGDOM
Birmingham—Wolverhampton
Blackpool

Bristol (T)
Douglas (T)
London†
Manchester*†
Newcastle upon Tyne*†
Sheffield*

UNITED STATES
Baltimore*†
Boston
Buffalo*
Cleveland†
Dallas*† (also T)
Denver*†
Detroit* (also T)
Fort Worth
Galveston (T)
Los Angeles*†
Memphis*(T)†
Miami*

Newark†
New Orleans†
Philadelphia
Pittsburgh†
Portland*†
Sacramento*†
San Diego*†
San Francisco†
San Jose*†
Seattle*(T)
St Louis*†

UZBEKISTAN
Tashkent

YUGOSLAVIA
Belgrade

SYSTEMS UNDER CONSTRUCTION

DENMARK
Copenhagen

FRANCE
Lyons
Montpellier
Orléans

GERMANY
Heilbron

ITALY
Florence
Sassari

PUERTO RICO
San Juan

PORTUGAL
Oporto

TURKEY
Bursa

UNITED KINGDOM
Croydon
Nottingham

UNITED STATES
Jersey City
Salt Lake City
Tampa (T)

VENEZUELA
Valencia

SYSTEMS PLANNED

AUSTRALIA
Brisbane

CANADA
Ottawa
Victoria

CHINA
Guangzhou

COLOMBIA
Cali

FRANCE
Bordeaux
Le Mans
Mulhouse
Toulon
Valenciennes

GERMANY
Aachen
Erlangen
Kiel

GREECE
Thessalonika

IRELAND
Dublin

ISRAEL
Beer Sheva
Jerusalem
Tel Aviv

ITALY
Bergamo
Bologna
Liverno
Padua
Palermo
Pisa
Verona

JORDAN
Amman

LUXEMBOURG
Luxembourg

MEXICO
Tijuana

NETHERLANDS
Gouda-Leiden

NEW ZEALAND
Auckland
Wellington

PAKISTAN
Karachi

SPAIN
Alicante
Barcelona
Bilbao
Donostia/San Sebastian
Madrid
Malaga

SWITZERLAND
Glattal

TURKEY
Adana
Isparta

UNITED KINGDOM
Bristol
Glasgow
Leeds
Llandudno
Maidstone-Medway
Portsmouth-Fareham

UNITED STATES
Cincinnati
Kenosha (T)
Minneapolis
New York
Norfolk
Orlando
Seattle
Trenton-Camden

WORLD URBAN TROLLEYBUS SYSTEMS

Around 300 trolleybus systems are operating in cities and towns worldwide, some serving urban areas too small to be covered in the following pages. Below is a comprehensive list of all urban trolleybus systems known to be operating. We are indebted to *Trolleybus Magazine* and the Trolleybus Museum Company upon whose records we have drawn in the compilation.

* SYSTEM CURRENTLY NOT OPERATING
† SYSTEM CURRENTLY OPERATING EXPERIMENTALLY

ARGENTINA
Córdoba
Mendoza
Rosario ()

ARMENIA
Erevan
Gümri

AUSTRIA
Innsbruck
Kapfenberg
Linz
Salzburg

AZERBAIJAN
Baku
Gyandzha
Mingechaur
Nakhichevan
Sumgait

BELARUS
Bobruisk
Brest-Litovsk
Gomel
Grodno
Minsk
Mogilev
Vitebsk

BELGIUM
Ghent

BOSNIA
Sarajevo

BRAZIL
Araraquara
Merida
Recife
Riberão Preto
Santos
São Paulo (2 systems)

BULGARIA
Burgas
Dobrich
Gabrovo
Kazanluk
Khaskovo
Pazardzhik
Pernik
Pleven
Plovdiv
Ruse
Sliven
Sofia
Stara Zagora
Varna
Veliko Turnovo
Vratsa

CANADA
Edmonton
Vancouver

CHILE
Valparaíso

CHINA, PEOPLE'S REPUBLIC
Anshan
Beijing
Benxi
Changchun
Chongqing
Dalian
Fuzhou

Guangzhou
Hangzhou
Harbin
Jilin
Jinan
Lanzhou
Luoyang
Nanchang
Nanjing
Nanning
Qingdao
Qiqihar
Shanghai
Shenyang
Taiyuan
Wuhan (2 systems)
Xi'an
Zhengzhou

CZECH REPUBLIC
Brno
České Budějovice
Chomutov
Hrádec Králové
Jihlava
Mariánské Lázně
Opava
Ostrava
Pardubice
Plzeň
Teplice
Ústí nad Labem
Zlín

DENMARK
Copenhagen

ECUADOR
Quito

ESTONIA
Tallinn

FRANCE
Grenoble
Limoges
Lyons
Marseille
Nancy
St Etienne

GEORGIA
Batumi
Chiatura
Gori
Kutaisi
Ozurgeti
Rustavi
Samtredia
Sukhumi
Tbilisi

GERMANY
Eberswalde
Essen*
Esslingen
Solingen

GREECE
Athens

HUNGARY
Budapest
Debrecen
Szeged

IRAN
Tehran

ITALY
Ancona
Bologna
Cagliari
Chieti*
Cremona
Genoa
Milan
Modena
Naples
Parma
Rimini
San Remo

KAZAKHSTAN
Akmola
Aqtöbe
Almaty
Karaganda
Kustanai
Petropavlovsk
Shymkent
Zhambyl

KIRGIZIA
Bishek
Naryn
Osh

KOREA, DEMOCRATIC PEOPLE'S REPUBLIC
Chongjin
Hamhung
Kimchek
Nampo
Pyongyang
Sinuiju
Wonsan

LATVIA
Riga

LITHUANIA
Kaunas
Vilnius

MEXICO
Guadalajara
Mexico City

MOLDOVA
Balţi
Bender
Chişinău
Tiraspol

MONGOLIA
Ulaan Baatar

NEPAL
Kathmandu

NETHERLANDS
Arnhem

NEW ZEALAND
Wellington

NORWAY
Bergen

POLAND
Gdynia
Lublin
Słupsk
Tychy

PORTUGAL
Coimbra
Oporto

ROMANIA
Baia Mare
Brăila
Braşov
Bucharest
Cluj
Constanţa
Galaţi
Iaşi
Mediaş
Sibiu
Slatina
Suceava
Targovişte
Timişoara
Vaslui

RUSSIA
Abakan
Almetyevsk
Archangelsk
Armavir
Astrakhan
Balakovo
Barnaul
Belgorod
Berezniki
Blagoveshchensk
Bratsk
Bryansk
Cheboksary
Chelyabinsk
Cherkessk
Chita
Dzerzhinsk
Engels
Grozniy*
Irkutsk
Ivanovo
Izhevsk
Kaliningrad
Kaluga
Kamensk-Uralskiy
Kazan
Kemerovo
Khabarovsk
Khimki
Kirov
Kostroma
Kovrov
Krasnodar
Krasnoyarsk
Kurgan
Kursk
Leninsk-Kuznetskiy
Lipetsk
Maikop
Makhachkala
Miass
Moscow
Murmansk
Nalchik
Nizhny Novgorod
Novgorod
Novocheboksarsk
Novokuybyshevsk
Novokuznetsk
Novorossiysk

Novosibirsk
Omsk
Orel
Orenburg
Penza
Perm
Petrozavodsk
Rostov-on-Don
Rubtsovsk
Ryazan
Rybinsk
Samara
Saransk
Saratov
Shakhty
Smolensk
Stary Oskol
Stavropol
Sterlitamak
St Petersburg
Taganrog
Tambov
Tolyatti
Tomsk
Tula
Tver
Tyumen
Ufa
Ulyanovsk
Vladikavkaz
Vladimir
Vladivostok
Volgodonsk
Volgograd
Vologda
Voronezh
Yaraslavl
Yekaterinburg
Yoshkar-Ola

SLOVAKIA
Banská Bystrica
Bratislava
Košice
Prešov
Žilina

SWITZERLAND
Basle
Berne
Biel
La Chaux-de-Fonds
Fribourg
Geneva
Lausanne
Lugano
Lucerne
Montreux-Vevey
Neuchâtel
Schaffhausen
St Gallen
Winterthur
Zürich

TAJIKISTAN
Dushanbe
Khudzhand

TURKMENISTAN
Ashgabat

UKRAINE
Antratsit
Artyemivsk
Bila Tserkov
Cherkasy
Chernigiv
Chernivtsi
Dnipropetrovsk
Dobropilya
Donetsk
Dzerzhinsk
Horlivka
Ivano-Frankivsk
Kharkov
Khartsyzsk
Kherson
Khmelnitsky
Kiev
Kirovograd
Kramatorsk
Krasnodon
Kremenchuk
Kriviy Rih
Lisichansk
Lugansk
Lutsk
Lviv
Makiyivka
Mariupol
Mikolayiv
Odessa
Poltava
Rivne
Sevastopol
Severodonetsk
Simferopol
Slavyansk
Stakhanov
Sumy
Ternopol
Vinnitsya
Vuglegirsk
Yalta
Zaporizhzhya
Zhitomir

UNITED STATES
Boston
Dayton
Philadelphia
San Francisco
Seattle

UZBEKISTAN
Almalyk
Andijon
Bukhoro
Fargona
Namangan
Nukus
Samarkand
Tashkent

YUGOSLAVIA
Belgrade

SYSTEMS UNDER CONSTRUCTION (*) OR ACTIVE DEVELOPMENT

BULGARIA
Blagoevgrad*
Dimitrovgrad*
Gorna Oryakhovitsa*
Lovech
Shumen*
Vidin*
Yambol*

GEORGIA
Tskhaltubo
Zestafoni

ITALY
Lido di Ostia

KAZAKHSTAN
Semipalatinsk

ROMANIA
Piatra-Neamţ*
Sfintu Gheorghe
Tirgu Jîu*

RUSSIA
Elektrostal
Nizhni Tagil*
Podolsk
Pskov
Serpukhov
Verkhnaya Pishma
Volzhski*
Zagorsk

SLOVAKIA
Nitra
Trencin

UKRAINE
Kamenits-Podolskiy*
Kerch*
Kolomyya*
Krasnyi Luch
Melitopol*

UNITED KINGDOM
Liverpool

UNITED STATES
New York
Oakland

AACHEN

Population: 252,000, region served 555,000
Public transport: Bus services provided by publicly owned transport and electricity company. Fares and services co-ordinated with DB rail services on two lines, regional bus services of Busverkehr Rheinland (BVR), an associated company of German Railway (DB) and other operators within the framework of Aachener Verkehrs Verbund (AVV). Also joint cross-border services run in conjunction with Belgian and Dutch operators

AVV

Aachener Verkehrsverbund GmbH (AVV)
Neuköllner Str 1, 52002 Aachen, Germany
Tel: (+49 241) 96 89 70   Fax: (+49 241) 968 97 20
General Manager: H J Sistenich

Current situation: Regional transit authority co-ordinates the services of six operators: ASEAG, BVR, Kreiswerke Heinsberg, Dürener Kreisbahn, Taeter Aachen and Deutsche Bahn (DB).

Passenger journeys: (1991) 76.5 million
(1992) 79.5 million
(1994) 82.6 million

ASEAG

Aachener Strassenbahn und Energieversorgungs AG
PO Box 500262, 52086 Aachen
Tel: (+49 241) 168 80   Fax: (+49 241) 168 82 36
Directors: Karlheinz Wontorra
    Dr Joachim Duttenhofer
Operating Manager: Hans-Peter Appel
Administration Manager: Uwe Peifer
Commercial Manager: Klaus Reinartz
Staff: 788 (transport division)

Current situation: Night service known as ASA (ASEAG Sammel Auto) using hired taxis operates half-hourly along certain routes from 00.30 to 03.45, serving 76 city stops; operates on 45 min prebooking by telephone; fares are double those in daytime.

Bus

Passenger journeys: (1995) 56.1 million
(1996) 56.5 million
(1997) 56.3 million
Vehicle-km: (1995) 17.8 million
(1996) 17.9 million
(1997) 16.2 million

Number of routes: 54
Route length: (One way) 1,012 km
On priority right-of-way: 12 km

Fleet: 267 vehicles, plus 76 contracted

Mercedes O305 (1982/85)	42
MAN SL200 (1979/85)	60
Mercedes O405 (1988)	12
MAN SL202 (1987/89)	31
Mercedes O405N low-floor (1991/92)	12
MAN NL202 low-floor (1991/93)	27
Mercedes O305G articulated (1983/84)	13
Mercedes O405G articulated (1987/88)	6
MAN SG242 articulated (1986/88/92)	47
Van Hool A508 midibus (1990)	10
MAN NG272 articulated (1993)	7

In peak service: 314
On order: 13

Most intensive service: 7 min
One-person operation: All routes
Fare collection: Prepurchase or payment to driver
Fare structure: Stages, single and multitickets, weekly and transferable monthly passes; day tickets
Fares collected on board: 26 per cent (74 per cent hold passes)
Fare evasion control: Roving inspectors
Arrangements for elderly/disabled: Free travel for disabled, reimbursed by Federal government
Operational control: All buses radio-equipped
Average peak-hour speed: 20.5 km/h
Operating costs financed by: Fares 77 per cent, subsidy/grants 23 per cent
Subsidy from: National 80 per cent and state 20 per cent governments
New vehicles financed by: Depreciation and subsidy

DKB

Dürener Kreisbahn GmbH
Kölner Landstrasse 271, 52351 Düren
Tel: (+49 242) 13 90 10   Fax: (+49 242) 139 01 88
Manager, Bus: Rolf Schorer
Staff: 199

Passenger journeys: (1995) 10.3 million
(1996) 10.7 million
(1997) 11.1 million

Current situation: County council owned operator providing urban and rural bus services in and around Düren (30 routes, 102 buses), and train services from Düren to Heimbach (30 km) and Jülich (16 km) with a fleet of 16 diesel railcars. The two rail routes carry about 3.7 million passengers a year.

BVR

Busverkehr Rheinland GmbH, Verkaufsbüro Aachen
Zollamtstrasse 3, 52064 Aachen
Tel: (+49 241) 43 33 36

Current situation: Bus company owned by DB provides suburban and rural services within the AVV region and beyond.

DB

Deutsche Bahn AG, Geschäftsbereich Nahverkehr
Regionalbereich Rheinland
Konrad-Adenauer-Ufer 3, 50668 Cologne
Tel: (+49 221) 141 33 30   Fax: (+49 221) 141 24 42

Type of operation: Suburban heavy rail

Passenger journeys: (1995) 5.4 million

Current situation: Stopping trains run on lines from Aachen to Düren (and onwards to Cologne) and Geilenkirchen (and onwards to Mönchengladbach), at least hourly with extra trains at peak periods. There is no fixed interval service. Electric locomotive-hauled trains with double-deck coaches are used.

UPDATED

Duewag's RegioSprinter on DKB local service
1996

AARHUS

Population: 282,000
Public transport: Bus services provided by municipal undertaking; limited local train service

Aarhus Sporveje Volvo B10M bus in town centre
1999/0045141

Aarhus sporveje

Aarhus sporveje
Bryggervej 35, 8240 Risskov, Denmark
Tel: (+45) 89 44 55 00   Fax: (+45) 89 44 55 44
e-mail: bus@aarhus.dk
Chair: Poul B Skou
Managing Director: Leif Marcussen

Developments: Free transfer started 1997 between buses and trains within municipal boundary. Last journey must be completed before bus pass or ticket expires, or fine of DKr250 incurred.

Bus

Passenger journeys: (1995) 45.5 million
(1996) 45.5 million
(1997) 45.2 million
Vehicle-km: (1995) 15.1 million
(1996) 15.2 million
(1997) 15.4 million

Number of routes: 39, plus 10 on Friday and Saturday nights only
Route length: (One way) 835 km

New bus waiting area at terminus of Aarhus Route 9
1999/0038743

Fleet: 227 vehicles
Leyland-DAB (1983-89)   90
DAB-Silkeborg (1988-97)   98
Volvo B10M (1994-97)   39
In peak service: 205
On order: 9 Volvo/Aabenraa and 7 Volvo/Säffle

Most intensive service: 10 min
One-person operation: All routes
Fare collection: Self-service with Autelca B-20 ticket vending machines, Almex M canceller, all on board

Fare structure: Zonal, with single and multitickets and season cards; free transfer to local trains and regional buses
Fares collected on board: 11.6 per cent (64.8 per cent of passengers use passes, 23.2 per cent multitickets)
Fare evasion control: 28 inspectors
Operational control: Mobile radio
Arrangements for elderly/disabled: Price reduction on season cards financed under social law
Average distance between stops: 500 m
Average peak-hour speed: In mixed traffic, 23 km/h

Bus priority: 4.6 km bus lanes
Operating costs financed by: Fares 63 per cent, other commercial sources 1 per cent, subsidy/grants 36 per cent
Subsidy from: Local council taxation
New vehicles financed by: Operating budget

UPDATED

ABERDEEN

Population: 209,000 (240,000 including environs)
Public transport: Bus services provided mainly by private companies; local rail service

First Aberdeen

First Aberdeen Ltd
395 King Street, Aberdeen AB24 5RP, Scotland
Tel: (+44 1224) 65 00 00   Fax: (+44 1224) 65 00 99
Managing Director: George Mair
Staff: 477

Current situation: Formerly the Regional Council's transport undertaking, the company was sold to its workforce in 1989. Subsidiary companies are Mairs Coaches of Dyce and Kirkpatrick of Deeside. GRT Bus Group, the parent company, is part of FirstGroup, the UK's largest bus operator.
Developments: Bus priority measures are being promoted following allocation of capital grants. Park-and-ride 'City Quick' service has been introduced on the King Street/Ellon Road corridor, while 'Gold Service' buses have been allocated to the busiest corridors. Hail-and-ride operates after 20.00 on some routes. Four further Gold Service routes introduced 1998 using low-floor Dennis Darts, with no double-deckers in service on Sundays and evenings.

Bus

Passenger journeys: (1992/93) 27.2 million
(1993/94) 26 million
(1996/97) 22.8 million
Vehicle-km: (1992/93) 10.9 million
(1993/94) 11 million
(1996/97) 11.2 million

Number of routes: 36
Route length: 190 km
On priority right-of-way: 800 m

Fleet: 190 vehicles, plus Mairs (3 buses, 21 coaches) and Kirkpatrick (4 buses, 5 coaches)
Leyland Olympian double-deck   31
Leyland Atlantean double-deck   57
Daimler CVG6   1
Coaches   12
MCW Metrorider   3
Mercedes minibus   14
Mercedes O405   49
Mercedes O405G articulated   1
Dennis Dart midibus   6
Dennis Dart SLF midibus   16
In peak service: 154

Most intensive service: 5 min
One-person operation: All routes
Fare collection: Pay-as-you-enter; electronic Wayfarer ticket issue and data collection equipment; stored value magnetic pass card
Fare structure: Stage; weekly/monthly/3-monthly passes
Fares collected on board: 76 per cent
Fare evasion control: Inspectors
Operational control: Route inspectors, mobile radio
Arrangements for elderly/disabled: Low maximum fare
Average distance between stops: 180 m
Average peak-hour speed: In mixed traffic, 16.5 km/h
Operating costs financed by: Fares 97 per cent, subsidy/grants 3 per cent
Subsidy from: Local council, for non-commercial routes put out to tender, plus concessionary fare reimbursement

Bluebird

Bluebird Buses Ltd
Bus Station, Guild Street, Aberdeen AB9 2DR
Tel: (+44 1224) 59 13 81   Fax: (+44 1224) 58 42 02
Managing Director: Tom Wileman
General Manager: Ian Mackintosh
Operations Director: Robert Andrew
Finance Director: Norman Strachan

Current situation: Formerly part of the state-owned Scottish Bus Group, the company was purchased in 1991 by Stagecoach. It operates the majority of commuter services into the city and routes throughout the Aberdeenshire, Highland, Moray and Perth & Kinross council areas.

Fleet: 377 buses
Single-deck   76
Double-deck   100
Coaches   108
Minibuses   93

ScotRail

ScotRail Railways Ltd
Caledonian Chambers, 87 Union Street, Glasgow G1 3TA
Tel: (+44 141) 332 98 11   Fax: (+44 141) 335 47 91

Current situation: Diesel commuter services provided from Dyce (10 km north, about hourly) and Portlethen (13 km south, limited).

UPDATED

Gold Service Optare-bodied Mercedes-Benz O405 with air conditioning   *1999*/0045140

ABIDJAN

Population: 3 million
Public transport: Bus and lagoon boat services in the metropolitan area and inner suburbs provided under concession from government by 'mixed economy' company part owned by vehicle manufacturer and responsible to Ministry. Private 'Gbaka' minibuses serve suburbs and outer areas

SOTRA

Société des Transports Abidjanais (SOTRA)
BP 2009, Abidjan 01, Côte d'Ivoire
Tel: (+225) 24 90 80   Fax: (+225) 25 97 21
President: Vincent-Pierre Lokrou
Director General: Pascal Yeboue-Kouame
Staff: 4,476

Passenger journeys: (1993/94) 205 million
(1994/95) 232 million
(1995/96) 256 million
Vehicle-km: (1993/94) 39.5 million
(1994/95) 42.7 million
(1995/96) 50.6 million

Current situation: SOTRA was created in 1960. A 39.8 per cent stake is held by the French manufacturer Renault, with almost all the remainder held by the Côte d'Ivoire government. SOTRA's council of administration comprises the President, five members appointed by the state, three by Renault and one by the city of Abidjan.

As well as conventional bus operations extending to

963 km on 65 routes and three ferry lines, a Taxi-Bagages service caters for passengers to and from the city's markets. Special school and workplace services are also provided.
Developments: SOTRA's exclusive area of operation was reduced in 1996, when provision of transport in the communes of Abobo and Yopougon was liberalised. Private bus operators may now compete in these areas, along with the Gbaka minibuses (see below). As a result, SOTRA has reduced its total fleet (though the number of serviceable vehicles has risen) and taken other steps in case it is forced to withdraw from the two communes.

In addition, at the end of 1997 SOTRA was awaiting the outcome of studies into proposals for its privatisation.

Fleet: 928 buses, of which 775 in service

Renault S105	468
Renault PR180-2	52
Renault SC10 (second-hand)	194
Renault PR180 (second-hand)	27
Renault SM8	27
Renault SG2/SG4	7
In peak service: 672	

Boat

Current situation: 12 vessels ply three routes on the Abidjan Lagoon totalling 7 km; they carry about 8 million passengers annually.

Minibus

Current situation: Most services to the outer suburbs are provided by private minibuses and shared taxis known as Gbakas, with 14-22 seats, operating on set routes but with no defined stops. Smaller minibuses and Saviem SG2 minibuses are widely used. Many services run in the peak periods only.

VERIFIED

ACCRA

Population: 2 million
Public transport: All services provided by private operators using 'tro-tro' midi and minibuses and shared taxis, plus wooden body trucks (mammy-wagons)

Minibus

Current situation: Following cessation of full-size bus operations by the Omnibus Services Authority, all public transport is provided by tro-tro midibuses and minibuses, shared taxis and mammy-wagons. Generally fixed routes are operated, and vehicles leave their terminals only when full.

There are some 12,000 tro-tros, carrying more than 50 per cent of the city's trips. Vehicle types include Volkswagen Kombis, Toyota Coaster and Willowbrook. Significant numbers of passengers also use taxis, of which there are thought to be more than 30,000.

Services are regulated by the Ghana Private Road Transport Union, which also sets fare levels.

VERIFIED

Toyota minibus bearing religious exhortation on Liberation Road, Accra   *1996*

ADDIS ABABA

Population: 1.9 million
Public transport: Bus services operated by public transport division of government-controlled Public Transport Corporation, operating both urban and intercity services. Shared taxi use is extensive and peak-only midibuses operate

General Ethiopian Transport

National Road Transport Corporation
Addis Ababa City Bus Services
PO Box 5780, Addis Ababa, Ethiopia
Tel: (+251 1) 15 31 17   Fax: (+251 1) 15 07 44
General Manager: Abdu Jemal
Operations Manager: Zelalem G Michael

Current situation: The city bus system operates under a number of constraints, including vehicle shortages, poor terminal and garage facilities, lack of an operations control system and a proliferation of short and duplicated routes running over very poor roads. Lack of capital hampers provision of spare parts and new vehicles.

As part of a transport study financed by the World Bank, recommendations have been made regarding the

Jonckheere-bodied Mercedes OF1621 of GET   *1996*

organisation and management of the Corporation, including operating methods, vehicle acquisition policy, maintenance arrangements and data processing

systems. Implementation is proceeding slowly, along with route rationalisation.

Bus

Passenger journeys: (1990/91) 119.4 million
Vehicle-km: (1990/91) 9.3 million

Number of routes: 40
Route length: (One way) 150 km

Fleet: Approx 200 buses, all single-deck standard length, comprising 160 Mercedes OF1621/Jonckheere, plus about 25 Volvo B7F with Italian Borsani bodies and a few Fiat 331A/Borsani. A small batch of 15 Mercedes was reported as having arrived in early 1995

Most intensive service: 5 min
Fare structure: Flat, higher for suburban journeys
Fare collection: Conductors on board in fixed location
Average peak-hour speed: 14.4 km/h
Operating costs financed by: Fares 88 per cent, subsidy/grants 12 per cent
Subsidy from: Government; PTC is exempted from government duties and taxes on fuel, spare parts, vehicles and workshop equipment and tools

VERIFIED

Toyota car-based 'Matatu' shared taxis in central Addis Ababa   *1996*

ADELAIDE

Population: 1.1 million
Public transport: Bus (including guided busway service), tram and suburban rail services administered by Passenger Transport Board and operated by state government authority, with competitive tendering started in 1995. A few private bus operators serve mainly country and outer-suburban areas

Passenger Transport Board

Passenger Transport Board
GPO Box 1998, Adelaide, South Australia 5001, Australia
Tel: (+61 8) 83 03 08 22   Fax: (+61 8) 83 03 08 28
Executive Director: Heather Webster
Director, Strategic Planning: Peter Hollister

Current situation: The Passenger Transport Board (PTB) was formed under the 1994 Passenger Transport Act and is responsible for administration and regulation of passenger transport throughout South Australia, including taxis, hire cars, charter bus operators (100 routes) and both country and metropolitan bus, train and tram services. The PTB is charged with the responsibility for overall integration of public transport in terms of services and ticketing. The PTB may not operate services itself.

The act requires that all regular intra-state passenger transport services be operated under contract to the PTB, subject to a limit of five years and a maximum fleet of 100 vehicles. It also guaranteed the existing operator TransAdelaide (the former State Transport Authority) the right to operate at least 50 per cent of bus, tram and train services until March 1997. The first round of competitive tendering for Adelaide metropolitan services started in March 1995.

TransAdelaide

TransAdelaide, SERCO
address above
e-mail: transadl@camtech.net.au
www: www.transadelaide.sa.gov.au
General Manager: Sue Filby
Staff: 2,101

Passenger journeys: (All modes)
(1995/96) 43.7 million
(1996/97) 38.4 million

Current situation: TransAdelaide, a statutory authority, is the major provider of bus, tram and rail service under contract to the PTB, which funds services and controls the integrated ticketing system.

Since 1995, private operators have tendered in competition with TransAdelaide for contracts to operate public transport services. During 1996/97, TransAdelaide submitted three tenders, and was awarded two contracts. Reduced traffic figures for 1996/97 reflect the loss of operating contracts for the Hills and Inner North areas, though services in Hills are now provided by a wholly owned subsidiary of TransAdelaide, Hills Transit.

Starting in late 1996, the government accelerated the pace of contracting-out, and the PTB negotiated with TransAdelaide for operation of the remaining bus service contracts and the metropolitan rail network. Negotiated

Blackwood interchange in Adelaide Hills   ***1998**/0007276*

contracts for bus service commenced in January 1997 and run for two years, whilst for rail service the period is two years, with an option to renew for a further three years. TransAdelaide holds 15 of the 16 metropolitan service contracts.

Developments: Several routes have been introduced operating exclusively with wheelchair-accessible vehicles and dedicated drivers. Other accessibility improvements include 'Flash Cards' for easy hailing of buses by visually impaired people. The service area of 'Night Moves', which co-ordinates buses and taxis to provide door-to-door transport between midnight and 04.00, has been doubled in size.

Bus
Staff: 1,150

Passenger journeys: (1995/96) 35.8 million
(1996/97) 35.2 million

Number of routes: 100
Average route length: (One way) 17 km

Fleet: 743 vehicles	
Volvo B59 standard (1977-79)	142
Volvo B58 (1981)	55
Volvo B58 articulated (1980)	35
Volvo B10M rigid (1981)	15
Volvo B10M articulated (1981)	5
MAN SL200 (1982)	130
MAN SL200 CNG-powered (1984)	10
MAN S6280 articulated (1986-88)	40
Mercedes-Benz O305G rigid (1985-1986)	41
Mercedes O305G articulated (1985)	51
MAN SL202 (1992)	25
MAN SL202 CNG-powered (1993)	100
MAN HOCL 11.190 midibus (1993)	50
MAN NL202 ultra-low-floor (1993/97)	44
In peak service: 672	
On order: 55 CNG-powered buses	

Most intensive service: 2 min
One-person operation: All routes
Fare collection: Pay-as-you-enter with passenger-operated ticket validating machines; prepurchase multitrip and day tickets: Crouzet ticketing system (magnetic strip tickets)

Fare structure: Zonal; single tickets valid 2 h for free transfer
Fare evasion control: Field supervisors, drivers
Integration with other modes: Fare system integrated with train and tram; 11 bus/rail interchanges
Operational control: Radio/mobile phone
Arrangements for elderly/disabled: Concessionary fare; low-floor kneeling buses with wheelchair ramps being introduced, also with user-friendly features such as seats with hip restraints and non-slip floor coverings; access ramps and extra handrails available on trains; wheelchair-access taxi cab scheme operated by the taxi industry
Average distance between stops: 300 m
Average peak-hour speed: 25 km/h

Guided bus
Current situation: The guided bus O-Bahn system provides high-speed (100 km/h) service on the 12 km corridor from Modbury in the northeastern suburbs to Gilberton just outside Adelaide's central business district. See *JUTS 1988* for history and description. In total 113 Mercedes buses (standard and articulated) are equipped with lateral guidewheels for busway operation.

Tramway
Staff: 72

Type of operation: Conventional tramway

Passenger journeys: (1995/96) 1.5 million
(1996/97) 1.5 million
Car-km: (Annual) 0.8 million

Route length: 9.5 km
Number of lines: 1
Number of stops: 21
Gauge: standard
Track: 40 kg/m rail, timber sleepers on ballast, sleepers on concrete on road areas
Electrification: 600 V DC, overhead

Service: Peak 10 min, off-peak 15 min
First/last car: 05.35/23.50
Fare structure: As bus

Rolling stock: 21 cars	
Pengelley Class H (1929)	M20
Class H restaurant tram (1990)	M1
In peak service: 10	

Developments: A 1 km extension through the city is under consideration.

Suburban railway
Staff: 328

Type of operation: Suburban heavy rail

Passenger journeys: (1995/96) 8.3 million
(1996/97) 8.2 million

Current situation: Services provided on six routes totalling 120 km (1,600 mm gauge) with 86 stations, every 20 min peak, 60 min off-peak. Zonal fare structure with all but six stations unstaffed.

Rolling stock: 100 dmu cars, M82 T18
In peak service: 88

Adelaide's 1929-vintage trams   ***1998**/0007277*   ***UPDATED***

AHMEDABAD

Population: 3.3 million
Public transport: Bus services provided by municipally owned undertaking

Ashok-Leyland Special Viking of AMTS

AMTS

Ahmedabad Municipal Transport Service
Transport House, PO Box 142, outside Jamalpur Gate, Ahmedabad 380022, India
Tel: (+91 79) 535 29 11/16   Fax: (+91 79) 535 45 68
Transport Manager: K C Patel
Staff: 6,548

Developments: AMTS has taken up route rationalisation to minimise bus transfers, reduce congestion inside major terminals and increase route lengths for enhanced crew utilisation.

Bus

Passenger journeys: (1994/95) 228.3 million
(1995/96) 250.2 million
(1997/98) 288.8 million
Vehicle-km: (1994/95) 43.8 million
(1995/96) 43.8 million
(1997/98) 51.73 million

Number of routes: 180
Route length: 2,219 km

Fleet: 852 vehicles
Ashok-Leyland single-deck   852
In peak service: 589
Average age of fleet: 10.5 years

Most intensive service: 10 min
Fare collection: Conductor
Fare structure: Stage
Fare evasion control: Random inspection with penalty
Average peak-hour speed: 18.3 km/h
Operating costs financed by: Fares 106.3 per cent, other commercial sources 3.5 per cent

UPDATED

ALBANY

Population: City 102,000, service area 769,000
Public transport: Fixed-route bus and paratransit services provided by governmental transit authority in 6,300 km² area including Albany, Schenectady, Rensselaer and Saratoga counties. The authority is governed by a nine-member board of directors. Four private operators run complementary routes within the service area

CDTA

Capital District Transportation Authority (CDTA)
110 Watervliet Avenue, Albany, New York 12206, USA
Tel: (+1 518) 482 11 25
Executive Director: Dennis J Fitzgerald
Director of Transportation: Charles Cohen
Director of Information: Carmino N Basile
Staff: 507

Current situation: CDTA was created in 1970 and began operations in 1971 when it assumed responsibility for routes of the Albany-Nassau Bus Co. In 1972 CDTA took over operations of four additional bus companies operating in the four-county service area. Five other counties (Green, Colombia, Montgomery, Fulton and Schoharie) may join the transit district by vote of the county legislature.
    CDTA operates local, express and special rural service routes between shopping and government centres. Paratransit service began in 1982 under the name STAR (Special Transit Available by Request). Operated seven

days a week, STAR provides kerbside service to persons unable to ride regular fixed-route buses.
Developments: ShuttleBug midibus service, introduced in 1996, links residential areas with suburban office developments. Operating on a 20 min frequency at peak hours, the shuttle serves individual office locations rather than conventional roadside stops.

Bus

Passenger journeys: (1992) 12.5 million
(1993) 10.8 million
(1994) 11.6 million
Vehicle-km: (1991) 10.3 million
(1992) 10.1 million

Number of routes: 60
Route length: 1,070 km

Fleet: 254 vehicles
Orion (1984/89)   105
Orion II (1991/92)   12
Ikarus 286 articulated   6
Orion V (1997)   103
Minibuses   5
NABI 35 ft low-floor (1998)   23
In peak service: 216

Most intensive service: 5-15 min
One-person operation: All routes
Fare collection: Pay-as-you-enter with GFI electronic fareboxes
Fare structure: Zonal, with additional charges for some

longer journeys; free transfers; reduced fare tokens and monthly passes; Express bus, STAR and rural service fares higher
Operational control: Route inspectors with radio cars, buses radio-equipped
Arrangements for elderly/disabled: Half fares (also for unemployed); STAR on-demand service (see above) carried 99,000 passengers in 1994; 28 fixed-route buses have wheelchair lifts
Integration with other modes: 3 CDTA-operated park-and-ride lots have Express bus service to downtown Albany; further 15 lots in shopping malls and other privately owned areas; free transfer to buses of Upstate Transit
Average distance between stops: 154 m
Average peak-hour speed: 19 km/h
Operating costs financed by: Fares 29 per cent, other commercial sources 1 per cent, subsidy/grants 62 per cent
Subsidy from: Mortgage/sales tax 41 per cent, state and FTA grants 59 per cent
New vehicles financed by: FTA and state grants

Other operators

Current situation: Services into Albany from surrounding districts are also operated by Adirondack Trailways (70 buses), Hendrick Hudson Bus Lines and Yankee Trails (48 buses).

UPDATED

ALEXANDRIA

Population: 3.5 million
Public transport: Bus, light rail and tram services provided by Transport Authority responsible to Governor of Alexandria; suburban rail service run by state railway (ER); metro proposed

Alexandria Passenger Transport

Alexandria Passenger Transport Authority
2 Aflatone Street, Chatby, PO Box 466, 21111 Alexandria, Egypt
Tel: (+20 3) 596 18 10/597 52 23
Chair: M S E Abd El-moneim
Staff: 8,829 (all modes)

Current situation: Two distinct tramway systems are operated — a network of street-running conventional lines in the west and south of the city and six light rail routes running into a terminus at Ramleh Square from the east.

Passenger journeys: (All modes)
(1986/87) 417.2 million
(1988/89) 396.5 million
(1989/90) 390 million

Operating costs financed by: (All modes)
Fares 66 per cent, other commercial sources 7 per cent, subsidy/grants 27 per cent
Subsidy from: Government

Bus

General Managers
Smouha garage area: Eng Mostafa A Haridy
Sidi-Bishr garage area: Eng Ahmed Abd El-Khalek
New Agamy garage area: Eng Nabil Ibrahim Mikhaiel
Staff: 2,678

Passenger journeys: (1986/87) 161.4 million
(1988/89) 137.5 million
(1989/90) 140 million
Vehicle-km: (1985/86) 27 million
(1988/89) 33 million
(1989/90) 40 million

Number of routes: 93
Route length: 1,557 km

Fleet: 483 vehicles
Saviem/Renault S105   129
Volvo-Saracakis   43
Nasr 411   131
Mercedes (Otomarsan) minibus   20
GM Egypt minibus NPR 59SLJ   160
New vehicles required each year: 75-100

One-person operation: On some minibus routes
Fare collection: Mostly conductors (seated)
Fare structure: Flat, with first and second class
Fare evasion control: Roving inspectors

Average peak-hour speed: 19 km/h
New vehicles financed by: State investments

City Tramway

General Manager: Eng Medhat Hafiz

Type of operation: Conventional tramway

Passenger journeys: (1985/86) 132 million
(1986/87) 137 million
(1989/90) 127 million
Car-km: (1985/86) 5.5 million
(1989/90) 6 million

Route length: 32 km
Number of lines: 16
Gauge: 1,435 mm
Electrification: 600 V DC, overhead

Rolling stock: 159 cars
Duewag articulated (1966 ex-Copenhagen)   M99
Kinki/Toshiba   M15 T15
Ganz-Mávag/Duewag (1986)   M15 T15

Light rail (Ramleh lines)

General Manager: Eng Abdel-Moneim Abdel-Ghani

Type of operation: Light rail, mostly on segregated right-of-way

Passenger journeys: (1985/86) 111 million
(1986/87) 118 million
(1989/90) 123 million
Car-km: 3.5 million (annual)

Route length: 16 km
Number of lines: 6
Gauge: 1,435 mm
Electrification: 600 V DC, overhead

Rolling stock: 48 three-car sets

Kinki Sharyo/Toshiba (1976)	108
Kinki Sharyo (1991)	18
Kinki Sharyo double-deck (1994)	M6
SEMAF (1995)	M12

Developments: Modernisation of track and catenary has been completed, along with installation of electronic signalling. New depot and workshops planned.

It is planned to upgrade the Ramleh lines to urban metro standards.

Egyptian National Railways
Egyptian National Railways
Station Building, Ramses Square, Cairo
Tel: (+20 2) 575 10 00   Fax: (+20 2) 574 00 00

Type of operation: Suburban heavy rail

Current situation: Frequent commuter services are operated to Abou Kir, east of Alexandria, and some commuter use made of other main lines. Services on the Abou Kir line run at 15 min intervals. The five-year plan from 1987 envisaged electrification and further improvements, though little progress has been made.

Minibus/shared taxi
Current situation: Extensive minibus/shared taxi system operates carrying some 20 per cent of public transport demand in up to 12-seaters (mostly Japanese-built) operating on fixed routes. A further substantial part of the

traffic is carried by a fleet of about 100 full-sized buses operated by individual employers.

Metro (proposed)
Current situation: An east-west metro line is proposed, running from Abou Kir via the city centre to El-Aamreya (55 km). French consultancy Systra was awarded a contract in 1997 for detailed studies of the whole line, and for design and pre-contract documentation of the 22 km first phase (Abou Kir to Misr), including a 12 km elevated or underground city-centre section. Start of construction planned for 2000.

Initial work is likely to focus on upgrading of two existing suburban lines, prior to linking them across the city centre.

The planning and construction authority for the line is the National Authority for Tunnels (see Cairo entry).

VERIFIED

ALGER
Population: 2.5 million
Public transport: Bus services mostly provided by municipal undertaking serving the city, suburbs and coastal area and which is also responsible for two public elevators and a funicular. Suburban railway operated by Algerian National Railways (SNTF); metro under construction. Further funiculars and cable cars planned. Taxi sharing extensive. Much company-sponsored transport provided privately

RSTA
Regie Syndicale des Transports Algérois (RSTA)
21 rue Alfred De Musset, PO Box 460, 21 Alger, Algeria
Tel: (+213 2) 66 33 75
Staff: 4,000

Bus
Passenger journeys: (Annual) 200 million
Vehicle-km: Approx 48 million (annual)

Fleet: Approx 700 vehicles

One-person operation: None
Fare collection: Pass or payment to conductor

Fare structure: Stages, with singles, 10-journey carnets, daily, weekly, monthly and annual passes; reductions for large families, students and handicapped
Fares collected on board: 86 per cent
Operational control: Route inspectors/mobile radio
Arrangements for elderly/disabled: Fare reductions; other plans under study
Operating costs financed by: Fares 100 per cent

Funicular
Current situation: One funicular carries about 6.3 million passengers annually. A further seven funiculars and cable cars are planned.

SNTF
Société Nationale des Transports Ferroviaires
21-23 Boulevard Mohamed V, Alger
Tel: (+213 2) 71 15 10   Fax: (+213 2) 61 96 93

Type of operation: Suburban heavy rail

Current situation: Service provided on routes from Alger Maritime to Blida (50 km) and Thenia (54 km) using 228 diesel-hauled push-pull cars.
Developments: The metro (see below) will take over

provision of suburban passenger service from SNTF, whose trains will terminate at interchanges at the two southern metro terminals.

Metro
Under construction
Entreprise du Metro d'Alger
13 chemin de Wilaya, No 4 Kouba, Alger
Tel: (+213 2) 58 67 68   Fax: (+213 2) 68 97 05
Director General: H Bellil

Current situation: Construction in progress on initial section of Line 1 (12.5 km, 16 stations) of the long-planned metro; 1,435 mm gauge, electrified 750 V DC third-rail, fleet of 120 cars required. Progress has been erratic since local contractors took over work from foreign companies in the early 1990s.

From Oued Koriche in the city centre, a 9 km underground section extends to Hamma where the line will come to the surface and take over existing SNTF tracks to Hai el Badr and a depot at Bachdjarah. Two other lines are proposed, linking Grande Poste with Bab Exxour (21 km, 18 stations) and Hussein-Bey with Birkhadem (10 km, 6 stations).

VERIFIED

ALMATY
Population: 1.185 million within city boundary (1994)
Public transport: Bus and trolleybus/tramway services run by separate municipal undertakings; non-municipal private buses operated by two main companies. Metro construction stopped since 1991. Aerial cableway to Kok-Tube Hill. Extensive use is made of paratransit 'gypsy cabs' whereby passengers hail private cars and negotiate fares with the driver.

Current situation: The director of each municipal undertaking has reported to the municipal Passenger Transport Department since the latter's creation in November 1996. A government decree of 1996 requires the provision of franchised bus services by competitive tendering. Tram and trolleybus services were exempted from the franchising requirement. A former Soviet-era master plan requiring expansion of the tram and trolleybus system has been discarded and the nine-route

tram network was reduced to three routes by 1996, whilst the trolleybus network has been reduced from 18 routes to 13.

Fare structure: Single-ride flat-fare tickets are issued. Monthly bus passes and 'uniform' passes (bus, trolleybus and tram) sold by concessionaires. Reduced price passes for school pupils and college students. Forty-four per cent of the population is entitled to free travel using privileges originally granted by the Soviet Union. The Motor Transport Trust runs a number of 'commercial routes' in addition to the basic 59-route network on which fares-exempt riders are not accepted. Private buses are also operated commercially.
Fare collection: Roving conductors on all vehicles, employed by drivers on buses and by the undertaking on trolleybuses and trams.

Upravlenie Automobil'novo Transporta
Upravlenie Automobil'novo Transporta (Motor Transport Trust)
Almaty, Kazakstan

Current situation: This is the larger of the two operators with responsibility for buses (and for taxis until about 1994).

Bus
Staff: (1995) 4,390

Passenger journeys: (1989) 441.3 million
Vehicle-km: (1989) 118.6 million
(1995) about 55.6 million

KTM-5 tram 1077 of 1990 on Route 6 in Almaty with passengers about to board (T V Runnacles)
1999/0045124

Number of routes: (1995) 59

Fleet: (Feb 1996) 1,255 buses

LIAZ 677	389
LIAZ 5256	103
Ikarus 280	136
Ikarus 260, 263, 354, 256 & 250	135
LAZ 695, 699	316
Mercedes O325 and O305*	49
Karosa	3
Iveco**	1
RAF, KVZ, PAZ (minibuses)	123

In course of delivery (1996):

MANAS SL232	200

*Some new Mercedes-Turk O325 and some ex-West Berlin Mercedes O305.
** By late 1996 a small number of Iveco midibuses had been added.
In peak service: (1996) 1,045

Tramvaino-Trolleibusnoe Upravlenie

Tramvaino-Trolleibusnoe Upravlenie (Tram and Trolleybus Trust)

Tramway
Staff: (1995) 650

Type of operation: Conventional tramway

ZIU9 trolleybus 1221 in Almaty (T V Runnacles)

Current situation: Routes 4, 6 and 10 in operation serving about 80 per cent of the original network length, which remained intact in 1996. Fleet reduced from 196 cars in 1991 to 52 by 1996. All remaining KTM-5 and RVZ-6 trams received cosmetic treatment in summer 1996. In April 1998 the Tramway Manager claimed that a contract had been signed with ČKD Dopravni Systemy to rebuild the depot in 1999, and to deliver 60 new cars to replace existing fleet and to enable most tram routes to be reopened.

Passenger journeys: (1989) 47 million
(1994) 18.6 million

Route length: Approx 40 km (non-duplicated) of which about 32 km is used by surviving routes
Number of routes: 3
Gauge: 1,524 mm

Rolling stock: (1996) 53 cars

Riga RVZ-6 (1984-86)	24
Ust-Katav KTM-5 (1989-91)	29

In peak service: (1996) 36

Trolleybus
Staff: (1995) 2,049

Current situation: By 1998, five routes had been closed but Route 6 was extended in 1996 to replace the outer end of closed tram routes 1 and 3. Several sections of wire

have been abandoned in recent years, all in the central area. The future of Almaty's trolleybus system does not appear to be defined in policy terms, although trolleybuses alone have retained their patronage at a reasonable level. Russian ZIU682 trolleybuses are imported as kits and assembled locally under the 'ElectroMash' brand, but a small number of Skoda vehicles acquired in 1998 was expected to be the start of a larger order.

Passenger journeys: (1989) 98.1 million
(1995) 89.4 million
Vehicle-km: (1989) 18 million
(1995) 12.3 million

Route length: (1996) approx 90 km (non-duplicated)
Number of routes: (1998) 13

Fleet: (1998) approx 270

Uritsky ZIU9 (1983-92)	approx 250
ElectroMash ZIU682G-012EM (1996-98)	approx 10
Skoda 14Tr (1998)	10

In peak service: (1998) 220

Private bus
Current situation: In addition to the two municipal undertakings, there have been premium-fare, private-sector bus services since 1993. These buses are individually owned, but they are formed into two groups which enjoy company status by virtue of small numbers of permanent staff who co-ordinate the operators' interests. In all about 800 buses are involved, mainly small and older types including RAF223, KAV Z-685, PAZ 672, LAZ 695N and LAZ 4202. Of these only about 250 are in regular use.

In 1996, the larger of the two groups ('Argymak') operated 198 vehicles on 24 routes and the smaller 'Briz' group had 76 buses serving three routes.

The city administration is now required to introduce franchised private bus services on a competitive tendering basis.

Metro
Construction suspended

Current situation: Construction started in 1984 of the initial 8.9 km section of Line 1 of a proposed three-line metro, which was expected to extend to some 40 km by 2010. Line 1 was scheduled to open in 1997, but construction ceased in 1991, at which time the civil works were largely complete. In 1997 a feasibility study was undertaken by SNC-Lavalin of Canada and Gurios of Turkey to provide preliminary design and a strategy to finance the project. Although the civil works are retained on a care and maintenance basis, the early completion of the metro remains in doubt, especially as capital city status was shifted from Almaty to the northwestern city of Akmola in 1996.

Aerial cableway
A 1.7 km long aerial cableway with two cabins was opened between Prospekt Abai and Kok-Tube Hill in 1967 but fell into disuse for several years before being resurrected in August 1996.

1999/0045125   *UPDATED*

AMSTERDAM
Population: 724,000
Public transport: Bus, metro, ferry, light rail and tram services operated by municipal transport department under national operating and financial framework. Suburban rail services provided by Netherlands Railways (NS) and buses by regional bus undertakings

GVBA
Gemeentevervoerbedrijf Amsterdam (GVBA)
Prins Hendrikkade 108-114, PO Box 2131, 1000 CC Amsterdam, Netherlands
Tel: (+31 20) 460 60 60   Fax: (+31 20) 460 60 66
Managing Director: André Testa
Deputy General Manager: Hans van Vliet
Technical Manager: Henk Waling
Staff & Personnel Manager: Jan Schermer
Manager, Metro/Light Rail: Henny van Haren
Manager, Tramway: Adri Bolier
Manager, Bus: Cas van Eerden

Manager, Ferry: Cor Molenaar
Staff: 4,527

Passenger journeys: (1995) 237 million
(1996) 235.7 million
(1997) 236.9 million

Operating costs financed by: Fares 25.3 per cent, other commercial sources 9.9 per cent, subsidy/grants 64.8 per cent
Subsidy from: City council, drawing a government contribution based on the number of paid journeys, and city council (ferries only)

Developments: GVBA's financial situation has deteriorated steadily since 1988, caused in part by substantial fare evasion and high operating costs. This led the government to seek an independent assessment of the organisation. A report published in 1996 highlighted poor management practices and overstaffing. A new managing director was appointed to implement the

report's recommendations, and in early 1997 the government increased GVBA's annual subsidy by G16 million. Going beyond the damage report's recommendations, the new management's Business Plans have resulted in a turn-around in late 1997 and early 1998, the balance on 1997 and the forecast on 1998 showing a small profit.

Conductors had been reintroduced in 1991 on some tram routes particularly hard hit by ticketless travel, and cancelling machines were withdrawn from buses in favour of driver inspection. The results were so good that all tram routes are to have conductors once again.

Bus
Passenger journeys: (1995) 53.4 million
(1996) 52.9 million
(1997) 51.9 million
Vehicle-km: (1997) 19.3 million

Number of routes: 51 (including 28 peak only and 11 night)

Route length: (One way) 422 km
On priority right-of-way: 34.6 km

Fleet: 276 vehicles
Standard buses	165
Articulated buses	85
Minibuses	16
Coaches	10

Most intensive service: 6 min
One-person operation: All routes
Fare collection: Prepurchase or payment to driver for strip tickets and day tickets, checked by driver. Onboard cancelling machines removed due to evasion problems, with all tickets now stamped by driver or shown
Fare structure: Zonal; prepurchase weekly, monthly and annual passes, multiday tickets and national Strippenkaart scheme tickets, last also available on board and valid for transfers; 1 h ride-at-will ticket; services operate all night with higher flat fare.

Under the Strippenkaart system, the Netherlands is split into zones of 4.5 km each. National prepurchase season tickets, weekly, monthly and annual, can be bought for one zone or more and used on all buses, metro, tramways and urban railways of all companies in the zone(s) paid for. Single rides can be made with the national Strippenkaart, prepurchased in 15 and 45 strips, or from drivers in 2, 3 and 8 strips, cancelling one strip for each zone, plus one 'boarding fee'
Fare evasion control: Bus driver and roving inspectors; spot fines
Operational control: Centralised control through centre linked to buses by mobile radio and with CCTV installed at a number of key points for observation; all buses equipped with VETAG
Average distance between stops: 495 m (intended maximum 5 min walking distance)
Bus priority: 34.6 km of reserved bus lanes and traffic light priority
Average peak-hour speed: 16.5 km/h
Integration with other modes: Interchanges at main stations; fully integrated fares and ticket system

Developments: New series of 55 standard buses (11 already delivered) and 6 minibuses (already delivered) ordered in 1997. Delivery in 1998/99.

Metro/light rail (sneltram)
Type of operation: Full metro and hybrid metro/light rail (sneltram)

Passenger journeys: (1995) 49.9 million
(1996) 49.7 million
(1997) 56.4 million
Vehicle-km: (1997) 6.4 million

Route length: 51 km
  in tunnel: 5.5 km
  elevated: 24 km
Number of lines: 4
Number of stations: 49
  in tunnel: 5
  elevated: 30
Gauge: 1,435 mm
Track: 49 kg/m S 49 rail, concrete sleepers on ballast
Tunnel: Mainly concrete caisson
Electrification: 750 V DC, third rail/600 V DC, overhead

Service: Peak 3¾-7½ min, off-peak 5-15 min
First/last train: 05.37/00.25
Fare structure: Nationwide zonal system
Revenue control: Ticket and cancelling machines in all entrances, roving inspectors, inspection at entrances
One-person operation: All trains up to 3 coupled sets
Central control: All operations monitored from central control room; CCTV on all platforms

Rolling stock: 44 two-car sets, 29 dual-voltage LRVs, 33 single-voltage (third rail) LRVs
Linke-Hofmann-Busch M1 (1973)	M8
Linke-Hofmann-Busch M2 (1976/77)	M66
Linke-Hofmann-Busch M3 (1980)	M14
BN dual-voltage Amstelveen line S1 (1990)	M13
BN dual-voltage S2 (1994)	M12
CAF dual-voltage S3 (1996)	M4

Current situation: Light rail line from Zuid-WTC to Amstelveen (Winkelcentrum) and Middenhoven opened 1990 (see below). The route is electrified at 600 V DC overhead, and is operated by cars with both third rail and

Latest Berkhof standard bus at Centraal Station interchange   *1999*/0045126

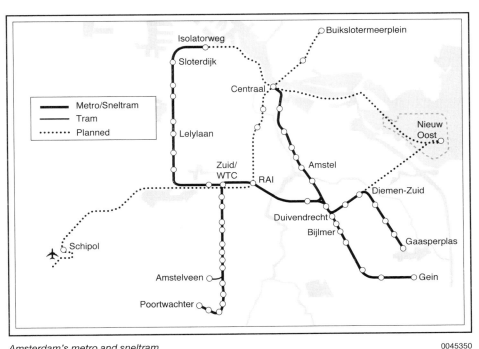
Amsterdam's metro and sneltram   0045350

Route 5 cars pass on the Leidseplein   *1997*

Former HTM (The Hague) PCC cars 1308 and 2104 in service on Line 3, Amsterdam (Quintus Vosman)
1999/0043455

overhead current collection to allow through running from the metro. Part of the route, between Amstelveen and Zuid-WTC (5 km), is also used by tram Route 5 (see below). A second new metro/sneltram opened in May 1997, the 11 km linking Isolatorweg with Zuid-WTC. This forms a ring line round the east, south and west sides of the city, with trains running through from Gein on the metro.

Developments: A further stage will see the ring extended from Isolatorweg to Centraal Station, with a later extension (the IJ line) proposed to run along the banks of the IJ to the future Nieuw Oost residential area.

A north-south line is also planned to run from the northern suburbs to Centraal and Zuid-WTC, with a later extension to Schiphol airport proposed. Government funding for this line, which is to be in bored tunnel, was approved in 1994 and construction was expected to start in 1999.

Extension of the Amstelveen line to Westwijk is a step nearer to construction after approval of government funding amounting to G36 million in 1996.

Tramway
Staff: 1,564

Type of operation: Conventional tramway

Passenger journeys: (1995) 133.7 million
(1996) 133.1 million
(1997) 128.7 million
Vehicle-km: (1997) 10.9 million

Route length: 138 km
  reserved track: 66 km
Number of routes: 17
Number of stops: 762

Gauge: 1,435 mm
Track: Ri60 60 kg/m rail, timber sleepers on concrete or ballast
Electrification: 600 V DC, overhead

Service: Peak 5-9 min, off-peak 6-12 min, evening 10-15 min, weekends 5-15 min
First/last car: 05.41/00.33
Fare structure: As bus and metro; nationwide zonal system
Revenue control: Conductors, roving inspectors
One-person operation: Conductors being reintroduced on all lines
Centralised control: Mobile radio contact between drivers and control room; automatic vehicle location and control on all lines, with countdown to departure information in cabs and real-time punctuality data displayed at stops. VETAG/VECOM detection system for traffic light priority, points control and vehicle identification

Rolling stock: 237 tramcars
Bijnes (1957/58/59/61/62)
Werkspoor (1964/66/67/68)
LHB (1974/75/79/80/81)
BN (1989/90/91)

Developments: Line 2 extended in 1994 to new residential areas in the western suburbs; further extension planned. Other proposed routes under consideration are to the old docklands area in east Amsterdam and to the University/Hospital area in the south. The initial stage of the sneltram ring route on the south and west opened May 1997. Order for new fleet of 70 cars planned for 1998/1999.

Ferry
Current situation: Frequent service operated by 10 vessels on four cross-IJ routes over 1.4 km; one route runs 24 h service. Subsidies are provided by the city council.

NS
Netherlands Railways
PO Box 2025, 3500 HA Utrecht
Tel: +(31 30) 235 91 11   Fax: (+31 30) 233 24 58

Type of operation: Suburban heavy rail

Current situation: Suburban and interurban services, electrified at 1.5 kV DC, radiate from Amsterdam Centraal station on several routes and carry heavy traffic. Nine stations within city boundaries served by 3 to 31 trains hourly, with more at peak times.

Because of the dense pattern of NS operations, differentiation of 'suburban' services is hard; no distinction is made by NS, nor separate traffic figures kept. Stations within city boundaries are included in the Strippenkaart system, and trains are used as alternatives to bus and trams, particularly for interchange with other NS services. There is also much longer distance commuting.

Developments: Two extra tracks between Sloterdijk and Centraal are now in service, while an extra platform at Amsterdam Centraal is planned for completion in 2001. The Amsterdam—Hoofddorp portion of the Amsterdam—Schiphol—Leiden line will gain two extra tracks by 2001, while Schiphol station will have three new tracks, the first of which opened in 1994. Several other capacity schemes are planned for the period 2000 to 2005.

Tram 710 (GVB Amsterdam) on Line 24 (Quintus Vosman)
1999/0043454

UPDATED

ANCHORAGE
Population: 250,000
Public transport: Fixed-route bus services and paratransit provided by municipal agency

Anchorage Transit System
Anchorage Transit System, Municipality of Anchorage
PO Box 196650, 3560 East Tudor Road, Anchorage, Alaska 99519-6650, USA
Tel: (+1 907) 343 84 02   Fax: (+1 907) 563 22 06

Director of Transit: Bob Kniefel
Operating Manager: Gary Taylor
Staff: 136

Current situation: The Anchorage Transit System is known as People Mover.

Bus
Passenger boardings: (1992) 3 million
(1994) 3 million
(1997) 3.2 million

Vehicle-km: (1992) 3.5 million
(1994) 3.2 million
(1997) 3.4 million

Number of routes: 18
Route length: (One way) 616 km

Fleet: 106 buses

Flyer D901 (1981/83)	21
GMC T6H 5307N (1984)	16
New Flyer D40 low-floor (1995)	18

Paratransit service:

Ford/Collins (1993)	5
Ford/Champion (1994)	3
Ford/Pioneer (1996)	6
Thomas Bus (1996)	1
Ford/Phoenix (1997)	11
Ford/Phoenix (1998)	7
Vanpool service:	
Chrysler Maxivan (1994)	12
Ford Super Club (1999)	6
In peak service: 39	

Most intensive service: 30 min
One-person operation: All routes
Fare collection: Payment to farebox
Fare structure: Flat; 10 cent transfer; prepurchase tokens and monthly passes
Fare evasion control: Driver supervision
Operational control: Shift supervisors
Arrangements for elderly/disabled: Services provided to ADA standards; 75 per cent discount on regular fares
Integration with other modes: Rideshare programme promotes carpools by providing matchlists with employer's help; funding from Federal Highway Administration grant; 837 pools, with 1,730 members; six park-and-ride lots served by Express buses to downtown
Operating costs financed by: Fares 17 per cent, other

Flyer D901 heads for Downtown on People Mover Route 45   *1997*

commercial sources 3 per cent, subsidy/grants 18 per cent, tax levy 62 per cent
Subsidy from: FTA and state grants, Municipal property tax

New vehicles financed by: FTA and state grants

UPDATED

ANKARA

Population: 3.5 million
Public transport: Municipally owned authority operates bus, metro and light metro services. Suburban rail services operated by State Railway. Also private operation of 'Minibus-Dolmus' services and conventional buses. Metro under construction

EGO

General Directorate of Electricity, Gas & Bus Management
Elektrik, Gaz ve Otobüs Işletmesi Genel Müdürlüğü (EGO)
Toros Sok No 12, Sihhiye-Ankara, Turkey
Tel: (+90 312) 229 12 84   Fax: (+90 312) 229 65 97
General Director: Altan Civan
Director: Ethem Lillidag
Staff: 5,182

Current situation: Though patronage is in decline as trips by private buses rise, EGO accounts for about 23 per cent of daily motorised trips. There is still substantial overcrowding, and considerable passenger waits are experienced, especially in peak hours. There has been pressure to maintain low fares despite high demand, but fares were increased twice in 1997 due to the high rate of inflation. Some areas of low demand are now served by midibuses.
Developments: Privatisation is under way, with EGO offering 41 routes (400 buses) to private-sector operators. Magnetic ticketing was introduced on EGO buses in August 1997.
The first section of heavy metro opened in December 1997.

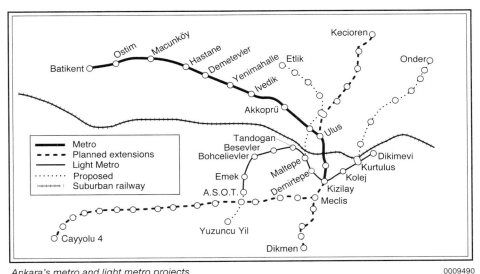

Ankara's metro and light metro projects   0009490

Bus
Passenger journeys: (1995) 262 million
(1996) 239 million
(1997) 216 million
Vehicle-km: (1995) 75.6 million
(1996) 76.1 million
(1997) 83.5 million

Number of routes: 329 (regular 229, express 41)
Route length: (One way) 7,000 km

Fleet: 1,331 buses

Mercedes O302	170
MAN standard	334
MAN articulated	50
Ikarus 280 articulated	350
Ikarus 260 standard	332
BMC Beldesan	50
Others	45

In peak service: 921
New vehicles required each year: 285

Most intensive service: 4 min
One-person operation: All routes
Fare collection: Prepurchase magnetic tickets with ticket box on vehicles
Fare structure: Flat; prepurchase full fare tickets, reduced-rate student tickets
Fares collected on board: None
Fare evasion control: By driver; 10 × standard fare surcharge
Operational control: At terminal and dispatching points and by route inspectors
Average peak-hour speed: In mixed traffic, 12-15 km/h; express services, 30 km/h
Operating costs financed by: Fares 76 per cent, subsidy/grants 24 per cent
Subsidy from: Municipality of Greater Ankara
New vehicles financed by: Municipality and General Directorate of EGO

Light metro
Type of operation: Light metro, opened 1996

Heavy metro train on trial prior to opening   *1998*/0007278

Passenger journeys: (1996/97) 44 million

Route length: 8.5 km
Number of lines: 1
Number of stations: 11
Gauge: 1,435 mm
Electrification: 750 V DC third rail

Rolling stock: 33 cars
Breda/Siemens (1994/95)   M33
In peak service: 27

Current situation: This light metro, built as part of the main metro project (see below), opened in 1996. It runs on fully segregated (mostly underground) alignment along the main east-west highway linking Dikimevi with Bahçeliever and the ASOT bus terminal. There is interchange with the heavy metro at Kizilay in the city centre.

Four other lines are proposed, from Kurtulus to Siteler (Phase 2) and from Maltepe to Etlik (Phase 3).

Metro
Type of operation: Full metro, opened 1997

Route length: 14.6 km
Number of lines: 1
Number of stations: 12
Gauge: 1,435 mm
Track: UIC54 rail on concrete sleepers, ballasted
Electrification: 750 V DC third rail

Rolling stock: 108 cars, formed in three-car sets
Bombardier (1995/97)   M108

Current situation: Line 1 links Kizilay in the city centre with new residential areas at Batikent in the west, running along the congested Atatürk Boulevard. It is fully segregated and capable of handling 31,500 passengers/h in each direction on opening, rising to 63,000/h in later stages.

Metro construction was initiated following recommendations in the Ankara Master Plan of 1986. The 1994 revision envisages a 130 km network comprising metro (44.5 km), light rail (22 km) and suburban rail (63.5 km), to be in full operation by 2015. Bids were sought in late 1998 for construction of Line 2 from Kizilay to Cayyolu (18.3 km), which is proposed for opening in 2005. Further plans for expansion are a 7.9 km line from Ulus to Kegiören (Phase 3) and TBMM to Dikmen.

TCDD

Türkiye Cumhuriyeti Devlet Demiryollari
İşletmesi Genel Müdürlüğü
06330 Gar, Ankara
Tel: (+90 312) 309 05 15   Fax: (+90 312) 312 32 15
Manager, Suburban: Feridun Akyüz

Suburban railway
Type of operation: Suburban heavy rail

Passenger journeys: (1994) 13.8 million
(1995) 15.2 million
(1996) 15 million

Current situation: Suburban operations extend over a 37 km route from Sincan through central Ankara to Kayas with 28 stations, electrified 25 kV 50 Hz. Flat-fare system.
Developments: Track-quadrupling between Ankara and Sincan was completed in 1994, with resignalling and other works to raise capacity finished in 1996. Feasibility studies have been carried out for introduction of double-deck trains in Ankara and Istanbul, and purchase of 11 six-car sets is proposed.

Rolling stock: 26 emu trains

Private buses
Passenger journeys: (1993) 53 million
(1994) 54.2 million
(1996) 60 million

Current situation: 18 private bus routes operate with

some 200 conventional vehicles, accounting for about 5 per cent of daily motorised trips. Their numbers and routes are regulated by the city's transport co-ordination body UKOME. Many other local operators also run services into Ankara from the surrounding area.

An additional 3,500 private buses are contracted by government institutions and some private firms for staff transport to work. Their numbers have increased substantially recently, and they now account for 18 per cent of daily motorised trips.
Developments: A group of new express bus routes was introduced in 1995 between Ataturk Bulvari, close to the city centre, and outlying suburbs, using MAN three-axle double-decks and run by private operator Ankara Özel Halk Otobusleri.

Minibus/shared taxi
Current situation: Over 2,200 Dolmus vehicles are operated by private owners providing services on 33 fixed routes mainly in outer suburbs, with numbers and routes subject to restriction by UKOME. Vehicles are 14-16 seaters, mainly Deutz chassis with Otokar bodies. They account for about 22 per cent of daily motorised trips.

Some 7,000 taxis operate, sometimes on a shared basis, accounting for about 6 per cent of daily trips.

UPDATED

Buses of EGO (background) and Dolmus at Dikmen   *1998*/0007279

ANSHAN
Population: 1.4 million, municipal area 3.3 million
Public transport: Municipal bus, trolleybus and tram services, also electrified passenger railway operated by the Anshan Steel Co. No detailed reports have been received for some time but it is assumed that the municipal organisation remains that of an umbrella undertaking, Anshan Public Transport Corp, with two operating subsidiaries — Anshan City Bus Company (bus only) and Anshan City Electric Traction Company (trolleybus and tram) — sharing responsibility for service provision with the City Planning Bureau. It is likely that some paratransit has been introduced, and there may also be competing or complementary bus services of other operators

Anshan City Bus
Anshan City Bus Company
Anshan, Liaoning Province, People's Republic of China

Current situation: A network of numbered services with its hub at the main railway station covers the city centre and various suburbs to the northeast, south and west, the entire northern quarter of the city being occupied by the steel plant. Many routes continue to more distant suburbs.

Bus
Number of routes: 24 (5 cross-city, 17 radial, 2 peripheral)

Fleet: Approx 300 buses, many articulated, mostly supplied by local builders

Fare collection: Cash payment to seated conductors, monthly passes
Fare structure: Stage
Integration with other modes: Central bus station located close to the main rail station, which is also served by trolleybus and tram routes and the electric railway, but there is no purpose-built interchange. Most radial and cross-city journeys can be made without change of mode or even vehicle, although two peripheral bus routes feed the tramway at its Taipingcun terminus. Monthly all-mode and trolleybus/tram passes available

Anshan City Electric Traction
Anshan City Electric Traction Company
Anshan

Current situation: The trolleybus network, consisting of two cross-city routes with a long common section linking northeast, southeast and northwest suburbs and a

rectangular route in the southwest quarter, has remained static since the mid-1980s, although fleet modernisation has taken place. The single tram route, which links northeastern and southern suburbs with the city centre and the eastern periphery of the steel plant, has not changed for many years, and the 13 trams built at Dalian around 1984 have not been followed by any more new cars. Trams dating from the late 1950s remain the mainstay of the fleet.

Trolleybus
Number of routes: 3
Route length: 25 km
Fleet: Over 100 articulated trolleybuses, recent deliveries are Shenyang SY561
Service: Every few minutes early morning to mid-evening
Fare collection: Cash payment to seated conductors, monthly passes
Fare structure: Stage

Tramway
Type of operation: Conventional tramway

Route length: 12.9 km
Number of routes: 1
Number of stops: 19
Gauge: 1,435 mm

Track: Railway type on side reservation and in centre of street
Electrification: 600 V DC, overhead

Service: Every few minutes, early morning to evening; extra cars run to cater for steel plant shift workers
Fare collection: Payment to roving conductors, monthly passes
Fare structure: Two flat-fare zones

Rolling stock: Approx 70 Dalian-built four-axle motored cars

Anshan Steel Co

Current situation: A public passenger service is operated over about 30 km of essentially industrial trackage with 22 stations. A circle line is electrified at 1.5 kV DC and a short branch line is diesel-worked. Irregular service to suit shift patterns at the steelworks. Industrial locomotives haul main line coaches.

VERIFIED

Dalian-built tramcars in Anshan

ANTWERP

Population: 529,000
Public transport: Bus and tramway/pre-metro services operated by publicly owned regional undertaking. An independent company operates five routes under contract. Suburban rail services operated by state railway

De Lijn (VVM)

Vlaamse Vervoermaatschappij (VVM)
Grotehondstraat 58, 2018 Antwerp, Belgium
Tel: (+32 3) 218 14 11   Fax: (+32 3) 218 15 00
Managing Director: L De Kesel
Operating Manager: D Swerts
Staff: 1,710

Passenger journeys: (All modes, Antwerpen urban area)
(1994) 57 million
(1995) 55 million
(1996) 52 million

Operating costs financed by: (All modes) fares 38.5 per cent, other commercial sources 2.7 per cent, government subsidy/grants 58.8 per cent

Current situation: In 1991, control of urban and regional public transport in the Vlaanderen region passed to VVM, known as De Lijn, which took over the former urban and national (SNCV) networks in the area. VVM is also responsible for all operations of the former National Bus Company (NMBV/SNCV) in Flemish-speaking regions.

De Lijn Antwerpen's bus operation extends to 45 routes operated by a fleet of 426 vehicles, while a further 31 routes are contracted to private operators. Details below refer to Antwerpen urban operations only.
Developments: Following opening of the latest section of pre-metro (underground tramway) in April 1996 (see below), plans for more tunnelling are in doubt and some completed sections may not now be opened.

Bus

Passenger journeys: (1994) 20 million
(1995) 18 million
(1996) 16.4 million
Vehicle-km: (1994) 7 million
(1995) 7.1 million
(1996) 7.2 million

Number of routes: 22
Route length: One-way 228 km, of which 109 km under contract (see below)
On priority right-of-way: 3.2 km

Fleet: 110 buses, plus 29 Mercedes on services under contract (see below)
Jonckheere-Mercedes O305 'TransCity' (1986)	80
Van Hool A300	30

In peak service: 82
New vehicles required each year: 11

Most intensive service: 10 min
One-person operation: All routes

Fare collection: Prepurchase multiride tickets, single-ride tickets only from driver; Prodata magnetic ticketing system
Fare structure: Flat 1-h tariff with free transfers, with 36 per cent discount for prepurchase of 8-ride multiride tickets (part of national scheme) and variety of day/period passes and tourist cards
Fares collected on board: (Bus and tram) single tickets 13 per cent, multiride 39 per cent, passes 26 per cent, pupil season tickets 22 per cent
Fare evasion control: Drivers and inspectors
Integration with other modes: Integration of services with tramway and regional bus lines
Operational control: Route inspectors/mobile radio; new radio system to be installed
Bus priority: 4 bus lanes totalling 3.2 km
Average distance between stops: 441 m, with some exceptions up to 1.4 km
Average peak-hour speed: In mixed traffic, less than 12 km/h
Operating costs financed by: Fares 28.5 per cent, other commercial sources 2.1 per cent, subsidy 69.4 per cent
New vehicles financed by: Loans

Bus (contracted)

Current situation: Five contracted routes totalling 109 km are operated with 29 buses by the De Polder company which is paid a per-km fee. A standard livery is used.

Tramway/pre-metro

Rolling Stock Manager: M Verdonck
Fixed Installations Manager: A Wittemans

Type of operation: Pre-metro, light rail, conventional tramway

Passenger journeys: (1994) 37 million
(1995) 37 million
(1996) 36 million
Car-km: (1994) 7.3 million
(1995) 7.3 million
(1996) 7.4 million

Route length: Pre-metro 15.2 km; tramway/light rail 101 km
  in tunnel: 15.2 km (pre-metro)
  on private right-of-way: 48.9 km light rail (in city 16.9 km, in suburbs 32 km)
Number of lines: Pre-metro 3, conventional 7
Number of stations: Pre-metro 6
Gauge: 1,000 mm
Track: 61.7 kg/m grooved or 50 kg/m flat-bottomed (vignole) rail, timber sleepers on ballast; 530 m section on concrete sleepers with resilient pads
Max gradient: 6%
Minimum curve radius: 18 m, new track 25 m
Tunnel: Bored double-track and cut-and-cover; new work shield tunnelling, single-track; stations built by roof pipe-jacking

PCC cars on Route 2 at Belgielei

1998/0007280

Electrification: 600 V DC, overhead

Service: Peak 4-6 min, off-peak 15 min
First/last car: 04.30/01.00
Fare structure: Flat (see above)
Revenue control: Prepurchase of tickets encouraged by discount; cancelling machines on board
Integration with other modes: As bus
Operating costs financed by: Fares 42.5 per cent, other commercial sources 3.7 per cent, government subsidy 53.8 per cent
One-person operation: All tram lines

Rolling stock: 166 cars
BN PCC (1960/61)   M39
BN PCC (1962)   M22
BN PCC (1966)   M40
BN PCC (1969/70)   M25
BN PCC (1974/75)   M40
Works cars   M8 T12
In peak service: 124

Developments: Further 6 km of pre-metro completed and awaiting tracklaying as funds become available. Further sections will open depending on design considerations and availability of finance. Preparatory studies made for further tramway extensions, based on studies completed in 1991.

Modernisation started 1989 of 105 PCC tramcars, which are being equipped with chopper control to improve operating characteristics for pre-metro routes.

Tram Route 3 has been upgraded to light rail standards, and extended to Linkeroever; futher extension from Astridplein to Sportpaleis opened 1996.

Construction was expected to start in 1998 on an extension to Zwijndrecht. New depot at Punt aan de Lijn opened February 1998.

SNCB

Belgian National Railways (SNCB/NMBS), North-East District
Koningin Astridplein 27, 2018 Antwerpen
Tel: (+32 3) 204 21 11   Fax: (+32 3) 204 29 00

Type of operation: Suburban heavy rail

Current situation: Local services run about hourly on five routes out of Antwerpen Centraal, electrified 3 kV DC.

UPDATED

ASHGABAT

Population: 500,000
Public transport: Bus and trolleybus services provided by municipal operators

Trolleybus
Current situation: Seven routes have been identified, but many streets are equipped with wires, but have no service. There is a fleet of about 30 Uritsky ZIU9s, plus a few Dniepropetrovsk PMZ, 10 ZIU10s and 3 LAZ 52522.

Bus
Current situation: Standard buses, mostly Ikarus 260/262/280 plus some LAZ 697R, are supplemented by a fleet of Iranian-bodied TAM midibuses. The latter also run fixed routes, some of which are shared with buses.

There are also two fleets of minibuses, Iranian-built on Iveco or Irankhodro chassis.

VERIFIED

Irankhodro Mercedes-type minibuses at Azadi   *1997*

ASUNCIÓN

Population: 460,000
Public transport: Bus and minibus services provided by private individual operators and groups. Government-operated tramway

Bus/minibus
Services under supervision of:
Seccion Transporte Publico
Direccion de Transporte Municipalidad
Oliva 579, Asunción, Paraguay
Tel: (+595 21) 477 19

Current situation: Extensive private bus operation largely employs 35-40 seat midibuses.

Passenger journeys: Bus 85 million, minibus 95 million (annual)
Vehicle-km: Bus 17 million, minibus 29 million (annual)

Number of routes: 37; bus 25, minibus 12
Route length: Bus 340 km, minibus 220 km

Fleet: About 1,000 vehicles (650 minibuses) including substantial numbers of Volvo 375 and some Henschel buses. Most popular mini/midibuses are Mercedes-Benz 608 derivatives and Austins

Fare collection: Mobile conductors
Fare structure: 2 zonal rates (city centre and elsewhere)

ATE
Administración de Transporte Electrico

Tramway
Type of operation: Conventional tramway

Buses of independent operators in Asunción   *1997*

Passenger journeys: 1.6 million (annual)

Current situation: A 5 km route remains, re-equipped with former Brussels cars. A 1983 consultants' study recommended retention and modernisation of the network. Infrastructure remains intact on two other routes, but rolling stock shortages prevent operation of a second route.

Developments: Service was suspended in 1994, though the line is not officially closed. Only one car is reported as being in working order.

Rolling stock: 5 cars
BN 9000 (ex-Brussels)   M5

VERIFIED

ATHENS

Population: 3.6 million

Public transport: Two independent state-owned companies, ETHEL (Thermal Bus Corporation) and ILPAP (Athens–Piraeus Azea Electric Buses), operate buses and trolleybuses. Suburban rail services are operated by ISAP. A fourth company, OASA, is responsible for overall planning of public transport, and for the financial support of the three operating companies; metro under construction

OASA

Urban Transport Organisation of Athens
15 Metsovou Street, 10682 Athens, Greece
Tel: (+30 1) 823 65 66   Fax: (+30 1) 821 22 19
Director, Planning & Development: P Kontogianis

Operating costs financed by: Fares 34 per cent, other sources (mainly loans) 44 per cent, subsidies/grants 22 per cent.

Current situation: OASA was established in 1993 as successor to the similar body OAS. It is responsible for transport planning throughout the city, for financial support of the three operating companies, and for marketing and promotion. OASA's subsidiary ETHEL was created in 1994 to operate all bus services.

Bus priority measures include 10 bus lanes (three contraflow) and three with-flow in middle of street.

ETHEL

Urban Transport Corporation (ETHEL SA)
Parnassou 6, 182 33 Athens
Tel: (+30 1) 493 30 02   Fax: (+30 1) 492 20 75
General Manager: K Kokkoris
Managing Director: A Batsos
Staff: 8,796

Current situation: Set up in 1994, ETHEL runs all the city's bus services, except the ISAP feeder routes.

Bus

Staff: 5,914

Passenger boardings: (1995) 469.3 million
Vehicle-km: (1995) 106.7 million

Number of routes: 282
Route length: (Both directions) 5,739 km

Fleet: 2,097 vehicles

Magirus-Deutz (1982)	283
Ikarus 260	1,047
Volvo (1983)	100
Leyland Olympian double-deck	20
Van Hool 507 midibus (1991)	33
Den Oudsten (1993)	71
Van Hool (1993)	111
Neoplan (1993)	95
Mercedes-Benz (1993)	337
In peak service: 1,644	

Most intensive service: 5 min
One-person operation: 100 per cent
Fare collection: Cancelling machines, tickets sold at kiosks.

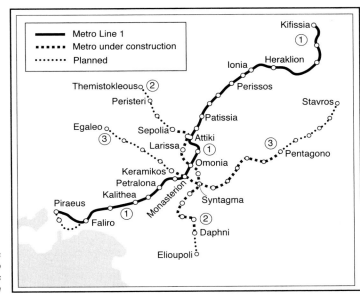

Fare structure: Flat; monthly passes
Fare evasion control: Roving inspectors
Average peak-hour speed: 16 km/h
Operational control: 300 bus controllers; computer monitoring planned
Operating costs financed by: Fares 34 per cent, other sources (mainly loans) 21 per cent, subsidies/grants 45 per cent

Developments: 750 new diesel buses and 130 CNG-powered buses have been ordered. Delivery is expected by 2001.

ILPAP

Athens-Piraeus Area Electric Buses (ILPAP)
Kirkis & Achaias Street, New Philadelphia, 14342 Athens
Tel: (+30 1) 258 33 00/33 01   Fax: (+30 1) 253 30 50
General Manager: K Chrisoulakis
Chairman: A Batsos
Staff: 2,055

Current situation: ILPAP operates the largest trolleybus fleet in western Europe. Environmental advantages favour trolleybuses; accordingly most of the routes serve the central business district.
Developments: On order are 280 trolleybuses including 192 dual-mode vehicles. Delivery is expected by 2001. The order includes 96 low-floor A300T trolleybuses, supplied by Van Hool and Alstom. Van Hool will build the vehicles and Alstom will supply the electrical equipment including its IGBT ONIX propulsion package. Van Hool has already supplied 33 midibuses and 111 low-floor 12 m buses to the city.

Trolleybus

Staff: 1,992

Passenger journeys: (1993) 80 million
(1995) 95 million
(1997) 69 million

Vehicle-km: (1993) 10.4 million
(1995) 11 million
(1997) 11.9 million

Number of routes: 18
Route length (both directions): 324 km

Fleet: 337 trolleybuses

Uritsky ZIU9/ZIU9B1 (1977-86)	236
Uritsky ZIU682 (1990–92)	101
In peak service: 300	

Most intensive service: 5 min
One-person operation: 100 per cent
Fare collection: Prepurchase ticket or monthly pass; cancelling machines on board
Fare structure: Flat; monthly passes
Fare evasion control: Random inspection
Operational control: Route inspectors; mobile radio
Average peak-hour speed: 11 km/h
Operating costs financed by: Fares 29 per cent, other sources (mainly loans) 27 per cent, subsidies/grants 44 per cent.
New vehicles financed by: Loans, barter deals

ISAP

Athens-Piraeus Electric Railways Co Ltd
Ilektriki Sidirodromi Athinon-Pireos AE (ISAP)
67 Athinas Street, 10552 Athens
Tel: (+30 1) 324 83 11   Fax: (+30 1) 322 39 25
President: Panagiotis Lampos
Managing Director: Konstantinos Vasiliadis

Operating costs financed by: Fares 37 per cent, other sources (mainly loans) 20 per cent, subsidies/grants 43 per cent

Current situation: ISAP operates the 750 V DC Athens-Piraeus Electric Railway linking Kifissia in the north with Athens and Piraeus, which is to become Line 1 of the

Athens-Piraeus Railway (Metro Line 1) and lines under construction

Legend:
— Metro Line 1
••••• Metro under construction
······ Planned

Eirini-bound train at Petralona   **1998**/0009564

Neoplan bus and Uritsky trolleybus in Athens   **1999**/0038744

metro (see below). It also runs a small complementary bus network.

Suburban rail
Staff: 1,514

Type of operation: Suburban rapid transit

Passenger boardings: (1995) 86.8 million
(1996) 86.7 million
(1997) 92 million

Route length: 51 km
  in tunnel: 3 km
Number of lines: 1
Number of stations: 23
  in tunnel: 3
Gauge: 1,435 mm
Track: Timber sleepers on ballast
Max gradient: 4%
Passenger **Minimum curve radius:** 160 m
Tunnel: Cut-and-cover
Electrification: 750 V DC, third rail

Service: Peak 3½ min
First/last train: 05.00/01.00

Fare collection: Ticket cancelling machines at entry
Fare structure: Metro, zonal; bus, flat with monthly passes

Rolling stock: 219 cars
MAN/Siemens (1958)	M15 T15
MAN/Siemens (1968)	M9 T9
MAN/Siemens/LEW (1983)	M44 T29
LEW G3 (1984)	M48
MAN/Siemens/Hellenic (1994/95)	M30 T20
In peak service: 135

Bus
Staff: 272

Current situation: Six routes are operated, extending to 57 route-km, with a fleet of 60 buses.

Attiko Metro
Attiko Metro AE

Current situation: Construction started 1992 on Lines 2 and 3 of a three-line network (Line 1 being the existing

Athens-Piraeus Railway). Line 2 will link Sepolia with Daphni (9.2 km), while Line 3 will run from Keramikos to Pentagono (8.4 km); 1,435 mm gauge, electrified 750 V DC third rail; total 21 stations.

Attiko Metro is a private company set up in 1992 to own and manage the metro, with two lines due to open in 2000. Initially, the lines will be signalled for manual operation at 2½ min headways, reducing to 1½ min when ATO is installed later. Ridership of 450,000 daily is expected in the first phase of operation.

Ten extensions totalling 44.3 km were assessed in planning studies completed in 1993, and four — including a deviation of Line 1 between Faliro and Piraeus — have been approved by the government for construction before the end of the century. These total 13.2 km, with 12 stations.

Also proposed are two tramway lines but construction has not yet started.

On order are 120 new cars to be delivered during 1999/2000.

UPDATED

ATLANTA
Population: 1.2 million
Public transport: Bus and metro services provided in Fulton and De Kalb counties and city of Atlanta by Transit Authority governed by 17-member representative board. Bus services in adjacent Cobb County link with metro; commuter rail proposed

MARTA
Metropolitan Atlanta Rapid Transit Authority (MARTA)
2424 Piedmont Avenue, Atlanta, Georgia 30324, USA
Tel: (+1 404) 848 50 00   Fax: (+1 404) 848 53 20
General Manager: Richard J Simonetta
Deputy General Manager: D L Brown
Senior Vice President, Operations: Nathaniel P Ford
Assistant General Manager, Bus: D Huber
Assistant General Manager, Rail: T Williams
Assistant General Manager, Transit System
  Development: Carolyn Wylder
Staff: 4,235

Passenger boardings: (1994) 142.7 million
(1995) 143.7 million
(1996) 144.8 million

Current situation: MARTA, created in 1965, became an operating agency in 1972 when it purchased the privately owned Atlanta Transit System, following the approval in 1971 of a 1 per cent sales tax in Fulton and De Kalb counties and the city of Atlanta, to apply until 2012 (later extended to 2032). The tax was rejected in Clayton and Gwinnett counties, and Cobb County declined to join altogether. The referendum mandated acquisition of ATS and provision of improved bus services, as well as construction of a 100 km metro network. No more than 50 per cent of the annual tax yield may be used to subsidise operating costs. Revenue bonds have been raised against the future tax yield to cover capital costs.

As each metro line opens, MARTA has integrated bus and rail, with bus routes diverted to feed rail lines. The result has been a significant reduction in bus traffic in the central business district.

Operating costs financed by: Fares 35 per cent, other commercial sources 7 per cent, subsidy/grants 5 per cent, sales tax 53 per cent
Subsidy from: FTA
New vehicles financed by: FTA grants (80 per cent) with local matching funds

Bus
Passenger boardings: (1994) 72.9 million
(1995) 73.3 million
(1996) 72.4 million
Vehicle-km: (1996) 29.8 million

Number of routes: 156
Route length: 2,526 km

Fleet: 704 vehicles	
Flxible Metro (1986/87/88)	272
New Flyer (1990)	160
New Flyer 35 ft (1990/92)	103
New Flyer low-floor (1994)	51
New Flyer low-floor CNG (1996)	118
In peak service: 586

Most intensive service: 6 min
One-person operation: All routes
Fare collection: GFI registering fareboxes
Fare structure: Flat, with free transfer within service area and to metro; transfer charge on 3 routes into Clayton and Gwinnett counties. Isolated higher fares outside regular service area. Weekly and monthly passes; tokens
Fare evasion control: Driver surveillance, electronic fareboxes
Operational control: Route inspectors/mobile radio; all buses radio-equipped; AVL on 250 buses
Arrangements for elderly/disabled: E-Bus is special door-to-door service for elderly; L-Van for disabled; half fare on regular routes at all times; wheelchair lift-equipped vans and conventional buses with kneeling capability used on request; 82 per cent of buses wheelchair accessible
Integration with other modes: Unified bus/metro fare system with free transfers. All bus routes feed at least one metro station; 9 park-and-ride lots with 2,386 spaces
Average distance between stops: 152 m
Average peak-hour speed: Mixed traffic, 15.3 km/h

Metro
Type of operation: Full metro, first line opened 1979

Passenger boardings: (1995) 70.4 million
(1996) 72.4 million
(1997) 78.4 million
Car-km: (1996) 59.4 million

Route length: 62.9 km
Number of lines: 3
Number of stations: 36
Gauge: 1,435 mm
Track: 52.1 kg/m 119RE continuously welded rail on

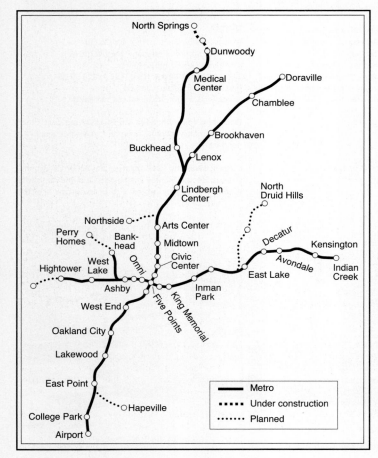

Atlanta metro

▬▬▬	Metro
▪▪▪▪▪	Under construction
••••••	Planned

concrete sleepers; elastomer springing under track in residential areas to reduce vibration; screens on surface and elevated sections to reduce noise
Max gradient: 3%
Minimum curve radius: 230 m
Electrification: 750 V DC, third rail

Service: 8 min
First/last train: 04.30/01.00
Fare structure: As bus
Revenue control: Automatic turnstiles accept coins, tokens, magnetic transfer tickets, smartcards and weekly and monthly passes; CCTV at all stations, which are unstaffed
Integration with other modes: Bus feeder services to all stations; 24 park-and-ride stations with 20,000 spaces
Arrangements for elderly/disabled: All stations wheelchair accessible

Bus feeders run to all MARTA metro stations

Signalling: ATP, ATO and automatic line supervision

Rolling stock: 240 cars
Franco-Belge 77A (1978/79)	M120
Hitachi/Itoh 82 (1985/86)	M120
In peak service: 160
On order: 100 cars from Breda for delivery starting in late 1999; Breda is also upgrading the traction equipment on the original fleet of 120 cars dating from 1978.

Developments: A 3.2 km extension to North Springs under construction for late 2000 opening.

New plans drafted under the MARTA 2000 programme by the Atlanta Regional Commission in 1989 envisage further metro routes to serve the northern suburbs, plus some 70 km of automated light metro, an exclusive busway and possible commuter rail service. At the end of 1997, studies were being made of a proposed 24 km line

1998/0007281

from Lindbergh Center to South DeKalb, which could be metro, light rail or monorail.

Cobb Community Transit
Cobb Community Transit
100 Cherokee Street, Suite 500, Marietta, Georgia 30090-9612
Tel: (+1 770) 528 16 10   Fax: (+1 770) 528 16 11
Transit Division Manager: Mary Shavalier
General Manager: Eric Estell
Staff: 111

Passenger journeys: (1995) 2.8 million
(1996) 2.9 million
(1997) 2.5 million
Vehicle-km: (1997) 1.9 million

Fleet: 55 vehicles
Flxible Metro 10.6 m (1989)	18
Flxible Metro 12 m (1989)	18
RTS-06 Suburban	19
In peak service: 43
Average age of fleet: 10 years

Current situation: Set up in 1989 to provide service in outer Atlanta suburbs in Cobb County; managed by Ryder/ATE Inc. Three express and one local route run to MARTA stations with through ticketing. Total 14 routes extending to 555 km; 55 buses; fares cover 35 per cent of operating costs.
Developments: A new bus transfer centre was opened in August 1998. Construction of a new operations, maintenance and administration centre has been delayed until 1999. Installation of seats and shelters at bus stops continues in phases.

Commuter rail (proposed)
Current situation: The Georgia Rail Passenger Authority has identified six routes over which commuter rail service could be revived and held public hearings on the project during 1995. Routes selected are from Athens, Bremen, Senoia, Gainesville, Madison and Canton to Atlanta.

UPDATED

AUCKLAND
Population: City 360,000, urban area 1.1 million
Public transport: A mix of commercial and non-commercial bus, train and ferry services is registered with the Regional Council, which also contracts and funds non-commercial services

Auckland Regional Council (ARC)
Auckland Regional Council
Private Bag 92012, Newton, Auckland, New Zealand
Tel: (+64 9) 379 44 20   Fax: (+64 9) 366 21 48
Transport Group Manager: Barry Mein

Current situation: Deregulation of public transport services was implemented in 1991. ARC contracts and funds non-commercial services, and also funds concessionary fares on all services.
Developments: A proposed 1 km rail extension into the city centre, where a new underground bus/rail interchange is to be built, remains bogged down in legal issues but construction could begin in 1999.

Progress is slow on the Auckland Rail Transit plan (see below) owing to difficulties in introducing an element of competition to a monopoly provider.

On the North Shore a bus/HOV lane is planned alongside the Northern Motorway.

Bus services in the North Shore and South Auckland are being reviewed with new services planned for 1999. In both areas trials of Output Based Funding, where operators are funded for passengers carried rather than providing service, will take place.

On 1 October 1998 a new funding agency was established to fund the public good element of transport and stormwater infrastructure. Infrastructure Auckland controls an asset fund of nearly NZ$900 million, from which it can make capital grants to contribute and give effect to regional growth and transport strategies.

MAN of Yellow Bus at Takapuna Transport Centre, North Shore

1997

Arrangements for elderly/disabled: The Total Mobility scheme provides half-price taxi fares for those who cannot use scheduled services; ARC also funds installation of wheelchair hoists in taxivans

Bus
Passenger boardings: (1995) 31.1 million
(1996) 32 million
(1997) 32.6 million

Operating costs financed by: Fares 44 per cent, property taxes and central government funding 56 per cent on contracted services. Commercial services are 100 per cent funded by fares apart from concessionary fare reimbursement.

Current situation: Services are provided by several operators. In 1997 Whenuapai Bus Travel and Devonport Bus Company were taken over by the Yellow Bus

Company. In 1998 the Yellow Bus Company was privatised and sold to Stagecoach Group which merged it with Cityline Auckland, which it already owned under the banner of Stagecoach Auckland. Stagecoach also took a controlling interest in ferry operator Fullers, giving Stagecoach a dominant position in the Auckland public transport market. The remaining operators are: Birkenhead Transport, Howick & Eastern Buses, Eastern Taxis, Gubbs, Hanham's, Ritchies and Taxi North Shore. Their combined fleets total 824 vehicles and they employ 1,365 staff.

Developments: Patronage grew by 2 per cent in 1996/97. All buses now have electronic ticket machines capable of handling smartcards as a first step in development of an integrated ticketing system.

Stagecoach Auckland has started taking delivery of 60 low-floor low-emission buses and is planning to buy another 200 between 1999 and 2001. This will substantially reduce the average age of buses in Auckland.

Four kilometres of peak-period bus lanes were introduced on the congested Dominion Road corridor in March 1998, leading to significant reductions in bus times and increases in patronage. More fragmented bus lane sections in Mt Eden Road have had a lesser impact. Further priority measure for buses are programmed for other major arterials.

The inner-city Link service, launched in 1997, is now carrying around 2 million passengers a year.

MAN bus in Stagecoach livery in Auckland   **1999**/0045127

Suburban rail
Operated under contract by Tranz Metro Auckland

Type of operation: Suburban heavy rail

Passenger journeys: (1995) 2 million
(1996) 2.1 million
(1997) 2.1 million

Current situation: Suburban trains operated by Tranz Metro covering three routes totalling 79 km with 38 stations — the Papakura (31 km) and Waitakere (31 km) lines, and the 17 km Harbour loop. Service at peak hours 15-30 min, 30-60 min off-peak and Saturday.
Developments: Increased patronage following the 1994 service revamp has led to capacity problems on the Waitakere line, which were overcome in 1997 with the lengthening of station platforms, allowing longer trains to run. Double-tracking of remaining single-track sections of the Waitakere line is proposed, to permit increases in service frequency.

It is proposed to upgrade the Harbour Loop line as a possible alternative to a proposed eastern arterial road. This upgrade includes station and train frequency upgrades and the relocation of Panmure station in association with a large park-and-ride area.

Rolling stock: 19 two-car dmus (ex-Perth)

Rail Transit Project
Current situation: An international expression of interest process for upgrading of the existing rail system was initiated in 1996. This process was varied in November 1997 due to the inability of Tranz Rail Ltd, the private owner of the rail corridor, and the Auckland Regional Council to conclude an access agreement. A subsequent Commerce Commission investigation highlighted the need for a transparent and competitive process for the upgrade of the rail service, and negotiations to resolve this impasse are in progress.

Ferry
Passenger journeys: (1995) 1.6 million
(1996) 1.8 million
(1997) 2 million

Current situation: Six ferry services operate in Waitemata Harbour and the Hauraki Gulf, linking central Auckland with Devonport, Stanley Bay, Birkenhead, Gulf Harbour, Bayswater and Waiheke, with routes to other Hauraki Gulf islands mainly for recreational purposes.
Developments: The Stagecoach Group took a controlling interest in dominant ferry operator Fullers in late 1998. Tenders have been issued for a new ferry service linking Half Moon Bay with Downtown Island.

UPDATED

AUGSBURG
Population: 253,000, region 648,000
Public transport: Bus and tramway services provided by municipal authority. German Railway (DB AG) provides commuter services. Suburban bus services provided by regional bus company and independent operators. Regional transit authority (AVV) integrates urban and suburban services

AVV
Augsburger Verkehrsverbund GmbH (AVV)
PO Box 101120, 86001 Augsburg, Germany
Tel: (+49 821) 15 70 07   Fax: (+49 821) 333 72
Managing Director: Helmut Hofmann

Passenger journeys: (1995) 17.4 million
(1996) 76.5 million
(1997) 75.2 million

Current situation: AVV, the regional transit authority, was created in 1985 by the city of Augsburg and surrounding local authorities to co-ordinate public transport in the region. The scheme includes six rail lines radiating from Augsburg and 97 regional bus routes operated by 19 companies with a route length of 2,653 km. Full integration of these was completed in 1992. Creation of 2,500 park-and-ride spaces and 780 cycle racks is planned at 20 stations.

Urban services in Augsburg (see below) were fully integrated into AVV during 1995, leading to the substantial rise in passenger journeys recorded above.

Operating costs financed by: Fares 56.7 per cent, other commercial sources 7.8 per cent, local authority subsidies 35.5 per cent

VGA
Stadtwerke Augsburg-Verkehrsbetriebe (VGA)
Hoher Weg 1, 86152 Augsburg
Tel: (+49 821) 324 25 65   Fax: (+49 821) 324 25 89
General Manager: Dr Werner Pusinelli
Operating Manager: Dipl-Ing P Lessing
Staff: 880

Passenger journeys: (1995) 50.8 million
(1996) 52.8 million
(1997) 51.8 million

Operating costs financed by: Fares 49.7 per cent, other sources 50.3 per cent
Subsidy from: City

Current situation: In order to improve the attractiveness of public transport in the region, frequency on bus and tram routes has been improved, and there are plans for more reserved rights-of-way for both buses and trams. Four suburban routes are served by shared taxis, operating to fixed schedule but on request by phone or radio-call from driver of connecting tram or bus.

Bus
Vehicle-km: (1995) 7.1 million
(1996) 6.8 million
(1997) 6.6 million

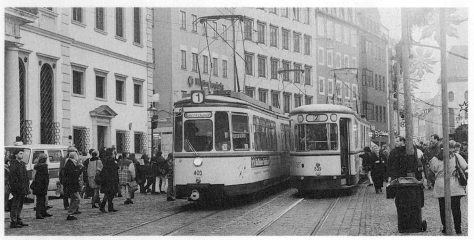

Ex-Stuttgart GT4 (left) on Augsburg's Karolinenstrasse   **1996**

MAN NG202 low-floor on Route 36 at Moritzplatz **1996**

Number of routes: 25
Route length: (One way) 203 km
On priority right-of-way: 2 km

Fleet: 139 vehicles, plus 5 subcontracted
MAN SL200 (1980/85)	9
MAN SG240H articulated (1981/86)	55
MAN SG242 articulated (1987/89)	22
MAN NL202 low-floor (1991)	20
MAN NG272 low-floor (1991)	22
MAN NG232 low-floor articulated CNG-powered (1996)	8
MAN NG313 low-floor CNG-powered (1998)	3

In peak service: 116

Most intensive service: 10 min
One-person operation: All routes
Fare collection: Payment to driver or prepurchase with validation/cancellation machines on board
Fare structure: Zonal, multitickets, day and period passes, annual subscription
Fares collected on board: 6 per cent (58 per cent hold passes)
Fare evasion control: Random inspection with penalty (DM60)
Operational control: Mobile radio
Arrangements for elderly/disabled: Free travel for disabled, reimbursed by government

Developments: VGA operates its own CNG filling station, which is also available to other users.

Tramway
Type of operation: Conventional tramway

Car-km: (1995) 2.7 million
(1996) 3.2 million
(1997) 3.5 million

Route length: 30.6 km
Number of routes: 4 (all cross-town)
Gauge: 1,000 mm
Electrification: 600 V DC, overhead

Service: All day 5 min
Fare structure: Zonal, as bus

Rolling stock: 75 cars
MAN GT8 (1976)	M12
Duewag/MAN M8C (1985)	M12
Esslingen GT4 (1965)	M20 T20
AEG GT6M low-floor (1995/96)	M11

In peak service: 44
On order: 16 Siemens Combino 7-section low-floor for August 1999 delivery

Developments: New Route 3 mostly on private right-of-

way from Hbf to Inninger Strasse to serve the university and Haunstetten opened 1996. A further extension of Route 3 from Haunsutetten to Königsbrunn Stadtgrenze is planned for construction starting in 1999. Plans for a northwards extension of Route 4 from Oberhausen to Oberhausen Nord (Gersthofen boundary) were finalised in August 1997 and construction started in summer 1998.

Plans also exist to divert Route 2 underground at Hbf to give a direct connection from tram to main line platforms.

DB
Deutsche Bahn AG, Geschäftsbereich Nahverkehr
Regionalbereich Süd-Bayern
Richelstrasse 3, 80634 München
Tel: (+49 89) 13 08 33 30   Fax: (+49 89) 13 08 19 31

Current situation: Commuter services are operated on six lines totalling 160 km, integrated in AVV (see above). Frequencies are irregular. Ordinary railway stock, both electric and diesel, is used.

RBA
Regionalbus Augsburg GmbH
Leonhardsberg 1, 86150 Augsburg
Tel: (+49 821) 50 21 50   Fax: (+49 821) 502 15 88
Managing Directors: Walter Jägle
  Ralph André
Staff: 211

Passenger journeys: (1994) 30.5 million
(1996) 27 million
(1997) 26 million
Vehicle-km: (1994) 22 million
(1996) 21.9 million
(1997) 21.9 million

Current situation: Formerly owned by DB, this regional bus company was sold to a group of private bus operators in 1992. There are 156 local and regional routes operated, extending well beyond the AVV area, totalling 5,250 km, with a fleet of 168 buses, plus 392 hired.

STWG
Stadtwerke Gersthofen
Augsburger Strasse 1A, 86368 Gersthofen
Tel: (+49 821) 249 14 80
Operating Manager: Hans Baumer

Current situation: Local authority operator runs a service between Gersthofen and Augsburg, and other local services, with a fleet of 25 buses.

UPDATED

AUSTIN
Population: 1 million
Public transport: Bus services in city and surrounding suburban areas provided by public authority through undertaking managed under contract, other services operated by private company; light rail proposed

Capital Metro
Capital Metropolitan Transportation Authority
2910 East 5th Street, Austin, Texas 78702, USA
Tel: (+1 512) 389 74 00   Fax: (+1 512) 389 12 83
General Manager: Justin T Augustine III
Assistant General Manager, Development: Jim Robertson
Chief Financial Officer: Alan Pegg
Chief Operating Officer: Gerald Robichaux
Chief Communications Officer: Rita Scott
Staff: 933

Current situation: Capital Metro was established in 1985 as a public authority for provision of transport in Austin and its suburbs. Today, it serves an area of 800 km² with a population of 621,000. Service includes park-and-ride routes, local routes, a downtown replica trolley service, vanpools, carpool-matching, door-to-door paratransit for mobility-impaired people, and rural feeder routes. The fleet includes the country's largest number of alternatively fuelled vehicles, and is 100 per cent accessible.
Developments: The Austin metropolitan area is growing

fast, and Capital Metro has moved swiftly to cater for changing transport needs. Its back-to-basics programme has focused on provision of quality service, resulting in major improvements for most passengers. Capital Metro is overseeing the Build Greater Austin programme which is providing $60.2 million over the 10 years to 2003 for street and pavement construction and repairs, and for other mobility projects throughout the region.

Proposals for a fixed-guideway system have been under development since 1986 (see below), when the City of Austin purchased the 261 km Giddings—Llano rail alignment from Southern Pacific. Now Capital Metro is to buy the route from the city and will take over management of various rail-related activities, such as freight service and tourist train operation. Funding was allocated in the 1998 budget for track and safety improvements.

Bus
Passenger boardings: (1993) 25.6 million
(1994) 26.3 million
(1996) 28 million

Number of routes: 60
Route length: 884 km

Fleet: 462 vehicles
Gillig Phantom (1985/86/89)	230
TMC RTS (1993)	30
TVI/SVMC trolley replicas (1985/86)	20
Various vans/minibuses	57
Low-floor buses	125

In peak service: 291

Most intensive service: 4-6 min
Fare structure: Flat, higher fare on Express routes, free transfer; 20-ticket books; monthly passes
Fare collection: Exact fare to farebox or prepurchase ticket
Integration with other modes: 11 park-and-ride lots served by a network of commuter Express bus routes, with 'Guaranteed Ride Home' taxi service available up to four times a year for $5 subscription; 115 vanpools
Arrangements for elderly/disabled: Demand-responsive service operated with 45 vans and 32 sedans, carried 452,000 passengers in 1996. Fixed-route fleet is 100 per cent lift-equipped, and there were 73,000 wheelchair boardings in 1996
Operating costs financed by: Fares 7 per cent, other sources 3 per cent, subsidy/grants 10 per cent, sales tax 80 per cent
Subsidy from: FTA and state of Texas

Light rail (proposed)
Current situation: Along with other options, a 22.5 km light rail line with 18 stations has been examined for the corridor north from the city centre to Parmer Lane and the University of Texas. In 1995, Capitol Metro's board proposed a 38 km starter line in the Northwest/North

Central Corridor, and authorised fast-track planning of the initial 22.5 km portion linking Leander with downtown Austin. Preliminary engineering studies were scheduled for 1998 at a cost of $3 million.

Portions of the Giddings—Llano rail alignment (see above) may also be utilised for light rail or commuter rail schemes, following demonstration service with a Siemens RegioSprinter railcar in 1997. Funding for engineering and environmental studies was approved in early 1997, with design work scheduled to start in 1999.

VERIFIED

BAKU

Population: 1.7 million
Public transport: Bus and trolleybus/tramway and funicular services operated by separate municipal authorities. Metro run by Ministry of Communications accounts for 25 per cent of journeys, with buses taking 50 per cent. Suburban rail services

Upravlenie Passajirskogo Transporta

Upravlenie Passajirskogo Transporta
Baku, Azerbaijan

Bus
Route length: 1,512 km

Fleet: 605 vehicles, including some articulated

One-person operation: All routes
Fare collection: Conductors
Fare structure: Flat
Average peak-hour speed: 18 km/h

Tramvaino-Trolleibusnoe Upravlenie

Tramvaino-Trolleibusnoe Upravlenie
Rosa Luxembourg Str 27, 370010 Baku
Tel: (+994 12) 93 50 05

Trolleybus
Route length: 175 km

Fleet: 340 vehicles
Škoda 9Tr
Škoda 14Tr   230
ZIU9

One-person operation: All routes
Fare collection: Conductors
Fare structure: Flat
Average peak-hour speed: 17 km/h

Tramway
Type of operation: Conventional tramway

Route length: 71 km
Gauge: 1,524 mm
Fare structure: Flat
Fare collection: Conductors

Baku metro

One-person operation: All routes

Rolling stock: 90 cars
RVZ6   M40
KTM5   M50

Developments: Trams were eliminated from the city centre after opening of the metro, but their use as feeders continues and further extensions are planned into areas where traffic density would not support a metro line.

Baku Metro

Bakinski Metropolitan
Azizbekov prospekt 33A, 370602 Baku
Tel: (+994 12) 98 25 00
Chief Executive: Y I Usifov
Chief Engineer: E E Muradov
Staff: 2,400

Type of operation: Full metro, first line opened 1967

Passenger journeys: (1991) 160 million

Route length: 29 km
Number of lines: 2
Number of stations: 18
Gauge: 1,524 mm

Max gradient: 4%
Minimum curve radius: 300 m
Tunnel: Baku chamber method developed to counter poor geological conditions; stations mostly cut-and-cover
Electrification: 825 V DC, third rail

Service: 2 min
First/last train: 06.00/01.00
Fare structure: Flat; monthly fare card
Fare collection: Automatic barriers
Signalling: Automatic train stop; radio-telephone communication between trains and central control

Rolling stock: 167 cars
E/Ex   M48
Ex3 (1975)   M76
Others   M43

Developments: Extensions are under construction totalling 4.1 km with three stations, and a further 10.2 km with six stations is in design. An eventual network of 52 km with 34 stations is envisaged.

Following the disastrous fire of late 1995, in which 286 people were killed, immediate efforts were made to tackle the backlog of infrastructure maintenance, though progress was hampered by shortage of finance.

UPDATED

BALTIMORE

Population: 750,000
Public transport: Bus, metro and light rail services operated by Mass Transit Administration, an agency of the Maryland Department of Transportation. Commuter services operated for MDoT under contract

Maryland MTA

Maryland Mass Transit Administration
6 Saint Paul Street, Baltimore, Maryland 21202-1614, USA
Tel: (+1 410) 767 39 43   Fax: (+1 410) 333 32 79
Administrator: Ron Freeland
Group Director, Operations and Engineering:
   Charles S Carnaggio
Staff: 301 (Administrative)

Passenger boardings: (All modes)
(1993) 92.4 million
(1994) 93.4 million
(1996) 101.2 million

MTA Baltimore light rail car in city centre
1999/0038749

Subsidy from: Canton and city

Current situation: Patronage has grown by some 29 per cent since introduction in 1983 of BVB's 'environmental' season ticket scheme, subsidised by all local authorities in the region, and congestion on tram routes in particular has led to examination of various capacity improvements (see below).

Developments: Rigorous cost-cutting, whilst maintaining service standards, helped reduce the deficit from roundly SWFr50 million in 1992 to SWFr39 million in 1993. But BVB ran into further financial difficulties in 1995/96, when the deficit reached SwFr48 million. Causes of the deficit include a reduction in the number of single tickets sold, reduced tariff income from TNW, and loss of income due to the popularity of BLT's tram routes in the city centre.

BVB has adopted a new marketing strategy *Bürgernah, Verfügbar, Bequem* (popular, accessible, comfortable).

Bus and trolleybus
Passenger journeys: (1993) 33.3 million
Vehicle-km: (1993) Bus 2.3 million, trolleybus 1.3 million

Number of routes: Bus 9, trolleybus 3
Route length: Bus 55.2 km, trolleybus 13.5 km

Fleet: 56 buses

Standard	35
Articulated	21

Fleet: 14 trolleybuses

Mercedes articulated (1982/83)	2
Neoplan low-floor articulated prototype (1992)	1
Neoplan low-floor articulated (1995)	11

Trolleybus electrification: 600 V DC

Most intensive service: 10 min
One-person operation: All routes
Integration with other modes: Full integration with tramway service
Average distance between stops: 400 m
Average peak-hour speed: 20 km/h
Subsidy from: City of Basle

Developments: 12 CNG-powered low-floor buses delivered late 1995.

Tramway
Type of operation: Conventional tramway

Passenger journeys: (1993) 120 million
(1994) 121 million
Car-km: (1993) 15.5 million

Route length: 61 km
Number of lines: 9
Gauge: 1,000 mm
Electrification: 600 V DC, overhead

Service: Peak 6 min, day 8 min, evenings 12 min
First/last car: 05.30/00.30
Fare structure: Zonal
Revenue control: Automatic ticket machines
Integration with other modes: Fully integrated with bus and trolleybus and BLT services, and bus services into Germany
One-person operation: All routes

Rolling stock: 338 cars, including 30 Be 4/6 owned by BVB but working on BLT (see below)

SWP Be 4/4 (1948/68)	M45
Duewag Be 4/6 (1967/73)	M58
Schindler Be 4/4 (1986/87)	M26
Schindler Be 4/6	M57
Trailers (various builders)	T113
Others	39

On order: 28 low-floor centre sections from Schindler to augment the 1990/91 fleet of Be 4/6 articulated cars. Trials with a prototype started in January 1998, and deliveries will run through to May 1999.

Developments: Completion of the reconstructed Wettstein bridge has allowed rerouting of Route 15 to provide better service between Klein-Basel north of the Rhein and the southeastern suburbs. Line 15 is also being extended through the Claragraben (where trams last ran 90 years ago) to reach industrial and shopping areas in the north of the city. Extensive works are planned to permit through running of BLT routes 10 and 11 to the main SBB station, for 1999 completion.

Gas-powered bus of BVB in Basle city centre   **1997**

Citroën Jumper on BVB's 1A minibus shuttle linking Messeplatz and Brombacherstrasse (Chris Bushell) **1997**

Neoplan low-floor trolleybus of BVB at Claraplatz in the city centre (Ken Harris)   **1999**/0043586

BLT

Baselland Transport AG
Granzweg 1, 4104 Oberwil
Tel: (+41 61) 406 11 11   Fax: (+41 61) 406 11 22
Managing Director: A Büttiker
Administrative and Financial Director: R Stöckli
Operating Manager: René Meury
Staff: 230

Passenger journeys: (1996) 50.5 million

Current situation: Formerly independent suburban tramways and a local light railway were merged in 1974 to form BLT, which was also given a remit to integrate bus services in the suburbs. The light rail Route 17 (the former Birsigthalbahn) was converted to tramway operation in 1984. All four routes use BVB tracks to reach central Basle, and 10 and 11 will be extended to the SBB station in 1999.

Tramway

Current situation: The two original tramways are Route 11 to Aesch and Route 14 to Pratteln (worked by BVB cars). A third, Route 10 serving Dornach, was extended in 1986 from its former terminus at Heuwaage into the city centre over BVB tracks and linked with Route 17 to Rodersdorf. This route passes through French territory and terminates in Solothurn canton; at 25.6 km it is the longest tram route in Switzerland. Total network 57 km of 1,000 mm gauge, electrified 600 V DC.

Route length: 51.5 km
Number of stations/stops: 77
Gauge: 1,000 mm
Track: Conventional sleepers on ballast and sleepers on concrete with resilient pads
Max gradient: 5%
Min curve radius: 12 m

Service: Peak 5 min, off-peak 10 min
First/last tram: 04.30/00.15

Rolling stock: 113 tramcars
Adtranz (Schindler)   M84 T17

Bus

Passenger journeys: (1994) 3.2 million
Vehicle-km: (1994) 1 million

BVB tram with Schindler Technik low-floor centre section at Claraplatz (Ken Harris)   **1999**/0043587

Number of routes: 7
Route length: 49 km

Fleet: 24 vehicles
Scania (1983/84)	3
Mercedes-Benz (1987–90/1993/1998)	18
Van Hool (1995)	3

Most intensive service: 10 min
Fare structure: Zonal
Operational control: Radio

SBB-CFF

Swiss Federal Railways

Type of operation: Suburban heavy rail

Current situation: As well as local services over its routes radiating from Basle, SBB operates the international S-Bahn service to Mulhouse in France, inaugurated in 1997 and expanded in 1998.

Developments: The first Regio S-Bahn route, the Green line, links existing routes from Laufenberg and Frick in the east with Basle SBB, the St Louis frontier, Habsheim and Mulhouse. An hourly service is provided by six Kolibri emus converted to run on 15 kV lines in Switzerland and Germany, and 25 kV in France; there are no border controls. A new station serves the residential and commercial development at Basle St Johann.

Several other routes have been proposed for better service or through running on the S-Bahn model, with the aim of improving cross-border services between Basle and neighbouring towns in France and Germany. The Swiss cantons of Basel-Stadt, Basel-Land and Aargau, and the French region of Alsace, paid for conversion of the Green line emus, and the next stage should see service extended into the German Land of Baden-Württemburg in 2001.

UPDATED

BEIJING

Population: City 7 million, region 10.5 million
Public transport: Bus, trolleybus and metro services operated by municipal agencies; extensive paratransit. Limited commuter service provided by Chinese Railways plays only a minor role in the city's transport; light rail planned

Public Transport Corporation

Beijing Public Transport Corporation
44 Nanlishi Lu, Beijing, People's Republic of China
Tel: (+86 10) 89 53 31/89 52 36

Current situation: Subsidiary companies run distinct bus and trolleybus systems and the metro, as well as

manufacturing over 1,000 buses and trolleybuses per year for Beijing and other cities.

Over five million bicycles and 300,000 cars make surface public transport severely congested. Average peak-hour speed is about 15 km/h. Computerised traffic control systems are in use, but rising traffic volume may be expected to offset any improvements.

Beijing City Bus

Beijing City Bus Company

Current situation: Bus services are operated throughout the metropolitan area. There is said to be a structure of area subsidiaries, but how this functions is not apparent. About 1,000 articulated buses of Type BK670 and about 500 similar but shorter buses of Type BK663 have entered service since the late 1970s, and these rather dated models continue to be delivered with only minor design changes. The rigid fleet used on less busy routes has been modernised and double-decks are in service on some trunk routes.

Bus

Passenger journeys: 2,000 million (annual)

Number of routes: Inner city 60; suburban and satellite towns 81; night routes 4
Fleet: Approx 3,000 vehicles, including 2,000 articulated, mainly Beijing types BK670 and BK663, and some Jiling double-decks

Fare collection: Payment to seated conductor, most passengers have monthly passes
Fare structure: Stage
Integration with other modes: There is little structured intermodal integration. Completion of metro Line 2 significantly improved journey times for passengers on

Beijing BD562 trolleybus of recent design   **1997**

certain routes, but interchange facilities between surface transport and metro are very poor, with few escalators and no purpose-built links for transferring passengers

Beijing City Trolleybus
Beijing City Trolleybus Company

Current situation: The trolleybus network is currently fairly static in size and the new all-articulated fleet delivered during the 1980s is about 10 per cent smaller than the original part-rigid, part-articulated fleet it replaced. Severe overcrowding still occurs and it is not clear whether the reduction in fleet size is deliberate or caused by the need to supply trolleybuses to other undertakings to replace worn-out vehicles. The system also suffers from severe traffic congestion which has worsened substantially in recent years.

Trolleybus services are augmented by bus routes separate from those of City Bus and recent expansion of the Trolleybus Company's network has been by introduction of more bus routes rather than new trolleybus routes. Two routes, 103 and 104, are worked by both buses and trolleybuses.

Bus
Number of routes: 16 (2 shared with trolleybuses)
Fleet: Approx 500 Beijing buses, over 75 per cent of which articulated, deliveries since 1982 being of type Beijing BK663. A few new Jinghua rigid buses have entered service recently

Fare collection: Payment to seated conductor, monthly passes
Fare structure: Stage

Trolleybus
Passenger journeys: 600 million (annual)

Number of routes: 13

Route length: 80 km
Fleet: Around 500 BD562 articulated

Fare collection/structure: As bus

Beijing Metro
Beijing Metro Corporation (BMRTC)
2 Beiheyan Road, Xicheng, 100044 Beijing
Tel: (+86 10) 68 02 45 66
General Manager: Feng Shuangsheng
Chief Engineer: Yao Jingdi
Staff: 10,000 including 1,600 engineers and technicians

Metro
Type of operation: Full metro, first line opened 1969

Passenger journeys: (1994) 530 million

Current situation: BMRTC is responsible to the city government for both construction and operation of the metro. The first line (east-west radial) opened in 1969, the second (a U-shaped loop) in 1984, and the system assumed its present ring-and-tangent form in 1987 when the radial and loop lines were linked, the former being cut back to an interchange at Fuxing Men and the latter extended to form a complete circle.

All construction is cut-and-cover, tunnels having a concrete rectangular frame with a wall separating up and down tracks. Most stations have island platforms, all 118 m long to accommodate six-car trains. Several stations have been designed as interchanges with future lines.
Developments: A British consortium was awarded a contract to upgrade the first section of metro opened in 1969. Included is complete resignalling of Line 1 with ATO, ATP, and ATS. A total of 32 six-car trains were equipped with ATP, 10 of which also have ATO for trials with automated driving.

Construction is in progress of a 13.6 km eastwards

extension of Line 1 to Bawangfen. Changchun Car Co is delivering 174 vehicles for the Bawangfen extension. A further 10 lines have been proposed, along with four new suburban rail routes to be built as feeders. North-south Line 4 (30 km) could be the next to be built, whilst 27 km Line 5 is under study.

Particularly heavy passenger flows have led to peak-hour controls on entry to the system, with only pass-holders allowed access.

Route length: 42 km, all in tunnel
Number of lines: 2
Number of stations: 29
Gauge: 1,435 mm
Track: Concrete slab, 50 kg/m welded rail, elastic fastenings
Max gradient: 3%
Minimum curve radius: 250 m
Tunnel: Cut-and-cover, 4.1 m wide, 4.35 m high
Electrification: 750 V DC, third rail

Service: Peak 3-4 min, off-peak 8 min, evenings 12 min
First/last train: 05.10/23.40
Fare structure: Flat
Signalling: Automatic block with 3-aspect colourlights and CTC; control-to-driver FM radio on Line 2. Modernisation will permit trains to run at 2 min headways, and Line 1 is being equipped with ATS/ATP/ATO

Rolling stock: 304 cars, standard formation six-car sets but shorter trains still in use. All cars built at Changchun (mechanical parts) and Xiangtan (electrical), apart from Japanese prototype set imported 1984. New generation of cars planned, 2.8 m wide and with GTO thyristor control

Light rail (planned)
Current situation: In 1994 Beijing Municipal Engineering Administration signed a build-operate-transfer contract with a California-based construction group for a 16.3 km line in the eastern suburbs to link Tongxian county with the Line 1 metro terminus at Bawangfen. It was expected to open at the same time as the metro extension to Bawangfen.

A separate 60 km line is planned to link the Asian Games village with the Ming Tombs and Great Wall tourist sites. A joint venture involving the Beijing Municipal Government and the Pacific Rim Construction consortium was established in 1994; it will fund construction and operate the line for 30 years, after which ownership will pass to the Chinese government. An agreement for construction of the line was signed in early 1995.

Paratransit
Current situation: Although conventional minibuses were introduced in Beijing in the early 1980s and subsequently spread to other cities, very few are now to be seen in the capital. Instead, several thousand microbuses ply the streets; they are based on Japanese designs and built in Jilin, Tianjin and elsewhere. Details of ownership and scope of operation are not known; they do not work numbered routes and are probably classed as collective taxis rather than small buses.

UPDATED

Beijing metro

BEIRUT
Population: 700,000
Public transport: Private shared taxis have provided the only public transport since municipal bus services were suspended in 1975. They are grouped into associations with routes covering specific areas. Local rail service resumed, and a new city transport authority, TCB, was set up in 1993

Shared taxis
Passenger journeys: 20 million (annual)
Vehicle-km: 10 million (annual)

Number of routes: 21

Fleet: Approx 450 vehicles, mostly Mercedes 5-seater taxis

One-man operation: All services
Fare collection: By driver
Fare structure: Distance-related, but subject to negotiation

CFL/TCB
Office des Chemins de fer et du Transport en Commun (CFL/TCB)
PO Box 109, Beirut, Lebanon
Tel: (+961) 44 70 07

Director General: Dr E Choueiri

Current situation: In 1986, a limited local service was started between Beirut and Jbeil (37 km north), with second-hand coaches purchased from the German Federal Railway (DB) making one return trip in each peak period. Further rehabilitation work was carried out in 1991/92.

A new fleet of 200 city buses was ordered from Renault in February 1996.

VERIFIED

BELFAST

Population: 297,000

Public transport: Bus and suburban rail services provided by state-owned company, which also operates rural bus services; also privately run shared taxi operations

Translink

Translink

Central Station, East Bridge Street, Belfast BT1 3PB, Northern Ireland

Tel: (+44 1232) 89 94 00   Fax: (+44 1232) 89 94 01

Managing Director, Group Operations: Ted Hesketh

Operations Director: Andy Watt

Manager, Central Area Buses: Frank Clegg

Manager, Railway Services: Seamus Scallon

Staff: 3,755 (all operations)

Current situation: In 1996 the management and operations of Belfast Citybus, Ulsterbus and Northern Ireland Railways were co-ordinated under the new name Translink. In a move that is completely opposed to the policy of deregulation in force in the rest of the UK, the then government saw co-ordinated public transport as a means of countering the province's high level of car use and traffic congestion.

Translink operates all urban and rural bus services, and all rail services, in Northern Ireland. Nevertheless, for the time being, the figures given below still reflect the former Citybus and NIR operations; they exclude rural bus services.

Citybus operates most urban bus services, while the Ulsterbus subsidiary Flexibus runs minibuses. Traditional boundaries between Citybus and Ulsterbus rural services are being revised as the two companies' routes in Greater Belfast are integrated.

Developments: Large numbers of low-floor buses entered service during 1997, and two Dennis SLF Darts were introduced in 1996 on Easibus services — 15 wheelchair-accessible routes — which operate in pairs on alternate days.

Flexibus park-and-ride routes were introduced in 1996 to the Northside car park. The Ulsterbus Airbus route with four Optare Metroriders links the city centre with the International Airport.

Bus (Belfast city operations)

Staff: 728

Passenger journeys: (1995/96) 25.7 million
(1996/97) 24.6 million
(1997/98) 23.1 million
Vehicle-km: (1995/96) 12.1 million
(1996/97) 11.7 million
(1997/98) 11.6 million

Number of routes: 60
Route length: 180 km
On priority right-of-way: 1 km

Sixty-two Volvo B10L buses have Alexander Ultra 44-seat bodywork. The skirt line shows the floor level (Andrew Jarosz)
1999/0045132

Fleet: 325 vehicles

Bristol single-deck	127
Leyland Tiger single-deck	110
Dennis Dart midibus	17
Dennis Dart SL2	2
Volvo B10M articulated	2
Volvo B10L ultra-low-floor	62
Mercedes minibus	1
DAF double-deck coach	1
Leyland double-deck	1
Daimler double-deck	1
Neoplan N4014	1
In peak service: 221	

Most intensive service: 7½ min
One-person operation: All routes
Fare collection: Onboard cancellation of prepurchased multijourney tickets, or payment of higher cash fare to driver
Fare structure: Zone; 4-fare multijourney ticket and Travelcards sold in shops
Fares collected on board: 75 per cent
Fare evasion control: Inspectors; penalty fare
Integration with other modes: Centrelink distributor links all main bus and rail stations with principal shopping areas; free to rail and most bus passengers
Operational control: Route inspectors/mobile radio
Arrangements for elderly/disabled: Blind persons carried free and over-65s at half fare with cost reimbursed by government

Bus priority: Bus lanes and vehicle-activated traffic signals
Average peak-hour speed: In mixed traffic 14.5 km/h
Operating cost financed by: Fares 98 per cent, grants 2 per cent
Subsidy from: Government
New vehicles financed by: Largely self-financed, 50 per cent government grant has been reduced — future position uncertain

Suburban rail

Type of operation: Suburban heavy rail

Passenger journeys: (1994/95) 6.1 million
(1995/96) 6.5 million
(1996/97) 6.2 million

Current situation: Trains run every 10-15 min inner suburban, 20-30 min outer suburban (peak hours), 30 min inner and 60 min outer (off-peak) over three routes extending to 151 km, 1,600 mm gauge, now fully integrated following opening of the cross-harbour link in 1994. Fare structure is graduated.
Developments: Reopening of the 23 km Belfast-Antrim direct line, closed in 1978, was approved in September 1998. Two new stations will be built, at Templepatrick and Mossley West, to be served by a frequent suburban service to and from Belfast Central. Opening is scheduled for mid-2000.

Rolling stock: 30 diesel-electric multiple-units

BREL Class 80 demu (1974/77)	M21 T36
BREL Class 450 demu (1985/86/87)	M9 T18

Shared taxi

Current situation: Some 350 London-type FX4 black taxis operate on shared travel basis on a limited number of high-density routes. Operations are supervised by two associations: West Belfast Taxis and the North Belfast Mutual Association. See *JUTS 1992* for details.

Services operate from informal city-centre termini, and from a West Belfast Taxi Association terminus in Castle Street, along fixed routes to points in the suburbs. Operating hours are from 06.00 to 02.00 and there is a basic two-stage (long and short journey) fare scale. Vehicles leave when full (maximum six passengers).

The shared taxis are estimated to account for between two-thirds and three-quarters of the public transport use on the corridors served, although buses continue to operate.

UPDATED

Volvo B10M articulated bus with Van Hool 71-seat bodywork at Europa Centre bus station on Goldliner service (Andrew Jarosz)
1999/0045131

BELGRADE

Population: 1.6 million
Public transport: Bus, trolleybus and tramway services operated by municipal undertaking and two other companies; suburban rail

GSP Beograd

Gradski Saobrácaj Beograd (GSP)
Zmaj Jovina 41, Belgrade, Yugoslavia
Tel: (+381 11) 62 74 11   Fax: (+381 11) 18 74 05
General Manager: Mihailo Glavičić
Staff: 8,854

Passenger journeys: (1993) 58.6 million
(1995) 85.5 million
(1996) 86 million

Operating costs financed by: Fares 52 per cent, other commercial sources 7 per cent, subsidy/grants 41 per cent and two other companies, suburban rail

Current situation: Bus is the basic mode of transport, supplemented by trolleybuses and trams. See earlier editions for background to GSP's development.
Developments: In the period 1996-2000 GSP is aiming to restore services to the level operating prior to the civil war. Purchase of 859 buses (349 articulated) is planned, mainly to replace obsolete vehicles, along with 81 trolleybuses and 61 tramcars. If patronage grows as expected, a further 332 buses (233 articulated), 93 trolleybuses and 84 trams will be required in 2000.

During the same period it is proposed to extend the tramway by 11.5 km, and trolleybus by 12.2 km. New garaging and maintenance facilities will be provided for 250 buses.

Bus and trolleybus

Passenger journeys: (1995) Bus 62 million, trolleybus 7.9 million
Vehicle-km: (1995) Bus 63.6 million, trolleybus 6.1 million

Number of routes: Bus 104, trolleybus 8
Route length: (One way) Bus 1,227 km, trolleybus 62 km
On priority right-of-way: 34.5 km

Fleet: 961 buses
Sanos	203
MAN-SU	18
MAN articulated	50
Ikarbus IK103	358
Ikarbus IK161 articulated	332
In peak service: 757	

Fleet: 134 trolleybuses
Uritsky ZIU9	133
Goša/Ansaldo	1
In peak service: 108	

Trolleybus electrification: 600 V DC

One-person operation: All vehicles
Fare structure: Zonal, including other operators and

Ikarbus IK103 on Route 37   *1997*

Tatra KT4D in advertising livery   *1997*

suburban rail. 95 per cent of passengers use employer-assisted season tickets. Multitickets sold through tobacconists, single tickets on board
Fare collection: On vehicle and prepurchase, with cancellers in vehicles
Fares collected on board: 0.5 per cent
Fare evasion control: 250 ticket inspectors

Integration with other modes: Full integration with tram service and other operators
Average distance between stops: Central area 300-350 m, suburban area 550-600 m
Bus priority: Bus lanes on most main roads

Tramway
Staff: 1,540

Type of operation: Conventional tramway

Passenger journeys: (1992/93) 82 million
(1995) 153 million
Car-km: (1995) 9.4 million

Route length: 118 km
Number of lines: 11
Gauge: 1,000 mm
Track: 60 kg/m Fenix rail, 'floating' track
Max gradient: 7.8%
Minimum curve radius: 20 m
Electrification: 600 V DC, overhead

Service: Peak 6-7 min, off-peak 10 min
First/last car: 04.30/24.00
Fare structure: As bus
Integration with other modes: As bus
One-person operation: All cars

Rolling stock: 197 cars
ČKD Tatra KT4D   M197
In peak service: 145
On order: 20 RT6N three-section articulated cars from ČKD

Vukov Spomenik station on suburban lines 1/2   *1997*

ZTP Beograd
Yugoslav Railways (JZ)
Nemanjina 6, PO Box 498, 11000 Belgrade
Tel: (+381 11) 68 44 59   Fax: (+381 11) 68 16 54
Director: M Maksimović

Type of operation: Suburban heavy rail

Current situation: Inner suburban services run on three routes to Batajnica, Pančevo and Resnik, totalling 52.4 km, 20 stations, electrified 25 kV, utilising 13 km of tunnel in the city centre. In addition, outer suburban trains run on four routes, total 367 km, extending to Novi Sad, Valjevo, Lapovo and Požarevac.
Developments: The urban development plan (see above) also recommended extension of suburban trains to nine

routes, but progress has been curtailed by political difficulties. May 1995 saw opening of a major city-centre underground station at Vukov Spomenik, and in 1996 two additional emus were commissioned, bringing the fleet to eight and allowing introduction of a 20 min service at peak hours.

VERIFIED

BELO HORIZONTE

Population: 2.2 million, metropolitan area 3.8 million
Public transport: Bus services for the city are provided by independent operators and co-ordinated by the municipally controlled BHTrans. Interurban bus services within the metropolitan area are the responsibility of the Minas Gerais state government (DER-MG), which also manages urban bus operations in 17 other municipalities making up the Belo Horizonte metropolitan area. Only the cities of Contagem and Betim manage their own bus operations. Suburban rail service run by separate authority Demetrô. Light rail plans appear to have been shelved for lack of finance

BHTrans
BHTrans
Empresa de Transporte e Trânsito de Belo Horizonte
Rua dos Inconfidentes, 1190-8° andar Funcionários,
CEP 30.120 Belo Horizonte, Minas Gerais, Brazil
Tel: (+55 31) 277 75 21/75 22/75 25
Fax: (+55 31) 277 75 99/75 75
President: Antônio Carlos Ramos Pereira
Director of Transport: Joao Luiz da Silva Dias

Current situation: BHTrans replaced the similar authority Transmetro in 1993 with a remit to plan, manage, co-ordinate, execute, delegate and oversee provision of public transport service in the Belo Horizonte municipality. Buses account for 68 per cent of daily journeys, car and taxi 25 per cent, Demetrô 2 per cent and other modes 5 per cent.

There is a uniform livery for each of the three types of service operated: Expresso or Semi-Expresso (red), Diametral (blue) and Circular (yellow). Vehicles are route-specific and have route numbers painted on.

The World Bank is financing implementation of an electronic management and monitoring system for the bus fleet, including centrally linked area-wide traffic light control. A condition of the funding is that the bus network is recast (see below) to feed Demetrô stations, where connections must also be improved and competing bus routes withdrawn.
Developments: The Bus 97 project aims to restructure the network by creating corridor routes which are served by feeder buses. Transfer stations are to be developed, along with integrated services and ticketing, and better interchange provided with Demetrô trains. The Via Norte corridor through the densely populated Venda Nova and

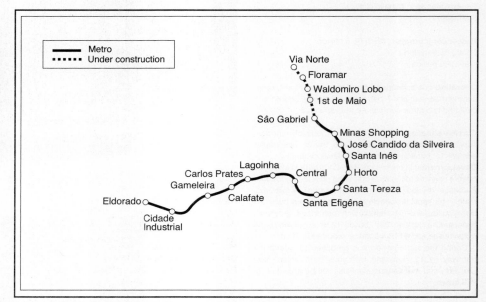

Belo Horizonte metro

Pampulha districts is the first to be commissioned. Two broad avenues, Antônio Carlos and Cristiana Machado, form the basis of the route, which will be operated on a concession basis using high-capacity buses. The area is currently served by 32 routes operated by nine companies with 485 standard buses. Under the new system, the fleet of conventional buses will be reduced to 161 working on routes reorganised to feed the main corridor, which will be served by 81 new articulateds and 51 standard buses.

BHTrans is seeking a loophole in legislation which classifies the Vetor Norte project as 'new', and for which new tenders must be invited before operating licences are granted. However, existing operators such as Venda Nova, which runs services on two routes with 80 vehicles and will see its operations reduced under Bus 97, claim that this is unfair.

Under Bus 97, six Demetrô stations will be served by circular distributor routes, the intention being to reduce the number of bus movements through the city centre and so cut pollution and congestion. But, at least initially,

Demetrô will not have the capacity to cope with all the proposed new ridership, necessitating retention of some parallel bus routes. Also to be created are some orbital routes which will not pass through the city centre; currently Belo Horizonte has only radial routes.

Private bus
Passenger journeys: (1990) 792 million
(1994) 438.6 million
Vehicle-km: (1990) 286 million

Number of routes: 255
Route length: City 7,800 km, including metropolitan region 16,157 km

Fleet: 2,677 vehicles	
Diametral services	1,342
Semi-express services	342
Auxiliary services	121
Others	872
In peak service: 2,529	
Average age of fleet: 4 years	

Operating costs financed by: Fares 100 per cent

Demetrô
Companhia Brasileira de Trens Urbanos
Av Afonso Pena 1500, 11° andar, CEP 30130-921, Belo Horizonte, Minas Gerais
Tel: (+55 31) 250 40 01   Fax: (+55 31) 250 40 04
e-mail: metrobh@gold.horizontes.com.br
Staff: 505

Type of operation: Regional metro, opened 1986

Passenger journeys: (1994) 13.1 million
(1995) 15.3 million
(1996) 16.2 million

Current situation: Surface metro network being developed using some existing rights-of-way and some new construction. Line 1 comprises 21.3 km with 13 stations; 1,600 mm gauge, electrified 3 kV DC overhead. Trains run every 7 min (peak) or 12 min (off-peak) from 05.45 to 23.00. Flat fare system with bus/rail transfers and integration on some routes. There is interchange with 120 bus routes operated by BHTrans and DER-BH. Fares cover 28 per cent of operating costs.
Developments: Demetrô, a division of the Brazilian Urban

A pair of Volvo B58Es (in front) on Route 2215 in central Belo Horizonte   **1998**/0007284

Railways Co (CBTU), is to be transferred to a new state and municipal authority in late 1998, when the extension to São Gabriel opens. World Bank finance for the remaining work is conditional on a recast of bus routes and withdrawal of competing services (see above).

The remaining 6.4 km to Via Norte is under construction for December 1999 opening. The existing CTC system is to be upgraded, and manual ticketing replaced by AFC using magnetic strip tickets.

Rolling stock: 15 four-car emus
Francorail TCO/Cobrasma (1985)   M20 T20
(1997/98)   M10 T10

VERIFIED

Demetrô's José Cândido station,
opened 1997
***1998**/0007283*

BERGEN

Population: 210,000
Public transport: Bus and trolleybus services in inner city provided by municipal undertaking working with private bus companies serving suburban areas; funicular; local trains run Bergen—Arna; light rail proposed

Bergen Buss

A/S Bergen Buss
Natlandsveien 89, 5030 Landaås, Norway
Tel: (+47) 55 28 13 30   Fax: (+47) 55 28 67 03
General Manager: Peer Frode Jarnung
Traffic Manager: Per Karl Blytt
Staff: 420

Developments: In 1998, the former Bergen Sporvei merged with suburban operators Pan Trafikk (55 routes, 279 buses) and Vest Trafikk (50 routes, 180 buses). Full details have not been received, and the figures below apply only to the former BS urban operation.

Plans for a light rail network (see below) could result in closure of the remaining trolleybus route, but at least two alignments have been proposed for new urban trolleybus lines, as well as longer-distance routes.

Bus and trolleybus

Passenger boardings: (1993) Bus 13.7 million, trolleybus 2.4 million
(1994) Both modes 15.4 million
(1995) Bus 12.6 million, trolleybus 1.8 million
Vehicle-km: (1993) Bus 5.9 million, trolleybus 0.7 million
(1995) Bus 6.3 million, trolleybus 0.5 million

Number of routes: 17 (bus 16, trolleybus 1)
Route length: (One way) 220 km (trolleybus 7.8 km)

Fleet: 118 buses	
Volvo	46
Mercedes	1
Scania-Vabis	49
Volvo articulated	1
Mercedes articulated	4
Scania articulated	9
Hino	1
Others	7

In peak service: 82
On order: 8 Volvo diesel buses

Fleet: 14 trolleybuses	
Mercedes-FBW/BBC articulated	5
Gräf & Stift-MAN/BBC articulated	6
Mercedes/ABB articulated duobus (1992/94)	3

In peak service: 9

Most intensive service: 7½ min
One-person operation: All routes
Fare collection: All types of ticket and card, except school pass, available from driver; onboard card reader
Fare structure: Zonal; common for all operators throughout county area; single or multijourney tickets, 30-day season, value card, off-peak card; one free transfer (1 h); higher fare for night services on Friday and Saturday
Fares collected on board: 93.3 per cent
Fare evasion control: Inspectors
Operational control: Central control with travelling inspectors in radio contact
Arrangements for elderly/disabled: Prebooked van services using 25 Mercedes minibuses with wheelchair access, paid for by grants from county council
Average distance between stops: 400 m
Average peak-hour speed: In bus lanes, 25 km/h; in mixed traffic, 16 km/h
Bus priority: 30 km of bus lanes with priority at traffic lights at some intersections
Operating costs financed by: Fares 92 per cent, other commercial sources 6.5 per cent, subsidy/grants 1.5 per cent
Subsidy from: Regional government
New vehicles financed by: Loans

Light rail (proposed)
Current situation: A light rail line has been proposed to link the airport with the city centre, and studies are being made by the municipal authorities.

UPDATED

Mercedes/ABB duobus of Bergen Buss

BERLIN

Population: 3.4 million
Public transport: Municipal authority provides metro, tram, bus and ferry services. Regional metro (S-Bahn) service provided by a subsidiary company of state railway DB, and outer-suburban rail services by DB. Some suburban tramways link with BVG, also tram and bus services run by municipal authority in neighbouring city of Potsdam. A regional transport authority (Verkehrsverbund) was inaugurated in 1997 to become operational in March 1998.

VBB

Verkehrsverbund Berlin/Brandenburg mbH
Lahnstrasse 52, 12055 Berlin, Germany
Tel: (+49 30) 682 97 10

Current situation: This new regional transport authority started operations during March 1998, taking over the role of the former Verkehrsgemeinschaft Berlin-Brandenburg which had been formed as a precursor. Its activities comprise joint promotion of all public transport services in the *Bundeslände* Berlin and Brandenburg.

Ownership of VBB is one-third by the state of Berlin, one-third by the state of Brandenburg, and one-third by cities within Brandenburg state. It covers an area of more than 30,000 km² and serves 6 million inhabitants, and is thus the biggest Verkehrsverbund (in terms of area) in Germany.

BVG

Berliner Verkehrsbetriebe (BVG)
Potsdamer Strasse 188, 10783 Berlin
Tel: (+49 30) 25 61   Fax: (+49 30) 216 41 86
General Manager: Rüdiger vorm Walde

Commercial Manager: Dr Joachim Niklas
Operations Manager: Dr Heino Dubbenkropp
Personnel Manager: Wilfred Mehner
Financial Manager: Dr Joachim Niklas
Staff: 17,003

Passenger journeys: (All modes)
(1995) 987 million
(1996) 818.4 million
(1997) 778.7 million

Operating costs financed by: Fares 33 per cent, other commercial sources 10 per cent, subsidy/grants 57 per cent
Subsidy from: Federal government 1 per cent, city 99 per cent

Current situation: Formed in 1929, BVG is a municipal authority operating two separate metro systems (large and small profile), an extensive bus network, tramways and ferries. BVG had been responsible for operation of S-Bahn services in west Berlin (taken over from the eastern authorities in 1984), but these were transferred to the DB subsidiary S-Bahn Berlin GmbH in 1994. BVG assumed management responsibility for the east Berlin operator BVB in 1990, and full merger of the two systems took place in 1992.

A number of through bus services to surrounding country areas have been inaugurated jointly with regional transport operators. All metro stations have been reopened on the routes previously passing beneath East Berlin without stops. A uniform route-numbering scheme now encompasses all routes in the VBB region.

A major upgrading of the metro is planned under the U-Bahn 2000 scheme (see below).

Bus
Staff: 7,675

Vehicle-km: (1995) 104 million
(1996) 97.9 million
(1997) 109.8 million

Number of routes: 157
Route length: 1,261 km (unduplicated)
On priority right-of-way: 73.6 km

Fleet: 1,540 vehicles, plus 358 contracted

Mercedes O305 (1980/84)	54
MAN SD200 double-deck (1982/85)	188
Mercedes O405 (1985/88)	46
Mercedes O402 midibus (1987)	16
MAN SD202 double-deck (1987/92)	464
Mercedes O405N (1990/95)	228
MAN ND202 (1990/91)	86
Neoplan N4009 midibus (1990)	6
Neoplan N4014 (1992)	10
MAN NG272 articulated (1992)	25
Neoplan N4021 articulated (1992)	18
Mercedes O405GN articulated (1993/97)	163
MAN ND202 double-deck (1995)	87
MAN NG312 articulated (1995/97)	46
MAN NL262 (1997)	39
Neoplan N4020/3 Megatr. (1997)	25
Volvo/Steyr B10L (1997)	30
Various	9
Ikarus 280 (in reserve)	30

In peak service: 1,592
On order: Tenders invited for 195 buses of different types.

Most intensive service: 2 min
One-person operation: All services
Fare collection: Single tickets sold on buses and at ticket offices on U-Bahn stations; 4-journey multiticket vending machines at some bus stops and special offices; daily, weekly and monthly passes; senior citizen passes; free daily travel for disabled. Automatic ticket vending machines for single and multitickets at U-Bahn stations. Transfers on single tickets within 2 h. Cancellation by machine or driver. Only 13 per cent use single tickets; all others travel on passes
Fare structure: Flat, with short-distance ticket
Fare evasion control: Inspectors with spot penalty
Operational control: Bus radio link to control centre
Arrangements for elderly/disabled: Lift- or ramp-equipped single-deck buses in operation on 39 routes. Separate 'Telebus' network of low-floor, wheelchair-accessible midibuses operated by special agency (see below)

MAN low-floor double-deck at Zoo (Chris Bushell)   1997

Integration with other modes: Full integration with tram, U-Bahn and S-Bahn services; transfers available; multimodal passes
Bus priority: 73.6 km network of city-centre bus lanes; long-term objective to secure 156 km of bus lanes
Average distance between stops: 396 m
Average peak-hour speed: Before 20.00, 18.4 km/h; after 20.00, 22.5 km/h

Developments: A rechargeable smartcard (known as the electronic purse) is on trial in a scheme funded by the Federal Ministry for Research & Technology (BMFT). Cards can be loaded with amounts up to DM999 and are valid for six months. Only 3,000 have been issued and their use is restricted to five bus routes.

Part of the bus network is subcontracted to private operators, following contracts for the first routes let in 1992. Door-to-door service is provided by contracted taxis on some of the all-night routes.

Long-term fleet planning envisages a reduction of double-deck buses to about 40 per cent of the total and only to be used in the central area.

Trials with CNG were stopped in 1997 due to cost. Other trials took place in 1998 with a diesel-electric Mercedes bus.

Metro
Staff: 5,033

Type of operation: Full metro, first line opened 1902

Car-km: (1995) 123.9 million
(1996) 133.7 million
(1997) 130.1 million

Route length: 144 km
  in tunnel: 120.2 km
  elevated: 10.2 km
Number of lines: 9
Number of stations: 169
Gauge: 1,435 mm
Track: 41 kg/m S 41 rail, conventional sleepers on ballast
Max gradient: 4%
Minimum curve radius: 74 m
Tunnel: Mainly cut-and-cover
Electrification: 780 V DC, third rail; bottom contact on large-profile lines

Service: Peak 3 min, off-peak 5-10 min
First/last train: 04.00/01.00
Fare structure: Flat, as bus
Integration with other modes: Fully integrated with bus, tram and S-Bahn
One-person operation: All trains
Signalling: Electromagnetic, Siemens; ATO on Line 4
Automatic control: Automatic operation on Lines 4 (SEL) and 9 (Siemens Seltrac)

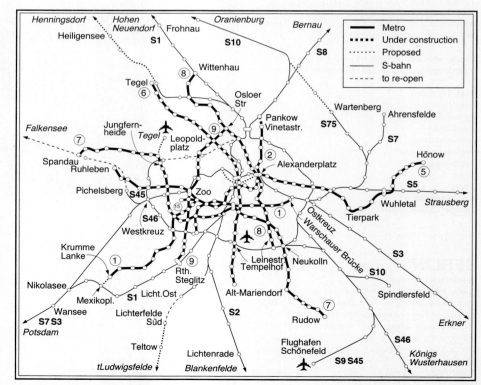

Berlin's metro and S-Bahn lines   0045351

Surveillance: CCTV at 18 stations for vehicle dispatching; trains also equipped with radio and radio telephone

Rolling stock: 1,528 cars (635 emus)
Small profile (2.3 m wide)

O&K A364 (1964)	M25 T25
DWM A366 (1966)	M11 T11
O&K A366 (1966)	M10 T10
O&K A3L66 (1966)	M4 T4
O&K A3L67 (1967/68)	M44 T44
O&K A3L71 (1971/73)	M69 T69
LEW G1 (1980)	M2 T2
Waggon Union A3L82 (1982/83)	M8 T8
LEW G1/1 (1988/89)	M51 T51
ABB A3L92 (1993/95)	M51 T51

Large profile (2.65 m wide)

O&K/DWM D57 (1956/58)	M19 T19
O&K/DWM D60 (1960/61)	M26 T26
O&K/DWM D63 (1963)	M59 T59
O&K D65/DL65 (1965)	M25 T25
O&K/DWM DL68 (1968/70)	M68 T68
O&K DL70 (1969/71)	M30 T30
O&K F74 (1973/75)	M28 T28
O&K/Waggon Union F76 (1976/78)	M41 T41
O&K/Waggon Union F79 (1980/81)	M43 T43
Waggon Union F84 (1984/85)	M39 T39
Waggon Union F87 (1986/87)	M21 T21
ABB F90 (1990/92)	M30 T30
ABB F92 (1992/93)	M55 T55
Adtranz H95 (1995/97)	M2 T2

Developments: The southern extension of U8 to Hermannstrasse (1 km, 1 station) opened in 1996, providing another link with the S-Bahn network. U2 is being extended by 1 km from Vinetastr to Pankow S-Bahn station, construction started October 1996. A new station at Mendelsohn-Bartholdy Park on U2 opened in late 1998. An extension of U5 from Alexanderplatz to Platz der Republik is expected to open in 2004.

A seven-year modernisation programme — U-Bahn 2000 — was approved in 1992. This will see introduction of automated train operation as part of a move to raise capacity, improve customer service and reduce operating costs. Together with the new trains and signalling required for driverless operation, there will be wide-ranging improvements to the station environment and passenger information systems. Non-passenger trials of driverless operation were expected to start on part of Line U5 in mid-1999, using two Adtranz H95 trainsets specially equipped.

To start the rolling stock replacement, a new fleet of 115 six-car trains with three-phase traction is being delivered from Adtranz. These have wide gangways and longitudinal seating, and are equipped with driver's cabs that can be removed once automatic train operation is commissioned. Two prototype sets delivered in 1995 entered service in 1997; further orders are expected as replacements for the entire fleet.

Tramway
Staff: 2,466

Type of operation: Conventional tramway

Car-km: (1995) 35.1 million
(1996) 35.7 million
(1997) 33.9 million

Route length: 176 km
Number of lines: 27 (4 night)
Number of stops: 359
Gauge: 1,435 mm
Electrification: 600 V DC, overhead

Service: Peak 5 min; 24 h service

Rolling stock: 558 cars

ČKD Tatra KTD4 (1980/87) modernised	M272
ČKD Tatra T6A2 (1988/90) modernised	M118 T64
AEG Adtranz GT6N low-floor (1994/98)	M104

On order: A further 60 Adtranz GT6N for delivery by the end of 1997 and 30 GT6N double-ended cars

Current situation: After merger of the two public transport operations, expansion of the tramway network into the western part of the city was proposed. The first such route, a 2.7 km extension of Route 23 along Osloer Strasse to Louise Schroeder Platz, was opened in 1995, and was further extended 2.8 km along Seestrasse to

S8 train at Bornholmer Strasse **1997**

Berlin's new low-floor tram (Chris Bushell) **1997**

Klinikum Rudolf Virchow in 1997. Work also continues on the Prenzlauer Tor—Alexanderplatz—Hackescher Markt route, planned for opening in October 1998. Unforeseen technical problems have pushed back opening to mid-1999.

An extension of Route 20 from Eberswalder Strasse westwards to Wedding (Nordbahnhof), planned for opening in 2000, has been met with local opposition. Work started on a short extension of Route 50 from Buchholz to Buchholz West at the end of 1997.

Private finance is being sought to fund construction of a 4.8 km line partly in tunnel from Alexanderplatz to Magdeburger Platz, on which work is expected to start in 1998. This will be a high-capacity route extending into the former western sector, and it is proposed that the tunnel under Leipziger Str will be used later for proposed metro Line 3.

Additionally, 45 km of extensions were proposed for construction in the longer term at a cost of DM600 million, including links to new and reopened metro and S-Bahn stations in the city centre. This was confirmed in the Local Transport Plan for Berlin by the Senate in January 1998.

Total modernisation of the existing network is in progress, including renewal of track and overhead, and depot and power supply modernisation. Refurbishment of 447 Tatra tramcars (M388 T59) has been completed, while a new fleet of low-floor cars has been delivered. An option for another 60 GT6 cars has been exercised, and a further 45 cars will be required to complete the fleet proposed for the end of the century. GT6 cars have started peak-hour operation in pairs, necessitating lengthening of tram stops.

In March 1998, BVG concluded a contract with the Berlin Senate in which some DM81 million would be invested in traffic management measures aimed at increasing the average operating speed of tram services from 17 to 21 km/h. The first route to be affected will be Route 6, where some 5 minutes is expected to be saved on the 15.5 km route section from Hellersdorf to Platz der Vereinigten Nationen.

Ferry
Passenger journeys: (1995) 0.3 million

Current situation: Six vessels ply six routes with a total length of 6.8 km, only one of which operates all year round.

S-Bahn Berlin
S-Bahn Berlin GmbH
Invalidenstrasse 130-131, 10115 Berlin
Tel: (+49 30) 29 71 98 01   Fax: (+49 30) 29 71 98 05
Chairman: Günter Ruppert
Director: Ernst-Otto Constantin
Staff: 4,660

Type of operation: S-Bahn

Passenger journeys: (1995) 245 million
(1996) 264 million

Number of stations: 154

Current situation: This subsidiary of DB took over operation of the S-Bahn network at the beginning of 1995.

Service is provided on 13 routes totalling 292 km with 146 stations; 1,435 mm gauge, electrified 800 V DC third rail; fares fully integrated with other modes. Peak-hour frequency on the busiest section is 2 min, with trains running every 3 min between Ostbahnhof and Alexanderplatz. Off-peak services run every 5-10 min; trains run from about 04.00 to 01.00; 20 min service to Schönefeld airport.

Developments: The section of the northern S-Bahn ring line between Westend and Jungfernheide reopened in April 1997, while on the southern section services between Neukolln and Treptower Park resumed in December 1997. According to the 'S-Bahn Netzplan 2010', published at the end of 1995, several other routes are to be reopened: Tegel—Hennigsdorf (8 km, December 1998), Westend—Schönhauser Allee (3.8 km, 2000), Lischerfelde Ost—Teltow Stadt (6.6 km, 1998/ 2002), Westkreuz—Falkensee (12 km, 1998/2003), and Jungfernheide—Schönhauser Allee (6.3 km, 1998/2000).

A standard emu has been designed for the merged S-Bahn network. This is the Series 481, based on the Series 480 stock; first-class accommodation is being reintroduced as these trains enter service. An order for 500 two-car sets has been placed with Adtranz for delivery through to 2004 to replace life-expired stock built between 1927 and 1941.

Some trains now offer a mobile catering service.

Rolling stock: 1,592 cars

Class 476 (1927/32, modernised 1979/89)	M195 T195
Class 477 (1938/41, modernised 1974/82)	M204 T204
Class 479	M3 T3
Waggon Union/AEG Class 480 (1986/90-94)	M168
LEW/AEG Class 485 (1987/92)	M166 T166
DWA/Adtranz Class 481 (1996/1997)	M10 T10
DWA/Adtranz Class 481 (1997/1998)	M134 T134

DB

Deutsche Bahn AG, Geschäftsbereich Nahverkehr
Regionalbereich Berlin-Brandenburg
Ruschestrasse 59, 10365 Berlin
Tel: (+49 30) 23 72 36 20   Fax: (+49 30) 29 72 41 77
Managers: Karl-Heinz Friedrich
    Hans Leister

Type of operation: Regional rail

Passenger journeys: (1995) 16,800 daily

Current situation: To complement the S-Bahn network, DB operates 18 regional routes, mostly electrified at 15 kV 16 ⅔ Hz. Services are fully integrated with the joint VBB tariff.
Developments: Starting in May 1998, a new network of six cross-city routes using mainly bilevel coaches was established by extending previously terminating services over the Stadtbahn between Zoo and Hbf.

Suburban tramways

Schöneicher-Rüdersdorfer Strassenbahn GmbH
Dorfstrasse 15, 15566 Schöneiche
Tel: (+49 30) 649 53 93   Fax: (+49 30) 649 89 84
General Manager: Jan Bleis

Trams in central Potsdam (Chris Bushell)   *1997*

Passenger journeys: (1994) 1.3 million
(1995) 1.2 million
(1996) 1.1 million

Current situation: Metre-gauge tramway providing S-Bahn feeder service over the Rüdersdorf—Schöneiche—Friedrichshagen route (14.5 km).

Strausberger Eisenbahn GmbH
Walkmülenstrasse 29, 15344 Strausberg

Current situation: Standard-gauge 6.2 km tramway connecting the town of Strausberg with the S-Bahn line S5 at Strausberg station.

Woltersdorfer Strassenbahn GmbH
Karl-Langowski-Strasse, 14789 Woltersdorf
Tel: (+49 33) 62 52 15

Passenger journeys: (1994) 1.2 million
(1995) 1 million
(1996) 0.5 million

Current situation: Standard-gauge tramway providing S-Bahn feeder service over Woltersdorf—Rahnsdorf route (5.6 km).

ViP

Verkehrsbetriebe Potsdam GmbH (ViP)
PO Box 601454, 14414 Potsdam
Tel: (+49 331) 37 50   Fax: (+49 331) 29 17 06
General Manager: Georg Dukiewicz

Passenger journeys: (1995) 35 million
(1996) 29.5 million
(1997) 29.4 million

Current situation: Potsdam is a neighbouring city to the south of Berlin, with a population of 149,000. Bus and

tramway services are provided by the municipal authority. Connections and through ticketing with BVG as part of VBB.
Developments: Short tramway extension opened 1997, between Robert Baberske Strasse and Kirchsteigfeld (1.3 km). Under proposals announced in January 1997, extensions over DB tracks from Potsdam Stern to Teltow, and Potsdam to Beelitz, are planned, while within Potsdam a link between Babelsberg and Stern is being considered. It is also planned to build a 2.9 km extension of the current Route 92 from Kappellenberg to Bornstedtler Feld in connection with the forthcoming Garden Show.

A new fleet of 48 low-floor Combino LRVs is on order from Siemens, of which 44 are five-section and the remainder seven-section. Delivery will be at five per year from 1998 to 2009. The first arrived in late 1998.

Bus
Vehicle-km: (1995) 3.3 million
(1996) 3.3 million
(1997) 3.3 million

Number of routes: 8
Route length: 125 km

Fleet: 48 buses

Mercedes O405N	39
Mercedes O405GN articulated	9

Tramway
Vehicle-km: (1995) 4.7 million
(1996) 4.5 million
(1997) 4.3 million

Number of routes: 7
Route length: 24.3 km
Gauge: 1,435 mm

Fleet: 98 cars

ČKD Tatra KT4DM modernised	M46 T39
ČKD Tatra KT4D	M9
Siemens Combino (1998)	M4

Havelbus

Havelbus Verkehrsgesellschaft mbH
Johannsenstrasse 12-17, 14482 Potsdam
Tel: (+49 331) 749 13 00   Fax: (+49 331) 751 61
General Manager: Hans-Joachim Knop

Passenger journeys: (1995) 19 million
(1996) 18.4 million
(1997) 17.4 million

Current situation: Regional bus company formed in 1992 by Potsdam and Nauen county councils to take over the regional bus services previously operated by ViP (see above). Several routes extend into the outskirts of Berlin, where they link with BVG services.

Bus
Vehicle-km: (1995) 11.2 million
(1996) 11.1 million
(1997) 10.9 million

Havelbus Mercedes awaits passengers in Potsdam (Chris Bushell)   *1997*

Number of routes: 48
Route length: 1,538 km

Fleet: 181 buses, plus 36 hired
Ikarus	71
Mercedes	55
MAN	49
Others	6

Telebus

Berliner Zentralausschuss für soziale Aufgaben eV
Telebus Fahrdienst für Behinderte in Berlin
Joachimstaler Str 15-17, 10719 Berlin
Tel: (+49 30) 88 00 30

Current situation: A fleet of wheelchair-accessible minibuses is available on demand-responsive service to those unable to use ordinary public transport. Services are operated by contractors.

UPDATED

BERNE

Population: City 131,000, metropolitan area 189,000
Public transport: Bus, trolleybus and tramway services operated by undertaking responsible to city council. Separate regional company RBS operates light rail and bus services. Swiss Federal Railway (SBB), BLS Lötschbergbahn (BLS) and the PTT postal coaches organisation provide suburban services; S-Bahn network

SVB

Städtische Verkehrsbetriebe Bern (SVB)
Eigerplatz 3, PO Box 3000, Berne 14, Switzerland
Tel: (+41 31) 321 88 88   Fax: (+41 31) 321 88 66
General Manager: H-R Kamber
Staff: 679

Passenger boardings: (All modes)
(1994) 127.7 million
(1995) 120.4 million
(1996) 119.4 million

Fare collection: Self-service with Autelca ticket issuing and validating equipment
Fare structure: Zonal, with ticket books and weekly, monthly and annual passes
Fare evasion control: Roving inspectors; penalty fare
Operating costs financed by: (All modes) Fares 60 per cent, other commercial sources 10.8 per cent, subsidy/grants 29.2 per cent
Subsidy from: City of Bern

Bus and trolleybus

Passenger journeys: (1994) Bus 28.6 million, trolleybus 44.3 million
(1995) Bus 28.9 million, trolleybus 43.1 million
(1996) Bus 28.2 million, trolleybus 43 million
Vehicle-km: (1994) Bus 3.5 million, trolleybus 2.2 million
(1995) Bus 3.5 million, trolleybus 2.1 million
(1996) Bus 3.4 million, trolleybus 2.2 million

Number of routes: Bus 11, trolleybus 5
Route length: (One way) bus 46 km, trolleybus 21.6 km
On priority right-of-way: Bus 1.3 km
Number of stops: 129

Fleet: 100 buses
FBW	21
Volvo	32
Volvo articulated	10
MAN low-floor articulated	37
In peak service: 78	

Fleet: 44 trolleybuses, all articulated
In peak service: 36
Trolleybus electrification: 600 V DC

Most intensive service: 15 min
One-person operation: All routes
Operational control: Route inspectors
Average distance between stops: 390 m
Average peak-hour speed: 17 km/h
New vehicles financed by: Canton of Berne

Tramway

Type of operation: Conventional tramway

Passenger journeys: (1994) 48.8 million
(1995) 48.4 million
(1996) 48.1 million
Car-km: (1994) 2.5 million
(1995) 2.5 million
(1996) 2.5 million

Route length: 17.2 km
   reserved track: 1.7 km
Number of lines: 3

Number of stops: 52
Gauge: 1,000 mm
Max gradient: 6%
Minimum curve radius: 15.5 m
Track: 60 kg/m Ri60 rail
Electrification: 600 V DC, overhead

Service: Peak 5 min, off-peak 6-12 min
First/last car: 05.40/23.45
Integration with other modes: Fully integrated with regional transport systems
One-person operation: All routes

Rolling stock: 63 cars
SWS/MFO Be 4/4 (1947/61)	M14
FFA/SIG/SWS B4 (1951/61)	T21
SWS/BBC Be 8/8 (1973)	M16
Vevey Be 4/8 low-floor (1989/90)	M12
In peak service: 29 motor cars	

Developments: It is proposed to convert trolleybus routes 13 and 14 — SBB station to Bimpliz and Gäbelbach — to tramway operation.

Two extensions are proposed — of Route 3 from Weissenbühl to Morillongut, and of Route 9 from Wabern to Kleinwabern.

SVB took delivery of eight Type BGT-N2 low-floor trolleybuses early in 1998. The 17.9 m 600 V DC articulated vehicles are powered by one 155 kW Škoda Type 2 ML 3550 K/4 asynchronous traction motor. The mechanical part was built by NAW and Hess with electrical equipment from Kiepe.

SVB took delivery of eight Type BGT-N2 low-floor trolleybuses early in 1998 (Milan Šrámek) **1999**/0038747

RBS feeder bus at Papiermühle interchange (Chris Bushell) **1998**/0009501

RBS

Regionalverkehr Bern-Solothurn (RBS)
Bahnhofhochhaus, PO Box 119, 3048 Worblaufen
Tel: (+41 31) 925 55 55   Fax: (+41 31) 925 55 66
General Manager: P Scheidegger
Staff: 365

Current situation: Two light railways, which had been under common management since 1965, were merged in 1984. They link Berne with Unterzollikofen, Jegensdorf, Solothurn and Worb. The undertaking also operates 12 bus routes.

Light railway

Type of operation: Suburban light rail

Passenger journeys: (1993) 17.6 million
(1994) 17.7 million
(1996) 17.7 million

Route length: 56 km
Number of routes: 5
Number of stations: 43
Gauge: 1,000 mm
Electrification: 1.25 kV DC (52 km), 600 V DC (11 km), overhead

Service: Peak 10-30 min, off-peak 15-30 min
Fare structure: Zonal
Integration with other modes: Part fare integration with SVB, full integration with other Swiss railways
Fare evasion control: Roving inspectors, penalty fare
Signalling: ATC; all trains single-manned

Rolling stock: 10 railcars, 32 emu sets, 9 articulated trainsets, 9 locomotives, 15 driving and 2 non-driving trailers

Developments: Extension of the Gümligen line to Bern Zytglogge over SVB tram routes 3 and 5 opened 1997.

Further double-tracking planned, and purchase of additional intermediate cars to increase capacity of emus.

Bus

Passenger journeys: (1996) 4.4 million

Current situation: Buses provide feeder services on 12 routes totalling 62 km serving a number of rail stations. Fleet of 53 buses, midibuses and rail service vehicles.

S-Bahn

Current situation: Suburban services of Swiss Federal Railways (SBB) and BLS Lötschbergbahn, and two local railways — Regionalverkehr Mittelland and Sensetalbahn — have been integrated and augmented to run as four cross-city routes providing S-Bahn style service.

UPDATED

BIELEFELD

Population: 324,000
Public transport: Bus and tramway services provided by municipal authority; urban and regional transport co-ordinated by the regional authority VOW

VOW

Verkehrsgemeinschaft Ostwestfalen-Lippe (VOW)
PO Box 102692, 33526 Bielefeld, Germany
Tel: (+49 521) 51 40 17   Fax: (+49 521) 51 41 41

Current situation: VOW co-ordinates urban services of Stadtwerke Bielefeld with suburban and regional bus services provided by BVO and several independent operators.

Stadtwerke Bielefeld

Stadtwerke Bielefeld GmbH
PO Box 102692, 33526 Bielefeld
Tel: (+49 521) 51 40 17   Fax: (+49 521) 51 41 41
Technical Manager: Dr Martin Proske
Operating Manager: Dipl-Ing Martin Klaiben
Commercial Manager: Wolfgang Brinkmann
Staff: 536

Passenger journeys: (All modes)
(1995) 32.3 million
(1996) 32 million
(1997) 32.6 million

Operating costs financed by: Fares 77.5 per cent, other commercial sources 1.7 per cent, subsidy/grants 20.8 per cent

Bus

Passenger journeys: (1995) 13.7 million
Vehicle-km: (1995) 5.4 million
(1996) 5 million
(1997) 5 million

Number of routes: 32
Route length: 489 km

Fleet: 74 buses, plus 25 contracted

Neoplan low-floor articulated	14
MAN low-floor articulated	7
MAN articulated	24
Neoplan standard	6
MAN standard/low-floor	16
Mercedes standard/low-floor	4
Neoplan Midi	3

In peak service: 64
On order: 22

Most intensive service: 10 min
One-person operation: All routes
Fare collection: Payment to driver
Arrangements for elderly/disabled: Free travel for disabled, reimbursed by government

Current situation: Shared taxi/dial-a-ride service runs in place of certain bus routes at off-peak periods, at supplementary fare.

Tramway/light rail

Type of operation: Conventional tramway upgraded to Stadtbahn, with tunnel section in central area

Passenger journeys: (1995) 18.6 million
(1997) 18.8 million
Car-km: (1995) 3.5 million
(1996) 3.6 million

Route length: 26.1 km
  in tunnel: 4.5 km
Number of routes: 6
Number of stops: 54
  in tunnel: 5
Gauge: 1,000 mm
Track: S41 rail on sleepers in ballast
Electrification: 750 V DC, overhead

Service: Peak 10 min, night 30 min
First/last car: 04.30/01.00
Fare structure: Zonal
Fare collection: Prepurchase from self-service machines or agencies
Control: Siemens ZUB 100 from central control room
Surveillance: CCTV on each platform

Rolling stock: 70 cars

Duewag M8C	M44
Duewag Stadtbahn M8D (1994/95)	M20
Duewag Stadtbahn M8D (1998)	M1 T5

In peak service: 59
On order: A further 15 M8D Stadtbahn

Developments: Patronage on the light rail lines has increased by up to 95 per cent since 1990 and two-car sets now run on weekdays on all routes. New cars have only one driving cab. Construction of new Line 4 to University started in 1998. Doubling of the northern end of Route 3 in Babenhausen was largely complete at the end of 1998. Plans issued in 1998 include extension of the route network by 27.1 km (to year 2007) and a further 2.8 km by 2015, at a total cost of DM404 million. Delivery of five new trailers, which will be coupled between M8D sets, took place in late 1998.

BVO

Busverkehr Ostwestfalen GmbH (BVO)
PO Box 100824, 33508 Bielefeld
Tel: (+49 521) 52 07 00   Fax: (+49 521) 520 70 70
Managing Directors: Heinz Georg Planz
　　Herbert Husser

Current situation: Railway-associated bus company providing suburban and regional bus services.

Fleet: 38 (Bielefeld services only)

UPDATED

BILBAO

Population: City 500,000, conurbation 1 million
Public transport: Most bus services provided by urban transport company, while separate company operates metro. Suburban rail lines operated by local government-controlled authority (Euskotren), and state railways RENFE (broad-gauge) and FEVE (narrow-gauge)

CTB

Consorcio de Transportes de Bizkaia
Calle Alameda Recaldé 18, 48009 Bilbao, Spain
Tel: (+34 94) 424 06 04   Fax: (+34 94) 423 10 88

Current situation: In 1975 the Bizkaia regional government founded the Bizkaia Transport Consortium to supervise construction of the metro in Bilbao and oversee

Low-floor Van Hool of Bilbobus
(Barry Cross)
1996

Opening day on the Bilbao metro (Barry Cross) **1996**

transport infrastructure planning generally. With metro Line 1 opened in 1995, it is expected that the organisation will become a unitary authority for overall control of public transport in Bizkaia.

Although details are not yet finalised, it seems likely that CTB will co-ordinate the activities of RENFE and FEVE (owned by the national government), ET/FE (Basque government), and TC's Bizkaiabus and Bilbobus networks (owned by CTB), and will be responsible for creating an integrated public transport network, elimination of competition between modes, and introduction of a unified tariff structure.

TC

Transportes Collectivos SA (TC)
Francisco Macía 4, 48014 Deusto Bilbao, Spain
Tel: (+34 94) 475 82 00   Fax: (+34 94) 475 03 55

Current situation: TC operates the Bilbobus (urban) and Bizkaiabus (suburban) bus networks.

Bus

Passenger journeys: (1993) 52.9 million
(1994) 51 million
(1995) 51.7 million

Number of routes: 37 urban, 25 suburban

Fleet: 209 vehicles
Urban fleet   117
Suburban fleet   92

Euskotren

Eusko Trenbideak — Ferrocarriles Vascos
Calle Atxuri 6, 48006 Bilbao
Tel: (+34 94) 433 95 00   Fax: (+34 94) 433 60 09
President: C Garcia
Director General: Oscar Gómez Barbero
Staff: 760

Type of operation: Suburban rail

Passenger journeys: (1994) 23.3 million
(1995) 31.6 million
(1996) 24.3 million

Current situation: Bilbao local services out of Atxuri (to Lemoa), San Nikolás (to Bolueta) and Calzadas (to Lutxana and Lezama) terminals form the rump of a 1,000 mm gauge network, electrified 1.5 kV DC overhead, following transfer of the San Nikolás—Plentzia line to the urban metro company in 1995. Also operates eight regional bus routes in Bizkaia, which carried 4.4 million passengers in 1994.
Developments: From a new interchange station with the metro at Bolueta, it is proposed to abandon the San Nikolás terminus in central Bilbao, instead rerouteing trains through a 1.5 km tunnel (open in 1997) to connect with services from Calzadas to Lezama. A new shuttle service will be introduced linking Calzadas with a new station at Bidarte.

In 1995, a 1.1 km extension opened from La Cruz to the centre of Lezama, with a possible 3.4 km further extension to Larrabetzu, dependent upon population growth. A new station has opened at Derio, replacing two existing sites, and another is planned at Elotxelerri. The depot and workshops at Lutxana are to be modernised.

Management of the Lutxana—Sondika branch is also to pass to the metro authority.

Rolling stock: 21 emu sets

Metro Bilbao

Elcana 3, 48001 Bilbao
Tel: (+34 94) 425 40 00   Fax: (+34 94) 425 40 39
Managing Director: Josu Sagastagoitia
Operating Manager: J M Ortega
Staff: 442

Type of operation: Full metro, opened 1995

Route length: 26.5 km
Number of lines: 1
Number of stations: 23

Gauge: 1,000 mm
Electrification: 1.5 kV DC, overhead

Service interval: Peak 5 min
First/last train: 06.00/23.00
Fare structure: Zonal; multijourney tickets and passes
Integration with other modes: Planned as part of future integrated transport authority in Bizkaia
Signalling: Manual operation prior to commissioning of ATO/ATP

Rolling stock: 96 cars
CAF/ABB (1995)   M48 T48

Current situation: Bilbao's first metro line, linking Plentzia and Casco Viejo, was opened in 1995 following transfer of the 20.5 km Plentzia line from ET/FV. This has been linked to a new 5 km city-centre tunnel to create metro Line 1.
Developments: Construction of Line 2, running 9.5 km from Lutxana to Santurzi with 9 stations, started in 1996 following approval of a Pta28.5 billion grant from the Bizkaia government. A further 10 four-car trains will be required for opening in 2000. Plans for a complementary light rail network have been abandoned.

FEVE

Ferrocarriles de Via Estrecha — Spanish Narrow Gauge Railways
General Rodrigo 6, 28003 Madrid
Tel: (+34 91) 533 70 00   Fax: (+34 91) 533 79 94

Passenger journeys: (1993) 1.5 million
(1994) 1.7 million
(1995) 1.8 million

Current situation: An hourly/half-hourly suburban service operates between Bilbao Concordia and Balmaseda (32 km, 18 stations), electrified 1.5 kV.

RENFE

Spanish National Railways
Avendia Ciudad de Barcelona 8, 28007 Madrid
Tel: (+34 91) 506 62 15   Fax: (+34 91) 506 73 26
Director, Bilbao: Angel Ibañez García
Staff: 310 (Bilbao area only)

Passenger journeys: (1994) 24.2 million
(1995) 23.5 million
(1996) 22.4 million

Current situation: RENFE operates suburban trains from La Naja station (adjacent to the main line terminus at Norte) to Santurzi and San Julian de Musques. Bilbao is RENFE's third busiest suburban network. Total 67 km, 1,668 mm gauge, on three routes with 39 stations; electrified 3 kV DC.
Developments: The La Naja—Santurzi service will be replaced by Line 2 of the metro, and the remaining service to Musques rerouted over a freight line (the Southern Variant) into Norte station, which itself is to be replaced by the new joint station with FEVE (see above).

Rolling stock: 22 three-car emus
Class 446   M44 T22

VERIFIED

BIRMINGHAM (UK)

Population: City 1 million, West Midlands conurbation 2.6 million
Public transport: Bus services operated by a major private company and over 50 other independent companies. As well as running commercial services, some operators are contracted for provision of supported services by Passenger Transport Executive (Centro), which also contracts for provision of local rail services. West Midlands area covers surrounding urban areas of Coventry, Wolverhampton, Walsall, Dudley, Solihull, West Bromwich. Light rail line

Travel West Midlands

Travel West Midlands Ltd
1 Sovereign Court, 8 Graham Street, Birmingham B1 3JR, England
Tel: (+44 121) 200 72 00   Fax: (+44 121) 233 12 17
Chief Executive: David Leeder
Chairman: Peter Snape MP
Commercial Director: Julie Giles
Financial Director: Paul Cox
Engineering Director: Jack Henry
Staff: 4,500

Current situation: TWM was created from the bus operating interests of the PTE and was sold by the Passenger Transport Authority to its workforce in 1991. Acquired by the National Express Group in 1995, it

A fleet of 14 CNG-powered Volvo B10Ls operates the 529 service between Walsall and Wolverhampton (Andrew Jarosz) **1999**/0045133

Low-floor Volvo B10BLE on first Quality Corridor route Line 33 in central Birmingham (Andrew Jarosz)   ***1999*/0045139**

remains the dominant bus operator in the area. Two subsidiaries operate in the area, Travel Your Bus and Travel Merry Hill, and NEG also owns Central Trains (see below) on a seven-year franchise awarded in 1997.

Developments: Recent initiatives have included branding of routes to create a colour-coded network throughout the region. Together with Centro and Birmingham City Council, TWM has introduced three 'Showcase' routes, with low-floor buses, attractive shelters and provision of real-time information bringing a 20 per cent increase in passengers.

Some £40 million has been invested in new buses, with 1998 deliveries including both the first low-floor double-decks in the UK and the first low-floor minibuses. Fourteen CNG-powered buses are also in operation.

TWM is participating in Centro's integrated travel programme, with one ticket valid for travel on all buses and trains in the West Midlands.

TWM is a member of the Altram consortium which is building the Midland Metro (see below); it will operate the line on opening in 1999.

A new subsidiary, Travel London, started with 31 low-floor buses on two routes during 1998. A website has been started.

Bus

Passenger journeys: (1993/94) 318.3 million
(1995/96) 328 million
(1996/97) 330 million
Vehicle-km: (1993/94) 104.2 million
(1995/96) 105 million
(1996/97) 106 million

Number of routes: 500
Route length: 7,524 km
On priority right-of-way: 7 km

Fleet: 1,763 vehicles

Daimler double-deck	1
MCW Metrobus double-deck	972
Scania N113 double-deck	40
Optare low-floor double-deck	2
Dennis single-deck	7
Volvo single-deck	6
Leyland Lynx single-deck	232
Leyland Tiger single-deck	18
DAF single-deck	21
Mercedes O405N single-deck	115
Coaches	20
Volvo B10B single-deck	72
Volvo B10L single-deck	87
Volvo B6LE single-deck	85
Scania L113 single-deck	3
Mercedes 709 minibus	20
Mercedes 811D minibus	20
Mercedes 814D minibus	20
MetroRider minibus	22

In peak service: 1,580
On order: Over 200 for 1999 delivery, including 105 Volvo B6LE, 20 Optare low-floor double-deck, 35 Optare Excel single-deck and 30 Optare Solo minibuses

Most intensive service: 2-3 min
One-person operation: All services
Fare collection: Autofare farebox with Wayfarer driver-operated ticket-issuing machine
Fare structure: Graduated stage fares with maximum off-peak fare; prepurchase travelcards for varying areas and time periods, including annual and off-peak only; direct-debit Faresaver
Fares collected on board: 36 per cent; travelcards advance sales 36 per cent; concessionary travel passes 23 per cent
Fare evasion control: Spot checks by revenue control inspectors

Operational control: Route inspectors/mobile radio
Arrangements for elderly/disabled: Passes for free bus travel, at all times, issued by Metropolitan District Councils to all blind persons and, at discretion, to disabled persons. Councils pay TWM to accept these for travel on bus and local rail services outside peak periods and up to 23.29 daily. Passes for free off-peak bus travel issued to the elderly by PTE (Centro)
Average distance between stops: 300 m
Integration with other modes: One-day 'Centrocard' and 'Daytripper' passes sold on buses, valid for all operators' buses and trains; rail travellers into West Midlands area can buy bus add-on tickets for all modes travel; many timed interchanges between bus and rail
Operating costs financed by: Fares 97 per cent, tendered service support 3 per cent

Midland Red West

Midland Red West Ltd
Heron Lodge, London Road, Worcester WR5 2EW
Tel: (+44 1905) 35 93 93   Fax: (+44 1905) 35 11 04
Managing Director: Ken Mills

Current situation: This former NBC subsidiary was purchased by its management in 1987 and is now owned by FirstGroup. Commercial minibus and full-size vehicle services have been developed after initial success with West Midland tendered services.

Fleet: 265 buses

Single-deck	114
Coaches	8
Minibuses	143

Birmingham Coach Company

Birmingham Passenger Transport Services Ltd
Hallbridge Way, Cross Quays Business Park, Tipton Road, Tividale B69 3HY
Tel: (+44 121) 555 55 22   Fax: (+44 121) 620 49 99
Managing Director: Geoff Howle
Staff: 145

Current situation: Established in 1984, the company grew quickly by introducing competitive and subsidised routes throughout the city. Acquired Sealandair of West Bromwich in 1994 and thus became the largest independent operator in the area.

Bus

Passenger journeys: (1993/94) 5.2 million

Number of routes: 16

Fleet: 126 vehicles

Leyland single-deck	88
DAF SB220 single-deck	3
Minibuses	10
Coaches	25

Chase

Chase Coaches Ltd
No Name Road, Chasetown WS7 8FS
Tel: (+44 1543) 68 69 37   Fax: (+44 1543) 68 64 32
Managing Director: G Dodd

Current situation: Operates both local and long-distance routes into north Birmingham; total 25 commercial and tendered routes operated by 80 buses and 12 coaches.

Other operators

Current situation: Among those providing commercial services are Banga Travel of Wolverhampton, Caves of Solihull, City Buses of Hockley, Claribel of Tile Cross, Flights of Handsworth, Green Bus of Great Wyrley, Lionspeed of West Bromwich, Ludlows Travel of Halesowen, Midland Choice of Willenhall, Midland Red North of Cannock, North Birmingham Busways, People's Express of West Bromwich, Pete's Travel of West Bromwich Great Barr, Red Arrow Express of Warley, Serveverse of Tamworth, Stagecoach Midland Red of Rugby, West Midlands Road Car and Zak's of Great Barr.

Centro

West Midlands Passenger Transport Executive
16 Summer Lane, Birmingham B19 3SD
Tel: (+44 121) 200 27 87   Fax: (+44 121) 214 70 10

Director General: Rob Donald
Passenger Services Director: Elizabeth Gilliard
Finance Director: Philip Severs
Staff: 280

Passenger journeys: (By operators in Centro's concessionary fares scheme)
(1995/96) 370.5 million
(1996/97) 355 million
(1997/98) 350.7 million

Current situation: Centro is the corporate name and identity of the West Midlands Passenger Transport Executive, the body which advises the WM Passenger Transport Authority (a political body) and carries out its policies. The PTA is a joint authority of the seven metropolitan councils of the West Midlands area — Birmingham City, Coventry City, and the metropolitan boroughs of Dudley, Sandwell, Solihull, Walsall and Wolverhampton. The PTA sets policies and budgets for public transport responsibilities in the area, and levies the councils for funds to carry out its work. The seven authorities and Centro submit a joint bid each year for central government funding of transport schemes.

Centro subsidises the local rail network. It operates and funds concessionary fares scheme, primarily one whereby senior citizens travel at off-peak times, free of charge. Centro provides public transport infrastructure, bus shelters, 12 bus stations and local rail stations. It finances socially necessary bus services, those withdrawn by private operators on commercial grounds but which it is deemed are essential to provide accessibility to all social groups. These services are awarded to private operators on a contract/tender basis. Centro funds the operation of the Ring and Ride door-to-door services for people with disabilities, operated by West Midlands Special Needs Transport Ltd, a registered charity.

Developments: In partnership with the local councils and the private sector, Centro has promoted the Midland Metro light rail project (see below) which opened in early 1999.

Early 1999 saw the public consultation process begin on a new 20-year strategy. The general approach to the revised strategy is to be inventive and visionary but realistic about potential funding, impacts and what is possible. The strategy will identify a core network of services and identify the most appropriate mode of high-quality value-for-money public transport for each corridor. The review of the strategy has drawn from the experience of other cities and countries with different funding levels.

Proposals for an increase to build a light rail network, adding to Midland Metro Line 1, have been taken on a 'bite-sized chunks' basis, as a piecemeal approach is more likely to gain funding approval than the whole of Lines 2 and 3. A prospectus was published in late 1998 outlining the case under the government's Private Finance Initiative to raise £172 million to fund the first three extensions to Midland Metro Line 1. These extensions are Wolverhampton Town Centre Loop, Wednesbury to Brierley Hill and a Birmingham City Tramway.

Centro is also implementing the Bus Showcase project which improves the quality of all aspects of bus travel in co-operation with local authority partners, bus operators and the police. The operators provide new easy-access buses. Centro provides state-of-the-art high-quality bus shelters and information — including real-time and 'talking' bus stops. The local authorities give bus priority in consultation with the police, and make improvements

Independent Midland Choice shares the second Quality Corridor route with TWM, operating four low-floor Optare Excels on Route 171 (Andrew Jarosz)   ***1999*/0045135**

Class 323 emu on Centro Service at Canlay station   **1999**/0045134

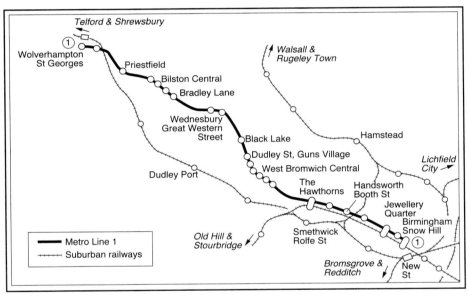

Birmingham's metro and suburban railways   0045352

to pavements at stops. The first 13 km route between Birmingham and Walsall came into operation in February 1997 and summer 1998 saw two more begin in Walsall and Coventry. Initial public reaction has been favourable and more routes are planned.

Contracted bus services
Current situation: 383 contracts. Cost £3.38 million. Subsidised services: 8.45 million km per year. 5.8 per cent of the total network is made up of subsidised services.

Contracted rail services
Operated for Centro by Central Trains Limited
PO Box 4323, Birmingham B1 1TH
Tel: (+44 121) 643 44 44   Fax: (+44 121) 644 44 61
Managing Director: Nick Brown

Franchisee
National Express Group PLC
Worthy Park House, Abbots Worthy, Winchester SO21 1AN
Chief Executive of Rail Division: Richard Brown
Franchise award: 17 February 1997
Franchise commencement: 2 March 1997

Type of operation: Suburban heavy rail

Passenger journeys: (1994/95) 19.7 million
(1995/96) 20.6 million

Current situation: Services operated with Centro support on nine routes with 71 stations totalling 177 km. Five routes are electrified at 25 kV 50 Hz and four are diesel-worked. Seven radial routes to Birmingham City Centre form three cross-city services.
Developments: Central Trains was privatised in 1997 under a seven-year franchise awarded to the National Express Group, which also owns Travel West Midlands. Operation of the West Midlands rail network is controlled under the franchise by a tripartite agreement between Centro, the Office of Passenger Rail Franchising and National Express.

In 1998 new services were introduced between Walsall and Wolverhampton and Birmingham to Rugeley services were extended to Stafford.

Other operators also run services that serve stations in the West Midlands on long-distance and intercity routes.

Light rail
Line 1: Commissioning testing for 1999 opening.
Future routes: Under planning process.

Current situation: Midland Metro Line 1 opened in early 1999. Line 1 (20.4 km, 23 stops) links Birmingham and Wolverhampton using former railway alignment and with a 2 km on-street running section in Wolverhampton town centre. A 23-year design, build, operate and maintain contract was awarded to the Altram consortium comprising Ansaldo Trasporti and civil engineering firm John Laing. Travel West Midlands later joined the consortium and their subsidiary company Travel Midland Metro operates the system.

UPDATED

Midland Metro Line 1
1999/0045235

BIRMINGHAM (USA)

Population: 750,000
Public transport: Fixed-route and specialised bus services provided under contract by Transit Authority, controlled by a Board of Directors. Several proposals for light rail lines under study by the Regional Planning Commission

MAX

Birmingham-Jefferson County Transit Authority
PO Box 10212, 3105 Eighth Avenue North, Birmingham, Alabama 35202-0212, USA
Tel: (+1 205) 322 77 01   Fax: (+1 205) 521 01 20
General Manager: Phil Gary
Operations Manager: Ray J Taylor
Staff: 311

Current situation: BJCTA is the principal transit operator, using the name Metro Area Express (MAX). The authority includes seven member municipalities and the unincorporated areas of Jefferson County.

In 1982 the Alabama state legislature approved a Levelised Beer Tax which guaranteed the authority a minimum $2 million per year in local funding. Subsequently, the hours of service and patronage have steadily increased. Routes have been reorganised for more efficient scheduling, bringing additional services without an increase in the workforce.

Maxpool co-ordinates and arranges carpools through a free computerised matching system. Private employer support is encouraged for the vanpool programme by purchase of a 7-15 seat van which is then maintained by MAX. Maxpool is also responsible for operation of park-and-ride lots throughout the service area.

Bus

Passenger journeys: (1991/92) 6.4 million
(1992/93) 6 million
Vehicle-km: (1991/92) 7.5 million
(1992/93) 7.8 million

Number of routes: 40
Route length: 2,703 km

Fleet: 143 vehicles

GMC RTS (1979)	19
Flxible 870 (1981)	37
Gillig Phantom (1987)	47
Boyertown trolley replicas (1990)	6
Flxible Metro (1997)	12
Blue Bird CS (1995)	22

In peak service: 76

Most intensive service: 10 min; no late evening service
One-person operation: All routes
Fare collection: Exact fare, registering farebox on board; Maxpass 7-day and monthly tickets
Fare structure: Flat, supplement for transfer
Operational control: Route inspectors/mobile radio
Arrangements for elderly/disabled: Accessible buses and door-to-door operation known as VIP Service
Integration with other modes: Maxpool encourages ride-sharing; extensive park-and-ride
Operating costs financed by: Fares 30.6 per cent, FTA subsidy/grants 22.5 per cent, state and local funds 44.9 per cent (Ad valorem and beer tax)
New vehicles financed by: 80 per cent FTA, 20 per cent local funding

Light rail (planned)

Current situation: The planning process started in 1992 for a proposed light rail link in the corridor connecting the city centre with the Birmingham Medical Centre and University of Alabama. Monorail link to the airport also discussed.

VERIFIED

BLANTYRE

Population: 1 million
Public transport: Bus services provided by company part-owned by the government, also responsible for services in other parts of Malawi. Large number of private minibuses

Stagecoach Malaŵi

Stagecoach Malaŵi Limited
PO Box 176, Blantyre, Malawi
Tel: (+265) 67 13 88   Fax: (+265) 67 00 38
Chief Executive: A Anderson

ERF Trailblazers at Blantyre Market

Current situation: In 1989 United Transport (Malaŵi) became 51 per cent owned by Stagecoach Holdings Ltd of Perth, UK, 34 per cent by the Malawi government (14 per cent directly and 20 per cent through Admarc, a parastatal organisation), and 15 per cent by an employee trust. This followed purchase by Stagecoach of the share formerly held by United Transport International. The change in company name took place in 1990. The company operates urban services in Blantyre, and intercity and country services throughout Malawi.
Developments: Rapidly increasing urbanisation of Blantyre has increased the total public transport market, but most growth has been absorbed by informal transit such as Matolas (pick-ups and government vehicles) and minibuses. With little regulation of these operations, legal services have been badly hit. In September 1997 Stagecoach Holdings plc withdrew its 51 per cent share holding in the company. These shares were then transferred to Admarc and the current share holding is now Admarc 71 per cent, Malawi Government 14 per cent and employee trust 15 per cent.

Bus

Blantyre urban operations only
Staff: 450

Passenger journeys: (1994/95) 21.3 million
(1995/96) 20.4 million
(1996/97) 16.9 million
Vehicle-km: (1994/95) 4.5 million
(1995/96) 4.3 million
(1996/97) 4.2 million

Number of routes: 13
Route length: 360 km

Fleet: 40 buses

Leyland Victory Mk2	27
ERF semi-auto	13
In peak service: 35	

One-person operation: Negligible
Fare collection: Floating conductors with Setright or Almex ticket equipment; two conductors on busy routes; prepurchase at certain central area stops
Fare structure: Per kilometre; graduated fares outside city
Operating costs financed by: Fares 98 per cent, other commercial sources (advertising) 2 per cent

Minibus

Current situation: Around 500 privately owned minibuses provide competing services. Most are poorly maintained, many are unlicensed and untaxed.

1997

UPDATED

BOCHUM-GELSENKIRCHEN

Population: 699,000, area served 975,000
Public transport: Bus and tramway/light rail services in Bochum, Gelsenkirchen and adjoining cities provided by public corporation within framework of Verkehrsverbund Rhein-Ruhr (VRR) (qv). Underground sections of tramway in both Bochum and Gelsenkirchen; standard-gauge Stadtbahn line U35 links Bochum and Herne. Area also served by DB S-Bahn

Bogestra

Bochum-Gelsenkirchener Strassenbahnen AG
Universitätsstrasse 58, 44789 Bochum, Germany
Tel: (+49 234) 30 30   Fax: (+49 234) 303 23 00
Directors: Dipl-Ing Gerd Liedtke
  Gisbert Schlotzhauer
  Dr Burkhard Rüberg
Marketing & Operations Manager: Heinz-Dieter Hartwich

Administration & Data Processing Manager:
  Wilfred Scheffer
Staff: 2,116

Passenger journeys: (All modes)
(1995) 105.9 million
(1996) 105.7 million
(1997) 105.6 million

Operating costs financed by: (All modes) fares 28.2 per cent, other commercial sources 7.6 per cent, subsidy/grants 64.2 per cent
Subsidy from: State (*Land*) and municipal government

Bus
Vehicle-km: (1995) 18.3 million
(1996) 17.6 million
(1997) 17.8 million

Number of routes: 69
Route length: 893 km
On priority right-of-way: 4 km shared with tramway

Fleet: 274 vehicles, plus 61 hired
MAN SL200 standard (1981/84)	23
MAN SL202 standard (1984/88)	54
Neoplan N416SL standard (1983/87)	18
MAN SG240H articulated (1980/84)	2
MAN SG242H/242 articulated (1986/88)	20
Mercedes O305G articulated (1980/82)	7
Mercedes O405G articulated (1987/90)	16
MAN NL202 low-floor (1989/94)	63
Neoplan N4016 low-floor (1989)	5
MAN NG272 low-floor articulated (1992/94)	35
Mercedes O405GN low-floor articulated (1995/98)	13
MAN NG312 low-floor articulated (1995)	7
MAN NL223 low-floor (1998)	11

In peak service: 267
On order: 17

Most intensive service: 10 min
One-person operation: All routes
Fare collection: Prepurchase monthly or weekly pass or multitickets with cancellers, cash to driver
Fare structure: Zonal
Fare evasion control: Roving inspectors
Average speed: Weekdays 22 km/h

Tramway/pre-metro
Type of operation: Conventional tramway with underground sections in city centre

Car-km: (1995) 5.6 million
(1996) 5.8 million
(1997) 5.8 million

Route length: 87.8 km
On private right-of-way: 63.4 km, reserved track 10.4 km, in tunnel 4.9 km with 6 stations
Number of lines: 7
Gauge: 1,000 mm
Electrification: 600 V DC, overhead

Fare structure: Zonal
Fare collection: Prepurchase, payment to driver; roving inspectors
One-person operation: All routes

Rolling stock: 99 cars
Duewag M65 6-axle (1976/77)	M33
Duewag M6C 6-axle (1981/82)	M22
Duewag/Siemens MGT6D 6-axle low-floor (1992/94)	M44

In peak service: 85

Light rail
Type of operation: U-Bahn/Stadtbahn with high platforms

Car-km: (1995) 2.3 million
(1996) 2.3 million
(1997) 2.4 million

Route length: 14.9 km
in tunnel: 10.7 km
Number of lines: 1
Number of stations: 21
Gauge: 1,435 mm
Tunnel: Cut-and-cover and bored
Electrification: 750 V DC, overhead

Service: Peak 5 min, off-peak 10-15 min
First/last train: 04.03/00.33
Surveillance: CCTV, emergency telephones

Operational control: Fully automated (microprocessor)

Rolling stock: 25 cars
Duewag/Siemens B80D (1989/93)	M25

In peak service: 11

Current situation: Bogestra's standard-gauge light rail (Line U35) opened in 1989 between Bochum and Herne, entirely in tunnel, replacing a metre-gauge street tramway. Southwards extension to Querenburg/Hustadt (5.9 km, of which 1.6 km in tunnel), converted from metre-gauge, opened 1993. The planned extension to Witten has been shelved, and U35 will now be Bogestra's only standard-gauge line.

Local transport plans announced in mid-1997 included a package of tramway improvements and developments for implementation by 2001. In particular, Route 306 is to be diverted into tunnel in Bochum, leaving the city-centre without surface rail transport.

Two short tunnel sections were under construction in 1997. Surface extension of tramway in Gelsenkirchen-Buer to S-Bahn station (2 km) is planned.

Regional bus
Current situation: Bogestra provides joint and/or connecting services with all neighbouring operators — Essen, Recklinghausen (Vestische), Herne, Dortmund and Wuppertal.

UPDATED

BOGOTA
Population: 4.6 million
Public transport: Part of bus service provided by public corporation. Other bus and minibus services run by more than 20 independent transport groups and co-operatives with more than 1,000 members, partly supported by state subsidies and under supervision of government agency. The Departamento Administrativo de Tránsito y Transporte (DATT) is the overall transport authority. There are also taxis and shared taxis; funicular; light rail proposed

EDTU
Empresa Distrital Transportes Urbanos (EDTU)
Calle 68 No 49-13, Apto Aereo 10648, Bogota, Colombia
Tel: (+57 1) 40 01 12

Current situation: Despite major vehicle purchases, EDTU operations provide less than 10 per cent of Bogota's transport.

SMB
Sistema Metrobus de Bogota (SMB)

Current situation: This company, formed in 1994, is a consortium of the UK's Stagecoach Holdings, Volvo Bus of Sweden, and Corporaciòn Financiera del Transporte. It is introducing a high-quality bus service in four corridors, along the lines of that operated in Curitiba, Brazil (qv). SMB was the chosen bidder from nine companies asked to offer solutions to the city's transport problems.

A fleet of 400 articulated buses will be built by Volvo in Brazil, mostly for local operators who will contract with SMB for provision of services.

Private bus/minibus
Current situation: Bus services are extensively operated by private companies and co-operatives, sanctioned by the government initially for one year and then progressively for longer periods after review.

There are more than 1,000 individual owner-operators each with one or two buses. Government provides special financial arrangements to assist private operators acquire vehicles through the Corporaciòn Financiera del Transporte. There are also arrangements for payment of government subsidy to some operations.

Services are categorised by the Ministry as either subsidised buses, non-subsidised buses (TSS) and minibuses. On non-subsidised buses and minibuses, including some premium 'Executivo' services, passengers pay an economic fare, but on the subsidised operations a 'social fare' is set at about half this level.

Light metro (proposed)
Current situation: Long-standing metro plans, rejected in the early 1990s on cost grounds, were superceded by proposals for a three-line light metro system extending to 35 km. In 1994 the city authorities called for expressions of interest from consortia which might bid for a concession to design, build and operate the system, though the choice of technology was left for bidders to specify. A consortium of Ingetec SA, Bechtel and France's Systra was selected to study various options in 1996.

Little progress was made, but metro plans were being discussed once again in mid-1998, and bids for a design-build-operate concession were to be sought by the end of the year.

UPDATED

BOLOGNA
Population: 386,000, conurbation 908,000
Public transport: Bus and trolleybus services provided by regional authority which operates both urban area and regional services. Light rail and local railway planned. Some suburban rail services by Italian Railways (FS) and a local railway Ferrovia Bologna—Porto Maggiore

ATC
Azienda Trasporti Consorziali Bologna (ATC)
Via di Saliceto 3, 40128 Bologna BO, Italy
Tel: (+39 051) 35 01 11   Fax: (+39 051) 35 01 77
e-mail: atc-dg@iperbole.bologna.it
Web: http://www.comune.bologna.it
Director: Armando Cocuccioni
Staff: 1,059

Current situation: ATC, controlled by the city and province of Bologna, serves not only the population of the Bologna urban area, but also the surrounding region with a total population of 908,000. Trolleybuses returned to this city in 1991 after closure in 1982; some 40 km of wiring had been retained on a care and maintenance basis. Reintroduction coincided with new restrictions on motor car access to the city centre on environmental grounds. Route 13 runs west to southeast from Borgo Panigale to San Ruffillo. A further route (14) is to be converted, for which 20 trolleybuses are on order.

ATC runs a number of special services, including the Videobus which runs to a regular timetable but requires prebooking by passengers, and the Freebus demand-response service which features stops equipped with 'call bus' buttons.

Interurban routes are being integrated with the local rail network. One line, Bologna—Galliera, offers through fares to feeder buses at several stations en route, and timetables have been revised to ensure better connections at interchanges.

Bus and trolleybus
(Urban area services only)

Passenger journeys: (1994) 107.5 million
(1995) 101.5 million
(1996) 96.4 million
Vehicle-km: (1994) 16.9 million
(1995) 17.2 million
(1996) 17.9 million

Number of routes: Bus 34, trolleybus 1
Route length: Bus 425 km, trolleybus 11.8 km
On priority right-of-way: 40 km

Fleet: 468 buses	
Fiat 480.12.21	46
Fiat 490.12.22	21
Fiat 409/Menarini	10
Fiat 421/A/Menarini	27
Fiat 421/AL/Menarini	116
Breda/Menarini M221/1 LU	10
Fiat 490E18mt	16
Menarini 201/LU	151
Fiat minibus	18
Fiat minibus for disabled service	5
BredaMenarinibus 230/1MU	15
MAN NL202 FU CAM low-floor	10
Iveco 491.12.22	11
BredaMenarinibus M321U	12

In peak service: 333
On order: 10 Pollicino battery-powered, 20 Carvin A9SE12 7.7 m, 4 Bassotto suburban, 6 Cacciamali TCM890 urban, 21 Mercedes O405 12 m suburban and 20 Van Hool AG300 low-floor

Fleet: 36 dual-mode trolleybuses	
Menarini M220 LU/4P (1990)	10
Breda 4001.12 (1990)	9
MAN NGT240 18 m low-floor	17

Most intensive service: 3 min
One-person operation: All routes
Fare collection: Tickets from machines and authorised vendors (newspaper kiosks, tobacconists, bars)
Fare structure: Flat, with time ticket (1 h), daily, transferable monthly and annual season tickets valid on all urban lines at varying rates for ordinary passengers, workers and students
Fare evasion control: Random inspection with penalty
Operational control: Inspectors/mobile radio
Arrangements for elderly/disabled: Reduced fares for persons on minimum pensions and disabled paid for by local authorities and included in subsidy provision below
Average distance between stops: 350 m
Average peak-hour speed: In mixed traffic, 15.4 km/h
Operating costs financed by: Fares 38.1 per cent, other commercial sources 5 per cent, subsidy/grants 56.9 per cent (including concessionary fares reimbursement)
Subsidy from: Region 97.6 per cent, national government 1.4 per cent, local and other sources 1 per cent
New vehicles financed by: Internal resources, with contribution from national transport fund

Light rail (planned)
Current situation: Recommendations for a three-line light rail system had been drawn up by consultants

Sisplan in a design study for the city, but lack of funding prevented any progress until the 1996 Finance Bill allocated Lit198 billion towards the estimated cost of Lit398 billion for building Line 1 of a 37 km four-line network, from Corticello to San Lazzaro (19 km). Local government will contribute Lit112.5 billion, regional government Lit3.5 billion, and ATC Lit85 billion. A fleet of 29 cars would be required.

A passenger service is also planned on the freight-only Casalecchio—Savignano—Vignola Railway (30 km, electrified 3 kV DC), for which three emus are under construction. At a later stage, through running to FS lines is planned.

FS
Italian Railways (FS), Bologna Division

Type of operation: Suburban heavy rail

Current situation: Irregular services provided on six routes. Upgrading and integration planned under a scheme approved in 1986.

UPDATED

BOMBAY (MUMBAI)

Population: Conurbation 12.6 million
Public transport: Bus and ferry services provided by municipal undertaking, and by state road transport corporation in suburban areas. Intensively used suburban rail network of Central and Western railways. Extensive use of taxis and autorickshaws and private company and school buses. Plans under consideration for metro, light rail and trolleybus networks

BEST
Bombay Electric Supply & Transport Undertaking (BEST)
Best Bhavan, Best Marg, PO Box 192, Bombay 400001, India
Tel: (+91 22) 287 39 61   Fax: (+91 22) 285 12 44
General Manager: Vinay Mohan Pal
Additional General Manager: Madhav Anant Shanbhag
Assistant General Manager, Traffic Operations:
   M K Prajapati
Public Relations Officer: V M Dhuri
Staff: 38,832

Current situation: BEST'S losses, subsided by its Electricity Supply Division, reached Rs670.8 million in 1995/96.
Developments: BEST is introducing India's first automatic fare collection system on its buses with prepaid smartcards. The system will be first implemented on air conditioned route A1. BEST plans to have a total of nearly 74 buses equipped with the system in the next few months. It is designed to generate real-time management information.

Bus
Passenger journeys: (1994/95) 1,752 million
(1995/96) 1,720 million
(1997/98) 1,531.4 million
Vehicle-km: (1994/95) 236 million
(1995/96) 230 million
(1997/98) 237.9 million

Number of routes: 339
Route length: (One way) 5,054 km

Fleet: 3,425 vehicles	
Ashok-Leyland double-deck	808
Ashok-Leyland single-deck	2,237
Midibus	54
Tata and others	325
CNG-powered	1

In peak service: 2,931
Average age of fleet: 9.3 years

Most intensive service: 1 min
One-person operation: None
Fare collection: Conductors issue preprinted tickets
Fare structure: Distance related/telescopic
Fare evasion control: Organised checking system
Operating costs financed by: Fares 97.7 per cent, other commercial sources and cross-subsidy from electricity supply activities 2.3 per cent
New vehicles financed by: Internal resources and loans from financial institutions

Ferry
Current situation: Ferry service is operated with two boats between Marve and Manori (1 km) on behalf of the Municipal Corporation of Greater Bombay, which meets any deficit.

MSRT
Maharashtra State Road Transport Corporation
Maharashtra Vahatuk Bhavan, Dr Anandrao Nair Marg, Bombay 400008
Tel: (+91 22) 307 15 24   Fax: (+91 22) 308 63 52
Managing Director: Norayan Vallun
Public Relations Officer: S S Bhogle

Current situation: MSRT operates extensive services throughout Maharashtra State. In 1997/98 the average size of the fleet was 16,253. The average age was 4.7 years. Total staff complement was 111,564, and 2,594.5 million passengers were carried.
MSRT provides service in the Thane, Raigad and Palghar divisions of the Bombay metropolitan region, though its city operations account for less than 5 per cent of the total.

Western Railway
Western Railway
Churchgate, 400020 Bombay
Tel: (+91 22) 203 80 16

Type of operation: Suburban heavy rail

Passenger journeys: (1995/96) 990 million
(1996/97) 1,028 million
(1997/98) 1,068 million

Current situation: Extremely heavy traffic is carried on WR's 1.5 kV DC electrified route between Bombay's Churchgate station and Virar (60.6 km, 28 stations). More than 900 trains run daily.
Developments: It has not been possible to increase the number of trains in proportion to the growth in patronage, but many trains have been extended from 9 to 12 cars.

Tracks, signalling and traction systems are being improved to permit aumentation of services. It has now been decided to finance the quadrupling of the Borivali—Virar section from Indian Railways' own budgetary resources since the BOLT scheme envisaged earlier for this project was not successful.

The work of converting the existing 1,500 V DC system to 25 kV AC traction is now being taken up on both Western and Central Railways due to several limitations of the existing 1,500 V DC system. VVVF-controlled three-phase drive equipments are being provided on the emus for dual voltage — 1,500 V DC/25 kV AC operation during the transition period.

Rolling stock: 710 emu cars   M244 T466

Central Railway
Central Railway
Victoria Terminus, 400001 Bombay
Tel: (+91 22) 262 15 51   Fax: (+91 22) 262 45 55

Type of operation: Suburban heavy rail

Passenger journeys: (1995/96) 1,082 million
(1996/97) 1,110 million
(1997/98) 1,135 million

Current situation: Following extension of service to New Bombay in 1996, CR now operates the most extensive suburban network in the country. It provides a service of 1,146 daily trains from Bombay Victoria to Karjat (100 km) and Kansara (120 km) on the main line, and to Khandeshwar (46 km), Andheri (21 km) on the Harbour branch and associated lines, electrified 1.5 kV DC.

The existing infrastructure of the suburban railway system has reached its limit of performance and there is pressing need to augment the capacity by implementing both short-term and long-term measures.
Developments: Some of the short-term measures taken in the recent past are operating 12-car emu rakes on through lines providing 71 services daily, respacing of signals to reduce headways, strengthening of track

structures and augmentation of power supply. As a long-term solution, provision of an independent corridor is essential for operation of suburban services, for which a major thrust is now being given for opening new corridors.

Rolling stock: 1,039 emu cars   M357 T682

Metropolitan Transport Project
Metropolitan Transport Project (Railways)
2nd Floor, Churchgate Station Annexe, 400020 Bombay
Tel: (+91 22) 208 00 15   Fax: (+91 22) 209 69 72
Chief Administrative Officer: O P Agarwal

Developments: This organisation is carrying out various projects for augmenting the capacity of Mumbai suburban rail network. Extension of the Mankhurd–Belapur line to Panvel was completed in March 1996. This line serves the developing island city of New Bombay, which is expected to have 2 million inhabitants by the end

of the century. The 23 km Belapur—Seawood—Uran link is under construction and the link from Thane to Vashi (19 km) is nearing completion at an estimated cost of Rs403 million on a cost-sharing basis between Indian Railways and the state government.

On the Western Railway, work on the fifth line between Santa Cruz and Borivali (15.8 km) at a cost of Rs641 million is in progress.

Mumbai Railway Vikas Corporation Ltd (MRVC): Another important development is that the Ministry of Railways and the Government of Maharashtra have signed a Memorandum of Understanding for the formation of a public-sector unit called Mumbai Railway Vikas Corporation for executing projects in the Mumbai area.

Private bus/taxi
Current situation: Significant numbers of private taxis,

autorickshaws and private buses operate, with transport for schools and factories often provided by contracted services.

Metro (planned)
Current situation: Further studies of a metro for the city, planned by the Metropolitan Regional Development Authority, have been funded by a World Bank loan. A 22.5 km line from Colaba to Wurli has been proposed, along with further improvements to the suburban rail network. Detailed feasibility studies and further discussions with the World Bank were in progress at the beginning of 1997.

UPDATED

BONN
Population: 311,000, population served 382,000
Public transport: Bus and tramway/Stadtbahn services operated by municipal authorities under common directorate. Some other bus services. All public transport in Cologne/Bonn area co-ordinated by Verkehrsverbund Rhein-Sieg (VRS) (see Cologne entry)

SWB/SSB
Stadtwerke Bonn (SWB) and Elektrische Bahnen der Stadt Bonn und des Rhein-Sieg-Kreises (SSB)
PO Box 180240, 53032 Bonn, Germany
Tel: (+49 228) 71 11   Fax: (+49 228) 71 17 70
Operating Director: Reiner Schreiber
Technical Director: Dipl-Ing Norbert Klein
Assistant Managing Directors: Horst Ruthenkolk
  Bus: Michael Althoff
  Rail: Jürgen Marx
Staff: 1,302

Passenger journeys: (All modes)
(1995) 64.9 million
(1996) 67.4 million
(1997) 69.2 million

Operating costs financed by: Fares 36 per cent, subsidy/grants 64 per cent
Subsidy from: City, state and national government

Current situation: The combined operating entity SWB/SSB has brought together the Bonn city transport undertaking, SWB, and the joint Bonn and Rhein-Sieg transport company, SSB.

SWB/SSB is a member of Verkehrsverbund Rhein-Sieg (VRS), providing a joint tariff scheme with Cologne, Rhein-Sieg Verkehrsgesellschaft (Siegburg/Troisdorf) and other

Mercedes-Benz O405 standard bus at Bonn main railway station (Wilhelm Pflug)   ***1999**/0043588*

operators in the area, including DB. At the start of 1998, the Bad Godesberg-Niederdollendorf vehicle ferry came under SWB ownership.

Bus
Staff: 488

Vehicle-km: (1995) 12.9 million
(1996) 13 million
(1997) 13.1 million

Number of routes: 35
Route length: (One way) 573 km

Fleet: 185 vehicles, plus 62 hired
Mercedes O305 standard (1983/86)	68
Mercedes O405 standard (1986/88/91)	52
MAN SL202 standard (1986/89)	14
Mercedes O405G articulated	6
MAN NL202 low-floor (1990/92)	30
Others	15

On order: 25 low-floor buses

Most intensive service: 5 min
One-person operation: All routes
Fare collection: Prepurchase with validation and cancelling machines or cash to driver
Fare structure: Zonal; prepurchase carnets or weekly, monthly, and annual passes
Fares collected on board: 13 per cent
Fare evasion control: Roving inspectors with penalty
Operational control: Route inspectors/mobile radio
Average peak-hour speed: 21.9 km/h
New vehicles financed by: Depreciation, subsidy and loans

Tramway/light rail
Staff: 180

Type of operation: Stadtbahn and conventional tramway

Car-km: (1995) 6.9 million
(1996) 7 million
(1997) 7.1 million

Route length: 64.2 km
Number of routes: 7 (3 tram, 4 LRT)
Gauge: 1,435 mm
Electrification: 750 V DC, overhead

SWB low-floor tram at Weberstrasse (Wilhelm Pflug)   ***1999**/0043589*

Rolling stock: 99 cars
Duewag B100C/S 6-axle articulated
(1973/84/92/93)   M75
Duewag R1 6-axle low-floor (1994/95)   M24

Current situation: Network comprises three routes of urban tramway and four of Stadtbahn, 1,435 mm gauge, including Routes 16 and 18 to Cologne over former Cologne-Bonn Railway operated jointly with KVB Cologne (qv).
Developments: Extension to Mehlem planned for opening after 2000. In connection with the opening of the ICE high-speed rail route from Cologne to Frankfurt, the terminus at Siegburg is being relocated underground at the new ICE station. Work will also include doubling of the existing single-line section from Siegburg Zange and completion is expected in 2001.

Suburban rail
Current situation: Extra trains introduced 1994 over the 10 km Bonn Hbf—Witterschlick section of the line to Euskirchen to provide a 15 min service during morning and evening peak hours. This service was extended a further 12 km to Rheinbach in late 1995. These additional trains are operated by DB under contract to SWB. Agreement was reached in March 1998 for an S-Bahn extension from Cologne to the Cologne/Bonn airport at Bonn-Oberkassel, due for completion by 2001. This is likely to be a Karlsruhe-style mixed Stadtbahn/S-Bahn operation.
Developments: In 1997, 38 of the newest vehicles were sold to a US trust company and leased back for a period of 27 years. SWB expects to save some DM10 million by this action.

RSVG

Rhein-Sieg Verkehrsgesellschaft mbH
Spicher Str 10, 53844 Troisdorf
Tel: (+49 2241) 49 90   Fax: (+49 2241) 49 92 98
Managing Directors: Herbert Lutz
    Dr-Ing Lothar Franz

Staff: 330

Passenger journeys: (1995) 16.9 million
(1996) 14.9 million
(1997) 16.8 million
Vehicle-km: (1995) 9.7 million
(1996) 9.3 million
(1997) 9.4 million

Fleet: 185 buses, plus 42 on hire

Current situation: Local authority-owned regional bus company providing services in the area around Bonn, especially on the right bank of the Rhine, and urban services in Siegburg, plus through routes to Bonn, as part of the VRS network.

UPDATED

BORDEAUX

Population: City 210,000, metropolitan area 650,000
Public transport: Bus services operated under contract to local authority consortium, through concession held by subsidiary of national company, for 27 towns of the Communauté Urbaine de Bordeaux (CUB) and three adjoining towns; light rail planned

CGFTE

Transport en Commun de la Communauté Urbaine de Bordeaux
Operated as concession by: Compagnie Générale Française de Transports et d'Entreprises (CGFTE) (part of the Vivendi Group)
25 rue du Commandant Marchand, 33082 Bordeaux Cedex, France
Tel: (+33 5) 57 57 88 00   Fax: (+33 5) 57 57 88 99
Chief Officer: Jean-Pierre Bonnet
Staff: 1,698

Developments: A major campaign against fare evasion was launched in 1997 with a 70 per cent increase in inspection staff and a major communication campaign. Four new circular routes around the edge of the city were introduced in 1998.

Bus
Passenger journeys: (1994) 59.4 million
(1995) 55.5 million
(1997) 58.2 million
Vehicle-km: (1994) 22.3 million
(1995) 20.6 million
(1997) 23.4 million

Number of routes: 62
Route length: (One way) 997 km
On priority right-of-way: 16.5 km

Fleet: 541 vehicles
Renault Mégabus   10
MAN NG272 articulated   23
Renault PR180-2 articulated   150
Renault PR100-2   192
Heuliez GX77   15
Renault PR100 MI   4
MAN NL222 low-floor   53
Renault Agora low-floor   53
Renault PR112   29
Mercedes O100 citybus   12
In peak service: 466
Average age of fleet: 6.1 years

Most intensive service: 3 min
One-person operation: All services
Fare collection: Cancellation by passengers with Camp CE 31 and electronic Camp needle-printing machines on board

Fare structure: Flat, multitickets, free transfers on up to 4 buses within 1 h; monthly/annual passes; 1- and 3-day and 1-month ride-at-will tickets, single route passes
Fares collected on board: 13.6 per cent
Fare evasion control: Inspectors
Operational control: 41 route inspectors/mobile radio
Arrangements for elderly/disabled: Reduced or free fares financed by city
Average distance between stops: 300 m
Average peak-hour speed: 16.5 km/h
Bus priority: Bus lanes totalling 14.2 km, of which 4.5 km physically separated and 3.3 km contraflow
Operating costs financed by: Fares 23.3 per cent, other commercial sources 1.7 per cent, subsidy/grants 75 per cent
Subsidy from: Dedicated payroll tax ('versement') and transport authority grant
New vehicles financed by: CUB

Light rail (planned)
Current situation: After various studies and altered proposals, a two-line automated metro on the VAL system was approved in 1990, but was abandoned in 1994.
    Light rail proposals were revived in 1997, when a three-line network recommended by consultants Systra/Sofretu was approved. In the 22.2 km first phase, Line A would run from Mériadeck in the east through the city centre and across the Garonne to Lormont in the north, with a short branch to Cenon-la-Morlette. Line B would link Quinconces just north of the city centre with Saige in the southwest, while short Line C would run from Quinconces to St Jean SNCF station with Line A interchange at Porte de Bourgogne. Phase I was expected to be approved in mid-1999, for opening in 2002/03. Phase II would see extensions built at each end of all three routes.

SNCF

French National Railways, Bordeaux Region
54 rue Amédée St-Germain, 33077 Bordeaux
Tel: (+33 5) 56 33 11 85   Fax: (+33 5) 56 33 10 10

Type of operation: Suburban heavy rail

Current situation: Limited suburban services provided on six routes, mainly with two-car Z2 emus, partially financed by Aquitaine Region. Busiest route is to Arcachon (59 km).
Developments: Several new or reopened stations are planned, in particular in the eastern suburbs on the line to Pointe de Grave. Phase III of the light rail scheme would involve Karlsruhe-style LRVs over rail lines.

UPDATED

Heuliez CNG bus in Bordeaux (David Haydock)

BOSTON

Population: 562,000, metropolitan area 2.6 million
Public transport: Bus, trolleybus, metro and light rail services operated by transport authority serving wide area with population of some 4.1 million, with some contracted services in outlying areas. Suburban rail services and ferries operated under contract

MBTA

Massachusetts Bay Transportation Authority (MBTA)
10 Park Plaza, Boston, Massachusetts 02116, USA
Tel: (+1 617) 222 31 06   Fax: (+1 617) 222 61 80
Secretary & MBTA Chairman: Patrick J Moynihan
General Manager: Robert H Prince Jr
Deputy General Manager: Philip Puccia
Chief of Staff: Mikel Oglesby
Chief Operating Officer: Michael Mulhern
Deputy Chief Operating Officer: Anne Herzenberg
Director of Subway Operations: Michael Francis
Staff: 5,815 plus 1,756 operating purchased service

Operating costs financed by: (All modes) Fares 30.2 per cent, other commercial sources 2.6 per cent, subsidy/grants 67.2 per cent
Subsidy from: Federal 1.8 per cent, Commonwealth of Massachusetts 47.5 per cent, local funding 17.9 per cent

Current situation: MBTA was created in 1964 as the forerunner of many regional transport planning and operating agencies. The MBTA area covers a total of 78 cities and towns in the greater Boston and eastern Massachusetts area. In addition, MBTA provides service to 52 communities outside the district, some provided under contract by 14 operators.

The metro network has its origins in an extensive system of street tramways. Today's light rail operation (the Green line) comprises four branches feeding into a city-centre tunnel with good interchange to metro and commuter trains.

Developments: Proposals for widespread contracting-out of bus services have been put on indefinite hold. Privatisation was seen as the only way of reducing the very high costs inherent in MBTA's operations. The undertaking's bus operating costs are roughly twice those of local private companies. Political difficulties and trades union opposition have delayed the process, and the plans were rejected by the state governor in 1997.

Bus and trolleybus

Passenger boardings: (1996) Bus 101.3 million, trolleybus 3.4 million
Vehicle-km: (1990/91) 41.5 million
(1996) Bus 40.9 million, trolleybus 1.2 million

Number of routes: Bus 155, trolleybus 4
Route length: Bus 1,100 km, trolleybus 25 km

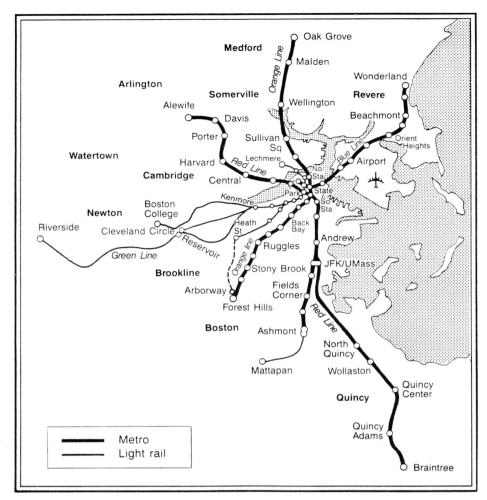

Boston's metro and light rail system

Fleet: 980 buses

GMC RTS T80-604 (1985, rebuilt 1992/93)	200
GMC RTS T80-606 (1986/87)	180
TMC RTS T70/80-606 12 m (1989)	170
TMC RTS T70/80-606 10.7 m (1989)	30
TMC RTS (1994)	122
Novabus RTS T80-206 (1995)	278

In peak service: 753
On order: Possible purchase of 25 12 m buses in 1999

Fleet: 43 trolleybuses

Flyer E800 (1976)	43

In peak service: 23

Most intensive service: 15 min
One-person operation: All routes
Fare collection: Coin to farebox; 1-, 3- and 7-day passes
Fare structure: Flat, some zone fares
Average peak-hour speed: Bus 18.3 km/h, trolleybus 19.5 km/h
Arrangements for elderly/disabled: 32 routes operated by lift-equipped buses. Call-A-Lift service will provide lift-equipped buses on any other route on request

Developments: Trolleybus operation was planned for Washington Street, to replace the relocated Orange line metro service. Progress had been delayed by protests in favour of a light rail line instead. Approval for the 4 km wiring was given in 1996 for 1998 opening, but there has been no progress and it is now thought that service will be provided by CNG-powered articulated buses running in reserved lanes. But this would not preserve the option to convert the alignment to light rail operation at a later date, as MBTA had been required to do.

A 3 km underground trolleybus 'transitway' is under construction to link the South Boston piers area with South station, with opening scheduled for 2000. FTA funding of $331 million has been granted towards the $413 million cost.

Plans were being developed for a new fleet of articulated trolleybuses with partial low floor, though a re-examination of requirements has changed the specification to 12.2 m rigid vehicles with full-length low floor. An initial batch of 50 is likely to be ordered; these will be dual-mode for operation away from the wires when required.

Metro/light rail

Type of operation: Full metro and light rail

Passenger boardings: (1993) Metro 110 million, light rail 69.6 million
(1994) Metro 114.3 million, light rail 69.9 million
(1996) Metro 107.6 million, light rail 69 million
Car-km: (1990/91) Metro 30.3 million, light rail 9 million
(1996) Metro 36.6 million, light rail 8.9 million

Route length: 125 km, comprising:
Orange line (full metro) 17.5 km
Blue line (full metro) 9.5 km

New Red line cars from Bombardier Transportation cross the Charles River Bridge at Boston (Van Wilkins)

1999/0038756

Red line (full metro) 47.5 km
Green line (light rail) 50 km
   in tunnel: 24 km
Number of stations: 84
   in tunnel: 28
   elevated: 3
Gauge: 1,435 mm
Track: 38.6 kg/m ASCE; 45.4 kg/m ARA-B; 68 kg/m RE rail on combination of conventional sleepers on ballast, wooden sleepers on steel and concrete sleepers with resilient pads. All new track continuous-welded on resilient pads
Tunnel: Cut-and-cover single-bored and caisson
Electrification: All 600 V DC. Collection: Red line, third rail, Ashmont—Mattapan light rail extension, catenary; Orange line, third rail; Blue line, third rail and catenary; Green line, catenary

Service: Peak 4½ min, off-peak 8 min
First/last train: 05.00/00.30
Fare structure: Flat on Orange and Blue lines; zonal on Green and Red lines; no free transfers to bus
Revenue control: Mechanical turnstiles accept tokens and electronically coded passes at all stations
One-person operation: Red line, 24 Series 1500 cars can be one-man operated, but there are no plans to run these cars as singles. Green line, one-man runs with LRV cars as single and multiple units, each added car with conductor
Automatic control: Red line, automatic speed control on approx 69 per cent of present route. Station stops and starts under driver's control; ATO being installed on Orange line
Surveillance: One end-of-line station (Braintree, Red line) equipped with CCTV monitored by local police

Rolling stock: 602 cars (Metro 408, Green line 194)

Pullman Standard 3000/3200 PCC (1946/47)	M11
Pullman Standard 01500/01600 (1969/70)	M74
Boeing Vertol 3400/3500 LRV (1977/83)	M68
Hawker Siddeley 0600 Blue line (1978/80)	M70
Hawker Siddeley 01200 Orange line (1979/81)	M120
Kinki Sharyo 3600 Type 7 LRV (1986/87)	M95
Kinki Sharyo 3800 Type 7 LRV (1997)	20
UTDC 01700 Red line (1987/89)	M58
Bombardier 01800 Red line (1993/94)	M86

Developments: Station modernisation continues to improve accessibility and attractiveness on all lines. Blue line platforms being extended to accommodate six-car trains. Major long-term improvement of the Green line in progress, including relocation of the Haymarket—Science Park section underground. A batch of 55 of the troublesome Boeing LRVs has been refurbished to keep them running for a further 10 years.

A low-floor car design similar to Grenoble's has been chosen for the Green line fleet renewal. Breda is building 100 cars with the entire fleet in service by 2001. Breda is also modifying the existing Kinki Sharyo cars to make them compatible with the new fleet.

Commuter rail
Type of operation: Suburban heavy rail (diesel)

Passenger journeys: (1996) 27 million
(1997) 29 million

Current situation: Service provided under contract to MBTA by Amtrak over 13 routes totalling 528 km with 116 stations. Five routes serve Boston's North station, eight run to South station; irregular service outside peak hours.
Developments: Service to the South Shore area started in 1997, when trains began running to Plymouth and Middleborough. This is the first phase of restoration of the three Old Colony lines (128 km), closed in 1959.

MBTA restored services on the branch from Ipswich to Newburyport in October 1998. Longer term plans exist for extension of commuter routes to serve Taunton, East Taunton, Freetown, Fall River and New Bedford from the Attleboro or Middleborough lines.

Rolling stock: 55 diesel locomotives and 287 coaches
On order: 25 rehabilitated diesel locomotives; plans to order 100 coaches in 2000

UPDATED

MBTA had old Boeings rebuilt to maintain service quality while awaiting delivery of new low-floor cars from Breda (Van Wilkins)   **1999**/0038757

Flyer E800 trolleybus of MBTA inbound on Route 73 in Cambridge   *1996*

BRASILIA

Population: With eight satellite cities, 1.8 million
Public transport: Bus services provided by one state-owned undertaking and eight private companies, all supervised by public transport department of the district government (DMTU/ST). Metro

DMTU/ST

Departamento Metropolitano de Transportes Urbanos
SCN-Galeria Oeste Norte, Brasilia DF 70710-500, Brazil
Tel: (+55 61) 321 17 99   Fax: (+55 61) 225 17 18
Director General: Ricardo Sampaio S

Caio bus of private operator Planeta
1997

Current situation: Services of state-owned TCB (280 vehicles) carry about 16.5 per cent of total passengers. DMTU/ST is responsible for licensing the other operators, and planning and supervising all services. The eight private operators are Alvorada (225 vehicles), Arco (107), Planeta (617), Viplan (541), Riacho Grande (37), Santo Antônio (37), São José (37) and Sol (370).

Government subsidies, which had been suspended in 1991, were resumed in 1993 to the tune of 5 per cent of operating costs.

Developments: Credit-card size magnetic strip tickets in both card and plastic are to replace the existing Edmondson system, giving compatibility between bus and metro ticketing and offering real-time information on ridership trends. Equipment is being supplied by the Isotech consortium.

Bus
Staff: 14,000

Passenger journeys: (1991) 217.3 million
(1992) 208 million
Vehicle-km: (1991) 302.8 million
(1992) 162 million

Number of routes: 414
Route length: 34.8 km (average)

Fleet: 1,930 vehicles, including Mercedes/Marcopolo, Thamco, Caio, Mafersa
In peak service: 1,636

Operating costs financed by: Fares 95 per cent, local government subsidy 5 per cent
Fare structure: Flat within Brasilia and each satellite city; higher fare for journeys between cities

Metro-DF
Cia do Metropolitano de Distrito Federal

Type of operation: Conventional metro, opened 1994

Route length: 20 km
  in tunnel: 9.5 km
Number of lines: 1
Number of stations: 8
Gauge: 1,600 mm
Track: Surface, ballasted; in tunnels, concrete slab; 57 kg/m rail
Minimum curve radius: 250 m
Electrification: 750 V DC, third rail

Service: Peak 5 min
Signalling: Full ATC
Surveillance: CCTV on all platforms

Rolling stock: 20 four-car emus
Mafersa (1993/94)   M40 T40

Current situation: The 20 km between Samambaia and Park Shopping Centre is the initial portion of a 38.5 km metro linking central Brasilia with the satellite cities of Guara I and II, Taguatinga, Ceilandia and Samambaia. It is being operated experimentally with a limited service prior to opening of the full route, now expected in 1999 or 2000. Alstom Transporte is to maintain the system's rolling stock and signalling under a contract awarded in 1998.

UPDATED

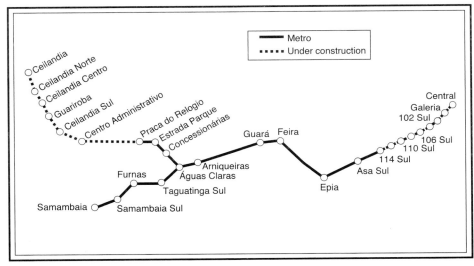

Brasilia's metro

BRATISLAVA
Population: 450,000
Public transport: Bus, trolleybus and tramway services provided by municipal department; metro planned

DPB
Dopravný podnik Bratislava a s
Olejárska 1, 81452 Bratislava, Slovakia
Tel: (+421 7) 59 50 11 11   Fax: (+421 7) 59 50 15 00
General Manager: Ján Zachar

Passenger journeys: (All modes)
(1993) 309 million
(1994) 262 million
(1996) 303 million

Current situation: DPB was reorganised in 1992 and again in 1994. It provides public transport throughout the city.

Developments: Proposals for conversion of tramways to standard gauge are reported to have been shelved, despite some 50 per cent of existing alignment having been rebuilt to facilitate the change. Nevertheless, plans for development of the network on the lines of Germany's Stadtbahn are still under consideration.

Renewal of the fleet with articulated buses is under way in collaboration with TAM-Bus, Slovenia. They are equipped with MAN engines.

Under proposals put forward in a study published in 1997, public transport is to be reorganised around a two-line core light metro network (see below).

Fare structure: Flat; 24 h, 48 h, 7 day, 1, 3, 6 and 12 month tickets
Fare collection: Prepurchase, cancelling machines
Fare evasion control: Roving inspectors
One-person operation: All routes

Tramway
Type of operation: Conventional tramway

Passenger journeys: (1994) 90.2 million
(1996) 92.7 million
(1997) 93.6 million
Car-km: (1994) 11 million
(1996) 11 million
(1997) 11 million

Number of routes: 11
Route length: 243 km
Gauge: 1,000 mm
Electrification: 600 V DC, overhead

Service interval: 12 min

Rolling stock: 227 cars
ČKD Tatra T3   M136
ČKD Tatra T6A5 (1992/93)   M56
ČKD Tatra K2 articulated   M35
In peak service: 145

Trolleybus
Passenger journeys: (1994) 16.1 million
(1996) 29.6 million
(1997) 29 million
Vehicle-km: (1994) 4.9 million
(1996) 5 million
(1997) 5 million

Number of routes: 13
Route length: 211 km
Electrification: 600 V DC

Fleet: 114 trolleybuses
Skoda 14Tr   93
Skoda 15Tr articulated   21
In peak service: 85

Newest articulated trolleybus Škoda 15Tr13/6M No 6617 in Bratislava   **1999**/0045137

Bus

Passenger journeys: (1993) 181.6 million
(1996) 180.4 million
(1997) 182.3 million
Vehicle-km: (1993) 32.1 million
(1996) 26.7 million
(1997) 26.3 million

Number of routes: 67
Route length: 1,477 km

Fleet: 555 buses

Karosa B731/B732	153
Karosa B741/C744 articulated	109
TAM	11
TAM articulated	34
Ikarus 415	44
Ikarus 280/283 articulated	108
Ikarus 435 articulated	96

In peak service: 481

Metro (proposed)

Current situation: After earlier plans for a 7 km VAL metro line to Petržalka were abandoned in 1992, the project was reactivated in 1994 when the city authorities asked Matra to review the plans. The urban transport study published in 1997 envisages a core network of two light metro lines totalling 32.5 km by 2030. Line 1, on which construction is expected to start in 2000 for opening in 2003, will run 9.7 km from Petržalka through the city centre, serving the main line railway station, and terminating at Trnavské Mýto. A later extension would run 3.9 km to Ružinov. A consortium including Siemens

New Ikarus 435 articulated bus and ČKD trams type T6A5 and T3SUCS at Dúbravka terminus

1999/0045138

Austria and Matra Transport was awarded a contract for Line 1 in late 1998.

Line 2 (18.9 km) will start at Dubravka in the west and loop south through the city centre to an interchange with

Line 1 before turning northeast to terminate at Rača. The technology selected is Matra's VAL system.

UPDATED

BREMEN

Population: 548,000; population served 598,000
Public transport: Bus and tramway services operated by member company of the Bremer Versorgungs und Verkehrsgesellschaft mbH (BVV), a public utility wholly owned by municipality of Bremen. Suburban rail services operated by DB. Bus services also run by private operators. Services co-ordinated by regional transit authority VBN

VBN

Verkehrsgemeinschaft Bremen/Niedersachsen
Otto-liliethalstrasse 23, 28129 Bremen, Germany
Tel: (+49 421) 17 49 40   Fax: (+49 421) 174 94 40
Managing Directors: Reiner Strenge
   Marc-André Hinrichs
   Walter-Jürgen Türkner

Passenger journeys: (1995) 94.4 million
(1996) 111.8 million
(1997) 114.1 million

Fare structure: Zonal

Current situation: Set up in 1989, this regional transit authority embraces the cities of Bremen and Delmenhorst and surrounding areas within a radius of 50-70 km from Bremen, covering 5,700 km² with a population of about 1.8 million (area further enlarged 1992). VBN co-ordinates services provided by BSAG (see below) with suburban rail services of DB and suburban and regional bus services provided by 30 public and private operators with a network of 247 routes. A uniform zonal tariff allows free transfers between modes and operators.
Developments: The area of VBN was expanded to include the cities of Bremerhaven and Oldenburg.

Construction of rail/road transit centres has started at several locations. Reorganisation of the regional bus network is planned.

BSAG

Bremer Strassenbahn AG
PO Box 106627, 28066 Bremen
Tel: (+49 421) 55 96 10   Fax: (+49 421) 55 96 302
Directors: Dr-Ing Herbert Felz
   Hubert Resch
   Karl-Heinz Witt
Manager, Corporate Planning: Hans-Dieter Griess
Manager, Traffic Planning: Lienhard Meyer

BSAG's GT8N low-floor tram

1997

Manager, Commercial: Wilhelm Richter
Manager, Engineering: Gerd H Sander
Staff: 2,401

Passenger journeys: (All modes)
(1995) 96.9 million
(1996) 95.2 million
(1997) 92.5 million

Fare collection: Payment to driver, prepurchase multitickets or pass; validation and cancelling machines on board
Fare structure: Zonal (area divided into 91 numbered zones); single tickets and day passes obtainable from driver; four and 10 multijourney tickets or weekly/monthly passes from booking offices; monthly/day passes transferable; a second person and up to four children may ride free after 19.00 and at weekends; football admission tickets valid for travel to and from stadium
Fares collected on board: 10.7 per cent
Operating costs financed by: (All modes) Fares 47 per cent, other commercial sources 8 per cent, subsidy/

grants 45 per cent; some subsidies made directly in respect of certain routes
Subsidy from: Deficits made good by Bremer Versorgungs und Verkehrsgesellschaft mbH as parent company. Part of the funds available for support come under Federal legislation providing for larger states to compensate smaller ones, like Bremen, for greater burden of providing local services. Contributions also received from neighbouring Lower Saxony municipalities

Developments: BSAG is participating in a new 'Norddeutsche Bahngesellschaft mbH (NBG)', together with EVB and OHE, with the objective of tendering for local railway lines currently operated by DB AG.

Bus

Vehicle-km: (1995) 16.2 million
(1996) 16.4 million
(1997) 16.9 million

Number of routes: 46
Route length: 558 km

Fleet: 325 vehicles

Neoplan N4021NG articulated (1988/92/95)	161
Mercedes O405N (1990/91)	27
Mercedes O405N2 (1994)	16
MAN NL202 (1990/92/94)	47
Neoplan N4014 (1991/92)	24
Mercedes O405GN (1997/98)	16
Others	34

Most intensive service: 5 min
One-person operation: All routes
Operational control: Traffic controllers on each route with mobile radio; computer-based control
Average distance between stops: 569 m
Average peak-hour speed: 21.9 km/h
New vehicles financed by: Leasing

Developments: A system of infra-red signalling enables buses to influence traffic signals. An automatic vehicle management system came into operation in 1996.

In mid-1997, a Neoplan low-floor articulated bus with diesel-electric transmission went into service on Route 26 for a three-year trial.

The bus fleet is now almost fully converted to low-floor vehicles.

Tramway
Type of operation: Conventional tramway

Car-km: (1995) 10.4 million	
(1996) 8.8 million	
(1997) 6.2 million	

Route length: 58.3 km
Number of lines: 8
Gauge: 1,435 mm
One-person operation: All routes

Rolling stock: 196 cars

Wegmann 4-axle articulated (1973/77)	M59 T57
Wegmann 6-axle double-articulated (1976/77, rebuilt 1992)	M2
AEG/Kiepe GT8N 8-axle low-floor (1993/95/96)	M78

Current situation: Eight-route network upgraded to Stadtbahn standards in suburbs, with street running maintained in city centre.
Developments: Line 4 extended eastwards to Horn (3.4 km), with later extension planned to Lilienthal. Line 6 extension to University was expected to be completed in September 1998 (2.2 km). The terminus of Line 5 at Flughafen has been relaid to serve the airport terminal directly.

In 1997, express trams started operating during the morning peak between Gröpelingen and the city centre, raising average speed from 20 to 28 km/h.

DB

Deutsche Bahn AG, Geschäftsbereich Nahverkehr
Regionalbereich Niedersachsen/Bremen
Joachimstrasse 8, 30159 Hannover
Tel: (+49 511) 286 33 30   Fax: (+49 511) 286 11 07
Manager: Peter Schatte

Type of operation: Suburban heavy rail

Current situation: Services operated on six routes radiating from Bremen Hbf, totalling 168 km with 32 stations, under VBN tariff (see above), carrying about 10 million passengers annually. The route from Bremen Hbf to Vegesack (17 km) and Verden (Aller) (35 km) has been upgraded to the City Bahn standards with fixed interval service (15 min peak, 30 min off-peak).

WEB

Weser-Ems Busverkehr GmbH
Friedrich-Rauers Strasse 9, 28195 Bremen
Tel: (+49 421) 30 89 70   Fax: (+49 421) 308 97 41
Managing Directors: Herbert Schlienkamp
   Manfred Tyborczyk

Current situation: Regional bus company owned by DB provides suburban and rural services on 24 routes within VBN area.

Wolters

Wolters Linienverkehrsbetriebe GmbH
Bremer Strasse 49, 28816 Stuhr
Tel: (+49 421) 89 99 81   Fax: (+49 421) 80 16 34
Managing Director: Gerhard Falke

Current situation: Independent bus operator providing suburban services on eight routes to the south of Bremen.

Delbus

Delbus GmbH
Bahnhofstrasse 22, 27749 Delmenhorst
Tel: (+49 4221) 919 20   Fax: (+49 4221) 91 92 20
Managing Director: Hubert Resch
Operating Manager: Carsten Hoffmann

Passenger journeys: (1995) 2.9 million
(1996) 3 million
(1997) 2.9 million
Vehicle-km: (1995) 1.5 million
(1996) 1.6 million
(1997) 1.5 million

Current situation: Subsidiary company of BSAG providing local bus service over 15 routes in Delmenhorst (population 80,000), with a fleet of 30 buses. Connection with BSAG services at two points; through ticketing.

Neoplan low-floor articulated bus at Bremen Hbf   *1996*   **UPDATED**

BRISBANE

Population: 751,000, metropolitan area 1.5 million
Public transport: Bus and ferry services provided by municipal undertaking, with all ferry and some bus services operated under contract. Suburban trains by Queensland Rail. Some suburbs served exclusively by private bus and ferry operators

Brisbane Transport

Brisbane City Council, Department of Transport
PO Box 1402, Fortitude Valley, 4006 Queensland, Australia
Tel: (+61 7) 38 67 38 80   Fax: (+61 7) 38 67 38 95
Chair, Transport Committee: M Hayes
Manager: N C Cagney
Staff: 1,612

Current situation: Brisbane Transport is a commercial unit of Brisbane City Council.

New bus interchange at Robina station on the Gold Coast line
1999/0038748

Bus

Passenger journeys: (1991/92) 42.9 million
(1992/93) 43.3 million
(1993/94) 44.8 million
Vehicle-km: (1991/92) 31.3 million
(1992/93) 30.4 million
(1993/94) 30.7 million

Number of routes: 83 plus 24 Cityxpress, Great Circle
outer suburbs and inner City Circle distributor routes
Route length: 875 km

Fleet: 630 vehicles

Volvo B59	46
MAN SL200	170
Volvo B10M	293
MAN CNG-powered	12
Leased buses	23
Volvo B10M/Fuji articulated	20
Volvo/Denning B10M articulated	1
Volvo/Volgren B10M articulated	6
Volvo/Austral B10M articulated	6
MAN midibus	7
Trambus	2
Mercedes minibus	4
Mercedes midibus	1
Others	39

In peak service: 491

Most intensive service: 15 min off-peak
One-person operation: All routes
Fare collection: Payment on boarding (change given) or
prepurchase
Fare structure: Zonal (5 zones); 50 per cent discount for
children, seniors and pensioners; bus/rail day ticket
Fares collected on board: 58 per cent
Fare evasion control: Random inspection and driver
control; spot fines
Integration with other modes: 5 bus/rail interchanges,
9 bus/bus interchanges
Operational control: By 82 inspectors and depot staff
Average distance between stops: 250-300 m (more than
1 km on Cityxpress/Great Circle routes)
Average peak-hour speed: 16 km/h (30-60 km/h on
Cityxpress/Great Circle routes)
Bus priority: 23 bus priority routes including the
Woolloongabba and City bus tunnels with dedicated right-
of-way, 2 HOV transit lanes, and 19 bus-only lanes
Operating costs financed by: Fares 46 per cent, other
commercial sources 4 per cent, subsidy 50 per cent
Subsidy from: State government 54 per cent, council 46
per cent
New vehicles financed by: Loans through Queensland
Treasury Corporation and self-funding through Council
sinking fund

Ferry (contracted)

Current situation: Cross-river ferry services operated
under contract on nine routes with 11 vessels. They carry
about 1.2 million passengers annually.

Citytrain

Queensland Rail
305 Edward Street, Brisbane, Queensland 4000
Tel: (+61 7) 32 35 12 37   Fax: (+61 7) 32 35 12 95

Queensland Rail ICE City train on Gold Coast line at Robina station **1999**/0038753

Group General Manager, Metropolitan & Regional
Services: Glen Dawe

Type of operation: Suburban/regional heavy rail

Passenger journeys: (1995/96) 39.2 million
(1996/97) 41.4 million
(1997/98) 41.5 million

Current situation: Suburban/interurban services
provided over network of 380 km on seven routes with
143 stations, electrified at 25 kV 50 Hz, 1,067 mm gauge.
Trains run every 10 min at peak times, every 15–30 min
off-peak; zonal fares.
Developments: Gold Coast railway extension opened
1996, linking the former suburban terminal at Beenleigh
with Helensvale (27.1 km) and bringing 30,000 new
journeys per week to rail. Further extension to Nerang
opened 1997, with service through to Robina open May
1998.
   Park-and-ride facilities are being promoted at Cityrail
stations, 21 of which have video surveillance and 26 have
locked car parks.
   Trainlink has been introduced to provide a dedicated
limited-stop service between Citytrain's Nambour station
and dedicated Trainlink bus stops at Eumundi, Noosaville
and Noosa Heads. Integrated ticketing is in force.

Rolling stock: 413 cars

Three-car suburban emus	100
Three-car interurban emus	10
ICE cars	20
Seven-car locomotive-hauled silver sets	9

Main supplier: Walkers Ltd Engineers & Founders, in joint
venture with ABB Transportation (now Adtranz) Australia
In peak service: 96 per cent
On order: 30 three-car SMU2 suburban emus for supply
April 1999–April 2001 by Walkers Ltd

Private bus

Current situation: Sixteen private bus lines provide
services in the metropolitan area, mostly to the suburbs.
Co-ordinated fares with rail offered on some routes.
Responsibility of State Department of Transport, which
also supervises some longer-distance ferry operations.

Light rail (proposed)

Current situation: A 1992 consultants' report prepared
for the city council recommended a core light rail route
from the city centre to the Fortitude Valley and Newstead,
with several branches. This initial route (14 km) was
confirmed by the Queensland government in May 1998,
and expressions of interest were invited from the private
sector for a concession for financing, developing and
operating an LRT system.

UPDATED

BRISTOL

Population: 400,000, metropolitan area 500,000
Public transport: Most bus services in city and
surrounding areas operated by private company, with
extensive minibus services. Local trains operated by
Wales & West Railways; ferry; light rail and guided dual-
powered bus system proposed

City Line

Bristol Omnibus Company Limited
Enterprise House, Easton Road, Lawrence Hill, Bristol
BS5 0DZ, England
Tel: (+44 117) 955 82 11   Fax: (+44 117) 955 12 48
Managing Director: Bob Holland
Staff: 1,797 (including Badgerline)

Current situation: The company trades as City Line,
operating most services within Bristol, and Badgerline
which runs routes into Bristol from the surrounding area

and local networks in neighbouring towns. Figures below
cover the joint operation.
Developments: Avon County Council's Bath Road park-
and-ride site, opened in 1994, is linked to the
city centre by a frequent high-quality bus service run by
City Line. In 1997, a second site was opened at Long
Ashton, linked to the city centre by a similar service
operated by Badgerline. Other park-and-ride services are
being developed, and a city-centre orbital route
introduced. CNG-powered and battery-powered buses
are on trial.

Bus

Passenger journeys: (1992) 38.1 million
(1993) 38.1 million
(1996) 56.7 million
Vehicle-km: (1992) 21.6 million
(1993) 21.7 million
(1996) 48.5 million

Number of routes: 98

Fleet: 725 vehicles

Bristol K double-deck	1
Bristol VR double-deck	31
Leyland/Volvo Olympian double-deck	107
Volvo B10M double-deck	13
Leyland National	3
Leyland Lynx	69
Dennis Lance	26
Dennis Lance SLF	6
Volvo B10M	14
Dennis Dart midibus	116
Mercedes minibus	192
Iveco minibus	18
Dennis Javelin coach	7
Volvo B10M coach	8
Volvo Olympian double-deck	60
Volvo B10BLE	19

Dennis Dart SLF	33
Tecnobus minibus	2

Most intensive service: 6 min
One-person operation: All routes
Fare collection: Stored value prepurchase cards or payment on board with Wayfarer electronic ticket machines linked to magnetic card validators
Fare structure: Zones, off-peak reductions; prepurchased magnetic tickets
Fares collected on board: 80 per cent
Operational control: Route inspectors/mobile radio
Arrangements for elderly/disabled: Fares at two-thirds normal rate funded by city council; new buses equipped to DPTAC standards
Average peak-hour speed: 16.1 km/h
Operating costs financed by: Fares 92 per cent

Other operators
Current situation: A small number of operators run some commercial and subsidised routes, including ABus, Bugler, Crown Coaches, Silverwing, Streamline, Swiftlink, Valley Travel and Westward Travel.

Bristol Electric Railbus
Bristol Electric Railbus Ltd
CREATE Centre, Smeaton Road, Bristol BS1 6XN
Tel: (+44 117) 930 09 01

Current situation: A tram service has started, linking Princes Street Bridge at the city end of the docks with the historic SS *Great Britain* ship and exhibition. It is operated on a 15 min frequency with a Parry flywheel-powered light tram carrying up to 30. The service runs daily throughout the year but not on days when the Bristol Harbour Steam Railway is running. The BER tram shares tracks with the steam train service for part of the route.

It is the first time that a Parry light tram has run in regular service and patronage is reported to be good. Expansion of the service is being planned by Bristol Electric Railbus.

Wales & West Railways
Wales & West Passenger Trains Ltd
Brunel House, 2 Fitzalan Road, Cardiff CF1 1SU
Tel: (+44 1222) 43 04 00   Fax: (+44 1222) 43 02 93
Managing Director: David Weir

Current situation: Suburban route operates about hourly to Avonmouth (14 km), with some trains extended to Severn Beach (22 km). Bristol City and South Gloucestershire councils contribute towards the cost of running this service. Local trains run irregularly on four other routes. The railway is operated on a seven-year franchise by Prism Rail.
Developments: A refurbishment programme has been undertaken for the company's fleet of Class 158 dmus with new colour scheme, seating, toilets and interior furnishings.

Ferry
Current situation: Bristol Ferry Boat Co operates three routes in the city docks, of which two run at commuting hours.

Light rail (proposed)
Bristol City Council
Planning, Transport & Development Services
Brunel House, St George's Road, Bristol BS1 5UY
Tel: (+44 117) 922 38 61   Fax: (+44 117) 922 38 86
Director: Diana Kershaw

Current situation: Parliamentary powers were granted in 1989 for an initial 16 km route linking Bristol city centre

ABus Optare Spectra low-floor double-deck bus at Bristol Temple Meads station (Andrew Jarosz)
1999/0045143

Parry light tram on Bristol Electric Railbus service (Tony Pattison)
1999/0024460

with Portishead on former railway alignment, but funding problems led to winding-up of the promoting company in 1992.

Avon County Council took over development of rapid transit proposals, adopting the name Westway, based on an initial route from Bradley Stoke in the north via Parkway station and Filton, using space on existing railway alignment to Lawrence Hill and then to Temple Meads station. From there the route runs to the city centre to terminate at Wapping Wharf.

With the abolition of Avon County Council in 1996, the project became the responsibility of Bristol City and

South Gloucestershire councils. These authorities have selected a private-sector consortium to form a joint venture to fund, build and operate Line 1 between central Bristol and Bradley Stoke (14 km). Railtrack will also be involved as LRVs are expected to share tracks with other services.

The council also administers 58 contracts with bus operators for provision of socially necessary services, and gives financial support to the Bristol–Severn Beach rail service.

UPDATED

BRNO

Population: 395,000
Public transport: Bus, trolleybus, tramway and boat services provided by municipal undertaking

Dopravní Podnik Města Brna

Dopravní Podnik Města Brna
PO Box 46, Hlinky 151, 65646 Brno, Czech Republic
Tel: (+42 5) 431 21 11   Fax: (+42 5) 432 11 72
e-mail: dpb@rat.fce.vutbr.cz
General Manager: Ing Petr Herzog
Operations Manager: Ing Josef Veselý
Commercial Director: Eva Lukavská
Staff: 3,406

Current situation: The system includes bus, trolleybus and tramway operations and a fleet of seven ships operating on the Brno-dam.
Developments: New trolleybus depot opened April 1997, presaging reinstatement of Route 140 currently bus-operated.

Passenger journeys: (All modes)
(1992) 365 million
(1996) 275 million

Operating costs financed by: Fares 35 per cent, subsidy/grants 65 per cent
Subsidy from: State and city council

Bus and trolleybus

Passenger journeys: (1996) Bus 89.1 million, trolleybus 34.5 million
Vehicle-km: (1996) Bus 15.8 million, trolleybus 7.1 million

Number of routes: Bus 45, trolleybus 14
Route length: Bus 466 km, trolleybus 98 km

Fleet: 299 buses
Karosa B731/732	226
Karosa B741 articulated	30
Ikarus articulated (1980-85/89)	43
In peak service: 246	

Fleet: 126 trolleybuses
Škoda 14Tr	98
Škoda 15Tr articulated (1990/91)	8
Šoda TrM14	20
In peak service: 112	

Brno's first low-floor tram on Line 4   *1998*/0007287

Most intensive service: 4 min
One-person operation: All routes
Fare collection: Prepurchase with onboard cancellation
Fare structure: Time and 3 zones
Fares collected on board: 29 per cent
Fare evasion control: Random inspection
Operational control: Route inspectors/mobile radio
Arrangements for elderly/disabled: Pensioners over 70 and disabled free

Tramway

Type of operation: Conventional tramway

Passenger journeys: (1996) 156.6 million
Car-km: (1996) 17.2 million

Route length: 68.5 km
Number of lines: 13
Gauge: 1,435 mm
Electrification: 600 V DC, overhead

Rolling stock: 324 cars
ČKD Tatra T2 (1958)	M2
ČKD Tatra T3/T3I/T3M/T3G/T3R (1986 on)	M157
ČKD Tatra K2/K2MM (1967/83)	M108
ČKD Tatra KT8D5 (1986/90)	M28
ČKD Tatra T6A5	M20
ČKD RT6N1 low-floor articulated	M4
ČKD KT8D5N low-floor (1998/99)	M5

In peak service: 298
On order: Delivery started in late 1998 of 60 low-floor cars from ČKD

Developments: Extension of Line 8 to Brno-Venkov opened in May 1998.

Ferry

Current situation: Seven ferries are operated on the Brno-dam.

UPDATED

BRUSSELS

Population: 1.1 million
Public transport: Bus, tramway, metro and pre-metro services provided by statutory undertaking with supervisory board of state, city and other representatives and under overall control of the Capital Region Ministry of Communications. Bus services also provided by regional operators TEC and De Lijn in city and suburbs, and suburban rail services by state railway SNCB/NMBS

STIB-MIVB

Société des Transports Intercommunaux de Bruxelles Maatschappij voor het Intercommunaal Vervoer te Brussel (STIB-MIVB)
Avenue de la Toison d'Or 15, 1060 Brussels, Belgium
Tel: (+32 2) 515 20 00   Fax: (+32 2) 515 32 84
Director General: Jacques Devroye
Deputy Director General: René Schoofs
Infrastructure: Luc Heyndrickx
Rolling Stock: Johnny Lanckriet
Manager, Traffic: Christian Dochy
Manager, Human Resources: Michel Leprince
Manager, General Utilities: Gunther Van Dyck
Manager, Technical Research: Robert Galle
Manager, Special Studies: Guy Verheulpen
Staff: 5,503 (all modes)

Current situation: STIB operations cover the 19 communes of the city and other suburban areas. Following devolution of powers to the regions in 1989, STIB is now funded solely by the Brussels regional government, which is also the overall planning authority. A five-year management contract agreed with the authority in 1991 gives STIB firm financial targets accompanied by more secure sources of finance.

Eight-axle 7900-Series car outside Midi station (Tony Pattison)   *1999*/0038755

The new administration voted in 1989 to give greater priority to public transport, and has been improving frequencies as well as completing current metro projects, studying further tramway extensions and segregation schemes, and expanding park-and-ride facilities.

The pace of converting pre-metro tunnels to full metro operation has been slowed by financial problems. Two sections totalling 12.1 km remain tram-operated, and these are more likely to become part of light rail conversions from existing tramway.

Further metro construction has been ruled out on cost grounds; instead more tramway is to be converted to paved reserved track usable also by buses where possible.

Passenger journeys: (All modes)
(1994) 210 million
(1995) 213.5 million
(1996) 213 million

Operating costs financed by: (All modes) fares 33 per cent, other commercial sources 5 per cent, subsidy/grants 62 per cent
Subsidy from: Regional government

Revenue control: Cancellers at inwards gates
Signalling: CTC; ATC with driver-only operation installed on Line 3
Surveillance: CCTV on platforms and escalators

Rolling stock: 380 cars

Mytischy EV1/EV3 (1969)	195
Mytischy 81-714/81-717 (1971)	186
Ganz-Mávag (1985)	6
Ganz Art-71 (Millennium Line 1973)	21
Ganz Art (Millennium Line 1987)	2
In peak service: 285	

Current situation: Millennium Line opened 1896, named to celebrate 1,000 years of the Hungarian State; first new metro line opened 1970.

Light rail/tramway

Type of operation: Light rail and conventional tramway

Passenger journeys: (1995) 350 million
(1996) 335.6 million
Car-km: (1995) 40.7 million
(1996) 38.7 million
(1997) 38.1 million

Route length: 209.3 km (unduplicated)
Number of lines: 31
Number of stops: 670
Gauge: 1,435 mm
Track: Vignole 48.5 kg/m, Phoenix 59 kg/m rail. About 75 km to light rail standards
Electrification: 600 V DC, overhead

Service: Peak 3-10 min, off-peak 5-15 min
First/last car: 04.00/23.45
Fare structure: Flat; day, weekly and monthly tramway season tickets valid on suburban railway, metro and trolleybuses, but not on buses, rack railway or river buses
Integration with other modes: Full integration, with buses acting as feeders for light rail and metro services
One-person operation: All routes

Rolling stock: 802 cars

Ganz-Mávag UV (1956)	M267 T64
Ganz-Mávag 8 articulated (1967)	M151
ČKD Tatra T5C5	M320
In peak service: 605	

Developments: Extension of Line 14 was due to be opened in 1998. Circular light rail routes are planned for the eastern suburbs. An association of public transport operators is planned.

Keeping the tracks clear near Vlahal terminus of Route 37 (D Trevor-Rowe) **1999**/0038750

Rack railway/chair lift/funicular
Current situation: The Varosmajor—Szechenyihegy rack line, 3.7 km, 1,435 mm gauge, is electrified at 1.5 kV DC. It carried 2.8 million passengers in 1996. There is also a chair lift linking Janoshegy and Zugliget (1 km), and the Buda Castle funicular.

Rolling stock: 7 two-car sets
SGP (1973)   M7 T7

Suburban railway (HEV)
Director: László Bársony

Type of operation: Suburban rail

Passenger journeys: (1995) 67 million
(1996) 63.2 million
(1997) 65.9 million

Rolling stock: 297 emu cars

Budapest rack railway arriving at upper terminus (D Trevor-Rowe) **1999**/0038751

Current situation: Ten routes are served from four main lines, total 176 km with 137 stations, 1,435 mm gauge, electrified 1.1 kV DC. Trains run every 5-15 min at peak times, 10-60 min off-peak, all one-man operated. Flat fare within city boundaries, zonal elsewhere. The HEV lines are owned jointly by the municipalities of Budapest and the districts served.

River ferries
Current situation: A fleet of 17 vessels operates a 20 min service on four routes (one summer only), carrying 204,000 passengers in 1995.
Developments: Ferries are now operated by a separate company.

MÀV
Hungarian State Railways (MÀV)
Népköztarsaság utja 75, 1940 Budapest VI
Tel: (+36 1) 122 06 60   Fax: (+36 1) 142 85 96

Type of operation: Suburban heavy rail

Current situation: Irregular services operated over several routes.
                                                            UPDATED

BUENOS AIRES
Population: City 2.9 million, conurbation 11 million
Public transport: Bus services provided by route associations of independent 'colectivo' mini and midibus owners and operators under general direction of national transport authority. Municipally owned metro with light rail extensions, and state-owned suburban railways, all run by private operators on a concessionary basis; also privately owned suburban light rail line

Comision Nacional de Transporte Automotor
Comision Nacional de Transporte Automotor
Buenos Aires, Argentina

Current situation: A new national transport authority was established in 1995 after plans for a Greater Buenos Aires transport authority were shelved. CNTA is controlled by three bodies — the National Transport Department (on account of the city's capital status), the Province of Buenos Aires (controlling routes which cross the city boundary), and suburban municipalities (controlling their own local networks). CNTA is not responsible for railways or the metro.

Mercedes LO1114, the traditional Buenos Aires vehicle, now being replaced by more modern types
1996

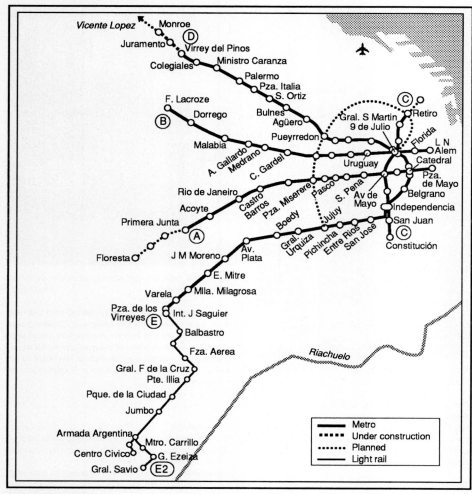

Buenos Aires metro

Legend:
- ▬▬▬ Metro
- ■■■■ Under construction
- •••• Planned
- ▬ Light rail

Developments:
A master plan for traffic improvements envisages a network of elevated highways built over existing railway alignments.

Private bus/minibus

Current situation: 'Colectivo' minibuses (more properly described as medium-sized), operating scheduled services, account for 80 per cent of all public transport trips and 54 per cent of total trips, amounting to some 7 million journeys daily in 1995.

Participants in the Empresas (route associations) can own more than one vehicle, but many are single vehicle operators and a third are owner-drivers. CNTA oversees fares and minimum frequencies for individual routes, governs the formation of new Empresas, and adjudicates tendering for new routes. In 1995 there were 104 operators, 24 fewer than in 1992. Services are provided on a wholly commercial basis, though fuel prices are subsidised. On some routes, higher-quality vehicles operate, offering seats to all passengers at a higher fare. Vehicles are powered increasingly by CNG rather than petrol.

Developments: Conductors were reintroduced on some routes in 1994 after the transport ministry banned driver-sales of tickets in an attempt to accelerate automation of fare collection. Fareboxes are now installed throughout the fleet, though some buses have a magnetic card reader to alleviate problems with cash shortages and the slow throughput of the fareboxes.

Increasing competition from taxis, illegal and paratransit minibuses and owner-operated old coaches has continued to erode patronage of scheduled services. Much business has also been lost to the suburban railways (see below), whose services were much improved following privatisation. In addition, traffic congestion, increased car ownership and recession have combined to cut sales of the popular *Diferencial* ticket by 50 per cent, thus putting operators under considerable financial pressure. Many smaller operators have been forced to close down, or have been taken over by larger groups.

Despite operators' requests for traffic control measures, experiments with bus lanes have met with only partial success due to the reluctance of some operators to use them, and they may be discontinued.

Fleet: 11,000, mainly Mercedes LO1114, OC1214, OF1315,OF1214, OH1314, OH1318, OHL1316, OH1418, OH1420 and old O170 types, plus a few El Detalle OA101, Arbus (one), Zanello (four) and Scania K112 demonstrator

Metrovías

Subterraneos de Buenos Aires (Subte)
Operated by Metrovías SA
B Mitre 3342, Buenos Aires 1201
Tel: (+54 1) 959 68 00   Fax: (+54 1) 866 30 37
e-mail: info@metrovias.com.ar
www: www.metrovias.com.ar
President: Cr Alberto Verra

Current situation: Metrovías is the concessionaire of the metros of Buenos Aires, the pre-metro LRT service and the Urquiza suburban line. Metrovías is part of the Roggio Group, a large Argentinian construction organisation, which has a 55.3 per cent shareholding. The company receives the technical assistance of Belgian consultants Transurb Consult SC. As part of that group, Metrovías took over overall operation of the metro and pre-metro light rail systems and the Urquiza line with 70 km of route and 103 stations, handling an annual ridership of 300 million passengers.

Developments: Demand has risen by 53 per cent since Metrovías took over operations in 1994 and it now carries 223 million out of the 612 million users of rail and road services in Buenos Aires, 36 per cent of the total.

Investment includes rebuilding of the interchange centre at 9 de Julio, improved control for Line B, mounting of murals by Molina Campos at metro stations and the acquisition of 30 metro cars from Nagoya fitted with pantographs by Metrovías for operation on Line D. A new signalling system is being installed and a magnetic ticketing system using AES Prodata equipment is being introduced in mid-1999.

Metro
Staff: 3,400

Type of operation: Full metro, first line opened 1913

Passenger journeys: (1994) 171.2 million
(1995) 217.6 million
(1996) 223.9 million

Route length: 36.5 km
Number of lines: 5
Number of stations: 63 (all in tunnel)
Gauge: 1,435 mm
Track: 44 kg/m or 45.5 kg/m rail on timber sleepers on stone ballast; concrete sleepers on new sections
Tunnel: All double-track; Line A, cut-and-cover; others bored
Electrification: Line A, 1.1 kV DC, overhead; Line B, 550 V DC, third rail; Lines C, D and E, 1.5 kV DC, overhead

Service: Peak 3-6 min, off-peak 10-12 min
Fare structure: Flat, with free transfer
Fare collection: Manual; token to turnstile
Operating costs financed by: Fares 67 per cent, other commercial sources 5 per cent, subsidy/grants 28 per cent

Rolling stock: 497 cars

La Brugeoise, Line A (1913/24, 12 rebuilt 1987)		M105
Siemens/O&K, Lines C, D, E		
(1934)		M29 T28
(1941)		M9 T9
(1944)		M14
Baseler, Lines C, D, E (1954)		T13
Fab Militares/Siemens, Line B (1978)		M20
Nat Movil y Const/GEE, Lines C, D, E (1964)		M30
Fab Militares, Lines C, D, E (1964)		T30
Fab Militares/GE, Line B (1965)		M20
Materfer/Fab Militares/Siemens		
Lines C, D, E (1980)		M30 T30
Ex-Tokyo Line B		M100
Ex-Nagoya Line D (1996/97)		30

Mercedes OA101 of operator Guido at Plaza Constitucion   *1996*

On order: 90 cars for Line A from Fiat/Siemens; some cars being refurbished by Morrison Knudsen

Light rail
Passenger journeys: (1991) 2.8 million

Current situation: The 7.4 km light rail line from Line E at Plaza de los Virreyes to Gen Savio opened in 1987; electrified 750 V DC; 13 stations. Further construction in progress to create a loop at the line's outer end. Plans exist for Line E1 to link Plaza de los Virreyes with the national airport.

Rolling stock: 17 cars
Fab Militares/Siemens LRV (1988)   M17

Suburban rail
Passenger journeys: (1993) 270 million
(1994) 337 million (includes Subte metro)
(1995) 543 million (includes Subte metro)

Current situation: All Argentine Railways (FA) suburban services were taken over by a holding company, Femesa, in 1991, prior to the offer of operating concessions to the private sector. All services are now in the hands of contractors. These are:
Metrovías, awarded the 20-year joint concession for the Urquiza lines (26 km) and the metro (see above).
Trenes de Buenos Aires, awarded a 10-year concessions for the Mitre (181 km) and Sarmiento (167 km) lines.
Transportes Metropolitanos SA, awarded 10-year concessions for the Roca (235 km), Belgrano South (52 km) and San Martin (55 km) lines.
Ferrovias, awarded a 10-year concession for the Belgrano North line (62 km).
　Suburban services operate out of six terminals on

LRV at Supermercado Jumbo on line E2   *1997*

1,000, 1,435 and 1,676 mm gauges, totalling 822 km with 276 stations. Five routes totalling 169 km out of Once and Retiro terminals are electrified at 600 and 800 V DC third rail, while the General Roca lines out of Plaza Constitucion to Glew and Ezeiza (40 km) are electrified at 25 kV 50 Hz with 52 three-car emus.
Developments: Proposals exist for electrification of the entire network.

Tren de la Costa
Tren de la Costa SA
J B de la Salle 653, San Isidro 1642
Tel: (+54 1) 732 60 00　Fax: (+54 1) 732 60 01
President: E Gonzalez del Solar
Staff: 114

Type of operation: Light rail, opened 1994

Passenger boardings: (1995) 2.9 million
(1996) 5 million

Current situation: This 15 km, 1,435 mm gauge light rail line, built on the formation of an abandoned railway, links Maipú and Delta in the northern suburbs. It is electrified at 1.5 kV DC overhead; fares cover 80 per cent of operating costs. The line serves a number of new commercial and leisure developments.

Rolling stock: 9 cars
CAF (1994)   M9

UPDATED

BUFFALO
Population: City 328,000, service area 0.9 million
Public transport: Bus and light rail services provided through operating subsidiary of Niagara Frontier Transportation Authority (NFTA), a New York State public benefit corporation created in 1967 and governed by Board of Commissioners

Metro
Niagara Frontier Transit Metro System Inc
181 Ellicott Street, PO Box 5008, Buffalo, New York 14205, USA
Tel: (+1 716) 855 76 31　Fax: (+1 716) 855 66 79
NFTA Chair: Robert D Gioia
NFTA Executive Director: Richard T Swist
Director, Surface Transportation: Karen J Rae (Acting)
General Manager, NFT Metro: Anthony J Schill
Staff: 1,100

Current situation: NFT Metro was created in 1973 as a

wholly owned subsidiary of NFTA to provide bus services in Erie and Niagara counties after acquisition of six independent companies. It is the major area operator.
　The light rail line runs along Main Street in a traffic-free area at the heart of the city's central business district, and service is fare-free over this section. The line is unusual as it runs on the surface in the city centre and in tunnel elsewhere.
　In 1990 NFTA obtained a dedicated source of revenue to fund its operating deficit. This consists of a percentage of a sales tax and a mortgage transfer tax. Nevertheless, NFTA remains short of its full requirement for capital expenditure.
Developments: Phased implementation of a paratransit network started in 1993. Expanded park-and-ride facilities and six new transit centres have been developed. Five CNG-powered buses are in service to evaluate use of alternative fuels.
　A restructuring of the network is likely to follow from studies started in 1996. The existing fixed-route system may be enhanced by a network of hubs linked by express bus and rail services, with local connecting routes operated by minibuses, vans or other appropriate vehicles, possibly on a demand-response basis.

Operating costs financed by: Fares 30.5 per cent, subsidy/grants 69.5 per cent
Subsidy from: FTA 15 per cent, state (general revenues and petrol tax) 30 per cent, and local (general revenues, sales and mortgage transfer tax) 55 per cent

Bus
Passenger boardings: (1994/95) 21.4 million
(1995/96) 20.5 million
(1996/97) 19.2 million
Vehicle-km: (1994/95) 15.5 million
(1995/96) 14.9 million
(1996/97) 14.7 million

Number of routes: 75
Route length: 1,980 km

Fleet: 322 buses
Orion (1985/91)	117
TMC TC40102A (1992)	17
Orion CNG-powered (1993)	5
New Flyer D40 (1993)	75
Ikarus USA 416.07 (1995)	67
Novabus TC40102A (1996)	41

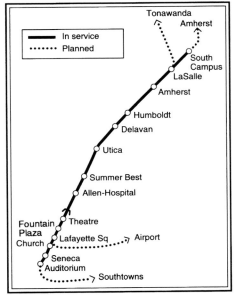

Buffalo's light rail line

Metro LRV on Buffalo's Main Street   *1998*/0007290

Orion city bus of Metro   **1997**

In peak service: 268
Average age of fleet: 5 years

Most intensive service: 10 min
One-person operation: All routes
Fare collection: Registering farebox
Fare structure: 4 zones
Arrangements for elderly/disabled: All buses wheelchair-accessible; reduced fares
Average distance between stops: 488 m
Integration between modes: Bus services integrated

with light rail; rail fare same as city bus with free transfer; 6 park-and-ride sites

Light rail
Staff: 157

Type of operation: Light rail, initial route opened 1985

Passenger boardings: (1994/95) 7.6 million
(1995/96) 7.1 million
(1996/97) 6.9 million

Car-km: (1994/95) 1.4 million
(1995/96) 1.4 million
(1996/97) 1.5 million

Route length: 10 km
 in tunnel: 7.7 km
Number of routes: 1
Number of stations: 14
 in tunnel: 8
Gauge: 1,435 mm
Electrification: 650 V DC, overhead

Service: Peak 5 min, off-peak 10-15-20 min
Integration with other modes: Full integration with bus system
Revenue control: Fare-free on city-centre surface section; AFC, no barriers on underground portion
Arrangements for elderly/disabled: Ramps and snow-melting equipment on surface section; lifts to underground platforms
Signalling: Centrally controlled cab signalling

Rolling stock: 39 cars
Tokyu Car LRV (1984/85)   M27
St Louis Car PCC (in store) (1946/49)   M12
In peak service: 23

Developments: Interim use of refurbished PCC cars was planned on the proposed Tonawanda extension, and 12 cars were bought from Cleveland in 1992. Lack of funding has delayed construction, which may not now take place. Three other extension proposals are included in the region's long-range transit development plan.

VERIFIED

BULAWAYO
Population: 550,000
Public transport: Bus services operated by company jointly owned by the government and United Transport, with fixed-route shared 'emergency taxis'

ZUPCO
Zimbabwe Passenger Company Ltd
Southern Division
Khami Road, PO Box 1779, Bulawayo, Zimbabwe
Tel: (+263 9) 672 91
General Manager, Southern Division: J Matsena
Staff: 1,365

Current situation: See Harare entry for details of ZUPCO. The company's Southern Division operates urban services in Bulawayo and three other towns, as well as a rural network. The figures below refer to the entire operation, except where noted.
Developments: Minibuses have been introduced to supplement full-size vehicle operations.

Future transport options for the city have been examined as part of a consultant's study of the four main urban areas in Zimbabwe.

Bus
Passenger boardings: (1992) 45 million
(1993) 50 million
(1996) 31 million
Vehicle-km: (1992) 23 million
(1993) 28 million
(1996) 23.9 million

Number of routes: Urban 69

Fleet: 296 vehicles
DAF/AVM 615/815
Scania
Toyota/Mazda minibuses
In peak service: 255

Most intensive service: 6 min
One-person operation: All services

Fare collection: By driver, plus sales to queues at major terminals from ticket agency booths
Fare structure: Graduated
Operational control: Inspectors
Operating costs financed by: Fares 100 per cent

Shared taxi
Current situation: 'Emergency taxis' were legalised by government in 1982. They are a form of paratransit shared taxi, with vehicles seating no more than seven passengers, supposed to operate on fixed routes at a maximum fare determined by the municipality. Recent growth of pirate taxis, with minibuses seating more than 20, has gone unchecked despite the breach of the franchise agreement terms.

VERIFIED

CAIRO
Population: 8.3 million, conurbation 16 million
Public transport: Bus services provided by government-owned transport authority, which also operates tramway networks in Cairo and Heliopolis, light rail line to Helwan, and cross-Nile ferries, and by second locally administered bus company. Other extensive fixed-route shared-taxi/minibus services by private operators, and minibuses run by the El Rayan Bus Company. Suburban rail and metro operated by state railway

Cairo Transport Authority
Cairo Transport Authority
Madenat Nasr, PO Box 254, Cairo, Egypt
Tel: (+20 2) 83 05 33

Current situation: CTA is responsible for a substantial bus operation, the tram networks in Cairo city and Heliopolis (absorbed in 1993), light rail line to Helwan and 12 cross-Nile ferry routes.

Bus
Passenger journeys: 1,000 million (annual)
Vehicle-km: 140 million (annual)

Number of routes: 220
Route length: 1,450 km

Fleet: 3,070 vehicles	
Nasr/Iveco	1,700
Iveco	340
Mercedes O302	330
Mercedes minibus	500
Iveco minibus	200

One-person operation: None
Fare collection system: Payment to conductor
Fare structure: City area, flat; elsewhere, distance-related
Fare evasion control: Roving inspectors

Tramway (Cairo city lines)
Type of operation: Conventional tramway

Route length: 54 km
Number of lines: 9
Gauge: 1,000 mm

Fare structure: Flat; monthly seasons
Fare evasion control: Roving inspectors
Fare collection: Coin to conductor

Rolling stock: 441 cars, plus about 280 cars of the Heliopolis network

Developments: Infrastructure improvements, including provision of some extensions on reserved track, and re-equipment of the rolling stock fleet, have helped to overcome the effects of a long period of underinvestment, but chaotic traffic conditions and poor trackwork still hamper operations on city-centre streets. Such sections will probably close when the urban metro lines are completed (see below). CTA took over operation of the Heliopolis tramway network in 1993. There has been some rationalisation of routes and fleets.

Tramway (Helwan line)
Current situation: 16 km route opened 1981 links Helwan with El Tibbeen, with branch (8 km) to May 15 City (opened 1984). It runs mostly on reserved track and is operated by Kinki Sharyo or Semaf wide-bodied cars.

Ferry
Current situation: A fleet of cross-Nile ferries is operated. Small launches are used on one main route (2 km) between the central business area and the old city.

Greater Cairo Bus

Greater Cairo Bus Company
Cairo
Tel: (+20 2) 82 86 56

Current situation: Operates services in part of Cairo in close co-operation with the CTA. A fleet of over 300 locally built Nasr buses is operated.

Heliopolis Company

Heliopolis Housing & Development Company
Heliopolis, Cairo

Egyptian National Railways

Egyptian National Railways
PO Box 466, Ramses Square, 11794 Cairo
Tel: (+20 2) 574 29 68   Fax: (+20 2) 574 29 50
General Manager, Metro: Mohamed Maher Moustafa

Type of operation: Suburban heavy rail, regional and urban metro

Current situation: ER operates the regional metro Line 1, the urban metro Line 2 and three conventional suburban routes (diesel-operated). Frequent cross-city service provided between El Marg, Cairo (Mubarak) and Helwan (42 km, 33 stations, electrified 1.5 kV DC). This upgraded suburban line is known as Line 1 of the metro. The initial phase of Line 2, the first urban metro route, was opened in 1996 and extended in 1997.

Rolling stock: 100 three-car emu sets, diesel-hauled trains

Metro
Type of operation: Full metro, opened 1996

Route length: 10.9 km
 in tunnel: 8.5 km
 elevated: 1.5 km
Number of lines: 1
Number of stations: 11
Gauge: 1,435 mm
Service: Peak 2 min

Rolling stock: 15 six-car trains
Mitsubishi (1994/95)   M45 T45

Current situation: The first section of urban metro Line 2, the 8 km from Shubra-el-Kheima to an interchange with Line 1 at Mubarak (Ramses Square), opened in 1996. The National Authority for Tunnels (see below) is the planning and construction authority, whilst the metro has been built by the French Alcatel-Alsthom group with Interinfra managing construction.

Phase IIA of Line 2, on which construction started in 1995, is a 5.1 km route with three stations from Tahrir Square to Cairo university, due to open in 1999. Phase IIB is a further extension to an interchange with ER's Upper Egypt line at El Giza (2.5 km, three stations), for which a construction contract was signed in 1997, for opening in 2000.

Studies for proposed Line 3 (10.8 km) started in 1998 with award of a two-year design contract to the Systra/Arab Consulting Engineers consortium. This would link Imbaba with Salah Salem to the west of Cairo, providing a third cross-city connection.

National Authority for Tunnels

PO Box 466, 11794 Cairo
Tel: (+20 2) 574 29 68/29 69   Fax: (+20 2) 574 29 50
Chairman: M E Abdel Salam

Current situation: This is the planning, design and construction authority for metros.

El Rayan Bus

El Rayan Bus Company
Cairo

Developments: El Rayan was given a licence by the city administration in 1985 for operation of a fleet of 600 Mercedes minibuses, the first officially authorised private bus services in Cairo since 1961.

Minibus/shared taxi
Current situation: Fixed-route jitney operations by shared taxi minibuses were permitted in the late 1970s, joining extensive illegal taxi sharing. Vehicles, licensed as taxis, normally wait until they have a full load before leaving their terminals and new passengers can only join at mid-route when passengers begin to be dropped off.

The most popular vehicles were originally locally assembled Ramses minibuses, but imported Japanese Nissan, Toyota and Mazda minibuses are now widely

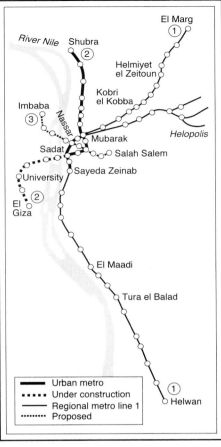

Cairo's metro and regional line

used. Most new vehicles are said to be owned by entrepreneurs outside the bus and taxi industry, who lease vehicles to drivers for 25 per cent of their fare collections. About 20 per cent of vehicles are owner-driven. Fares are three to four times normal bus levels, but demand is high.

UPDATED

CALCUTTA

Population: Conurbation 10 million
Public transport: Bus services provided in part by state-owned undertaking and also by substantial groupings of private bus and minibus owner-operators. State-owned tramway. Suburban rail and metro services provided by Indian Railways

CSTC

Calcutta State Transport Corporation (CSTC)
45 Ganesh Chandra Avenue, Calcutta 700013, India
Tel: (+91 33) 27 12 12   Fax: (+91 33) 26 44 77
Managing Director: S K De
Staff: 10,805

Current situation: CSTC operates urban services in Calcutta and longer distance routes in the state of West Bengal. Its urban services face strong competition from private operators and have been affected by changing travel patterns; in addition, high operating costs and inefficiency have dogged attempts to boost patronage. These problems are being addressed by the RITES consultancy, which has drawn up an operational, technical and financial improvement programme designed to bring CSTC to financial viability by the end of the century.

Great effort has been put into raising productivity, with the staff:bus ratio cut from 22 in 1984 to 13 in 1997. During the same period the number of daily kilometres run per employee has doubled to 15.7. Measures such as optimal fleet utilisation to reduce fuel consumption, fare evasion controls and better scheduling have also helped improve performance.

Bus
Passenger journeys: (1995/96) 282.9 million
(1996/97) 283 million
(1997/98) 269 million

Vehicle-km: (1995/96) 61.5 million
(1996/97) 67.8 million
(1997/98) 63.1 million

Number of routes: 89 urban, 122 long-distance
Route length: 23,332 km

Fleet: 1,061 vehicles
Ashok-Leyland single-deck   433
Ashok-Leyland semi-articulated double-deck   4
Tata single-deck   624
In peak service: 1,000

Most intensive service: 5 min
Fare collection: Payment to one or two conductors
Fare structure: Stage
Fare evasion control: Roving inspectors, penalty
Average peak-hour speed: 8 km/h
Operating costs financed by: Fares 43.9 per cent, other commercial sources 1.3 per cent, state government subsidy 54.8 per cent

Calcutta Tramways

Calcutta Tramways Co Ltd
12 R N Mukherjee Road, Calcutta 700001
Tel: (+91 33) 248 26 81/92 58   Fax: (+91 33) 244 55 03
Chairman & Managing Director: D K Chakraberty
Chief Operating Manager: K Bhattacharya
Staff: 7,567

Type of operation: Conventional tramway

Passenger journeys: (1991/92) 185 million
(1992/93) 119.4 million
(1993/94) 124.5 million

Vehicle-km: (1991/92) 10.4 million
(1992/93) 6.2 million
(1993/94) 7.4 million

Current situation: Tram operations are severely affected by traffic congestion, as a result of which in 1990 the West Bengal government confirmed a long-term policy of abandonment. In an attempt to reduce losses and improve reliability, in 1992 CTC started operating buses in parallel with some tram routes; fleet of 165 buses.
Developments: On behalf of the West Bengal government, ICF Kaiser, USA has formulated a revival package for the century-old tramway. In the meantime Avto export of Russia is shortly going to submit its final report on feasibility of replacing the existing dilapidated tramway by trolleybuses. On receipt of this report, the state government will decide on one of these two options.

Tramway
Number of routes: 30
Route length: 67 km
Number of lines: 29
Number of stops: 447
Gauge: 1,435 mm

Service: Peak 3 min
First/last car: 04.15/24.00
Fare structure: Graduated
Operating costs financed by: Fares 21 per cent, other commercial sources 1 per cent, state government subsidy 35.6 per cent

Rolling stock: 374 cars
Articulated   M147
Streamlined   M227
In peak service: 225

Metro train coming out of tunnel (K K Gupta) **1999**/0043590

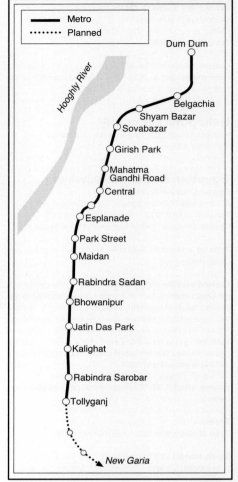

Calcutta's metro

Metro

Metro Railway, Metro Rail Bhavan
33/1 Chowringhee Road, Calcutta 700071
Tel: (+91 33) 29 10 53/226 76 80   Fax: (+91 33) 29 45 81
General Manager: R P Madan

Type of operation: Full metro, opened 1984

Passenger journeys: (1995/96) 128,000 daily
(1996/97) 171,000 daily
(1997/98) 240,000 daily

Route length: 16.5 km
  elevated: 1.6 km
Number of lines: 1
Number of stations: 17
Gauge: 1,676 mm
Track: UIC 60 kg/m rail; ballastless track with reinforced
concrete bed
Max gradient: 2%
Min curve radius: 300 m
Electrification: 750 V DC, third rail

Service: Peak 10 min
First/last train: Weekdays 07.20/21.20, Sunday 15.00/
21.00
Fare structure: 4 zones; reduced price carnets
Fare evasion control: AFC with magnetically encoded
tickets and microprocessor-controlled entry/exit gates
Integration with other modes: None
Signalling: Colourlights, ATP
Surveillance: CCTV
One-person operation: None; all cars suitable

Rolling stock: 144 cars
ICF A   M108
ICF B   T36

Current situation: Through service on the entire section
from Tollyganj to Dum Dum was introduced over three
years ago (in September 1995) but the ridership on the
system is still rather low. Several measures, including
increase in frequency of services during peak hours in
phases from 10 to 6 minutes, are contemplated to
improve the ridership and earnings.
Developments: A final location survey for the planned
extension from Tollyganj to Garia was completed in 1996.
In addition, a techno-economic survey for a northern
extension from Dum Dum to Barrackpore (13.5 km) is in
progress.

Eastern Railway

Eastern Railway
17 Netaji Subhas Road, Calcutta 700001
Tel: (+91 33) 220 68 11
General Manager: S Ramanathan
Chief Operations Manager: M C Shrivastava

Type of operation: Suburban heavy rail

Passenger journeys: (1995/96) 410 million
(1996/97) 414 million
(1997/98) 431 million

Rolling stock: M358, T748

South Eastern Railway

South Eastern Railway
Garden Reach, Calcutta 700043
Tel: (+91 33) 439 12 81
General Manager: A K Malhotra
Chief Operating Manager: P K Chatterjee

Emu at Lakshmikantapur station of Eastern Railway's Sealdah (South) Division (K K Gupta) **1999**/0043592

South Eastern Railway suburban train, Calcutta (K K Gupta)   **1999**/0043591

Type of operation: Suburban heavy rail

Passenger journeys: (1994/95) 57.1 million
(1995/96) 59.2 million
(1996/97) 61.28 million

Rolling stock: M88, T183

Current situation: Two major terminals serve the city — Sealdah and Howrah — to the east and west of the central business district. Sealdah is served by ER trains and Howrah by both ER and SER services; together they handle about 900 daily suburban trains. At peak times, emus are overcrowded heavily in excess of crush loads. Most routes are electrified at 25 kV, 1,676 mm gauge. Both railways are now operating dmu services on several non-electrified sections and main line emus on several main line electrified sections.

Developments: Circular Railway (on ER) is already in operation from Dum Dum to Princep Ghat. In view of the problem which commuters face in switching over from metro to the suburban system at Dum Dum station, it has been decided to electrify the section from Dum Dum to Tala on the Circular Railway so that in peak hour commuter services can be started for the northern suburbs. A survey is in progress for the extension of the Circular Railway from Princep Ghat to Majerhat.

On SER, construction of a new terminal at Shalimar is in progress to ease the congestion at Howrah. Trains will reach Shalimar by a link from SER's main suburban route at Santragachi, some 7 km from Howrah.

Private bus/minibus
Current situation: Private bus operations account for about half of the public transport trips and two-thirds of

bus trips in the city — around 1,000 million journeys annually. Route associations, generally one for each route, have developed. Owners retain control over operations and retain fares but the associations govern relationships between members and set operating standards. Private bus crews are paid a percentage of the fares, which keeps fare evasion below the high levels suffered by CSTC, and are allotted to individual vehicles, improving maintenance responsibility.

The state regional transport authority allocates licences for private buses and minibuses, as well as taxis.

Fleet: Over 2,200; full-size buses are all Tata, whilst the minibuses comprise Tata, Toyota and Hindustan

UPDATED

CALGARY
Population: 790,498
Public transport: Bus services and light rail system operated by municipal department

Calgary Transit
City of Calgary Transportation Department
928-32 Avenue Connector NE, PO Box 2100, Postal Station M, Calgary, Alberta T2P 2M5, Canada
Tel: (+1 403) 277 97 11   Fax: (+1 403) 230 11 55
General Manager: R H Irwin
Assistant Controller: Beng Koay
Superintendent of Operations: J Pawson
Staff: 1,827

Current situation: In 1997 Calgary Transit continued to experience a significant increase in ridership of 9 per cent due largely to the improving economic and employment situation. Accessible transport is now provided on 23 of Calgary Transit's 133 routes and at all of its light rail stations.

The Community Shuttle service, using 38 minibuses each seating 20, continues to expand as the service grows to serve developing suburban areas. The less expensive Community Shuttle continues to replace larger service buses on routes that do not meet the minimum performance of 20 passengers per operating hour.
Developments: Expansion of the Community Shuttle service on a further five routes. Accessible service is now provided at all of the 31 light rail stations.

Passenger journeys: (All modes)
(1995) 56.3 million
(1996) 60.5 million
(1997) 66.1 milion

Operating costs financed by: Fares 54.9 per cent, other commercial sources 0.9 per cent, provincial grants 2.1 per cent, municipal support (tax levy) 42.1 per cent

Bus
Passenger journeys: (1995) 33.8 million
(1996) 36.3 million
(1997) 39.7 million
Vehicle-km: (1995) 31.5 million
(1996) 31.7 million
(1997) 33.9 milion

Number of routes: 133 including community shuttle
Route length: (One way) 2,790 km
On priority right-of-way: 2 km shared with light rail

Fleet: 622 vehicles
Standard motor bus	449
Low-floor bus	135
Community shuttle (minibus)	38

In peak service: 507
On order: 44 for December 1998 delivery

Most intensive service: 3 min
One-person operation: All routes

Fare collection: Exact fare to farebox, prepurchase tickets, day/monthly passes, transfers
Fare structure: Flat
Fares collected on board: 17 per cent (cash)
Fare evasion control: By driver and inspectors
Integration with other modes: Bus and light rail routes integrated; feeder and main line buses serve stations; park-and-ride (300 spaces on bus routes, 7,016 at stations)
Operational control: Supervisors/radio control
Arrangements for elderly/disabled: Low-floor accessible service on 23 routes; reduced-rate annual pass for seniors depending on income
Average distance between stops: 300 m
Average peak-hour speed: 24 km/h
New vehicles financed by: Debentures/Provincial cost-sharing programmes

Light rail
Type of operation: Light rail, initial route opened 1981, extended 1985, 1989 and 1990

Passenger journeys: (1995) 22.5 million
(1996) 24.2 million
(1997) 26.4 milion

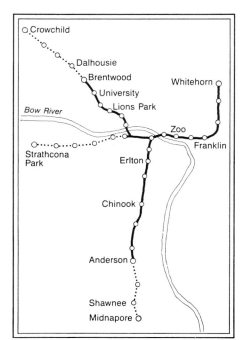

Calgary light rail

Calgary LRV at 7th Avenue Transit Mall station

Train-km: (1995) 2.9 million
(1996) 2.8 million
(1997) 2.8 million

Route length: 29.3 km
in tunnel: 2 km
Number of routes: 3
Number of stations: 31
Gauge: 1,435 mm
Track: 60 kg/m Ri-60 girder rail on ballasted concrete sleepers, 50 kg/m ARA 100T welded rail on concrete slab in tunnel and city-centre sections
Electrification: 600 V DC, overhead

Service: Peak 3-5 min, off-peak 10-15 min
First/last car: 05.01/01.19
Fare structure: Flat, as bus; free fare zone on 2 km downtown section of 7th Avenue
Fare collection: Self-service ticket dispensers and prepaid ticket cancellers on platforms; monthly passes; transfer from bus
Integration with other modes: Feeder buses at most stations; park-and-ride (7,016 spaces)
Fare evasion control: Roving inspectors
One-person operation: 100 per cent
Signalling: Automatic block with interlockings at all junctions and terminals; auto-switching and station signs

controlled by onboard VETAG in transit mall; all train movements monitored at radio control centre

Rolling stock: 85 cars

Siemens-Duewag U2 (1981)	M27
Siemens-Duewag U2 (1983/85)	M56
Siemens-Duewag U2 AC propulsion	M2

In peak service: 72

Developments: Extensions to the South and Northwest lines are planned for opening within the next five years, with timing dependent on availability of funding.

UPDATED

CANBERRA

Population: 307,000
Public transport: Bus services provided by Australian Capital Territory government through a division of the Department of Urban Services, with some independent operations

ACTION

Australian Capital Territory Internal Omnibus Network (ACTION)
200 Scollay Street, PO Box 1155, Tuggeranong, ACT 2901, Australia
Tel: (+61 2) 62 07 80 00   Fax: (+61 2) 62 07 80 80
Executive Director: Guy Thurston
Staff: 729

Current situation: Public transport is based on an integrated feeder-express system which reflects the distinctive urban design of Canberra — a series of discrete 'towns' with major concentrations of government, business, retail and recreational activity in each town centre. Bus interchanges in the four town centres (City, Woden, Belconnen and Tuggeranong) are linked by a 29 km intertown express route. Local services link suburban areas to their local town centre interchange, or to the two adjoining interchanges. During peak periods this network is supplemented by express services providing direct links between outer suburbs and the city centre.
Developments: A new network has been designed for implementation in early 1999. The basis of this network has been designed on the concept of through routeing in order to minimise bus transfers within interchanges. In line with the route changes a new zonal-based fare system will be introduced.

The introduction of a new bus route and the extension of another to the new Gungahlin Town Centre, the fifth satellite in Canberra's plan. The introduction to service of 25 low-floor accessible Dennis Dart buses.

In late 1998 consultants were examining the feasibility of a tramway linking the city centre with the National Museum site.

Bus

Passenger boardings: (1994/95) 24 million
(1995/96) 24 million
(1996/97) 17.9 million
Vehicle-km: (1994/95) 20.9 million
(1995/96) 20.9 million
(1996/97) 19 million

Circular Route 307 in Canberra city centre   *1997*

Number of routes: 128
Route length: 2,383 km
Fleet: 383 vehicles

Mercedes O305	2
Renault PR100-2	259
Renault PR180-2	34
Renault PR100-3	42
Dennis Dart SLF	25
Others	21

In peak service: 334

Most intensive service: 4-7 min, intertown express
One-person operation: All routes
Fare collection: Cash to driver, or prepurchase magnetic tickets
Fare structure: Flat fare on boarding for cash payers; prepurchase 4 or 10 single-ride, daily, weekly, monthly and quarterly magnetic tickets
Fares collected on board: 20 per cent
Operational control: Route and ticket inspectors; two-way radio; movements monitored through all interchanges

Arrangements for elderly/disabled: Concession fares with reimbursement provided by ACT government. New buses built to low-floor design with ramp and carefully placed handrails for ease of entry and exit; bell push-buttons placed low down; raised bay numerals at interchanges assist blind people; reserved bus seating identified by upholstery colour
Average distance between stops: 300 m
Average peak-hour speed: Local feeder buses 30 km/h, express 35 km/h
Bus priority: All interchanges are bus-only areas; 13.7 km of bus-only lanes on arterial roads; priority sections of road and/or priority traffic signals at some intersections; additional bus-only lanes planned
Subsidy from: ACT government
New vehicles financed by: Grant and loan funding

Other operators

Current situation: Suburban bus services are operated into central Canberra by Deane's from Queanbeyan in the southeast (three routes) and by Transborder from Yass in the north.

UPDATED

CAPE TOWN

Population: 4.1 million
Public transport: Scheduled bus services throughout metropolitan area provided by privately owned group. Substantial numbers of 'Kombi-taxi' minibus services, many of which are illegal. Transport policy is co-ordinated under a Metropolitan Transport Advisory Board

Golden Arrow

Golden Arrow Bus Services (Pty) Ltd
PO Box 1795, Cape Town 8000, South Africa
Tel: (+27 21) 507 88 00   Fax: (+27 21) 548 88 18
Chair: N S Cronjé
General Manager: H J Grebe
Staff: 1,941

Current situation: The present Golden Arrow company was set up in 1992 when the management of the former

City Tramways gained control of the operation from Tollgate Holdings. It serves the metropolitan Cape Peninsula and Cape Flats areas, encompassing the cities of Cape Town and Tygerberg and four other municipalities, totalling some 1,350 km².
Developments: New concepts of franchising services and small business units are being developed with a view to increasing community and worker involvement in the company's activities. In addition, GA is expanding the concept of integrating driver, bus and route as a single unit to improve operating efficiency. Electronic ticketing is being assessed in a pilot scheme on the Simonstown routes, and limited trials of through ticketing have also been made in co-operation with Metro Rail.

A rehabilitation programme is under way in which four buses a month are being turned out with rebuilt front and rear ends, wider entrances, improved cabs, electronic destination indicators and better suspension. A batch of 40 of the oldest vehicles is being fitted with new AAD

17M250A mid-engine chassis, giving better weight distribution and easier passenger access than the old front engines.

Bus

Passenger boardings: (1994/95) 36.7 million
(1996/97) 39.5 million
(1997/98) 38.3 million
Vehicle-km (1994/95) 35 million
(1996/97) 38 million
(1997/98) 38.2 million

Number of routes: 900
Route length: 18 km (average)

Fleet: 703 vehicles

Leyland Victory J double-deck	155
Leyland Victory J single-deck	430
ERF Trailblazer	91

GA buses in the high-occupancy lane of highway N2 **1998**/0007132

Mercedes 1624	10
AAD	1
AAD minibus	3
Nissan minibus	1
Leyland minibus	6
Coaches	6

In peak service: 650
Average age of fleet: 11 years

Most intensive service: 5-10 min
One-person operation: All routes
Fare collection: Setright for cash fares collected on board; 10-ride weekly and 48-ride monthly clipcards issued by Wayfarer machines. Electronic Wayfarer machines in test phase
Fare structure: Stages, discount clipcard
Fares collected on board: 40 per cent
Fare evasion control: Random inspectors
Operational control: Multichannel selective calling two-way radio with 150 field staff under centralised operations control centre with computerised database
Ticket integration with other modes: Integrated tickets available from Metrorail for specified services. Considering expansion
Average peak-hour speed: 30 km/h
Bus priority: Bus lanes on four major corridors
Average distance between stops: 750 m
Subsidy from: Recoverable discount system on clipcards, operated in collaboration with government-administered fund
New vehicles financed by: Own resources

Metro Rail

South African Rail Commuter Corporation Ltd
Western Cape Metropolitan Area
Private Bag X2, Sunninghill, Johannesburg 2157
Tel: (+27 11) 804 29 00   Fax: (+27 11) 804 38 52

Type of operation: Suburban heavy rail

Passenger journeys: (1994/95) 127.1 million
(1995/96) 126.8 million
(1996/97) 139.1 million

Current situation: Frequent suburban service on 12 routes in the Western Cape area, serving 102 stations on

the Cape Peninsula, total 305 km, 1,065 mm gauge, electrified 3 kV DC. Up to 35 trains per hour in the peak, off-peak services every 30 min. Fares cover 38 per cent of operating costs.
Developments: Two routes totalling 15 km — the Blue Downs line and the Khayelitsha extension — are proposed in Metro Rail's 10-year capital development programme.

Rolling stock: 1,055 emu cars

Union Carriage & Wagon (1957 on)	M289 T714
Siemens (1984)	M4 T4
Hitachi (1984)	M6 T6
Hitachi-Dorbyl (1987/88)	M16 T16

Shared taxis
Current situation: Estimates put the total number of Kombi-taxi operators at about 6,000 with some 7,500 vehicles. They run variable routes and schedules outside the normal bus licensing system. Their growth has had a major effect on the patronage of licensed bus operators. The Kombis were legalised under a government transport policy review in 1987, though some still operate illegally.
Developments: In 1997, the provincial government implemented a new regulatory regime for the Kombis, designed to control their numbers. Taxis can only obtain route permits if they belong to a registered association. At the cut-off date, some 92 associations and 2,450 operators with 3,800 vehicles had registered.

Light rail (proposed)
Current situation: The city council is considering several options for guided transit, including a three-line light rail network extending to 22 km.

UPDATED

Forty new buses are being introduced to the Golden Arrow fleet this year. The chassis were ordered from local manufacturers AAD and the vehicle bodies have been built by the company's own engineering division, Multimech **1999**/0043533

CARACAS

Population: 3.5 million
Public transport: Bus services mostly provided by private operators; 'Por Puestos' minibus services provided by about 80 associations, plus unlicensed pirates. Jeep transport provided by about 50 associations in the poor areas on steep mountain slopes surrounding the city where only four-wheel drive vehicles can operate. Metro; commuter railway planned

Private bus operators
Passenger journeys: (1995) 90.2 million

Number of routes: 15
Fleet: Approx 350

Current situation: There are about 50 operators; most have poor premises and inadequate maintenance facilities resulting in lack of roadworthy vehicles and operational unreliability. Attempts are made to impose

minimum standards of maintenance in the light of accidents, but prosecution has been limited as a general clampdown would provoke a public transport crisis. Few operators can afford new vehicles and closures occur when fleets reach the end of their useful life.

Caracas Metro

Compania Anonima Metro de Caracas
Apartado 61036, Caracas 1060, Venezuela
Tel: (+58 2) 206 76 11   Fax: (+58 2) 266 33 46
President: A Combellas Lares
Staff: 4,725

Current situation: As well as running the metro, the company operates a network of feeder bus routes.

Metro
Type of operation: Full metro, initial route opened 1983

Passenger journeys: (1994) 271 million
(1995) 289 million
(1996) 289 million

Route length: 42.5 km
Number of lines: 3
Number of stations: 40
Gauge: 1,435 mm
Track: 54 kg/m continuously welded rail, on Stedef twin-block sleepers laid on concrete (tunnels) or ballast (surface)
Tunnel: Cut-and-cover and bored
Electrification: 750 V DC, third rail

Service: Peak 1½ min
Fare structure: Zonal; magnetically encoded 10-trip tickets
Revenue control: Entrance and exit turnstiles, ticket-issuing machines

Caracas metro   *1999*/0021697

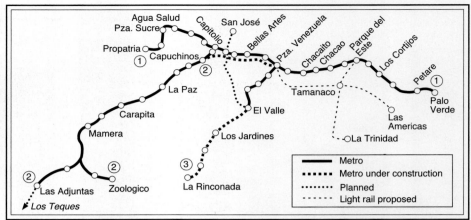

Caracas metro

Signalling: Full ATC

Operating costs financed by: Fares 58 per cent, other commercial sources 5.8 per cent, subsidy/grants 36.2 per cent

Rolling stock: 456 cars

CIMT Type A (cab)	M110
CIMT Type B	M268
GEC Alsthom Type C (cab) (1995)	M34
GEC Alsthom Type D (1995)	M22
GEC Alsthom Type R (1995)	T22

In peak service: 345
On order: 44 cars from Alstom

Current situation: Line 3 from Plaza Venezuela to La Rinconada (12.1 km, 10 stations) under construction, of which the 5.6 km section to El Valle opened in 1994. Line 4 from Capuchinos to Plaza Venezuela (5.5 km) also under construction, to relieve the busiest central section of Line 1.

A suburban extension (9.5 km) of Line 2 from Las Adjuntas to Los Teques is planned, along with a light rail route in the southeast suburbs.

Bus
Staff: 1,018 (included above)

Passenger journeys: (1991) 26.5 million (1994) 30.2 million (1995) 34 million

Current situation: MetroBus feeder buses were introduced in 1987 on a single route and the network has expanded each year. In 1996 there were 25 routes extending to 502 km. Fares cover 29.3 per cent of operating costs.

Fleet: 274 buses

Leyland National Mk1	22
Renault PR100-2	99
Pegaso 6424	99
Renault Unicar Fanabus	54

In peak service: 160

Minibus

Current situation: Most vehicles are now 15 to 24 seaters. With additional (legal) standing capacity for 10 to 15 passengers, they compete directly with conventional buses and have grown at their expense, particularly in the light of bus operational shortcomings.

Fares charged are graduated and generally the same as buses, though with higher levels at evenings and weekends. Authorised operations are grouped into associations covering a number of routes, often in competition, with an estimated fleet of at least 15,000, including pirates outside the associations to which the authorities turn a blind eye. Fleet sizes of the associations vary from 10 to about 100 vehicles.

Commuter rail (planned)

Current situation: The long-planned high-speed commuter link through the 43 km corridor between Caracas and Tuy Medio came a step closer to realisation in 1996 when the government signed an agreement for its construction with the Contuy consortium of Venezuelan, Japanese and Italian companies. Work started during 1997 for opening in 2001.

UPDATED

CARDIFF

Population: 300,000
Public transport: Bus services provided by local authority-owned company, with some suburban operations by others; local rail services; light rail proposed

Bws Caerdydd/Cardiff Bus

Cardiff City Transport Services Ltd
Leckwith Depot, Sloper Road, Cardiff CF1 8AF, Wales
Tel: (+44 1222) 78 77 00   Fax: (+44 1222) 78 77 42
Managing Director: Alan Kreppel
Staff: 760

Current situation: CCTS was established as a private company in 1986. Its sole shareholder is Cardiff City Council. Fleet composition has been changed from mainly double-deck to a mix of double-deck, single-deck and midibuses.

Bus
Passenger journeys: (1995/96) 29.2 million
(1996/97) 29.7 million
(1997/98) 30.6 million
Vehicle-km: (1995/96) 16.3 million
(1996/97) 15.1 million
(1997/98) 15.7 million

Brewers Plaxton-bodied Dennis Dart leads Cardiff Bus Olympian out of central bus station
(Andrew Jarosz)   *1999*/0043593

Number of routes: 173
Route length: 430 km
On priority right-of-way: 3.5 km

Fleet: 278 vehicles

Leyland Olympian double-deck	26
Bristol/VRT double-deck	31
Volvo Ailsa double-deck	49
Scania double-deck	10
Leyland Lynx single-deck	41
Scania single-deck	21
Dennis Dart single-deck	7
Optare Excel low-floor single-deck	15
Optare Metrorider midibus	74
MCW midibus	4

Most intensive service: 3 min (2-3 min on sections with more than one service)
One-person operation: All routes
Fare collection: Driver-operated ticket issue by Wayfarer 2 electronic machine; Multiride all-route ticket (weekly, monthly etc) sold at sales offices in Cardiff city centre and Barry; all-route 'Capital' daily ticket for visitors sold on buses
Fare structure: Zonal; reduced off-peak fares 09.15-15.45 weekdays

Operational control: Route inspectors; all vehicles have mobile radio contact with central control
Arrangements for elderly/disabled: Free travel for over-75s; other seniors and disabled have half fare financed by Cardiff County Council concessionary fares scheme; 165 vehicles have DPTAC features, 15 have low-floor wheelchair access and 22 have kneeling facility
Average peak-hour speed: 17 km/h
Bus priority: Bus lanes used to assist on all services in short sections in city centre; recently introduced lanes have distinctive green finish
Subsidy from: County Council for specific services secured by tender

Other operators

Current situation: South Wales Transport, Brewers Motor Services, Rhondda Buses, Stagecoach Red & White, Newport Transport, Bebbs, Shamrock and Islwyn Borough Transport operate into the city from outlying areas.

Cardiff Railway

Cardiff Railway Co Ltd
Brunel House, Fitzalan Road, Cardiff CF2 1SA
Tel: (+44 1222) 43 00 00   Fax: (+44 1222) 48 04 63
Director: Tom Clift
Staff: 293

Type of operation: Local rail

Passenger journeys: (1994) 5.5 million
(1996) 5.9 million
(1997) 6.1 million

Current situation: Diesel suburban services run at 15-60 min intervals on seven routes (137 km, 67 stations); fares cover operating costs, but not all infrastructure costs. Operations are franchised to Prism Rail.
Developments: Resignalling of the busy section between Cardiff (Radyr) and Pontypridd has reduced headway to 5 min. Under its franchise agreement, Prism now runs several through trains daily to Pontypridd from its adjacent Wales & West operation, and is rehabilitating both trains and stations.

Rolling stock: 29 two-car dmus

UPDATED

Cardiff Bus low-floor Optare Excels operate on the Easyrider quality corridors (Andrew Jarosz)
1999/0043594

CHANGCHUN

Population: 2 million
Public transport: A single municipal company operates bus, minibus, trolleybus and tram services; light rail planned

CCGJ

Changchun City Public Transport Co (CCGJ)
49 Da Jing Road, Changchun, Jilin Province, People's Republic of China
Tel: (+86 431) 897 27 31   Fax: (+86 431) 891 35 48
General Manager: Zhang Yun Xi
Deputy General Manager: Zhu Xing Hua
Staff: 11,000

Passenger journeys: (All modes)
(1990) 350 million
(1991) 330 million

Current situation: CCGJ was set up in 1987 following merger of the former bus and trolleybus operating companies. As well as regular bus, trolleybus and tram services in the city and suburbs, CCGJ runs a minibus fleet, taxis, tourist buses, a hotel and a hospital, and

SY561 articulated on urban route
1998/0009927

several other businesses. Since formation, extensive minibus operations have been introduced, the trolleybus fleet has been modernised, and one of the three remaining tram routes closed.

Bus, trolleybus and tram services continue to operate at fares which, although about 100 per cent higher than in the mid-1980s, have not been increased in line with inflation. Minibuses run over the same routes at premium fares which may be 400 per cent higher. All vehicles carry conductors, those in buses and trolleybuses being seated.

All old trolleybuses have been replaced, but several routes have been closed, and only two remained in operation in 1997.

The tramway, already reduced to two suburban routes, saw further contraction in April 1996 when Route 52 was closed. Though light rail proposals have been mooted several times in the past decade, there is no evidence of any progress and complete abandonment now seems likely.

Bus/minibus
Number of routes: 86
Route length: 1209 km

Fleet: Approx 400 buses (mostly articulated), mainly from the Nanchang and Shanghai factories, and about 300 minibuses, some by Siping

Trolleybus
Number of routes: 2
Route length: 31 km

Fleet: 74 trolleybuses, Shanghai SK561GF and Shengyang SY561

Tramway
Type of operation: Conventional tramway

Number of routes: 1
Route length: 7.64 km
Gauge: 1,435 mm gauge

Rolling stock: 40 four-axle cars

Light rail (planned)
Current situation: A 9.05 km line is proposed, with 10 stops.

UPDATED

Minibus passengers transfer to Changchun's last tram route
1998/0009928

CHARLEROI
Population: 580,000
Public transport: Bus and tramway/light rail services provided by regional publicly owned undertaking. Suburban rail services by state railway (SNCB)

TEC Charleroi
Société de Transport en Commun Charleroi
Place des Tramways 9/1, 6000 Charleroi, Belgium
Tel: (+32 71) 23 41 11   Fax: (+32 71) 23 42 09
www: http://www.tec-charleroi.be
Director General: Gilbert Delva
Staff: 895

Passenger journeys: (Both modes)
(1995) 22.1 million
(1996) 21.5 million
(1997) 21.8 million

Current situation: TEC was created in 1991 under the reorganisation of local transport that saw control pass to the new regional body Société Regional Wallonne du Transport. TEC replaced the former operators STIC and SNCV and brought public transport in Charleroi under single management. It serves a total of 20 communes covering an area of some 1,100 km². Four longer-distance bus routes are run by private operators.

Part of the former network of interurban tramways in Charleroi and the surrounding area has been converted into a light rail system. Services feed into an 8 km city-centre line, mostly elevated, which may eventually form a loop. The initial section was opened in 1976, though subsequent progress has been intermittent.

A further section to Janson and Parc opened in 1996, when two new routes were introduced.
Developments: Magnetic ticketing system introduced in late 1996.

Bus
Number of routes: 65
Route length: 1,544 km

Fleet: 283 vehicles
Van Hool A120	159
Van Hool A500	26
Van Hool A600	11

TEC Van Hool A500 bus   **1999**/0038764

Renault R312	41
Mercedes	2
Others	44

One-person operation: All routes
Fare collection: Payment to driver or prepurchase
Fare structure: Zonal; ticket cards; various passes; free transfers; national system of common zonally valid multijourney strip tickets
Fares collected on board: 19.1 per cent
Fare evasion control: Inspectors; penalty
Operational control: Route inspectors/mobile radio
Arrangements for elderly/disabled: Passes at reduced rates

Average distance between stops: 700 m
Average peak-hour speed: In mixed traffic, 15 km/h
Operating costs financed by: Fares 28.4 per cent, other commercial sources 3.6 per cent, subsidy/grants 68 per cent
Subsidy from: Regional government
New vehicles financed by: Loans

Tramway/light rail
Type of operation: Conventional tramway/light rail

Route length: 16 km (new construction), total 25 km
Number of stations: 20
Gauge: 1,000 mm
Track: 50 kg/m rail on 'Angleur' tie-plates inclined 1/20; 20/40 ballast
Electrification: 600 V DC, overhead

Service: Peak 5 min, off-peak 30 min
First/last car: 05.00/20.00
Fare structure: Zonal
Fare collection: Prepurchase tickets, or cash to driver
Fare evasion control: Roving inspectors, spot fines
Integration with other services: Bus feeders at many stations
Operating costs financed by: Fares 15.3 per cent, subsidy/grants 84.7 per cent

Rolling stock: 33 articulated cars
BN/ACEC (1980)	M33

SNCB
Belgian National Railways (SNCB/NMBS), South-West District
Quai de la Gare du Sud 1, 6000 Charleroi
Tel: (+32 71) 60 21 11   Fax: (+32 71) 60 23 91

Type of operation: Suburban heavy rail

Current situation: Services operate about hourly on seven routes out of Charleroi Sud station, electrified 3 kV DC.

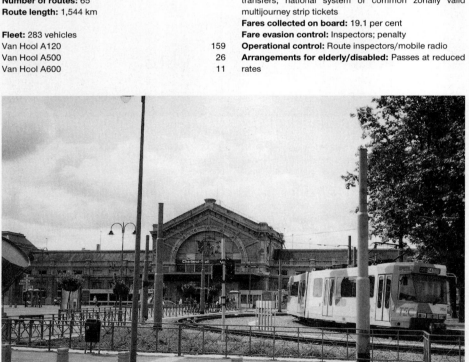

TEC tram outside Charleroi station   **1999**/0038761   ***UPDATED***

CHARLOTTE
Population: Metropolitan area 1.2 million
Public transport: Bus services provided by the City of Charlotte under contract

Charlotte Transit
Transit Management of Charlotte
901 N Davidson, Charlotte, North Carolina 28206, USA

Tel: (+1 704) 336 24 20   Fax: (+1 704) 336 40 58
Assistant Manager: Bob Williams
Communications Officer: Olaf Kinard
Staff: 360
Managed by ATE/Ryder Transportation Services

Current situation: CT was established in 1976. It provides local and express bus service within the Charlotte city limits. A no-fare zone operates in the main

shopping area during off-peak hours. Express bus passengers, mainly commuters whose services run only in peak times, have 'Guaranteed Ride Home' facility for urgent journeys between the peaks.
Developments: Earlier start to weekday services introduced 1997.

Bus
Passenger journeys: (1994) 12 million

(1995) 12.3 million
(1996) 12.5 million
Vehicle-km: (1995) 8.2 million
(1996) 8.3 million

Number of routes: 43
Route length:

Fleet: 161 buses

Flxible ADB (1982)	42
Flxible (1991)	40
MAN (1987)	39

RTS TMC (1990)	10
Goshen (1996)	6
Gillig (1997)	20
AVS electric bus (1995)	4
In peak service: 133	

Most intensive service: 10 min
One-person operation: All routes
Fare collection: Farebox, no change given
Fare structure: Flat, surcharge for express routes; free transfers; weekly and monthly passes
Arrangements for elderly/disabled: Reduced off-peak

fares; passes at reduced rates; most buses have kneeling capability; wheelchair lifts on 50 buses; demand-responsive service for those who cannot use fixed-route bus/mobile radio
Average distance between stops: 700 m
Average peak-hour speed: In mixed traffic, 15 km/h
Operating costs financed by: Fares 31.4 per cent, other commercial sources 3.3 per cent, subsidy/grants 65.3 per cent

VERIFIED

CHELYABINSK
Population: 1.1 million
Public transport: Bus and trolleybus/tramway services provided by separate municipal undertakings; metro under construction

Bus
Number of routes: 73
Fleet: Ikarus 260/260, LIAZ 677 and Hyundai
Fare collection: Prepurchase, cancellers on board

Tramvaino-Trolleibusnoe Upravlenie
Tramvaino-Trolleibusnoe Upravlenie
Ul Truda 66, 454000 Chelyabinsk, Russia
Tel: (+7 3512) 33 77 52

Current situation: This is one of the best Russian tramway systems in terms of maintenance standards and reliability. Metro construction started in 1992 and has progressed erratically; there is no likelihood of opening before 2000.

Trolleybus
Number of routes: 22
Fleet: About 400 vehicles, ZIU9 and ZIU10

Tramway
Passenger journeys: (1989) 185 million

Number of routes: 16
Track length: 155 km

Rolling stock: About 370 cars

KTM5 (1982-92)	M320
KTM8 (1990-96)	M50

VERIFIED

ZIU10 articulated trolleybus crossing the central square   **1997**

KTM8 car at Pobedy Prospekt   **1997**

CHEMNITZ
Population: 259,000, area served 263,000
Public transport: Bus and tramway services provided by municipal company account for 95 per cent of all public transport journeys; some suburban services of state railway (DB) and regional bus company Autobus Sachsen. Interurban light rail planned

VMS
Arbeitsgemeinschaft Verkehrsverbund Mittelsachsen GbR c/o CVAG (address below)

Current situation: Regional transit authority created in 1998 to co-ordinate public transport in Chemnitz, Mittweida, Freiberg, Erzgebirge, Zwickau and West-sachsen regions. Introduction of a uniform tariff scheme planned.

CVAG
Chemnitzer Verkehrs AG (CVAG)
PO Box 114, 09001 Chemnitz, Germany
Tel: (+49 371) 237 00   Fax: (+49 371) 237 06 00
Director: Dipl-Ing-Ök Gert Gottschalk
Managers: Ilka Caspary
   Reinhart Seidel
Staff: 944

Passenger journeys: (1995) 56.7 million
(1996) 55.8 million
(1997) 50.7 million

Current situation: CVAG serves an area of 118 km². The bus system is more extensive than in many eastern German cities as the former 925 mm gauge tram network was replaced largely by buses rather than total conversion to 1,435 mm gauge. Conversion was completed in 1988.
Developments: Bus routes are being replanned as feeders to an extended tram network, including new light rail routes into surrounding areas, some of which may take over existing DB routes. Tram service now replaced by buses at times of low demand.

Operating costs financed by: Fares 29.1 per cent, subsidy/grants 60 per cent, other 10.9 per cent (bus and tram combined)

Bus
Staff: 555

Passenger journeys: (1995) 32.7 million
(1996) 31.8 million
Vehicle-km: (1995) 8.7 million
(1996) 8.6 million
(1997) 7.8 million

Number of routes: 32
Route length: 309 km including duplication, unduplicated 239 km
On priority right-of-way: 1.1 km

Fleet: 151 vehicles, plus 18 contracted

Ikarus 280 articulated (1987/90)	9
Mercedes O405N low-floor (1991/93)	66
MAN NG272 low-floor articulated (1991/93)	31
Neoplan N4014/2 low-floor (1992/94)	10
Mercedes O405GN low-floor articulated (1993/97)	24
Neoplan N4032 Megashuttle double-deck (1993/94)	7
Others	4
In peak service: 115	

Average age of fleet: 5.25 years
New vehicles required each year: 9-17

Most intensive service: 7.5 min
One-person operation: All routes
Operational control: Computer-based system planned
Fare structure: Time-based single or multiride ticket; daily, weekly, weekend and monthly passes, annual subscription
Fare collection: Prepurchase only, no driver sales but onboard vending machines introduced; onboard validation; 78 per cent hold passes or multiride tickets
Fare evasion control: Roving inspectors
Average distance between stops: 622 m
Average speed: 20.7 km/h
Operating costs financed by: Fares 32 per cent, subsidy/grants 68 per cent
Subsidy from: City of Chemnitz 100 per cent

Developments: Covered parking space for 162 buses is under construction at Werner-Seelen Binder Strasse depot for 1998 completion. One bus route operated jointly with Autobus Sachsen (see below)

Tramway
Staff: 396

Type of operation: Conventional tramway

Passenger journeys: (1995) 24 million
(1996) 24 million
Car-km: (1994) 6 million
(1997) 5.1 million

Number of routes: 4
Route length: 23.6 km
    reserved track: 21.2 km
Gauge: 1,435 mm
Electrification: 600 V DC, overhead

Service: Peak 7 min
Number of stops: 50
Average distance between stops: 476 m
Average speed: 18.6 km/h
Type of rail: Ri60 (60.5 kg/m); S49 (49.1 kg/m)
Max gradient: 53.69%
Min curve radius: 27 m
Fare evasion control: Roving inspectors
Operating costs financed by: Fares 41 per cent, subsidy/grants 59 per cent

Rolling stock: 151 cars

ČKD Tatra T3D/B3D 4-axle (1968/78)	M80 T20
ČKD Tatra T3D-M/B3D-M modernised	M36 T14
ABB Variobahn 6NGT 6-axle articulated (1993)	M1

In peak service: 105
On order: 23 Variobahn low-floor cars (of which five will be bidirectional) from Adtranz/DWA for late 1998 delivery, with an option for a further 30

Developments: A 4.5 km extension from Falkeplatz to Stolberger Strasse was expected to open in November 1998. Other extensions planned including some over DB tracks to Stollberg, Limbach-Oberfrohna and Burgstädt (see below).

Autobus Sachsen

Autobus GmbH Sachsen Regionalverkehr
Zwickauer Strasse 58, 09112 Chemnitz
Tel: (+49 371) 380 80   Fax: (+49 371) 380 81 13
General Manager: Rolf Kuhfahl
Staff: 331

Passenger journeys: (1995) 9.5 million
(1996) 9.2 million
(1997) 8.9 million
Vehicle-km: (1995) 7.9 million
(1996) 6.2 million
(1997) 7.2 million

Current situation: Local government-owned bus company providing regional services in the area around Chemnitz with a fleet of 151 buses plus 12 on hire.

City-Bahn Chemnitz

City-Bahn Chemnitz GmbH

Current situation: Company founded in 1997 jointly by CVAG (80 per cent) and Autobus Sachsen for planning of the light rail line from Stollberg to Chemnitz. First section due to open in 1998. A double-ended version of the 'Variobahn' will be used.

UPDATED

CHENGDU

Population: 3 million
Public transport: Bus services are supplemented by large numbers of minibuses. Chinese Railways operates a suburban service of five trains daily on the line from Chengdu main station to Jiwuduan, with journey time of 15-17 min. Metro and light rail planned

Chengdu City Transport

Chengdu City Transport
Chengdu, Sichuan Province, People's Republic of China

Current situation: The trolleybus system is reported to have closed in 1997.

Bus
Number of routes: About 50
Fleet: Approx 500, including some 200 articulated
Fare collection: Stage fares paid to seated conductor; monthly passes

Metro and light rail (planned)
Current situation: Plans for a 20 km three-line metro were announced in 1993. These envisaged a 5 km north-south line from Chengdu to Chengdu South station, a 6 km east-west line from Wuguiqiao to the Emei Film Studios, and a 9 km orbital line beneath the main boulevard encircling the city centre. Private finance was to be sought in Hong Kong to augment the public funds to be allocated.

This scheme seems to have foundered, as a new proposal for a 12 km metro line and 189 km of light rail routes was announced in 1994. A design-build-operate contract was expected to be awarded to a Canadian company.

VERIFIED

CHIBA

Population: 800,000
Public transport: Situated 40 km to the east of central Tokyo, Chiba has seen recent large-scale commercial and residential development and a rapid increase in population, many of whom commute to Tokyo. JR and private rail services; monorail operated by third-sector company; privately operated bus services

Keisei Dentetsu

Keisei Electric Railway
10-3 Oshiage, 1-chome, Sumida-ku, Tokyo 131, Japan
Tel: (+81 3) 36 21 22 31

Interurban rail
Managing Director: H Hosokawa
Staff: 2,169

Passenger journeys: (1991/92) 276 million
(1992/93) 279 million
(1993/94) 281 million
Car-km: (1992/93) 76 million
(1993/94) 76 million

Current situation: Operates from Ueno station in Tokyo to Chiba-Chuo (42.6 km) with nine stations in Chiba city. A reciprocal through service is operated with Chiba Kyuko Dentetsu (see below).

Rolling stock: 496 emu cars
Various builders   M442 T54

Bus
Managing Director: K Sato
Staff: 2,200

Passenger journeys: (Tokyo conurbation, including Chiba)
(1991/92) 138.8 million
(1992/93) 135.3 million
(1993/94) 136.5 million

Current situation: Keisei's bus division runs 980 buses, of which about 730 are operated on routes in Chiba city and prefecture, including feeder services to monorail stations.

JR East

East Japan Railway Company
Higashi Nihon Ryokaku Tetsudo
2-2 Yoyogi 2-chome, Shibuya-ku, Tokyo 151
Tel: (+81 3) 53 34 11 51   Fax: (+81 3) 53 34 11 10
Chair: S Yamanouchi
President: M Matsuda

Current situation: Chiba is the eastern terminus for cross-Tokyo Sobu line local emus which operate to Mitaka via Shinjuku every 3-14 min. These are supplemented by frequent limited stop rapid service emus between Kurihama, Yokohama, Tokyo and Chiba, with hourly trains continuing to Narita airport, and by Limited Expresses running between Tokyo, Chiba and Choshi. Chiba is also the terminus for regional local services on the Sobu, Narita, Uchibo and Sotobo lines.

In 1990 a second JR line was completed between Chiba and Tokyo, with five stations in Chiba city; the Keiyo line serves major new development projects alongside Tokyo Bay including Disneyland, the Nippon Convention Centre and the Chiba Port commercial and residential development zone. Keiyo line local and rapid service emus run between Tokyo and Soga (Chiba), supplemented by Uchibo and Sotobo line Limited Expresses which call only at Soga.

Chiba Urban Monorail

Chiba Urban Monorail Company
199-1, Hagidai-cho, Inage-ku, Chiba-shi 263
Tel: (+81 43) 287 82 11   Fax: (+81 43) 252 72 34
President: T Numata
Vice President: Y Yamaguchi

Current situation: Chiba Urban Monorail is a third-sector company; shareholders include Chiba city, Chiba prefecture and Keisei Electric Railway. The Chiba master plan envisages a 40 km monorail system to serve expanding commercial and residential development areas. The initial route, Line 2 linking Chiba and the new residential suburb of Chishirodai via the Sports Centre, was opened in 1988 and completed in 1991. The first section of Line 1 between Chiba and Chiba Port, with one intermediate station, opened in 1995, the service running through from Line 2.

A 0.7 km extension of Line 1 from Chiba to the Prefectural Government Office was under construction for 1998 opening, following which separate services will be introduced on the two lines. A further 4 km extension of Line 1 beyond the Government Office is planned.

Monorail
Type of operation: Townliner suspended monorail, opened 1988

Passenger journeys: (1993/94) 13.3 million
(1994/95) 13.3 million
(1995/96) 15.5 million
Car-km: (1993/94) 2 million
(1994/95) 2 million
(1995/96) 2.2 million

Route length: 13.5 km
Number of lines: 2, operated as a single route
Number of stations: 15
Electrification: 1.5 kV DC

Service: 5 min
First/last train: 05.30/00.10
Fare structure: Graduated
One-person operation: All cars
Signalling: CTC

Rolling stock: 17 two-car sets
Mitsubishi (1991/93)   M34

Chiba Kyuko Dentetsu

Chiba Express Electric Railway
250-1 Shinmei-cho, Chuo-ku, Chiba-shi
Tel: (+81 43) 245 26 75   Fax: (+81 43) 245 26 77

Interurban rail
Current situation: This company is building a 15 km line from Chiba Chuo to an interchange with the Kominato Railway (see below) at Ama-ariki; 1,067 mm gauge; electrified 1.5 kV DC overhead. The first 4 km opened in 1992 with a reciprocal through service to the Keisei system, and a further 6.7 km opened in 1995.

Major shareholders comprise Keisei Electric Railway (43.9 per cent), Chiba city (12.9 per cent) and Chiba prefecture, Kominato Railway and the Housing & Urban Development Agency (8.3 per cent each).

Rolling stock: 2 four-car emus

Kominato Tetsudo
Kominato Railway
810 Shioda-cho, Chiba 260
Tel: (+81 472) 61 51 42

Bus
Passenger journeys: (1990/91) 14.6 million

(1991/92) 15.2 million
(1992/93) 14.5 million
Vehicle-km: (1990/91) 5.1 million
(1991/92) 5.1 million
(1992/93) 5.1 million

Current situation: Operates 250 buses on services in Chiba city and prefecture, also a 39.1 km railway elsewhere in Chiba prefecture.

Chiba Chuo Bus
Chiba Chuo Bus
2-27-4 Nagasu, Chiba-shi 280
Tel: (+81 472) 24 37 71

Bus
Passenger journeys: (1990/91) 12.3 million
(1991/92) 12.6 million
(1992/93) 11.8 million
Vehicle-km: 4 million
(1991/92) 4.1 million
(1992/93) 4.1 million

Current situation: This Keisei Group company operates 95 buses on services in Chiba; also owns 57 coaches.

VERIFIED

CHICAGO
Population: 2.8 million, city region 7.8 million
Public transport: Bus, metro and commuter rail services in a 6,000 km² area encompassing the city of Chicago and suburban Cook County, and the surrounding counties of Will, McHenry, DuPage, Kane and Lake, controlled by Regional Transportation Authority through three service boards. City operations are undertaken through Chicago Transit Authority (CTA) under local representative board; regional metro and suburban rail services through the Commuter Rail Service Board (Metra) and operated by Metra and independent railway companies; other RTA-controlled bus services run by suburban bus board (Pace) through independently administered mass transit districts in certain suburbs, based on previously independent operations; local personal rapid transit proposed

RTA
Regional Transportation Authority
181 W Madison Street, Suite 1900, Chicago, Illinois 60602, USA
Tel: (+1 312) 917 07 00   Fax: (+1 312) 917 13 44
Chair: Thomas McCracken
Executive Director: Richard J Bacigalupo

Passenger journeys: (All modes)
(1991) 642 million
(1992) 603 million
(1994) 600 million

Current situation: The RTA, established in 1974, exercises overall planning and financial control of public transport in the Greater Chicago area, provision of which is in the hands of three service boards. Operations in Chicago itself are run by CTA, regional and commuter rail services through Metra, and suburban bus operations by Pace, the Suburban Bus Division, serving parts of Chicago and suburbs including Oak Park, Waukegan, Harvey and Oak Lawn. Some local private bus operators are also supported.

A sales tax (1 per cent in Cook County, 0.25 per cent in other counties) provides about one-third of RTA revenue, while the Illinois State Public Transportation Fund adds 25 per cent of the annual sales tax proceeds. Some 85 per cent of these funds are allocated to the service boards. As a condition of receipt of state funds, the regional transit system as a whole must recover at least 50 per cent of its operating expenses from system-generated revenue (primarily fares). For recent history see earlier editions.

CTA
Chicago Transit Authority (CTA)
Merchandise Mart Plaza, PO Box 3555, Chicago, Illinois 60654
Tel: (+1 312) 664 72 00   Fax: (+1 312) 661 01 12
Chair: Valerie Jarrett

MAN articulated bus with CTA on Michigan Avenue (Bill Luke)   *1999*/0038762

President: Frank Kruesi
Executive Vice Presidents
    Transit Operations: R Winston
    Customer Service, Facilities & Development:
        Jack Hartman
    Management & Performance: Jeff Morales
Vice President, Rail: William Mooney
Vice President, Bus: vacant
Staff: 12,531

Passenger boardings: (All modes)
(1995) 441.5 million
(1996) 445.4 million
(1997) 419 million

Operating costs financed by: Fares 46.3 per cent, other commercial sources 2.9 per cent, subsidy/grants 50.8 per cent

Bus
Passenger journeys: (1995) 182.7 million
(1996) 180.9 million
(1997) 287.6 million
Vehicle-km: (1994) 115 million
(1995) 115.7 million
(1996) 115.5 million

Number of routes: 128
Route length: (One way) 1,523 km

Fleet: 1,872 vehicles	
MAN articulated (1982)	73
Flyer (1983)	110
MAN standard (1985)	337
TMC RTS T80 208 lift-equipped (1991)	475
TMC RTS T80 608 narrow body (1991)	15
Flxible lift-equipped (1991)	467
Flxible lift-equipped (1995)	330
New Flyer lift-equipped (1995)	65

In peak service: 1,657
Average age of fleet: 4 years

Most intensive service: Peak 1.8 min, off-peak 10 min
One-person operation: All routes
Fare collection: Exact fare; $ bill, coin, token, pass or transfer; monthly pass accounts for less than 20 per cent of revenue
Fare structure: Flat; monthly pass; discounted tokens; 30 cent transfer good for 2 bus/rail transfers, magnetic cards
Operational control: Route inspectors/mobile radio; on-line monitoring for emergencies
Arrangements for elderly/disabled: Half fare at all times; 57 main line services operated by 1,241 lift- or ramp-equipped buses, limited special funding provided; 4 competing private carriers contracted to provide demand-responsive door-to-door service for disabled; voucher system provides taxi service to disabled people at double main line fares; paratransit services carried 1.2 million passengers in 1996

Low-floor New Flyer CTA bus on Michigan Avenue (Bill Luke)   *1999*/0038767

Pace Nova Bus on regional suburban service at Michigan Avenue (Bill Luke)   *1999*/0038763

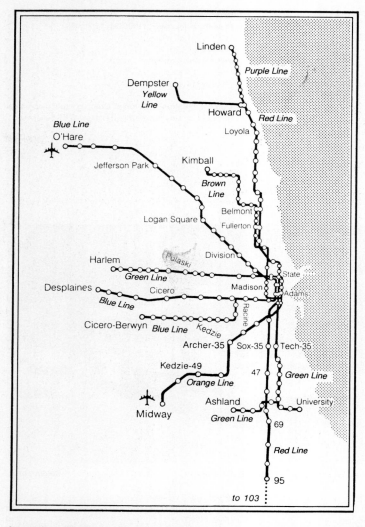

Chicago's metro

Integration with other modes: Bus service links central area rail stations and surrounding areas
Average weekday speed: 20 km/h
New vehicles financed by: Federal grant 80 per cent, local share 20 per cent

Developments: Satellite-based vehicle location and management system being installed for 1999 completion.

NovaBUS Corporation, Saint Eustache, Quebec has won a contract to build 150 40 ft low-floor buses for CTA. The contract, estimated at nearly US$40 million, is accompanied by an option for 320 additional vehicles, bringing the potential total number of buses to 470 over the next few years.

Metro (Rail)

Type of operation: Full metro, initial route opened 1892

Passenger journeys: (1994) 78 million
(1995) 79.7 million
(1996) 84 million
Car-km: (1994) 74 million
(1995) 73.5 million
(1996) 77.9 million

Route length: 173 km
 in tunnel: 18 km
 elevated: 62.3 km
Number of lines: 7
Number of stations: 140
 in tunnel: 20
 elevated: 112
Gauge: 1,435 mm
Track: Flat-bottom rail; timber sleepers on ballast (212 track-km); sleepers on concrete trackbed with resilient pads (37.1 km); timber sleepers on iron/steel elevated structure (151.8 km)
Tunnel: 5.4 m diameter tube and cut-and-cover
Electrification: 600 V DC, third rail; overhead on 4 km section of Skokie line

Service: Peak 3-8 min, off-peak 10-20 min
First/last train: 2 routes operate 24 h service; others run 22 h (Brown), 19 h (Orange), 17 h (Yellow), 21 h (Green)

and 22 h (Douglas branch Blue); no weekend service on Yellow line and Douglas branch Blue line
Fare structure: Flat; monthly pass; discounted tokens; 30 cent transfer good for 2 bus/rail transfers
Revenue control: Magnetically coded fare cards sold at all stations
Arrangements for elderly/disabled: Half fare at all times; 30 stations have ramps or lifts
Signalling: Cab signalling on 124.4 km of route, automatic block on remainder; long-term plans for cab signalling throughout
One-person operation: All routes

Rolling stock: 1,192 cars
Budd 2200 (1969/70)	M144
Boeing 2400 (1977/78)	M194
Budd/Transit America 2600 (1981/87)	M597
Morrison Knudsen 3200 (1992/93)	M257
In peak service: 918	

Developments: The Green line reopened in 1996 on completion of a two-year $350 million reconstruction. The new Washington/Wells station on the Loop has replaced Madison/Wells and Randolph/Wells. Library-State/Van Buren station in the Loop opened June 1997.

The Budd/Transit America cars built between 1981 and 1987 have been refurbished and converted for one-person operation.

Magnetic tickets were introduced throughout the metro network in September 1997.

Metra

Northeast Illinois Regional Commuter Railroad Corporation (Metra)
547 West Jackson Boulevard, Chicago, Illinois 60661-5717
Tel: (+1 312) 322 69 00
Chair: Jeffrey R Ladd
Executive Director: Philip A Pagano
Deputy Executive Director: G Richard Tidwell
Chief Operating Officer: Vaughn Stoner
Director of Media Relations: Frank Malone
Staff: 2,300

Type of operation: Suburban heavy rail

Passenger journeys: (1995) 73.1 million
(1996) 73.3 million
(1997) 75.2 million

Current situation: Metra evolved from the Northeast Illinois Railroad Corporation to operate the commuter lines of the former Rock Island Railroad (79 route-km) and later those of the Milwaukee Road (135 km), which had been purchased and leased respectively by the RTA. NIRC also had purchase of service agreements for other commuter services provided by the Illinois Central (125 km), Burlington Northern (59 km), Chicago & North Western (249 km), Norfolk Southern (39 km) and Chicago, South Shore & South Bend (between Chicago and the Illinois/Indiana border, now the South Shore Line) railroads.

In 1984 the Commuter Rail Service Board took over, adopting the service name Metra. Today NIRC (Metra) owns and operates (through NIRC) the former Rock Island, Milwaukee, IC (Metra Electric) and Norfolk Southern (taken over in 1993) lines. Trains on other lines operate under purchase of service agreements. Metra is responsible for setting fare and service levels, and provides for capital improvements, planning and marketing for all lines.

Operations extend to 537 route-km of 1,435 mm gauge on 11 routes and four branches serving 250 stations, of which 66 km (two routes) are electrified at 1.5 kV DC overhead. Other routes are worked by diesel push-pull trainsets. Trains run every 5-20 min at peak times, and every 1, 1½ or 2 h off-peak; limited service evenings and weekends. Zonal fare structure, with monthly tickets giving an opportunity to purchase monthly bus pass (Link-up Passport) at a reduced rate. Fares account for 55 per cent of operating costs.

In addition the South Shore Line has 117 km of 1,435 mm gauge route electrified at 1.5 kV DC overhead and operates interurban service from Chicago to Gary, Michigan City and South Bend in Indiana. This route is subsidised 22 per cent by Metra and 78 per cent by the Northern Illinois Commuter Transportation District, which purchased the line in 1991.

Rolling stock: 130 diesel locomotives, 861 coaches, 223 emu cars

Developments: The North Central route, a 67 km extension to Antioch with 11 stations, opened in 1996.

Pace

550 West Algonquin Road, Arlington Heights, Illinois 60005
Tel: (+1 847) 228 23 02 Fax: (+1 847) 437 81 16
Executive Director: T J Ross
Deputy Executive Director, Operations: Melinda Metzger
Chair: Florence Boone
Staff: 1,320

Passenger journeys: (1995) 37.2 million
(1996) 37.5 million
(1997) 37.9 million

Current situation: Pace was established in 1984 to assume operational responsibility for the three existing RTA-controlled suburban bus divisions and other operations, together covering the 5,500 km², 4.5 million population, six-county suburban region of Chicago.

Pace provides funding for 235 bus routes serving 235 communities. It owns and operates nine suburban carriers, subsidises three municipal carriers and contracts with 12 private operators, primarily running express routes serving suburban employment centres and feeders to 132 CTA metro and Metra rail stations. A uniform fare structure exists for most Pace services.

Some 82.8 per cent of passengers are carried by Pace-owned operations, 7.9 per cent by private contract carriers, 2.8 per cent by municipal services, 4.4 per cent by paratransit and 2.1 per cent by vanpools.

Paratransit services to all parts of the area (excluding that covered by CTA) have seen increasing patronage. They are operated mainly by dial-a-ride shared taxi, fixed route deviation types of service on 60 routes. There are also four 'mobility limited' routes. There are 56 local operators and six private contractors; Pace-owned lift-equipped vehicles are used. All satellite cities have fully accessible service.

Developments: Several capital projects are under way in the Comprehensive Operating Plan, including provision of more transit centres and park-and-ride sites. A transit vehicle management system is to be installed, with passenger counting and automatic vehicle location facilities as well as traffic signal pre-emption.

The VIP vanpool programme continues to expand, with over 200 vehicles, despite the reduced emphasis now placed on the Employee Commute Options programme.

Fleet: 638 buses; 354 paratransit vehicles; 356 vanpool vans (minibuses)

Gillig (1986)	20
Orion I (1988/93)	454
Ikarus USA (1992)	71
Chance RT52 (1995)	15
Nova (1996)	22
Eldorado (1997)	56
Paratransit	
Ford/Goshen (1990/91)	21
Ford/Eldorado (1994)	110
Chance (1995)	3
Eldorado minibuses/buses (1995/97)	220

In peak service: 588 buses, including contractors' vehicles
Average age: 6.9 years (fixed route)

Most intensive service: 5 min
Fare structure: Primarily flat
Fare collection: Registering farebox collects cash, CTA tokens and stored value card receipts
Arrangements for elderly/disabled: Paratransit operations serve 224 municipalities
Integration with other modes: Full integration with CTA; bus and rail passes co-ordinated with CTA and Metra rail
Average peak hour speed: 22.4 km/h
Bus priority: Slip ramp from Tollway is used to access CTA station; signal priority in demonstration phase
Operating costs financed by: Fares 36.3 per cent, subsidy/grants 63.7 per cent

Newly opened Library station on Van Buren Loop   ***1999**/0043534*

Subsidy from: RTA provides support drawn from sales tax, federal operating assistance and state subsidy via the public transportation fund

UPDATED

CHIŞINĂU
Population: 676,000
Public transport: Extensive trolleybus network and smaller feeder bus system operated by separate undertakings controlled by Ministry of Transport. These are supplemented by small buses known as 'marshroutniy taxis'

City Trolleybus Company
Chişinău City Trolleybus Company
Chişinău, Moldova

Current situation: The trolleybus network forms the basis of the city's public transport and services are extremely crowded.

Trolleybus
Number of routes: 20 regular, plus 3 at shift-change hours only
Fleet: Approx 450 trolleybuses, Uritsky ZIU9 and some ZIU10
Fare structure: Flat
Fare collection: Single tickets purchased from driver or from kiosks, cancelling machines on board; calendar monthly and semi-monthly passes
Fare evasion control: Roving inspectors

City Bus Company
Chişinău City Bus Company

Current situation: Buses play a smaller, mainly feeder role. The fleet is mostly Ikarus 260/280; fare structure is the same as for trolleybuses, but with single tickets 50 per cent higher.

VERIFIED

CHONGQING
Population: 3 million, metropolitan area 14 million
Public transport: The city centre occupies a hilly peninsula at the confluence of the Yangzi and Jialing rivers. Suburbs fan out from the neck of land west of the centre and are also located north of the Jialing and west of the Yangzi. Each river is crossed by only one road bridge. Public transport is of particular importance because the hilly terrain is considered unsuitable for cycling, though the topography is ideal for trolleybus operation and Chongqing adopted this mode in 1955. An extensive network of bus services complements the trolleybuses. Rail plays little part in local transport; though a direct line exists between the centre and the outer trolleybus terminal at Shapingba, a 7 km tunnel restricts operation of suburban services to two trains morning and afternoon between Chongqing and Chongqing West. A few local trains also run between Chongqing and Chongqing South (7 km); light rail proposed

Chongqing City Transport
Chongqing City Transport Department
Chongqing, Sichuan Province, People's Republic of China

Current situation: A tree-shaped network of overlapping trolleybus routes runs from the river confluence up the spine of the peninsula to three suburban terminals, one route crossing the Jialing bridge. The busiest part of the system has sections of duplicated overhead to increase capacity. There is also an intersuburban route. In 1989 the network had remained unchanged for many years apart from an alteration near the central junction to conform to a one-way traffic scheme.

Bus
Passenger journeys: (1985/86) 568 million
Vehicle-km: (1985/86) 54 million

Number of routes: 50
Route length: 500 km
Fleet: Approx 800 buses, including many articulated, all Chongqing including types CQ643, CQ650 (two-axle), CQ662, CQ663 and CQ670 (articulated)
Fare collection: Stage fares paid to seated conductor; monthly passes

Trolleybus
Passenger journeys: (1985/86) 57 million
Vehicle-km: (1985/86) 5.4 million

Number of routes: 5
Route length: 30 km
Fleet: Approx 150 Chongqing trolleybuses, including about 130 articulated; current type is CQ563 articulated
Fare collection: As bus

Other modes
Current situation: There is an aerial cableway across each river but ferries remain the principal cross-river links away from the two bridges. Three funiculars provide short-distance transport at difficult locations.

VERIFIED

CHRISTCHURCH

Population: City 310,000
Public transport: Bus and ferry services overseen by the Canterbury Regional Council. Bus and ferry services are provided by a mixture of public and privately owned companies

Canterbury Regional Council

Canterbury Regional Council (CRC)
PO Box 345, Christchurch, New Zealand
Tel: (+64 3) 365 38 28   Fax: (+64 3) 365 31 94
Passenger Services Manager: Wayne Holton-Jeffreys

Current situation: Deregulation of public transport services was implemented in 1991. CRC contracts and funds all but four bus services in Christchurch, which are provided commercially.

Responsibility for transport is split between the city council and Canterbury Regional Council. CRC is responsible for the registration of all passenger transport services in the Canterbury region including bus, rail, taxi and ferry services. It contracts provision of bus and ferry services in Christchurch and other smaller centres in the Canterbury region where these would not otherwise be provided at a desired level on a commercial basis.
Developments: Bus services in the northeast and north-west were restructured in 1997. Increases in frequency and introduction of 20 super-low-floor buses have seen patronage in these areas grow by 20 per cent. Inter-operator transfers allowing the use of a single ticket for journeys between different bus companies were also implemented in 1997.

Construction of a new central city bus interchange started early in 1998. The Christchurch City Council has made a commitment to development of a central city shuttle service using hybrid diesel-electric midibuses.

Widespread public consultation is currently being undertaken to determine the future role of public transport in Christchurch.

Arrangements for elderly/disabled: The Total Mobility scheme provides a 50 per cent subsidy for taxi fares up to NZ$20 for those who cannot use scheduled services; CRC also funds installation of wheelchair hoists in taxivans

Bus

Passenger boardings: (1994/95) 7.7 million
(1995/96) 8.1 million
(1996/97) 8.5 million
Vehicle-km: (1995/96) 8 million

Low-floor Dennis Dart of Christchurch Transport in New Brighton   **1998**/0010002

Operating costs financed by: Fares 50 per cent, property taxes and central government funding 50 per cent

Current situation: Services are provided by four main operators, the largest of which, Christchurch Transport, is a city council owned local authority trading enterprise. Leopard Citylines has a growing presence, running several major services in the western area of the city as well as the service to the port of Lyttelton. Other operators include Astro Coachlines and Ritchies Transport Holdings.

Number of routes: 32

Fleet: 150 vehicles

SLF Dennis Dart (1997)	14
SLF MAN 11190 (1997)	6
MAN SL202 (1986/90)	54
MAN 22240 (1990)	9
MAN 10150 (1990)	1
Volvo B10M ex-Wellington trolleybuses, dieselised 1996	12
Isuzu LR312 (1986)	3
Nissan Civilian (1986)	1
Mercedes 305 (1975-1984)	30
Bristol Hess (1981)	15
MAN SL200	4
Others	1

Fare collection: Prepurchase 12-ride tickets and monthly pass or cash to driver
Fare structure: Zonal with 1 & 2 section ticket for short trips

Passenger ferry

Current situation: A passenger ferry service connects the small community of Diamond Harbour with the port of Lyttelton.

The ferry service is provided by Lyttelton Harbour Cruises on contract to the Canterbury Regional Council.

VERIFIED

CINCINNATI

Population: 364,000, city region 867,000
Public transport: Bus services in city and environs provided by operating arm of Southwest Ohio Regional Transit Authority, governed by representative Board of Trustees. Services also run into the city from Covington and Newport across the Ohio river in Kentucky, operated by similar undertaking

Metro

Southwest Ohio Regional Transit Authority (SORTA)
1014 Vine Street, Cincinnati, Ohio 45202-1122, USA
Tel: (+1 513) 621 94 50   Fax: (+1 513) 621 52 91
www: http://www.sorta.com
President, SORTA Board of Trustees: Peter R Gomsak Jr
General Manager: Paul C Jablonski
Assistant General Manager, Operations: Michael L Brown

Assistant General Manager, Administration: Barry Frank
Manager, Marketing & Communications: Rita D Potts

Current situation: Metro, SORTA's bus operating subsidiary, was established in 1973 when voters approved a tax increase to fund purchase of the Cincinnati Transit bus system. It serves a total population of 867,000; 34 per cent of riders live outside the city of Cincinnati in other parts of Hamilton and Clermont counties, and are served by 18 per cent of vehicle-km operated.
Developments: Informal proposals exist for light rail in a corridor where a moribund rail route could be utilised. Purchase of rail rights-of-way was authorised in 1992, and in 1994 the city bought a share in the 25.6 km former Conrail freight line running northeast to Evendale.

Bus

Passenger journeys: (1995) 23.7 million
(1996) 23.3 million
(1997) 23.6 million
Vehicle-km: (1995) 19.8 million
(1996) 20.1 million
(1997) 20.1 million

Number of routes: 48
Route length: (One way) 1,993 km

Fleet: 429 vehicles

Flxible Corp (1987)	94
Neoplan (1989/90)	163
Gillig Phantom (1995/96/97)	147
Eldorado National (1997)	18
Minibuses (1995/6)	7
In peak service: 328	

Metro bus on 71 service to Fields Ertel, Cincinnati   **1999**/0038760

COLUMBUS

Population: 634,000, metropolitan area 1.3 million
Public transport: Bus services provided for 961,400 residents of Franklin County in central Ohio by Regional Transit Authority under control of representative Board of Trustees. Service area includes small portions of Delaware, Fairfield, Licking and Pickaway counties whose boundaries adjoin Franklin County

COTA

Central Ohio Transit Authority (COTA)
1600 McKinley Avenue, Columbus, Ohio 43222-1093, USA
Tel: (+1 614) 275 58 00　Fax: (+1 614) 275 59 33
President: Mathew G Kallner
General Manager: Ronald L Barnes
Assistant General Manager, Marketing & Communications: Raymond C Miller
Staff: 716

Current situation: COTA operates three types of regular routes: Locals, which make all stops and travel through or terminate downtown; Expresses, which make few or limited stops and start or terminate downtown; and Crosstowns, which operate between two non-downtown points. See earlier editions for history.
Developments: Funding was approved at the beginning of 1997 for the GO BUS! scheme which allows unlimited free travel on COTA buses for students of Ohio State University. Three new or enhanced routes were provided to cater for the additional patronage, including late-night and weekend service between the Campus and the Brewery District.
　　COTA received grants in 1997 to develop transit centres in the fast-growing Easton development, and in impoverished Linden. Ohio DoT also granted funds for expansion of suburban services, including an east-west crosstown route to alleviate congestion in the Northern Outerbelt area, and circulators in the northern suburbs of Westerville and Dublin.
　　Having adopted a schedule of service improvements for the period through to 1999 under the Short Range Transit Plan published in 1995, COTA approved a resolution to double the size of the bus network by 2005.
　　Lack of funding precluded progress with an earlier plan to develop a 17.8 km light rail line running northwards from the city centre.

Bus

Passenger boardings: (1994) 17.1 million
(1996) 17.5 million
(1997) 17.8 million
Vehicle-km: (1994) 9.5 million
(1996) 9.7 million
(1997) 9.7 million

Number of routes: 57
Route length: (One way) 1,644 km

Fleet: 302 vehicles
Grumman/Flxible Metro (1984/91/93)　　　235
GMC (1987)　　　67
Plus 32 Flxible 870 (1982) in reserve to provide additional services at times of fuel shortage, when ridership can increase by 20 per cent at short notice
In peak service: 248

Most intensive service: 4 min
One-person operation: All routes
Fare collection: Cash to electronic counting farebox with dollar bill facility

Fare structure: Flat, no change, or prepurchase tickets; monthly passes for Local and Express routes; 10 cent transfers, premium for Express services
Fare evasion control: Driver monitors payment
Operational control: Two-way radio
Arrangements for elderly/disabled: Reduced fares; 32 fixed routes accessible to wheelchairs. Project Mainstream provides transport for those who cannot use fixed-route services — Subscription riders make the same journey at least once a week, whilst Reservation riders request trips as required. Since 1987, Project Mainstream operations have been contracted to DAVE Transportation Services. SCOT (Senior Citizens on the Town) provides group demand-responsive service for the elderly during mid-day and evening hours. Demand-responsive services carried 92,000 people in 1994
Integration with other modes: Some 26 park-and-ride lots have a total of 2,218 spaces, and there are two parking loops with 12 spaces each. Development of five additional lots planned, mostly around the I-270 orbital highway; guaranteed ride home scheme reimburses participants 90 per cent of fare of four taxi rides per year at times when regular buses do not run
Average peak-hour speed: 22.3 km/h
Bus priority: Peak-hour priority lane in central business district
Operating costs financed by: Fares 24.8 per cent, other commercial sources 2 per cent, subsidy/grants 11.8 per cent, tax levy 61.4 per cent
Subsidy from: FTA 4.5 per cent, state 7.3 per cent, local 86.2 per cent, other 2 per cent
New vehicles financed by: FTA (80 per cent) and local grants (20 per cent)

UPDATED

COPENHAGEN

Population: 1.7 million
Public transport: All bus services in the metropolitan area are planned and co-ordinated by the public authority Hovedstadsområdets Trafikselskab (HT). The area is also served by local and regional trains of Danish State Railways (DSB) and five local railways. The common fare system allows for transfer between buses and trains throughout the region. Mini-metro under construction

HT

Hovedstadsområdets Trafikselskab (HT)
Toftegårds Plads, Gammel Køge Landevej 3, 2500 Valby, Denmark
Tel: (+45) 36 44 36 36　Fax: (+45) 36 44 01 19
www: www.ht.dk
Staff: HT 280, contractors 3,700

Current situation: Development of fully integrated services has been a major feature of HT, which was formed in 1974 and until 1989 was responsible for overall supervision of all public transport in the region. In 1990 the Greater Copenhagen Council was abolished and overall control of local rail services passed back to DSB. HT's role is now confined to inviting tenders, service planning and co-ordination, and marketing. It receives all fare income and pays operating costs to contractors for provision of service.
　　Deregulation in the Copenhagen region takes the form of competition on service quality and costs amongst operators. Based on the existing operations of both publicly owned and private contractors, deregulation has been implemented in phases from 1990. In 1997, the extent of deregulated services reached 70 per cent. The remaining services which have not yet been tendered are operated by HT's former bus division, now constituted as an independent limited company known as Bus Danmark.
　　The tendering process has brought about decreases in contract prices of up to 25 per cent. HT has developed a quality and incentive system. If the operator renders services above the targeted figures, a bonus of up to 5 per cent of the bus-hour payment is earned. If target figures are not met, then payment is reduced by up to 1 per cent. Quality measurements have been conducted regularly since 1994, and incentives were introduced in 1996.
Developments: Deregulation is to be completed in 2002. HT's former bus division Bus Danmark is allowed to bid on equal terms with private contractors. The number of private contractors has dropped since the first round of tendering in 1990, from 19 to nine in 1997.

S-Bus express service Route 350 S　　　　　*1998*/0007914

　　A mini-metro connecting Copenhagen city with the island of Amager is under construction and is scheduled to open in 2000. The project is divided into three phases. The first phase is 11 km and is to be operational in 2000. The plans for phases two and three expect operation to start in 2001 and 2003 respectively.
　　Twenty-three stations are to be built, 20 m below, 7 m below and 5 m above ground level. Stations will be unmanned and the platforms will be provided with automatic screen doors for passenger safety.
　　The client Ørestadsselskabet I/S, the organisation for implementation of the system in Copenhagen, was established in 1993 as a partnership between Copenhagen municipality and the Danish State Ministry of Finance.
　　A consultant was employed from early 1994 with the initial task of recommending the optimal choice of system.
　　The metro is an automatic, driverless, frequent, small-unit train system monitored from a control centre and staffed by service personnel boarding the cars.

　　Implementation of the full system takes place in three stages: a stage 1 within Copenhagen municipality running from Nørreport to Ørestad, branching off to Lergravsparken, thereby connecting Copenhagen city with the densely populated areas of Amager.
　　Stage 2 from Nørreport to Vanløse enters Frederiksberg municipality and takes the municipality in as a partner in Frederiksbergbaneselskabet. Stage 3 runs from Lergravsparken to Copenhagen airport.
　　The metro will run in a separated double-track right-of-way for the full 22 km, following existing railway tracks from Vanløse to Frederiksberg, diving into 8 km tunnels under Copenhagen city to Lergravsparken and to Brygge Islands, passing the University development area in Ørestad on elevated structures and finishing on a low embankment through the south part of Ørestad.
　　Ørestadsselskabet employs COWI for contract management and supervision of the contracts entered into for the implementation of the metro system.
　　Each three-car trainset will be 39 m long and accommodate 300 passengers. The maximum driving

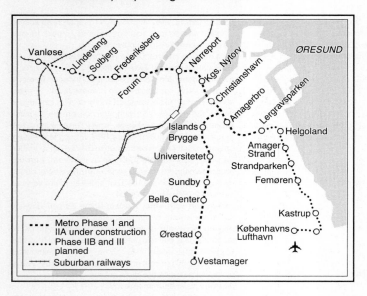

Copenhagen light metro under construction

Developments: Upgrading is in progress between Ballerup and Frederikssund, including installation of double track on the Ballerup—Veksø section and construction of two new stations. Completion of the double-tracking in 2000 will permit introduction of a 10 minute interval service. Work on the remaining section to Frederikssund will be complete in 2002.

A proposal for an outer circle route to link all the radial branches of the S-Bane, by extending the existing line from Hellerup to Vanløse round to Sjaelør, is undergoing further study.

The first prototypes of a new generation of S-Bane trains were delivered by Siemens/Linke-Hofmann-Busch in 1995. The trains are to a four-section articulated design with single steerable wheelsets. Following successful trials, DSB's option on a series-production of 112 sets was taken up in April 1997. Delivery of the new fleet started in early 1999 and will run through to 2005.

Rolling stock: 582 emu cars (S-Bane), 12 diesel railcars

Scandia/GEC MM/FS (1967/78)	M275 T275
Scandia/ASEA (1986)	M16 T16
LHB/Siemens prototypes	8
Diesel railcars	M7 T5

speed is 80 km/h with 40 km/h as average speed including stops at stations.The specification includes flush-floor/platform levels, good ventilation and large window panels. The system will operate a 90 second interval in rush hours. Travel time across the city from Nørreport to the University will be seven minutes.

The system is powered by 750 V DC from a protected third rail. Passenger information and communication are provided by the control centre working with remote control and video surveillance.

Bus

Passenger journeys: (1995) 248 million (1996) 256 million

Number of routes: 251
Route length: (One way) 4,500 km

Fleet: 1,139 buses	
12 m single-deck	1,071
Articulated	57
Tele-bus vehicles	11

In peak service: 981
Average age of fleet: 4.5 years

Most intensive service: 4-5 min
One-person operation: All services
Fare collection: Preprinted tickets issued by driver with manually operated ticket machine; multijourney tickets sold by bus drivers, at 123 rail ticket offices and by about 80 agents. Multijourney tickets cancelled in buses and at stations, about 2,000 ticket cancellers in use
Fare structure: Zonal; all tickets valid for free transfer between buses and between bus and rail; single, multijourney and season tickets (monthly). Tourist cards including bus and rail travel and admissions to attractions
Fares collected on board: 30 per cent of bus and train tickets sold on buses; 15 per cent use single tickets, 35 per cent multijourney tickets, 50 per cent season tickets
Fare evasion control: On-the-spot penalty payment to inspectors
Operational control: Route inspectors/mobile radio/traffic centre
Arrangements for elderly/disabled: 3-month off-peak season tickets at one-tenth normal adult price; no special finance provided

Operating costs financed by: Fares 52 per cent, other commercial sources 1 per cent, subsidy/grants from HT member counties 47 per cent

Developments: Two Mercedes/AEG duobuses were tried out over a two-year period, but the high capital and running costs led to a decision in 1995 not to order a fleet. In September 1997, a fleet of 51 LPG-powered buses went into service.

Development continues of the network of 'S-line' express bus routes established in 1993 to provide orbital links between S-Bane rail stations.

In 1995 HT started trials of real-time information provision to customers, along with active traffic signal priority for buses by means of satellite positioning. Two test areas have been chosen — part of the suburban ring road and a major radial street with heavy traffic in central Copenhagen.

Light rail (planned)
Current situation: Three routes are proposed — Hellerup—Glostrup via the city centre, Herlev—Nørrebro—Nørreport, and an orbital route Lyngby—Herlev—Glostrup—Ishøj.

DSB

Danish State Railways (DSB), S-Train
Kalvebod Brygge 34, 1560 Copenhagen V
Tel: (+45) 33 14 04 00   Fax: (+45) 33 12 21 47
Operations Manager: Erik Maglehøj

Suburban rail (S-Bane)
Passenger journeys: (1992) 95.6 million
(1993) 93.4 million
(1996) 92.9 million

Operating costs financed by: Fares 77 per cent, other commercial sources 9 per cent, national subsidies 14 per cent

Current situation: Extensive and frequent services (peak, 10 min) operated over network of 170 route-km, with 80 stations, 1,435 mm gauge, electrified 1.65 kV DC overhead. Integrated fares system applies with automatic ticket vending/cancelling machines. Also operates 25 km local railway linking Hillerød and Helsingør.

Regional rail
DSB Regional, address as above
Tel: (+45) 33 14 04 00   Fax: (+45) 33 93 06 16
Operations Manager: Stig Næsh

Current situation: Other DSB regional, local and suburban services link Copenhagen with Helsingør (electrified 25 kV, 20-min service), west and southern Zeeland via Roskilde (three routes), and Roskilde—Køge—Næstved.
Developments: A link to Kastrup airport was opened in September 1998, served by electric trains from Helsingør and a new direct hourly service from the Roskilde line, bypassing Central station.

Local railways
Current situation: Four railways, the Helsingør-Hornbaek-Gilleleje Bane (HHG), the Gribskov and Hillerød-Frederiksvaerk-Hundested Jernbane (GDS/HFHJ), and the Lyngby-Naerum Jernbane (LNJ) provide local services, with some connections to S-Bane services.
Developments: In 1997, HFHJ and GDS received three two-car sets of Flexliner dmu from the batch of 13 ordered in 1994 by the Association of Danish Private Railways on behalf of members.

Mini-metro
Under construction
Ørestadsselskabet
Grøns Pakhus, Holmens Kanal 7/4, 1060 Copenhagen K
Tel: (+45) 33 11 17 00   Fax: (+45) 33 11 23 01
Director: Anne-Grethe Foss
Project Manager: Helge Erlandsen

Current situation: A new urban development corporation, Ørestadsselskabet, was set up in 1993 to promote development of the Ørestad area close to Copenhagen's international airport on Amager island. A key element in the development is a rapid transit link with the city centre, now under construction.

With all three phases completed, the system will extend to 22 km (8 km in tunnel) with 24 stations; it is expected to be carrying some 70 million passengers a year by 2005.

UPDATED

CÓRDOBA
Population: 1.2 million
Public transport: Bus and trolleybus services provided by private companies and route co-operatives supervised by municipal transport department

Direccion del Transporte Publico
Palacio 6 de Julio, Córdoba, Argentina
Director of Transport: Lic Gustavo Reartos

Current situation: This authority supervises all public transport in Córdoba, which is provided by private operators. An exception has been the trolleybus network,

which has variously been in private and municipal hands. Public transport co-operatives were merged by the municipal authorities in 1970 into 13 route associations. Excessive competition between members led in 1980 to reorganisation of services by route-corridor, which were then put out to tender.

Bus
Current situation: There are 50 routes concentrated along nine corridors, plus three radial and 12 other routes. Mergers and takeovers have reduced the number of operators to six, employing some 3,400. These are: Dr Belgrano, Ciudad de Córdoba, El Coniferal, Union 12 de Octubre, America and Konfort.

Developments: An air conditioned express network of 12 midibus routes has been set up, run in part by new operator Konfort and using Mercedes LO709 and Toyota Coaster vehicles.

A new fare collection system is planned to replace the existing clipcard/token arrangements.

Passenger journeys: (1994) 200 million
Vehicle-km: (1994) 80 million

Number of routes: 65
Route length: 2,123 km
Fleet: 1,025 vehicles, mainly Mercedes midibuses but with some Brazilian-bodied Mercedes buses and an

increasing number of El Detalle OA101s; there are also some Fiat-Iveco AU130s and re-engined Zanellos, both built locally; the Express network is operated by Mercedes LO710/OF1215 and Toyota Coasters

Fare collection: Prepurchase ticket or token to driver
Fare structure: Flat, with transfer permitted to two orbital routes
Average peak-hour speed: 16 km/h

Trolleybus
Current situation: A trolleybus system opened in stages between 1989 and 1994, and now comprises three routes with a total route-length of about 30 km. The infrastructure and vehicles are owned by the municipality, while operation and maintenance have usually been carried out by a private company under contract. However, operations have been hampered by difficulties, with the municipality taking over from the three private companies that have so far attempted to run the system. A new private operator TroleCor was selected in 1997, and has promised new vehicles for 1999.

Electrical equipment from 31 ex-Montevideo vehicles was acquired for renovation in 1993.

Passenger journeys: (1994) 13 million
Vehicle-km: (1994) 2.5 million

Fleet: 44 trolleybuses
ZIU 682 (1989/93)	32
ZIU 683 (1990/92)	12

UPDATED

San Miguel-bodied Diferencial of Ciudad de Córdoba   **1996**

ZIU 682 trolleybus with centre doors removed to increase seating capacity
1998/0009728

CURITIBA
Population: 1.6 million
Public transport: Integrated bus services provided by 10 independent companies contracted by city authority, which is responsible for provision of system of busways and terminals and setting of fares and service levels

URBS S/A
Urbanização de Curitiba S/A
Empresa Gerenciadora do Transporte Coletivo, Prefeitura Municipal de Curitiba
PO Box 17017, Av Presidente Affonso Camargo 330, CP 80060-090, Curitiba, Paraná, Brazil
Tel: (+55 41) 322 48 46   Fax: (+55 41) 232 94 75
President: Carlos Eduardo Ceneviva

Current situation: The highly integrated service network is operated by 10 private companies, each allocated a share in the different types of express, conventional, feeder, intersuburb, neighbourhood, executive and the new direct routes.

The contract with public transport companies, extended for 10 years in 1981, was later declared null and void. Operating companies are no longer franchise holders and operate under contract on the authority of the governor, in accordance with regulations which ensure

that they meet quality standards set by URBS, a municipal company established as the only franchise holder. Failure to comply with URBS requirements may result in permission to operate a particular line being withdrawn.

The arrangement has overcome artificial area boundaries inhibiting planning of the transport system and prohibiting one company from picking up passengers while crossing the 'territory' of another, and creating an operating monopoly.

Remuneration of operating companies is made on the basis of km actually covered — journeys not made and timetables cancelled are not paid for, potentially resulting in fines.

Income from the system has become public; the daily takings of each bus are deposited in a local authority account with Banestado, managed by URBS. A balance sheet is published each month so that the receipts of the system can be clearly monitored.

Developments: Schlumberger Smart Cards & Terminals has been chosen to supply a new ticketing system.

In the first phase of the project, 30,000 municipal employees will be given a smartcard which functions as a local identity and access card, a payment card for retailers and a passport to preferential services with a participating bank. These applications will be followed by electronic ticketing for local bus services which will operate in contactless walk-by mode. Starting in 1999, the

programme was due to be extended to families of municipal employees and then to the city's entire urban population of 1.5 million.

Operating companies:
Auto Viação Marechal Ltda
Transporte Coletivo Glória Ltda
Auto Viação Nossa Senhora da Luz Ltda
Empresa Cristo Rei Ltda
Auto Viação Nossa Senhora do Carmo Ltda
Auto Viação Redentor Ltda
Auto Viação Agua Verde Ltda
Auto Viação Curitiba
Auto Viação Mercês
Leblon Transporte de Passageiros Ltda (operating a feeder route from the suburb of Fazenda Rio Grande)
Total staff: 8,425

Bus (contracted)
Passenger journeys: (1991) 323 million
(1992) 320 million
Vehicle-km: (1991) 90 million
(1992) 98 million

Number of routes: Total 277, including 114 conventional, 13 express, 90 feeder, 12 very fast (Ligeirinho)
Route length: 1,217 km, including express routes (reserved corridors) 53.7 km, feeders 294 km, intersuburb 176 km, very fast 200 km

Fleet: 1,206 vehicles, including Mercedes, Fiat, Scania and Volvo (Padron and articulated), also Volvo bi-articulated
Conventional/intersuburb/feeder routes	863
Express routes	71
Very fast	135
Express articulated	108
Express bi-articulated	29

Fare structure: Flat; set by city. Double for executive midibus services and lower for city centre and neighbourhood routes
Fare collection: By driver or prepurchase from roadside ticket machines on main routes
Fares collected on board: 60 per cent
Operational control: Route inspectors
Arrangements for elderly/disabled: Free travel for over-65s/blind persons

Volvo B58 double-articulated bus loading at a 'tube station' (Bill Luke)   **1999**/0038758

Volvo Padron on 'conventional' Route 285   **1997**

Bus priority: 56 km of busways and bus lanes under city pro-public transport policy (see below), and priority at junctions by bus actuations or area traffic control
Operating costs financed by: Fares 100 per cent
New vehicles financed by: Municipality, with fares recovery element

Current situation: An extensive system of reserved busways and bus lanes has been implemented by the city authority under an integrated land use/transport policy favouring public transport dating from 1974 (see *JUTS 1991* for details). Introduced between 1974 and 1981, the 'Integrated Transport Network' expanded the length of express bus exclusive lanes, and patronage rose from 25,000 per day to 997,000 per day by 1993.

The north-south corridor of 26.2 km is operated by a fleet of 168 standard and articulated buses, and caters for 250,000 passengers a day with peak-hour flows of 14,000 passengers/direction. Volvo/Marcopolo bi-articulated buses were introduced in 1995 to cope with increased demand. This corridor serves 56 'stations' and seven terminals. Operation is in the hands of three companies — Glória, Redentor and Cidade Sorriso — all members of the Golin group.

The Boqueirão corridor of 12.4 km has a fleet of 33 bi-articulated buses catering for 146,000 passengers a day and 14,116 in the peak hour, the East 12.2 km corridor has 44 vehicles carrying 6,525 in the peak hour and the West corridor is served by 17 vehicles carrying 46,000 passengers a day.
Developments: Rapid growth of patronage was addressed by the Ligeirinho (very fast) system introduced on two corridors in 1991, and later extended. These routes are served by high-capacity luxury buses running on limited-stop schedules, providing an additional level of service and comfort within the existing network. They serve 'tube stations', which are stylish cylindrical glass shelters with a ticket machine at the single turnstile access and same-level entry to the buses from two side turnstiles. Stations have since been upgraded to allow the bi-articulateds to open three or more doors at once, so reducing dwell time from 23 to 19 sec.

The buses have no steps; instead extending platforms reach out to bridge the gap with the station platform. Loading is about four times faster than at conventional stops. Several new routes and extensions are planned, with a further north-south corridor converted in 1995 (see below).

In a further step to reduce overcrowding, 1992 saw introduction of bi-articulated buses to raise capacity from 160 to 270 passengers.

Onboard computers are being fitted throughout the fleet to control passenger flow and monitor adherence to the timetable.

URBS is now proposing implementation of its integrated system to neighbouring cities, to help solve their problems of traffic congestion and stagnation of public transport.

Trolleybus (planned)
Planning authority: The Research & Urban Planning Institute of Curitiba (IPPUC)
Rua Bom Jesus 669, CEP 8000 Curitiba
Tel: (+55 41) 352 14 14   Fax: (+55 41) 252 66 79
President: Cassio Taniguchi

Current situation: Detailed plans have been prepared by IPPUC, responsible for the municipality's planning, for the introduction of trolleybus operations on a 59 km network, based on the current dedicated radial express bus corridors with central area distribution. Designed to enhance capacity and achieve energy savings, the four corridors at present cater for some 50 per cent of the city's passengers.

The plans envisaged a phased conversion programme beginning with the most congested north-south corridor, with 87 articulated trolleybuses carrying about 235,000 passengers a day. No progress has been reported, and it now appears that the plans have been shelved in favour of further extensions of the Ligeirinho network.

UPDATED

DAKAR
Population: 1.8 million
Public transport: Bus services provided by mixed public-private company, established by government and vehicle manufacturer, and route associations of independent operators in suburban area. Ferry service to offshore island. Suburban rail service

SOTRAC
Société de Transports en Commun du Cap Vert (SOTRAC)
BP 4036, Route de Ouakam Km 4, Dakar, Senegal
Tel: (+221 8) 23 14 43   Fax: (+221 8) 23 33 29
Director General: Babacar Diop
Director of Operations: Ibou Diouf
Staff: 2,560

Current situation: Established in 1971 as a joint company between the government (which now owns 67 per cent) and French vehicle builder Renault (holding 24 per cent); private-sector involvement accounts for 9 per cent.

The operation has struggled to cope with an expanding population in a widely spread urban area split between industrial and commercial centres around the port and Plateau, and a number of dormitory towns up to 20 km from the city centre. Growth of competition from private services has reduced SOTRAC's share to about one-third, with competitors creaming off traffic from the most profitable routes. It is required to carry schoolchildren and soldiers at reduced rates, such traffic amounting to some 10 per cent of the total. Other problems include high absenteeism, poor vehicle availability and corruption.

A period of losses was followed by introduction of state subsidies. A system of three-year 'contract-plans' setting out agreement between SOTRAC and the state came into operation in 1981. This was intended to put finances on a firmer footing and allowed purchase of 50 new buses. In place of subsidy an agreed state contribution is made in advance, with the state also fixing fares levels (unchanged for political reasons, except from flat to zonal, since 1980). But SOTRAC has been so badly run that it has not been able to meet its obligations despite some CFAFr4.4 billion in annual grants and tax exemptions.

Some 80 million passengers a year were being carried at the beginning of the 1990s with a fleet of mainly Saviem S105 buses.

Dakar's commuter train   **1998**/0007905

Minibus
Current situation: Between 2,000 and 3,000 minibuses and other small vehicles are operated by private firms in competition with SOTRAC. These are the so-called 'cars rapides'; they are not licensed to operate in the Plateau (city centre area).

There are no formal unions or co-operatives, but some 85 per cent of operators are loosely affiliated to religious brotherhoods. Only 12 operators own more than 10 minibuses, the largest having a fleet of 100.

Vehicles are Renault SG2 with 25 seats and Mercedes 407D with 32 seats, all operated with driver and conductor. Standees are not permitted. Fares are nominally the same as SOTRAC's, but widespread malpractice means that many journeys cost twice as much as by conventional services.

Between 3,000 and 4,000 taxis operate, carrying up to five passengers.

In Pikine, a satellite town with a population of 600,000 and no surfaced roads, all public transport is by shared taxi. These are still referred to as 'Clandos' (clandestine), although they have been recognised officially for several years.

Ferry
Current situation: The Dakar port authority operates a passenger ferry to the island of Gorée. Journey time is 25 min.

RCFS
Regie des Chemins de Fer du Senegal
PO Box 175, Cité Ballabey, Thies
Tel: (+221) 51 10 13   Fax: (+221) 51 13 93

Passenger journeys: (1996) 5.8 million

Current situation: Diesel-hauled suburban trains marketed as *Le Petit Train Bleu* run to Tiaroye (13 km), Rufisque and Bargny about hourly.

VERIFIED

DHAKA

Population: 1.5 million
Public transport: Bus services provided by national road transport corporation and about 10,000 independent 'autorickshaw' three-wheeler taxis; suburban rail; metro proposals studied

BRTC

Bangladesh Road Transport Corp (BRTC)
Paribahan Bhaban, 21 D I T Avenue, Dhaka, Bangladesh
Tel: (+880 2) 23 50 51
Staff: 3,500

Bus

Passenger journeys: 170 million (annual)
Vehicle-km: 54.2 million (annual)

Route length: 1,200 km
Fleet: 576 vehicles, including Nissan, Isuzu, Ashok Leyland double-deck

One-person operation: None
Fare collection: Payment on board
Fare structure: Stages
Average peak-hour speed: 15.6 km/h

Bangladesh Railway

Bangladesh Railway
Headquarters Building, Chittagong
Tel: (+880 2) 50 01 20

Type of operation: Suburban heavy rail

Current situation: Frequent local diesel trains run between Dhaka and Narayanganj (12 km), metre-gauge.

VERIFIED

DNIPROPETROVSK

Population: 1.2 million
Public transport: Bus and trolleybus/tramway services provided by separate municipal undertakings. Metro

Upravlenie Automobil'novo Transporta

Upravlenie Automobil'novo Transporta
Dnipropetrovsk, Ukraine

Bus

Number of routes: 35
Route length: 330 km
Fleet: 125 vehicles, Ikarus and Liaz 677

Fare collection: Conductors
Average speed: 19 km/h

Dnipromis'k elektrotrans

Dnipromis'k elektrotrans
Prospekt K Marksa 119A, 320038 Dnipropetrovsk
Tel: (+380 56) 242 65 24
Director: V T Karpenko

Current situation: Dnipropetrovsk's public transport reflects the city's better economic situation than other parts of Ukraine. Frequency and maintenance of both tram and trolleybus networks is good, and there is no severe overcrowding as is common in other cities. So-called trolleybus-taxi services have been introduced using YuMZ-T2 and ZIU9 vehicles. They run on all main routes and stop only on request; if necessary, normal service trolleybus must give way.

Tram routes in the city centre, which had been closed during metro construction, were reopened in 1996, along with a major extension into the northern suburbs.

KTM5 car on Route 3 at Ostrouskogo Square, the city's main tram terminus **1998**/0009732

Examples of both Russian KTM8M and locally built Tatra T3Yug cars were delivered in 1996/97, and further orders are planned.

The trolleybus fleet is also being augmented by new YuMZ-T1 and -T2 vehicles from the local Yuzhmash works.

Trolleybus

Number of routes: 22
Route length: 131 km

Fleet: 285 vehicles
ZIU9 (1980/93) 189
ZIU10 (1991/92) 17

YuMZ-T1 (1992/95) 55
YuMZ-T2 (1994/96) 24

One-person operation: All routes
Fare collection: Conductors
Fare evasion control: Roving inspectors check tickets as passengers exit
Average speed: 19 km/h

Tramway

Type of operation: Conventional tramway

Route length: 153 km
Number of lines: 16
Number of stops: 338
Gauge: 1,524 mm

Fare collection: As trolleybus
One-person operation: All routes

Rolling stock: 362 cars
ČKD Tatra T3	M212
KTM5	M113
KTM8	M7
KTM8M (1996/97)	M24
Tatra T3Yug (1996/97)	M6

Metro

Current situation: Line 1 extends to 11.2 km from Oktyabrskaya in the east to Kommunarovskaya in the west, of which the 7.8 km from Kommunaro'skaya to Vokzalnaya (main station) was opened in 1995. Construction of the remaining section with three stations is reported to have ceased. Line 2 would run north-south.

YuMZ-T2 running as trolleybus-taxi at Karl-Marx Prospekt **1998**/0009733

VERIFIED

DONETSK

Population: 1.1 million
Public transport: Bus and trolleybus/tramway services provided by separate municipal undertakings; also private-sector and hired buses; metro under construction

Bus

Number of routes: 66
Fleet: Mainly Ikarus 260/ 280, LIAZ 677, and LAZ 695

Fare collection: Prepurchase, cancellers on board, or cash to conductor

Tramvaino-Trolleibusnoe Upravlenie

Tramvaino-Trolleibusnoe Upravlenie
Donetskaya ul 39, 340086 Donetsk, Ukraine
Tel: (+380 62) 293 46 29
Director: V Belichkov

Current situation: Donetsk has suffered from the problems of its chief industry — coal mining — and since independence has experienced shortages of funding and technical expertise, and considerable unemployment. Operation of trams and trolleybuses is erratic, being plagued by spare parts and electricity supply problems. No new tramcars have been delivered since 1988.

The trolleybus network has expanded from 16 to 22 routes since 1993, and Route 7 runs to the neighbouring town of Makeyevka but does not connect with the system there.

Fare collection: Conductors; monthly ticket valid on trolleybus and tram

Trolleybus
Number of routes: 22

Fleet: About 300 vehicles; some ZIU9s run in double traction

ZIU9 (1980/95)	About 240
ZIU10 (1990/94)	14
YuMZ-T1/T2 (1992/97)	43
LAZ 52523	1

Tramway
Passenger journeys: (1994) 57.6 million

Number of routes: 13
Track length: 131 km

Rolling stock: About 200 cars

ČKD Tatra T3 (1967-87)	M200

VERIFIED   Tatra T3 cars at Donetsk main station   *1997*

DORTMUND

Population: 596,000, area served 680,000
Public transport: Bus and tramway services provided by municipal company, also responsible for other public utilities, operating as part of Rhein-Ruhr Verkehrsverbund, co-ordinating fares and services with regional rail (S-Bahn); people mover

Dortmunder Stadtwerke

Dortmunder Stadtwerke AG
PO Box, 44127 Dortmund, Germany
Tel: (+49 231) 955 00   Fax: (+49 231) 955 33 00
Directors: Harald Heinze
   Karl-Heinz Faust
Transport Division: Dr Erhard Schrameyer
Technical/Transport Manager: Udo Griebsch
Operating Manager: Dipl-Ing Ernst Helmich
Administration Manager: Gerhard Pitt
Personnel: Joachim Basista
Staff: 1,752

Passenger journeys: (All modes)
(1995) 107.1 million
(1996) 106.8 million
(1997) 103.6 million

Fare structure: Zonal; as Rhein-Ruhr (qv), plus various special fares

Operating costs financed by: Fares 30 per cent, other commercial sources 5.3 per cent, subsidy/grants 24.4 per cent including cross-subsidy from gas and water supply, remainder as deficit
Source of subsidy: Region 91.7 per cent, local 8.3 per cent

Current situation: DSW took over operation of DB's Dortmund—Lüdenscheid line (57 km) in May 1998, having been awarded a five-year contract jointly with MVG (the Lüdenscheid transport operator). A joint subsidiary company has been formed to operate the line.

Bus
Passenger journeys: (1995) 45.9 million
Vehicle-km: (1995) 9.6 million
(1996) 11.9 million
(1997) 11.9 million

Number of routes: 46
Route length: (One way) 623 km

Fleet: 143 vehicles, plus 51 contracted

MAN SL200 standard (1983/85)	15
MAN SG242H articulated (1987/88)	33
MAN NG272 low-floor articulated (1989/94)	41
MAN NL202 low-floor (1991/93)	36
Van Hool AG300 articulated (1994)	2
Van Hool A360 low-floor (1996)	6
Mercedes O405N low-floor (1997)	6
MAN NG312 low-floor articulated (1997)	2
Others	2

In peak service: 130

Most intensive service: 10 min
One-person operation: All routes
Fare collection: Prepurchase pass or multitickets with validation and cancelling machines; payment to driver
Fare evasion control: Roving inspectors
Integration with other modes: At passenger's request, bus and tram drivers may summon a taxi to any stop
Average speed: 22 km/h
Operating costs financed by: Fares 32.2 per cent, other commercial sources 5.6 per cent, subsidy/grants 27.2 per cent, remainder as deficit

Tramway/light rail
Type of operation: Conventional tramway; 5 routes upgraded under the Rhein-Ruhr Stadtbahn project with city-centre tunnels

Passenger journeys: (1995) 61.2 million
Vehicle-km: (1995) 7 million
(1996) 7.6 million
(1997) 8 million

Route length: 76.3 km (tramway 51.3 km, light rail 25 km)
   reserved track: 50.6 km
   in tunnel: 13.7 km
Number of routes: 3 tramway, 5 light rail
Number of stops: 215
Gauge: 1,435 mm
Electrification: 600 V DC, overhead

Rolling stock: 114 cars

Duewag N8C articulated (1978/80/82)	M52
Duewag GT8 (1974)	M8
Duewag B6 6-axle articulated (1986/93)	M43
Duewag B8 8-axle articulated (1994)	M11

In peak service: 102
On order: 10 three-section B80 cars from Duewag

Current situation: 12.8 km of new reserved track in operation with 20 stations, comprising Line 80 from Hacheney through city centre, and other short sections. Work completed 1992 on the initial northern section of Line 90, 10.3 km, to be followed by the two southern branches totalling 5.2 km, the first section (0.7 km) of which was opened in 1995. Line 95 and other extensions still in planning stage.
   Under the Rhein-Ruhr Stadtbahn plan, which comprises four stages through to 2000, 10 branches of the tramway network are being linked by three cross-city tunnels to create a light rail system of 41 km, with 59 stations, of which 20 km will be in tunnel. The remainder will be upgraded tramway, though much of the present system is already at or close to Stadtbahn standards (see under Rhein-Ruhr).

Duewag N8C Stadtbahn at Dortmund Wickede station on Route 408 (Norman Griffiths)   *1999*/0043536

Integration with other modes: Services co-ordinated with rail
Arrangements for elderly/disabled: Concessionary fares
Average peak-hour speed: 20 km/h
Operating costs financed by: Fares 46.8 per cent, other commercial sources 4.4 per cent, subsidy/grants 48.8 per cent
Subsidy from: Government and city council (rates and general services fund)

Metro Rail

South African Rail Commuter Corporation Ltd
Durban Metropolitan Area
Private Bag X2, Sunninghill, Johannesburg 2157
Tel: (+27 11) 804 29 00   Fax: (+27 11) 804 38 52

Type of operation: Suburban heavy rail

Passenger journeys: (1994/95) 73.2 million
(1995/96) 77.7 million
(1996/97) 76.3 million

Current situation: Frequent suburban services in the Natal metropolitan area on eight routes totalling 273 km, 1,067 mm gauge, electrified 3 kV DC; up to 22 trains per hour at peak times, every 30 min off-peak. Fares cover 22.8 per cent of operating costs.
Developments: 3 km Inanda extension proposed under Metro Rail's 10-year capital investment programme.

Rolling stock: 825 emu cars
Union Carriage 5M2A (1957 on)   M227 T598

PUTCO

Current situation: See Johannesburg entry for general description of PUTCO. The company's Durban operation

carries commuters on medium and long-distance journeys (20-35 km); some 80 per cent of routes are peak-only.

_____

Private bus/minibus

Current situation: There are extensive and growing operations by private minibuses known locally as 'kombi-taxis', licensed as taxis but operating illegally as shared-taxis and accused of poaching passengers from conventional bus routes, as well as over 100 other private bus operations mostly running from suburban areas, including Kwa Zulu bus service and around 80 small Indian operators.

UPDATED

DÜSSELDORF

Population: 571,000, area served 1.2 million
Public transport: Bus, tramway, light rail and leisure ferry services provided in city and surrounding area by municipal company and suburban rail services by DB, both operating as part of Rhein-Ruhr Verkehrsverbund (VRR), co-ordinating fares and services. See also Rhein-Ruhr entry

Rheinbahn

Rheinische Bahngesellschaft AG
PO Box 104263, 40033 Düsseldorf (Oberkassel), Germany
Tel: (+49 211) 582 01   Fax: (+49 211) 582 19 66
Directors: Dipl-Ing Georg Püttner (Chair)
    Personnel: Walther Hülshoff
    Commercial: Gert Blumenthal
Infrastructure Manager: Frank Dix
Workshops & Technical Manager: Helmut Döpfer
Operations Manager: Volkmar Pfaff
Personnel Manager: Ulrich Reisenhauer
Purchasing Manager: Michael Becker
Staff: 3.533

Passenger journeys: (All modes)
(1995) 196 million
(1996) 196.5 million
(1997) 197.6 million

Operating costs financed by: Fares 57 per cent, subsidy/grants 43 per cent

Bus
Vehicle-km: (1995) 24.7 million
(1996) 25.3 million
(1997) 24.4 million

Number of routes: 71
Route length: 1,065 km

Fleet: 371 vehicles, plus 45 contracted
Mercedes O305/O405 standard	100
Mercedes O405N low-floor	21
Mercedes O305G/O405G articulated	61
MAN SL200/202 standard	60
MAN NL202 low-floor	39

MAN SG242 articulated	35
MAN NG272 low-floor articulated	17
Neoplan N4016NF low-floor	6
Mercedes O405GN low-floor articulated	23
MAN NG312 articulated (1997)	9
In peak service: 352	

Most intensive service: 10 min
One-person operation: All routes
Fare collection: Prepurchase tickets or pass with validation and cancelling machines; payment to driver
Fare structure: Zonal; prepurchase multiride tickets, weekly and monthly passes, Jobticket (see below)
Fares collected on board: 16 per cent
Fare evasion control: Roving inspectors
Arrangements for elderly/disabled: Free travel for disabled, reimbursed by government
Operational control: Route inspectors/mobile radio
Average peak-hour speed: 19 km/h

Tramway/light rail
Type of operation: Stadtbahn and conventional tramway

Car-km: (1995) Tram 12 million, LRT 9.4 million
(1996) Tram 11.9 million, LRT 9.3 million
(1997) Tram 11.5 million, LRT 9.3 million

Route length: Tramway 82.2 km, LRT 64.2 km (in tunnel 6 km)
Number of lines: 17 (LRT 3, tram 14)

Current situation: Plans envisage a 4-line LRT network of some 68 km, of which 15 km will be in tunnel. Under the Rhein-Ruhr Stadtbahn scheme, the existing tramway is being upgraded and transformed. Tunnels now extend to 6 km and are used by five routes, including the interurbans to Neuss, Krefeld and Duisburg. At Hbf there is interchange with the S-Bahn. Restaurant facilities are available on the interurban services to Krefeld and Duisburg.
Developments: Construction of east-west light rail line from Grafenberg to Bilk (7.4 km), with a tunnel in the city centre, which was approved in 1991 for opening in 1994/96, will not now be ready before 2001. In January 1997, construction started on the 1.8 km section from Oberbilcer Markt to Siegburger Strasse.

In June 1997, the city council in neighbouring Neuss voted to remove the tramway (operated by RBG) from the pedestrian zone in the city centre. It is planned to reroute Line 709 into the parallel Promenadenstrasse, for 2003 completion. The Neuss terminus and routeing of Line U75 will also be affected.

Conversion of two DB routes to Stadtbahn operation proposed (see below).

Rolling stock: 352 cars
Duewag 4-axle (1955/66)	T62
Duewag GT6 6-axle articulated (1956/61)	M25
Duewag GT8 8-axle articulated (1958/69) some ex-GT6	M56
Duewag GT8S 8-axle articulated (1974/75)	M29
Duewag GT8SU 8-axle articulated (1973/75)	M38
Duewag B80D 6-axle articulated Stadtbahn (1981/93)	M104
Duewag NGT6D low-floor articulated	M37
On order: 18 cars from Duewag, with options for a further 68

Ferry
Current situation: Four boats operate leisure services on the Rhein.

Rhein-Bus
Rhein-Bus Verkehrsbetriebe GmbH
Hildener Strasse 72, 40549 Düsseldorf
Tel: (+49 211) 97 15 00   Fax: (+49 211) 971 50 50

Current situation: This low-cost bus company was formed as a joint venture between Rheinbahn and independent operator Taeter of Aachen. Rhein-Bus operates services under contract to Rheinbahn. Fleet includes Volvo/Steyr buses.

DB
Deutsche Bahn AG

Type of operation: Regional metro (S-Bahn)

Current situation: Düsseldorf is served by four lines of the Rhein-Ruhr S-Bahn (see under Rhein-Ruhr), and by other (non-S-Bahn) suburban services of DB.

Regio-Bahn
Regionale Bahngesellschaft Kaarst-Neuss-Düsseldorf-Erkrath-Mettmann mbH

Current situation: Founded by various local authorities, this company will take over operation from DB of the Kaarst—Neuss and Düsseldorf—Mettmann lines (total 34.2 km, 18 stations) starting in May 1999. Operation will be contracted to Deutsche Eisenbahn Gesellschaft (DEG).

Rolling stock: 8 dmus on order

Regional bus
Current situation: Regional bus services provided by Busverkehr Rheinland (HBVR), an associated company of DB. For full details see under Rhein-Ruhr entry.

Duewag low-floor cars with Rheinbahn

UPDATED

EDINBURGH

Population: 450,000
Public transport: Most bus services provided by company owned by local councils, with some by private operators. Local rail services

Lothian Region Transport

Lothian Region Transport plc
1-4 Shrub Place, Edinburgh EH7 4PA, Scotland
Tel: (+44 131) 554 44 94   Fax: (+44 131) 554 60 38
Chairman: Alexander Kitson
Managing Director: Pilmar Smith
Commercial Manager: George B Kirk
Staff: 1,740

Current situation: Following abolition of Lothian Regional Council in 1996, LRT is 91 per cent owned by the new City of Edinburgh Council. The company operates commercial services and submits competitive tenders for any contracted operations. A comprehensive city route network is supplemented by routes extending into surrounding towns.
Developments: Lothian Region Transport is taking five Alexander ALX400s.

Bus

Passenger journeys: (1992/93) 97.8 million
(1995/96) 90.3 million
(1996/97) 90.6 million
Vehicle-km: (1992/93) 32.1 million
(1995/96) 21.2 million
(1996/97) 20.4 million

Number of routes: 78
Route length: 1,370 km
On priority right-of-way: 10 km

Fleet: 596 vehicles

Leyland/Atlantean/Alexander double-deck	66
Leyland Olympian/ECW double-deck	127
Leyland Olympian/Alexander double-deck	200
Volvo Olympian/Alexander double-deck	101
Leyland National single-deck	20
Leyland Lynx single-deck	12
Dennis Dart single-deck	12
Volvo B10L low-floor single-deck	1
Leyland Atlantean open-top double-deck	30
Coaches	27
In peak service: 424	

New vehicles required each year: 34 double-deck

Most intensive service: 6 min (2-3 min on combined routes)
One-person operation: All routes
Fare collection: Wayfarer electronic machines with farebox on board; passes and season tickets
Fare structure: Stage; 4-week, 1-week and annual 'Rida Cards'; flat fare on all-night buses, 1-day tickets
Fares collected on board: 54 per cent
Fare evasion control: Inspectors
Operational control: Patrol inspectors in vans/mobile radio
Average peak-hour speed: In mixed traffic, 15.6 km/h
Operating costs financed by: Fares 90 per cent, other commercial sources 10 per cent

Airport express services of LRT and Guide Friday (behind) compete at the Waverley station bus stand (Andrew Jarosz) **1999**/0043542

Subsidy from: Company operates fully commercially with specific support from council's rate fund for any contracted services won by tender

SMT

Lowland Omnibuses Ltd
14-16 Eskbank Road, Dalkeith, Midlothian EH22 1HH
Tel: (+44 131) 663 19 45   Fax: (+44 131) 660 39 89

Bus (Operations in Lothian area only)
Passenger journeys: (1991) 38 million
(1992) 36.8 million
(1993) 36.4 million
Vehicle-km: (1991) 26.6 million
(1992) 26.4 million
(1993) 26.4 million

Fleet: 168 buses

Single-deck	44
Double-deck	60
Coaches	6
Minibuses	58

Current situation: Eastern Scottish (now Lowland) was purchased from the Scottish Bus Group in 1990 by its workforce and became a subsidiary of FirstGroup in 1995. It operates a substantial proportion of the bus services in the Lothian area, including Edinburgh. There is a network of services to surrounding towns including commuter express workings.

Management has been merged with the FirstGroup subsidiary Lowland Scottish, and SMT is only used as a brand-name to denote Lothian region operations.

The first new buses for the SMT fleet for over 10 years have been delivered. They are 21 Volvo Olympians with Alexander Royale bodywork and are operating on a cross-city route in Edinburgh which uses Edinburgh's new priority Greenway route between Corstorphine and the city centre.

Other operators

Current situation: Guide Friday of Stratford on Avon has established a base in the city and challenges LRT on sightseeing services and the Airport Express route. Stagecoach Fife works some services from towns across the Forth bridge. First Midland and First Lowland Scottish operate services from the south and west.

ScotRail

ScotRail Railways Ltd
Caledonian Chambers, 87 Union Street, Glasgow G1 3TA
Tel: (+44 141) 332 98 11   Fax: (+44 141) 335 31 25

Type of operation: Local rail

Current situation: Hourly/half-hourly diesel services provided on several routes, plus electric trains to North Berwick (36 km).
Developments: Proposed reopening of the Edinburgh south suburban loop line to passenger services has been problematic on account of track capacity constraints at Edinburgh's Waverley station. However, in 1997 reopening was proposed of a short freight line to Millerhill in the southeast to create a cross-city route with the existing Bathgate service to the west. Four new stations are planned, along with a 10 km extension from Millerhill to Gorebridge utilising former railway alignment.

Class 170 Turbostar trains are being introduced on the Glasgow to Edinburgh line with 15 minute interval service.

Light rail/busway (planned)

Planning authority: City of Edinburgh Council
1 Cockburn Street, Edinburgh EH1 1ZL
Tel: (+44 131) 529 35 98   Fax: (+44 131) 469 37 77
Director, City Development: Dr George McL Hazel

Alexander-bodied Volvo Olympian picks up on Edinburgh's cobbled Royal Mile (Andrew Jarosz)
1999/0043544

Plaxton-bodied Dennis Dart of SMT on one of Edinburgh's Greenway bus priority lanes on the Balerno service (Andrew Jarosz) **1999**/0043543

Current situation: Development of north-south and east-west light rapid transit routes remains the council's long-term aim, but these cannot be afforded at present. In addition, a line linking the city centre with Leith and Newhaven has been proposed by a private company, the Edinburgh Tram Company.

Approval has been given for the City of Edinburgh Rapid Transit (CERT) project, which is a bus-based scheme linking park-and-ride sites, the airport and west Edinburgh with the city centre, and including a 9 km busway. The scheme has been developed by the council as a private finance initiative project, and is expected to start operations in 2000.

The Greenways bus priority scheme started in 1997 on the A8 and A900 roads, adding 26 km of bus lanes to the city's network. A further three routes are expected to be in operation in the second half of 1999. Priority will be extended in the city centre to both Princes Street, where non-bus traffic is already banned in the eastbound direction, and Leith Walk.

UPDATED

EDMONTON

Population: 637,000
Public transport: Bus, trolleybus and light rail services operated by municipal undertaking with two small suburban bus systems

Edmonton Transit System

Edmonton Transit System
PO Box 2610, Edmonton, Alberta T5J 3R5, Canada
Tel: (+1 403) 496 57 40   Fax: (+1 403) 496 42 44
Manager of Transit: Wayne Mandryk
Director, LRT: L J McLachlan
General Supervisor, Security & Risk Management:
  D Kowalchute
Director, Community Relations: L Stewart
Director, Service Development: K Koropeski
Director, Business Development: P Waisman
Director, Ferrier Bus Operations: J Sirovyak
Director, Mitchell Bus Operations: D Geake
Director, Westwood Bus Operations: W Broadhead
Director, Custom Transportation: D Nowicki
Staff: 1,478

Current situation: Edmonton's public transport operation functions as a branch of the municipal transportation and streets department, reporting to the general manager. Bus services have been reshaped to feed the light rail line, but the route is poorly placed in relation to several of the area's major traffic generators.

'Stop Request' system operates, under which buses will stop for passengers to alight at any safe location on the regular route after 18.30.

Developments: Trolleybus operation has experienced problems related to high costs and inefficiency, and the system's future had been in doubt. But in 1994 it was decided to spend an additional C$6.7 million on a four-year programme to upgrade the infrastructure.

A new service strategy comprising Base and Community networks was implemented in 1997.

An experimental commuter bus service began in 1998 between Leduc and Edmonton. Leduc City Council approved a pilot project to run the bus service. A stop is also to be made to serve the community of Nisku. Greyhound Lines of Canada also operates five round trips every day between Leduc and Edmonton but with limited stops.

Passenger journeys: (All modes)
(1995) 37.1 million
(1996) 38.7 million
(1997) 38.9 million

Operating costs financed by: Fares 43 per cent, other commercial sources 5.5 per cent, tax levy 51.5 per cent
Subsidy from: Disabled transport grants from Province of Alberta

Bus and trolleybus
Vehicle-km: (1995) 29.4 million
(1996) 32.1 million
(1997) 28.9 million

Number of routes: Bus 130, trolleybus 7
Route length: Bus 2,593 km, trolleybus 200 km

Fleet: 657 buses, 78 trolleybuses	
GMC	488
Flyer	12
New Flyer low-floor (1993/94)	139
Community buses	18
GMC-Brown Boveri (1981/82) trolleybuses	78
In peak service: 586	

Most intensive service: 7-8 min
One-person operation: All routes
Fare collection: Exact fare payment to farebox; prepurchase multitickets or monthly pass
Fare structure: Flat; monthly passes, 10-journey discount multitickets, free 90 min transfers; ET tickets and passes valid on suburban operators' buses within city limits
Arrangements for elderly/disabled: Discount annual senior passes. Door-to-door Disabled Adult Transportation System (DATS) operated with special vehicles; 139 low-floor buses available for service on 22 routes with kneeling capability, hydraulic ramp and two wheelchair positions
Integration with other modes: Common fare for buses and LRT, free transfers apply; free central area rides on LRT 09.00-15.00; cycle racks used on one route since 1995

Light rail
Type of operation: Light rail, initial route opened 1978

Car-km: (1995) 2.5 million
(1996) 2.7 million
(1997) 2.6 million

Route length: 13.7 km
Number of lines: 1
Number of stations: 10
Gauge: 1,435 mm
Tunnel: Cut-and-cover and bored
Electrification: 600 V DC, overhead

Service: 5 min
First/last car: 05.30/01.31
Integration with other modes: Common fare systems on bus and LRT; Jasper Avenue section in city centre fare free 09.00-15.00 weekdays and 09.00-18.00 Saturdays; cycles carried off-peak.

Rolling stock: 37 articulated cars	
Duewag/Siemens (1978)	M14
Duewag/Siemens (1979)	M3
Duewag/Siemens (1982)	M20
In peak service: 27	

Current situation: Proposed extensions put on indefinite hold in 1993, but the next section likely to be built is the short extension to Health Sciences.

Other operators
Current situation: Operators in the adjacent localities of St Albert and Sherwood Park run services through to downtown Edmonton, and issue passes valid on ET services. These are St Albert Transit (29 vehicles) and Strathcona County Public Transit (31 vehicles).

UPDATED

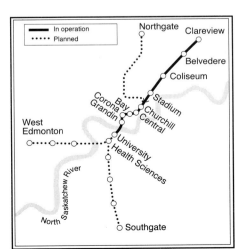

Edmonton's light rail system

Trolleybus on Route 42 at 105th Street Bridge

EREVAN

Population: 1 million
Public transport: Bus and trolleybus/tramway services operated by separate authorities; metro

Upravlenie Automobil'novo Transporta

Upravlenie Automobil'novo Transporta
Erevan, Armenia

Bus

Passenger journeys: 110 million (annual)

Route length: 500 km
Fleet: 350 vehicles

One-person operation: All routes
Fare collection: Farebox or prepurchase with cancellation
Fare structure: Flat

Tramvaino-Trolleibusnoe Upravlenie

Tramvaino-Trolleibusnoe Upravlenie
Prospekt Ordzhonikidze 18, 375023 Erevan
Tel: (+374 2) 52 79 79

Trolleybus

Passenger journeys: 100 million (annual)

Route length: 170 km
Fleet: 320 vehicles, including Uritsky and Škoda

One-person operation: All routes
Fare collection: By conductors
Fare structure: Flat

Tramway

Rolling stock: 150 cars

ČKD Tatra KTM5	M50
RVZ6	M100

Erevan Metro

Erevan Metro
76 Marshal Bagramanian Avenue, Erevan 375033
Tel: (+374 2) 27 45 43   Fax: (+374 2) 15 13 95
General Manager: Hrant Beglarian
Chief Engineer: Pailak Yayloyan
Staff: 1,198

Type of operation: Full metro, initial route opened 1981

Passenger journeys: (1992) 52.3 million
(1993) 58.6 million
(1995) 36 million

Route length: 10.5 km
Number of lines: 1
Number of stations: 9
Gauge: 1,520 mm
Track: 50 kg/m rail on timber or concrete sleepers
Max gradient: 4%
Minimum curve radius: 250 m
Tunnel: Bored and cut-and-cover
Electrification: 825 V, third rail

Service: Peak 3½ min, off-peak 5 min
First/last train: 06.00/24.00
Fare structure: Flat
Fare collection: Manual
Operating costs financed by: Fares 47.6 per cent, government subsidy 52.4 per cent

Rolling stock: 70 cars

81-M/81-N	M70

Current situation: First line opened 1981 linking the principal industrial area at Druzhba with Sasuntsi David through the city centre, and extended 1986. Further 3.9 km from Barekamutian to Achapniak under construction, though delayed following earthquake damage and other problems. The initial portion of Line 2 from Hanrapetutian Hraparak to Yeraz is at the planning stage.

VERIFIED

Erevan metro

Skoda trolleybus of TTU in central Erevan   *1998*/0010051

ESSEN

Population: 611,000, area served 652,000
Public transport: Bus, Stadtbahn, tramway and bus/guided bus services operated by municipal company and suburban rail and bus services by DB, both operating as part of Rhein-Ruhr Verkehrsverbund (qv) co-ordinating fares and services. Tramway sections being upgraded as part of Rhein-Ruhr Stadtbahn. See also under Rhein-Ruhr

EVAG

Essener Verkehrs-AG
Zweigertstrasse 34, 45115 Essen, Germany
Tel: (+49 201) 82 60   Fax: (+49 201) 826 10 00
Directors: Wolfgang Meyer
    Johannes Werner Schmidt
    Falkobert Obst
Operations Manager: Hans Ahlbrecht
Marketing Manager: Helmut Kanand
Personnel Manager: Wolfgang Daub
Infrastructure Manager: Michael Mertin
Staff: 2,274

Passenger journeys: (All modes)
(1995) 106 million
(1996) 105.5 million
(1997) 106.7 million

Duewag Stadtbahn M car in Essen Dinnendahlstrasse on Route 109 (Norman Griffiths)   *1999*/0043545

Operating costs financed by: Fares 47 per cent, other commercial sources 10 per cent, subsidy/grants 43 per cent

Subsidy from: Federal government and state Nordrhein-Westfalen for tunnel construction; from state and city for operations

Current situation: Changing urban activity and travel patterns in the Rhein-Ruhr conurbation have led to development of the interurban Stadtbahn upgraded from existing tramways under the Rhein-Ruhr Verkehrsverbund. EVAG has also pursued a number of its own technical and operational developments to enhance local services. Three Stadtbahn lines have been developed, one in conjunction with the neighbouring undertaking in Mülheim. The second is under way in conjunction with neighbouring undertaking of Bochum-Gelsenkirchen.

With funding from the Federal Ministry of Research & Technology EVAG has introduced an innovative guided bus system, linked to the operation of dual-mode trolleybus/diesel routes using a fleet of 18 'Duobuses'; 8.9 km of guided busway is in operation. In 1997 EVAG signed a co-operation agreement with the neighbouring municipal operators of Mülheim and Oberhausen.

Bus

Vehicle-km: (1995) 14.8 million
(1996) 14.9 million
(1997) 15.2 million

Number of routes: 46
Route length: (One way) 316 km

Fleet: 248 vehicles

Mercedes O405 standard (1984/85/87)	33
Mercedes O405GTD articulated duobus (1986/87)	18
Mercedes O405N low-floor (1990/96)	76
Mercedes O405GN low-floor articulated (1993/97)	63
MAN NL202 low-floor (1993/97)	37
MAN NG272 articulated (1998)	21

Most intensive service: 5 min
One-person operation: All services
Fare collection: By driver or prepurchase at vending machines and from newspaper kiosks; cancelling equipment on all vehicles
Fare structure: Zonal with multiride tickets and weekly and monthly passes standardised under Rhein-Ruhr Verkehrsverbund
Fares collected on board: 8 per cent
Fare evasion control: Roving inspectors
Integration with other modes: Integrated transit system for all modes in Rhein-Ruhr Verkehrsverbund
Operational control: Mobile radio; computer-aided control system under implementation

Arrangements for elderly/disabled: Free travel for disabled, reimbursed by government; most buses are low-floor vehicles
Average distance between stops: 542 m
Average peak-hour speed: On separate right-of-way 25-35 km/h; in mixed traffic, 20 km/h
New vehicles financed by: 30-40 per cent from state funds

Developments: New express bus route opened betweeen Essen and Bottrop in October 1997, which led to a 20 per cent increase in passengers on this route. Journey time was reduced by 10 minutes or 25 per cent.

Guided bus/duobus
Current situation: See *JUTS 1989* for history and development.

Joint running with trams through an existing city-centre tunnel was suspended in 1995 and has not yet resumed.

Fleet: 18 Daimler-Benz O405GTD articulated duobuses with dual propulsion (diesel engine with automatic transmission plus electric traction motor with GTO chopper control). These buses are equipped for guideway operation and fitted with off-side doors to serve island platforms on the tunnel sections. The vehicles currently operate in diesel mode only.

Tramway/light rail
Type of operation: Light rail (U-Stadtbahn), conventional tramway

Car-km: (1995) Tram 5.8 million, Stadtbahn 1.7 million
(1996) Tram 5.8 million, Stadtbahn 1.8 million
(1997) Tram 5.8 million, Stadtbahn 1.8 million

Route length: 73.47 km
U-Stadtbahn (1,435 mm gauge): 13.9 km (in tunnel 5.3 km, segregated 4.7 km, on street 1.8 km)
(mixed gauge): 1.9 km (in tunnel)
Tramway (1,000 mm gauge): 59.5 km (in tunnel 5.1 km, segregated 5 km, on street 47.5 km)
Number of lines: 3 LRT, 9 tramway
Gauge: U-Stadtbahn 1,435 mm; tramway 1,000 mm
Track: S49, Ri59, Ri59N, Ri60, Ri60N rail, conventional sleepers on ballast
Tunnel: Cut-and-cover; bored single track; bored stations
Electrification: 750 V DC, overhead

First/last car: 04.30/00.15
Fare collection: Cancelling equipment on all cars
Fare evasion control: Travelling inspectors
One-person operation: All services
Average speed: Stadtbahn 28 km/h; tramway 20.4 km/h
Average distance between stops: Stadtbahn 683 m, tramway 548 m

Rolling stock: 141 cars; also operates and maintains 7 B80 LRVs owned by Mülheim for use on joint routes
Standard-gauge

Duewag LRV B80 (1976/85)	M24
LHB P86 ex-London Docklands (1986/89)	M21

Metre-gauge

Duewag M8S 8-axle articulated (1975/76)	M19
Duewag M8C 8-axle articulated (1979/90)	M57
Duewag 8-axle articulated (1960/66)	M20

On order: An order for 12 metre-gauge low-floor trams was placed in 1997 with DWA/Adtranz for delivery by 1999/2001

Current situation: Essen's Stadtbahn lines are part of the much larger Rhein-Ruhr (qv) development. Network of 58 km planned, of which 12.5 km will be underground. Tunnel sections (1.5 km) to Westendstrasse opened in 1991, further section of U17 between Karlsplatz and Altenessen (2.5 km) opened in 1998. Metre-gauge operation beyond Altenessen to Gelsenkirchen-Horst ceased in June 1998, pending conversion of the remainder of the route to standard-gauge; approximately 2.5 km is under construction and another 4 km on surface is planned for 2001.

There is joint operation of Stadtbahn Line U18 to Mülheim, and tram routes to Gelsenkirchen and Mülheim.
Developments: EVAG is evaluating proposals to take over and operate as Stadtbahn a former Krupp industrial railway to the north of the city. This would serve new industrial and residential areas and a park-and-ride.

Introduction of tram priority at traffic lights in progress, along with computerised data transmission radio. Job creation programme for information and passenger service personnel under way at major stations.

A computerised passenger information system FIS (*Fahrgast Informations System*) has been introduced experimentally on the Stadtbahn route in northern Essen. It provides information on real-time arrivals, transfer possibilities, delays and breakdowns.

DB
Deutsche Bahn AG, Geschäftsbereich Nahverkehr
Regionalbereich Rhein-Ruhr
Am Hauptbahnhof 3, 45127 Essen
Tel: (+49 201) 182 33 30   Fax: (+49 201) 182 44 75
Manager: Volker Theis

Type of operation: Regional metro (S-Bahn)

Current situation: Essen is served by Lines S1, S3 and S6 of the Rhein-Ruhr S-Bahn (see under Rhein-Ruhr), and by other DB suburban services. DB associated company Busverkehr Rheinland (BVR) provides some suburban bus services.

UPDATED

FLORENCE
Population: 393,000, region 604,000
Public transport: Bus services provided by undertaking belonging to consortium of local authorities serving region as well as city, with some additional privately owned regional services. Suburban services by state railway (FS). Light rail and metro proposed

ATAF
Azienda Trasporti Area Fiorentina (ATAF)
CP 4140, Viale dei Mille 115, 50131 Florence, Italy
Tel: (+39 055) 565 01   Fax: (+39 055) 565 02 09
e-mail: talluri@ataf.fi.it
Administrative Director: Piero Lullia
Lines Director: Piero Sassoli
Technical Director: Massimo Ruini
Staff: 1,416

Developments: There are now four 'Blue Line' routes operated by Gulliver electric minibuses serving the historic city centre. Route 16 (FS—Scandicci) has joined the airport bus (Route 62) as ATAF's second 'direct' service running on reserved right-of-way and with limited stops. ATAF also operates dial-a-bus in some parts of the city, with both the stop and time specified by the caller.

A fleet of 50 low-floor buses has been delivered, and trials with gas-powered buses were made in 1997.

ATAF's legal status changed in 1996, bringing the undertaking greater autonomy and more responsibility for

its financial performance. ATAF now has a contract with the Comune (city council) for provision of service.

Bus
Passenger journeys: (1994) 72 million
(1995) 76.4 million
(1997) 77.3 million
Vehicle-km: (1994) 19.1 million
(1995) 19.2 million
(1997) 19.8 million

Number of routes: 69
Route length: 630 km
On priority right-of-way: 24 km

Fleet: 506 vehicles

Fiat, Menarini and Inbus standard	301
Fiat, Menarini and Inbus low-floor	35
Fiat 412 double-deck	1
Fiat 470.18.24 and Iveco articulated	51
Fiat 470.18.24 and Iveco articulated low-floor	51
Various small/minibuses	33
Technobus electric minibuses	20
Iveco CNG low-floor (1996)	14

In peak service: 382
On order: 50 buses a year

Most intensive service: 2 min
One-person operation: All single-deck routes
Fare collection: Coin to farebox or prepurchase passes with cancelling machine on bus

ATAF's Technobus electric low-floor bus in the centre of Florence   **1999**/0038775

Fare structure: Mainly flat; time-tickets, multitickets, monthly passes
Fare evasion control: Roving inspectors
Integration with other modes: Several lines terminate at rail stations
Operational control: Mobile radio
Arrangements for elderly/disabled: Half and free fares
Average distance between stops: 292 m

Average peak-hour speed: 15.9 km/h
Operating costs financed by: Fares 39.8 per cent, other commercial sources 3.3 per cent, subsidy/grants 56.9 per cent
Subsidy from: National government 88 per cent, local taxes 12 per cent
New vehicles financed by: National transport fund and local authorities

FS

Italian Railways (FS), Firenze Division

Type of operation: Suburban heavy rail

Current situation: Trains run frequently between Florence and Pisa airport, Pistoia and Arezzo; irregular services on other routes. Electrified 3 kV DC, 1,435 mm gauge.
Developments: Track quadrupling is to be undertaken between Florence and both Prato and Empoli to permit segregation of suburban and long-distance services. When completed, trains will run every 10/20 min to Prato, and 20/30 min to Empoli and Pisa airport. The Faentina line is also to be rehabilitated.

An integrated ticketing system known as the Orange Card has been introduced experimentally in daily, weekly and monthly versions; it can be used on FS, ATAF and Co-operativa Autolinee Pratesi buses.

ATAF's Iveco CNG low-floor bus, the first of 14   *1999*/0038774

Light rail (proposed)
Current situation: Feasibility studies have made for a proposed two-line light rail system. Line A would link Piazza Magrini with the FS suburban station at Varlungo (17 km, 27 stations), while Line B runs from Scandicci to Bagno a Ripoli (15 km, 22 stations).

Construction of part of Line B, from Scandicci to Sta Maria Novella (7.2 km, 15 stops), was approved by the city council in 1994. A consortium known as Tranvia Fiorentina has been formed to build the line, which could open in 2000.

The scheme was allocated Lit94 billion (about 50 per cent of the total cost) by the government in the 1996 finance bill.

UPDATED

FORTALEZA

Population: 1.8 million
Public transport: Bus services provided by municipal operator and 22 private companies. Regional metro system being developed from suburban rail lines

CTC

Supervised by: Secretaria de Transporte da Prefeitura Municipal de Fortaleza
Fortaleza, Brazil

Passenger journeys: (1994) 300 million
Vehicle-km: (1994) 93.4 million

Current situation: Bus services are co-ordinated by the Secretaria de Transporte which allocates concessions to private operators.

The municipal company CTC and 22 private operators run about 150 routes using 1,500 vehicles whose average age is 4 years. Flat fare, 50 per cent discount for students.
Developments: Swipe-card readers have been installed on buses for use with students' identity cards. This has

reduced fraud considerably, with the number of 'students' using the inter-campus route operated by São José de Ribamar having fallen from 60 to 40 per cent of the total. The down-side is increased fraud by conductors, who charge full fare to passengers but record them as students using forged or stolen passes. All Fortaleza area buses are now equipped with card-readers.

Metrofor

Autarquia de Regiao Metropolitana de Fortaleza
Rua Jose Laurenco, Aldeota, Fortaleza 60000
Tel: (+55 85) 212 40 34

Type of operation: Suburban heavy rail

Passenger journeys: (1994) 35,000 daily
(1995) 7.6 million

Current situation: Two separate metre-gauge routes (43 km, 17 stations) have been upgraded and resignalled to form the first stage of a commuter railway. Fares cover 18 per cent of operating costs.

Developments: Metrofor, the local branch of CBTU, was transferred to Ceará state government control at the beginning of 1998. The move has triggered reactivation of a US$268 million loan from Japan's Eximbank, which had been frozen since 1992. The funds will cover track-doubling and electrification of the 23 km southern line, together with provision of nine new stations, and construction of a 3.5 km elevated link between the two lines. A turnkey order worth US$87 million has been won by Alstom for the supply of 10 four-car trainsets and the signalling system. The overall system will be manufactured by Alstom's factories in São Paulo, with the traction equipment supplied by Alstom's plant in Tarbes, France. Alstom is also responsible for the management of the project and the integration and installation of the complete electrical and mechanical system. With cross-city service established, by 2001 some 420,000 daily journeys are expected.

Rolling stock: 6 diesel locomotives, 45 coaches

UPDATED

FORT WORTH

Population: 475,000
Public transport: Bus services managed under contract for Regional Transit Authority. Privately operated light rail line

The T

Fort Worth Transportation Authority
PO Box 1477, 2304 Pine Street, Fort Worth, Texas 76101, USA
Tel: (+1 817) 871 62 21   Fax: (+1 817) 871 62 17
Managed by McDonald Transit Associates Inc
Chair: Walker C Friedman
General Manager: John P Bartosiewicz
Assistant General Manager: Anthony V Johnson
Manager of Transportation: David Harris
Manager of Development: Nancy Amos
Staff: 377

Current situation: In 1983 responsibility for the former City Transit Service of Fort Worth (Citran) passed to a new Regional Transportation Authority, created by a vote which also authorised the raising of dedicated funds from a ¼ per cent sales tax; this was increased to ½ per cent in 1989. Lake Worth, Richland Hills and Blue Mound joined the RTA area in 1992. The RTA makes an annual payment to the cities' funds for improvements to streets served by bus routes.

Flxible Metro bus of The T

A gradual expansion of services has taken place over the past few years. Central area services are fares-free. A ride-sharing programme operates vanpools. In 1992 The T inaugurated a programme for conversion of all buses to CNG power by 1998.

Developments: A five-year plan approved in 1996 emphasised the importance of the planned Railtran commuter rail service between Fort Worth and Dallas, a project jointly managed by the two cities. Trains are due to start operations in 1999. See Dallas entry for details.

Other aspects of the plan cover fleet renewal and expansion, provision of increased express service and expansion of vanpooling.

Bus
Passenger boardings: (1992) 4.3 million
(1993) 4.7 million
(1995) 6 million
Vehicle-km: (1992) 9.5 million
(1993) 10.4 million
(1995) 9.8 million

Number of routes: 37
Route length: 570 km

Fleet: 184 vehicles

Flxible Metro (1986)	35
Flxible Metro (1987)	33
Flxible Metro (1990)	7
Flxible Metro (1991)	9
Flxible Metro (1992)	32
Flxible Metro (1995)	13
MCI coach (1984)	3
MCI coach (1990)	2
Vans/minibuses (disabled service)	33

Champion Route (1994)	12
Eldorado Route (1996)	5
In peak service: 116	

Most intensive service: 15 min
One-person operation: All services
Fare collection: Registering farebox on vehicle, tokens or passes
Fare structure: Exact flat fare; monthly passes, tokens; free transfers; free central area travel
Fare evasion control: Driver supervision
Operational control: Route inspectors/mobile radio
Arrangements for elderly/disabled: On-demand minibus service with 32 vehicles carried 269,000 passengers in 1995
Average peak-hour speed: 13 km/h
Bus priority: Peak-hour bus lanes on some inner radial routes
Integration with other modes: 21 park-and-ride sites, 13 served by special express routes; ride-sharing/vanpools promoted; special service to airport with vans
Operating costs financed by: Fares and other commercial sources 14.8 per cent, FTA subsidy/grants 16 per cent, state and local sales tax 69.3 per cent

New vehicles financed by: FTA 80 per cent, 20 per cent FWTA funds (sales tax)

Tandy
Tandy Center Subway
100 One Tandy Center, Fort Worth, Texas 76102
Tel: (+1 817) 336 52 48   Fax: (+1 817) 338 23 88
General Manager: Jim Lincecum
Vice President, Operations: Jim Giese

Type of operation: Light rail

Passenger journeys: (Annual) 1.5 million

Current situation: Tandy Corp operates a 1.6 km light rail line, partly underground, to link its downtown headquarters building and department store with a 3,000-vehicle parking lot. Free service is provided.

Rolling stock: 8 cars

PCC (rebuilt 1977/78)	M8

VERIFIED

FRANKFURT AM MAIN
Population: 649,000; RMV area 5 million
Public transport: Bus, tramway and Stadtbahn (light rail) services provided by municipal company operating as part of Rhein-Main Verkehrsverbund (RMV) co-ordinating fares and services with regional bus and rail services provided by DB and other operators

RMV
Rhein-Main Verkehrsverbund GmbH (RMV)
Am Kreishaus 1-5, 65719 Hofheim, Germany
Tel: (+49 6192) 20 15 15   Fax: (+49 6192) 20 16 23
www: www.rmv.de
Director: Volker Sparmann
Deputy Director: Uwe Stindt
Corporate Manager: Herbert Jack
Traffic Planning Manager: Gerhard Stanek
Marketing Manager: Hansjörg Rörich

Passenger boardings: (All modes)
(1994) 223.5 million (FVV figure)
(1995) 520 million
(1996) 550 million

Current situation: The regional transit authority RMV was set up in 1994; it became operational in 1995 as successor to Frankfurter Verkehrsverbund (FVV). It is the largest regional transit authority in Germany, covering an area of 14,000 km² with a population of 4.8 million. Extending from Marburg in the north to Erbach in the south and from Limburg in the west to Fulda in the east, the area includes the cities of Darmstadt, Frankfurt, Offenbach and Wiesbaden, seven other cities and 15 rural authorities.

RMV is responsible for implementation of decisions taken by politicians at state, county or city level, and for management of services which are provided by both public and private operators. It is mainly aimed at regional transit, while purely local services remain the responsibility of cities and counties. Tickets are interavailable. An integrated fixed-interval rail timetable was implemented in 1995, with S-Bahn trains running every 15 min at peak periods and 30 min off-peak, and regional trains every 30 or 60 min.

While FVV was an association of transport operators, RMV is formed by local authorities and buys in services from existing operators. RMV embraces 50 rail routes and 250 bus routes (8,009 km), served by 4,100 buses run by 140 operators. There are 350 ticket sales outlets.

In 1993, there were 3.9 million daily journeys made in the RMV area and modal split was 14 per cent by public transport, 23 per cent walking/cycling and 63 per cent by private transport. By the year 2000 it is expected that daily journeys will total 4.2 million, and RMV hopes to raise public transport's share to 25 per cent.

Developments: In 1998 RMV and the Nordhessiche Verkehrsverbund placed a joint order for some 15 lightweight GTW 2/6 diesel units. These will be made

MAN NL202 on ESWE's Route 3 at Biebrich Rheinüfer   **1998**/0007651

available to potential new rail operators for use on local services within the region when existing contracts with DB become due for renewal.

The success of a pilot scheme with 'chip cards' (stored-value tickets) in Marburg will lead to their progressive adoption by RMV within the next two years.

A multimodal mobility and transport information centre (MOTIC) or 'Verkehrsinsel' has been opened in the centre of Frankfurt. Information and services are provided for urban transport, DB rail, airport, road traffic situation, cycling, taxi, hire cars and package express services. This facility is part of the EU research project called 'Enterprice'.

Fare structure: Zonal; single tickets (reduced fares during off-peak hours), passes (weekly/monthly), day tickets. Short-distance tickets and other special offers; all ordinary passes transferable; no ticket sales on board rail vehicles (S-Bahn, Stadtbahn, tram), but vending machines at every station/stop; free transfers
Operating costs financed by: Fares and grants 53 per cent, subsidy 47 per cent
Subsidy from: Federal government 47 per cent, state government 12 per cent, local authorities 41 per cent

Stadtwerke Frankfurt
Stadtwerke Verkehrsgesellschaft Frankfurt am Main mbH
60276 Frankfurt am Main
Tel: (+49 69) 21 30   Fax: (+49 69) 21 32 27 40
Directors: Manfred Ott (Commercial)
    Werner Röhre (Personnel)
Technical Managers: Christian Lambrecht (Vehicles)
    Klaus Gierse (Track)

Finance Manager: Klaus-Jürgen Burdack
Marketing Manager: Walter Noé
Manager, Traffic Management: Rolf Valussi
Staff: 2,738 (all modes)

Passenger journeys: (All modes)
(1994) 154.9 million
(1995) 151.8 million
(1996) 151.5 million

Operating costs financed by: Fares 45.3 per cent, subsidy/grants 43.6 per cent, other 11.1 per cent
Subsidy from: City budget

Current situation: On 1 August 1996 the municipal transport authority was transformed into a commercial company (GmbH), entirely owned by the city of Frankfurt. Most central area services are provided by Stadtbahn, tram or S-Bahn, with buses acting as feeders and serving suburban areas. Surface tramways were due to be eliminated from the city centre, leaving the metro and S-Bahn as the only means of cross-city-centre transport, but in 1989 the newly elected city council resisted and there was strong public pressure to retain the trams.

Although overall journeys rose, there was a decline in city-centre trips of 10 per cent, and it was felt that eliminating trams would accelerate the decline. One cross-city-centre tram route was retained; a 0.7 km city-centre link was under construction for 1998 opening.
Developments: In late 1996 the city agreed a rail transport plan (GVP) that would commit DM640 million to Stadtbahn and tramway improvements. Proposals include a further 11 km of Stadtbahn and 10 km of tramway, plus two new S-Bahn stations.

Arrangements for elderly/disabled: 1 tram and 7 urban bus routes served by lift-equipped low-floor vehicles; installation of lifts at metro stations in progress. A large fleet of low-floor trams and buses has entered service in the last few years.

Bus

Staff: 609

Passenger boardings: (1997) 36.1 million
Vehicle-km: (1995) 12.6 million
(1996) 12.6 million
(1997) 12.8 million

Number of routes: 44
Route length: 307 km
On priority right-of-way: 15.5 km; extension planned
Fleet: 194 vehicles, plus 70 contracted; including 32 articulated and 81 low-floor, all Mercedes and Neoplan
In peak service: 219

Most intensive service: 10 min
One-person operation: All routes
Fare structure: Zonal (see RMV)
Fare evasion control: Roving inspectors; penalty fare
Average speed: 18-20 km/h

Developments: Introduction of bus priority lanes under study. Passengers may leave buses other than at designated stops after 20.00, except in the central area. Rail feeder minibuses in northern suburbs run by independent operator under contract.

The workshops at Rebstock have been reorganised and now also undertake work for outside customers.

Light rail (Stadtbahn)

Staff: 694 (including tramway)

Type of operation: Light rail (Stadtbahn) runs underground in the city centre, but largely on converted tram routes in the suburbs; initial route opened 1968

Passenger boardings: (1997) 91 million
Car-km: (1994) 15.6 million
(1995) 15.1 million
(1996) 15.5 million

Route length: 56.1 km
Number of lines: 7
Number of stations: 82
Gauge: 1,435 mm
Tunnel: Box section
Electrification: 600 V DC, overhead

Buses of SWF at Frankfurt Hbf

1998/0007650

Service: Peak 2 min
Fare structure: Zonal (see RMV)
Integration with other modes: Common tariff structure throughout RMV area

Rolling stock: 396 cars (including tramway, type Pt cars are also used on tram routes)

Duewag U2 (1968/85)	M101
Duewag U3 (1980)	M34
Duewag U4/2000 (1996)	M39
Duewag Pt (1972/77)	M100
Crede K (1954)	M4
Fuchs 2-axle (1954)	T6
Duewag N eight-axle	M30
Duewag O (1969)	M8
Duewag R (1993/94/96)	M39
Others	35

Current situation: The U6 extension from Zoo to Ostbahnhof (0.6 km) is expected to open in 1999. Eleven km of extensions were approved in 1996 under the GVP plan (see above). Completion of delivery of the U4/2000 vehicles has enabled cascading U2 types onto Line U7, permitting transfer of Pt trams to pure tram routes and replacement of the oldest Duewag tramcars of types M and N. Fifty-four Pt trams have been rebuilt as Ptb with extended steps for Lines U5 and U6, to enable use at common platforms with the wider U2 and U3 types. Line U5 was extended over the existing U4 route from Konstablerwache to Hauptbahnhof in 1998 with Ptb vehicles.

Developments: Experiments with fully automated driverless operations are planned for 1999. Funding for the project will be provided by the Federal Ministry for Research & Technology (BMFT).

New Ost depot for 150 cars is planned for 1999 opening, replacing three central area facilities.

Tramway

Car-km: (1995) 8.3 million
(1996) 8.2 million
(1997) 7.8 million

Route length: 58.4 km
Number of routes: 8

Developments: Construction of 2.3 km from Bockenheim to Rebstock has been approved by the city council amongst 10 km of extensions, but citizens have protested against cutting-down of trees along the route and the supervisory authorities have refused to permit single-track operation.

Route 16 to Offenbach was closed beyond the Frankfurt city boundary in 1996, following opening of the S-Bahn extension to Offenbach (see below). Large-scale withdrawal of Duewag M and N type cars has been permitted by the cascading of Pt trams from U-Bahn Line U7.

DB

Regio Deutsche Bahn Gruppe
Lyoner Strasse 15, 60528 Frankfurt am Main
Tel: (+49 69) 26 53 50 00   Fax: (+49 69) 26 53 50 02
Manager: Jochen Schiebeler

Regional metro

Type of operation: Regional metro (S-Bahn)

Passenger journeys: (1994) 92 million
(1995) S-Bahn 98 million, other RMV routes 55 million
(1997) 85 million

Current situation: S-Bahn services are operated over seven routes on the north bank of the River Main converging at Hbf and continuing in tunnel via Konstablerwache in the central business district and under the River Main to Offenbach and Südbahnhof (4.3 km), with two routes running through to Stresemannallee and extended to Darmstadt and Langen in 1997. Outer termini at Wiesbaden, Offenbach Ost, Niedernhausen, Bad Soden, Kronberg, Friedrichsdorf, Friedberg, Hanau and Mainz; latter route also serving the airport. Total S-Bahn routes 288 km, 1,435 mm gauge, electrified 15 kV 16⅔ Hz. In addition, DB operates over 46 other routes within the RMV area, totalling about 1,200 km.

Work on branches to Dietzenbach and Rödermark was approved in 1997 for possible opening in 2001/02. Planned construction of separate S-Bahn tracks on the Frankfurt—Bad Vilbel section is due to begin in 2000. Construction has started on an S-Bahn station at the fairground (Messe). After 21.00 hrs every S-Bahn train is to be accompanied by a security guard.

Rolling stock: 130 ET 420 plus 147 double-deck coaches, 639 other coaches, 34 diesel railcars
Most intensive service: 15 min peak, 30-60 min off-peak (more frequent on overlapping sections)

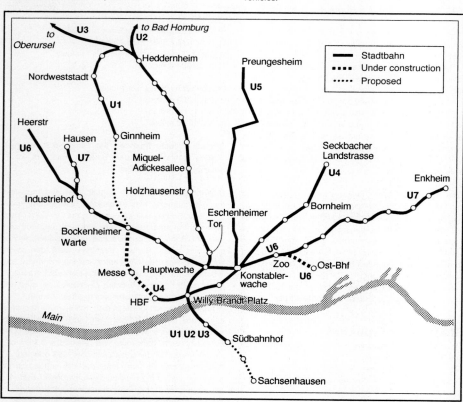

Frankfurt Stadtbahn

0009500

VU

Verkehrsgesellschaft Untermain GmbH (VU)
Mainzer Landstrasse 189, 60327 Frankfurt
Tel: (+49 69) 758 09 50
Directors: Wolfgang Hietel
Manfred Bohr
Staff: 370

Current situation: Railway subsidiary regional bus company operating services within the RMV area and in adjacent parts of Bovaria with a fleet of 122 Mercedes buses, plus 365 contracted.
Developments: Services in the Frankfurt–Darmstadt corridor were substantially revised on start-up of S-Bahn operations in 1997. Most buses from and to the south now terminate at Neu-Isenburg S-Bahn station rather than running through to Frankfurt, despite protests from users. The number of low-floor buses in the fleet is increasing. All vehicles (own and contractors) are radio-controlled.

Bus

Passenger journeys: (1995) 20.5 million
(1996) 20.6 million
(1997) 21.6 million
Vehicle-km: (1995) 24.3 million
(1996) 24.2 million
(1997) 21.6 million

Number of routes: 113

FKE

Frankfurt-Königsteiner Eisenbahn AG
Bahnstrasse 13, 61462 Konigstein
Tel: (+49 6174) 290 10   Fax: (+49 6174) 29 01 15
Director: P Berking
Staff: 168

Passenger journeys: (Both modes)
(1994) 5.1 million
(1997) 5.3 million

Current situation: Local railway operating diesel railcars between Frankfurt-Höchst and Königstein (25 km), the Höchst–Bad Soden line (part of S3 taken over from DB in 1992), total 46 km, and local bus feeder services in the Frankfurt-Höchst/Kelkheim/Hofheim/Königstein area. Company owned by state of Hessen via Hessische Landesbahn holding. Connects with S-Bahn at Höchst, but during peak hours some trains continue over main line tracks to Frankfurt Hbf. Operation of the DB line from Friedrichsdorf to Friedberg (16 km) was taken over in May 1998. New GTW 2/6 diesel units from DWA are being delivered for this service.

FKE also operates the HLB-owned Taunusbahn (TSB), from Friedrichsdorf to Grävenwiesbach. In 1997, extension of this line for a further 8 km over former DB tracks to Brandoberndorf was approved.
Developments: A prototype new-generation diesel railcar was evaluated in 1997.

Bus

Vehicle-km: (1995) 5.1 million
(1996) 5.2 million
(1997) 15.2 million

Number of routes: 21
Route length: 366 km
Fleet: 36 buses, plus 94 contracted

Local railway

Car-km: (1995) 1.6 million
(1996) 1.6 million
(1997) 1.6 million

Rolling stock: 23 diesel railcars

OVB

Offenbacher Verkehrsbetriebe GmbH
Heberstrasse 14, 63065 Offenbach
Tel: (+49 69) 80 05 80   Fax: (+49 69) 80 05 81 90
Director: Claus Steinberg
Staff: 213

Current situation: Municipally owned company provides bus service in the city and county of Offenbach.

Bus

Passenger journeys: (1995) 12.1 million
(1996) 10.6 million
(1997) 10.2 million
Vehicle-km: (1995) 3.4 million
(1996) 3.4 million
(1997) 3.7 million

Number of routes: 12
Route length: 196 km

Fleet: 66 buses, plus 10 contracted
Mercedes	25
MAN	40
VW/Auwärter	1

ESWE

Stadtwerke Wiesbaden AG Verkehrsbetriebe (ESWE)
Kirchgasse 2, 65184 Wiesbaden
Tel: (+49 611) 78 00   Fax: (+49 611) 780 23 39
Chair: Dr Gerhard Heunemann
Directors: Klaus Kopp
Diether Sammet
Operations Manager: Uwe Cramer
Staff: 708

Bus

Passenger journeys: (1995) 54.9 million
(1996) 52.5 million
(1997) 52.5 million
Vehicle-km: (1995) 10.6 million
(1996) 11.6 million
(1997) 11.4 million

Number of routes: 42
Route length: (One way) 573 km
On priority right-of-way: 12 km

Fleet: 181 vehicles, plus 40 contracted
Mercedes O405 (1987/89)	51
Mercedes O405G articulated (1988/92)	41
Mercedes O405N low-floor (1990/94)	49
Mercedes O405GN low-floor articulated (1997)	12
MAN NL202 low-floor (1993)	23
Others	5

In peak service: 183

Most intensive service: 5 min
One-person operation: All routes
Fare structure: As RMV
Fares collected on board: 35.7 per cent
Operational control: Route inspectors/mobile radio. Computer-based bus control system RBL with infra-red beacons along routes activated by onboard equipment; activation of traffic signals for bus priority
Arrangements for elderly/disabled: Disabled travel free, partly funded by government; low-floor buses have wheelchair ramp at centre door
Integration with other modes: Cross-river routes to Mainz operated jointly with Stadtwerke Mainz
Average peak-hour speed: 20.1 km/h
Operating costs financed by: Fares 42.5 per cent, other commercial sources 28.6 per cent, subsidy/grants 28.9 per cent
Subsidy from: In part by cross-subsidy from other municipal enterprises which are part of the company (electricity, gas, water etc) and in part from city and state

HEAG

HEAG Verkehrs-GmbH
Jägertorstrasse 207, 64289 Darmstadt
Tel: (+49 6151) 70 90   Fax: (+49 6151) 709 41 05
www: www.heag.de/verkehrs-gmbh
Directors: Horst Blechschmidt
Siegfried Bittner
Staff: 454

Passenger journeys: (1995) 29.9 million
(1996) 30.2 million
(1997) 29.1 million

Current situation: Municipally owned company provides bus and tramway services in Darmstadt and the surrounding area.
Developments: A controversial feasibility study recommends closure of the tramway and replacement by a private bus service running partially over exclusive busways. Consultants believe this action could turn HEAG's annual deficit of DM45 million into a profit of DM8 million.

Bus

Vehicle-km: (1995) 4.9 million
(1996) 4.9 million

Route length: 270 km

Fleet: 58 buses, plus 34 contracted
Mercedes O405GN low-floor articulated	19
Mercedes O405G articulated	7
Mercedes O405N low-floor	13
Mercedes O405 standard	6
MAN NG272 low-floor articulated	13

Tramway

Car-km: (Annual) 4.2 million

Route length: 37.7 km

Rolling stock: 73 cars   M43 T30

Funicular

ESWE also operates a 500 m funicular with 2 cars.

Light rail (planned)

A study has been commissioned for a planned light rail line from Wiesbaden to Bad Schwalbach (21.8 km). Of this, 7.1 km would be on private right-of-way in the city and the remainder on former DB tracks. Initially 20 vehicles would be required.

U6 train at Konstablerwache

FUKUOKA

Population: 1.3 million
Public transport: Bus services provided by private company also operating two separate commuter railways. Metro operated by municipal undertaking; suburban rail services provided by Japan Railways (JR); ferry services across Hakata Bay

Nishi Nippon Tetsudo 'Nishitetsu'

Nishi Nippon Railway
1-11-17 Tenjin, Chuo-ku, Fukuoka-shi 810-0001, Japan
Tel: (+81 92) 761 66 31   Fax: (+81 92) 722 14 05
President: G Kimoto

Current situation: Operates the local bus network, a 75 km interurban/commuter railway and a separate 21 km suburban railway. A 5 km tramway is operated in Kitakyushu.

Nishi Nippon is the largest bus operator in Japan. Bus operations generate about 55 per cent of income and include urban networks in Fukuoka, Kitakyushu, Kurume and Omuta as well as rural, interurban, express and sightseeing services. Of note is the network of frequent motorway express services linking Fukuoka, Fukuoka airport, Kitakyushu and other towns in northern Kyushu.

Associated companies include Nishi Nippon Shatai, bus body manufacturers, and Fukuoka Nishitetsu Taxi Company.

Bus
(Fukuoka operations)
Passenger journeys: Approx 150 million (annual)

Number of routes: 122 including 7 express routes and an airport service

Fleet: Total 3,020 buses and 472 coaches. Approx 1,000 buses committed to Fukuoka local operations; types include Nishi Nippon Shatai-bodied Nissan Diesel, Hino, Isuzu and Mitsubishi. Recent deliveries include Mitsubishi MP747M 'non-step' low-floor buses.

Fare structure: Flat fare zone covering central and inner Fukuoka with stage fares beyond. Some routes entirely flat fare. Prepurchase coupon tickets, season tickets, one-day city bus tickets (valid in flat fare zone)
Fare collection: Payment to farebox by driver on alighting, or prepurchase
One-person operation: All routes

Suburban railway
Staff: 916 (including tramway)

Type of operation: Suburban/interurban railway

Passenger journeys: (Whole network, including Kitakyushu tramway)
(1990/91) 156 million
(1991/92) 159 million
(1992/93) 155 million
Car-km: (1992/93) 11 million (including Kitakyushu tramway)

Rolling stock: 362 emu cars
1,435 mm gauge	M201 T126
1,067 mm gauge	M23 T12

Current situation: Nishi Nippon operates a 116 km rail network including the 75 km Fukuoka—Omuta main line with branches, 1,435 mm gauge, electrified 1.5 kV DC, and the 21 km 1,067 mm gauge Miyajidake line from Kaizuka in the eastern suburbs of Fukuoka to Tsuyazaki. Interchange with metro Line 2 at Kaizuka.
Developments: A 3.6 km section of the Miyajidake line is to be upgraded to allow extension in 2004 of Line 2 metro trains to a new station at Kashii.

Fukuoka-shi Kotsu Kyoku

Fukuoka Municipal Transportation Bureau
2-5-31 Daimyo, Chuo-ku, Fukuoka 810-0041
Tel: (+81 92) 732 41 07   Fax: (+81 92) 721 07 54
Superintendent, Transportation: K Nishi

Metro
Staff: 651

Type of operation: Full metro, initial route opened 1981

Series 1000 metro train   1996

Passenger journeys: (1992) 96 million
(1994) 111 million
(1997) 116 million

Route length: 17.8 km (trains also operate over 44.8 km of JR tracks)
  in tunnel: 16.7 km
Number of lines: 2
Number of stations: 19 (trains also serve 16 JR Chikuhi line stations)
Gauge: 1,067 mm
Electrification: 1.5 kV DC, overhead

Service: Peak 3-6 min, mid-day 4-8 min; Line 1 trains operate through to JR Chikuhi line destinations every 15-30 min
First/last train: 05.30/23.50
Fare structure: 4-section distance-related scale; one-day/monthly passes; prepaid 'F-Card' introduced 1995
Fare collection: Full AFC
Arrangements for elderly/disabled: Free travel for over 70s and severely disabled
One-person operation: All trains
Signalling: Full ATO, ATC
Operating costs financed by: Fares 38.8 per cent, other commercial sources 3.2 per cent, subsidy/grants 30.6 per cent

Rolling stock: 144 cars formed into six-car sets
Kinki Sharyo, Toshiba, Hitachi and Mitsubishi
Series 1000	M68 T34
Series 1000N	M4 T2
Series 2000	M24 T12

Current situation: Line 1 connects with JR Chikuhi line at Meinohama and a through service is operated between Fukuoka-kuko (airport) and Nishi-karatsu (57.9 km) using metro and JR rolling stock. Interchange between Line 2 and Nishitetsu Miyajidake line at Kaizuka.
Developments: Proposed Line 3 between Tenjin in central Fukuoka and Hashimoto in the western suburbs (12.7 km, 16 stations) is due to open in 2006. The 1,435 mm gauge small-profile line will be operated by six-car linear-motor-powered trains. An extension from Tenjin to Hakata Waterfront and a branch from Watanabe-dori to Hakata JR station, totalling 4 km, are also planned but not yet authorised for construction.

It is also proposed to extend Line 2 trains over 3.6 km of the Nishitetsu Miyajidake line to a new station at Kashii in 2004.

Fukuoka City Ferries

Fukuoka City Ferries
13-6, Chikko-honmachi, Hakata-ku, Fukuoka 812-0021
Tel: (+81 92) 291 10 85

Current situation: Fukuoka municipality operates passenger ferry services across Hakata Bay.

JR Kyushu

Kyushu Railway Company
Kyushu Ryokaku Tetsudo
1-1 Chuogai, Hakata Eki, Hakata-ku, Fukuoka 812-8566
Tel: (+81 92) 474 25 01   Fax: (+81 92) 474 97 45
Chair: Y Ishii
President: K Tanaka

Type of operation: Suburban/interurban heavy rail

Passenger journeys: (Fukuoka city only)
(1990/91) 51.4 million

Current situation: JR Kyushu operates frequent 'Town Shuttle' emus between Fukuoka, Kokura and Moji, with some trains running through from Kurume, Omuta and Kumamoto. Diesel services run to Nogata (41 km), with some trains continuing to Kurosaki in Kitakyushu. Also diesel railcar service on the 25 km Kashii line in Fukuoka's eastern suburbs. A fleet of six-car Series 103 emus operates the through service between the Chikuhi line and Line 1 of the metro.
Developments: Work has started on upgrading 11.1 km of the Chikuhi line from single to double track, including elevation of a 1.8 km section, to provide greater capacity for growing commuter traffic from new dormitory suburbs to the west of the city. JR Kyushu, Fukuoka city and central government are all contributing towards the ¥16.2 billion cost of the project, which is due for completion in 1999.

JR West

West Japan Railway Company
Nishi Nihon Ryokaku Tetsudo
4-24, Shibata 2-chome, Kita-ku, Osaka 530-0012
Tel: (+81 6) 375 89 81   Fax: (+81 6) 375 89 19
Chair: T Tsunoda
President: M Ide

Type of operation: Suburban/interurban heavy rail

Passenger journeys: (1994/95) 1.6 million

Current situation: JR West operates a unique local passenger service using shinkansen trains running on the 8.5 km 1,435 mm gauge line between the Sanyo shinkansen terminus at Hakata and the shinkansen depot at Hakata Minami; runs about hourly with no intermediate stops.

UPDATED

FUSHUN

Population: 1.2 million, municipal area 2.1 million
Public transport: Two distinct public transport systems: extensive network of municipal bus services and frequent electric train service on the tracks of the Fushun Mining Administration; developing paratransit services

Fushun City Bus

Fushun City Bus Company
Fushun, Liaoning Province, People's Republic of China

Current situation: No recent report has been received but it is assumed that the extent of the bus system remains largely unchanged. Paratransit almost certainly exists in Fushun as in other Chinese cities, but it is not known whether operations are in the hands of Fushun City Bus or other agencies.

Bus

Number of routes: Approx 30
Fleet: Approx 400 buses, including many articulated supplied by Shenyang and other factories in northeast China
Fare collection: Payment to seated conductors, monthly passes

Fushun Mining Administration Railway

Type of operation: Conventional heavy rail

Current situation: Operates a public passenger service on 2 routes (25 stations) over more than 30 km of its 600 km of standard-gauge railway. This operation is the only true urban/suburban electric railway using multiple-unit rolling stock in China, apart from the metros at Beijing, Shanghai and Tianjin. Electrified 1.5 kV DC overhead, with trains every 20-60 min.

Rolling stock: Approx 20 trains comprising 5 to 7 cars, including some articulated. Trains are mostly emu sets, but there are a few sets of coaches hauled by industrial-type electric locomotives.

VERIFIED

GDANSK

Population: Gdansk 480,000, Sopot 50,000
Public transport: Bus, tramway and seasonal ferry services provided by local authority agency; suburban rail services

PKM

Przedsiebiorstwo Komunikacji Miejskie
ul Jaskowa Dolina 48, 80952 Gdansk-Wrzeszcz, Poland
Tel: (+48 58) 41 00 21
Staff: 3,200

Current situation: The former public transport operator WPK, which served the three cities of Gdansk, Gdynia and Sopot, was split into three undertakings in 1989, PKM becoming responsible for operations in Gdansk and Sopot.

Bus

Passenger journeys: (1989) 150 million
Vehicle-km: (1989) 15.3 million

Number of routes: 53
Route length: (One way) 618 km

Fleet: 322 vehicles
Ikarus 280 articulated	172
Ikarus 260	59
Jelcz M11	74
Jelcz PR110	2
Mercedes O405N low-floor	15

Most intensive service: 10 min
Fare collection: Prepurchase tickets with validation/cancellation machines on board
Fare structure: Flat

Tramway

Type of operation: Conventional tramway

Passenger journeys: (1989) 130 million
Vehicle-km: (1989) 12.5 million

Neoplan Megatrans of ZKM in Gdansk   *1998*/0007652

Number of lines: 8
Route length: 50 km
Number of stops: 368

Rolling stock: 265 cars
Konstal 105N	M114
Konstal 105NA	M151
Konstal 105NG low-floor (1997)	

Suburban bus

Current situation: Several private operators run bus/minibus services from central Gdansk to suburban destinations beyond the city limits. ZKM Tczew, the municipal operator of that town, also has a route to central Gdansk. P.PKS is the government-owned regional bus company.

PKP

Polish State Railways (PKP)
ul Chalubinskiego 4, 00928 Warsaw
Tel: (+48 22) 620 45 12   Fax: (+48 22) 621 27 05

Type of operation: Suburban heavy rail

Passenger journeys: 120 million (annual)

Current situation: At least five trains per hour run in the electrified Gdansk—Gdynia urban corridor (27 km), some extended to Wejherowo (44 km). Also Gdansk to Tczew (32 km) about hourly, Gdansk to Gdansk Nowy Port two or three trains per hour, and from Gdynia southwards to Koscierzyna every 2 h.

VERIFIED

GENEVA

Population: 399,000
Public transport: Bus, trolleybus and tramway services operated by municipal authority. Swiss Federal Railways services on local lines; also French National Railways local route to Geneva Eaux-Vives. Lake steamers providing mostly tourist services

TPG

Transports Publics Genevois (TPG)
Route de la Chapelle 1, PO Box 950, 1212 Grand-Lancy 1, Switzerland
Tel: (+41 22) 308 33 11   Fax: (+41 22) 308 34 00
President: Jean-Pierre Etter
General Manager: Christoph Stucki
Staff: 1,286

Passenger boardings: (All modes)
(1993) 102.9 million
(1994) 101.3 million
(1995) 101.2 million

Trams, trolleybuses and diesel buses serve the interchange just outside the SBB/SNCF Cornavin station
(Tony Pattison)   *1999*/0038779

Operating costs financed by: (All modes)
Fares 39 per cent, other commercial sources 8 per cent, subsidy/grants 53 per cent
Subsidy from: Canton, plus 2 per cent from government for country routes

Current situation: The authority has been successful in raising patronage despite high car ownership. An increase in the number of articulated vehicles has helped cope with peak capacity problems. Several tramway/light rail extensions have been considered, including a route to Annemasse in France, and an automated light metro is proposed.

Bus and trolleybus
Passenger boardings: (1993) Bus 55.1 million, trolleybus 30.1 million
(1994) Bus 54.2 million, trolleybus 29.8 million
(1995) Bus 51.1 million, trolleybus 30 million
Vehicle-km: (1993) Bus 10.1 million, trolleybus 3.3 million
(1994) Bus 10 million, trolleybus 3.3 million
(1995) Bus 9.8 million, trolleybus 3.3 million

Number of routes: Bus 42, trolleybus 4
Route length: Bus 299 km, trolleybus 29 km

Fleet: 221 buses	
Standard	56
FBW articulated	31
Volvo B10M articulated	25
Mercedes O405	40
Mercedes O405G articulated	48
Mercedes O405GN articulated	21
In peak service: 190	

Fleet: 73 trolleybuses	
Saurer/Hess/BBC-Sécheron articulated (1982/83)	24
FBW	16
NAW/Hess/BBC-SE (1988)	20
NAW/Hess/Siemens	13
In peak service: 56	

Trolleybus electrification: 600 V DC

Most intensive service: 5 min
One-person operation: All routes
Fare collection: Self-service, from machines at stops; no fares payable on board
Fare structure: Flat for 1 h transfer tickets and 3-stop only tickets; multitickets of both types; monthly and annual passes, monthly passes also valid on all public transport in Canton of Geneva; passes to be introduced to include journeys on SNCF route (see below)
Fares collected on board: None
Fare evasion control: Roving inspectors
Average distance between stops: 300 m
Average peak-hour speed: In mixed traffic, 15-20 km/h

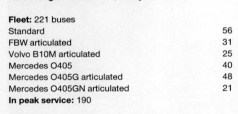

Trolleybus heads towards the waterfront near Lake Geneva (Tony Pattison) *1999*/0038780

The pedestrianised main shopping street is shared by trams, trolleybuses and diesel buses (Tony Pattison) *1999*/0038782

Tramway
Type of operation: Conventional tramway

Passenger boardings: (1994) 17.3 million
(1995) 20.1 million
(1996) 27.6 million
Car-km: (1994) 2.1 million
(1995) 2.2 million

Route length: 10.8 km
Number of lines: 3
Number of stops: 59
Gauge: 1,000 mm
Electrification: 600 V DC, overhead

Service: Peak 5 min, off-peak 10 min
First/last car: 05.30/00.30
Fare structure: As bus
One-person operation: All trams

Rolling stock: 46 cars	
Vevey/Duewag B4/6	M46
In peak service: 40	

Developments: 1.2 km extension from Bachet de Pesay to Les Palettes opened 1997, served by Route 13. Further construction is proposed to serve two major park-and-ride sites, in the north at Sécheron (Place des Nations) and at Etoile in the south, for opening by 2005.

Light metro (proposed)
Current situation: The 8.5 km tram line originally proposed to serve the airport and Meyrin is now planned as a light metro eventually linking the two areas of France that surround the city. Running from Meyrin to the airport and Cornavin SBB station, the line would then continue to Annemasse (16 km, 30 stations).

SBB-CFF
Swiss Federal Railways, Lausanne Division
PO Box 345, 1001 Lausanne

Tel: (+41 21) 318 91 11 Fax: (+41 21) 323 37 00
Divisional Manager: Philippe Gauderon

Type of operation: Suburban heavy rail

Current situation: Local trains run half-hourly to La Plaine, hourly (half-hourly at peak times) to Nyon and Lausanne, and frequently to Geneva airport.

SNCF
French National Railways

Type of operation: Local railway

Current situation: The electrified line from Annemasse extends across the Swiss border to serve Geneva at Eaux-Vives in the southeast of the city. Trains run about hourly.

Ferries
Current situation: Two companies, Mouettes Genevoises and Compagnie Générale de Navigation sur le Lac Léman, operate regular ferry services on Lake Geneva linking ports on the Swiss and French shores.

UPDATED

A park-and-ride bus in overall pink livery pulls in to the interchange just outside Cornavin station (Tony Pattison) *1999*/0038781

GENOA
Population: 652,000
Public transport: Urban and suburban bus and trolleybus networks operated by municipal undertaking also responsible for regional services, 9 elevators, 2 funiculars and 1 rack railway, and a light rail route

AMT
Azienda Mobilita e Trasporti Genova
Via L Montaldo 2, CP 1756, 16137 Genoa, Italy
Tel: (+39 010) 558 22 32 Fax: (+39 010) 558 24 00
Principal Officers: Ing Cavagnetto, Ing Pizzorno, Ing Niola, Ing Cappai, Ing Sordini, Ing Testoni, Dott Pesci, Dott Schena, Rag Lepera
Staff: 3,008

Passenger journeys: (1996) 157.3 million

Current situation: Distinct urban and suburban/regional route networks are operated, the latter in conjunction with other local undertakings. There are 122 bus and one trolleybus routes served by 147 buses; they carried 3.2 million passengers in 1996.

Initial section of light rail opened 1990. Construction of a 17 km three-route trolleybus network started 1994, and operation of the 7 km route between S Benigros and Foce started in 1997.

City-centre circular route 'CompraBus' serving mainly pedestrian streets runs weekdays 09.30-13.00 and 16.30-20.00.

Developments: 1996 brought a change of name and legal status for AMT, which now has greater autonomy and more responsibility for its financial performance. AMT now has a contract with the Comune (city council) for provision of service.

A new city circular route, the Artbus, was introduced in 1998, serving main attractions in the city.

An Altrobus service is running in the city, sponsored by the EU Thermie programme, the Ligurian Regional Council and the City Council. A fleet of 10 hybrid Iveco citybuses take power from traction batteries which are kept charged by a diesel generator. This is switched off in the city centre. They are running on Route 19, a 7 km route which crosses the city centre.

Bus and trolleybus (urban operations only)
Passenger journeys: (1995) 169.4 million
(1996) 155 million
(1997) 157.3 million
Vehicle-km: (1995) 32.1 million
(1996) 30.5 million
(1997) 30.8 million

*Göteborgs Spårväger BOVA Futura FLD 15-340
Magnum*   *1999*/0038776

also authorised, and specifications were being prepared
in late 1997.

Developments: The bus tendering procedure has been
delayed and former contracts have been prolonged after
the five-year period came to an end.

Passenger journeys: (Bus and tram/light rail)
(1994) 85 million
(1995) 89.3 million
(1996) 87.5 million

Fare structure: Within the city, there is a flat fare, but the
fare system is integrated with the regional fare structure
valid in Gothenburg and the 12 other municipalities
administered by GLAB; magnetic tickets and monthly
passes

Fare collection: Validators for magnetic ticket; tickets
and monthly passes (valid 30 days from validation) are
both magnetic; drivers sell tickets for single journeys, and
magnetic tickets; prepurchase at reduced rate; stored-
value cards cheaper if bought at kiosks

Fares collected on board: Less than 15 per cent

Fare evasion control: Roving inspectors; spot penalty

Operating costs financed by: Fares 54 per cent, city
council subsidy 46 per cent

Arrangements for elderly/disabled: Responsibility of a
separate organisation; fare structure decided by
Trafikkontoret. A fleet of 90 vehicles is run by five
operators, along with 175 contract taxis; they carry 5,000
passengers a day. A computer-based system is used to
arrange ride-sharing. A 'Service Line' with low-floor buses
operates on a regular route in areas where many senior
citizens live, connecting with day centres and hospitals.
This route is operated by GS as part of the regular bus
system and regular passes are valid.

Bus

Vehicle-km: (1996)13.8 million
(1997) 14.3 million

Number of routes: 58
Route length: 939 km

Fleet: 133 buses

Scania CN112 (1987)	3
Scania CN113 (1990)	2
Scania CN113 (1991)	24
Volvo B10M (1988)	17
Volvo B10M CNG (1993)	19
Ontario II (1989)	6
Ontario II (1990)	1
Volvo B10MA (1991/95/96/97)	42
Volvo B10BLE CNG (1994/96/97)	19

In peak service: 115

Most intensive service: 8 min

Bus priority: Traffic management system for central
Gothenburg divides the area into five sections to which
access for private traffic is only possible for internal
movement, thereby preventing through traffic, though
buses and trams can move freely

Light rail/tramway
Type of operation: Light rail/tramway

Car-km: (1994) 12.9 million
(1996) 13.1 million
(1997) 13.1 million

Route length: 140 km
   reserved track: 90 per cent

Göteborgs Spårväger tram at Härlanda (N Griffiths)   *1999*/0043549

Number of lines: 9, plus one peak-hours only
Gauge: 1,435 mm
Max gradient: 6 per cent
Minimum curve radius: 17 m
Electrification: 750 V DC, overhead

Service: Peak 8-10 min, off-peak 12-20 min

Rolling stock: 204 cars

Hägglunds M29 (1969/72)	58
ASEA/ASJ M28 (1965/67)	66
ASEA/ABB M21 articulated (1984/91)	80

In peak service: 168

Developments: The batch of M21 cars of 1984/91 (80
vehicles) is to be rebuilt with a low-floor centre section. At
the same time, some M28 cars will be refurbished and
equipped with new electronics; the number to be
overhauled will depend on how many new cars are
ordered.

Styrsöbolaget

Styrsöbolaget
PO Box 5085, 42605 Västra Frölunda
Tel: (+46 31) 69 64 00   Fax: (+46 31) 69 42 85
General Manager: Ove Boström
Operations Manager: Gunnar Söderberg
Staff: 54

Ferry
Passenger journeys: (1996) 2.7 million
(1997) 2.8 million
(1998) 2.7 million

Current situation: Ferry services on the River Göta
between Lilla Bommen and Klippan and from Saltholmen to
the southern archipelago operated under contract to
Stadstrafiken by the city-owned shareholding company
Styrsöbolaget with nine vessels; four routes total 43 km. All
ferries are integrated into the fares system, and there is no
transfer fee. Fares cover 35 per cent of operating costs.

Developments: Demand for ferry service has increased
over the past few years, due to opening of a new college at
Lindholmen and housing development on the northern
bank of the Göta.

Linjebuss

Linjebuss Sverige AB
Toltorpsgatan 137, 43141 Mölndal
Tel: (+46 31) 87 01 90   Fax: (+46 31) 27 04 83
Manager: Jan Glans

Current situation: In 1993 this private operator took over
some routes totalling 94 km in the western part of the city
and in 1997 another route (35 km) was added. Linjebuss
also operates a number of regional bus services.

Bus
Vehicle-km: (1996) 2.1 million
(1997) 2.1 million

Fleet: 40 buses

Scania N113 (1990)	2
Scania N113 (1993)	13
Volvo B10B (1993)	7
Volvo B10M (1993/94/95)	7
Volvo B10M (14.5 m, three axles)(1997)	11

Styrsöbolaget's River Göta ferry   *1996*

Swebus Sverige AB

Kruthusgatan 7, S-41104 Gothenburg
Tel: (+46 31) 10 38 00   Fax: (+46 31) 10 31 92
Manager: Wille Mark

Background: Swebus is owned by UK company Stagecoach.
Current situation: Since June 1997 Swebus operates a number of routes for Stadstrafiken. It also operates regional routes for the regional authority Göteborgsregionens Lokaltrafik AB (GLAB).

Fleet: 55 buses

Neoplan NE7 (1990)	2
Neoplan 8012 (1995)	1
Scania CN2 (1989)	2
Scania Cn3 (1990/92)	3
Volvo B10R (1987)	1
Volvo B10M (1988–1996)	17
Volvo B10L (1997)	17
Volvo B10LA (1997)	12

SJ

Swedish State Railways (SJ)
PO Box 1522, 40158 Gothenburg
Tel: (+46 31) 10 41 00   Fax: (+46 31) 10 41 03
Area Manager: L-A Antonsson

Type of operation: Suburban heavy rail

Current situation: Services operated on several routes under contract, electrified 15 kV 16⅔ Hz.

UPDATED

GRAZ

Population: 240,179
Public transport: Bus, tramway and funicular services operated by municipal undertaking, part of public utility trading company responsible also for gas, electricity and water services

Grazer Stadtwerke

Grazer Stadtwerke AG, Verkehrsbetriebe
Steyrergasse 114, 8010 Graz, Austria
Tel: (+43 316) 887   Fax: (+43 316) 88 77 88
Chair: Dr Alfred Edler
Directors: Dr Ott
Manager of Verkehrsbetriebe: Prok Dr Scholz
Staff: 711 (transport 396)

Passenger journeys: (All modes)
(1995) 98.1 million
(1996) 95.4 million
(1997) 92.8 million

Fare collection: Ticket purchase on buses, from shops or machines at main stations; validating equipment on board
Fare structure: Zonal, flat within zones; prepurchase 10-zone and zonal 24 h, weekly and monthly passes, annual tickets
Fares collected on board: 8.2 per cent
Operating costs financed by: Fares 78 per cent, other commercial sources (cross-subsidy) 17 per cent, subsidy 5 per cent
Subsidy from: Government and city (5 per cent)

Developments: In 1997 a total of 50 operators in Steiermark joined in formation of the Verkehrsverbund Steiermark tariff region, extending a uniform zonal fare structure to a population of some 1.2 million. Finance comes from the national government, the Province of Steiermark and the city of Graz .

Bus

Staff: 236 (operating)

Passenger journeys: (1995) 42 million
(1996) 38.9 million
(1997) 39.4 million
Vehicle-km: (1995) 8.7 million
(1996) 8.7 million
(1997) 8.9 million

Number of routes: 30
Number of stops: 280
Route length: (One way) 184.5 km
On priority right-of-way: 10.3 km

Fleet: 131 buses

MAN/Steyr/Gräf & Stift standard	52
MAN/Gräf & Stift/Neoplan low-floor	31
MAN/Gräf & Stift/Neoplan standard articulated	21
MAN/Mercedes-Benz/Neoplan low-floor articulated	22
Mercedes-Benz midibus	1
Steyr Citybus	4
In peak service: 107	

On order: 4 low-floor city buses

Most intensive service: 6 min
One-person operation: All routes
Fare evasion control: Inspectors
Operational control: Route inspectors/mobile radio with computerised online monitoring
Arrangements for elderly/disabled: Reduced rate monthly and annual passes for unrestricted travel on weekdays after 08.15 and at weekends
Average distance between stops: 405 m
Average peak-hour speed: 18.9 km/h

Tramway

Staff: 160

Type of operation: Conventional tramway

Passenger journeys: (1995) 56.1 million
(1996) 56.5 million
(1997) 53.1 million
Car-km: (1995) 8.5 million
(1996) 8.4 million
(1997) 8.3 million

Route length: 49 km
Number of lines: 7
Number of stops: 76
Gauge: 1,435 mm
Track: 66 kg/m Ri60 rail on concrete
Electrification: 600 V DC, overhead

Service: Peak 5 min, off-peak 15 min
First/last car: 04.30/00.30
One-person operation: All cars
Average distance between stops: 360 m
Average peak-hour speed: 15.9 km/h

Rolling stock: 60 cars

SGP 260 (1963)	M9
Lohner Wien 260 (1963)	M10
Duewag 520 (1971)	M17
SGP 500 (1978)	M10
SGP 600 (1986)	M12
GVB 580	M2
In peak service: 56	

Developments: New workshops under development.

Funicular

Current situation: The Schlossbergbahn Funicular carries 0.4 million passengers annually.

Light rail (proposed)
Current situation: A regional light rail network has been proposed for the greater Graz area, sharing existing OBB and local railway alignments.

UPDATED

Grazer Stadwerke bus and Duewag tram share tracks in the city centre   *1999*/0038838

Taxi meets tram in Graz city centre   *1999*/0038836

GRENOBLE

Population: City 150,000, area served 370,000
Public transport: Bus and trolleybus services mostly provided under contract concession by company formed by 23 local authorities covering 212.5 km² in city region with 10 per cent provided by arrangement by second company (VFD), owned by Département. Light rail network; limited local service provided by state railway

TAG

Société d'Economie Mixte des Transports en Commun de l'Agglomération Grenobloise (Semitag)
PO Box 258, 38044 Grenoble Cedex 9, France
Tel: (+33 4) 76 20 66 11   Fax: (+33 4) 76 20 66 99
Chairman: M Charles Descours
Director General: André Magnon
Staff: 813

Passenger journeys: (All modes)
(1995) 47.3 million
(1996) 47.3 million
(1997) 46.7 million

Operating costs financed by: Fares 49.1 per cent, other commercial sources 7.6 per cent, subsidy/grants 43.3 per cent

Subsidy from: Consortium of local authorities owning Semitag, and through 1.75 per cent payroll tax on employers

Current situation: Semitag (marketed as TAG) operates as a 'mixed economy' company responsible to the Syndicat Mixte des Transports en Commun (SMTC) representing 23 local authorities in the city region. Semitag is 65 per cent owned by SMTC, 27 per cent by Transcet. The network is 94 per cent operated by Semitag directly, with the remainder provided under contract by VFD. Figures below include both operations.

The light rail network has been an unqualified success, and has become the model for many recent light rail projects worldwide. Two core routes have replaced the city's busiest bus routes, around which other bus lines have been replanned as feeders. Light rail now accounts for 45 per cent of all public transport trips. Many city-centre streets traversed by the trams have been pedestrianised, and several new car parks have been built at the fringes of the central area. Removal of street traffic has also permitted restoration of the historic city-centre area.

Bus and trolleybus

Passenger journeys: (1995) 26.1 million
(1996) 24.5 million
(1997) 23.8 million
Vehicle-km: (1995) 9.7 million
(1996) 10.6 million
(1997) 10.2 million

Number of routes: Bus 18 (of which 4 operated by VFD), trolleybus 2
Route length: (One way) bus 177 km, trolleybus 28 km
On priority right-of-way: 17.2 km

Fleet: 213 buses

Heuliez GX107	33
Berliet/Renault PR100	55
Renault R312	16
Heuliez GX187 articulated	44
Renault PR180/182 articulated	21
Gruau MG36 minibus	14
Breda minibus	6
Heuliez GX317	6
Renault Agora low-floor	18
In peak service: 177	

Fleet: 33 trolleybuses

Renault ER100	33
In peak service: 30	

Trolleybus electrification: 620 V DC

Most intensive service: 2 min
One-person operation: All services
Fare collection: Prepurchase carnets or daily/weekly/monthly passes, or payment to driver; validation on board buses or at tram stops
Fare structure: Flat; single ticket gives free transfer within 1 h; carnets/passes
Fares collected on board: 9.5 per cent
Fare evasion control: Inspectors
Operational control: Route inspectors/mobile radio
Arrangements for elderly/disabled: 8 minibuses operate services for disabled; free or reduced-rate travel for over-60s and invalids
Average distance between stops: 300 m
Bus priority: On-vehicle traffic-light control by Philips VETAG; plus SAE central control and reporting system
New vehicles financed by: SMTC

Light rail
Type of operation: Light rail, initial route opened 1987

Passenger journeys: (1995) 21.2 million
(1996) 22.8 million
(1997) 22.9 million
Car-km: (1995) 1.6 million
(1996) 1.9 million
(1997) 2.0 million

Route length: 18.7 km
Number of lines: 2
Number of stops: 38
Gauge: 1,435 mm
Track: 55 kg/m Type 35G grooved rail on twin-block sleepers with elastic fastenings, resting on rubber pads and mounted in concrete slab
Electrification: 750 V DC, overhead

Grenoble light rail at Denis Papin terminus on the latest extension to open, in 1997 (D Trevor Rowe)
1999/0043550

Grenoble trolleybus 746 on Route 31 at Malpertuis terminus (D Trevor Rowe)   *1999*/0043551

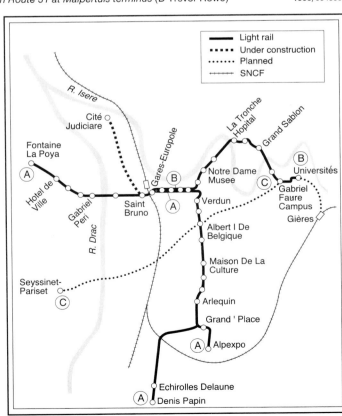

Grenoble light rail
0045354

Service: Peak 2 min, off-peak 6-10 min
First/last car: 04.51/24.00
Fare structure: As bus

Integration with other modes: 3 major city-centre interchanges; bus routes replanned as feeders; park-and-ride at 3 stops; full access for wheelchairs

Rolling stock: 53 six-axle low-floor articulated cars

Alsthom-Francorail (1986/87)	M20
Alsthom-Francorail (1989)	M18
GEC Alsthom (1996)	M15

In peak service: 49

Current situation: Line A was extended 3.4 km southwest from Grand' Place to Echirolles Delaune, opening in two sections in 1995 and 1996. Line A was further extended 0.5 km from Echirolles to Village II, a dense housing development, in December 1997.

Extension of Line B to Cité Judiciaire is under construction (opening date end 1999) and that to Gières is under study. In the longer term it is planned to refurbish the city's principal boulevards to incorporate an east-west Line C from Seyssinet-Pariset to Universités.

SNCF

French National Railways, Chambéry Region

Type of operation: Suburban heavy rail

Current situation: Limited service on routes to Valence and Veynes. A 30 minute service to/from Rives (peak) and a 20 minute service to/from Chambéry (peak) is provided, with a limited service off-peak.

UPDATED

GUADALAJARA

Population: 4 million

Public transport: Trolleybus and some bus services operated by state authority. Light rail service; most bus services provided by independent operators who are mostly members of a co-operative

Sistecozome

Sistema de Transporte Colectivo de la Zona Metropolitana (Sistecozome)
Antiguo Central Camionera, Guadalajara, Mexico
Tel: (+52 3) 619 08 20   Fax: (+52 3) 650 04 85
Director General: Javier Ramírez Acuña
Staff: 458

Current situation: Sistecozome is a public corporation formed in 1974. It also supervises a network of Colectivos on 41 routes. Sistecozome owns all vehicles and leases them to individual drivers. Originally intended as a trolleybus feeder service, the Colectivos now form a network in their own right, running into the central area in competition with buses. This is said to be the only profitable activity of Sistecozome. The fleet comprises 760 Volkswagen 9-seaters. Of the five trolleybus routes, one (Route 300) is out of service due to road construction work.

Developments: New trolleybus Route 600, which opened in February 1995, is one of two north-south routes almost completed in 1988 but then postponed because there was no finance available for sufficient vehicles to run these high-density routes. The new state administration that took office in 1989 had no interest in the project, but nearly all the infrastructure was left in place and the substations were maintained. Work on Route 600 resumed in October 1994 with the intention of opening before the city and state elections to be held on 12 February 1995, and thereby helping the incumbent party.

Infrastructure of the second route (700) remains largely intact, and nearly all the material to complete it is still in store, but there are no funds to finish the job or purchase vehicles. Furthermore, the metropolitan area has since grown beyond the planned termini, so further wiring would be necessary before the route could fulfil its proper role. There also remains the problem of restricting competition from the many private motor bus operators on the corridor.

The city's first articulated vehicles entered service in late 1994, and all 18 were in service on opening of Route 600. Sistecozome's parallel bus Route 60 continues to operate.

Ex-Mexico City MASA trolleybus on Route 400 'Par Vial' in the city centre   1998/0009734

Bus and trolleybus

Passenger journeys: 60 million (annual)
Vehicle-km: 10 million (annual) (320 km per vehicle per day)

Number of routes: Bus 8, trolleybus 5
Route length: 105 km
On priority right-of-way: 5 km

Fleet: Approx 145 trolleybuses

MASA-Toshiba (1982/85)	97
MASA/Toshiba articulated (1985/87 ex-Mexico City)	18
Marmon-Herrington (1951/52) in store	approx 30

Fleet: Approx 225 buses

Most intensive service: 5 min
Fare collection system: Payment to driver
Fare evasion control: Roving inspectors
Average distance between stops: 300 m
Average peak-hour speed: 18 km/h
Operating costs financed by: Fares 75 per cent, other commercial sources 5 per cent, subsidy/grants 20 per cent
Subsidy from: Government
New vehicles financed by: State and federal governments

Siteur

Sistema de Tren Eléctrico Urbano (Siteur)
Calz del Federalisimo Sur 217, 44100 Guadalajara
Tel: (+52 3) 613 18 26   Fax: (+52 3) 613 45 17

e-mail: siteur@foreigner.class.udg.mx
Director General: Horacio González Ponce
Director, Technical: Victor M Monraz Ponce
Director, Operations: Arturo Herrera Ramírez
Director, Rolling Stock & Engineering:
  José M Romo Perez
Director, Public Relations: Sandra Carballo Flores
Staff: 678

Current situation: Situer operates the light rail network and a small network of feeder buses. Initial 8.5 km section of east-west Line 2 opened 1994, linking Benito Juarez and Tetlan. This line (including the proposed 4.3 km western extension to Minerva, if built) is entirely underground except for a large new maintenance depot just beyond Tetlán terminus. Three additional lines are planned for opening by 2010.

Light rail

Type of operation: Light rail, first line opened 1989

Passenger journeys: (1994) 30.8 million
(1995) 34 million
(1996) 40.6 million

Route length: 24 km
  in tunnel: 15.1 km
Number of lines: 2
Number of stations: 29
Gauge: 1,435 mm
Track: 115RE 52 kg/m rail on concrete sleepers
Electrification: 750 V DC, overhead

Guadalajara light rail

Trains at the Line 2 terminus at Juárez   1996

Service: Peak 5 min, off-peak 10 min
First/last car: 06.00/23.00
Fare structure: Stage; transfer fee payable between Lines 1 and 2
Fare collection: Coin or token to turnstile
Integration with other modes: Bus feeders to each terminal
Operating costs financed by: Fares 60 per cent

Rolling stock: 48 cars
Concarril/Melmex TLG88 (1989)   M16
Bombardier/Siemens TEG90 (1993/94)   M32
In peak service: 40

Bus
Passenger journeys: (1996) 3 million

Current situation: Seven routes extending to 29 km are operated as feeders to the light rail network, run under contract with 27 vehicles.

Private bus
Current situation: There are two major operators — Alianza, an owners' co-operative, and Servicios y Transport, a franchised private company with 99 per cent of shares now held by the state of Jalisco.

Alianza, formed in 1957, has 730 licence-holders who between them own 1,642 buses; the maximum number of buses that can be owned by any licence-holder is five. Operations are divided into seven sectors of 10-15 routes each. Alianza oversees operations with a small staff; all

maintenance is contracted out. New vehicles are financed from a renewals fund supplied by 20 per cent of daily fares receipts.

Servicios y Transport runs a fleet of about 900 vehicles.

Passenger journeys: 500 million (annual)
Vehicle-km: 130 million (annual)

Number of routes: 140
Route length: 1,351 km

One-person operation: All routes
Fare collection: Payment to driver, or prepurchase
Fare structure: Flat, depending on route
Average speed: 15 km/h
                                                          VERIFIED

GUANGZHOU

Population: 3.3 million, municipal area 8 million
Public transport: Bus, trolleybus and ferry services provided by state/municipal enterprises with three separate bus companies, a trolleybus company itself with four motor bus divisions, a ferry company, minibus and taxi companies. Private/State joint venture bus companies have expanded in the past five years and local private bus operators depart for the outer suburbs with their conductors touting for business as buses slow past bus stops. The legislative position of these latter operations is unclear.

Guangzhou Public Utilities Bureau

Guangzhou, Guangdong Province, People's Republic of China
Director: Liang Zhu Ze
Staff: 30,000 (transport)

Current situation: The Bureau is responsible for planning and management of Guangzhou's public transport, water transport, water and gas supply and other utilities.

Subsidiaries include the Guangzhou City No 1, No 2 and No 3 Bus Companies, the Guangzhou City Trolleybus Company, passenger ship company, Guangzhou Taxi Company, Baiyun Taxi and Minibus Company and the Bureau oversees the state's involvement in joint venture bus operations.

Manufacturing subsidiaries assemble and overhaul buses. Fleet numbers are issued in blocks to the various public and private bus companies, each has an appropriate prefix so that No 2 Bus Co is prefixed 1-, Trolleybus Company D (dien che - electric car), and similar.

Guangzhou City No 1 Bus Co

Current situation: This state-owned company can trace its origins back to 1951 when it was known as the Guangzhou City Bus Company. This was changed to Guangzhou City No 1 Bus Co circa 1977 when the No 2 Bus Co was formed. According to the company's own

Zhujiang-built single-deck bus on Xin Fok Lei Bus Co Route 188 (Mike Davis)   *1999*/0043553

briefing at the 1995 UITP conference in Shanghai, then it operated 47 per cent of city bus routes, had 1,224 vehicles, 10,000 staff and ran 77 routes. Further expansion has since taken place. A pioneer in the use of imported second-hand double-deck buses in 1988, these were all transferred to the then newly formed No 3 Bus Co in 1995. No 1 does, however, operate about 20 Chinese-built FeiHe double-decks fitted with Steyer engines. All other buses are single-deck of various ages, including GZ644s, GZA6120s and newer 25-seaters. By 1998, all articulated buses had been converted to front-entrance rigid and the fleet is 100 per cent one-person operated. As with most state-owned bus operations, there are companies within companies and these are indicated by secondary prefixes to fleet numbers – the first indicating the core operation.

Guangzhou City No 2 Bus Co

Current situation: This company, also state-owned, was formed in 1977. When, in 1995, it presented its company profile at the UITP Shanghai meeting it had a fleet of 746 vehicles and a staff of 7,400. Of the bus fleet, 15 per cent were air conditioned with a target of 50 per cent by 1998.

The number of routes operated was not specified but routes were divided into three categories, urban, suburban and interurban. Suburban routes were described as being of 30 to 40 km, while interurbans were of 100 km and more.

In addition to its fleet of single-deck buses, the company operates a number of second-hand Leyland Fleetline double-decks imported from Kowloon Motor Bus (Hong Kong). By 1998, most of these were out of service but a number, including most which had been converted to left-hand drive, were being rebodied by Guangzhou Cityview Bus Installation Co, brand name 'Eagle', for further service. It is felt, however, that many of the remainder will be scrapped in the near future. The company has recently acquired a number of Eagle single-decks to supplement its ageing fleet of GZ644s and newer GZA6100s. All buses are two-axle rigid and one-person operated. Secondary fleet number prefixes indicate secondary companies as in No 1 Bus Co.

Guangzhou City No 3 Bus Co

Current situation: A third state bus company was formed in 1995. This was to take over 'special' vehicles from No 1 Bus Co, including all foreign-made buses which, in addition to ex-Hong Kong, Singapore and Berlin double-decks, included 23 Neoplan single-decks ex-Pittsburgh. Soon after its formation, additional operating centres were established to operate single-decks and an assortment of older GZ644s and GZA6100s appeared, to be followed by Eagle single-decks and, more recently, growing numbers of smaller 25-seat HDK6702s.

Of the double-decks, by October 1998 only the ex-Berlin MANs remained in service, together with very few ex-London and Hong Kong DMS and KMB Fleetlines, a Dennis Dominator and a few ex-Singapore Atlanteans. Many were seen in a scrap condition at the depot. No 3 Bus Co is no exception to the secondary company principle and within it the 'foreign' vehicles are operated by a 'special' company with an S prefix.

Fares structure: Flat fare: double for air conditioned services

Guangzhou City Trolleybus Bus Co

No 3 Nolingxia Road, Guangzhou
Contact: Huang Hai Jing

Current situation: The Guangzhou City Trolleybus company has five 'companies within the company'. D1

SK5102GB dual-mode trolleybus, built in Shanghai, with traction batteries for negotiating road works and other blockages, on Zhong Shan No 3 Street, Guangzhou (Mike Davis)   *1999*/0043552

operates the trolleybus fleet of 130 vehicles, whilst D2 to D5 operate motor buses. There is also a joint venture with a Macau bus company trading as Xin Fok Lei. The trolleybus system was curtailed along its main east-west corridor on Zhongshan No 3 and No 2 Roads during construction of the cut-and-cover metro, but the full line was restored in October 1998. An extension to the wiring was due to open in late 1998 with the overhead in place in early October. This is to connect the west of the system with the north via Zhongshan No 8, Liwan Road and Dongfeng Road West to rejoin the northern line towards the main rail station and airport via Renmin Road.

Thirty new trolleybuses were delivered in 1998, built in Shanghai and of the SK5102GP type. They have traction batteries weighing 400 kg capable of driving the vehicle at 15 km/h for a distance of 10 km. All older trolleybuses have been converted from articulated to two-axle rigid, with the front of the vehicle, including the driver, moved forward to permit a front entrance ahead of the axle facilitating one-person operation.

Number of routes: 6; plus one awaiting introduction November 1998

Fleet: 130 trolleybuses, all two-axle
Guangzhou GZ664	21
Shanghai SK541	34
Guangzhou GZK6100	20
Hua Yu	15
Shanghai SK5102	40

Electrification: 500 V DC

Fleet: buses
Guangzhou GZ6100
Guangzhou GZK6100A
Guangzhou GZ644
Double-deck buses no longer operated

Service: 4-5 min most routes
Fares structure: Flat fare: Yuan 1 non-air conditioned, Yuan 2 air conditioned

Guangzhou Kwoon Chung Bus Co Ltd
95 Zeng Cha Lu, G/F, Luo Chong Wei, Guangzhou 510160
Tel: (+86 20) 879 04 36 Fax: (+86 20) 879 04 35
Director and General Manager: Patrick Ng King yee

Current situation: Guangzhou Kwoon Chung is a joint venture between Guangzhou No 2 Bus Co and the Kwoon Chung Bus Group of Hong Kong which commenced operations in 1994. The Group also provides management advisory and support services to Guangzhou No 2 Bus Co, to which it makes available 100 buses.

Number of routes: 4

Fleet: 86 buses (plus 100 provided for Guangzhou No 2 Bus Co)

Other bus companies
Xin Fok Lei Bus Co: This is a joint venture between Fok Lei of Macau and Guangzhou Trolleybus Company, with 12 routes and approximately 250 buses.
Guangzhou Jumbo Bus Co: Commenced operating in 1996 and was established as a joint venture owned by Guangzhou No 3 Bus Co and Equity Concepts Ltd, a Hong Kong advertising agency associated with the CNT Group which owns Citybus Ltd in Hong Kong. Ten routes by 1996; 120 buses.

Former BVG Berlin MAN-built double-deck bus opposite Guangzhou railway station (Mike Davis)
1999/0043554

Fu Yu: Commenced mid-1995. Operates services to/from Grand World Scenic Park. Air conditioned and non-air conditioned buses.
Guangzhou Jockey Club Bus Co: Commenced operation 1994/5 on two routes, one air conditioned, one not, based on the Jockey Club.
Sun Sui: Commenced 1994/5 using air conditioned buses on two routes and non-air conditioned on two others.

Other outer suburban services are offered by numerous unidentified buses of various sizes, usually quite old, crewed by a tout who hangs from the vehicle at bus stops seeking business.

Guangzhou City Ferry
Guangzhou Passenger Ship Company

Current situation: The company is mainly responsible for ferry services across the Pearl River, but also serves tourist needs.

Passenger journeys: (1986) 107.9 million
Fleet: 58 vessels

Guangzhou City Taxi & Minibus
Baiyun Minibus & Taxi Company

Minibus
Current situation: Ten paratransit routes were introduced around 1983 with minibuses built in China, bought new from Japan and second-hand from Hong Kong. The operation is thought to have expanded substantially since.

Taxi
Current situation: A fleet of over 6,500 taxis carried 68.7 million passengers in 1986.

Metro
Guangzhou Subway Company
204 Huan Shi Road, Guangzhou 510010
Tel: (+86 20) 667 32 76 Fax: (+86 20) 667 82 32
Project Manager: Jin Feng
Deputy Chief Engineer: Ning Zi Rong

Current situation: The Guangzhou Subway Corporation was incorporated in 1992 to oversee construction of Line

1 of the city's metro, which began in early 1994 after a complicated bidding process. A German consortium headed by Siemens and Adtranz is providing the rolling stock, power supply equipment and other items, while Balfour Beatty Power Construction of the UK is providing the catenary.

Five stations on a 5 km section of Line 1 opened as a 'one-train-in-service' shuttle in June 1998 to test the system 'live' in passenger service. Twenty six-car trains are used in rotation until completion of signalling to allow the use of additional trains in service. The remainder of Line 1 was due for December 1998 opening. The line will eventually cover 18.5 km east-west from East Station of Chinese Railways to the Guangzhou Iron and Steel Works at Huang Sha, running mostly underground with a crossing of the Pearl River and Fang-cun; it will have 16 stations.

A second line was included in the feasibility study completed in 1988 and build-operate-transfer bids for this were called for in 1994. Line 2 will run 26 km roughly north-south from Xinshi, north of the main railway station, to the university, requiring a second crossing of the Pearl River. It will have 22 stations, an interchange with Line 1 at Hai Zhu Square and a depot at the north end.

Line 3 will be a 5.2 km link between the university end of Line 2 and the eastern end of Line 1, where a new sports centre is planned. A 7.8 km extension would run along the riverbank to Xinshou.

Light rail (proposed)
Current situation: Several schemes have been proposed for light rail feeders to the metro. In 1994 the agency which is funding the metro unveiled a plan for a 26 km line with 18 stations along the north bank of the Pearl river between the eastern end of metro Line 1 and a new development zone at Xiagang.

Previously the city was reported to be studying conversion of a 5 km underground air-raid shelter into a tram subway, which was estimated to require two years to complete.

A third scheme, originally promoted by the Foshan Communications Development Corp, would see construction of an 18 km line from Foshan to connect with the western end of metro Line 1 near the steelworks. It is thought that responsibility for this project has passed to the same agency which is promoting the waterfront line, which may have been given a higher priority.

UPDATED

THE HAGUE
Population: 564,000
Public transport: Bus and tramway services (including interurban route to Delft) provided by company owned by the city, with additional suburban bus services operated by regional bus undertakings. Suburban rail services provided by Netherlands Railways (NS)

HTM
NV Gemengd Bedrijf Haagsche Tramweg-Maatschappij (HTM)

Postbus 28503, Dynamostraat 10, 2502 KM The Hague, Netherlands
Tel: (+31 70) 384 84 84 Fax: (+31 70) 384 87 29
Director General: G A Kaper
Staff: 1,829

Current situation: HTM is constituted as a private company, but all shares are owned by the city. From the start of 1996, the regional authority Stadsgewest Haaglanden became the overall co-ordinating body for public transport. It receives subsidy funding from the national government and transfers to HTM such subsidy

as it is entitled to. Services extend beyond the city boundary to serve a total population of some 656,000, and there is close integration of routes and fares with regional bus services. The national standard tariff 'Strippenkaart' multiticket system applies (see Amsterdam for details).

Developments: The tramway Route 17 extension to Rijswijk Steenvoorde was due to open in late 1998. Two other routes are planned to serve the new residential areas of Ypenburg and Wateringse veld. These extensions of the system will start running in 2000. Construction of a tram tunnel under Grote Marktstraat, the city's main shopping street, started in March 1996 as part of a major project to revitalise the city centre. It will be completed in 2000.

HTM is also participating in the RandstadRail project. In co-operation with the rural operator ZWN and Netherlands Railways, a plan has been drawn up to convert main line rail operations on the Zoetermeer and Rotterdam Hofplein lines to light rail, and at the same time integrate the lines with existing tram routes. The intention is to help ease traffic congestion in the southern Randstad area by providing more frequent services and better interchanges. The first stage of this project has been approved for completion in 2003. A tender will be prepared for both infrastructure and operations.

Passenger boardings: (1995) 114.9 million
(1996) 110.1 million
(1997) 115.4 million

Operating costs financed by: Fares 30 per cent, other commercial sources 4.2 per cent, subsidy/grants 65.8 per cent
Subsidy from: Government

Bus

Passenger boardings: (1995) 38.7 million
(1996) 34.1 million
(1997) 36.4 million
Vehicle-km: (1995) 9 million
(1996) 9.5 million
(1997) 9.7 million

Number of routes: 19
Route length: 210.5 km
On priority right-of-way: 9.1 per cent

Fleet: 207 vehicles
DAF 201 (1980/88)	79
Neoplan N4016 low-floor (1990/91)	70
Mercedes low-floor	40
MAN (1997)	2
Den Oudsten articulated (1997)	16

In peak service: 162

Service: Peak 5-15 min, evening 15 min
One-person operation: All routes
Fare collection: Prepurchase pass or ticketcard with card validation on board by driver; or payment to driver
Fare structure: Zonal; prepurchase passes and national Strippenkaart multitickets valid on all modes, Strippenkaart also available from driver
Fare evasion control: Check by driver on boarding; roving inspectors
Bus priority: Philips VETAG/VECOM, also used for point setting and passenger information on tramway
Integration with other modes: Services co-ordinated with those of neighbouring regional bus operators; Strippenkaart gives nationwide standard tram, bus and metro fares
Average speed: 20 km/h

Tramway

Type of operation: Conventional tramway

Passenger boardings: (1995) 76.2 million
(1996) 76.2 million
(1997) 79 million
Car-km: (1995) 8.3 million
(1996) 8.4 million
(1997) 8.5 million

Route length: 131.1 km
  reserved track: 81.8 per cent
Number of lines: 10
Gauge: 1,435 mm
Electrification: 600 V DC, overhead

Service: Peak 5-10 min, evening 15-20 min
One-person operation: All routes
Fare structure: As bus
Fare collection: Pass, prepurchase ticket card or payment to driver; boarding at other doors with cancelling machines
Fare evasion control: Roving inspectors
Tram priority: As bus
Average speed: 18.5 km/h

Rolling stock: 147 cars, plus 10 PCC cars in store
PCC 1100 (1957/58)	M1
PCC 1300 (1971/72)	M9
BN GTL8-1 double-articulated (1981/84)	M100
BN GTL8-2 double-articulated (1992/93)	M47

In peak service: 132

NS

Netherlands Railways
PO Box 2025, 3500 HA, Utrecht
Tel: (+31 30) 235 91 11   Fax: (+31 30) 233 24 58

Type of operation: Suburban heavy rail

Tram at the stop near the new City Hall of The Hague   *1999*/0024980

Mercedes-Benz low-floor bus on newly introduced night bus weekend services   *1999*/0043556

HTM tram passing alongside the new Grote Marktstraat tram tunnel under construction   *1999*/0024981

Current situation: Services provided on five routes into Centraal station. There are seven stations within the city boundaries, served by 5 to 20 trains per hour, more at peak times.

Developments: An additional platform has been built at Centraal station, along with two four-tracking projects to raise capacity.

UPDATED

HAKODATE

Population: 350,000
Public transport: Bus and tramway services operated by municipal undertaking. Privately operated buses serve Hakodate and surrounding areas

Hakodate-shi Kotsu Kyoku

Hakodate City Transport Bureau
4-13 Shinome-cho, Hakodate-shi, Hokkaido 040, Japan
Tel: (+81 138) 26 01 31

Bus

Staff: 108

Passenger journeys: (1994) 10.1 million
Vehicle-km: (1994) 3.4 million

Number of routes: 31
Route length: 95 km
Fleet: 107 vehicles, including Hino and Mitsubishi
In peak service: 92

One-person operation: All routes
Fare collection: Farebox
Fare structure: Stage; prepurchase cards, 1- and 2-day tickets, 1- and 3-month seasons, 1- and 3-month off-peak discount seasons ('Shopper's Season Ticket'), all valid for bus and tram
Operational control: Bus location system

Tramway

Staff: 101

Type of operation: Conventional tramway

Passenger journeys: (1994) 8.3 million
Car-km: 1.1 million

Route length: 11 km
Number of routes: 2
Number of stops: 26
Gauge: 1,372 mm
Electrification: 600 V DC, overhead

Alna Koki car 3001 on Hakodate Route 2   **1996**

Service: Peak 10 min, off-peak 10-20 min
First/last car: 06.30/22.00
Fare collection: Farebox
Fare structure: As bus
One-person operation: All cars

Rolling stock: 35 cars

Nippon Sharyo Type 500 (1948-50)	M3
Nippon Sharyo Type 1000 (ex-Tokyo, 1955)	M3
Niigata Type 710 (1959-61)	M10
Niigata Type 800 (1963-66)	M4
Niigata Type 8000 (rebodied 1990-97)	M8
Alna Koki Type 2000 (1993/94)	M2
Alna Koki Type 3000 (1993/94/96)	M4
Historical car (1993)	M1

In peak service: 23 cars

Hakodate Bus

Hakodate Bus
10-1 Takamuri-cho, Hakodate-shi, Hokkaido 040-0024
Tel: (+81 138) 51 39 60

Bus

Passenger journeys: (Annual) 16 million

Fleet: 204 buses, 13 coaches

Current situation: Hakodate Bus is a subsidiary of the Tokyu Corporation, which has extensive bus and rail interests in the Tokyo area.

UPDATED

HALIFAX

Population: 330,000
Public transport: Bus and ferry services provided by undertaking under control of municipal authority

Metro Transit

Metro Transit, Regional Operations
200 Ilsley Avenue, Dartmouth B3B 1V1, Canada
Tel: (+1 902) 490 66 14   Fax: (+1 902) 490 66 88/66 14
Director of Business Operations: Brian T Smith
Manager, Metro Transit: Brian R Taylor
Manager, Fleet Maintenance: Paul A Beauchamp
Supervisor, Marketing & Public Relations: Lori Patterson
Staff: 420

Current situation: The former Metropolitan Transit Commission, established in 1981 to bring together separate Halifax and Dartmouth transit undertakings, was absorbed in 1986 by its parent body, the Metropolitan Authority. In 1996, Metro Transit became part of the Halifax Regional Municipality under the amalgamation of four municipal units as a single regional authority. The bus and ferry service is now part of a larger Regional Operations Department, which also covers municipal engineering and public works.
Developments: Metro Transit is completing a C$2 million

upgrade of its GoTime automatic vehicle location system. In 1996, a private rural transport operation was absorbed, becoming a Community Transit service. Also in 1996, the 16-vehicle Access-A-Bus operation was transferred from a private contractor to Metro Transit following a public tendering process.

Bus

Passenger journeys: (1994/95) 13 million
(1995/96) 15.4 million
(1996/97) 15.3 million
Vehicle-km: (1995/96) 8.7 million
(1996/97) 8.7 million
(1997/98) 8.7 million

Number of routes: 45
Route length: (One way) 622 km

Fleet: 195 vehicles	
MCI Classic	32
NovaBUS (1993/96)	33
GMC	38
GM New Look	54
Articulated	14
Orion (1990)	4
Paratransit vehicles	20

In peak service: 147 (fixed-route)

Most intensive service: 10 min
Fare collection: Prepurchase or exact fare to farebox
Fare structure: Flat; prepurchase adult, senior and children's tickets; monthly passes
Fares collected on board: 68 per cent
Integration with other modes: Free transfer to ferry; routes serve carpool areas and 11 park-and-ride lots
Operational control: Route inspectors/mobile radio/AVL computers
Arrangements for elderly/disabled: 16 lift-equipped vehicles known as Access-A-Bus, plus hired taxis; 3,374 registered users made 78,800 trips in 1996/97, with a further 40,400 transported by taxi; funded 92 per cent by municipality
Average peak-hour speed: 20.8 km/h
Operating costs financed by: Fares 68 per cent, other commercial sources 3 per cent, tax levy 29 per cent
New vehicles financed by: Metro Transit

Ferry

Current situation: Services between Dartmouth and Halifax are provided every 15 min on a route which is the oldest such salt water operation in North America.

UPDATED

HALLE

Population: 270,000, area served 330,000
Public transport: Tramway and bus services provided by municipal company. State railway runs regional metro (S-Bahn) and two regional bus companies provide suburban services

MDV

Mitteldeutscher Verkehrsverbund (MDV)

Current situation: This is the regional transit authority planned for the Halle/Leipzig region. For details see Leipzig entry.

HAVAG

Hallesche Verkehrs AG (HAVAG)
PO Box 200658, 06007 Halle, Germany
Tel: (+49 345) 56 85 50   Fax: (+49 345) 568 54 40
www: www.havag.com

Technical Director: Rene Pietsch
Commercial Director:
   Dipl Ing/Dipl Wirtsch-Ing François Girard
Technical & Maintenance Manager: Gerd Blumenau
Permanent Way Manager: Peter Thomas
Staff: 1,302

Passenger journeys: (1994) 70.6 million
(1995) 68.3 million
(1996) 67 million

Operating costs financed by: Fares 26.8 per cent, other commercial sources 10.5 per cent, subsidy/grants 62.7 per cent
Subsidy from: Regional government 31 per cent, local government 69 per cent

Current situation: HAVAG provides tramway and feeder bus services in the Halle/Merseburg area, serving a total population of 352,000. Bus services in Halle-Neustadt were taken over from Omnibusbetrieb Saalekreis GmbH when the latter town was incorporated into Halle in 1991. A regional transit authority, Verkehrs- und Tarifgemeinschaft, co-ordinates the services of HAVAG, the S-Bahn and regional bus companies Omnibusbetrieb Saalekreis GmbH and Regiobus Merseburg GmbH.

Bus

Passenger journeys: (1996) 15.5 million
Vehicle-km: (1995) 6.4 million
(1996) 6.5 million
(1997) 6.7 million

Number of routes: 34
Route length: (One way) 272 km
On private right-of-way: 3.6 km
Fleet: 75 vehicles, plus 31 contracted

Standard 2-axle	5
Low-floor Mercedes/Neoplan	50
Neoplan low-floor CNG-powered	2
Standard articulated	7
Low-floor articulated	6
Low-floor articulated CNG-powered	5

In peak service: 79

Most intensive service: 10 min
One-person operation: All routes
Fare collection: Fare to driver or prepurchase; 57 per cent of passengers use passes; 14 sales outlets plus vending machines

Fare structure: Flat, single and multijourney tickets, short-distance ticket valid 10 min; off-peak/daily/monthly passes; annual subscription
Integration with other modes: Joint fare scheme with HAVAG and DB S-Bahn
Arrangements for elderly/disabled: Reduced fares for disabled
Average distance between stops: 610 m

Developments: A 3.6 km private right-of-way was inaugurated in 1993 on the Neustadt—Hallorenring route, and is used by 50 buses/h/direction in the morning peak.

Tramway

Type of operation: Conventional tramway

Passenger journeys: (1996) 51.5 million
Car-km: (1995) 16 million
(1996) 15.8 million
(1997) 15.2 million

Number of routes: 12
Route length: 79.1 km
Average distance between stops: 696 m
Gauge: 1,000 mm
Electrification: 600 V DC, overhead
Service: Peak 10 min

Rolling stock: 368 cars

Esslingen GT4 4-axle articulated	
(ex-Stuttgart/Freiburg 1959/64)	M38
ČKD Tatra T4D/B4D 4-axle (1971/86)	M142 T13
ČKD Tatra T4D/B4D 4-axle (1971/86,	
modernised 1992/94)	M82 T41
Duewag MGT6D 6-axle low-floor (1992/99)	M52

In peak service: 335
On order: Option for 96 Adtranz/Siemens/DWA low-floor for delivery through to 2004

Developments: Extensions planned to Halle-Nord and Halle-Neustadt (7.8 km), plus two short links between existing routes. Construction of the 7.8 km route to Halle-Neustadt started in 1998, with opening projected for the first section in 2000 and the whole line in 2005.

Studies have been made of plans to deliver goods to businesses in the historic central area by tram. Though technically feasible, this would be more expensive than using road vehicles, as at present.

A new depot at Rosengarten opened in late 1997.

DB

Deutsche Bahn AG, Geschäftsbereich Nahverkehr Regionalbereich Sachsen-Anhalt/Leipzig
Ernst-Kamieth-Strasse 2, 06112 Halle
Tel: (+49 345) 215 33 31   Fax: (+49 345) 215 17 05
Manager: Thomas Hoffmann

S-Bahn

Type of operation: Regional suburban rail (S-Bahn)

Passenger journeys: (1996) 30.1 million (all regional services)

Current situation: The S-Bahn runs 22.8 km over a U-shaped loop from Halle-Trotha in the northeast via Halle Hbf and Halle-Neustadt to Halle-Dölau in the northwest. Most intensive service is every 20 min, provided by seven push-pull sets of double-deck cars hauled by electric locomotives.
Developments: Introduction of park-and-ride is planned at the Trotha and Dölau terminals, which are to be linked by the year 2000 to provide a full circular service. The connection would serve a new housing development.

Construction work started in 1997 on a new link from Halle to Leipzig (32.3 km, 12 stations), scheduled for completion in 2001 and it is expected that double-deck trains will be used.

UPDATED

HAMBURG

Population: 1.7 million, area served 2.3 million
Public transport: All public transport in Hamburg and the adjoining metropolitan area is co-ordinated by a public transit authority, Hamburger Verkehrsverbund (HVV). Bus and metro services are provided by city transport company, ferry services by city shipping company, urban and regional rail (S-Bahn) by DB subsidiary HSBG, other regional services by three bus companies and a local railway (AKN), and park-and-ride facilities by a separate company, all government-owned

HVV

Hamburger Verkehrsverbund (HVV)
Steinstrasse 7, 20095 Hamburg, Germany
Tel: (+49 40) 302 30   Fax: (+49 40) 302 31 12
www: www.hvv.com
Chairman: Peter Kellermann
Director: Lutz Aigner
Transport & Infrastructure Manager: Bernd Rust
Commercial Manager: Jörg Mampe
Purchasing Manager: Hans-Heinz Kirchhoff

Passenger journeys: (All modes)
(1995) 481 million
(1996) 478 million
(1997) 477 million

Fare collection: Single tickets (payment to driver or from vending machine), day tickets, weekly or monthly passes, annual subscription, bulk sales of passes to employers at reduced rates; Card+Ride introduced 1994; onboard sales (bus only) 19 per cent. As an experiment, 50 HHA ticket machines have been adapted to accept payment by a smartcard which also serves as a telephone card
Fare structure: Zonal, transfers free, premium for express bus or first class on S-Bahn; reduced price passes for off-peak travel
Fare evasion control: Random inspection; penalty
Arrangements for elderly/disabled: Reduced rate passes for disabled, paid by government
Operating costs financed by: Fares 52 per cent, contractual grants 7 per cent, subsidy 41 per cent

Current situation: HVV, which was formerly a co-ordinating body of transport operators in the conurbation,

was restructured in 1996. It is now controlled by the city of Hamburg (85 per cent), the *Land* of Schleswig-Holstein (2 per cent) and six rural districts (Kreis/Land Kreis). The total HVV area is around 3,000 km², with a population of 2.3 million, for which a route network of 2,163 km and 2,989 stopping points is provided.

HVV has established a zonal ticket system allowing free intermodal transfer and integrated services with an overall passenger information system. Park-and-ride sites total 84 with 14,590 spaces, and developers wishing to provide inner city parking are required to pay for construction of an equal number of parking places at a suburban park-and-ride station.

About 300 cycle lockers were introduced at 32 stations in 1998.

Hamburger Hochbahn

Hamburger Hochbahn Aktiengesellschaft (HHA)
PO Box 102720, 20019 Hamburg
Tel: (+49 40) 328 80   Fax: (+49 40) 32 88 45 62
Board of Directors: Dipl Econ Günter Elste
  Dipl-Ing Holger Albert
  Dr Ulf Lange
Operating Manager, Bus: Dipl-Ing Herbert Hussmann

Operating Manager, Metro: Dipl-Ing Ulrich Sieg
Staff: 4,475

Passenger journeys: (All modes)
(1995) 402 million
(1996) 400 million
(1997) 348 million

Operating costs covered by: (All modes) Fares 51 per cent, other commercial sources 10 per cent, subsidy/grants 35 per cent
Subsidy from: State and city

Current situation: HHA provides services both direct and through 14 subsidiary companies and affiliated divisions. These include the shipping lines HADAG (see below) and ATG Alster-Touristik, the bus undertaking Jasper, the central bus station, the cleaning company TEREG, a bus company, a staff accommodation service, and a security company. HHA also operates the vehicle research and development company FFG and has a consulting subsidiary Hamburg-Consult.

Arrangements for elderly/disabled: All future bus purchases will be of low-floor types with wheelchair ramp;

Mercedes-Benz Citaro bus of HHA at Hamburg Harburg (Wilhelm Pflug)   **1999**/0043557

Hamburger Hochbahn DT4 trainset by Hamburg harbour   ***1999**/0043559*

70 per cent of the fleet is currently accessible. Lifts have been installed at 25 metro stations; guidelines being installed in platform floors for visually impaired and blind people

Bus
Staff: 2,025

Passenger journeys: (1995) 224.1 million
(1996) 222.8 million
(1997) 222.3 million
Vehicle-km: (revised figures)
(1995) 52.6 million
(1996) 51.4 million
(1997) 50.5 million

Number of routes: 119
Route length: (One way) 750 km
On priority right-of-way: 21 km
Average distance between stops: 566 m ordinary, 691 m express

Fleet: 647 vehicles, plus 312 contracted
Mercedes O405 standard (1984/86)   95
Mercedes O405G articulated (1987)   50
Mercedes O405N low-floor (1991/97)   392
Mercedes O405GN low-floor articulated (1992) 75
Mercedes Citaro (1997)   35
In peak service: 501
New vehicles required each year: 40
Average age of fleet: 5 years

Most intensive service: 3-5 min
One-person operation: All routes
Fares collected on board: 26 per cent
Operational control: Computer-aided control system RBL
Integration with other modes: Tickets interchangeable between all modes; single ticket covers any journey by any combination of modes. Computerised passenger information system provides personalised optimal travel details. Many stations have bus feeders, with other main corridors served by express buses to the city centre; park-and-ride encouraged. At Dehnhaide metro/bus interchange signals warn bus drivers of late running of metro trains so they may wait for transferring passengers; more such installations under construction
Average speed: 19.7 km/h ordinary, 21.9 km/h express
New vehicles financed by: Leasing

Developments: There are five bus depots, with managers who since 1996 have taken over a wide range of responsibilities formerly vested in head office, including staffing, vehicles, infrastructure and subcontracting.
    A fleet of 245 rigid and 75 articulated buses has been leased from Mercedes-Benz Charter-Way rather than purchased. Maintenance is the responsibility of the lessor.

A first batch of Mercedes-Benz Citaro buses entered service in 1997/98. Work on a major rebuild of the central bus station in Hamburg (ZOB) began in 1998.

Metro
Staff: 1,631 (total)

Type of operation: Full metro, first line opened 1912

Passenger journeys: (1995) 178.2 million
(1996) 177.1 million
(1997) 176.7 million
Car-km: (1995) 58.4 million
(1996) 58.1 million
(1997) 60.2 million

Route length: 100.7 km
  in tunnel: 41.5 km
  elevated: 9 km
Number of lines: 3
Number of stations: 89
Gauge: 1,435 mm
Track: 49 kg/m S49 rail, sleepers on ballast
Max gradient: 5 per cent
Minimum curve radius: 70 m
Tunnel: Bored single-track, concrete caisson, bored double-track
Electrification: 750 V DC, third rail

Service: Peak 2-5 min, off-peak 5-10 min
First/last train: 04.05/01.16
Surveillance: CCTV on most platforms
Fare evasion control: Random inspection, penalty fare

Series ET474 LHB/Adtranz S-Bahn stock at Hamburg Ohlsdorf   ***1999**/0043558*

Rolling stock: 836 cars
LHB DT2 (1962/66)   M300
LHB DT3 (1968/71)   M252
LHB DT4 (1989/95/97)   M284
In peak service: 687
On order: Further 15 DT4 four-car sets for 1999 delivery

Developments: 'Trainscreen' visual information system installed in metro cars provides service information, news, entertainment and commercials. LCD flat screens and wireless data transfer technology is used.
    Station staff are expected to be eliminated by 2000, when new technology will permit 'self dispatch' of trains by drivers.

Ferry
Operated by ATG Alster-Touristik GmbH

Current situation: 17 ships operate one short crossing of the Alster plus tourist cruises.

HADAG

HADAG Seetouristik und Fährdienst AG
St Pauli Fischmarkt 28, 20359 Hamburg
Tel: (+49 40) 311 70 70   Fax: (+49 40) 31 17 07 10
www: www.hadag.de
Director: Jens Wrage

Ferry
Staff: 113

Passenger journeys: (1994) 2.2 thousand
(1995) 2.2 thousand
Ship-km: (1993) 640.5 thousand
(1994) 636.3 thousand

Current situation: This subsidiary of HHA operates 18 vessels on eight routes in the harbour and on the River Elbe, with a total route length of 27.6 km and a frequency of 15 minutes (at peak times). Its 50 per cent shareholding in Elbe-City-Jet (see below) was sold in 1997.

S-Bahn Hamburg

Hamburg S-Bahn GmbH
Steinstrasse 12, 20095 Hamburg
Tel: (+49 40) 39 18 39 04   Fax: (+49 40) 39 18 21 84
Directors: Peter Hofmann
    Wolfgang Wöbken
Staff: 1,259

Type of operation: Urban heavy rail

Passenger journeys: (1994) 148.9 million
(1996) 149.6 million
(1997) 139.7 million

Current situation: HSBG was created at the beginning of 1997 as a wholly owned subsidiary of DB. The network comprises six routes with 59 stations extending to 110 km, 1,435 mm gauge, electrified at 1.2 kV DC third rail. Trains run every five minutes in the peak, 10-20

minutes off-peak, with service 04.00-24.00. Most stations are unstaffed, and all trains are driver-only operated. Fares cover about 60 per cent of operating costs.
Developments: Upgrading of stations and signalling installations on the Wedel—Poppenbüttel line planned, along with a computer-based system to guarantee connections for the 50 per cent of passengers who transfer to or from other modes. In 1997, Line S21 was extended to Reinbek, with a further extension to Aumühle due to open in 2000.

Long-term plans envisage extension of third-rail S-Bahn routes beyond present terminals to Buxtehude, Elmshorn (at present served by regional rail, see below), Quickborn and Ahrensburg. Plans for a route from Ohlsdorf to Fuhlsbüttel airport have now been proposed. A decision on this extension is not expected before 2000.

New rolling stock to replace Series 471 and 470 emus commenced delivery in 1997, but was beset with teething problems. Linke-Hofmann-Busch and Adtranz are supplying 103 three-car ET474 series emus, delivery of which started in 1997.

Number of stations: 59
Operational control: CCTV on platforms
Fare evasion control: Roving inspectors

Rolling stock: 169 three-car emus
Series 471/871 (1939/58)   M122 T61
Series 470/870 (1959/70)   M90 T45
LHB/MBB Series 472/473 (1974/84)   M186
LHB/Adtranz Series ET474 (1997/98)   M3
On order: 103 three-car emus for delivery through to 2002

Regionalbahn Schleswig-Holstein
Regionalbahn Schleswig-Holstein GmbH
Walkerdamm 1, 24103 Kiel

Type of operation: Suburban heavy rail

Passenger journeys: (1994) 11.4 million
(1996) 11.5 million

Current situation: RSH is a wholly owned subsidiary of DB. Amongst other services, it runs outer-suburban trains in the HVV area over 38 route-km serving 12 stations. Statistics apply only to services within the HVV area.

Rolling stock: 47 coaches, push-pull trains propelled by main line AC electric or diesel locomotives

AKN
Altona-Kaltenkirchen-Neumünster Railway
PO Box 106322, 20019 Hamburg
Tel: (+49 40) 73 33 41   Fax: (+49 40) 73 33 42 88
Director: Dipl-Ing Johannes Kruszynski
Staff: 314

Type of operation: Local rail

Passenger journeys: (1995) 6.6 million
(1996) 5.7 million
(1997) 4.6 million

Current situation: Provides suburban services over three routes run in connection with metro and S-Bahn lines, totalling 50 km with 29 stations.
Developments: Since September 1996, one of the former AKN routes is operated under contract to a local authority, hence the reduction in passenger journeys. AKN also operates a rural 61 km line under contract for DB.

Rolling stock: 68 diesel railcars

VHH
Verkehrsbetriebe Hamburg-Holstein AG
Curslacker Neuer Deich 37, 21029 Hamburg
Tel: (+49 40) 725 60 70   Fax: (+49 40) 72 56 07 22
Board of Directors:
  Dipl-Volksw Josef Hoffstadt
  Dipl-Ing Holger Albert
Staff: 927

Bus
Passenger journeys: (1995) 38.2 million
(1996) 38.8 million
(1997) 38.7 million
Vehicle-km: (1995) 15.6 million

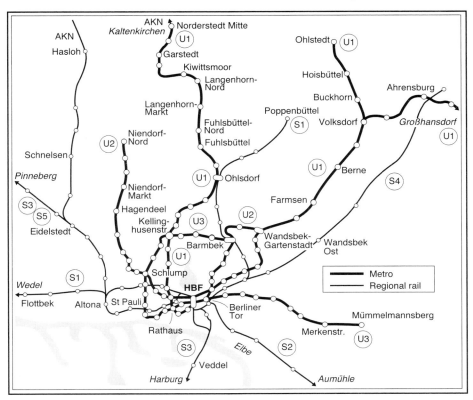
Hamburg's metro and S-Bahn

(1996) 17.4 million
(1997) 16 million

Number of routes: 68
Route length: 726 km

Fleet: 279 buses, plus 45 contracted

Current situation: Under the same management as HHA, VHH provides regional bus services under the auspices of HVV. Some routes also operated outside the HVV area (not included in statistics above).

PVG
Pinneberger Verkehrsgesellschaft mbH
PO Box 1326, 22860 Schenefeld
Tel: (+49 40) 83 99 40   Fax: (+49 40) 83 99 42 80/81
Director: Ralf-Dieter Pemöller
Staff: 439

Bus
Passenger journeys: (1995) 5.9 million
(1996) 5.8 million
(1997) 6 million
Vehicle-km: (1995) 1.6 million
(1996) 1.6 million
(1997) 1.7 million

Number of routes: 8 (in HVV area)
Route length: 81 km

Fleet: 191 buses (all services)

Current situation: PVG, majority-owned by the city of Hamburg, provides local bus services in the western part of Hamburg and Pinneberg region (both within and outside the HVV area), and in the western part of Hamburg on behalf of HHA. Statistics above apply only to operations directly for HVV. A total of 24 routes is operated (eight direct for HVV, 11 on behalf of HHA and five in the Pinneberg region).

PVG wants to expand its activities and has participated in a competitive tendering scheme outside its traditional operations area. Third-party maintenance work is also carried out.

KVG
Kraftverkehr GmbH
PO Box 1525, 21655 Stade
Tel: (+49 4131) 606 10   Fax: (+49 4131) 60 61 24
Directors: Heinz-Dieter Pohl
  Reinhard Stüttgen

Bus
Passenger journeys: (1994) 2.5 million
(1996) 2.5 million
Vehicle-km: (1994) 1.4 million
(1996) 1.5 million

Fleet: 30 buses

Current situation: Regional bus company, formerly associated with DB. The company, which was taken over by local government in 1996, provides rural and urban transit in area south of River Elbe from Cuxhaven in north to Luneburg in south. Only 10 out of a total of 197 routes are integrated in HVV. Statistics apply only to operations within the HVV area.

Elbe-City-Jet
SAL Schiffahrtskontor/Altes Land GmbH & Co
Bürgerei 29, 21720 Steinkirchen
Tel: (+49 4142) 818 10   Fax: (+49 4142) 35 11
Managing Director: Hans Heinrich

Current situation: This joint venture between operator SAL and KG Seetourist of Flensburg was formed to run a commuter ferry route on the River Elbe between Hamburg and Stade, which was inaugurated in 1996 using two jet catamarans. Claimed to offer a much faster journey than road or rail, the service did not immediately attract substantial patronage. In late 1996, there were only some 150 regular passengers of the estimated 16,000 daily commuters between the two cities.
Developments: A third catamaran has been acquired to run a tourist service between Hamburg and Cuxhaven, causing the original partner HADAG to pull out.

P+R
P+R Betriebsgesellschaft mbH
Steinstrasse 20, 20095 Hamburg
Tel: (+49 40) 32 88 25 53   Fax: (+49 40) 32 88 28 74
Managing Director: Dipl-Ing Axel von Knobloch

Current situation: At 85 stations in the Hamburg area some 16,000 park-and-ride spaces are available. Expansion in 1998 will raise this figure to 18,500. Cycle lockers were introduced at some locations in 1996.

P+R, a management company for park-and-ride, operates sites at 18 stations with some 6,164 spaces. It became a full member of HVV in 1990. It is controlled by the City of Hamburg commercial holding, with the German Automobile Club (ADAC) having a 5 per cent shareholding.

UPDATED

HAMILTON

Population: 400,000
Public transport: Bus services provided by publicly owned company operating as a division of Regional Transportation Department

Hamilton Street Railway

The Hamilton Street Railway Company
330 Wentworth Street North, Hamilton, Ontario L8L 5W2, Canada
Tel: (+1 905) 528 42 00   Fax: (+1 905) 528 54 10
Chair, Transportation Services: Terry Anderson
Commissioner of Transportation: Dale Turvey
Director of Operations: Don Hull
Staff: 721

Current situation: HSR is publicly owned by the Regional Municipality of Hamilton-Wentworth.

Bus

Passenger boardings: (1993) 27.8 million
(1994) 26.7 million
(1995) 26.3 million

Number of routes: 31
Route length: 300 km (one way)

Fleet: 214 buses
GM Canada	75
Flyer (1979)	20
GMC articulated (1982)	12
MCI Canada (1987/88)	29
GMC natural gas-converted	8
Orion (1989)	15
Orion CNG-powered (1991/92)	30
New Flyer low-floor (1996)	25

In peak service: 175

Most intensive service: 4-6 min
One-person operation: All routes

CNG-powered New Flyer low-floor of HSR at Gore Park (Bill Luke)   **1999**/0043560

Fare collection: Exact fare to electronic farebox or prepurchase
Fare structure: Flat; free transfer to next available bus; monthly passes, student semester passes
Fare evasion control: By driver
Operational control: Mobile radio on all vehicles, with automatic passenger counting as part of AVLC project; emergency button access to control room
Arrangements for elderly/disabled: 25 low-floor buses on regular service; special service provided by another regional department; 45 buses have kneeling capability; accessible taxi service. 'Easier Access' programme designed to improve access to public transport for elderly and disabled people
Average peak-hour speed: 21 km/h
Operating costs financed by: Fares 40.5 per cent, other commercial sources 5.3 per cent, subsidy/grants 54.2 per cent
Subsidy from: Region of Hamilton and Ontario government
New vehicles financed by: 75 per cent government of Ontario, 25 per cent Regional Municipality

VERIFIED

HANGZHOU

Population: 1.4 million
Public transport: Bus and trolleybus services provided by municipal agency; extensive paratransit services by private operators; light rail planned

Hangzhou Public Transport

Hangzhou Public Transport Company
195 Kaixuan Road, Hangzhou, Zhejiang Province, People's Republic of China
Tel: (+86 571) 604 98 00   Fax: (+86 571) 604 91 01
Chief Engineer: Jin Ling

Current situation: A citywide bus network is operated using two-axle and articulated buses, supplemented by four trolleybus routes. Ex-Hong Kong double-deckers run on one scenic route. One trolleybus route, though complete and shown on maps, seems not to have been opened.
Developments: Three light rail routes are planned, totalling 37.7 km.

Bus
Staff: 6,500

Vehicle-km: (1994) 35.6 million

Number of routes: 63
Route length: 869 km

Fleet: 738 vehicles, including 240 articulated. All Hangzhou except for 100 Chang Jiang CJ6922CH recently delivered and a few Daimler double-deck from Hong Kong

Fare collection: Stage fares paid to seated conductor; monthly passes

Trolleybus
Staff: 2,000

Hangzhou central bus station   **1996**

Vehicle-km: (1994) 7.3 million

Number of routes: 4
Route length: 40.1 km
Fleet: 142 Hangzhou 561 articulated, also about 40 buses for suspended trolleybus route (Hangzhou 661 and 641 articulated)

Fare collection: Stage fares paid to seated conductor; monthly passes
Integration with other modes: Suburban trolleybus terminals are interchange points for bus services to outer suburbs

VERIFIED

Carrus-bodied Volvo low-floor CNG-powered bus in the HKL fleet **1999**/0043565

Fares collected on board: 17 per cent of total revenue
Fare evasion control: Roving inspectors for bus, tram and metro; spot fine

Current situation: There is a common flat fare system on all modes operating within the city, including the contracted bus and rail services, and the ferry, with revenue pooling through HKL or the Metropolitan Area Council, and payment to operators according to their contribution.
Developments: The growth in public transport journeys continued in 1997. The metro extension (with three stations) was opened in August 1998. Tram stops have been renewed with higher platforms, new shelters and better information. All new buses are low-floor and the first natural gas buses have been operating since spring 1998. Projects for improvement of customer information include a website, which has been operating since 1997. Real-time information in bus and tram stops and inside vehicles started operation at the end of 1998.
The first round of tendering in bus traffic was implemented in 1997-98. The second round will be in operation from the beginning of summer 1999.
New low-floor tramcars are being delivered from the end of 1998 and all 20 cars by 2000. Twelve two-car metro car sets will be delivered 2000-2002.

Bus (HKL)
Staff: 975

Passenger boardings: (1994) 70.8 million
(1995) 70.7 million
(1996) 69.9 million
Vehicle-km: (1994) 18.3 million
(1995) 18.8 million
(1996) 19.1 million

Number of routes: 55 (46 regular, 9 peak-only)
Route length: 450 km

Fleet: 378 buses

Volvo B10M (1986/87/88/89/90/91)	192
Volvo B10BLE low-floor	23
Volvo-Wiima articulated	72
Volvo-Wiima articulated low-floor	2
Scania N112CL60 (1988)	25
Scania N113CLB low-floor	11
Scania L113TLL low-floor	4
Scania MaxCi N113CLL (1997)	21
MAN LPG-powered (1991)	1
Mercedes O405 N2 low-floor	4
Volvo B10L (1997)	6
Volvo B10L CNG (1998)	11
Volvo B10B (1998)	4
DAB low-floor midibus (1998)	1
Ikarus low-floor midibus (1998)	1
In peak service: 315	

Most intensive service: 5 min; about 20 sec on route with several lines
One-person operation: All routes
Fare collection: Prepurchase or single tickets from driver with Almex-M self-service cancellers
Average distance between stops: 400 m

Average peak-hour speed: 26.5 km/h
Bus priority: 42 km of bus lanes
Integration with other modes: Full integration of fares and services
Operational control: Mobile radio on all vehicles; central control room and radio patrol cars
New vehicles financed by: Municipal grant

Contract bus services (SLH/STA)
SLH (private companies in joint fares arrangement) and STA (Suomen Turistauto Oy)
Operated under contract to HKL
Staff: 761

Passenger boardings: (1995) STA 16.4 million, SLH 16 million
(1996) STA 16 million, SLH 15 million
(1997) STA 16.2 million, SLH 15.5 million
Vehicle-km: (1995) STA 6.4 million, SLH 8.3 million
(1996) STA 6.5 million, SLH 8.3 million
(1997) STA 6.5 million, SLH 8.4 million

Number of routes: 30 (STA 9 regular, 5 peak-only; SLH 13 regular, 3 peak-only)
Route length: STA 185 km; SLH 246 km

Fleet: 273 vehicles
In peak service: 227

Metro
Type of operation: Full metro, initial route opened 1982

Passenger boardings: (1995) 38.8 million
(1996) 40.6 million
(1997) 42.3 million
Car-km: (1995) 8.6 million
(1996) 9.1 million
(1997) 8.95 million

Route length: 21.1 km
  in tunnel: 6.5 km
Number of stations: 16
  in tunnel: 7
Gauge: 1,524 mm
Max gradient: 3.5%
Minimum curve radius: 300 m
Electrification: 750 V DC, third rail

Service: 3-10 min
First/last train: 05.25/23.23

Rolling stock: 42 two-car sets
Valmet Oy/Strömberg Oy   M84
In peak service: 18 trains
On order: 12 two-car sets from DWA, with delivery starting in mid-2000

Current situation: The line is the first of a planned network agreed by the city council in 1969. A 4 km branch from Itäkeskus to Vuosaari with three stations was opened in August 1998.

Tramway
Type of operation: Conventional tramway

Passenger boardings: (1995) 51.6 million
(1996) 52.6 million
(1997) 53.6 million
Car-km: (1995) 5.2 million
(1996) 5.3 million
(1997) 5.7 million

Route length: 76 km
  on reserved track: 54 km
Number of lines: 12
Max gradient: 8%
Minimum curve radius: 15 m
Electrification: 600 V DC, overhead

Service: Peak 5 min
First/last car: 05.30/01.30
One-person operation: All routes

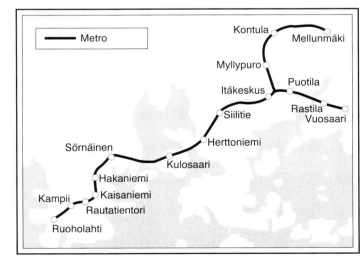

Helsinki metro
0009919

Rastila metro station, Helsinki, opened in 1998 **1999**/0043566

Rolling stock: 104 cars

Karia/Valmet 4-axle (1959)	M22
Valmet 6-axle articulated (1973/75)	M40
Valmet 6-axle articulated (1983/87)	M42

In peak service: 90
On order: 20 low-floor cars from Adtranz and Rautaruukki Oy; delivery started in November 1998 and will run through to the end of 2000

VR

VR Ltd
S-Train Unit, Helsinki
PO Box 488, 00101 Helsinki
Tel: (+358 9) 70 71   Fax: (+358 9) 707 28 95
Route Manager: Kari Pekka Rosenholm

Type of operation: Suburban heavy rail

Passenger journeys: (1995) 33.2 million
(1996) 36 million
(1997) 38 million

Current situation: VR operates suburban trains on three routes out of Helsinki, to Karjaa, Vantaankoski and

Riihimäki, totalling 173 km, 52 stations, electrified 25 kV 50 Hz. Minimum one or two trains per hour (four trains peak hours, every 5 min between Helsinki and Tikkurila); zonal fares.

In the Helsinki metropolitan area, VR has an agreement with the Helsinki Metropolitan Area Council (YTV) regarding provision of suburban service, under which tickets issued by the participating municipalities are valid on VR trains. Outside the metropolitan area only VR's zonal tickets are valid. The traffic figures above apply to the whole Helsinki suburban operation.

Developments: The current agreement between VR and the Helsinki Metropolitan Area Council runs through to the end of 1999, and will remain in force thereafter unless new provisions are required to encourage competing services.

VR is refurbishing suburban trains at a rate to ensure that half the services currently purchased by the council will be operated by refurbished units by 1999. The council pays VR a special fee linked to the number of refurbished trains in operation. VR ordered 10 two-car emus from Fiat for introduction in late 1998.

Under traffic plans for Helsinki in the period through to 2020, additional tracks are proposed from Helsinki to Leppävaara and later Espoo Centre, as well as from Tikkurila to Kerava.

The agreement also allows for implementation of the LILI programme of co-ordination with other operators, designed to improve feeder services at many stations. The unified ticketing system is being extended, and smartcards are being introduced in 1998. The ultimate aim is for electronic ticketing to cover the whole metropolitan area.

Rolling stock: 110 two-car emus, 57 coaches, 6 electric locomotives

Valmet Oy Sm1 (1968)	M50 T50
Valmet Oy Sm2 (1975)	M50 T50
Fiat Sm4 (1999)	M10 T10
Coaches VR Pasila works (1982)	T57

Ferry

Current situation: 10 routes operate both short inner-harbour crossings and longer routes to off-islands. One ferry operates all year round.

UPDATED

HIROSHIMA

Population: 1 million, metropolitan area 1.1 million
Public transport: Bus, light rail and tramway services provided by private company. Three other main private bus operators. Commuter rail services run by JR West. Astram automated guideway

Hiroshima Dentetsu 'Hiroden'

Hiroshima Electric Railway Company
2-9-29 Higashi Senda-machi, Naka-ku, Hiroshima 730-8610, Japan
Tel: (+81 82) 242 35 25   Fax: (+81 82) 242 35 92
President: Tetsuya Ota
Managing Director: Hitoshi Sato
Staff: 1,890

Current situation: Hiroden is responsible for a substantial proportion of the Hiroshima area public transport. Tramways serve the inner city; a through service is operated across the city centre over tramway tracks to the main railway station from Hiroden's Miyajima light rail line. Bus services are provided by Hiroden and five other companies.

Other commercial activities, including the New Hiroden Hotel, retail stores and housing development, assist the public transport operation to remain generally subsidy-free apart from support to maintain bus services to outlying areas. Bus services account for 54.7 per cent of income, trams and light rail 30.5 per cent, and other activities 14.8 per cent.

Bus
Staff: 990

Passenger journeys: (1997/98) 52.4 million, city routes 25 million
Vehicle-km: (1997/98) 32 million, city routes 8.3 million

Hiroden Mitsubishi low-floor non-step bus heading for University Hospital (A W Phipps)   **1999**/0043570

Number of routes: 439, including 14 city routes
Route length: 2,192 km (city routes 107 km)
On priority right-of-way: 128.3 km

Fleet: 644 buses and coaches, of which 235 buses used on city routes

Most intensive service: 2-3 min
One-person operation: All routes
Fare collection: Payment to farebox by driver on alighting, or prepurchase
Fare structure: Stage; 1-, 3- and 6-month passes; prepurchase coupons and stored fare 'Prepaid Card' valid for all six bus operators, tramway, light rail and Astram
Fare evasion control: Penalty payment
Integration with other modes: Bus operations fully integrated with light rail and Astram

Average distance between stops: 300-400 m
Average peak-hour speed: In mixed traffic, 12-13 km/h; in bus lanes, 20 km/h
Operational control: Computerised bus location and passenger information system on city routes

Bus priority: Bus lanes. Onboard traffic light control to give priority as bus approaches. A 'Centre Line Transfer System' was introduced on National Road Route 54, which connects the northwest area with the city centre, with one bus every 30 s in peak hours and one every 2 min at other times. One lane of a four-lane 5.7 km section of road is exclusively available to buses in peak hours.
New vehicles financed by: Internal funds. New low-floor buses part-subsidised by city and prefecture.

Current situation: Operations include a network of numbered city routes and a large number of unnumbered outer suburban and rural routes mainly serving the western half of Hiroshima prefecture.
Developments: Hiroden and Hiroshima Bus each acquired eight Mitsubishi MP747K 'non-step' low-floor buses in December 1997, partly funded by Hiroshima city and prefecture, to upgrade urban services. These vehicles feature kneeling suspension, wheelchair ramp and an 'idling-stop' system to reduce emissions.

Light rail
Staff: (Light rail and tramway) 584

Type of operation: Light rail transit (Miyajima line)

Passenger journeys: (1997/98) 20.7 million

Route length: 16.1 km
Number of lines: 1
Number of stops: 20
Gauge: 1,435 mm
Electrification: 600 V DC, overhead

Service: Peak 3 min, off-peak 6-7 min
First/last train: 05.50/23.33

Hiroden Green Liner Class 3950 LRV at Hiroshima station (A W Phipps)   **1999**/0043571

One-person operation: None
Fare structure: Graduated; day tickets (city tramway and light rail); 1-, 3- and 6-month passes, 'Prepaid Card' valid for all six bus operators, tramway, light rail and Astram
Fare collection: Payment to farebox on alighting; at Hiroshima station pavement conductors collect fares with mobile fareboxes

Rolling stock: 41 articulated trams, 4 two-car sets and a single car; fleet includes 2 Duewag cars ex-Dortmund

Developments: Six new Type 3950 'Green Liner' three-section articulated cars were delivered by Alna Koki between December 1997 and March 1998. Hiroden's first low-floor car is on order for delivery in 1999, with a total of 12 due in service on the Miyajima line by 2001.

Tramway
Type of operation: Conventional tramway

Passenger journeys: (1997/98) 44.9 million
Car-km: (1997/98) 4.9 million

Route length: 18.8 km
Number of lines: 7
Number of stops: 61
Gauge: 1,435 mm
Electrification: 600 V DC, overhead

Service: Peak 5-10 min; off-peak 5-11½ min
First/last tram: 06.00/23.03
Fare structure: Flat; day tickets (city tramway only and city tramway/light rail), 1-, 3- and 6-month passes, 'Prepaid Card' valid for all six bus operators, tramway, light rail and Astram
Fare collection: As light rail
One-person operation: All routes

Rolling stock: 86 bogie cars and 3 two-axle historical cars used on city routes; includes many second-hand cars from other Japanese systems

Kinami Sharyo (1940/42)	M7
Fuji Car (1950)	M3
Naniwa Koki (1953/55/57/58)	M27
Kobe Municipal Transport (1954)	M3
Kawasaki Rolling Stock (1956/60)	M7
Kisha Seizo Kaisha (1958)	M2
Osaka Sharyo Kogyo (1957/60)	M12
Alna Koki (1982/83/85/87/89/90/92/97)	M25
Osaka Sharyo (1984) (historical car)	M1
Class 150 (1987) (historical car)	M1
Class 200 ex-Hannover	M1

Current situation: The city tramway system has a centralised control system. The location of cars is shown on an indicator board in the control centre and instructions to drivers are given by means of light signals at some stops. At some stops passenger information about the route of the next car is shown by light signals.

Hiroshima Kosoku Kotsu
Hiroshima Rapid Transit
2-12-1, Choraku-ji, Asa minami-ku, Hiroshima-shi 731-0413
Tel: (+81 82) 830 31 11   Fax: (+81 82) 830 31 14
President: T Fukushima
Staff: 221

Type of operation: Rubber-tyred guideway system Astram

Passenger journeys: (1997) 18.2 million
Car-km: (1994/95, 9 months) 5.7 million

Route length: 18.4 km
Number of lines: 1
Number of stations: 21
Track: Elevated with side guidance
Electrification: 750 V DC

Service: 3-20 min
First/last train: 06.00/23.50
One-person operation: All trains
Fare structure: Graduated distance-related; commuter and student passes; bus/Astram transfer tickets; stored fare 'Astram Card'
Fare collection: AFC

Hiroshima Kawasaki-built 1155 on Route 3 to Koi (Colin Brown)   **1999**/0043568

Fare collection at Hiroshima station tram terminus (A W Phipps)   **1999**/0043569

Rolling stock: 23 six-car trains
Niigata/Mitsubishi (1994/98)   M138
In peak service: 114 cars

Current situation: This third sector line opened in 1994 linking central Hiroshima and the Asian Games stadium in the northern suburbs. Feeder bus routes link residential areas with several Astram stations.

Hiroshima Kotsu 'Hiroko'
Hiroshima Transport Company Limited
14-17 Misasa-machi 3-chome, Nishi-ku, Hiroshima 733-0003
Tel: (+81 82) 238 77 55
President: Morito Mae
General Manager: Katsuhiko Hiraoka
Staff: 470

Bus
Passenger journeys: (Annual) 26 million

Number of routes: 21
Fleet: 274 vehicles, including Nissan Diesel and Mitsubishi Fuso
Operating costs financed by: Fares 100 per cent
Bus priority: Services use 'Centre Line Transfer System' on National Road Route 54 (see above)

Hiroshima Bus
Hiroshima Bus Co Ltd
13-13 Osuga-cho, Minami-ku, Hiroshima-shi 732-0821
Tel: (+81 82) 261 51 41
Staff: 603

Bus
Passenger journeys: (Annual) 26.5 million
Vehicle-km: (Annual) 8.4 million

Number of routes: 45, including 10 city routes
Fleet: 202 buses, 43 coaches including Nissan Diesel and Mitsubishi Fuso

Current situation: Hiroshima Bus operates a network of numbered city bus routes.
Developments: Eight Mitsubishi MP747K 'non-step' low-floor buses entered service in December 1997, part-subsidised by the city and prefecture, to upgrade urban services.

Geiyo Bus
Geiyo Bus
Showa-machi, Saijo, Higashi Hiroshima-shi 739-0014
Tel: (+81 82) 422 31 21

Bus
Passenger journeys: 15 million (annual)

Fleet: 109 vehicles including Hino

Current situation: This Hiroden subsidiary operates suburban and longer-distance routes to the east of Hiroshima.

JR West
West Japan Railway Company
Nishi Nihon Ryokaku Tetsudo
4-24, Shibata 2-chome, Kita-ku, Osaka 530-0012

Tel: (+81 6) 375 89 81   Fax: (+81 6) 375 89 19
Chair: T Tsunoda
President: M Ide

Type of operation: Suburban/interurban heavy rail

Passenger journeys: (Hiroshima operations only)
(1993/94) 56 million

Current situation: Frequent all-stations interurban/commuter emu services run on the Sanyo main line, Hiroshima—Iwakuni (41 km) with some trains continuing to Ogori (138 km) or Shimonoseki (206 km) and Hiroshima—Shiraichi (41 km) with some continuing to Okayama (162 km). A number of trains start/finish at Hiroshima whilst others run through, for example Iwakuni—Hiroshima—Okayama. Also emu service on Kure line, Hiroshima—Kure—Mihara (96 km), and the Kabe line, Hiroshima—Kabe (17 km). A dmu service runs on the Geibi line, Hiroshima—Miyoshi (69 km).

UPDATED   JR West Kabe line emu (A W Phipps)   *1999*/0043567

HOBART
Population: 180,000
Public transport: Bus services provided by state government business enterprise. Private operators run services to some suburbs

Metro
Metropolitan Transport Trust
PO Box 61, 212 Main Road, Moonah 7009, Tasmania, Australia
Tel: (+61 03) 62 33 42 32   Fax: (+61 03) 62 72 87 70
Manager, Business Services: Stuart Davies
Staff: 467 (Hobart operations 354)

Current situation: The Trust was formed in 1954 to provide public road transport in the metropolitan areas of Hobart, Launceston and Burnie; its business name is Metro. Its Hobart operating area is within a 22 km radius of the general post office. Metro does not operate exclusively within this area, and private operators are licensed to serve some districts.

In addition to local services, express buses link outer suburbs with the city centre, and midibuses provide a high-frequency service to the university.

Bus (Metro Hobart operations only)
Passenger journeys: (1993/94) 8.7 million
(1994/95) 8.8 million
(1995/96) 8.6 million
Vehicle-km: (1993/94) 8.5 million
(1994/95) 8.8 million
(1995/96) 8.9 million

Number of routes: 114
Route length: (One way) 320 km

Fleet: 161 vehicles
Scania N112/N113 (1990/94)   130
Volvo B58 articulated (1980)   3
Volvo B10M articulated (1985)   19
MAN 10-180 midibus (1990)   9
In peak service: 147
Average age of fleet: 5.5 years

Most intensive service: 10 min
One-person operation: All routes

Passengers board a Metro service in suburban Hobart   *1997*

Fare collection: Payment to driver for single and daily multitrip tickets; prepurchase 10-trip, 10-day and monthly tickets
Fare structure: Sections; 20 per cent discount for prepurchase multitickets; flat fare for children and concession travellers
Fares collected on board: 50 per cent
Fare evasion control: Electronic warning on ticket validator; inspectors
Operational control: Supervisors/mobile radio
Arrangements for elderly/disabled: All buses have kneeling capability, low-floor buses on trial
Average peak-hour speed: 26.5 km/h
Average distance between stops: 400 m
Operating costs financed by: Fares 46 per cent, other commercial sources 10.5 per cent, subsidy/grants 46.9 per cent
Subsidy from: State government consolidated revenue fund
New vehicles financed by: Own resources

Other operators
Current situation: Three private operators are licensed to provide service within Metro's operating area. Tasmanian Redline Coaches runs two routes and TigerLine three. The services together carry about 15,000 passengers weekly. Apart from a few Hobart Coaches peak-hour services, there is no common ticketing with Metro.

UPDATED

HO CHI MINH CITY
Population: 4 million
Public transport: Bus services provided by public authorities, and also widely by employers and other organised groups. Extensive use of shared taxis, 'Xiclos' (pedicabs) and 'Selam' (scooter taxis)

Doan Thanh Mien Cong San
City Bus Administration
Ho Chi Minh City, Vietnam

Bus
Current situation: Bus services in Ho Chi Minh City are provided with a fleet of Hino RC and Karosa B731 buses, plus some Isuzus second-hand from Japan, DAF MB200s from the Netherlands, IFA, Desoto and LAZ.

Suburban and out-of-town services are run with a varied assortment of older vehicles including Renault and BMC van-derived mini- and midibuses and various types surviving from the US presence in Saigon, including Dodge, Ford and Desoto models. Most have provision for the carriage of roof luggage, including bicycles.

A Dutch operator, VSN International, started running some city routes in 1995.

Shared taxis
Current situation: There is extensive use of shared taxis, 'Xiclos' (pedicabs) and 'Selam' (scooter taxis).

VERIFIED

HOHHOT

Population: 500,000
Public transport: Bus services provided by municipal authority

Hohhot City Bus

Hohhot City Bus Company
Hohhot, Neimongol Province, People's Republic of China

Current situation: A network of routes worked largely by modern buses covers the urban area. Unusually for Chinese cities, few articulated buses are in use, distributed over several routes alongside two-axle vehicles.

Bus

Number of routes: 18

Fleet: Approx 110 buses, including Beijing BK645 and Siping SP642
Beijing BK663 articulated: approx 10

Most intensive service: Approx 10 min

One-person operation: None
Fare collection: Payment to seated conductors, monthly passes
Fare structure: Stage

VERIFIED

HONG KONG

Hong Kong Special Administrative Region of The People's Republic of China
Population: 5.5 million
Public transport: Main bus services provided by four large government-franchised operators. The traditional exclusive area franchise principle is gradually being replaced by competitive tendering, the clearest change in this area being Hong Kong Island where, since 1933, the exclusive area franchise had been held by China Motor Bus (CMB) until challenged by government to improve its services in the early 1990s. The result was, first, the transfer in 1993 of 26 former CMB routes to Citybus, hitherto a non-franchised operator, followed by a further 14 two years later. In 1998 the CMB franchise was terminated and the remaining routes either put to public tender or were transferred to Kowloon Motor Bus and Citybus. A new company, New World First Bus Services Ltd, successfully tendered and commenced operations on 88 former CMB routes in September 1998.

The government-owned Mass Transit Railway operates in the urban area and provides an express link to the new airport at Chek Lap Kok on the north shore of Lantau Island and the Kowloon Canton Railway provides regional metro services on its existing line and plans a second. It also provides light rail services in the Northwest New Territories and feeder buses to both light and heavy rail systems.

Government-licensed 16-seat 'Public Light Buses' and maxicabs supplement other modes and 'Residents' Services' coaches are licensed to serve specific housing developments.

A funicular is operated by a private operator.

Total operations cater for over 10 million daily journeys. Overall policies are formulated by the Secretary for Transport, advised by a Transport Advisory Committee. The major operators are introducing a smartcard ticketing system.

The Government of Hong Kong SAR has been presented with proposals for trolleybus operation in an effort to reduce pollution in Hong Kong. The franchised bus operators, on the other hand, have been invited to explore the feasibility of using LPG-fuelled buses. Currently all taxi operators have been encouraged to replace diesel with LPG before the end of 2005.

All operations except railways are under the direct supervision of the Commissioner for Transport.

Commissioner for Transport

41/F Immigration Tower, 7 Gloucester Road, Wanchai, Hong Kong SAR
Tel: (+852) 28 29 52 00   Fax:(+852) 28 24 04 33
Commissioner: Robert Footman

Kowloon Motor Bus

Kowloon Motor Bus Co (1933) Ltd
A wholly owned subsidiary of Kowloon Motor Bus Holdings Ltd
1, Po Lun Street, Lai Chi Kok, Kowloon, Hong Kong
Tel: (+852) 27 86 88 88   Fax: (+852) 27 45 03 00
Chairman: Woo Pak Chuen
Managing Director: John C C Chan
General Manager: Charles C Y Lui
Staff: 12,000

Current situation: Operations are in Kowloon and the New Territories. In addition, services are operated through the three cross-harbour tunnels to Hong Kong Island.

KMB is Hong Kong's largest public transport operator, having been first granted a franchise in 1933. In 1997 this franchise was extended to July 2007.

Population increase, particularly in the New Towns of the New Territories, continues and further routes are introduced to meet demand. Air conditioned double-deckers have gained general acceptance and further air conditioned routes are being introduced to meet demand for higher quality services.

Developments: Kowloon Motor Bus Co (1933) Ltd, together with Long Win Bus Co Ltd and Sunbus Ltd, now forms part of Kowloon Motor Bus Holdings. Art East Ltd is a 50:50 joint venture company between KMB Group and a Shenzhen-based company and runs shuttle-buses between the boundary at Huanggang and Lok Ma Chau in the New Territories. Dalian HK Macau Bus Motor Bus Services Ltd is a joint venture between KMB, a Macau-based company and an established Dalian (northeast China) state-owned operator and is an example of the KMB Group's continued efforts to enter new markets.

Smartcard (Octopus), now 25 per cent in use, is to be extended to all vehicles over three to four years.

Passenger boardings: (1995) 996 million
(1996) 1,032 million
(1997) 1,051 million

Vehicle-km: (1995) 271 million
(1996) 285 million
(1997) 300 million

Fleet: 3,973 vehicles, of which 2,061 air conditioned
Double-deck

Dennis Jubilant	185
Leyland Olympian	122
Volvo Olympian 3-axle	30
Dennis Dominator	40
Mercedes-Benz	41
Leyland Olympian 3-axle	620
MCW 3-axle	254
MCW 9.7 m	82
Dennis Dragon 3-axle	538
Volvo Olympian 3-axle air conditioned	867
Dennis Dragon 3-axle air conditioned	714
Dennis Trident 3-axle air conditioned	30
Leyland Olympian 3-axle air conditioned	150
Scania 3-axle air conditioned	22

Single-deck

Dennis Dart air conditioned	53
Dennis Lance air conditioned	24
Dennis Falcon coach air conditioned	19
Mitsuibishi air conditioned	182

On order: Includes last batch of Dennis Dragon, Tridents, Neoplan SLF and Volvo Olympian SLF

One-person operation: All services
Fare collection: Payment to farebox on board or (25 per cent) smartcard (Octopus)
Fare structure: Sectional and flat
Fares collected on board: 100 per cent
Fare evasion control: Inspectors
Operational control: Route inspectors/mobile radio
Arrangements for the elderly/disabled: Reserved seats, more handholds, coloured and textured stanchions, half-fare for over 65s. More low-floor buses for mobility handicapped
Average speed: 18.6 km/h
Bus priority: On the congested Lion Rock Tunnel Road, Turn Mun Highway and Tsing Yi Bridge and other smaller scale measures in conjunction with Transport Department
Integration with other modes: Smartcard (Octopus) valid with other major operators; bus routes to MTR and KCR stations
Operating costs financed by: Fares 99 per cent; other commercial sources 1 per cent
New vehicles financed by: Loans from banks and Export Credit Guarantee

Long Win Bus

Long Win Bus Co Ltd
A wholly owned subsidiary of Kowloon Motor Bus Holdings Ltd
1, Po Lun Street, Lai Chi Kok, Kowloon, Hong Kong
Tel: (+852) 27 86 87 88   Fax: (+852) 27 45 03 00
Chairman: Woo Pak Chuen
Managing Director: John C C Chan
Deputy Managing Director: Charles C Y Lui
Staff: 400

Current situation: This subsidiary of Kowloon Motor Bus Holdings holds a franchise to operate 12 routes serving the new airport and Tung Chun New Town and services to the major New Towns in the New Territories. LWBC started operations with a fleet of brand new low-floor double-decks. Environmental protection includes Euro-2 engines in all new buses; water purification measures at depots to prevent contaminated waste entering the drainage system

Kowloon Motor Bus Volvo Olympian with Alexander air conditioned body approaching Kowloon Star Ferry pier (M C Davis)   **1999**/0043582

Number of routes: 12

Fleet: 140 buses
Dennis Trident low-floor   140

One-person operation: All services
Fare collection: Sectional and flat
Fares collected on board: 100 per cent
Fare evasion control: Bus captains and service co-ordinators
Operational control: Control centre, service co-ordinators/mobile radio
Arrangements for elderly/disabled: All buses fully accessible to wheelchairs; reserved seats, more handholds, coloured and textured stanchions; half-fare for over-65s
Average speed: 32.7 km/h
Bus priority: None
Integration with other modes: Smartcard (Octopus) valid with other major operators
Operating costs financed by: Fares 100 per cent
New vehicles financed by: Loans from banks and Export Credit Guarantee

Sun Bus

Sun Bus Ltd
A wholly owned subsidiary of Kowloon Motor Bus Holdings Ltd
1, Po Lun Street, Lai Chi Kok, Kowloon, Hong Kong
Tel: (+852) 27 86 87 88   Fax: (+852) 27 45 03 00
General Manager: Simon Tu

Current situation: Sun Bus Limited is the first business in the newly formed Non-franchised Transport Services Division KMB, designed to provide services in niche markets, including residential, employee, hotel, student and contract hire services.

China Motor Bus

China Motor Bus Co Ltd

Current situation: This company ceased to be a franchised operator in August 1998; its routes and most buses were transferred to New World First Bus, Citybus Limited and Kowloon Motor Bus. Ten vehicles are retained for non-franchised operations.

New World First Bus Services

New World First Bus Services Ltd
25/F, Eight Commercial Tower, No 8 Sun Yip Street, Chai Wan, Hong Kong
Tel: (+852) 21 36 21 40   Fax: (+852) 21 47 36 11
Managing Director: Hsu Huang
Operations Director: Mark Savelli

Current situation: New World First Bus Services is Hong Kong's newest franchised bus company. Established in early 1998 to bid for 88 routes formerly operated under franchise by China Motor Bus, which the government of the SAR put out to tender in February 1998 for commencement on 1 September. The company will operate a fleet of 700 buses on 88 routes, 59 on Hong Kong Island and 29 cross-harbour routes. New World First Bus is a joint venture between New World Services Limited and FirstGroup plc — the largest bus operator in the United Kingdom, with over 9,000 buses.
Developments: New World First Bus is investing HK$2 billion over the franchise period to improve buses, depots and passenger facilities. Five hundred new buses will be introduced over the first two years of operation with 200 in service by the end of 1998. All new buses will have wheelchair access and facilities for the disabled, and will be equipped with the Octopus smartcard fare payment system.

Initially New World First Bus operated 710 former China Motor Bus vehicles in diminishing numbers alongside increasing numbers of new vehicles with improved facilities. All new buses will meet Euro-2 engine emission requirements. A safety officer has been appointed, a first in the Hong Kong bus industry, to monitor safety standards and driver performance.

Fleet: 710 buses
Air conditioned

DA Dennis Condor 12 m	92
DC Dennis Dart	20
LA Leyland Olympian 12 m	25
VA Volvo Olympian 12 m	62

Non-air conditioned

DS Dennis Jubilant two-axle	29
DM Dennis Condor 11 m	28
DL Dennis Condor 12 m	48
LF Leyland Fleetline	72
LM Leyland Olympian 11 m	10
LV Leyland Victor	163
MB MCW Metrobus 11 m	39
MC MCW Metrobus	10
ML MCW Metrobus 12 m	84
SF short Fleetline	28

As new vehicles become available, it is intended that former China Motor Bus non-air conditioned buses be disposed of, with the aim of attaining an all-air conditioned fleet by 2001.

New Lantao Bus

New Lantao Bus Co (1973) Ltd
A 99.99 per cent owned subsidiary of Kwoon Chung Motors Co Ltd
1205 Eastern Harbour Centre, 28 Hoi Chak Street, Quarry Bay, Hong Kong
Tel: (+852) 29 84 83 61   Fax: (+852) 29 84 88 12
Chairman and Managing Director:
   Matthew Wong Leung-pak

Current situation: New Lantao Bus was formed in 1973 by an amalgamation of smaller companies. It was franchised in 1979 to serve Lantau for nine years, subsequently extended. The company was acquired by Kwoon Chung Motors in 1992. In March 1998, NLB was operating 13 (1997: 9) franchised bus routes on Lantau (two further routes since added). For the year ended March 1998, the bus service derived turnover of NLB was approximately HK$57 million, representing an increase of 43.6 per cent as compared with that of 1996/97 of HK$39.7 million. The significant increase was due to the opening of the Tsing Ma Bridge in May 1997, bringing a substantial rise in the number of passengers travelling from North Lantau to South Lantau, particularly during weekends and holidays. An airport service, A35, provides direct connections from South Lantau to the new Hong Kong International Airport at Chek Lap Kok, North Lantau.

Passenger journeys: (1993) 5 million
(1996) 4.7 million

Number of routes: 15

Fleet: 84 vehicles

Isuzu single-deck	74
Dennis Dart low-floor	3
Toyota Coaster	2
Mercedes-Benz 45-seat coaches	5

Developments: Land granted by SAR government for construction of a depot at Siu Ho, North Lantau. Plans to consolidate present position and to expand into North Lantau New Towns when tenders are offered. Expansion into Ma Wan is proposed when a resort village is developed there.

Kwoon Chung Bus

Kwoon Chung Bus Holdings Ltd
1205 Eastern Harbour Centre, 28 Hoi Chak Street, Quarry Bay, Hong Kong

Current situation: Through its subsidiary companies, the core Kwoon Chung Motors, Good Funds Services and Tai Fung Coach Co, the Kwoon Chung Group is one of the largest, non-franchised bus operators in Hong Kong. The Group also has operations in eight cities in China, the largest being the 800-bus Shanghai No 5 Bus Company. In Hong Kong, the group has become the leading school-bus provider and has a strong position in resident and employee services. The network was extended during 1998 to the new Chek Lap Kok airport. The acquisitions of Tai Fung Coach Co Ltd and Holiday Rental in April 1997 has enabled the Group to become the biggest provider, in terms of bus fleet size, of tour buses and coaches to hotels and tour operators in Hong Kong. Buses and coaches are also provided under contract to the Mass Transit Railway for use on Airport Express shuttle services. The group, through subsidiary New Lantao Bus Co (1973) Ltd, provides franchised bus services on Lantau Island (see above).

Citybus

Citybus Limited
17/F, King Kong Commercial Center, 9 Des Voeux Road West, Hong Kong
Tel: (+852) 29 63 48 88   Fax: (+852) 25 79 02 02
e-mail: webmaster@citybus.com.hk
Managing Director: Lyndon Rees
General Manager: Samuel Cheng

Current situation: This is a franchised operation. In July 1998 it became the second largest franchised bus operator in Hong Kong, both in terms of passengers carried and in fleet size. Part of this expansion was the result of the introduction of new routes to serve the new Hong Kong International Airport at Chek Lap Kok which opened in July 1998. A fleet of 62 low-floor air conditioned coaches was purchased to operate the new Cityflyer routes, providing a premium quality service between the new airport and Hong Kong/Kowloon.

In April 1998 the last non-air conditioned bus was withdrawn, making Citybus the first franchised operator to have a fully air conditioned fleet.

In September 1998 Citybus took over another 12 routes from China Motor Bus, which established Citybus as the major operator on Hong Kong Island.

The entire Citybus fleet has been fitted with smartcard equipment.

Despite the economic turmoil in Asia during 1998, Citybus has maintained significant passenger growth.

Passenger journeys: (1998, 9 months) 130.7 million
Vehicle-km: (1998, 9 months) 43.5 million

Number of routes: 107

Fleet: 960 buses

Citybus operates a fleet of Dennis Trident Cityflyer double-decks on a number of express routes serving the new Chep Lap Kok airport (M C Davis)

Single-deck	
Volvo B6	61
Dennis Dart	36
MAN NL262	60
Double-deck	
Dennis Dragon 10.3 m	40
Dennis Dragon 12 m	80
Dennis Trident 10.6 m	1
Dennis Trident 12 m	124
Leyland Olympian 10.4 m	34
Leyland Olympian 11 m	13
Leyland Olympian 12 m	55
MAN	1
Volvo Olympian 10.4 m	10
Volvo Olympian 11 m	140
Volvo Olympian 12 m	305

On order: 40 Dennis Trident double-decks, with options on 11 MAN double-decks

Most intensive service: 3 min
One-person operation: 100 per cent
Fare collection: Farebox on board, mobile fareboxes on selected routes in peak hours to allow boarding through centre doors. Smarcard equipment is fitted to all buses.
Fare structure: Stage/flat fare
Operational control: Inspectors with patrol cars and mobile radio. Route regulators.
Arrangements for elderly/disabled: 50 per cent concession fare for elderly. All new buses are low-floor, and most have space for a wheelchair. All buses have most DiPTAC features.

Citybus non-franchised operations
Current situation: Citybus was a pioneer of the Residents' Services in the early 1980s and has progressively developed this business based on high-quality three-axle double-deck coaches, although single-deck vehicles are used where appropriate. From the commencement of its cross-border services into mainland China, also in the 1980s, Citybus has employed mainly double-deck buses and coaches. The present Guangzhou service is being maintained by five Jonckheere Monaco luxury coaches.

In September 1998 Citybus became the first residential coach operator to use the Octopus smartcard system for fare payment on its buses, with all routes being converted by October 1998.

The passenger figures include residential, cross-boundary and Ocean Park only.

Passenger journeys: (1998, 9 months) 12 million
Vehicle-km: (1998, 9 months) 11.6 million

Number of routes: 19 (residents)

Fleet: 133 vehicles

Single-deck	
Norinco Neoplan	3
Volvo B10M	12
Double-deck	
AEC Routemaster	3
Leyland Olympian	5
Leyland Olympian 11 m	82
Leyland Olympian 12 m	16
Volvo Olympian 12 m	7
Volvo B12	5

HK Tramways double-deck tram and other operators' buses including KMB bus on Route 101 (M C Davis)
1999/0043579

Hongkong Tramways
Hongkong Tramways Limited
A wholly owned subsidiary of Wharf (Holdings) Ltd
Whitty Street Tram Depot, Connaught Road West, Western District, Hong Kong
Tel: (+852) 25 59 89 18   Fax: (+852) 28 58 36 97
General Manager: Frankie Yick
Operations Manager: Allan Leech

Type of operation: Conventional tramway, first line opened 1904

Passenger journeys: (1995) 114.1 million
(1996) 107.8 million
(1997) 101.9 million
Car-km: (1995) 6.8 million
(1996) 6.8 million
(1997) 6.8 million

Route length: 23.8 km
Number of routes: 7
Number of stops: 122
Gauge: 1,067 mm
Track: Ri60 grooved 60.5 kg/m rail directly fixed to concrete slab embedded in road surface (some special work Ri59)
Electrification: 500V DC, overhead
Current collection: Trolley pole

Service: Peak 2-6 min
First/last car: 05:16/01:00
Fare structure: Flat fare, pay on exit (planned to commence pay on entry early 1999); monthly tickets; tourist tickets (joint with 'Star' Ferry Co); seniors concessionary fare
Operating costs financed by: Fares 86.8 per cent; other commercial sources 13.3 per cent
One-person operation: 100 per cent

Rolling stock: 163 double-deck cars mainly built by local contractors and Hongkong Tramways Workshops
Two-axle   M161
Open-top leisure cars   M2
In peak service: 155

Developments: Routes, services and running times are regularly reviewed to take account of changing travel and traffic patterns. Replacement of existing timber-framed bodies by new bidirectional alloy structures is planned. A new control system is currently being installed and all cars are being rewired during overhaul. A computerised scheduling and rostering system is being introduced.

Two route extensions are proposed of which one is a link to the Central and Wanchai reclamation areas, and lies parallel to the existing tram route between Central and Causeway Bay. The second line would extend the Kennedy Town service into a new housing estate, park and leisure area planned on reclaimed land at Green Island, or may operate as an independent light rail line by linking up with the Central and Wanchai reclamation extension.

A longer-term project is being studied for a light rail line, which would run from Central/Admiralty to Aberdeen, with a possible link to the existing system.

Air conditioning is being studied in possible conjunction with the next car rebody programme, but also dependent upon review of available power supply.

Mass Transit Railway
MTR Corporation
MTR Tower, Telford Plaza, 33 Wai Yip Street, Kowloon Bay, Hong Kong
Tel: (+852) 29 93 21 11   Fax: (+852) 27 98 88 22
Chairman & Chief Executive: Jack C K So
Operations Director: Phil Gaffney
Project Director: Russell Black
Staff: 8,486

Type of operation: Full metro, first line opened 1979

Passenger journeys: (1995) 813 million
(1996) 817 million
(1997) 812 million
Car-km: (1995) 86.4 million
(1996) 87.8 million
(1997) 88.2 million

Route length: 84 km
  in tunnel: 43.2 km
  elevated: 16.2 km
Number of lines: 4
Number of stations: 44
Gauge: 1,432 mm
Track: BS 90A 40 kg/m continuously supported FB rail, discretely supported on overhead sections of Tsuen Wan extension; UIC60 60 kg/m continuously supported FB rail in tunnels of Island line and Eastern Harbour crossing, discretely supported on overhead sections
Max gradient: 3%
Minimum curve radius: 300 m

Buses and trams interchange with the MTR outside Queensway Plaza, which is accessed by footbridge from the platforms. The MTR Admiralty station is below Queensway Plaza (M C Davis)   *1999*/0043574

Tunnel: Bored single-track, bored double-track and cut-and-cover

Electrification: 1.5 kV DC, overhead

Service: Peak 112 sec, off-peak 3-10 min
First/last train: 06.00/01.00

Airport Express

Type of operation: Dedicated express rail link to Chek Lap Kok Airport, commenced 6 July 1998

Route length: 34.8 km
  in tunnel: 7.5 km
  elevated: 9.5 km
  ground level: 17.8 km
Number of lines: 1
Number of stations: 4
Integration with other modes: In conjunction with its Airport Express service, the MTR operates a fleet of shuttle-buses under contract connecting major hotels with its Hong Kong and Kowloon stations. These are operated free of charge but are strictly for airport passengers only.

Fare structure: Zonal, with single and stored value tickets
Integration with other modes: Common stored value ticket valid for travel also on KCR, Citybus and HYF and some bus routes of KMB
Revenue control: AFC at all stations
Operating costs financed by: Fares 90 per cent, other commercial sources 10 per cent
One-person operation: All trains
Automatic control: All tracks except within depots
Surveillance: CCTV on platforms and concourses

Rolling stock: 943 cars

Metro-Cammell (1979/81)	M210
Metro-Cammell (1981184)	T362
Metro-Cammell (1984)	T31
Metro-Cammell (1989)	M68
GEC Alsthom (1994/95)	M88
Adtranz/CAF Airport Express (1997)	M55 T33
Adtranz/CAF Lantau (1997)	M60 T36

In peak service: 648

Developments: In 1993 a seven-year investment programme was unveiled, designed to further raise capacity and provide a better environment for both passengers and staff. Signalling on all three lines has been renewed to reduce headways so that 34 trains/h can be run; Alstom has installed the SACEM system. In addition, complete refurbishment of the rolling stock fleet is being carried out in a programme extending to 2001.

Public service started in June/July 1998 on the 34 km line serving the new airport at Chek Lap Kok and Tung Chung New Town on Lantau Island. It runs from Central on Hong Kong Island, across the harbour serving reclaimed areas with stations at Kowloon and Olympics (Tai Kok Sui) before making interchange with the Tsuen Wan line at Lai King. This section provides relief for the existing line in the Nathan Road corridor. From Lai King the route runs partially on reclaimed land to separate terminals at the airport and Tung Chung.

Refurbished KCRC emu at Sheung Shui (T V Runnacles)   ***1999****/0043576*

Two levels of service operate – the Tung Chung mass transit and Airport Express – running at up to 135 km/h. Journey time from Central to the airport and Tung Chung is 23 min. Initially, the Airport line service runs every 8 min, with a 4 min service on the Tung Chung line, of which alternate trains turn back at Tsing Yi.

Construction is also in progress of a 1.7 km extension of the Kwun Tung line from its Quarry Bay terminus to North Point on the island line. This will relieve the existing interchange between the two lines at Quarry Bay, and is intended to form the first stage of a duplicate Island line which would serve newly reclaimed land on the north shore.

An extension of the Kwun Tung Line to Tseung Kwan O (12.5 km, five stations) was approved in October 1998, for completion in 2002.

Kowloon-Canton Railway

Kowloon-Canton Railway Corporation
KCR House, 9 Lok King Street, Fo Tan, Sha Tin, New Territories, Hong Kong
Tel: (+852) 26 88 13 33   Fax: (+852) 26 88 09 83
Chairman and Chief Executive Officer: Yeung Kai-yin
Director, KCR East Rail: K K Lee
Director, KCR West Rail: Ian McPherson
Staff: 3,512

Current situation: KCRC, formerly a government department, was vested as a public corporation in 1983. It operates a high-intensity urban and suburban rail network, marketed as East Rail, on the line between Kowloon and the boundary with mainland China. This line forms the southern part of the main line over which KCRC shares in the operation of through passenger rail services to Guangzhou, Dongguan, Foshan and Zhaoqing.

Additionally, KCRC operates one of the world's busiest light rail networks in the Northwest New Territories, as well as feeder buses to both the heavy rail and light rail operations. A new commuter passenger line is under construction branded West Rail.

KCRC East Rail

Type of operation: Regional metro line, opened 1910. East Rail serves 13 stations along 34 route-km

Passenger journeys: (1995) 232 million
(1996) 247 million
(1997) 261 million

Route length: 34 km
Number of lines: 1
Number of stations: 13
Gauge: 1,435 mm
Track: 54 kg/m rail on concrete sleepers
Max gradient: 1%
Minimum curve radius: 200 m
Electrification: 25 kV 50Hz, overhead

Service: Peak 3 min; off peak 5-6 min
First/last train: 05.35/00.25
Fare structure: Zonal
Revenue collection: Automatic machines and entrance/exit barriers
Integration with other modes: KCR light rail; stored value Octopus smartcard also valid on MTR, KMB, Citybus and HYF
Operation financed by: Fares

Rolling stock: 351 emu cars, 12 coaches, 12 diesel locomotives

Metro-Cammell L	M120
Metro-Cammell S	T60
Metro-Cammell (1987/91)	M75
GEC Alsthom (1989-91)	M96
Kinki Sharyo double-deck (1997)	T12

A three-year programme of train refurbishment is halfway through. Additional sliding doors and new front ends have been added and the seating in standard class has been brought into line with the requirements of a high-density metro.

Developments: A short extension of East Rail is being built restoring the connection between the Hung Hom terminus of the present line with Tsim Sha Tsui, a link lost in 1983. This will then connect with West Rail at Yen Chow Street when that line opens in 2003 (see below).

Ma On Shan Line: East Rail is also to build an extension from an interchange with the main line at Tai Wai. The new line will then head northeasterly towards Ma On Shan and Lee On via the east bank of the Shing Mun River and will include such transport nodes as City One Shatin.

KCRC West Rail

Construction started in October 1998 of KCRC's West Rail project, which will connect the western New Territories with Kowloon. Originally proposed as part of a network to include long-distance passenger services into China, as well as a freight link to relieve road congestion in

Airport Express train serving the new Hong Kong airport about to pass through Olympic station. Note baggage car at the leading end of the train (T V Runnacles)   ***1999****/0043575*

New Goninan LRV on the Tuen Mun light rail network (T V Runnacles)   **1999**/0043572

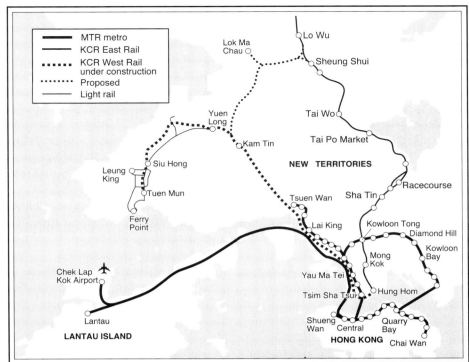

Hong Kong's metro and rail   0045355

the container port area at Kwai Chung, the whole was given an estimated cost of HK$75 billion. As a result, it was decided to implement the scheme in phases. Phase I comprises the West Rail domestic passenger line, reducing the initial cost of the project to HK$64 billion by removing the long-distance proposal. Construction of the route from Kowloon to Tuen Mun started in late 1998 for completion by the end of 2003. Phase II will include cross-boundary and through trains and a rail freight system pending further study.

The total length of Phase I is 30.3 km, running from Tuen Mun to Yen Chow Street, with seven stations and a depot at Pat Heung occupying an area of 43 ha. The western section will be mostly on viaduct, while in the urban area there will be a mixture of tunnel and enclosed at-grade structure. Tai Lam Tunnel, at 5.5 km, will be the longest bored tunnel in Hong Kong, excluding tunnels of the underground Mass Transit Railway, with which West Rail will have two interchanges as well as four connections with the Tuen Mun LRT system. Interchanges will be set up at West Rail stations, integrating services with various feeder services, including buses, minibuses, and taxis.

Route length is 30.3 k, with 9 stations. Track gauge is 1,435 mm and the track is UIC 54 kg/m rail on concrete sleepers. Electrification is 25 kV 50Hz, overhead. Rolling stock comprises 250 cars in 7-car sets.

KCRC Light Rail
55-65 Lung Mun Road, Tuen Mun, New Territories, Hong Kong
Tel: (+852) 24 68 76 00   Fax: (+852) 24 55 00 30
Director: Jonathan Yu

Type of operation: Light rail; first line opened 1988

Passenger journeys: (1995) 123 million
(1996) 125 million
(1997) 126 million

Route length: 31.8 km
  reserved track: 28 km
Number of routes: 8
Number of stops: 57
Gauge: 1,435 mm
Track: UIC54 kg/m flat bottom on concrete sleepers and some grooved rail; 3 km paved track in concrete
Max gradient: 6.1%
Minimum curve radius: 23 m
Electrification: 750 V DC, overhead

Service: Peak 5-10 min, off peak 10-13 min
First/last car: 05.30/00.30
Fare structure: Five zones, three fare steps, Octopus – charged by distance travelled and number of trips taken (eight fare steps)
Revenue control: Ticket vending machines on all platforms, inspectors, spot penalty
Integration with other modes: KCR feeder buses

Rolling stock: 119 cars

Comeng (1987/88)	M69
Kawasaki (1992/93)	M20 T10
Goninan (1997/98)	M20

In peak service: 108

Current situation: Ridership and revenue continued to grow in 1997 (by 1 per cent and 6 per cent respectively)
Developments: Service improvements followed commissioning of the 20 cars from Goninan and the introduction of a new contactless smartcard ticketing system.

KCRC Bus
Passenger journeys: (1995) 32 million
(1996) 38 million
(1997) 39 million
Vehicle-km: (1995) 5.8 million
(1996) 6 million
(1998) 5.8 million

Fleet: 105 buses

Current situation: Feeder services provided to KCR stations (9) and light rail stops (12).
Developments: A further two air conditioned double-deck buses were delivered at the end of 1998.

Hongkong & Yaumati Ferry
Hong Kong Ferry (Holdings) Co Ltd
West Kowloon Reclamation Area Lot No SSP Misc 58, Po Lun Street extension, Lai Chi Kok, Kowloon, Hong Kong
Tel: (+852) 27 86 93 83   Fax: (+852) 27 86 90 01

Group General Manager: David C S Ho
Staff: 1,297

Passenger journeys: (1994) 38.5 million
(1995) 35.8 million
(1996) 38.7 million

Operating costs financed by: Fares 100 per cent

Current situation: Operates cross-harbour passenger (six routes) and vehicle (one route) ferries, eight routes to new towns and outlying districts and four excursion routes on a 15-year franchise which ends in 1999. Also operates hoverferry service Hong Kong to China (Whampoa and Shekou) and Macau. Fleet of 84 vessels. Stored-value ticketing system installed 1996.
Developments: With the completion of three cross-harbour tunnels and the bridges to Lantau, the company's business has decreased. In August 1998, the Government of Hong Kong SAR announced that HYF would lose its franchise at the end of 1999.

Star Ferry
Star Ferry Company Limited
16F Ocean Centre, Harbour City, Canton Road, Kowloon, Hong Kong
Tel: (+852) 21 18 52 23   Fax: (+852) 21 18 60 28
Operations Manager: Johnny T H Leung
Staff: 325

Passenger journeys: (1995) 34.9 million
(1996) 35.2 million
(1997) 32.5 million

Star Ferry (M C Davis)   **1999**/0043578

MTRC train on Island Line approaching Chai Wan on the open-air eastern section (M C Davis)
1999/0043577

Peak Tramway (Andrew Jarosz)   *1999*/0043580

Central to Mid-Levels escalators climb some 200 m from Central Market and are over 1 km in length (Andrew Jarosz)
1999/0043581

Current situation: Operates three cross-harbour passenger routes from Edinburgh Place to Tsim She Tsui and Hung Horn, and Kowloon Point to Wan Chai, totalling 7.1 km, with a fleet of 12 vessels. Fares cover 59 per cent of operating costs.

Franchised ferries
Current situation: Eight operators have franchises granted by the Commissioner for Transport. They ply minor routes and carried 9 million passengers in 1996.

There are also 85 local services called 'Kaitos', with 85 operators.

Public Light Bus/Red Minibus and Green Minibus

Current situation: Legalised in 1969, the Public Light Buses were carrying an estimated 25 per cent of all trips within three years. The Government then fixed the number of vehicles permitted and Red and Green Minibus now account for about 17 per cent of trips.

PLBs (now known as 'Red Minibuses') concentrate on main urban corridors and are demand-responsive. There are no fixed routes, stops or fares, though they are

prohibited from certain areas and there are some restrictions on pick-up points to avoid congestion.

Green Minibus services have been licensed additionally to act as feeders to major routes (see below).

Red Minibus
Independent 'Public Light Bus'
Licensed by: Transport Department
Staff: 3,400 drivers

Passenger journeys: (1996) 0.9 million daily
(1997) 0.8 million daily

Fleet: 2,148 minibuses (16-seat)

One-person operation: All services
Fare collection: Driver collected
Fare structure: Stage, not controlled; surcharge generally applied for peak and night services
Operating costs financed by: Fares 100 per cent

Green Minibus
Represented by: GMB Maxicab Operators General Association Limited

Shop 14 G/F, Kam Po Court, Sai Kung, New Territories
Tel: (+852) 27 92 29 48

Hong Kong Scheduled (GMB) Licensee Association
12/F ABBA Commercial Building, 233 Aberdeen Main Road, Hong Kong
Tel: (+852) 28 73 68 08
Supervised by: Transport Department

Passenger journeys: (1996) 0.9 million daily
(1997) 1 million daily

Current situation: Green Minibuses are scheduled PLB services on specified routes, with fixed timetables and fare scales approved by the Transport Department. In 1997 there were 287 routes — 69 on Hong Kong Island, 66 in Kowloon and 152 in the New Territories, with a total of 2,102 16-seat vehicles. Fares are distance-based.
Developments: It is the Transport Department's intention to convert more 'Red' PLBs to 'Green' PLBs. In 1997, 27 new Green Minibus routes were opened for competitive bidding. The government stresses that there are no plans to increase the 16-seat limit imposed on PLBs.

Residential coaches
Current situation: To cater for the peak-hour transport demand of residential areas which did not have adequate access to franchised buses and Green Minibuses, Residents' Services (RS) were introduced in 1982. New RS are introduced to supplement franchised bus services during peak hours but, where demand justifies, some RS may be approved to operate outside the peak periods, provided that the operational arrangements are acceptable and there is no significant impact on other modes. RS all operate under a Passenger Service Licence.

Passenger journeys: (1997) 111,000 daily
(1998) 117,710 daily

Number of routes: 222
Fleet: 824

Non-franchised buses
In addition to the franchised bus fleet in Hong Kong, there are nearly 3,000 non-franchised vehicles used on contract hire, private hire, school bus transport, hotel and airport transfers and similar work, and on services operating into Mainland China.

Funicular/cable car
Peak Tramways Company Ltd
No 1 Lugard Road, The Peak
Tel: (+852) 28 49 76 54   Fax: (+852) 28 49 62 37
General Manager: Anthony Williams

Current situation: The Peak Tramway and Ocean Park Cable Car are almost entirely leisure operations, and carry about 3 million passengers annually.

UPDATED

HONOLULU
Population: 900,000
Public transport: Bus and paratransit services provided by private non-profit undertaking under contract to public transit authority which co-ordinates bus and paratransit services

Department of Transportation Services
City & County of Honolulu
711 Kapiolani Boulevard, Suite 1200, Honolulu, Hawaii 96813, USA
Tel: (+1 808) 527 68 90   Fax: (+1 808) 596 23 80
Director: Cheryl D Soon

Public Transit Division Chief: Paul B Steffens
Fixed Route Operations Branch Chief: Alvin K Morimoto
Staff: 23

Current situation: On 1 July 1997 the Honolulu Public Transit Authority was dissolved and the public transport function transferred to the Department of Transportation

Services, City & County of Honolulu. A Public Transit Division was created to assist in the city's contract of the operation of bus and paratransit to Oahu Transit Services, a private non-profit corporation.

Bus (TheBus) and paratransit (The Handi-Van)
Operated under contract by Oahu Transit Services Inc
President: James E Cowen
Staff: 1,600

Passenger boardings: (1995/96) 77.9 million
(1996/97) 75 million
(1997/98) 73.1 million
Vehicle-km: (1995/96) 30.9 million
(1996/97) 31.6 million
(1997/98) 31.9 million

Number of routes: 80
Route length: (One way) 2,475 km
Number of stops: 3,720

Fleet: 526 vehicles

Gillig Phantom (1983/84)	104
Scania CN112 (1985/87)	64
Neoplan (1985)	7
TMC RTS-06 (1991)	35
TMC RTS-08 (1992/93)	94
Gillig (1994/95)	132
Gillig (1996)	22
Gillig 300 (1997/98)	68

In peak service: 413

Most intensive service: 4 min
One-person operation: All routes
Fare collection: Exact fare, farebox on bus
Fares collected on board: 25 per cent cash
Fare structure: Flat or prepaid monthly adult, senior, student, disbaled and tourist bus passes
Fare evasion control: By driver
Operational control: Radio and inspectors
Arrangements for elderly/disabled: 360 buses have wheelchair lifts; Handi-Van paratransit service carried 660,000 passengers in 1997/98
Average distance between stops: In high-density areas, 160 m; in rural areas, 305 m
Average peak-hour speed: In mixed traffic, 22.5 km/h; in bus lanes/HOV, 32-40 km/h
Operating costs financed by: Fares 28 per cent, subsidy/grants 72 per cent
Subsidy from: City government 93 per cent, FTA 7 per cent
New vehicles financed by: FTA grants (80 per cent) and city government (20 per cent)

UPDATED

Gillig of Oahu Transit on Waikiki Beach service *1998*/0007908

TheBus RTS bus in Honolulu (Bill Luke) *1999*/0038840

HOUSTON

Population: 1.7 million; service area 2.6 million
Public transport: Bus services provided by Metropolitan Transit Authority of Harris County, controlled by representative board

METRO

Metropolitan Transit Authority of Harris County
PO Box 61429, 1201 Louisiana, Houston, Texas 77208-1429, USA
Tel: (+1 713) 739 40 00   Fax: (+1 713) 759 95 37
Chair: Robert D Miller
General Manager: Robert G MacLennan
Deputy General Manager, Transit Operations:
   Fred Gilliam
Staff: 3,407

Current situation: Voters in Harris County approved creation of the MTA in 1978, allowing the State to collect a 1 per cent sales tax to partially fund the authority. After the 1983 rejection of a bond issue to finance an initial metro line, voters approved in 1988 a $2.6 billion 13-year programme of public transport improvements known as the Phase 2 Mobility Plan. As a result, by 1998 14 transit centres, 24 park-and-ride sites, over 1,600 bus shelters and 115 km of high-occupancy transitways had been commissioned. Also approved in 1988 was a measure to set aside at least 25 per cent of sales tax revenue for general mobility projects such as road, bridge and pavement construction.

Houston METRO added 26 replica tramcar buses to its fleet in 1998 *1999*/0038841

Developments: In the fiscal year 1998, METRO set a new ridership record with 71.4 million passenger trips made on buses. METRO also replaced its Downtown circulator buses with 26 trolley buses (not trolleybuses – these vehicles, mainly seen in the USA are replica tramcars on bus chassis), providing expanded routes and hours of operation.

In addition, the Authority began work on a five-year $177 million reconstruction of transit streets in the central business district.

In 1992 the board approved the Regional Bus Plan – a $1 billion long-range plan for bus and related capital improvements to be implemented throughout the 3,300 km² service area by 2010. Federal funding of $500 million towards the project was granted in 1994. Building on the existing network, the plan includes improvements to speed up bus operations, an increase in the fleet by some 400 buses, increased service to suburban employment centres, and expansion of local routes. A sixth bus maintenance depot opened at Fallbrook in 1997, capable of housing 250 vehicles.

The bus fleet is being renewed and expanded to about 1,600 during the plan period; all will be lift-equipped. General mobility plans also call for extension of transitways to some 183 km, to be served by 19 transit centres and 2,100 sheltered stops. All bus routes are to be fully accessible to disabled people by 2000. Vanpooling is being encouraged in areas where bus service is limited, with subsidies offered to employers who participate. The MetroVan scheme, started in 1994, attracted 115 companies in its first year of operation, and has grown to over 200 vans.

METRO is now conducting a major investment study examining transport options for a corridor running from the central business district to major activity centres south of Downtown. One possible transit option is light rail.

Bus
Passenger journeys: (1996) 59 million
(1997) 63.9 million
(1998) 71.4 million
Vehicle-km: (1996) 87.6 million
(1997) 94.4 million
(1998) 97.2 million

Number of routes: 130
Route length: 4,158 km

Fleet: 1,427 vehicles (includes paratransit)

Eagle 10 coaches (1985)	87
GMC RTS-II 04 (1982/83)	257
Neoplan 40 ft (1986)	10
Flxible (1985)	135
Neoplan 30 ft (1986)	21
Ikarus 40 ft (1990/91/92/93/94)	300
S&S Mercedes (1992/93)	29
Neoplan articulated (1992/93/96/97/98)	175
Neoplan 45 ft (1993/94)	51
Collins van (1992)	17
MetroTrans vans (1996)	98
New Flyer low-floor (1997/98)	76
Ferroni 29 ft suburban (1993)	84
New Flyer (1996/97/98)	157
Chance Trolley (1998)	26

In peak service: 1,108
On order: 36 articulated buses from Neoplan, 243 New Flyer low-floor 40 ft, 32 New Flyer low-floor 29 ft, 103 New Flyer 45 ft, all for 1998–2001 delivery

Most intensive service: 3 min
One-person operation: All routes
Fare collection: Coin, prepurchase ticket or token, weekly or monthly pass; stored value fare card
Fare structure: Local and express, flat; commuter, zonal; volume discount
Average peak-hour speed: 25.3 km/h
Integration with other modes: 24 park-and-ride sites have 26,579 spaces; buses, carpools and vanpools (20.8 million riders in 1997) use the transitways
Arrangements for elderly/disabled: MetroLift demand-responsive service operated under contract carried 1,058,000 in 1997 using 115 lift-equipped vans on prebooked journeys, supplemented by subscription taxi service and subsidised on-demand service of commercial taxis; 57 regular routes accessible; reduced fares on regular routes
Bus priority: Barrier-separated transitways on five freeways available to buses, high-occupancy vehicles and carpools; reversible HOV lanes extend to over 115 km
Operating costs financed by: Fares 21.1 per cent, tax levy 78.9 per cent

Busway
Current situation: Transitways are barrier-separated, one-direction single carriageways for use inbound from 05.00 to 11.00 and outbound from 14.00 to 20.00. They provide direct links with most park-and-ride lots and are open to all high-occupancy vehicles. Plans envisage a network of more than 183 km.

UPDATED

HULL

Population: 262,000
Public transport: Most bus services provided by two private companies

Stagecoach (KHCT)

Kingston upon Hull City Transport Ltd
Foster Street, Hull HU8 8BT, England
Tel: (+44 1482) 22 23 33   Fax: (+44 1482) 21 76 23
Managing Director: Ken Clarke
Operations Director: Paul De Santis
Engineering Director: Wilson Clark
Finance Director: David Reay
Staff: 300

Current situation: Formerly owned by the city council, KHCT was sold to Cleveland Transit of Stockton in 1993, with employees holding 49 per cent of shares. KHCT and its parent company were bought by Stagecoach in 1994.
Developments: KHCT rationalised its core facilities in Hull prior to sale to Cleveland Transit. Co-ordination with East Yorkshire has been developed on city routes, and the two operators have established joint ticketing arrangements. Limited-stop 'Stagecoach Express' services introduced to Leeds, Sheffield and Grimsby.

Bus
Passenger journeys: (1991/92) 18.4 million
(1992/93) 17.7 million
(1995/96) 14.3 million
Vehicle-km: (1991/92) 7.1 million
(1992/93) 7.9 million
(1995/96) 7.5 million

Number of routes: 85
Route length: 416 km

Fleet: 107 vehicles

Dennis Dominator/Alexander double-deck	5
Dennis Dominator/East Lancs double-deck	33
Volvo Olympian/Northern Counties double-deck	3
Dennis Lance single-deck	1
Leyland National single-deck	1
Scania/East Lancs single-deck	6
Scania/East Lancs double-deck	17
Volvo B10M/Northern Counties single-deck	20
Mercedes-Benz 709D/Alexander minibus	10
Mercedes-Benz O814D/Alexander minibus	2
Volvo B10M coach	9

In peak service: 100

East Yorkshire's newest buses are Northern Counties bodied Volvo Olympians and work the North Hull services (Andrew Jarosz)   *1999*/0043583

Most intensive service: 8 min
One-person operation: All services
Fare collection: Wayfarer equipment with change-giving; magnetic stored-value cards
Fare structure: Coarse stages; daily, weekly, monthly and 11-journey cards
Fares collected on board: 86 per cent (14 per cent of journeys by card holders)
Fare evasion control: Ticket inspectors
Operational control: Inspectors; mobile radios
Arrangements for elderly/disabled: Low flat fare at all times paid for by county council subsidy; 'Handyrider' wheelchair-accessible bus operates on different services each day; new vehicles conform to DPTAC standards

Bus priority: Bus lanes on Beverley road; pedestrianisation in city centre around Queen Victoria Square does not prohibit buses
Operating costs financed by: Fares 84 per cent, other commercial sources 2 per cent, subsidy/grants (for specific services/concessions) 14 per cent
Subsidy from: City and county council grants

East Yorkshire

East Yorkshire Motor Services Ltd
252 Anlaby Road, Hull HU3 2RS
Tel: (+44 1482) 271 42   Fax: (+44 1482) 21 20 40
Chairman & Chief Executive: Peter Shipp

JACKSONVILLE

Population: 732,000
Public transport: Bus and people mover services provided by transit authority governed by appointed board

JTA

Jacksonville Transportation Authority
PO Drawer O, 100 N Myrtle Avenue, Jacksonville, Florida 32203, USA
Tel: (+1 904) 630 31 81   Fax: (+1 904) 630 31 66
Chair: Carol S Miner
Executive Director: Miles N Francis Jr
Director of Mass Transit: Michael J Blaylock
Marketing & Media Relations: Charles Dixon
Staff: 464

Current situation: JTA, formed in 1972, provides public transport throughout Duval county. Dedicated funding for transit services was assured from 1989 when a ½ per cent sales tax was instituted. Unlike the former bridge and highway tolls, the sales tax can be used for both road construction and support of public transport, and $5 million was earmarked for bus service improvements through to 1995.

Bus

Passenger boardings: (1993) 9.6 million
(1994) 9.2 million
(1995) 9.1 million

Vehicle-km: (1993) 10.2 million
(1994) 10.2 million
(1995) 10 million

Route length: (One way) 936 km

Fleet: 184 buses	
Flxible 870 (1982)	63
Ikarus (1983)	2
Flxible Metro (1986)	30
Boyer trolley replica (1987)	1
Ikarus (1989)	8
Neoplan (1990/91)	37
Flxible Metro (1992/93)	23
Flxible Metro (1995)	20
In peak service: 138	

Most intensive service: 7 min
One-person operation: All routes
Integration with other modes: 7 Express Flyer routes serve suburban park-and-ride sites; also park-and-people mover shuttle in downtown
Fare structure: Flat, surcharge for special services; reduced rate multiride pass books; weekly passes
Fare collection: Coin to farebox
Arrangements for elderly/disabled: 63 lift-equipped buses provide fixed-route services; 100 minibuses and other vehicles operate a contracted-out dial-a-ride service; over-60s travel free
Operating costs financed by: Fares and parking revenues 26 per cent

People mover

Passenger journeys: (1993) 492,000
(1994) 409,000
(1995) 401,000

Current situation: A 1 km demonstration line opened 1989, based on VAL technology, was to have formed the nucleus of a 10 km 'Skyway Express' elevated people mover.
Developments: In 1994, Bombardier's UTDC Systems Division was awarded a contract to substitute its UM-III monorail technology on the 1 km route and build 1 km extensions at each end to serve Florida Community College and San Marco, across the St Johns River. When completed, nine vehicles will serve eight stations. Further extension approved late 1998, to bring the route to 4 km.

Suburban rail/light rail (proposed)

Current situation: JTA and Florida DoT collaborated in a 1995 systems planning study to consider options for commuter rail and long-range mass transit services.
   Light rail is proposed for four alignments — northwest to Edgewood Avenue, east to Neptune Beach, southeast to The Avenues, and southwest to Kingsley Avenue. An extensive network of park-and-ride lots is also proposed.

UPDATED

JAIPUR

Population: 1.5 million
Public transport: Bus services provided by State Road Transport Corporation; autorickshaws, tempos and minibuses operated by private companies

Rajasthan State Road Transport

Rajasthan State Road Transport Corporation
PO Box 210, Parivahan Marg, Jaipur 302001, India
Tel: (+91 141) 36 91 09   Fax: (+91 141) 37 30 04
Managing Director: Umesh Kumar
Staff: (State-wide total) 25,720

Current situation: Provides services throughout Rajasthan with a total fleet of 5,002 vehicles in 1997/98.
   The present bus service in Jaipur is inadequate for the rapidly growing population, and much of the city's transport is provided by private operators.

Bus

(Jaipur city service only)
Passenger journeys: 30 million (annual)
Vehicle-km: 5 million (annual)

Number of routes: 10
Route length: 250 km

Fleet: 100 buses, including Ashok Leyland and Tata

Fare collection: Floating or seated conductor
Fare structure: Stage

Minibus

Current situation: Private 'Matador' minibuses seating about 20 passengers, three-wheelers seating about 12, and cycle rickshaws provide much of the city's public transport. These are considered wasteful of road space, and congestion on city streets is increasing rapidly.

Light rail (proposed)

Current situation: A draft report on a proposed light rail system for the city was put forward by consultants RITES in 1991, recommending a 50.4 km network to be built in phases. Subsequently the government selected the Central Road Research Institute (CRRI) to carry out studies of suitable rapid transit systems, including a high-speed tramway. CRRI recommended phased construction of light rail routes extending to 58.7 km with 48 stations. The state government is now considering ways of financing and implementing the project.

UPDATED

JAKARTA

Population: 8.4 million
Public transport: Two main bus companies, one government-owned, the other private, cater for less than half of public transport provision. The remainder is supplied by two private minibus co-operatives (using vehicles with a maximum of 25 seats), and a large fleet of independent Mikrolets (microbuses with 10-15 seats), supplemented by some short-distance Bemo routes run by vehicles with fewer than 10 seats. There are also some 13,000 Becak trishaws. State railway Perumka provides suburban service, being upgraded to regional metro; metro and light rail planned

Dllajr Dki Jakarta

Highway Transportation & Traffic Agency of the Jakarta City Government
Jalan Taman Jatibaru 1, Jakarta 10150, Indonesia
Tel: (+62 21) 37 53 67

Passenger journeys: (All modes)
(1990) 1,379 million

Current situation: This city government authority is responsible for co-ordination and licensing of all public road transport. It also operates 14 bus terminals and maintains bus shelters. Three of the terminals serve as interchange points between urban and interurban buses, the latter not permitted to penetrate the central area.
Developments: A guided busway runs through the city centre on elevated alignment. The route runs from Kota in the central business district to the Blok M bus terminal in the suburb of Kebayoran Baru.

Bus

Current situation: Several companies, including government-owned PPD, operate throughout the city, with nearly 200 routes and some 1,500 vehicles, mainly double-deck. PPD runs a separate network of school buses as crews of service buses often refused to admit students (paying reduced fares) during peak hours.

One-person operation: None
Fare collection: 2 conductors per vehicle; no tickets issued
Fare structure: Flat; surcharge for express (100 per cent) and air conditioned (300 per cent) services

Double-deck bus in the central business district (Bill Luke)   *1999*/0043182

Mikrolets touting for business (Bill Luke)
1999/0043181

Fares collected on board: 100 per cent
Arrangements for elderly/disabled: None
Average peak-hour speed: Urban 8 km/h; suburban 17 km/h
Bus priority: Bus lanes along some main routes, not always respected by other vehicles
Integration with other modes: Interchange with interurban buses at three terminals

Minibus

Current situation: Four co-operatives operate minibus services within Jakarta. Metro Mini was founded in 1962 and originally restricted to vehicles of not more than 15 seats, but was reorganised in 1977 and authorised to operate vehicles with up to 25 seats. Kopaja was founded in 1980, and two other co-operatives (Koantas Bima and Kopami Jaya) came into being more recently. Together they operate more than 4,000 vehicles, mainly Mitsubishi, Isuzu and Daihatsu with local bodywork.

All vehicles carry conductors and charge fares 20 per cent higher than ordinary city buses.

Mikrolet

Current situation: Two co-operatives, Koperasi and APK, operate Mikrolets (vehicles with 10-15 seats) on regular routes, one within the city and the other mainly on suburban routes. Their combined fleets total more than 8,000 vehicles. Mikrolets do not operate into the central business district.

Vehicles are either owned by their drivers or by investors and hired out on a daily basis. The city government specifies a number of types which are eligible for Mikrolet operation, which may then be further restricted by the co-operative. City government also defines a uniform livery and lettering.

Toyokos touting for business (Bill Luke)
1999/0043183

Bemo

Current situation: Public service vehicles with fewer than 10 seats are officially referred to as Bemos. These are not licensed by the city government, but by the various districts. They operate on short intra-neighbourhood routes which may change frequently according to demand. There are a total of 1,096 three-wheel scooters with longitudinal seats for six passengers, also known locally as Toyokos. It is estimated that each carries some 35 passengers a day, amounting to around 14 million annual journeys.

Perumka

Perum Keteta Api (Perumka)
Jalan Perintis Kemerdekaan No 1, Bandung, Java Barat
Tel: (+62 22) 43 00 39/43 00 54
Fax: (+62 22) 43 00 62

Type of operation: Suburban heavy rail

Current situation: Services operate over 50 route-km between Jakarta and Bogor with 19 stations, and over a loop line in Jakarta, electrified at 1.5 kV DC. Sporadic diesel-hauled trains operate over several other routes. Together they carry about 20 million passengers a year.

The existing suburban network is being upgraded into a regional metro to serve the Jabotabek planning region, a 6,000 km^2 area covering Jakarta and its satellite towns of Bogor, Tangerang and Bekasi, with a total population of 13.6 million. Of these, 40 per cent use motorised transport every working day, the modal split being 60 per cent for public buses, 25 per cent for private cars and only 2 per cent for rail. By the year 2005, it is planned that the regional metro should achieve a 20-30 per cent share.

Developments: Electrification and double-tracking of the Tangerang line is in progress, with a planned link to Soekarno-Hatta (Cengkareng) international airport. Project engineering is being carried out by JARTS. Two more construction projects were approved in early 1995, including replacement of further sections of suburban railway on elevated alignment.

Plans for a major multimodal interchange and commercial development on Perumka land at Manggerai were approved in 1995. It would be the first instance of a joint public/private enterprise involving development of railway land.

Rolling stock: 50 two-car emus, plus 25 diesel railcars/coaches
On order: 40 four-car emus being supplied by PT Inka following joint production with BN of Belgium and Holec of the Netherlands of 7 four-car sets; also 8 trainsets from Hyundai

Aeromovel

Coester SA

Type of operation: Demonstration people mover, powered by compressed air

Current situation: A 3.2 km circular track has been built in the Taman Mini-Indonesia theme park as a demonstrator, and is now used for pleasure rides. The three cars serve six stations. It is not part of the public transport network.

Metro/light rail (planned)

Current situation: Successful bidder to build an 82 km light rail network linking central Jakarta with Tangerang and Bekasi, adjudicated in 1995, was a consortium of local companies. Some routes could use the alignments of existing suburban railways (see above).

At the beginning of 1995, the government approved plans for a US$1.4 billion initial metro network, extending to 14.5 km in tunnel with 14 stations. A German/British/Japanese consortium of ABB/AEG, Ferrostaal, Siemens, Taylor Woodrow and Itochu is financing the design stage of the project, and hopes to win the construction contract. The project underwent a technical and financial review in late 1997.

UPDATED

JERUSALEM

Population: 250,000, region 608,000
Public transport: Most bus services provided by local members of national transport co-operative society; light rail proposed

EGGED

Israel Transport Co-operative Society Ltd (EGGED)
PO Box 13178, Jerusalem 91131, Israel
Tel: (+972 2) 30 44 44

Current situation: The Jerusalem Region is the smallest of EGGED's three divisions, extending from Beit Shemesh to the Jordan Valley. For details of EGGED operations see Tel Aviv entry.

Bus

(Jerusalem Region operations only)
Staff: 1,760

Passenger journeys: Specific figures not available

Fleet: 667 buses

One-person operation: All routes
Fare collection: Manually by driver from ticket board
Fare structure: Flat
Fares collected on board: 100 per cent
Fare evasion control: Inspectors
Average peak-hour speed: In bus lanes, 20 km/h; in mixed traffic, 18.6 km/h
Bus priority: 3.9 km of bus lanes; further 4.8 km planned
Subsidy from: Government

Light rail (proposed)

Current situation: Plans have been announced for a light rail network of eight lines. The Ministry of Transport and

the city council plan to carry out and operate the scheme in stages, financed and run by the private sector, and the prequalification tender for groups invited to bid for construction of the line was to be issued early in 1999.

Phase A of the project is to be completed by 2004 and will comprise a 15 km double track serving Mount Herzel, University, Municipality Square, French Hill, Shuafat and Pisgat Zeev.

Preliminary construction work has started and includes the diversion of underground installations, allocation of dedicated bus lanes, and clearance of interfering structures.

At the same time Jerusalem city council, backed by the Ministry of Transport, is no longer granting planning permission for new commercial and office developments with large-capacity dedicated car parks.

UPDATED

JILIN

Population: 1.4 million
Public transport: Single municipal transport operator providing bus, minibus and trolleybus services

Jilin City Transport

Jilin City Transport Company
Jilin, People's Republic of China

Current situation: The backbone of transport is a trolleybus system which has remained static in extent for many years, but which is now worked by a second generation of articulated vehicles, many received since 1985, although it is not clear whether they were new or cascaded from Shanghai. Only about 20 per cent of the fleet consists of trolleybuses, however, and the bus network covers a far larger area of the city. Minibuses at

premium fares, thought to have been introduced around 1986, duplicate some bus and trolleybus services.

Bus

Number of routes: Approx 30

Fleet: Approx 300 buses, of which about 130 articulated, mainly Jiangcheng and Siping types

Fare collection: Payment to seated conductors, monthly passes
Fare structure: Stage
Integration with other modes: Number of bus routes act as feeders to trolleybus system; minibuses augment ordinary services

Minibus
Number of routes: At least 4

Fleet: Over 100 Siping SP320N, SOK6650 and SP6651 minibuses

Fare collection: Payment to conductors
Fare structure: Probably flat

Trolleybus
Number of routes: 3

Fleet: Approx 62 trolleybuses, all articulated
Shanghai SK561G	about 57
Shenyang	5

Service interval: Every few minutes

Fare collection: Payment to seated conductors, monthly passes
Fare structure: Stage
Integration with other modes: Bus routes from outer suburbs terminate at two suburban trolleybus termini; premium-fare minibuses augment services

VERIFIED

JOHANNESBURG
Population: 1.7 million
Public transport: Bus services provided for part of city by municipal undertaking, with network of suburban commuter routes by private company (PUTCO) and shared 'Kombi-taxis'. Suburban rail services operated by SA Rail Commuter Corp

Johannesburg Transportation
City of Johannesburg Transportation Directorate
Transportation House, Raikes Road, PO Box 1787, Newtown, Johannesburg 2000, South Africa
Tel: (+27 11) 339 57 16   Fax: (+27 11) 339 68 13
Executive Director: S Verrier
Staff: 1,100

Bus
Passenger journeys: (1991/92) 48.1 million
Vehicle-km: (1991/92) 12.1 million

Number of routes: 73
Route length: (One way) 630 km

Fleet: 505 buses
Leyland Fleetline double-deck	73
Mercedes O305 double-deck	284
Mercedes O305 single-deck	46
AEC Mk V	1
MAN midibus	1
Busaf (1996)	100

In peak service: 312

Most intensive service: 10 min
One-person operation: All services
Fare collection: Monthly tickets and prepurchase coupons with cancellation machines or payment to driver
Fare structure: Zonal (4 and 5 zones); monthly tickets (peak or off-peak); 10-trip coupons
Operational control: Mobile inspectors with radio communication and computerised online monitoring
Arrangements for elderly/disabled: Free off-peak travel for persons over 70, low flat fare for pensioners. Cost of concessions included in city council's compensation for the undertaking's deficit
Average peak-hour speed: 17 km/h
Bus priority: With flow and contraflow bus lanes
Operating costs financed by: Fares 42 per cent, other commercial sources 3 per cent, subsidy/grants 55 per cent
Subsidy from: Johannesburg ratepayers 48 per cent, other local authorities 4 per cent, Central Witwatersrand regional services council 3 per cent
New vehicles financed by: Loans

Metro Rail
South African Rail Commuter Corporation Ltd
Johannesburg Metropolitan Area
Private Bag X2, Sunninghill, Johannesburg 2157
Tel: (+27 11) 804 29 00   Fax: (+27 11) 804 38 52

Type of operation: Suburban heavy rail

Passenger journeys: (1994/95) 134 million
(1995/96) 157 million
(1996/97) 159 million

Current situation: Extensive network of 1,065 mm gauge suburban trains on 14 routes serving the whole southern Transvaal (Witwatersrand—Vereeniging area, population 5.5 million), totalling 305 km with 167 stations, electrified at 3 kV DC. Links with northern Transvaal area services (see under Pretoria). Up to 35 trains per hour run at peak times on the busiest sections, while off-peak the normal frequency is hourly. Fares cover 20.3 per cent of operating costs.
Developments: As well as proposals for two new lines totalling 16 km in northern Johannesburg, the Corporation is also planning a route to serve the Baralink commercial and residential development in the south-west of the city. Comprising a loop and branch, the 20 km alignment would be built with private-sector finance.

A start has been made with fleet renewal; bids were sought in mid-1998 for five 12-car trains intended for service on the Johannesburg—Soweto line.

Rolling stock: 1,757 emu cars, mostly four-car sets
UCW Steam side door (1932 onwards)	T14
UCW 5M2A (1957 onwards)	M521 T1,222

PUTCO
Putco Ltd
PO Box 3, Wendywood 2144

Current situation: PUTCO operates extensive long-distance commuter services. Separate eastern and western networks have a combined fleet of about 1,600 buses, carrying about 90 million passengers a year. The Department of Transport provides a fares subsidy of about one-third.

Shared taxis
Current situation: Since the 1977 Road Transportation Act there has been major growth in the numbers of Kombi-taxis, mostly Volkswagen minibuses operating variable routes and schedules. Originally illegal, the Kombi-taxis are now licensed, though deregulation is planned.

Light rail (proposed)
Current situation: Plans for a light rail system were prepared in 1985, but were superseded by proposals for an extensive metro network in 1987. This plan was rejected on cost grounds. In 1991 the Masstran Consortium of local authorities recommended a seven-line light rail network, and in 1994 go-ahead was given for construction of Line 1 from the city centre to the suburb of Observatory. Work had been expected to start in 1995, but the project was reported shelved in early 1995.

UPDATED

KAGOSHIMA
Population: 540,000
Public transport: Bus and tramway services provided by municipal undertaking. Additional private bus services operated by three main firms; JR suburban rail services; ferry

Kagoshima-shi Kotsu Kyoku
Kagoshima City Transport Bureau
43-41 Korai-cho, Kagoshima-shi, Kyushu 890-0051, Japan
Tel: (+81 992) 57 21 11   Fax: (+81 992) 58 67 41
General Manager: T Tsutsui
Staff: 661

Bus
Passenger journeys: (Annual) 25 million

Number of routes: 26
Route length: 335.6 km
Fleet: 182 vehicles, including Isuzu, Hino, Nissan and Mitsubishi

One-person operation: All routes (except tours)
Fare collection: Payment to farebox by driver or cancellation of multitickets or passes
Fare structure: Zonal; multitickets, monthly pass or one-day tickets (bus/tram)
Arrangements for elderly/disabled: Half fare for elderly
Average peak-hour speed: 15 km/h

Tramway
Type of operation: Conventional tramway

Passenger journeys: (1995) 10.9 million
Car-km: (Annual) 2 million

Route length: 13.1 km
  on reserved track: 6.4 km
Number of lines: 2
Number of stops: 35
Gauge: 1,435 mm
Electrification: 600 V DC, overhead

First/last car: 06.00/23.00
Fare structure: Flat; multitickets, monthly and 3-monthly passes, one-day tickets (bus/tram)
Fare collection: Coin to farebox on alighting, or prepurchase
One-person operation: All cars

Rolling stock: 53 cars
Toyo Koki Type 500 (1955/56)	M13
Hitachi Type 600 (1959)	M4
Naniwa Koki Type 600 (1960)	M4
Teikoku Sharyo Type 600 (1962/63)	M4
Naniwa Koki Type 800 (ex-Osaka) (1968)	M4
JR Kyushu Type 2100 (1989/91/92/94)	M11
Alna Koki Type 9500 (rebuilt 1995/96/97/8)	M11
Alna Koki Type 9700 (1998)	M2

Developments: Fleet modernisation continued in 1998 with the delivery of a further three rebuilt ex-Osaka Naniwa Koki cars and two new Type 9700 cars from Alna Koki.

Kagoshima Kotsu
Kagoshima Kotsu Co Ltd
12-12 Kamoike-shinmachi, Kagoshima-shi 890-0064
Tel: (+81 992) 23 11 10
Staff: 703

Current situation: Private operator runs part of Kagoshima city bus services, as well as sightseeing tours and travel services.

Bus
Passenger journeys: (Annual) 16.6 million (including tours)
Vehicle-km: (Annual) 18.8 million (including tours)

Number of routes: 258 (including 25 city routes)
Route length: (One way) 2,044 km
Fleet: 420 buses (including charter vehicles)

Operating costs financed by: Fares 91 per cent, other commercial sources 7.5 per cent, subsidy/grants 1.5 per cent
Subsidy from: Government and local authorities

Nangoku Kotsu

Nangoku Kotsu
11-5 Chuo-machi, Kagoshima-shi 890-0053
Tel: (+81 992) 55 21 41

Bus
Current situation: Operates some 200 vehicles with routes serving the Kagoshima area.

Hayashida Sangyo

Hayashida Sangyo Kotsu Co Ltd
12-10 Terukuni-cho, Kagoshima-shi 892-0841

Tel: (+81 992) 23 11 22
General Manager: Kouichi Kawaharazono
Staff: 350

Current situation: Private operator runs part of services in Kagoshima, plus substantial tourist-related operations, on a fully commercial basis.

Bus
Passenger journeys: (Annual) 8.5 million
Vehicle-km: (Annual) 8.5 million

Number of routes: 149

Fleet: 210 vehicles, including Isuzu, Mitsubishi and Hino

JR Kyushu

Kyushu Railway Company
Kyushu Ryokaku Tetsudo
1-1 Chuogai, Hakata Eki, Hakata-ku, Fukuoka 812-8566
Tel: (+81 92) 474 25 01   Fax: (+81 92) 474 97 45

Chair: Y Ishii
President: K Tanaka

Type of operation: Interurban/suburban railway

Passenger journeys: (Kagoshima operations only) (1990/91) 10 million

Current situation: Local emu services operate from Nishi Kagoshima to Sendai and beyond on the Kagoshima main line. Local stations towards Hayato on the Nippo main line have a mixed emu/dmu service. A dmu service operates to Kiire, 29 km south of Kagoshima, with some trains continuing to Yamakare (55 km).

Ferry
Current situation: Sakurajima municipality operates a ferry service across Kagoshima Bay from Kagoshima Port to the volcanic Mt Sakurajima. The crossing takes 15 min and vessels run every 10-15 min.

UPDATED

KALININGRAD

Population: 430,000
Public transport: Bus, trolleybus and tramway services provided by two public enterprises and other operators; suburban rail

MGP ATP

MGP ATP Kaliningrad
Kaliningrad, Russia

Current situation: This public enterprise is still the largest operator. Additional services are provided by Stalena, Swetlowskie Linii, Kron Auto and others. Their fleets comprise a mixture of former Soviet types and second-hand imports from Germany and, to a lesser extent, Poland.

Fare collection: Prepurchase
Fare structure: Flat; various concessions; passes

Route Taxis
Current situation: About half the city's buses operate as 'Route Taxis'. There is a co-operative, Associacija Taxobus, but other operators, including ATP, participate as well. Fleets are the same mixture as ordinary buses; there are no minibuses.

Fare collection: Roving or seated conductor
Fare structure: Flat, 25 per cent above ordinary buses; no concessions; no passes issued or accepted

TTU

Tramvaino-Trolleibusnoe Upravlenie
Ul Kievskaya 17, Kaliningrad 236039
Tel: (+7 0112) 44 43 33   Fax: (+7 0112) 44 15 72
Director: Ivan Kravtsov
Technical Manager: Alexander Firsov
Trolleybus Manager: Evgueni Alexine

Current situation: This public enterprise runs trolleybus and tramway services; they are slower than buses and apparently run less frequently.

Trolleybus
Number of routes: 6
Fleet: 66 trolleybuses, all ZIU9

Tramway
Number of routes: 12

Fleet: About 165 cars	
Tatra T4	M123
Tatra KT4	Over M40
Duewag ex-Mannheim	M2

RZD

Russian Railways, Kaliningrad Region
Ul Kievskaya 1, Kaliningrad 236039
Tel: (+7 0112) 49 33 00   Fax: (+7 0112) 44 34 12

Current situation: Suburban service operated by emus on three lines, with infrequent diesel trains serving the remaining area of Kaliningrad Oblast.

Suburban/regional bus
Current situation: Kenig-Avto, a state enterprise, and other operators provide suburban and regional service into the city.

VERIFIED

Tatra tram and Ikarus bus in central Kaliningrad
1998/0009697

KAMPALA

Population: 478,000
Public transport: Bus services operated by minibus/shared taxi owners

Minibus/shared taxi
Current situation: With the abandonment of conventional bus services in the early 1990s, following liquidation of Uganda Transport and Peoples Transport, minibus and shared taxi services now cater for all the public transport needs of the city. The small-scale operators and owner-drivers are members of either the Uganda Taxi Operators & Drivers Association or the Uganda National Taxi & Travel Organisation, between which there is much rivalry.

Operations are reportedly unlicensed as to route or quantity of vehicles, though pick-up and terminal points are strictly regulated by Kampala City Council staff and the police. Vehicles are mainly second-hand Toyota Hiace and Nissan minibuses seating 8 or 14; conductors collect a flat fare.

VERIFIED

KANPUR

Population: 2.1 million
Public transport: Extensive private bus and 'tempo taxi' operations provide most of the city's public transport needs; limited local trains of Northern Railway

Bus
Licensed by: Regional Transport Office
Sarvodaya Nagar, Kanpur 208005, India

Current situation: Following withdrawal of the Uttar Pradesh State Transport's operations in the city, private operators licensed by the Regional Transport Office run 43 bus routes. Most journeys are catered for by the tempo taxis, usually eight-seaters.

Fleet: 320 buses, mainly Tata, Eicher, DCM and Swaraj Mazda; 2,200 tempo taxis, mainly Bajaj Auto and Vikram

Fare structure: Stage
Fare collection: Cash to conductor on buses, to driver on tempo taxis

Northern Railway

Northern Railway

Current situation: Runs eight return dmu services at commuting times between Kanpur and Lucknow (72 km), and one pair of main line emu trains between Kanpur and Etawah.
Developments: NR plans to introduce another two emus; consultancy RITES is carrying out a study for a high-capacity mass transit system for the city.

UPDATED

Odakyu limited express and suburban trains at Mukogaoka-yuen   **1998**/0007911

General Director: Yasuo Usui
Staff: 849

Current situation: Kawasaki-shi Kotsu Kyoku and private operators' routes are numbered in a common system. Municipal and private operators also share a common flat fare with prepurchase ticket strips valid on all routes within Kawasaki except that operated by Yokohama-shi Kotsu Kyoku.

Bus
Passenger journeys: (1991/92) 59.1 million
(1992/93) 58.3 million
(1996) 40 million
Vehicle-km: (1991/92) 13 million
(1992/93) 13 million
(1996) 12.5 million

Number of routes: 28
Route length: 189 km
On priority right-of-way: 16.8 km

Fleet: 354 vehicles
Isuzu   160
Mitsubishi   150
Hino   32
Nissan Diesel   12
Fleet includes 18 low-emission vehicles (CNG or diesel-electric hybrid)
In peak service: 302
New vehicles required each year: 25

Most intensive service: 1 min
One-person operation: All routes
Fare collection: Payment to farebox by driver or prepurchase ticket strips
Fare structure: Flat; prepurchase ticket strips; monthly and 3-monthly passes; one-day 'Ecology' pass
Integration with other modes: Services integrated with JR and other railways
Average distance between stops: 380 m
Operating costs financed by: Fares 83.6 per cent, other commercial sources 3 per cent, subsidy/grants 17 per cent
New vehicles financed by: Public bonds, subsidy and internal funds

Developments: Premium fare late journeys introduced on six 'Midnight Bus' routes.

Kawasaki Tsurumi Rinko Bus
Kawasaki Tsurumi Rinko Bus
15-2 Nishin-machi, Kawasaki-ku, Kawasaki-shi 210-0024
Tel: (+81 44) 233 65 01

Current situation: This private company operates in Kawasaki and Yokohama; 30 of the routes (including five express) serve Kawasaki, some jointly with Kawasaki City Bus.

Bus
Passenger journeys: (1990/91) 53.2 million
(1991/92) 53.6 million
(1992/93) 53 million

Vehicle-km: (1990/91) 11.9 million
(1991/92) 12.2 million
(1992/93) 12.2 million

Number of routes: 36
Route length: 162 km

Fleet: 360 vehicles

JR East
East Japan Railway Company
Higashi Nihon Ryokaku Tetsudo
2-2, Yoyogi 2-chome, Shibuya-ku, Tokyo 151-8578
Tel: (+81 3) 53 34 11 51   Fax: (+81 3) 53 34 11 10

www: http://www.jreast.co.jp
Chair: S Yamanouchi
President: M Matsuda

Type of operation: Inner and outer suburban heavy rail

Current situation: Kawasaki is linked to both Tokyo and Yokohama by frequent Keihin-Tohoku line inner suburban E-den trains and by outer suburban services on the Tokaido main line. Outer suburban trains on the Yokosuka line link Shin-Kawasaki with Tokyo and Yokohama.
    E-den trains on the 35.5 km Nambu line serve 18 stations in Kawasaki providing a link between central Kawasaki and suburban areas to the northwest.
    E-den service also on 4.1 km branch from Shitte to Hama-Kawasaki and on 7 km Tsurumi line from Tsurumi to Ogimachi.

Keihin Kyuko Dentetsu 'Keikyu'
Keihin Express Electric Railway
20-20 Takanawa 2-chome, Minato-ku, Tokyo 108-0074
Tel: (+81 3) 32 80 91 22   Fax: (+81 3) 32 80 91 93
President: I Hiramatsu

Interurban railway
Current situation: Keihin-Kawasaki station on the main line between Tokyo and Yokohama serves central Kawasaki. Through services are operated to central Tokyo via the Toei Asakusa line metro and on to the Keisei Railway. The 4.5 km Daishi branch links Keihin-Kawasaki with Kojima-Shinden (see main entry under Tokyo).

Bus
Current situation: Operates buses in Kawasaki, Yokohama and other parts of Kanagawa Prefecture as well as in Tokyo.

Local service of Tokyu Bus   **1997**

Odakyu's monorail   **1998**/0007912

Tokyu/Odakyu/Keio Teito

Suburban/interurban railways

Current situation: These railways serve areas to the northwest of central Kawasaki which function largely as outer suburbs of Tokyo. All three railways operate through trains to the Tokyo metro system. The Tokyu Toyoko line from Tokyo to Yokohama serves two stations in Kawasaki (through service to Hibiya line metro) and the Denentoshi line serves six stations (through service to Hanzomon line metro). The Odakyu Odawara line serves seven Kawasaki stations (through service to Chiyoda line metro) with three other stations served by the Tama branch line. Keio Teito has two stations in Kawasaki on the Sagamihara line (through service to Shinjuku line metro). (See main entries for these railways under Tokyo.)

Bus

Current situation: Tokyu Corp has two bus depots in Kawasaki and operates 23 local routes, including one demand-responsive, with some of the 300 buses allocated for Yokohama and Kawasaki operations.

Odakyu Bus also operates routes in Kawasaki. Both operators also serve Yokohama and Tokyo.

Monorail

Current situation: Odakyu operates a 1.1 km 750 V DC Lockheed straddle monorail between Mukogaoka-yuen on the Odawara line and the company's nearby amusement park. The service is provided by a single two-car train which carries about 2,000 passengers daily.

UPDATED

KAZAN

Population: 1.1 million
Public transport: Bus and trolleybus/tramway services provided by separate municipal undertakings; metro under construction

Bus
Number of routes: 40

RVZ6 and KTM8M cars at Tatarstan street

1998/0009735

Fleet: Ikarus 260/280, LIAZ 677, Mercedes-Benz Türk O325, Karosa B731/B741

Fare collection: Conductors

Gorelektrotransport
Ul Yershova 1, Kazan 420045, Russia
Tel: (+7 8432) 36 76 52

Current situation: In terms of maintenance levels and frequency, this is a medium-scale tramway. No new track has opened so far during the 1990s, but a new 10 km route is under construction in the east of the city.

Trolleybus
Number of routes: 12

Fleet: Approx 270 vehicles, ZIU9 plus 1 Jelcz/Nordtroll

Fare collection: Conductors

Tramway
Passenger journeys: (1989) 152 million

Number of routes: 18
Track length: 151 km
Fare collection: As trolleybus

Rolling stock: Approx 410 cars

RVZ6 (1977/87)	About M220
KTM5 (1988/92)	M147
KTM8 (1993)	M24
LM93 (1993/96)	M7
KTM8M (1995/97)	M14

Metro
Under construction

Current situation: Construction of east-west Line 1 of the proposed three-line metro is reported to have started in mid-1997, for opening in 2004.

UPDATED

KHARKOV

Population: 1.6 million
Public transport: Bus and trolleybus/tramway services provided by separate municipal undertakings, also private and hired bus operations; metro

Upravlenie Automobil'novo Transporta
Upravlenie Automobil'novo Transporta
Kharkov, Ukraine

Bus
Passenger journeys: 269 million (annual)
Vehicle-km: 41 million (annual)

Route length: 597 km

Fleet: 741 vehicles, including some articulated

Fare collection: Conductors
Fare structure: Flat

Gorelektrotrans
Gorelektrotrans
Ul Molodoy Gvardii 5, Kharkov 310006
Tel: (+380 57) 227 56 58
Chief Engineer: V Matriyenko

Current situation: Gorelektrotrans struggles to maintain its networks despite lack of funds and deteriorating vehicles and infrastructure, though it has the support of the city government which tries to restrict competing private-sector buses and minibuses to less-important routes. Trolleybuses no longer penetrate right to the city centre, their routes having been cut back to terminate at

Trolleybuses leaving the depot thread their way through the central market

1998/0009795

four metro stations on the edge of the centre, dividing the system into three separate networks. In addition, some tram routes have been closed or shortened.

Trolleybus
Passenger journeys: 200 million (annual)
Vehicle-km: 26 million (annual)

Route length: 134 km
Number of routes: 28

Fleet: 503 vehicles

ZIU9 (1983/91)	372
ZIU10 (1992/94)	9
DAC 217E (1989/90)	47
Rocar 217E (1995)	28
YuMZ-T1 (1993/94)	47

Fare collection: Conductors
Fare structure: Flat

Tramway

Type of operation: Conventional tramway

Route length: 166 km
Number of lines: 20
Number of stops: 350
Gauge: 1,524 mm

Fare collection: Conductors
Fare structure: Flat

Rolling stock: 649 cars
T3 (1967/87)	M549
KTM5 (1978/91)	M47
T3M (1988/91)	M53

Kharkov Metro

Kharkov Metropolitena
Ul Engelsa 29, Kharkov 310012
Chief Executive: Nikolai Yakovlevich Bessonov
Chief Engineer: Leonid Ivanovich Vstavskii

Type of operation: Full metro, initial line opened 1984

Passenger journeys: (1991) 250 million

Route length: 26 km
Number of lines: 3
Number of stations: 27
  in tunnel: 23
Gauge: 1,524 mm
Max gradient: 4%
Minimum curve radius: 300 m
Electrification: 750 V DC, third rail

Service: Peak 2½ min, off-peak 6 min
First/last train: 06.00/01.00

Kharkov metro

Fare structure: Flat, monthly season card
Revenue control: Prepurchase token or magnetic-strip season ticket activate access gates
One-person operation: None
Signalling: Automatic train stop; cab signalling, with automatic speed control; no signals; radio communication between control and trains

Rolling stock: 287 cars in five-car sets
EJ-79	M287

Current situation: Line 1 was originally planned as a suburban rail cross-city route, hence the non-standard 750 V DC traction supply. The initial section of Line 3 in the city centre was opened in 1995; northwards extension to Peremohi under construction.

VERIFIED

KIEV

Population: 2.6 million
Public transport: Bus and trolleybus/tramway services provided by separate undertakings. Metro; funicular operated by city authority; suburban rail services; river ferries; private-sector minibuses

Current situation: Strong competition has broken out between state-owned buses and trolleybuses and private minibus operators established in 1996/97. New Ford and GAZ minis run parallel to the busiest bus and trolleybus routes in the west and south of the city, even using the same route numbers. The minibuses are not obliged to carry the large number of passengers who are entitled to free travel, while 70 per cent of trolleybus passengers fall into this category and around half the remainder simply refuse to pay. Thus revenue of state-owned services has fallen steeply.

New trolleybus Route 24 in the north opened in 1996, since when no further tram or trolleybus extensions are under construction. No new trams have been received since 1995, and there is no money to fund purchase of the Tatra-Yug vehicles developed by Yuzhmash. Some YuMZ-T1 (articulated) and -T2 vehicles were supplied in 1996/97, but there are no orders for the articulated Kyiv 12, two prototypes of which are confined to the depot, or

Škoda's 14TrM, four of which were delivered in 1997 for trials.

Fare collection: Conductors
Fare structure: Flat, higher for bus; single, monthly and quarterly seasons
Arrangements for elderly/disabled: Free travel

Kyivelektrotrans

Kyivelektrotrans
Nabereshne Chose 2, Kiev 254070, Ukraine
Tel: (+380 44) 291 04 70
Director General: S P Beikul
Staff: 8,820

Current situation: Trolleybus is the principal mode in the city centre. The tramway includes a 9.5 km fully segregated section used by Routes 1/1k and 3 to satellite housing developments southwest of the city, equipped with ATC and operated by three-car sets.
Developments: After many difficulties in the period immediately following independence, the network has begun to settle down, but trolleybuses came under intense pressure from minibuses in 1997 (see above). Some new construction and rehabilitation has been

Kiev metro Line 6 showing the river crossing and station   **1999**/0043195

carried out on the infrastructure of both modes. Trolleybus wiring has been extended to Tereshchenkivska Str and the major Bessarabsky interchange rebuilt, while tram tracks on Esplanadna and Zhilyanska have been rehabilitated. A new express tramway link is under construction to Livoberezhna metro station.

Widespread fare evasion has been countered by reintroduction of conductors in September 1996.

Small quantities of Yuzhmash locally built trolleybuses and tramcars are entering service, allowing withdrawal of obsolete vehicles.

Operating costs financed by: Fares 32.6 per cent, other commercial sources 3.3 per cent, subsidy/grants 51.5 per cent

Trolleybus
Passenger journeys: (1996) 100.5 million

Number of routes: 34
Route length: 329 km

Fleet: 657 vehicles
Skoda 14Tr (1982-91/97)	314
Skoda 15Tr articulated (1989/95)	45
DAC 217E articulated (1988/90)	230
YuMZ-T1 articulated (1993/96)	53
YuMZ-T2 (1996/97)	15
In peak service: 410	

Tramway
Type of operation: Conventional tramway/light rail

Passenger journeys: (1996) 104.7 million

High-speed reserved track express tramway on Line 3 (D Trevor-Rowe)   **1999**/0043194

Number of lines: 25
Route length: 287 km
Gauge: 1,524 mm

Rolling stock: 672 cars
ČKD Tatra T3SU (1966/87)   M576
ČKD Tatra T3M (1985/91)   M94
Tatra-Yug T3M   M2
In peak service: 410
On order: 35 Tatra-Yug T3M for 1998 delivery; may be delayed by lack of funding

Kiev Metro

Kyivskiy Metropoliten
Prospekt Peremogi 35, Kiev 252055
Tel: (+380 44) 228 90 21   Fax: (+380 44) 229 18 57
General Manager: N E Balatskiy
Chief Engineer: V I Fedorenko
Staff: 5,315

Type of operation: Full metro, first line opened 1960

Passenger journeys: (1996) 268 million
(1997) 266 million
(up to September 1998) 205 million

Route length: 48.9 km
   in tunnel: 41.7 km
Number of lines: 3
Number of stations: 39
Gauge: 1,524 mm
Max gradient: 4%
Minimum curve radius: 400 m
Electrification: 825 V DC, third rail

Service: Peak 1 min 35 s, off-peak 3-6 min
First/last train: 06.00/24.00
Fare structure: Flat, monthly season card
Revenue control: Prepurchase token or magnetic-strip season ticket activate access gates
Integration with other modes: With tram/trolleybus/bus
One-person operation: All lines
Signalling: Automatic train stop; radio communication between trains and control; CTC; CCTV at stations

Rolling stock: 537 cars (operational)
Mytischy D60 (1960/89)   M259
Mytischy E79 81-714/715 (1979)   M248
Others   M30

Developments: In 1999 the Syretsko–Pecherska line is due to open, with a further extension to the Vinogradar residential area. Also in 1999 the Obolon depot is due to be refurbished. The extension of the Sviatoshino–Brovarska line to Novo-Belichi is under development. An automatic sprinkler system has been installed.

Bus

Current situation: Buses play only a limited and decreasing supporting role to the other modes. Operations are in the hands of six local ATPs (Automobil'novo Transporta Pasagirskogo), with a fleet of mainly Ikarus 280 plus some 260 and 263, and LAZ. No new buses have been delivered since 1995.

YuMZ-T1 trolleybus at Nivki metro station terminus   *1998*/0009796

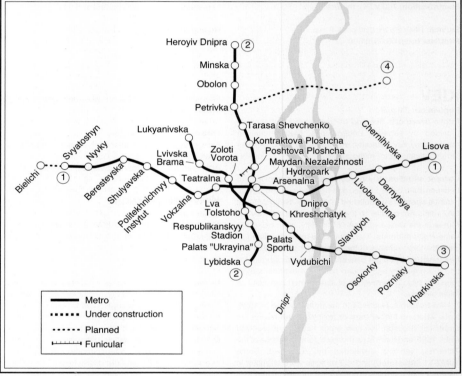

UPDATED   *Kiev metro*   0009920

KINGSTON

Population: 500,000
Public transport: Bus services provided by franchised operators regulated by transport authority; also cross-harbour ferry

Transport Authority

PO Box 9000, Kingston, Jamaica
Tel: (+1 809) 926 91 70   Fax: (+1 809) 926 28 35
Managing Director: John McFarlane
General Manager, Operations: Charles C Campbell

Passenger journeys: (1996) 262 million

Kingston's new Mercedes buses
1998/0007913

Fleet: 584 vehicles

Ikarus 260	39
Ikarus 280 articulated	189
Jelcz M11	171
Jelcz 120M	130
Scania CR111/112	20
Scania CN113LAB (1992/93)	20
Scania MaxCi	11
MAN SG242/SL200	3
Jelcz MN121M	1

In peak service: 446

Most intensive service: 5 min
One-person operation: All services
Fare collection: Prepurchase with validation/cancellation equipment on board, or payment to driver
Fare structure: Urban, flat; suburban, zonal
Fare evasion control: Roving inspectors
Operational control: Traffic regulators and route inspectors; control by mini-computer to be introduced

Arrangements for elderly/disabled: Disabled soldiers, pensioners, students, scholars half fare; over-75s and blind people with escorts, free
Average distance between stops: 690 m
Average peak-hour speed: 18 km/h
New vehicles financed by: Central budget

Tramway
Type of operation: Conventional tramway/light rail

Car-km: (1992) 25.6 million
(1993) 24.6 million
(1994) 24.8 million

Route length: 79.5 km
Number of lines: 28
Gauge: 1,435 mm

Fare structure: As bus
One-person operation: All routes

Rolling stock: 525 cars

Konstal 102N articulated	M95
Konstal 105N	M372
MAN/Siemens T4/B4 ex-Nürnberg	M27 T27
T6	M4

In peak service: 352

PKP
Polish State Railways (PKP)
ul Chalubinskiego 4, 00928 Warsaw
Tel: (+48 22) 620 45 12   Fax: (+48 22) 621 27 05

Type of operation: Suburban heavy rail

Current situation: Trains run about hourly to Skawina (21 km), and to Wieliczka/Niepolomice. Also irregular services on several other routes.

UPDATED

KREFELD
Population: 243,000, area served 537,000
Public transport: Municipal company provides local bus and tramway services and regional bus services in an area extending to Geldern in the north and the Dutch border in the west. Bus service to Mönchengladbach provided jointly with that town's operator. Interurban LRT line to Düsseldorf operated by Rheinbahn of Düsseldorf (qv). DB operates local trains on four lines plus some regional bus services. All services co-ordinated by Rhein-Ruhr Verkehrsverbund (VRR) (qv)

SWK
Städtische Werke Krefeld AG
PO Box 2760, 47727 Krefeld, Germany
Tel: (+49 2151) 980   Fax: (+49 2151) 98 25 03
www:www.swk.de
Directors: Horst Hannappel (Chair)
    Klaus Evertz
    Dr Dirk König
Staff: 326 (transport division only)

Passenger journeys: (All modes)
(1995) 33.7 million
(1996) 33.7 million
(1997) 33.4 million

Operating costs financed by: Fares 38 per cent, other commercial sources 7 per cent, subsidy/grants 55 per cent
Subsidy from: City and Nordrhein-Westfalen Land government and other communities served

Current situation: The former municipal transport operator Krefelder Verkehrs AG was merged in 1990 with other public utilities into a single authority, SWK.
    Tramway services continue to be improved by double tracking and driver control of traffic signals to give tram priority. Further bus routes have been contracted out and such buses now account for 41 per cent of all bus-km.

Bus
Vehicle-km: (1995) 7.4 million
(1996) 7.2 million
(1997) 7 million

Number of routes: 25
Route length: 515 km

Fleet: 96 vehicles, plus 38 contracted

MAN SL200 standard (1985)	5
MAN SG220 articulated (1984)	8
MAN SG242H articulated (1988/90)	22

MAN NL202 low-floor bus of SWK at main railway station (Wilhelm Pflug)   *1999*/0045272

Mercedes O505 (1988)	10
MAN NL202 low-floor (1993/94)	20
MAN SU242 (1991)	8
Van Hool AG300 low-floor articulated (1996/97)	23

Most intensive service: 15 min
One-person operation: All routes
Fare collection: Prepurchase of tickets, passes, with validation/cancelling machines on board, or payment to driver
Fare structure: Zonal; multiride tickets, weekly and monthly passes, reduced off-peak fares
Fare evasion control: Roving inspectors
Average peak-hour speed: 23.1 km/h

Tramway
Type of operation: Conventional tramway

Car-km: (1995) 2.3 million
(1996) 2.2 million
(1997) 2.3 million

Route length: 37.7 km
Number of lines: 4
Gauge: 1,000 mm
Fare structure: As bus
Most intensive service: 10 min

Rolling stock: 41 cars

Duewag 8-axle articulated (1964/76)	M21
Duewag M8C articulated (1980/81)	M20

Current situation: Upgrading in progress, with street sections being replaced by reserved tracks; 0.5 km extension opened 1993. New main workshops at Weeserweg completed 1996.

Rhein-Ruhr Stadtbahn Route U76 runs to Düsseldorf (1,435 mm gauge, operated by Rheinbahn, Düsseldorf).
Developments: A proposed extension of Route 044 in Hüls has met political opposition there, despite having broad popular support.

DB
Deutsche Bahn AG, Geschäftsbereich Nahverkehr
Regionalbereich Rheinland

Type of operation: Suburban heavy rail

Current situation: Though not part of the Rhein-Ruhr S-Bahn network, two DB suburban rail routes provide frequent links to the S-Bahn at Duisburg and Düsseldorf. Parallel bus route to Duisburg has been withdrawn at request of VRR. DB subsidiary company also operates some regional bus services.

West-Bus
West-Bus GmbH
St Töniser Str 270, 47804 Krefeld
Tel: (+49 2151) 98 48 01   Fax: (+49 2151) 98 48 04
Director: Pieter Harre
Operations Manager: Ralf Poppinghuys
Staff: 70

Current situation: This low-cost operation was formed in 1996 as a joint venture of four municipal transport companies, including SWK and Möbus of Mönchengladbach (50 per cent), and independent Taeter of Aachen (50 per cent). Buses are hired from the municipal companies (without drivers), and then operated for them by West-Bus staff.

UPDATED

KUALA LUMPUR
Population: 1.2 million
Public transport: Conventional bus services in metropolitan area provided by eight main area-franchised private companies with many owner-operated route-licensed 'Bas Mini' fixed-route minibuses and metered taxis licensed by government board as well as special school and factory buses. Suburban rail; light rail; mini-metro under construction

Bus (franchised operators)
Regulated by: Road Transport Licensing Board
Ministry of Public Enterprise
Blok A, Komplek Pejabat Damansara, Jalan Dungun, Damansara Heights, 50620 Kuala Lumpur, Malaysia
Tel: (+60 3) 254 90 44

Current situation: The two main operators are Park May Bhd and Intrakota Consolidated Bhd. Other operators include: Sri Jaya Kenderaan; Toon Fong; Foh Hup; Kuala Lumpur, Klang & Port Swettenham Bus; Selangor Bus; Len Bus; Len Seng; Len Chee. Each main bus operator is franchised to serve a specific sector of the city. Fleets range from 30 to 361 vehicles, with over 1,000 vehicles operated in total. Services run 06.00-24.00 on most routes at intervals varying from 2 minutes to hourly. There is considerable overlapping of routes.

Minibus (Bas Mini)

Regulated by: Road Transport Licensing Board

Current situation: Conventional services are largely duplicated by minibus routes, which have drawn business from buses and led the conventional operators into Bas Mini operation too. Minibuses were introduced in 1975; each is licensed for a particular route. A flat fare is set.

The largest bus operator, Sri Jaya Kenderaan, runs a fleet of Mercedes O309 minibuses on more lightly used routes.

Developments: The Board started franchising of minibus routes in 1994 as a direct replacement for Bas Mini operations, in an attempt to improve vehicle and passenger standards. The Optare Metrorider was selected as the fleet vehicle, and is equipped with air conditioning, tinted glazing, wide doors and low entry steps. The minibuses, known as Pekanriders, are imported in knocked-down form for local assembly by Diversified Resources Bhd (DRB), though there will be an increasing proportion of local content. A total of 1,000 is being delivered over a five-year period starting in 1996, to replace 800 Bas Mini vehicles.

Eight cross-city routes have been franchised to Intrakota, which is a subsidiary of DRB.

KTM

Malayan Railways (KTM)
PO Box 100001, 50050 Kuala Lumpur
Tel: (+60 3) 274 94 22   Fax: (+60 3) 230 39 39

Type of operation: Local railway

Passenger journeys: (1996) 25,000 daily

Current situation: Cross-city 'Komuter' suburban service between Seremban, Rawang and Pelabuhan Klang, total 153 km, metre-gauge, electrified 25 kV 50 Hz.

Developments: The immediate success of electric trains, introduced in 1995, led KTM to order two further batches of 22 emus.

Rolling stock: 62 three-car emus
Hunslet TPL/Holec (1993/94)   M18 T36
Mitsubishi/Hyundai (1996/97)   M22 T44
Union Carriage (1996/97)   M22 T44

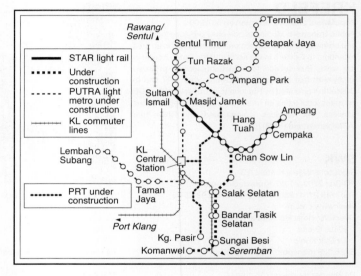

Komuter emu of KTM   1997

Kuala Lumpur's railways, operating and under construction

STAR

Sistem Transit Aliran Ringan Sdn Bhd
PO Box 39, Jalan Ampang, 68000 Ampang, Selangor Darul Ehsan
Tel: (+60 3) 494 25 50   Fax: (+60 3) 494 25 54
Chief Executive Officer: Zainal Abdul Ghani
General Manager, Operations: Guido Vandenbril
Manager, Operations: Peter Gillen
Manager, Engineering: Leong Yee Foong
Staff: 480

Current situation: STAR operates this light metro system on a 60-year franchise from the Malaysian government. Phase I, the 12 km section from Ampang to Sultan Ismail, was opened in December 1996, while Line 2 from Chan Sow Lin to Komanwel was due to open in late 1998. A

3.2 km northwards extension of Line 1 from Sultan Ismail to Sentul Timur, elevated and with four stations, was under construction for opening at the end of 1998.

Type of operation: Light rail, opened 1996

Passenger journeys: (1996/97) 20 million

Route length: 24.3 km
Number of lines: 2
Number of stations: 21
Gauge: 1,435 mm
Electrification: 750 V DC, bottom contact third rail

Service interval: Peak 2 min
First/last car: 06.00/24.00

Fare structure: Distance-based; single and stored-value tickets
Fare collection: Ticket machines with automatic barriers at all stations
Signalling: Non-permissive automatic block, CTC and ATS with computer-based scheduling and headway regulation

Rolling stock: 90 cars
Walkers/AEG (1995)   M34
Walkers/AEG (1996/97)   M56

PUTRA

PUTRA Sdn Bhd
Ground Floor, MUI Plaza, Jalan P Ramlee, 50250 Kuala Lumpur
Tel: (+60 3) 241 88 66   Fax: (+60 3) 248 35 15
Chairman: Zulfikli Mahmood

Mini-metro
Under construction

Current situation: Construction in progress of a 29.2 km automated light metro line, designated LRT System 2 — Phase I, linking western and eastern suburbs across the city centre. This is has been built by concessionaire Projek Usahasama Transit Ringan Automatik Sdn Bhd (PUTRA), a subsidiary of the investment company Renong. The technology and vehicles, based on Vancouver's SkyTrain system, have been supplied by Canadian companies Bombardier and SNC-Lavalin under contracts worth C$961 million signed in 1994.

PUTRA has a concession from the Malaysian government to build the infrastructure, which comprises a 4.4 km tunnel beneath the city centre, 22 km on viaduct, and the remainder at grade. There will be 24 stations on the complete system. The Canadian consortium is supplying mechanical and electrical equipment, and a fleet of 70 linear-motor powered cars — sufficient to provide initial capacity of 10,000 passengers/h in each direction, though this will rise to 16,000/h in Phase II.

STAR LRV in Kuala Lumpur   1997

Phase II will extend the line eastwards to Keramat and then north to Wangsa Maju, with the third segment continuing to Gombak (Terminal PUTRA). The entire route should be operating by mid-1999.

Express Rail Link

Express Rail Link (ERL)
Chief Executive: Adnan Aminuddin

Current situation: This consortium was awarded a 30-year concession by the government in 1997 to design, build, operate and maintain a 57 km line to the new international airport which opened at the end of 1997. Construction is expected to start in early 1999 following confirmation of the contract in October 1998. Designed to 1,435 mm gauge and to be electrified at 25 kV, the line will offer a rapid service for airline passengers as well as trains stopping at the three intermediate stations. A fleet of 12 four-car emus will be supplied by Siemens for the start of services in early 2001.

People mover
Under construction

Current situation: Construction of a 16 km automated straddle monorail people mover linking the Pekeliling bus terminal at Jalan Tun Razak with Kg Pasir via the central business district started in December 1996. The initial 9 km phase from Tun Razak to KTM's Central station is due to open late 1998 and throughout in 1999. There will be 20 stations and a fleet of 14 trains supplied by Hitachi.

UPDATED

KUMAMOTO

Population: 632,000
Public transport: Bus and tram services operated by municipal undertaking with additional bus services provided by private operators, one of which also runs suburban railway. JR suburban/interurban rail

Kumamoto-shi Kotsu Kyoku

Kumamoto City Transportation Bureau
5-1-40 Oe, Kumamoto-shi 862-0971, Japan
Tel: (+81 96) 361 52 11   Fax: (+81 96) 363 59 55
Staff: Bus 303; tramway 128

Passenger journeys: (All modes)
(1989/90) 28 million
(1991/92) 29.5 million

Operating costs financed by: Fares 65.5 per cent, other commercial sources 15.3 per cent, subsidy/grants 19.2 per cent
Subsidy from: City and regional government

Bus

Passenger journeys: (1989/90) 19.2 million
(1991/92) 19.7 million
Vehicle-km: (1991/92) 6.9 million

Number of routes: 27
Route length: 167.6 km

Fleet: 190 vehicles
Isuzu	50
Hino	45
Nissan Diesel	50
Mitsubishi	45
In peak service: 181
On order: 10 buses

Fare collection: Payment to farebox or prepurchase
Fare structure: Stage; prepurchase discount strip tickets, 1- and 3-month season tickets, 1-day tickets (bus/tram); pre-paid card
Operating costs financed by: Fares 69.2 per cent, other commercial sources 8.4 per cent, subsidy/grants 22.4 per cent
Subsidy from: City and regional government
Bus priority: Peak-hour bus lanes, 07.00-09.00 and 17.00-19.00

Tramway

Passenger journeys: (1993) 10.3 million
(1994) 10.2 million
(1995) 10.2 million
Car-km: (1991/92) 1.6 million

Route length: 12.1 km
Number of routes: 2
Gauge: 1,435 mm
Electrification: 600 V DC, overhead

Service: Peak 4-15 min, off-peak 5-17 min
First/last car: 06.00/23.40
Fare collection: Farebox
Fare structure: As bus
One-person operation: Almost all cars
Operating costs financed by: Fares 58.4 per cent, other commercial sources 28.4 per cent, subsidy/grants 13.2 per cent
Subsidy from: City government

Rolling stock: 43 air conditioned cars
Hirose Sharyo (1951)	M1
Shin Kinami Sharyo (1954)	M3

Japan's first European-style low-floor tramcar at Kumamoto station   *1998*/0009480

Toyo Koki (1954/55/57/58/60)	M20
Kawasaki articulated (1957) ex-Nishitetsu	M4
Nippon Sharyo (1982)	M2
Alna Koki (1985/86/88/91/93/94)	M12
Niigata low-floor articulated (1997)	M1
On order: Two Adtranz/Niigata low-floor articulated cars

Developments: Japan's first new-generation low-floor tram was delivered to Kumamoto in 1997. The 18.5 m four-axle articulated car was built by Niigata Engineering to an Adtranz design.

Plans for extensions into residential areas and for town-centre underground sections are under consideration.

Kumamoto Denki Tetsudo 'Kumaden'

Kumamoto Electric Railway
3-7-29 Kurokami, Kumamoto-shi 860-0862
Tel: (+81 96) 343 41 91

Bus

Current situation: Operates 109 buses on services to the north of Kumamoto.

Suburban railway

Passenger journeys: (Kumamoto city only)
(1990/91) 1 million

Current situation: Operates a 9.7 km suburban rail service from Kumamoto, Fujisakigumae, to Miyoshi, plus a shuttle service on the 3.4 km branch from Kita-Kumamoto to Kami-Kumamoto. All trains are one-person operated.
Developments: Two former Tokyo (Toei) Series 6000 metro cars entered service in December 1995, re-formed as a two-car set and converted from 1.5 kV to 600 V DC.

Rolling stock: 12 cars, including second-hand cars from the Tokyu and Toei systems in Tokyo

Kyushu Sangyo Kotsu

Sanko Bus
3-35 Sakura-machi, Kumamoto-shi 860-0805
Tel: (+81 96) 325 11 11   Fax: (+81 96) 322 27 30

Bus

Passenger journeys: (1994/95) 20 million

Current situation: Many of the Sanko fleet of more than 600 buses are used on services in the Kumamoto area where a network of 75 urban/suburban routes is operated. Fleet includes lift-equipped vehicles. Services are also provided throughout Kumamoto Prefecture with some express routes serving cities such as Fukuoka and Nagasaki in adjoining prefectures.
Developments: A stored-fare card is being introduced. Two Neoplan N4001 'non-step' low-floor buses were delivered in 1998.

JR Kyushu

Kyushu Railway Company
Kyushu Ryokaku Tetsudo
1-1 Chuogai, Hakata Eki, Hakata-ku, Fukuoka 8128566
Tel: (+81 92) 474 25 01   Fax: (+81 92) 474 97 45
Chair: Y Ishii
President: K Tanaka

Type of operation: Suburban/interurban heavy rail

Passenger journeys: (Kumamoto city only)
(1990/91) 7.6 million

Current situation: Local emu and occasional dmu services on Kagoshima main line; dmus serve suburban stations on the Hohi main line.

Kumamoto Bus

Kumamoto Bus
11-18 Shinichi-machi, Kumamoto-shi 860-0803
Tel: (+81 963) 366 92 11

Bus

Current situation: Runs a fleet of some 75 buses on services to the south of Kumamoto.

UPDATED

KUNMING

Population: 3 million
Public transport: Bus services provided by municipal agency, also minibus and microbus paratransit operations. Chinese Railways operates a suburban service of two trains each way daily on the metre-gauge line from Kunming Bei to Wangjiaying (23 km), and on the 1,435 mm gauge lines from Kunming to Zhongyicun (53 km) and Jinmacun (15 km); on the latter route another pair of trains runs between Kunming and Kunming Dong (7 km). Light rail proposed

Kunming City Bus

Kunming City Bus Company
Kunming, Yunnan Province, People's Republic of China

Current situation: Articulated buses predominate in the city centre, with two-axle buses in use on routes with lighter traffic. New buses have been received from factories in Beijing, Guangzhou and elsewhere. Competition exists from paratransit, with probably several hundred minibuses and microbuses in service, but demand is sufficiently high for both modes to co-exist.

Bus

Number of routes: 30

Fleet: Approx 450 vehicles, including many articulated; types include CC641 (two-axle), CC660-3 (articulated), Beijing BK670 articulated, Guangzhou articulated and two-axle, Chongqing CQ643 (two-axle) and CQ662 (articulated) and others

Fare collection: Stage fares paid to seated conductor; monthly passes

Minibus

Current situation: Two levels of service are offered at premium fares above those of city bus services. Many minibuses built all over China to designs based on the Japanese Coaster are in operation, along with a smaller number of microbuses, also based on Japanese designs.

Light rail (proposed)

Current situation: Consultants from VBZ, the operator in Kunming's twin city of Zürich, have recommended a 12 km tram line on the city's busiest corridor, along with improvements to the bus network.

VERIFIED

KYOTO

Population: 1.5 million
Public transport: Bus and metro services provided by municipal undertaking. Suburban services by JR, private railways and bus company

Kyoto-shi Kotsu Kyoku

Kyoto Municipal Transportation Bureau
48 Bojocho, Mibu Nakagyo-ku, Kyoto-shi 604-8804, Japan
Tel: (+81 75) 822 91 15   Fax: (+81 75) 822 92 40
Chair: T Tanabe
General Manager: S Miura
Staff: 2,814

Passenger journeys: (All modes)
(1991) 245.4 million
(1992) 245.3 million
(1993) 244.3 million

Operating costs financed by: Fares 82.4 per cent, other commercial sources 11.3 per cent, subsidy/grants 6.3 per cent
Subsidy from: City, prefecture and government

Bus

Staff: 2,113

Passenger journeys: (1991) 171.6 million
(1992) 171.5 million
(1993) 170.6 million
Vehicle-km: (1991) 37.1 million
(1992) 39.6 million
(1993) 36.8 million

Number of routes: 89
Route length: 469 km
On priority right-of-way: 94.9 km; 40 bus priority signals; staff patrol during peak hours to prevent illegal parking and ensure observance of lane discipline

Fleet: 928 vehicles, including Isuzu, Mitsubishi, Hino and Nissan, all air conditioned; tram replica buses operate on sightseeing services; two Mitsubishi New Aerostar 'non-step' low-floor buses introduced 1997

One-person operation: All routes
Fare collection: Farebox on vehicle
Fare structure: Flat; coupon tickets, transfer tickets (bus/bus, bus/metro); 1-, 3- and 6-month passes, day passes (bus/metro)
Fares collected on board: 31.8 per cent
Fare evasion control: Driver inspection; penalty
Average distance between stops: 420 m
Average peak-hour speed: In bus lanes, 17 km/h; in mixed traffic, 14 km/h
Operational control: Inspectors; computerised bus location and passenger information systems installed on some routes
Arrangements for elderly/disabled: Fleet includes four lift-equipped 'non-step' and low-floor buses
Operating costs financed by: Fares 85.8 per cent, other commercial sources 8.2 per cent, subsidy/grants 6 per cent
Subsidy from: City and prefecture
New vehicles financed by: Debenture

Developments: A computerised total bus operations system has been introduced, comprising bus location, passenger information and data collection.

Kyoto municipal buses (right) and JR buses at Kyoto station (Colin Brown)   **1999**/0045273

Certain routes withdrawn and others rationalised with Kyoto Bus services in 1997 to reduce duplication and feed into the extended metro at Kokusai Kaikan.

Metro

Staff: 713

Type of operation: Full metro, initial route opened 1981

Passenger journeys: (1992) 73.8 million
(1993) 73.7 million
(1994) 74 million

Car-km: (1991) 6.7 million
(1992) 7.3 million
(1993) 7.3 million

Route length 26.4 km
Number of lines: 2
Number of stations: 27
Gauge: 1,435 mm
Track: 60 kg/m rail; sleepers on concrete with resilient pads, partly conventional sleepers on ballast
Max gradient: 3.2%
Minimum curve radius: 260 m

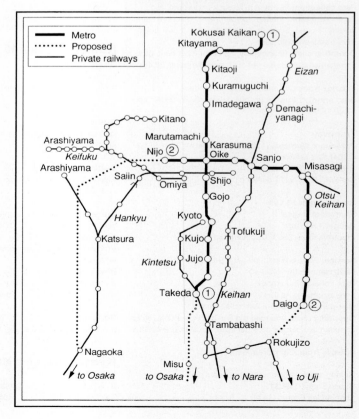

Kyoto metro and connecting lines
0043198

Tunnel: Bored plus some cut-and-cover
Electrification: 1.5 kV DC, overhead

Service: Peak 4-5 min, off-peak 6-7½ min
First/last train: 05.21/23.28

Fare structure: Four-section fare scale; coupon tickets, bus/metro transfer tickets; 1-, 3- and 6-month passes; bus/metro day passes
Revenue control: AFC
Operating costs financed by: Fares 75.4 per cent, other commercial sources 17.7 per cent, subsidy/grants 6.9 per cent
Signalling: CTC and ATC

Rolling stock: 204 cars, in six-car sets

Hitachi/Kinki Sharyo Series 10	M80 T40
Kinki Sharyo Series 50	M56 T28

Current situation: A through service is operated over Kinki Nippon Railway track from Takeda to Shin Tanabe (16 km) using metro and Kintetsu stock.

Developments: The first 12.7 km section of Kyoto's second metro, the 1,435 mm gauge 1.5 kV DC Tozai line, opened in 1997. The line runs east-west through central Kyoto from JR's Nijo station to Daigo via Oike, for interchange with the existing metro line, and Keihan's Sanjo terminus. Between Sanjo and Misasagi the metro replaces the parallel on-street section of Keihan's Keishin line and a through running service is operated from Shiyakusho-mae to Otsu.

The 3.5 km section between Sanjo and Misasagi was built by the third sector Kyoto Rapid Railway (51 per cent owned by Kyoto municipality, 12 per cent by Keihan Electric Railway and 37 per cent by other investors), with the remainder constructed by Kyoto municipality. Extensions are projected at both ends to provide a 30 km line between Nagaoka and Rokujizo.

Also opened in 1997 was a 2.6 km northern extension to Kokusai Kaikan (International Hall), and a southern extension to Rakunan-Shintoshi is planned.

Keihan Denki Tetsudo

Keihan Electric Railway
2-27, Shiromi 1-chome, Chuo-ku, Osaka 540-6034
Tel: (+81 6) 944 25 21   Fax: (+81 6) 944 25 01
Chair: M Miyashita
President: A Kimba
Staff: 3,424

Interurban rail

Current situation: Frequent limited-express, express and local trains on Keihan main line compete with Hankyu and JR for Kyoto—Osaka traffic. Direct services run between Yodoyabashi (Osaka) and Demachi-yanagi in north Kyoto (for interchange with the Eizan Railway) via a 5.1 km underground link through central Kyoto. Also Kyoto—Uji local service (see Keihan entry under Osaka).

Light rail

Passenger journeys: (1995/96) 30.4 million
(1996/97) 29.4 million
(1997/98) 22.9 million

Keihan's Type 600 two-car set approaching Keihan Ishiyama (Andrew Phipps)   **1999**/0043196

Car-km: (1996/97) 3.7 million
(1997/98) 4.2 million

Route length: 21.6 km
Number of lines: 2
Number of stations: 27
Gauge: 1,435 mm
Electrification: 1.5 kV DC, overhead

Fare structure: Zonal; prepurchase coupon tickets, season tickets
One-person operation: None

Rolling stock: 62 cars formed into 8 four-car and 15 two-car sets

Keihan Type 600 (rebuilt 1984/88)	M20
Keihan Type 700 (rebuilt 1992/93)	M10
Kawasaki Series 800 (1997)	M32

Current situation: Keishin line runs 7.5 km from Misasagi to Hama-Otsu, with a through service to the Tozai line metro. The 14.1 km Ishiyama—Sakamoto line runs north-south through Otsu connecting at Hama-Otsu.

Developments: The 3.5 km part-street-running section of the Keishin line between Misasagi and Keishin Sanjo was closed in 1997 and replaced by a through service to the newly opened Tozai line metro. Upgrading for through running involved introduction of Series 800 trains, raising the voltage to 1.5 kV, lengthening platforms and converting rolling stock depots and generating stations. Double-tracking of the Ano—Sakamoto section of the Ishiyama—Sakamoto line was completed in 1997.

Keihan Bus

Keihan Bus Company
5 Minami Ishida-cho, Higashi-Kujo, Minami-ku, Kyoto-shi 601-8033
Tel: (+81 75) 682 23 10   Fax: (+81 75) 682 23 27

Bus
(Entire operations)
Passenger journeys: (1991/92) 79.6 million
(1992/93) 77.4 million
(1996/97) 67.6 million
Vehicle-km: (1991/92) 18.8 million
(1992/93) 19 million
(1996/97) 22 million

Number of routes: 512
Route length: 627 km
Fleet: 506 vehicles

Current situation: Keihan Bus, a subsidiary of the railway, operates approx 150 air conditioned buses on Kyoto area services. About 100 do double duty on sightseeing tours, especially at weekends. Most of the remainder operate in the Osaka area. Vehicles include Hino and Mitsubishi.

Keifuku Denki Tetsudo

Keifuku Electric Railway
3-20 Mibu-kayo-gosho-machi, Nakagyo-ku, Kyoto 604-8811
Tel: (+81 75) 841 93 81

Current situation: This Keihan group company operates two connecting lines in Kyoto's western suburbs — the 7.2 km Arashiyama main line and 3.8 km Kitano line. Mostly reserved track but some street running on Arashiyama line. Also operates an interurban rail network and a 290-bus fleet in Fukui City, about 140 km from Kyoto.

Light rail

Passenger journeys: (1990/91) 12 million
(1991/92) 12.1 million
(1992/93) 11.8 million
Car-km: (1990/91) 1 million
(1991/92) 1.1 million
(1992/93) 1.1 million

Route length: 11 km
Number of lines: 2
Number of stations: 20
Gauge: 1,435 mm
Electrification: 600 V DC, overhead

Service: Peak 7-10 min, off-peak 16-25 min
First/last car: 05.57/23.19
Fare structure: Zonal; 1-, 3- and 6-month passes
One-person operation: All cars

Rolling stock: 28 cars

Mukogawa Sharyo (1971)	M2
Mukogawa Sharyo (1975/84/85-rebuilt)	M10
Mukogawa Sharyo (1990/92/93/95/96)	M14
Mukogawa Sharyo 'retro' historic cars (1994)	M2

Eizan Dentetsu 'Eiden'

Eizan Electric Railway
25-3, Tanaka-kamiyanagi-machi, Sakyo-ku, Kyoto-shi 614-8205
Tel: (+81 75) 702 81 10   Fax: (+81 75) 702 45 22
President: M Asada

Keihan's Series 800 trains for through running to the Tozai line metro   **1998**/0009481

Interurban rail
Staff: 140

Passenger journeys: (1995/96) 8 million
(1996/97) 8 million
Car-km: (1996/97) 1.5 million

Current situation: Eizan, a Keihan subsidiary, operates a 1,435 mm gauge 600 V DC line north from Demachi-yanagi in Kyoto to Yaseyuen (5.6 km, 8 stations) with a branch to Kurama (8.8 km, 9 stations); fleet of 24 cars. Also Keifuku funicular (1.3 km) and cable car (aerial ropeway, 0.5 km) ascend Mt Hiei from the Eizan Yaseyuen terminus.
Developments: Type 900 panoramic two-car train 'Kirara' entered service in October 1997 followed by a second set in 1998.

Kyoto Bus
Kyoto Bus
1-1 Miyojo-cho, Saga, Ukyo-ku, Kyoto-shi 616
Tel: (+81 75) 871 75 21

Bus
Passenger journeys: (1990/91) 11.7 million
(1991/92) 11.7 million
(1992/93) 11.6 million
Vehicle-km: (1990/91) 4.3 million
(1991/92) 4.4 million
(1992/93) 4.3 million

Current situation: Part of the Keihan group, Kyoto Bus operates 42 routes extending to 203 km, mainly linking central Kyoto with outer suburbs; fleet of 94 vehicles. A day ticket is valid on city bus and metro and Kyoto Bus services.
Developments: Certain routes reorganised in June 1997 to feed the extended metro at Kokusai Kaikan.

Hankyu Dentetsu
Hankyu Corporation
16-1, Shibata 1-chome, Kita-ku, Osaka 530-8389
Tel: (+81 6) 373 50 92   Fax: (+81 6) 373 56 70

Current situation: Frequent limited-express, express and local trains on Kyoto main line between Hankyu-Kawaramachi and Umeda (Osaka). Portion in central Kyoto runs underground with four stations. Connecting service on 4.1 km Hankyu—Arashiyama line in western suburbs (see main entry under Osaka).

Eizan Electric Railway Type 900 'Kirara' cars (Andrew Phipps)   ***1999**/0043197*

Kinki Nippon Tetsudo 'Kintetsu'
Kinki Nippon Railway
6-1-55, Uehommachi, Tennoji-ku, Osaka 543-8585
Tel: (+81 6) 775 34 44   Fax: (+81 6) 775 34 68
President: W Tashiro

Current situation: Kinki Nippon's Kyoto line is served by frequent limited-express, express and local trains to Nara. Also longer distance limited-expresses to Kashikojima. A reciprocal through service is operated between the Kyoto line and Kyoto's Karasuma line metro via a connection at Takeda (see main entry under Osaka).

JR West
West Japan Railway Company
Nishi Nihon Ryokaku Tetsudo
4-24, Shibata 2-chome, Kita-ku, Osaka 530
Tel: (+81 6) 375 89 81   Fax: (+81 6) 375 89 19

Chair: T Tsunoda
President: M Ide

Type of operation: Suburban/interurban heavy rail

Passenger journeys: (Kyoto operations only)
(1990/91) 67 million
(1993/94) 106 million
(1994/95) 54 million

Current situation: Kyoto is a major hub on JR West's urban network; frequent local and rapid service emus operate on routes to Osaka, Kobe, Maibara, Nara and Sonobe.
Developments: New Kyoto station completed 1997, includes commercial development, hotels, convention halls and parking lots.

UPDATED

LAGOS
Population: 6 million
Public transport: Bus services provided by state transport corporation responsible to Ministry of Public Transportation, six private bus companies, several thousand independent minibuses and 'Molue' and 'Danfo' paratransit modes based on trucks. Ferry services to Lagos Island. Some peak-hour commuter trains run by Nigerian Railway Corporation. Metro project cancelled, alternatives being considered to ease serious traffic congestion problems

Lagos State Transport
Lagos City Transport Service
Lagos State Transport Corporation
State Highway, Ilupeju, PO Box 2137, Lagos, Nigeria
Tel: (+234 1) 96 34 55/90 07 71
Staff: 1,500

Current situation: Government involvement in bus operations began in the 1960s following private enterprise developments and the LSTC was gradually established to provide services in the state's five administrative divisions with a zonal management structure. Services provided are mostly urban, and in early 1995 were reported to be operating at a very low level compared with some 36 million annual journeys in 1989.

Engineering difficulties led to availability as low as 25 per cent in the mid-1980s, but subsequent efforts to improve fleet management through better repair and maintenance and spares control, and a policy of standardisation with Mercedes/Van Hool buses, brought some relief. For history see *JUTS 1991*.

Traffic congestion in Lagos is severe and in 1983 the Corporation obtained approval for construction of a 28.5 km metro, but due to the country's economic problems this was cancelled in 1985. In 1990, however, moves were made to resume work on the project, though there has been no progress. The population of Lagos has been increasing by up to one million annually. Major investment in new equipment will be needed to improve services and studies have been initiated to determine possible alternative mass transit provision.

It is the intention of the government to improve LSTC's operations so it may account for a greater share of public transport provision, and it does not figure in the recent programme of selling-off public companies. Increases in the cost of fuel during 1993 led to substantial disruption to services.

Bus
Number of routes: 172
Route length: 1,200 km

Fleet: Over 500 vehicles, Mercedes 1617/Van Hool 280, plus O608/508D midibuses and minibuses. Latest delivery of Van Hool citybuses completed 1991

Most intensive service: 15 min
One-person operation: Less than one-third
Fare collection: Conductors or payment to driver
Fare structure: Graduated
Fare evasion control: Random inspection with special squads as well as checking inspectors; penalty surcharge/prosecution; evasion widespread
Operational control: Route inspectors/mobile radio
Average peak-hour speed: 9 km/h

Integration with other modes: Private minibus services not permitted onto Lagos Island
Operating costs financed by: Fares 85 per cent, other commercial sources 15 per cent
Subsidy from: None provided, except for capital expenditure
New vehicles financed by: Loans

Nigerian Railway Corp
Nigerian Railway Corporation
Ebute Metta, Lagos
Tel: (+234 1) 80 20 00

Type of operation: Suburban heavy rail

Current situation: Diesel-hauled trains are operated on weekdays between Lagos Terminus/Apapa and Oshodi, Agege, Agbado and Ifaw (48 km). Monthly season tickets issued. Services are overcrowded. Fares cover about one-third of costs.
Developments: NRC was granted funding in 1992 for purchase of rolling stock to upgrade these services as a means of helping to tackle the city's notorious traffic problems, but no progress has been reported.

Private bus/minibus
Current situation: Six main private bus companies with around a dozen buses each and several thousand private midi- and minibuses operate, mainly using Volkswagen 'Kombi' types, as well as 'Molue' and 'Danfo' paratransit vehicles based on locally built Mercedes and Bedford TJ

light truck chassis with bus bodies. Due to traffic congestion and unruly operating practices they are prohibited from entering Lagos Island where LSTC vehicles and taxis only are permitted. Private-sector bus operations have been reduced due to much increased costs of vehicles and spares with strict foreign exchange controls.

Further competition for regular bus service has come from a trend for scooter riders to offer paid lifts.

There are four main operators' associations which also function as co-operatives for the purpose of, for example, bulk purchase of supplies.

Ferry

Current situation: Ferry services link Lagos Island and the mainland, run by the state-owned Lagos State Ferry Services (which shares a common board with LSTC) and the Federal Inland Waterways Division Ferry Services.

LSFS runs two large vessels (over 100 passengers) from Mile 2 to Marina, and the Federal operation connects Apapa with Marina, also with two vessels.

VERIFIED

LAHORE

Population: 3.9 million
Public transport: Bus services in city and surrounding districts provided by provincial government-owned road transport corporation with monopoly on urban routes. Punjab government issues permits for extensive paratransit operations by private buses, horse-drawn 'tongas', autorickshaws and taxis. Suburban trains operated by Pakistan Railways. Light rail plans approved

PRTC

Punjab Road Transport Corporation
Transport House, 11-A Egerton Road, Lahore, Pakistan
Tel: (+92 42) 631 62 06
Managing Director: Imtiaz Ahmed Sadiq
Staff: 4,702

Current situation: PRTC operates both urban services in Lahore and interurban elsewhere in the Province of Punjab. Lahore services are extensively challenged by paratransit and, with only a small proportion of the fleet required to service demand, PRTC patronage has declined dramatically. About 35 per cent of passengers are students who pay only some 5 per cent of the regular fare, thus contributing further to a substantial operating deficit.
Developments: Considerable progress has been made in reducing staff levels from the 12,000 or so employed countrywide in 1993, when a redundancy payment scheme was instituted. A reorganisation of urban services was carried out in 1994.

Bus

Passenger journeys: (1992/93) 13.4 million
(1993/94) 6.2 million
(1995) 5.5 million
Vehicle-km: (1992/93) 6.3 million
(1993/94) 3.2 million
(1995) 3 million

Number of routes: 12
Route length: (One way) 264 km

Fleet: 707 vehicles, including Fiat, Hino, Isuzu and Volvo B57, of which 95 in roadworthy condition
In peak service: 44

Most intensive service: 10 min
Fare collection: Conductors
Fare structure: Stage; single tickets and monthly passes
Fares collected on board: 95 per cent
Fare evasion control: Checking squads and fines by special traffic magistrates
Operational control: Route inspectors
Arrangements for elderly/disabled: Special free buses financed by government subsidy
Average peak-hour speed: 17 km/h
Operating costs financed by: Fares 6 per cent, subsidy/grants from Punjab government 93 per cent
New vehicles financed by: Government grant

Private bus/minibus

Current situation: Privately operated buses and minibuses (Suzuki vans) run, along with horse-drawn 'tongas'; they are subject to Punjab government permits and not officially supposed to ply in the city itself. They nevertheless carry the bulk of the city's traffic.

PR

Pakistan Railways
31 Sheikh Abdul Hamid bin Bades, Lahore
Tel: (+92 42) 654 50

Type of operation: Suburban heavy rail

Current situation: Services run between Lahore Junction, Jallo and Wagah (39 km) at peak hours, plus irregular services on three other routes.

Light rail (planned)

Current situation: Plans for a light rail system have been studied by the city authorities and consultants, and metro plans were examined by the Punjab government and Lahore Development Authority. In 1992 the government approved construction of Line 1 (14.6 km, 15 stations) of a light rail network, which is to be partly funded by Japan. The 1,435 mm gauge line, linking Chowk Bhaati and Kok Lakhpat, will be largely elevated above the city's busy Ferozepur corridor. A fleet of 105 cars would be required.
Developments: Following completion of pre-feasibility studies funded by the World Bank, bids were to be sought from consortia interested in financing and building the line.

VERIFIED

LA PAZ

Population: 1 million
Public transport: Bus services provided by confederation of independent owners and drivers operating minibuses, known as 'micros', formed into 45 route associations and regulated by Servicio Nacional de Transito (a state police department). Suburban and light rail plans

Bus

Regulated by: Servicio Nacional de Transito
Av Mariscal Santa Cruz 1000, La Paz, Bolivia
Tel: (+591 2) 37 99 81

Current situation: All bus services are operated by small vehicles known locally as 'microbuses', but including some larger vehicles seating up to 35 and often carrying up to 50 with standees. Each route (designated by letters or numbers) is operated by a 'comite' of owner-drivers or company-operated vehicles. Several owners share each route, though there are some large firms. Longer-distance routes tend to be served by licensed passenger-carrying lorries able to carry up to 200 on perimeter bench seats and standing or sitting on the floor. Maximum loads are indicated on the side of the vehicles, which also carry goods.

Passenger journeys: Approx 140 million (annual)
Vehicle-km: Approx 25 million (annual)

Number of routes: 45
Route length: 380 km

Fleet: Mostly Ford or Dodge short chassis with either US school bus (mostly Blue Bird) or local bodies

Most intensive service: Frequent
One-person operation: 60 per cent
Fare collection: By driver
Fare structure: Flat in central area; fares fixed by Ministry of Transport
Average peak-hour speed: 11 km/h

Light rail (proposed)

Current situation: The National Railways (ENFE) has studied several schemes for a fixed guideway transit system to relieve severe road traffic congestion. Amongst them is upgrading of the freight-only La Paz–Alto tramway (8.3 km) to form a light rail route to the airport, for which design and construction supervision bids were sought in mid-1995.

Another proposed scheme would see electrification of existing ENFE lines around the city.

VERIFIED

A Dodge 'microbus' is overtaken by a Japanese minibus
1997

LAS VEGAS

Population: 260,000, area served 1.1 million
Public transport: Bus services in city and surrounding area of Clark County operated under contract to Regional Transportation Commission; leisure monorail

CAT

Citizens Area Transit (CAT)
3210 Citizen Avenue, North Las Vegas, Nevada 89030, USA
Tel: (+1 702) 636 04 23   Fax: (+1 702) 636 06 31
Director, RTC: Kurt Weinrich
General Manager: David A Boggs
Operations Manager: Jim Wolf
CAT operated under contract by ATC/Vancom Inc
Staff: 1,000

Current situation: The Regional Transportation Commission of Clark County was set up in 1965 and is governed by an eight-member board. A new public transit operation, CAT, was inaugurated in 1992 to provide co-ordinated fixed-route service in Clark County, which has seen rapid population growth. At the same time, privately owned Las Vegas Transit ceased operation of almost all its routes and CAT assumed responsibility for these also. Funding for CAT comes from a ¼ per cent sales tax which was approved by voters in 1990.

Paratransit services are now operated under separate contract by ATC/Vancom. The contract was awarded in January 1998 for three years with two one-year options.
Developments: New bus maintenance depot in North Las Vegas, with capacity for 250 buses and 150 paratransit vehicles opened in January 1998. It is intended that all new buses should be LNG-powered.

Agreement of a new 5-year contract with ATC/Vancom at the end of 1996 paved the way for further development of this rapidly growing system. Services have increased substantially to cope with the city's 29 million annual visitors, and new Crosstown Express and Strip Express routes have been introduced.

Bus

Passenger journeys: (1995) 26 million
(1997) 41 million
(1998) 45 million
Vehicle-km: (1993) 10.3 million
(1997) 15.4 million

Number of routes: 42

Fleet: 241 vehicles
New Flyer D40/D40LF (1992/94)	90
GMC/TMC T80204/80206	10
Gillig Phantom (1990)	13
New Flyer low-floor (1995)	44
New Flyer articulated (1991/95/96)	18
El Dorado 33 ft	20
NABI 436 60 ft	46

A Gillig phantom loads at CAT's downtown transit centre   *1998*/0009482

New NABI 60 ft (18 m) articulated bus inside new integrated bus maintenance facility, Las Vegas
1999/0045274

Most intensive service: 7 min; 10 routes operate 24 h to serve the resort corridor
One-person operation: All routes
Fare collection: Coin to farebox
Fare structure: Flat, reduced off-peak; monthly passes
Arrangements for elderly/disabled: All buses lift-equipped
Operating costs financed by: Fares 25 per cent

Monorail

The Monorail Company

Current situation: A 2 km monorail link between the MGM Grand and Bally's Resort hotels was opened in

Monorail train approaches the MGM Grand Hotel
1998/0009483

1995. Designed initially for hotel patrons only, the line could become part of an initial core route to the airport. The two trains shuttle back-and-forth on their own tracks, carrying about 15,000 passengers daily, fare-free.
Developments: A new-technology system, Cable Liner Shuttle, is planned to link casinos and the centre. Built by Doppelmayr (see New Technology section), cable-powered cars will link the Mandalay Bay, Luxor and Excalibur casinos with Tropicana Intersection.

Rolling stock: 2 six-car trains
                                                  UPDATED

LAUSANNE

Population: 244,000
Public transport: Bus, trolleybus and light rail services provided by publicly owned undertaking, controlled by representative board. City-owned rack line, known locally as Metro. Rail services by Swiss Federal Railways, local railway and lake steamers

TL

Transports Publics de la Région Lausannoise SA (TL)
PO Box 3960, 1002 Lausanne, Switzerland
Tel: (+41 21) 621 01 11   Fax: (+41 21) 312 40 30
Chair: M Blanc
General Manager: Jean-Pierre Kallenbach
Staff: 849

Current situation: TL is owned by the canton of Vaud (26 per cent), local communities (67 per cent), the Vaud Cantonal Bank (4 per cent) and private individuals (3 per cent). It operates buses and trolleybuses, owns the vehicles and operates the light rail route built by TSOL (see below), and also embraces the Metro LO rack line. Though separately constituted, the three undertakings are operated under a single administration.
Developments: The trolleybus fleet, which dates from the closure of street tramways in 1964, is to be modernised.

TL trolleybus and trailer near the main station   *1998*/0010325

The computer-controlled monitoring system SAE has been fitted to 113 trolleybuses, 84 buses and 64 trailers.

Though patronage is stable and farebox recovery has risen, rationalisation of operations is urgently necessary

to reduce costs, following enactment of the Federal Transport Law of 1994 which raises the charges falling upon local authorities. In particular the complex historic ownership structures of the city's transport undertakings

Lausanne's 1.5 km Ouchy—Flon rack metro (Milan Šrámek)   **1999**/0043199

demands action, and negotiations are in progress to amalgamate them into a single modern management structure.

Bus and trolleybus
Passenger journeys: (1991) 69.3 million
(1992) 72.5 million
(1994) 73.6 million
Vehicle-km: (1991) 11.5 million
(1994) 11.3 million

Number of routes: Bus 21, trolleybus 11
Route length: Bus 120 km, trolleybus 61.7 km
On priority right-of-way: 9.4 km

Fleet: 108 buses
Standard buses   82
MAN SG280H articulated   17
Trailers   9
Average age of fleet: Buses 12 years, trailers 18 years

Fleet: 118 trolleybuses
FBW/BBC   76
NAW/Lauber/BBC-Sécheron   42
Hess trailers   62
Average age of fleet: Trolleybuses 15 years, trailers 18 years
Trolleybus electrification: 600 V DC

Most intensive service: 6 min
One-person operation: All routes
Fare collection: Prepurchase tickets, passes or carnets; or payment to driver; Autelca and Sadamel prepurchase equipment at stops, Almex (urban) and Prodata (suburban) on board
Fare structure: Zonal system covers suburban and interurban operators and SBB trains; 10-ticket carnets (from shops), monthly passes, 24 h and 3-day tourist tickets
Fare evasion control: Roving inspectors; penalty
Operational control: Route inspectors/mobile radio
Arrangements for elderly/disabled: Reduced rate monthly passes
Average peak-hour speed: 15 km/h

Operating costs financed by: Fares 49.1 per cent
Subsidy from: State and city councils
New vehicles financed by: Loans

Metro Ouest
Société du Tramway du Sud-Ouest Lausannois SA (TSOL)
Address as TL (above)

Type of operation: Light rail, opened 1991

Passenger journeys: (1992) 7.5 million
(1993) 8.3 million
(1994) 7.2 million
Car-km: (1991) 0.5 million
(1993) 0.9 million
(1994) 0.8 million

Route length: 7.8 km
    in tunnel: 0.7 km
Number of routes: 1
Number of stops: 15
Gauge: 1,435 mm
Electrification: 750 V DC, overhead

Service: 10 min, evening 15 min; being reduced to 7½ min
First/last car: 05.23/24.00
Fare structure: As TL, through passes to Metro LO and SBB/CFF services

Rolling stock: 12 cars
Vevey (1990/91)   M12
On order: Further 5 cars from Vevey/ABB

Current situation: Runs from the city centre at Flon westwards to the Institute of Technology and the suburb of Renens (SBB/CFF station). Single-track route with 12 passing loops mostly at grade and segregated; interchange with SBB trains at Renens and with the LO metro at Flon, to which the LEB local railway is being extended.

Developments: A 7½ min interval service is to be introduced as soon as track-doubling of the University section is complete.

Metro LO
Metro Lausanne-Ouchy SA
PO Box 3333, 1002 Lausanne
Tel: (+41 21) 621 03 80   Fax: (+41 21) 312 40 30
Staff: 73

Type of operation: Rack railway

Passenger journeys: (1992) 7.3 million
(1993) 7.6 million
(1994) 7.2 million

Current situation: 1.8 km former funicular (now rack-operated) with 10 cars links the lakeside at Ouchy with the centre of Lausanne, known locally as the 'Metro'. It was acquired by the municipality in 1985.
Developments: A 4.6 km extension northeast to Croisettes (Epalinges) is planned as a rubber-tyred light metro. The existing line would be converted to provide a through service.

SBB/CFF
Swiss Federal Railways, Lausanne Division
PO Box 345, 1001 Lausanne
Tel: (+41 51) 224 11 11   Fax: (+51 224) 34 17
Divisional Manager: Philippe Gauderon

Type of operation: Suburban heavy rail

Current situation: Hourly or half-hourly services, electrified 15 kV 16⅔ Hz, provided on routes to Geneva, Vallorbe, Yverdon, Payerne, Fribourg and Aigle. More frequent service on line to Renens (5 km), connecting with light rail services.

LEB
Lausanne-Echallens-Bercher Railway
Place de la Gare 5, 1040 Echallens
Tel: (+41 21) 881 11 15   Fax: (+41 21) 881 59 95
Manager: U Gachet
Staff: 54

Type of operation: Local railway

Passenger journeys: (1991) 1.8 million
(1995) 1.7 million

Current situation: Electric trains (1.5 kV DC) run half-hourly from Lausanne-Chauderon to Echallens, extended hourly to Bercher (23 km). A 1.1 km tunnel is under construction from Chauderon to Flon to link with LO and light rail services. The initial 0.3 km section to a new underground station at Chauderon opened in 1995.

Rolling stock: 10 emu cars, 7 trailers

CGN
Compagnie Générale de Navigation sur le lac Léman
PO Box 116, 1000 Lausanne 6
Tel: (+41 21) 614 04 44   Fax: (+41 21) 614 04 45

Current situation: Runs boats on Lake Geneva, linking Geneva, Lausanne and St Gingolph, and from Lausanne to Evian and Thonon, carrying about 1.6 million passengers annually. Fleet of 16 boats including eight vintage paddle-wheel boats.

UPDATED

LEEDS-BRADFORD
Population: Leeds 714,000, Bradford 464,000, conurbation 2 million
Public transport: Bus services in the West Yorkshire area including Leeds and Bradford and surrounding towns such as Huddersfield, Halifax and Wakefield, are provided by more than 40 operators, the largest of which is FirstGroup. Other major operators include Arriva and Blazefield. The Passenger Transport Executive is responsible for contracting non-commercial bus services by competitive tender, local rail services, passenger facilities, information and policy development in partnership with district councils

Yorkshire Rider
Yorkshire Rider Ltd
Kirkstall Road, Leeds LS3 1LH, England
Tel: (+44 113) 245 16 01   Fax: (+44 113) 242 97 21
Yorkshire Divisional Director: Ray O'Toole
Staff: 3,000

Current situation: Yorkshire Rider was established in 1986 from the former PTE bus operations as a separate operating company, wholly owned by West Yorkshire PTA, which sold it to a management/workforce consortium in 1988. Yorkshire Rider was bought by Badgerline in 1994, becoming part of FirstGroup in 1995.

Further reorganisations within the Rider Group split the five operations in Leeds, Halifax, Huddersfield, Bradford and York into five separate trading divisions — Leeds (Leeds CityLink, now First Leeds), Bradford (Bradford Traveller, now First Bradford), Halifax (CalderLine), Huddersfield (Kingfisher), with York remaining unchanged under the name Rider York.
Developments: The first phase of the Leeds guided busway was launched in 1995 on the A61 Scott Hall Road. The second phase opened in late 1996, with the third in 1997. Further extensions, including a park-and-ride, opened in 1998 and 1999. All Scania single-deck low-floor buses are equipped with

guidewheels on their front axles. The group received government approval for its 'twin track' matched investment plan for the East Leeds Quality Partnership. FirstGroup will contribute £3.7 million, Arriva £1.3 million and the government £5 million towards the £10 million infrastructure and highway costs. The two operators will then introduce £6 million worth of new buses to complete the partnership.

Work on the York Road and Selby Road corridor will comprise 2.5 km of guided busway, 2.8 km of additional bus priority lanes, and upgrading of a further 1 km of bus lanes. Construction started in 1999, and the corridor should be completed by late 2000.

Bus

Passenger journeys: (1992/93) 183 million
(1993/94) 180 million
(1994/95)
Vehicle-km: (1992/93) 65 million
(1993/94) 63 million
(1994/95) 64 million

Number of routes: 170

Most intensive service: 3 min
One-person operation: 100 per cent
Fare collection: By driver with Wayfarer; exact fare to farebox in Bradford, prepaid sales through 300 outlets
Fare structure: Stage, with off-peak maximum fare; weekly, monthly, quarterly and annual 'Metro Cards'; District Rider cards; Day Rover
Fares collected on board: 70 per cent of passengers pay cash
Fare evasion control: Roving staff
Integration with other modes: Prepurchase tickets/passes interavailable between bus and rail
Operational control: Route inspectors/mobile radio; radio communication between drivers and inspectors based at four district control rooms; some vehicles radio-equipped
Arrangements for elderly/disabled: Concessionary fares financed by PTE (half adult fare in peak hours, nominal inter-peak)
Operating costs financed by: Fares 73 per cent, concessionary fares reimbursement 12.5 per cent, contracted services 11.5 per cent, other income 3 per cent
Subsidy from: PTA levy for contracted services

First Leeds

Kirkstall Road, Leeds LS3 1LH
Tel: (+44 113) 245 16 01   Fax: (+44 113) 244 02 90
Managing Director: Steve Graham
Operations Director: Richard Harris
Finance Director: Martin Wilson
Engineering Director: John Gilchrist

Fleet: 487 vehicles (including FirstQuickstep subsidiary)
Leyland Atlantean double-deck	129
Leyland Olympian double-deck	28
MCW Metrobus double-deck	57
Volvo Olympian double-deck	22
Scania N113 double-deck	42
Dennis Dart single-deck	75
Scania N113 single-deck	55
Scania L113 single-deck	20
Scania L94/Wright low-floor	10
Dennis Dart SLF/Plaxton low-floor	3
Dennis Lance single-deck	23
Mercedes minibus	6
Optare Solo low-floor midibus	6
Volvo B10M coach	8
Dennis Javelin/Plaxton coach	3

First Bradford

Bowling Back Lane, Bradford BD4 8SP
Tel: (+44 1274) 73 48 33   Fax: (+44 1274) 73 67 68
Managing Director: Gary Raven
Operations Director: Khadim Hussain
Financial Director: Christina Haigh
Engineering Director: Steve Adkin

Fleet: 231 vehicles
Leyland Atlantean double-deck	39
Leyland Olympian double-deck	116
Scania L113/Wright low-floor	11
Volvo Olympian double-deck	26
Volvo B10BLE/Wright low-floor	19
Mercedes minibus	20

Low-floor Scania on Scott Hall Road guided busway (Andrew Jarosz)   ***1999**/0045275*

Dennis Dart SLF low-floor bus of First Leeds operates the Metro contracted service from Leeds/Bradford airport (Andrew Jarosz)   ***1999**/0045278*

Alexander Royale-bodied Volvo Olympian of First Leeds in Farsley (Andrew Jarosz)   ***1999**/0045276*

Low-floor Optare Solo followed by First Leeds Metrobus (Andrew Jarosz)   ***1999**/0045277*

Arriva Yorkshire

Arriva Yorkshire Ltd
24 Barnsley Road, Wakefield WF1 5JX
Tel: (+44 1924) 37 55 21   Fax: (+44 1924) 30 01 06
Managing Director: Peter Harvey
Operations Director: Justin Davies
Engineering Director: Vernon Barfoot
Staff: 1,029

Current situation: Formerly the Yorkshire Bus Group, the company is being rebranded as Arriva Yorkshire. It operates as three companies, with West Riding and Yorkshire Woollen in the Leeds/Bradford area. There is a network of services to the east of Leeds and to the south and west of the two cities. The company was privatised in 1987, was later sold to Caldaire Holdings, and became part of Arriva in 1996.

Bus
Number of routes: 180

Fleet: 447 vehicles	
Leyland Olympian double-deck	89
Leyland Lynx single-deck	131
Volvo Olympian double-deck	3
Volvo B10B single-deck	33
Dennis Lance single-deck	30
Dennis Dart SLF low-floor single-deck	30
DAF SB220 low-floor single-deck	50
Optare Metrorider midibus	34
Mercedes minibus	41
Scania coaches	4
DAF coaches	2

Most intensive service: 10 min
One-person operation: 100 per cent
Fare structure: As Yorkshire Rider, but Rider card not available

Black Prince

Black Prince Buses Ltd
York Cottage, Texas Street, Morley, Leeds LS27 0HG
Tel: (+44 113) 252 60 33   Fax: (+44 113) 253 60 82
Managing Director: Brian Crowther
Chief Engineer: David Crowther
Commercial Manager: Jack Berry
Staff: 90

Current situation: The company developed commercial services from Morley to Leeds city centre in 1986, and moved progressively into other areas. Uses route colour for different groups of routes and also operates as 'Leeds Suburban Buses'.

Bus
Number of routes: 17
Route length: 32.2 km

Fleet: 46 vehicles	
Leyland PD2 double-deck	1
Volvo B10M double-deck	1

Scania double-deck	24
Optare Vecta single-deck	4
Mercedes O405/Optare single-deck	4
Scania single-deck	9
Optare Metrorider minibus	3

Most intensive service: 10 min
One-person operation: 100 per cent

Other commercial operators
Current situation: Blazefield Holdings subsidiaries Keighley and District, Harrogate and District and Yorkshire Coastliner operate into the area. A number of smaller operators also run commercial or tendered services but none is of any considerable size: Taylors Coaches, Optional Travel and Bigfoot Buses.

Metro

West Yorkshire Passenger Transport Executive
Wellington House, 40-50 Wellington Street, Leeds LS1 2DE
Tel: (+44 113) 251 72 72   Fax: (+44 113) 251 73 33
Director General: Kieran Preston

Passenger journeys: (Bus and rail)
(1995/96) 246 million
(1996/97) 231 million
(1997/98) 231 million

Current situation: Metro is the corporate name adopted by the Passenger West Yorkshire on behalf of the Passenger Transport Authority. Metro's activities include securing subsidised bus services to complement the commercial network, specifying and financing the local rail network, administration of all concessionary travel and prepaid ticketing schemes, provision and maintenance of all bus stops, most shelters and the majority of bus stations, timetable and promotional information, planning new systems, and working with the district councils' planning and highway teams to promote increased use of public transport.

MetroTrain service is contracted from Northern Spirit, with North Western Trains handling the Manchester—Huddersfield—Wakefield service.

Contracted bus services
Current situation: Changes in the market and better appreciation by operators of the commercial basis of their operations cause constant change in the bus network, and Metro is required to secure socially necessary services when commercial operators withdraw. Subsidised services run about 20.6 million km a year, and the average cost per km has fallen due to competition and increased efficiency.

Contracted rail
Operated by Northern Spirit Ltd
Station Rise, York YO1 1HT
Tel: (+44 1904) 65 30 22   Fax: (+44 1904) 52 30 75
Director: P G Davison

Passenger journeys: (1995/96) 16 million
(1996/97) 16 million
(1997/98) 18 million

Current situation: Local rail services operated to Metro's specifications on 15 routes totalling 295 km with 64 stations, and on the Manchester—Huddersfield—Wakefield route (69 km), supported jointly with Greater Manchester PTE and operated by North Western Trains.
Developments: The long-planned restoration of service between Bradford and Huddersfield was awarded a grant of £4 million under the Environment Department's Capital Challenge scheme; an agreement on operating subsidy was reached between the PTA and Northern Spirit in late 1998. The project involves restoration of two short sections of route (total 3.5 km) and construction of new stations at Elland and Brighouse, for opening in May 2000.

A long-awaited order for new trains for the area's electrified network was placed in March 1998. Siemens is building 16 three-car emus for delivery in late 2000.

Rolling stock: 102 dmu cars, 65 emu cars

Light rail (planned)
Current situation: The Leeds Transport Strategy of 1991 proposed a three-line light rail network, together with two initial routes for guided bus, designed to supplement the existing local rail network focused on Leeds. The aim was to provide a fixed-track service on all major radial routes into the city.

The South Leeds line, running 12 km from the city centre to Tingley and Stourton, received Royal Assent in 1993. The Eurotrans consortium, comprising Taylor Woodrow, Morrison Construction, Cristiani & Neilsen, Arriva and Bombardier, was selected in 1996 as preferred bidder for a design, build, operate and maintain contract for this line. Private-sector funding is being sought and a bid made for government funds to enable a start on construction in 2000 for opening in 2002.

Approval is being sought for extensions to bring the network to 28 km. Line 2 would link the universities, hospitals and residential areas of Headingley, Seacroft and Harehills to the city centre.

Guided bus
Current situation: The first four phases of guided busway along Scott Hall Road were completed in July 1998 and included a 160-space park-and-ride site. Development was under way with local bus operators of a second route along the A64 York Road. That scheme, costing £10 million, was given the government go-ahead in December 1998.

In the first partnership of its kind, bus operators First-Group and Arriva will jointly contribute £5 million towards infrastructure costs which will be matched equally by a contribution from the government. Construction started in 1999 and most traffic measures should be completed by the end of 2000.

UPDATED

LEICESTER

Population: 282,000
Public transport: Most bus services provided by former municipally owned company and local private companies; local rail service

First Leicester

Leicester Citybus Ltd
Abbey Park Road, Leicester LE4 5AH, England
Tel: (+44 116) 251 66 91   Fax: (+44 116) 253 82 70
Managing Director: Ian Humphreys
Operations Director: Julian Heubeck
Finance Director: Jeremy Hollis
Engineering Director: Colin Stafford
Staff: 450

Current situation: On deregulation the city council established its transport undertaking as a separate company. This was offered for sale in 1993 and is now owned by FirstGroup. A co-ordinated network has been developed with Midland Fox.
Developments: Double-deck replacement by high-capacity single-decks continued, with delivery of 10 low-floor Optare Excels in 1997, and 18 low-floor Scanias in 1998. A quality partnership with the city council is planned for the Belgrave Road corridor. Preliminary work starts in 1999 with real-time and a satellite tracking experiment. Highway management, infrastructure improvements and low-floor bus introduction is planned for 2000.

Bus
Passenger journeys: (1990/91) 25.4 million
(1991/92) 25.6 million
(1992/93) 25.3 million
Vehicle-km: (1990/91) 9.8 million
(1991/92) 10.3 million
(1992/93) 10.5 million

Number of routes: 55
Route length: 800 km
On private right-of-way: 3.6 km

Fleet: 186 vehicles	
Leyland Titan PD2 double-deck	1
MCW Metrobus double-deck	1
MCW Metrobus/Alexander double-deck	11
Dennis Dominator/East Lancs double-deck	71
Volvo B10M/Alexander double-deck	1
Dennis Falcon/East Lancs single-deck	9
Dennis Falcon/NC single-deck	9
Mercedes O405/Optare single-deck	10
Optare Excel low-floor single-deck	10
Scania L113/Wright low-floor single-deck	15
Scania L94/Wright low-floor single-deck	3
LAG/Volvo/Leyland coaches	9
Iveco/Carlyle minibus	1
Renault/Northern Counties minibus	15
Renault/Wright minibus	20

Most intensive service: 8 min
One-person operation: All services
Fare collection: Driver with Wayfarer equipment
Fare structure: Stage; single, return, weekly and monthly tickets
Operational control: All buses have two-way radio; 12 locations monitored by CCTV
Operating costs financed by: Fares 86 per cent, other commercial sources 12 per cent, tenders 2 per cent
Subsidy from: County Council for pensioners' concession fares and specific contracted routes

FirstGroup standard Wright-bodied low-floor Scanias have been delivered to First Leicester (Andrew Jarosz) ***1999**/0045279*

Arriva Fox County

Midland Fox Ltd
PO Box 613, Leicester LE4 8ZN
Tel: (+44 116) 264 04 00   Fax: (+44 116) 260 56 05
Managing Director: Mark Bowd
Staff: 675

Current situation: 'Fox Cub' minibus services cover Leicester and surrounding towns, while conventional buses run interurban services and a number of longer-distance out-of-town routes, branded as Urban Fox. It is a subsidiary of the Arriva Group.

Bus (Whole company operations)
Passenger journeys: (1994) 26 million
(1995) 27 million
(1996) 28.6 million

Vehicle-km: (1994) 21 million
(1995) 22 million
(1996) 23 million

Number of routes: 87
Route length: (One way) 1,035 km

Fleet: 340 vehicles
MCW Metrobus double-deck	10
Volvo Olympian double-deck	43
Leyland Olympian double-deck	48
DAF/Optare double-deck	2
Scania double-deck	28
Leyland National single-deck	4
Scania single-deck	14
Greenway single-deck	10
Dennis Dart single-deck	6

Iveco minibus	30
Mercedes minibus	110
Coaches	35
In peak service: 324	

One-person operation: All services
Fare collection: Payment to driver with Wayfarer ticket machine; magnetic card system introduced 1997
Fare structure: Single, day return, season and area tickets
Fares collected on board: 74 per cent
Operational control: VHF radio for inspectors
Operating costs financed by: Fares 88 per cent, other commercial sources 12 per cent

Other operators
Current situation: Hylton & Dawson of Glenfield operates three routes and Kinchbus of Barrow-on-Soar some tendered services. Virgin and TRS operate limited commercial services.

Central Trains

Central Trains Limited
Po Box 4323, Birmingham B1 1TH
Tel: (+44 121) 643 44 44   Fax: (+44 121) 654 44 61
Managing Director: Nick Brown

Type of operation: Local rail

Current situation: Trains run about hourly to local stations on two routes.
Developments: In a scheme approved in 1992, restoration of services was planned over a freight line to Coalville and Burton on Trent (the Ivanhoe line — 48 km) with eight new stations, creating a circular route linking the new stations with Leicester and Derby. Provision of finance to implement the scheme was rejected by the Department of Transport in 1996, but a revised proposal agreed in late 1997 envisages reopening from Leicester to Ashby-de-la-Zouch only (34 km), with four stations.

UPDATED

LEIPZIG

Population: 439,000, area served 599,000
Public transport: Central area served almost entirely by tramways operated by municipal company which also runs bus services in the suburbs; regional bus company; suburban rail services by German Railway (DB)

MDV

Mitteldeutscher Verkehrsverbund (MDV)
Naunhofer Strasse 50, 04299 Leipzig, Germany
Tel: (+49 341) 862 87 16/87 17

Current situation: This regional transit authority became operative in March 1998, LVB holding 23 per cent of the shares. A unified fares system should be introduced in May 1999. The authority comprises the cities of Halle and Leipzig and four rural counties, covering an area of 3,500 km² with a population of 1.3 million. MDV integrates the services of 13 operators, carrying about 200 million passengers annually.

LVB

Leipziger Verkehrsbetriebe GmbH (LVB)
PO Box 100910, 04009 Leipzig
Tel: (+49 341) 49 20   Fax: (+49 341) 492 10 05
Directors: Wilhelm Hanss (Chair, Personnel)
   Technical: Wolfgang Jähnichen
   Marketing & Finance: Heinz-Jörg Panzner
Manager, Personnel: Angelika Büttner
Manager, Finance: Dr Brigitte Teltscher
Manager, Technical Equipment: Siegfried Gentsch
Manager, Maintenance: Klaus-Jürgen Stöhrer
Staff: 2,639

Passenger journeys: (Revised figures)
(1995) 99.8 million
(1996) 92.9 million
(1997) 87.2 million

Operating costs financed by: Fares 26.2 per cent, other commercial sources 18.6 per cent, subsidy/grants 55.2 per cent

Current situation: The former state-owned undertaking passed to Leipzig municipality in 1993; it is now a joint stock company, the shares of which are held entirely by the city and county of Leipzig (Kreis Leipziger Land). Fares were raised to a level closer to those charged in west German cities in 1995, and increased again in 1997. To attract passengers back to public transport after a 25 per cent decline in patronage, some 500 modern shelters have been erected, low-floor buses and trams introduced, and cycles can be carried on trams and buses outside peak hours.

Measures have also been taken to improve operating efficiency, including computerised recording of bus fuel consumption and vehicle-km. Despite these measures, passenger figures have continued to decline seriously, and

this is causing concern among the local authorities responsible for funding the company, in particular the Kreis Leipziger Land.

Studies into possible modernisation of the city's public transport have been undertaken by LVB, Daimler-Benz and TransTec, the consulting arm of the transport undertaking in Leipzig's west German partner city of Hannover. However, the idea of putting central area tramways underground has been discarded as too expensive and offering only limited benefits.

A cross-border lease agreement for 205 trams was concluded with FBBC Leasing Corporation of New York in April 1996. Worth US$180.5 million, the deal is valid for 30 years.

MAN low-floor bus and Tatra trams at Leipzig Hbf (Bill Luke) ***1999**/0043200*

Graf & Stift trolleybus in front of Linz railway station (Bill Luke)   **1999**/0043202

Bus and trolleybus

Passenger journeys: (1994) Bus 16.9 million, trolleybus 26.1 million
(1995) Bus 17.1 million, trolleybus 26.3 million
(1996) Bus 16.3 million, trolleybus 26.7 million
Vehicle-km: (1994) Bus 3.8 million, trolleybus 1.5 million
(1995) Bus 3.9 million, trolleybus 1.4 million
(1996) Bus 4.2 million, trolleybus 1.3 million

Number of routes: Bus 22, trolleybus 4
Route length: Bus 131 km, trolleybus 18.8 km

Fleet: 90 buses

Gräf & Stift NG272 articulated (1993/94/95/96)	31
Gräf & Stift GSGU280M18 articulated (1981/82)	15
Gräf & Stift GSLH200M12 (1984/85)	12
Steyr SS11 HU200 (1988/89/90)	14
Steyr SN12 HUA285 (1994)	1
Steyr SN12 HUA245 (1996)	13
Volvo City III (1995)	4
In peak service: 75	

Fleet: 21 trolleybuses

Gräf & Stift GSGE150 M18 articulated (1983/84/85)	17
Steyr STS11HU (1988)	4
In peak service: 16	

Most intensive service: 5 min
One-person operation: All routes
Fare collection: Prepurchase, and automatic machines for ticket issuing and cancellation at all stops
Fare structure: Stage; ticketcards, passes (weekly, monthly and annual)
Fares collected on board: None
Fare evasion control: Random inspection
Operational control: Route inspectors/mobile radio

Average peak-hour speed: Bus 20 km/h, trolleybus 20 km/h, tram 19 km/h
New vehicles financed by: Free financing and credit

Tramway

Type of operation: Conventional tramway

Passenger journeys: (1994) 37.7 million
(1995) 38.1 million
(1996) 38.1 million
Car-km: (annual) 2 million

Route length: 15.3 km
Number of lines: 2
Number of stops: 39
Gauge: 900 mm
Max gradient: 4%
Minimum curve radius: 18 m
Electrification: 600 V DC, overhead

Service: Peak 4-6 min, off-peak 6-15 min
First/last car: 04.01/23.48
Fare collection: Prepurchase and automatic machines for ticket issuing and cancellation at all stops
One-person operation: All vehicles

Rolling stock: 43 cars

Bombardier-Rotax GTW8 (1970/71)	M8
Bombardier-Rotax GTW8 (1970/71 rebuilt 1973/74)	M7
Bombardier-Rotax GTW10 (1977 rebuilt 1979/80)	M12
Bombardier-Rotax GTW10 (1985/86)	M16
In peak service: 35	

Local railway (Bergbahn)

Current situation: ESG also operates the Bergbahn, a 2.9 km railway with eight stations running from Bergbahnhof at the tramway Line 3 terminal to Pöstlingberg, operating on 600 V DC catenary. It carries about 500,000 passengers a year.

Rolling stock: 13 cars

UPDATED

LISBON

Population: 610,000, city region 2.5 million
Public transport: Bus and tramway services provided in city area by public company also responsible for three funiculars and a public elevator. Metro operated by separate public undertaking, suburban rail lines by Portuguese Railways (CP), cross-river ferries by CP and Transtejo, and suburban bus services by municipally owned bus company and private operators. Though fares are integrated, no overall authority directs transport planning for the region, but the Basic Law of Land Transport passed in 1991 allows for creation of such a body. Rail infrastructure planning and construction is undertaken by a quasi-autonomous transport ministry department. Other arrangements apply in the south Tagus conurbation (see separate section below)

Carris

Companhia Carris de Ferro de Lisboa SA (Carris)
Rua Primeiro de Maio N° 101-103, 1399 Lisbon, Portugal
Tel: (+351 1) 363 02 66   Fax: (+351 1) 364 93 99
President: Helder Jacinto de Oliveira
Commercial Director: António Proença
Staff: 4,729

Passenger boardings: (All modes)
(1994) 381 million
(1995) 379.2 million
(1996) 376.2 million

Operating costs financed by: Fares 64.9 per cent, government subsidy 27.4 per cent, deficit 7.7 per cent

Current situation: Carris operates as exclusive concessionnaire for provision of public transport to the framework followed by the previous owners, Lisbon Electric Tramways Ltd, taken into public ownership in 1978. Moves to integrate and co-ordinate the five publicly owned transport operations have been under discussion, and a multimodal pass system extends to part of the suburban area.

New Mercedes O405N of Carris in Lisbon   **1999**/0043203

Developments: In 1997 Carris received 30 new articulated buses and 27 low-floor rigid buses with air conditioning. In 1998 28 buses outstanding from 1997 were received, together with 55 from the 1998 intake.

In 1998 a special service to support the Expo '98 exhibition was set up, with four routes to serve the Gare do Oriente, the main public transport connection for the exhibition.

Bus

Passenger boardings: (1994) 354 million
(1995) 354 million
(1996) 351.9 million
Vehicle-km: (1994) 44.3 million
(1995) 44.3 million
(1996) 43.5 million

Number of routes: 93
Route length: (One way) 595 km
On priority right-of-way: 38.4 km

Fleet: 802 vehicles

Volvo B10R	94
Volvo B59	266
Volvo B10M articulated	85
MAN SL200F	86
MAN SL200	112
MAN 10150 HOCL (1990/91)	40
Magirus/Fiat-Iveco 470	82
Volvo B58 articulated	1
Renault B120 minibus	30
Renault for disabled service	4
Mercedes 412 D40	2
In peak service: 681	

Most intensive service: 8-10 min
One-person operation: All routes
Fare collection: Payment to conductor or driver, prepurchase tickets and passes, 10-journey carnets; cancellers at entrance
Fare structure: Flat, city centre; zonal, outside (3 zones); monthly passes; tourist passes for 4 or 7 days
Fares collected on board: 14.3 per cent of revenue; prepurchase 20 per cent, passes 65.7 per cent
Fare evasion control: Roving inspectors
Arrangements for elderly/disabled: 6 lift-equipped minibuses including 4 Renault SG3/Grau and 2 Mercedes 412 D40

Integration with other modes: Passes valid on all services in Lisbon area in different zone combinations; minibus link to airport
Average distance between stops: 394 m
Average peak-hour speed: In mixed traffic, 14.8 km/h
Operating costs financed by: Fares 73 per cent
New vehicles financed by: Loans

Developments: A radio-based traffic management system known as SICRA has been installed throughout the fleet, with completion at the end of 1997.

Tramway
Type of operation: Conventional tramway, plus one light rail line

Passenger boardings: (1994) 22.4 million
(1995) 22 million
(1996) 20 million
Car-km: (1994) 3.2 million
(1995) 3 million
(1996) 2.5 million

Route length: 53 km
On priority right-of-way: 11.2 km
Number of lines: 6
Number of stops: 100
Gauge: 900 mm
Track: 45 per cent conventional sleepers on ballast, 55 per cent on concrete with resilient pads
Max gradient: 14%
Minimum curve radius: 10 m
Electrification: 580 V DC, overhead

Service: Peak 6-11 min, off-peak 8-18 min
First/last car: (Line 15) 05.05/01.55
Fare structure: Zonal, but flat-fare season tickets across the network account for most journeys
One-person operation: All routes
Operating costs financed by: Fares 22 per cent

Rolling stock: 60 cars
CCFL NF51 various ages rebuilt   M45
CCFL DB1/K33   M5
Siemens LRV (1995)   M10
In peak service: 50

Current situation: A total of 50 heritage cars have been rebuilt with modern electrical and mechanical equipment, whilst retaining their original exterior appearance.

The five hill routes have been developed as a tourist attraction whilst continuing their traditional public transport role in the narrow, steeply graded streets of the old city. Some streets are barely wide enough for a single track, and the section between São Tome and Graca (Route 28) has interlaced track on sharp curves.
Developments: Waterfront Route 15 is being upgraded to near light rail standards, including creation of 4.2 km of reserved track and introduction of 10 three-section

Carris bus at the Expo '98 Oriente station   *1999*/0043207

New LRV at Algés terminal, Lisbon (Bill Luke)   *1999*/0043206

articulated cars, for which upgraded depot facilities have been provided at Santo Amaro. These are currently operating between Praça Figueira and Belém, although further upgrading work should see operations extended to a terminus at Cruz de Quebrada, where a park-and-ride is planned.

Similarly, Route 18, which shares part of its alignment with Route 15, is to be upgraded to light rail standards and extended once again to Santa Apolónia CP station, although this would necessitate exercising of options for a

further 20 LRVs from Siemens. Also Line 12 is to be extended to form a circular route round Castelo de S Jorge.

Should money become available, Carris would like to reopen its lines to the suburb of Benfica, upgrading them to light rail standards. In addition, the northern suburb of Odivelas urgently needs some form of fixed-track transport system, and the government is paying Carris to undertake a feasibility study to determine whether light rail would cater for its needs or if it would be better served by the metro. A 14 km route is also proposed from central Lisbon to the CP suburban station at Póvoa, requiring 20 cars.

Funiculars/elevator
Passenger journeys: (1994) 4.8 million
(1995) 4.5 million
(1996) 4.3 million

Current situation: Carris operates three funicular (cable tram) routes and one vertical public elevator.

Lisbon tram heading through the narrow streets of Alfama district (Andrew Jarosz)   *1999*/0045280

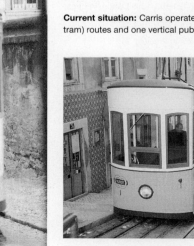
Bica Ascensores upper level, Lisbon (Bill Luke)   *1999*/0043204

New ML95 trainset at ML's depot   **1999**/0043208

ML

Metropolitano de Lisboa EP (ML)
28 Avenida Fontes Pereira de Melo, 1069 Lisbon Codex
Tel: (+351 1) 355 84 57   Fax: (+351 1) 357 49 08
President: A Santos Machado
Managing Director, Operations: A Pinto Dantas
Fixed Installations: A Cerdeira Baptista
Rolling Stock: P Vazão de Almeida
Staff: 2,026

Type of operation: Full metro, opened 1959

Passenger journeys: (1995) 123.9 million
(1996) 128 million
(1997) 117 million
Car-km: (1994) 10.3 million
(1995) 10.5 million

Route length: 19 km
  in tunnel: 17 km
Number of lines: 2
Number of stations: 25
Gauge: 1,435 mm
Track: Vignole (FB) 50 kg/m U50 profile rail on timber
sleepers, normally on ballast, with resilient pads; new
lines twin-block Stedef sleepers; on concrete at stations
Max gradient: 4%
Minimum curve radius: 150 m (some 100 m)
Tunnel: Cut-and-cover except 1 km bored
Electrification 750 V DC, third rail

Service: Peak 3 min, off-peak 6 min
First/last train: 06.30/01.00
Fare structure: Flat
Fare collection: AFC at all stations, open access
Fare evasion control: Spot checks at stations or on trains
Integration with other modes: Fares integrated with
suburban bus, ferry and rail services through monthly
zonal passes
Surveillance: CCTV on all platforms
Operating costs financed by: Fares 27 per cent, other
commercial sources 11 per cent, government subsidy/
grants 62 per cent

Rolling stock: 197 cars, in four-car sets except for two
ML90 three-car prototypes

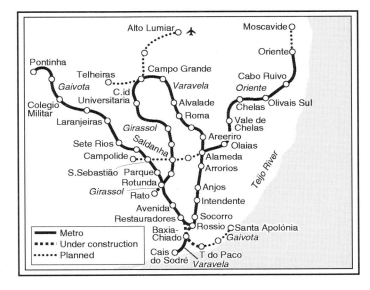

Lisbon metro
0045357

Linke-Hofmann-Busch ML7 (1959)	M20
Linke-Hofmann-Busch ML7 (1964)	M14
Sorefame ML7 (1972)	M32
Sorefame ML7 (1975)	M14
Sorefame ML79 (1984)	M40
Sorefame ML79 (1985/88)	M16
Sorefame ML90 prototype (1992)	M4 T2
Sorefame ML90 (1995/96)	M38 T17

On order: 114 ML95 cars are on order from Adtranz
Portugal, with options for a further 120

Developments: A major expansion programme now
under way is transforming the present network into
three separate lines and adding a new cross-city
route, effectively doubling the size of the network
by the end of the century, when annual patronage of
200 million is expected. There will be eight interchanges
with CP suburban trains and three with cross-Tagus
ferries; park-and-ride facilities are planned at six outlying
stations.

In 1995, the existing 19 km single route was split into
two wholly separate lines, the 5.3 km Girassol line
(formerly Line B) being segregated from the remaining
network thanks to inauguration of a second station at
Rotunda. An extension to Rato opened in late 1997, along
with a 3 km extension of the Gaivota line (Line A) to a new
terminus at Pontinha. A Varavela line (Line C) extension to
CP's Cascais line station at Cais do Sodré opened in
1998.

Further extensions to all three routes are planned. The
Gaivota line will be extended to CP's Santa Apolonia
terminal, the Girassol from Campo Grande to Alto do
Lumiar, and the Caravela from Campo Grande to Telheiras.

The new Oriente line (formerly Line D) from Alameda to
Oriente opened in 1998 to serve the Expo 98 site. Later,
extensions are proposed northwards to Moscavide and
westwards across the city centre to Campolide, where

there will be interchange with CP suburban trains on the
future cross-Tagus line.

A fifth line is under study, linking the southwest
riverside suburb of Belem with Oriente, while a proposed
line to serve Loures is now to be built as light rail rather
than full metro. By the end of the century the network will
comprise four lines totalling some 40 km and serving 50
stations.

All existing stations are undergoing refurbishment and
lengthening of platforms. By 1998 all stations were able to
handle six-car trains.

Lisbon Rail Development Board

Gabinete do Nó Ferroviário de Lisboa
Estaçao do Rossio, 4° piso, 1200 Lisbon
Tel: (+351 1) 342 09 69/09 47   Fax: (+351 1) 342 33 00
President: Dr Braamcamp Sobral

Current situation: GNFL was set up by the Ministry of
Public Works, Transport & Communications in 1987 as a
quasi-autonomous government department to oversee
railway development. Its remit is to modernise
infrastructure serving the city, adapt the network to meet
current requirements, build new lines where necessary,
and to create conditions under which the cross-Tagus rail
link can be built. However, its functions were expected to
pass in 1997 to a new national infrastructure authority.
Developments: GNFL is working on seven projects:
upgrading the ring railway, including the Alcântara
branch; modernising the Sintra line; extending suburban
service on the western line to Torres Vedras; upgrading
the Cascais line; restructuring the northern line to
Azambuja to permit introduction of suburban service;
building a new main terminal in Lisbon; implementing
the cross-Tagus line, and planning a second such link.

Construction of the cross-Tagus link, which is to be
incorporated into the lower deck of the existing road bridge,
is costed at Esc78 billion. Initial build-operate-transfer bids
from the private sector were rejected on cost grounds, and
separate contracts are now to be let for each aspect of the
project. So far, contracts have been awarded for the rail link
itself and for strengthening of the bridge.

Cross-Tagus rail service was due to start in 1999, with
trains running through from Azambuja on CP's northern
line to Pinhal Novo and Setúbal on the south side via the
ring line. Thirty four-car double-deck emus are on order
from Alstom/CAF/Adtranz.

CP

Caminhos de Ferro Portugueses (CP)
Calcada do Duque 20-1, 1294 Lisbon Codex
Tel: (+351 1) 346 31 81   Fax: (+351 1) 347 65 24

Suburban rail
Type of operation: Suburban heavy rail

Passenger journeys: (1995) 139 million

Current situation: Suburban services provided by CP on
three routes. From Santa Apolónia electric trains (25 kV
50 Hz) run hourly (peak half-hourly) on the northern line to
Azambuja (54 km), with a shuttle serving the orbital line
between Alcântara and Areeiro (10 km), and an irregular

ML's Chelas station on Oriente/Red line   **1999**/0043205

hourly service to Sacavém. Some 15 trains run to destinations further afield. From the Cais do Sodré terminus a frequent service is operated to Estoril and Cascais (26 km), electrified at 1.5 kV DC. Lisbon's most intensive service is on the Sintra line (electrified 25 kV 50 Hz) out of Rossio station, where there is a 16 min service throughout the day, plus a similar inner-suburban service between Terminal Av 5 and Cacém (18 km).

Developments: The Sintra line carries the heaviest traffic of any CP route. It has been completely modernised, with four tracks being provided as far as Cacém. Track and catenary have been upgraded with modern signalling including CTC. A new fleet of 52 four-car emus has been delivered by Adtranz Portugal.

The Cascais line is also being modernised. Track is being rehabilitated, level crossings eliminated, catenary remodelled, new substations built, stations refurbished and platforms lengthened to accommodate 10-car trains, and new interchange facilities introduced. The fleet is being increased from 10 to 13 trains.

On the orbital route, colourlight signalling will permit 15 min frequency, thereby allowing some Cascais line trains to run to Areeiro and so reduce pressure on Cais do Sodré. This route will eventually be used by the cross-Tagus service from Azambuja to Setúbal.

Under a proposed reorganisation, management of suburban routes in Lisbon will be grouped into one or more profit centres better to identify costs, although central government will continue to provide subsidy. The Sintra line will be the first to be granted this level of autonomy, and will market itself under a separate brand name.

Ferry
Current situation: CP's cross-Tagus ferries from Terreiro do Paco pier to Barreiro were transferred in 1993 to a subsidiary, Soflusa. Eight vessels operate between 05.45 and 02.45, providing a 10-min peak service, 30-45 min off-peak.

In addition, Transtejo provides frequent services across the estuary from three points on the north shore to five on the south. Main departure point in Lisbon is Terreiro do Paço, with vehicle ferries leaving from Cais do Sodré. Belem, 5 km west of the city, handles departures for downstream destinations.

There are seven routes totalling 37 km, operated by 26 vessels (five carrying vehicles); about 44 million passengers are carried annually.

LISBON - SOUTH TAGUS
Population: 440,000
Public transport: The south bank communities of Almade, Seixal, Barreiro and Moita form the third largest conurbation in Portugal. Ferry services provide a link with Lisbon, while CP operates suburban rail services from its Barreiro station. Bus services are provided by a number of operators, notably Transportes Colectivos and Rodoviário Sul do Tejo. A four-line light rail network is planned

CP
Address as above

Current situation: About hourly (peak half-hourly) service provided from 05.00 to 02.05 between Barreiro, where there is connection with the cross-Tagus ferries, and Setúbal (29 km).
Developments: Cross-Tagus rail link being built to improve access to central Lisbon; initial services should start in 1999. Improvements on the south bank include a new line to the bridge with six stations, an 8,000-space park-and-ride at Penalva, and electrification and upgrading between Pinhal Novo and Setúbal.

Private bus
Current situation: The former state-owned Rodoviário Sul do Tejo, which is now owned by Barraqueiro, provides suburban bus services on the south bank.

Transportes Colectivos do Barreiro
Rua Resistentes Antifascistas, 2830 Barreiro
Tel: (+351 1) 207 83 54   Fax: (+351 1) 207 83 68
General Manager:
   Pedro Alberta Correira de Andrade Canário
Staff: 234

Number of routes: 14
Route length: 129 km

Fleet: 65 vehicles, plus 12 hired

Current situation: A municipal bus service is provided in Barreiro on the south bank of the Tagus, connected to Lisbon by ferry. Fares cover 88 per cent of operating costs.

Light rail (proposed)
Current situation: With the population of the four south bank municipalities expected to double by 2030, a four-line light rail network has been recommended by a feasibility study. The 41 km would serve 55 stops, linking the four towns and ferry terminals, as well as the university, hospital and local beaches. A 25.8 km core network would be built initially, requiring a fleet of up to 47 cars. Construction started in 1997 for 1999 opening.

On completion of the cross-Tagus rail link, CP's existing Barreiro—Moita line will no longer be a main route and will be converted to light rail.

UPDATED

LIVERPOOL
Population: City 470,000, Merseyside county area 1.5 million
Public transport: Main bus services provided by employee-owned company, with other services operated by private firms. Passenger Transport Executive, under direction of a joint board of local districts and trading as Merseytravel, has direct responsibility for ferry operation, the Mersey road tunnels, subsidising contracted non-commercial bus services, rail services within Merseyside county area, including central area metro loop line, operated under contract, service promotion, and provision of bus station facilities; rapid transit options being evaluated

MTL
MTL Services Ltd
9th Floor, Rail House, Lord Nelson Street, Liverpool L1 1RQ, England
Tel: (+44 151) 330 44 00   Fax: (+44 151) 330 44 01
Managing Director: Peter Coombes
Operations Director: Henry Sherman
Commercial Director: Dominic Brady
Engineering Director: Robert Dawson
Financial Director: Colin Fuller
Staff: 2,490

Current situation: Established in 1986 from the former PTE bus operation as a separate company wholly owned by the PTA, the company was sold to its workforce in 1992. It operates a network of commercial services throughout the Merseyside area, plus subsidised services both wholly within Merseyside and running into neighbouring areas of Lancashire and Cheshire.
Developments: The company expanded with the takeover of Fareway Passenger Services, Blue Triangle of Bootle, Heysham Travel and Liverbus. MTL later bought London Buses' subsidiary London Northern, and subsequently acquired London Suburban Buses and R&I Tours, both based in north London. The company was awarded the franchise to operate the Merseyrail network in 1996, and Regional Railways North East (now Northern Spirit) in 1997. In 1998 Village Group of Liverpool was acquired, but London operations were sold to Metroline of Harrow, and Sightseers coaching operation was sold to Hardings.

Merseybus operates three 17-seat Neoplan 4009 minibuses on behalf of Merseytravel (Andrew Jarosz)
1999/0045283

Bus
Passenger journeys: (1992/93) 134 million
Vehicle-km: (1992/93) 48 million

Number of routes: 110
Route length: 651 km

Fleet: 920 vehicles

Leyland Atlantean double-deck	167
MCW Metrobus double-deck	28
Leyland Olympian double-deck	84
Leyland Titan double-deck	208
Volvo Olympian double-deck	59
Scania double-deck	11
Volvo B10 single-deck	135
Leyland National single-deck	72
Neoplan N4016 single-deck low-floor	12
Scania single-deck low-floor	20
Volvo B6 midibus	49
Dennis Dart midibus	9
Neoplan N4009 low-floor midibus	3
Dennis Dart SLF low-floor midibus	40
Optare Metrorider midibus	11
Mercedes midibus	12

Most intensive service: 5 min
One-person operation: All routes
Fare collection: Prepurchase season tickets/passes, or payment to driver for single tickets
Fare structure: Zonal for season tickets, stage for single fares
Fare evasion control: Inspectors and other measures
Average distance between stops: 400 m
Average peak-hour speed: In mixed traffic, 20 km/h

Fleet: 598 vehicles

AEC Routemaster double-deck	41
MCW Metrobus double-deck	153
Leyland Olympian double-deck	23
Volvo Olympian double-deck	73
Optare Delta single-deck	9
Leyland National single-deck	24
MAN/Optare Vecta single-deck	8
Dennis Dart single-deck	236
Leyland Lynx single-deck	6
Dennis Lance SLF single-deck	10
Optare Metrorider minibus	9
Optare Excel low-floor single-deck	6

On order: 24 single-deck

Metroline

Metroline Travel Ltd
118-122 College Road, Harrow HA1 1DB
Tel: (+44 181) 861 40 80   Fax: (+44 181) 427 33 04
Managing Director: Declan O'Farrell

Current situation: This employee-owned company operates services in northwest London from five depots.
Developments: The company acquired Brents Coaches and Atlas Bus of Watford in 1996, and was floated on the London stock market in 1997. London Northern was acquired from MTL Group in 1998, and the two companies are being integrated.

Fleet: 864 vehicles

AEC Routemaster double-deck	98
MCW Metrobus double-deck	355
Leyland Titan double-deck	16
Volvo Olympian double-deck	38
Dennis Dart single-deck	199
Dennis Lance SLF single-deck	14
Dennis Dart SLF single-deck	28
MAN single-deck	29
Minibuses	57
Coaches	30

Stagecoach East London

East London Bus & Coach Company Ltd
2-4 Clements Road, Ilford IG1 1BA
Tel: (+44 181) 553 34 20   Fax: (+44 181) 477 72 00
Managing Director: Barry Arnold
Staff: 2,000

Passenger journeys: (1996/97) 12.6 million

Current situation: Operates 55 routes in east London from six depots.

Fleet: 611 vehicles

AEC Routemaster double-deck	64
Leyland Titan	256
Scania double-deck	50
Volvo Olympian double-deck	51
Optare Delta single-deck	26
Dennis Dart single-deck	124
Scania low-floor single-deck	16
Optare Starrider minibus	24

In peak service: 518
On order: 78

Stagecoach Selkent

South East London & Kent Bus Company Ltd
180 Bromley Road, Catford, London SE6 2XA
Tel: (+44 181) 695 07 07   Fax: (+44 181) 695 92 32
Managing Director: Barry Arnold
Staff: 1,100

Current situation: Operates services in south London from three depots.

Fleet: 374 vehicles

Leyland Olympian double-deck	87
Leyland Titan double-deck	135
Volvo Olympian double-deck	52
Dennis Dart single-deck	60
Dennis Lance single-deck	12
Optare minibus	28

Travel London

Travel West Midlands Ltd
1 Sovereign Court, 8 Graham Street, Birmingham B1 3JR
Tel: (+44 121) 200 72 00   Fax: (+44 121) 233 12 17

Current situation: This company was set up by Travel West Midlands to operate two contracted services using

London United Volvo Olympian on Airbus service at King's Cross railway station (Andrew Jarosz)
1999/0045287

Alexander-bodied Volvo Olympian of Metroline leaving the bus station next to Victoria railway station
1999/0045289

Optare Excel low-floor bus on Stationlink service, operated by Thorpes (Andrew Jarosz)   *1999*/0045288

low-floor minibuses. The fleet is based at the Gatwick Express depot in Battersea.

Fleet: 31

Optare Excel low-floor single-deck	21
Optare Solo low-floor midibus	10

Suburban bus

Current situation: Bus service in suburban areas around London are provided by six main companies and several smaller operators. Unlike London itself, bus operations in these areas were deregulated in 1986. For history see *JUTS 1989*.

Between them the companies provide an extensive network of local bus services, including many routes feeding stations on the rail network in London's outer suburban centres such as Watford, Croydon, Bromley, Uxbridge, Enfield and Romford, and towns further afield.

London Underground

(address as for LT)
Chair: Denis Tunnicliffe
Director of Passenger Services: Hugh Sumner
Staff: 16,000

Type of operation: Full metro, first line opened 1863

Passenger journeys: (1995/96) 784 million
(1996/97) 772 million
(1997/98) 832 million
Train-km: (1995/96) 57.2 million
(1996/97) 58.6 million
(1997/98) 62.1 million

Route length: 392 km
  in tunnel: 171 km
Number of lines: 12
Number of stations: 267 (including 21 managed by Railtrack)
Gauge: 1,435 mm
Track: Running rail, 47 kg/m BH and 54 kg/m FB; conductor rail (open and subsurface), 74 kg/m FB and 53 kg/m FB; conductor rail (tube tunnel), 64 kg/m rectangular; conventional sleepers on ballast (concreted in tube tunnels)
Tunnel: Bored single-track (tube) and cut-and-cover double-track; 5 lines cut-and-cover, remainder bored tunnel
Electrification: 630 V DC, third and fourth rail

Service: Peak in central area, 2 min
Revenue control: Fully automated system with self-service machines at nearly all stations; automatic checking on entry and exit at all central area and some suburban stations; random on-train inspection; penalty fare
One-person operation: All lines except Northern; Victoria line has full automatic train control ATO/ATP
Surveillance: CCTV at almost all stations
Operational control: Two-way radio on all lines
Operating costs financed by: Fares 125 per cent (before depreciation and renewals)

Rolling stock: 4,912 cars
Tube stock (small profile)
Metro-Cammell
  (1959/62) Northern line (being withdrawn) M410 T164
  (1972) Mk I/II Bakerloo/Northern lines   M238 T175
  (1967/72) Victoria line (ATO fitted)   M172 T172
  (1973) Piccadilly line   M349 T174
ABB Transportation (1992) Central/W&C lines   M700
GEC Alsthom (1996/97) Jubilee line   M354
GEC Alsthom (1997/98) Northern line (entering service)   M636
Surface stock (normal profile)
Cravens A60/62 Metropolitan/E London
  lines   M226 T227
Metro-Cammell C69/C77 (1969/77) District/
  Circle/Hammersmith lines   M138 T138
  D78 (1978) District line   M300 T150

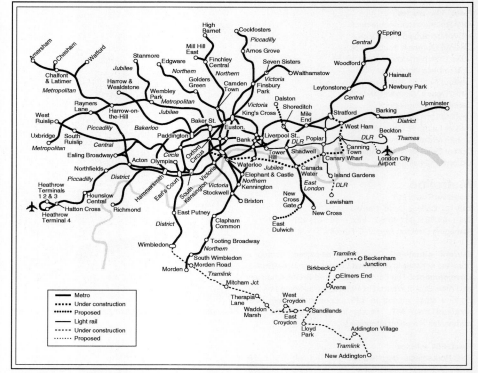

London's metro system and light rail   0045358

Developments: Opening of the 20 km extension of the Jubilee line from Green Park to Stratford via London Bridge, the Docklands development area and the Millennium Dome site at Greenwich has been delayed by engineering and signalling problems. The extension will not now open until 21 December 1999, one-and-a-half years late, and barely days before the start of Millennium celebrations. The escalating delay in completing the extension led to appointment in September 1998 of US engineering and construction management company Bechtel to manage the final stages of the project.

Modernisation of the Central line, with new trains, signalling and ATO, is nearing completion. Refurbishment of Bakerloo and Metropolitan line trains has been completed, and work on the Piccadilly line fleet is in progress.

The first new cars for the Northern line entered service in 1998. These were built on a leasing and maintenance contract with GEC Alsthom, which financed construction of the trains, and will maintain them at Northern line depots under a 20-year service contract valued at £40 million annually. The Northern line is also being equipped with track-to-train CCTV to permit one-person operation.

A substantial backlog of engineering work was tackled in 1997, though reopening of the East London line, closed for complete refurbishment in 1995, was further delayed until March 1998.

Steps were taken to obtain powers to extend the Piccadilly line to the proposed Terminal 5 at Heathrow airport, and approval has been granted to extend the East London line northwards to Dalston and possibly to Highbury & Islington. Future extensions will be the responsibility of Transport for London.

Suburban rail
Type of operation: Suburban heavy rail

Current situation: Suburban services run on all routes out of London to a distance of over 100 km, with an extensive network of inner-suburban routes serving east and northeast London, and the area south of the River Thames which is poorly served by metro. Much of the network is electrified — south of the Thames at 660/750 V DC, the remainder mostly at 25 kV 50 Hz. Operations are franchised to 10 private-sector companies. They run over track owned by the privatised infrastructure company Railtrack, with trains leased from the privatised rolling stock leasing companies.

Trains run generally from about 05.00 to 24.00. Off-peak the service interval is 10-30 min, stepped up in the peak hours to every few minutes at some stations. Fares are graduated, though zonal all-modes passes are available within Greater London. Most stations have self-service ticket machines; inspection is largely manual, though some of the franchisees are installing automatic barriers at busy stations to help reduce fraud.

The area served by the 10 train operating companies created in 1994, and now franchised, extends far beyond the London commuting area, and separate data for London suburban operations is not available. Figures given in the entries below cover the companies' entire operations. An eleventh company, Gatwick Express, runs the dedicated service linking Victoria station in central London with Gatwick airport (43 km). Service to Heathrow airport (Heathrow Express, see below) from Paddington station, operated by the airports authority BAA, was inaugurated in 1998.

Developments: In the privatisation regime implemented by the Conservative government, franchises for all 10 railways had been awarded by March 1997.

A major London scheme, Thameslink 2000, is one of the two proposed Railtrack infrastructure projects. This proposal would raise capacity of the existing Thameslink cross-city line to provide a 5 minute service, and comprises construction of a flyover on the approaches to London Bridge station, enlarged stations at Blackfriars and St Pancras, and provision of a connection to the Great Northern suburban lines in the north. Funding for the £650 million scheme was approved in 1996. Completion is scheduled for 2002.

The loop line between Streatham, Wimbledon and Sutton, operated by Thameslink, has been improved with the refurbishment of eight stations. The line is an important link both locally for travel between Streatham, Wimbledon and Sutton, and also to provide links with London, Luton and stations to the north. The stations, managed by Thameslink, are owned by Railtrack which

New Jubilee line train at Kingsbury on the original portion of the route   **1998**/0010329

jointly invested in, and carried out, the improvements, with Kier Rail as main contractor.

In late 1998 proposals surfaced once again for construction of links between the metro network and certain suburban lines, with the aim of creating new cross-city connections.

Chiltern

The Chiltern Railway Co Ltd/M40 Trains
Western House, 14 Rickfords Hill, Aylesbury HP20 2RX
Tel: (+44 1296) 33 21 00   Fax: (+44 1296) 33 21 26
Director: Adrian Shooter
Staff: 300

Passenger journeys: (1995/96) 7.5 million
(1996/97) 8.1 million
(1997/98) 8.8 million

Current situation: Trains run northwest to Aylesbury by two routes, Banbury and Birmingham, extending to 245 km. Operation is franchised to M40 Trains.
Developments: Chiltern has introduced a faster service between London and Birmingham, using a new fleet of five four-car express dmus from Adtranz.

Rolling stock: 99 dmu cars

Connex Rail

Connex South Eastern Ltd, Connex South Central Ltd
Friars Bridge Court, 41-45 Blackfriars Road, London SE18 8NZ
Tel: (+44 171) 620 50 00   Fax: (+44 171) 620 55 00
Chairman, Connex Rail: Colin Webster
Vice Chairman and Chief Executive, Connex Rail:
    Antoine Hurel
Chief Operating Officer: Geoff Harrison-Mee

Type of operation: Suburban rail/commuter rail

Passenger journeys/boardings: (1996) 198.4 million
(1997) 200 million

Current situation: Routes serve south London, Kent, Surrey and Sussex. Connex launched a revamp of its inner-suburban services under the South London Metro banner, with improved frequencies at many stations and a new livery in late 1997.

Both Connex South Eastern and Connex South Central are operated on 15-year franchises by Connex Rail.
Developments: Connex South Eastern and Connex South Central were both brought under one roof following a reorganisation at the end of 1998. Further orders of Class 375 trains are expected to eliminate slam-door stock on Connex South Eastern by 2006.

Route length: 1,407 km
Number of lines: 39
Number of stations: 413
Electrification: 750 V DC (25 kV AC Willesden to Rugby section)

Fare evasion control: Penalty fares system over parts of network
Integration with other modes: Integrated fares with local bus operators and cycle hire at Tonbridge and Canterbury West
One-person operation: All Connnex Metro and Kent Link services

Rolling stock: 2,276 cars
Connex South Central   M249 T665
Connex South Eastern   M592 T770
On order: 210 Class 375 from Adtranz, 120 of which are to be delivered by 2000

First Great Eastern

33 Artillery Lane, London E1 7LP
Tel: (+44 171) 904 33 00   Fax: (+44 171) 904 33 01
Managing Director: Bob Breakwell
Staff: 1,320

Passenger journeys: (1996/97) 43.5 million
(1997/98) 51.6 million

Current situation: Runs extensive suburban services in east London and Essex, almost entirely electrified at

Thameslink Class 319 from Sutton entering newly refurbished South Merton station on the Wimbledon loop line (Tony Pattison)   *1999*/0043214

Chiltern Railways Adtranz dmu on commuter service to London   *1999*/0043213

Connex South Eastern Networker Express Class 365 on London service to the Kent coast   *1999*/0045286

25 kV AC, serving 57 stations. Operation is franchised to the FirstBus group. Fares cover 78 per cent of operating costs and 90 per cent of trains are one person operated.
Developments: Refurbishment of the oldest rolling stock started 1998, along with provision of improved disabled access and repainting at many stations. Ten-minute off-peak service planned for 1999 implementation at inner-suburban stations.

Rolling stock: 576 emu cars

Thameslink Class 319 emu in new livery pulls away from Blackfriars station, London (Monitor Photography)   **1999**/0043211

LTS Rail

LTS Rail Ltd
Central House, Clifftown Road, Southend-on-Sea SS1 1AB
Tel: (+44 1702) 35 78 89   Fax: (+44 1702) 35 78 23
Managing Director: Ken Bird

Passenger journeys: (1993/94) 23 million
(1996/97) 21.3 million
(1997/98) 23.7 million

Current situation: Running commuter trains between London Fenchurch Street, Southend and Shoeburyness, Basildon, Grays, Upminster and Barking, LTS is a Prism Rail 15-year franchise. LTS Rail serves 25 stations with a 26th built at West Ham and due to open in 1999 to coincide with completion of the Jubilee line extension.

Also in 1999, 44 Class 357 Electrostar four-car units are going into service on the route, built by Adtranz. Extensive station refurbishment is taking place along the route with £75 million being invested by Railtrack and an additional £14 million by LTS Rail. An £11.5 million project to install ticket gates at all stations will be completed in 1999.

Rolling stock: 324 emu cars

Silverlink

Silverlink Train Services Ltd
Melton House, 65-67 Clarendon Road, Watford WD1 1DP
Tel: (+44 1923) 20 77 77   Fax: (+44 1923) 24 64 80
Managing Director: Charles Belcher
Staff: 998

Passenger journeys: (1993/94) 32 million
(1996/97) 28 million
(1997/98) 30.7 million

Current situation: Operates outer-suburban route running north from London to Milton Keynes, Northampton and Birmingham (electrified 25 kV), along with several local lines in north London (750 V DC third rail, dual 750 V/25 kV, diesel) and one rural route; total eight routes, 278 km, 97 stations. Operation is franchised to the National Express Group.
Developments: Formerly North London Railways, the company rebranded itself as Silverlink in 1997.

Rolling stock: 20 dmu and 217 emu cars

South West Trains

South West Trains
Friars Bridge Court, 41-45 Blackfriars Road, London SE1 8NZ

Tel: (+44 171) 928 51 51   Fax: (+44 171) 620 55 50
Managing Director: Graham Eccles
Staff: 3,900

Passenger journeys: (1995/96) 90 million
(1996/97) 110.6 million
(1997/98) 118.2 million

Current situation: Serves the southwest London suburbs, Surrey, Hampshire, Dorset and Devon; extending to 940 route-km with 203 stations; mostly electrified at 750 V DC third rail. Operation is franchised to the Stagecoach group.
Developments: A new fleet of 30 four-car trains is being delivered in 1999 for service on the London Waterloo—Reading line.

Rolling stock: 66 dmu and 1,048 emu cars

Thameslink

Thameslink Rail Ltd
Friars Bridge Court, 41-45 Blackfriars Road, London SE1 8NZ
Tel: (+44 171) 620 52 22   Fax: (+44 171) 620 50 99
Managing Director: Euan Cameron

Passenger journeys: (1995/96) 25.6 million
(1996/97) 26.8 million
(1997/98) 30.2 million

Current situation: Operates the cross-city link from Bedford in the north to Brighton in the south, plus a south London suburban service; electrified 750 V DC/25 kV AC. Operation is franchised to the Govia consortium.

Rolling stock: 264 emu cars

Thames Trains

Victory Railway Holdings
Venture House, 37-43 Blagrave Street, Reading RG1 1RY
Tel: (+44 1734) 57 59 77   Fax: (+44 1734) 57 96 48
Website: www.thamestrains.co.uk
Director: Euan Cameron
Staff: 850

Passenger journeys: (1993/94) 21 million
(1996/97) 26.8 million
(1997/98) 28.5 million

Current situation: Thames Trains operates a passenger rail service principally between London Paddington and Oxford via Maidenhead and Reading, with certain of these services extending to Stratford-on-Avon and via Worcester to Hereford. Thames Trains also operates a

service between London Paddington and Bedwyn via Reading and Newbury. Branch line services include those connecting Slough with Windsor, Maidenhead with Marlow and Twyford with Henley-on-Thames. Thames Trains also operates between Reading and Gatwick Airport via Guildford and Reading and Basingstoke. Thames Trains serves a number of tourist destinations including Stratford-on-Avon, Windsor and Oxford.

Thames Trains is operated on a seven-and-a-half year franchise by the Victory Railway Holdings consortium. Victory Railway Holdings was formed to bid for the Thames Trains franchise in 1996 and was a joint venture between the Go-Ahead Group plc and the management and employees of Thames Trains. The franchise for Thames Trains was awarded to Victory Railway Holdings from October 1996 to March 2004. Ownership of shares was 65 per cent Go-Ahead Group and 35 per cent management and employees of Thames Trains. In May 1998 the Go-Ahead Group bought back the 35 per cent share in Victory Railway Holdings held by the management and employees of Thames Trains Ltd. From that date Thames Trains became a wholly owned subsidiary of the Go-Ahead Group.

Rolling stock: 63 Class 165/166 dmus, comprising 164 cars

WAGN

West Anglia & Great Northern Railway
Hertford House, 1 Cranwood Street, London EC2A 2AA
Tel: (+44 171) 928 51 51   Fax: (+44 171) 713 21 16
Managing Director: David Burton
Staff: 1,750

Passenger journeys: (1994/95) 45 million
(1996/97) 50.5 million
(1997/98) 52.8 million

Current situation: WAGN operates 15 routes serving 104 stations running north from London to Peterborough, Cambridge and King's Lynn, extending to 415 km; mostly electrified at 25 kV DC. Operation is franchised to Prism Rail.

Rolling stock: 543 emu cars

Docklands Light Railway

Docklands Railway Management Limited
PO Box 154, London E14 0DX
Tel: (+44 171) 363 95 00   Fax: (+44 171) 363 95 32
Chairman: David Quarmby
Managing Director: Malcolm Hutchinson
Staff: 300

Current situation: DLR was owned by the London Docklands Development Corporation until that body was abolished in March 1998. In 1997 operation was franchised to Docklands Railway Management Ltd for seven years. Its trains are driverless but carry a Train Captain whose job in normal circumstances is to close doors and initiate the start from each station, as well as making ticket checks and assisting passengers. Docklands Railway Management Ltd – a private-sector company controlled by Serco Group plc – took over the operations and maintenance of the DLR in 1997 on a seven-year franchise. DLR Ltd is the holding company, owned by the Department of Environment, Transport and the Regions, responsible for managing the franchise and the Lewisham Extension Concession, developing the railway's assets and planning its future.
Developments: A 4.2 km cross-river extension from Island Gardens to Greenwich and Lewisham is under construction for opening in 2000. The project is being financed and built by a private-sector consortium City Greenwich Lewisham Rail Link.

Good progress is being made on another DLR extension, approved by government, to London City Airport. Feasibility studies will start shortly on the £35 million extension due to open between 2002 and 2004.

Other proposals to emerge from an Horizon Study – which examined the potential for DLR extensions to serve regeneration and integration – include extending the London City Airport link to North Woolwich, a DLR link under the Thames to Woolwich Arsenal, and a DLR service across the proposed Thames Gateway Bridge to Thamesmead. DLR Ltd also has the government's

Rolling stock: 180 cars

Alsthom Lines A and B	M64 T32
Alsthom Rack Line C	M12
GEC Alsthom Line D (1991)	M72

In peak service: 130 cars

Current situation: Line D, which is fully automated on the Maggaly system, opened in stages during 1991/92. In contrast to Lille, platform screens and doors are not provided. Instead, an infra-red beam system detects an obstruction or a person falling on to the track. Train doors have sensitive edges so that passengers' clothing does not become trapped.

Developments: The 1.8 km extension of Line D northwards to a new park-and-ride and bus interchange at Vaise opened in 1997. Extension of Line B from Jean Macé to Gerland (2.4 km, three stations) is under construction for opening in September 2000.

The supervised car park at Bonnevay station was extended to 700 spaces in 1996. Drivers buy a special ticket covering the parking charge and TCL travel.

Funiculars

Passenger journeys: (1994) 14,000 daily
(1995) 13,000 daily

Current situation: Routes run from St Jean to St Just (max gradient 12%, four cars) and Fourvière (max gradient 17%, two cars), total 1.2 km, five stations.

Electrification: 600 V DC, overhead

SNCF

French National Railways, Lyons Region
10 Cours de Verdun, 69286 Lyons
Tel: (+33 4) 72 40 11 10   Fax: (+33 4) 72 40 10 16

Type of operation: Suburban heavy rail

Current situation: Limited suburban services provided on eight routes, plus about hourly service to St Etienne, carrying about 1 million passengers a year. Routes from St Paul station to Brignais, Sain Bel and Lozanne provide interchange with metro Line D at Gorge de Loup.

New platforms at Peruche now allow a through north-south service and frequencies have been improved on all routes.

UPDATED

Driverless train at Parilly on metro Line D   **1997**

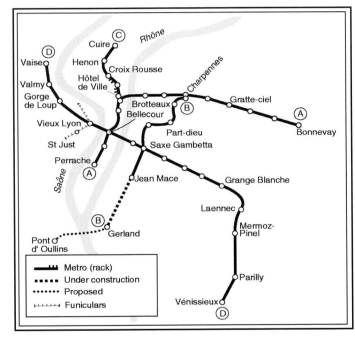

Lyons metro
0045360

MADRAS (CHENNAI)

Population: 5.4 million

Public transport: Most public transport needs are met by bus services provided by metropolitan division of State Transport Corporation which was split into two operations in 1994. District services division also runs suburban routes. Suburban rail service provided by Indian Railways on three routes, with initial 9.2 km section of regional metro completed in 1997. Local paratransit

Metropolitan Transport I

Metropolitan Transport Corporation Ltd (Chennai Division I) (formerly Pallavan Transport Corporation Ltd)
Pallavan House, Anna Salai, Madras 600002, India
Tel: (+91 44) 56 60 63   Fax: (+91 44) 56 61 00
Managing Director: Dr M Koteeswaran
Staff: 11,836

Current situation: Over the past 20 years several infrastructure works have been carried out by the Metropolitan Development Authority, with World Bank loans. MTCL-I has augmented its fleet by 1,800 vehicles over a seven-year period, financed by the World Bank. It has introduced limited-stop services on all main routes, and made other improvements, but it has struggled to cope with growth in demand averaging 9 per cent a year.

Developments: Under a reorganisation scheme, Pallavan

Transport Corporation has been renamed as Metropolitan Transport Corporation (Chennai Division I) Ltd.

Bus (metropolis services)
Passenger journeys: (1994/95) 657 million
(1995/96) 706.3 million
(1997/98) 767.4 million
Vehicle-km: (1994/95) 98.9 million
(1995/96) 110.2 million
(1997/98) 118.9 million

Number of routes: 254
Route length: 5,586 km

Fleet: 1,515 vehicles	
Ashok Leyland single-deck	1,247
Evan battery-powered midibus	4
Others	264

In peak service: 1,092
Average age of fleet: 4.6 years
On order: 100 buses

Most intensive service: 3 min
One-person operation: None except few buses on airport and point-to-point service
Fare collection: Payment to conductor
Fare structure: Stages; monthly season tickets; tokens
Fare evasion control: Random inspection; penalty

Operational control: Over 400 route inspectors (checking and timekeeping); over 80 sets of mobile radio
Arrangements for elderly/disabled: Some seats reserved; free passes for blind and disabled at operator's cost
Operating costs financed by: Fares 98.7 per cent, other commercial sources 1.5 per cent

Metropolitan Transport II

Metropolitan Transport Corporation Ltd (Chennai Division II) (formerly Ambedkar Transport Corporation Ltd)
4 Anderson Street, Ayanavaram, Madras 600023
Tel: (+91 44) 61 72 19   Fax: (+91 44) 644 34 32
Managing Director: Dr M Koteeswaran
Staff: 10,209

Current situation: Under a reorganisation, Ambedkar Transport Corporation Ltd (Chennai Division II) has been renamed as Metropolitan Transport Corporation.

Bus (metropolis services)
Passenger journeys: (1997/98) 725.5 million
Vehicle-km: (1997/98) 96.8 million

Fleet: 1,330 vehicles
Average age of fleet: 4.6 years

Operating costs financed by: Fares 93.7 per cent, other commercial earnings 13.4 per cent

SR

Southern Railway
Park Town, Madras 600003
Tel: (+91 44) 56 31 57   Fax: (+91 44) 535 14 39

Type of operation: Suburban heavy rail

Passenger journeys: (1993/94) 213 million
(1994/95) 192 million
(1995/96) 199 million

Current situation: SR runs suburban services over three routes electrified at 25 kV 50 Hz, out of Madras Central and Beach stations to Gummipundi (46 km) and Tiruvallur (41.6 km) on broad-gauge, and from Madras Beach to Tambaram/Chengalpattu (60 km) on metre-gauge. Principal traffic is on the section to Tambaram (29 km), which carries 340,000 passengers daily. On this section, SR has been operating the country's first all-woman emu since October 1997.

Some 210 broad-gauge and 325 metre-gauge suburban emu trains run daily. The railway handles an estimated 20 per cent of urban travel in Chennai.

Developments: In addition to capacity improvements already completed, a broad-gauge line between Madras Beach and Tambaram has been commissioned as part of extensive gauge-conversion work. Remodelling is in progress of Madras Central suburban terminal.

Rolling stock: 497 emu cars
ICF metre-gauge	M75 T192
ICF broad-gauge	M69 T161

Regional metro (RTS)

Under construction
Metropolitan Transport Project (Railways)
Periar EVR High Road, Madras 600008
Tel: (+91 44) 532 29 53

Current situation: The initial section of a city circle route from Madras Beach to Luz became fully operational in October 1997 with opening of the Chepauk—Luz portion. The 2.7 km from Beach to Park Town with three stations is on surface and the remaining 6.2 km with five stations is elevated; electrification is at 25 kV.

Interrunning with the existing broad-gauge suburban network is planned, and it is expected that the line will contribute to reducing traffic congestion in the city.

Extension of this line by 10.3 km to Velachery at a cost of Rs6 billion has been taken up by SR in co-ordination with Tamil Nadu state government which has agreed to bear two-thirds of the cost, besides providing government land available along the alignment free of cost.

Further plans, for which feasibility and other studies have been completed, propose a rapid transit line extending 35 km from Taramani to Villivakkam (on the broad-gauge route to Tiruvallur (see above)) and Tiruvottiyur on the Gummipundi line. This would form an inner circle rail system.

A spur is also proposed linking Anna Nagar with Villivakkam, to permit direct running to Madras of emus serving the growing residential area around Anna Nagar and so relieve bus services on the main road into central Madras.

UPDATED

MADRID

Population: 2.8 million, conurbation 5.1 million
Public transport: The Consorcio Regional de Transportes oversees public transport in the autonomous region of Madrid, which includes the city and surrounding conurbation. Main bus services provided by a municipal undertaking, while the metro is jointly owned by the municipality and the region and operated under a concession from CRTM. Suburban rail services run by Spanish National Railways (RENFE); some private suburban bus operations

CRTM

Consorcio Regional de Transportes de Madrid (CRTM)
Plaza Descubridor Diego de Ordás 3, E-28003 Madrid, Spain
Tel: (+34 91) 580 45 32   Fax: (+34 91) 580 46 34
Managing Director: José Ignacio Iturbe

Current situation: CRTM was set up in 1985; it includes representatives from the central, regional and municipal government authorities, as well as from trades unions, private bus operators and users' associations. The organisation has overall responsibility for policy and co-ordination of urban and suburban public transport provision in the autonomous region of Madrid, except for suburban rail, control of which remains with RENFE.

CRTM maintains contractual agreements with private bus operators to provide suburban services on a local monopoly basis. This may take the form of own-risk operation, guaranteed revenues, contracted price or management contract. Metro infrastructure planning, bus lanes, interchange facilities, planning and allocation of transport services, control of service levels, fares and ticketing policy, information, marketing and public image all fall within the competence of CRTM. Monthly or annual zonal travel cards, used by 58 per cent of passengers, are issued, along with other heavily discounted passes for students and the elderly.

EMT

Empresa Municipal de Transportes de Madrid SA (EMT)
Alcantara 24, E-28006 Madrid
Tel: (+34 91) 406 88 00   Fax: (+34 91) 406 88 01
President: José Ignacio Echeverría Echániz
Director General: Tomás Burgaleta Hernando
Staff: 6,233

Current situation: EMT was formed in 1971 to take over service provision from the former private operator. The company operates urban buses in the Madrid municipality and also a special service to Barajas airport. It is also responsible for a parking administration in central Madrid.

Bus

Passenger boardings: (1995) 530 million
(1996) 551 million
(1997) 555 million

Vehicle-km: (1995) 89.5 million
(1996) 91.7 million
(1997) 93.9 million

Number of routes: 174
Route length: (One way) 1,431 km
On priority right-of-way: 96 km

Fleet: 1,820 vehicles
Pegaso 6038 Wilson (1985/86)	245
Pegaso 6038 Voith (1985/86)	81
Pegaso 5317 (1987/88)	109
Pegaso 6424 (1988-94)	624
Pegaso 6425A articulated (1991/94)	73
DAF SB220 Urban (1988/89/91/94/97)	259
DAF SB220 Express (1988)	15
DAF SB220 Airport (1989)	9
Iveco 5522 Standard (1994)	5
Iveco 5522 CNG-powered (1995/96/97)	32
MAN NL low-floor (1994-97)	98
Iveco 623E/II (1995-97)	167
Mercedes O405N low-floor (1995-97)	95
Renault PR118 articulated (1995)	8

In peak service: 1,692
Average age of fleet: 6.8 years
On order: 29 MAN NL low-floor, 46 Mercedes O405 low-floor, 40 Renault Citybus low-floor, 160 Iveco CityClass plus 18 CNG-powered, and 136 MAN 14220 HOCL low-floor

Most intensive service: Peak 2-8 min, off-peak 4-12 min
One-person operation: All routes
Fare collection: Prepurchase 10-journey tickets validated on board or pass, or payment to driver
Fare structure: Flat; prepurchase 'Bono bus' 10-journey tickets, monthly and annual CRTM passes cover urban/suburban buses and rail
Fares collected on board: 5.1 per cent (63.8 per cent use CRTM travelcards, 31.1 per cent EMT passes and 10-trip tickets)
Fare evasion control: Roving inspectors; minimal fraud attributed to widespread use of discounted travelcards
Operational control: Inspectors/14 mobile radio cars/integral/elemental SAE
Arrangements for elderly/disabled: Low-floor buses used on routes with high proportion of elderly passengers
Average peak-hour speed: 14.7 km/h
Bus priority: Extensive system of central area bus lanes totalling 18.2 km solely for buses, 78.2 km also available for taxis
Operating costs financed by: Fares 81.6 per cent, subsidy/grants 24.7 per cent, other commercial sources 2.4 per cent

Developments: An electronic traffic management system is being developed involving 800 vehicles linked to a central monitoring station. Buses will have traffic light priority at junctions and real-time information on bus arrival times will be available at major stops. A new system of ticket validation has been installed on all buses.

Low-floor Mercedes-Benz O405N bus on Route C (circular) (Bill Luke)   *1999*/0038886

In 1996, EMT sought tenders from private operators to run some outer-suburban routes.

Metro de Madrid

Metro de Madrid SA
Cavanilles 58, E-28007 Madrid
Tel: (+34 91) 552 49 00/84 00   Fax: (+34 91) 552 39 52
General Manager: R Lopez Mancisidor del Rio
Staff: 5,568

Type of operation: Full metro, first line opened 1919

Passenger journeys: (1993) 391 million
(1994) 392 million
(1995) 397 million
Car-km: (1993) 82.3 million
(1994) 86 million
(1995) 90.2 million

Route length: 120.8 km
Number of lines: 11
Number of stations: 164
Gauge: 1,445 mm
Track: 45/54 kg/m rail
Max gradient: 5 per cent
Min curve radius: 90 m
Tunnel: Mostly bored
Electrification: 600 V DC, overhead

Service: Peak 2-4 min, off-peak 3-5 min
First/last train: 06.00/01.30
Fare structure: Flat, single and 10-journey tickets; CRTM monthly and annual travelcards integrated with urban and suburban buses, and suburban railways
One-person operation: All lines
Signalling: CTC and ATP on all lines, ATO on Lines 1, 3, 6, 7, 8, and 9
Surveillance: CCTV at all stations
Operating costs financed by: Fares 51 per cent, CRTM grants 49 per cent

Rolling stock: 1,142 cars

CAF 300 (1961/82)	M40 T12
CAF 1000 (1964/68)	M134 T18
CAF 5000 (1974/94)	M332 T12
CAF 2000 (1984/94)	M262 T250
CAF/Alstom/Siemens/Adtranz 6000 (1998/99)	M76 T6

Developments: CRTM has produced a Metro Development Plan for the years 1994-2001, with the twin objectives of extending the metro to areas currently unserved and improving connections between existing lines in the city centre. The plan envisages completion of 10 sections totalling 30 km by mid-1999, with 31 new stations. Longest of these is extension of Line 7 from Avenida de America to Lacoma (10.7 km) opened in stages in late 1998.

A 20 km single-track suburban extension of Line 9 from its new terminus at Vicálvaro to Arganda is under construction. This is being funded, built and operated on concession by a consortium known as Transportes Ferroviarios de Madrid comprising Metro de Madrid and several contractors. The concession will run until 2020.

Also line from Mar de Cristal on Line 4 to Barajas airport, 4.5 km, for 1999 opening.

RENFE

Spanish National Railways (RENFE)
Avenida Ciudad de Barcelona 6, E-28007 Madrid
Tel: (+34 91) 506 62 15   Fax: (+34 91) 506 73 26
Director, Madrid: Cecilio Gömez Comino
Staff: 1,349

Type of operation: Suburban heavy rail

Passenger journeys: (1993) 142.5 million
(1994) 147.7 million
(1995) 171.8 million (new method of calculation)
(1996) 180.1 million

Current situation: Suburban services are operated on 10 routes or groups of routes totalling 278 km with 118 stations, from terminals at Príncipe Pío, Atocha and Chamartin, the last two linked by a cross-city tunnel; 1,668 mm gauge, electrified 3 kV DC overhead (except for one line, 19 km, metre-gauge, electrified 1.5 kV DC overhead). Most trains run half-hourly off-peak, but

Low-floor MAN NL bus   *1999*/0038887

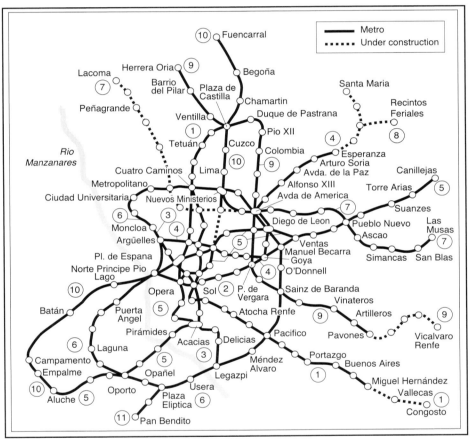

Madrid metro   0045361

Rebuilt Class 440/470 emu of RENFE at Vilaverde Baja, south of Atocha   *1996*

average 10 minutes in the peak, when some inner-suburban sections have metro-style service.

Developments: Patronage has more than doubled since the mid-1980s and is expected to grow each year until the end of the century as rising house prices in the city force more people to commute from developing satellite towns.

As part of the strategic plan for suburban rail expansion in the period 1996-2001, major additions to the network are in progress. New lines are under construction to serve Alcobendas and San Sebastián de los Reyes, and there will be a link to Barajas airport. Pta98.4 billion is being spent on infrastructure to segregate suburban trains from long-distance and freight traffic wherever possible, and Pta34.8 billion is earmarked for new trains. There will also

be some new stations on existing lines, with the aim of providing rail service for all communities of more than 30,000 population.

Over Pta1 billion was spent on station modernisation in 1996, and more automatic barriers were installed; introduction of smartcards is being considered. It is proposed to order another batch of Class 447 emus, and existing Class 440 trains are to be refurbished.

Line 7 has been extended to Canal, which is part of a further extension to Pitis.

Rolling stock: 696 emu cars

Class 440 three-car emu	M21 T42
Class 446 three-car emu	M286 T143
Class 470 three-car emu	M24 T48
Class 450 six-car bi-level emu	M40 T80
Class 442 two-car emu metre-gauge	M6 T6

Private bus

Passenger journeys: (1993) 169.1 million
(1994) 174.7 million
(1995) 191.6 million
Vehicle-km: (1993) 75.5 million
(1994) 78 million
(1995) 89.4 million

Current situation: A total of 41 private operators provide monopoly services, either urban routes in the outer municipalities or interurban within the conurbation. All services are co-ordinated by CRTM.

Main operators are De Blas, Martín, Autocares Urbanos del Sur, Llorente, Interbus and Continental Auto.

Number of routes: 186 suburban, 7 night and 45 urban (in municipalities other than Madrid)
Route length: (One way) 14,436 km

Fleet: 958 vehicles
Pegaso	447
Scania	263
Setra	16
Volvo	209
Others	23

Average age of fleet: 5.6 years

Most intensive service: 3 min
One-person operation: All routes
Fare structure: Zonal or distance-based, according to route; CRTM monthly and annual travelcards integrated with urban and suburban buses, and suburban rail
Fare collection: Driver sells single tickets; prepurchase 10-journey tickets, CRTM travelcards
Bus Priority: 12.5 km exclusive bus and HOV double lanes in northwest corridor, also 4 km bus-only lane
Operating costs financed by: Fares 100 per cent

Renault articulated bus on Route 27 at Place Castilla (Peter Newman)   **1999**/0045311   **UPDATED**

MAGDEBURG

Population: 262,000
Public transport: Bus, tramway and ferry services provided by municipal company; S-Bahn operated by DB; regional bus services

MVB

Magdeburger Verkehrsbetriebe AG (MVB)
Otto-von-Guericke Strasse 25, D-3910 Magdeburg, Germany
Tel: (+49 391) 54 80   Fax: (+49 391) 543 00 46
www: http://mvb.magdeburg.de
Directors: Dr-Ing Herbert Preil (Commercial)
    Hans-Dieter Hakke (Technical)
Staff: 1,044

Passenger journeys: (1995) 63.2 million
(1996) 61 million
(1997) 58.1 million

Operating costs financed by: Fares 48 per cent, subsidy/grants 52 per cent

Developments: A co-operation agreement concluded between MVB, DB and bus operators from four surrounding counties in 1996 envisages introduction of joint timetables and tariffs. Discussions have taken place about the possibility of creating a regional transport authority (verkehrsverbund) for Magdeburg and its surrounding local authorities.

In September 1998, the first step towards a common fare system was taken with the mutual recognition of

season tickets for tram and bus journeys in the greater Magdeburg area.

Bus

Vehicle-km: (1995) 3.2 million
(1996) 3.4 million
(1997) 3.5 million

Number of routes: 11
Route length: 83 km

Fleet: 59 buses
MAN NL202 low-floor	12
MAN NG272 low-floor articulated	10
Mercedes O405N low-floor	24
Mercedes O405GN low-floor articulated	13

In peak service: 47

Most intensive service: 10 min
One-person operation: All routes
Fare collection: By driver
Fare structure: Flat transferable daily, weekly, monthly and annual passes, also valid in certain other cities by mutual agreement; reduced price for passes after 09.00; surcharge for onboard tickets
Arrangements for elderly/disabled: Free travel for disabled, reimbursed by government
Integration with other modes: Through-ticketing (passes only) with DB regional services and connecting urban buses in Burg, Genthin and Haldensleben
Average distance between stops: 570 m
Average speed: 20.7 km/h

Tramway
Type of operation: Conventional tramway

Car-km: (1995) 13.2 million
(1996) 11.2 million
(1997) 11.2 million

Magdeburg low-floor tram on Line 10 (Quintus Vosman)   **1999**/0045315

Number of routes: 9

Route length: 59 km
Number of stops: 116
Gauge: 1,435 mm
Minimum curve radius: 30 m
Electrification: 600 V DC, overhead

Service: Peak 10 min
First/last car: 04.15/23.00
Average distance between stops: 540 m
Average speed: 19.2 km/h

Rolling stock: 235 cars
ČKD Tatra T4D/B4D 4-axle (1968/86)   M82 T25
  (modernised 1991/94)   M64 T22
ČKD Tatra T6A2 4-axle (modernised 1995/97)   M11 T6
LHB NGT8D 8-axle low-floor articulated (1994/95) M25
In peak service: 227
On order: Further 28 NGT8D cars from Adtranz/DWA/
LHB for 1999/2000 delivery

Developments: New workshops under construction for 1999 completion. Tatra cars are now programmed to remain in service until 2015, as fewer new cars were ordered than originally planned. Similarly, the use of trailer cars is being progressively abandoned.

Several tram stops have been fitted with real-time information displays showing the actual arrival time of the next tram. Extension of Route 5 under construction.

Ferry
Current situation: Three vessels ply two short cross-Elbe routes and operate excursions, carrying around 100,000 passengers a year.

DB
Deutsche Bahn AG, Geschäftsbereich Nahverkehr
Regionalbereich Sachsen-Anhalt
Ernst-Kamieth Strasse 2, D-06112 Halle

Tel: (+49 345) 215 33 31   Fax: (+49 345) 215 17 05
Manager: Thomas Hoffmann

Current situation: S-Bahn services from Zielitz and Haldensleben feed into a single cross-city route extending to Schönebeck. Four fare zones.

Regional bus
Current situation: Services radiating from the city are provided by several independent and local government operators.

UPDATED

MALAGA
Population: 600,000
Public transport: Local bus and midibus services provided by municipal company, with longer-distance services to neighbouring resorts in the hands of private operators; local rail service; light rail network planned

EMT
Empresa Malaguena de Transportes SAM
Camino de San Rafael s/n, E-29006 Malaga, Spain
Tel: (+34 95) 235 72 12   Fax: (+34 95) 235 88 07
Director General: Rafael Fernandez Barrera
Director of Operations: Manual Fernandez Andrade
Staff: 605

Developments: Introduction of split-shift working by drivers has allowed increased capacity at peak periods and stimulated an additional 1.5 million journeys. Routes which terminate at Muelle de Heredia may be diverted into the city centre, with the aim of increasing their patronage.

EMT has begun to replace its oldest vehicles and augment the fleet to meet growing demand, with delivery of 68 buses in 1996/97. The electronic vehicle management system Siclic, which uses satellite tracking, was fully implemented in 1997.

Bus
Passenger journeys: (1993) 33.4 million
(1994) 34.8 million
(1996) 34.7 million
Vehicle-km: (1993) 7.7 million
(1994) 8.6 million
(1996) 8.5 million

Number of routes: 35
Route length: 238 km

Fleet: 200 buses
Pegaso 6038 citybus (1984/85/86)	59
Pegaso 6424 (1991/93)	31
Pegaso 5317 midibus (1990/91/92)	28
Iveco 623E2 (1996)	21
Renault Citybus (1996/97)	35
Volvo B10M articulated (1997/98)	9
Mercedes O405 (1998)	10
Others	7

Average age of fleet: 6 years

Most intensive service: 10 min
Fare structure: Flat
Fares collected on board: 31.1 per cent
Arrangements for elderly/disabled: Special Route 48 operated for disabled
Operating costs financed by: Fares 64.6 per cent, other commercial sources 1.6 per cent, subsidy/grants 33.8 per cent

RENFE
Spanish National Railways (RENFE)
Avenida Ciudad de Barcelona 8, E-28007 Madrid
Tel: (+34 91) 506 61 27   Fax: (+34 91) 506 69 39
Managing Director, Suburban: Abelado Carrillo Jiménez
Director, Malaga: Rafael Rodríguez Rebollo
Staff: 122 (Malaga area)

Type of operation: Local railway

Passenger journeys: (1994) 7.3 million
(1995) 7.3 million
(1996) 7 million

Current situation: Electric trains (3 kV DC) run half-hourly from Malaga Centro-Alameda to Fuengirola and Alora, two routes totalling 68 km with 24 stations. A 30 min service runs to the airport on the Fuengirola line, which carries heavy tourist traffic.
Developments: A rolling programme of investment in stations is in progress, including provision of ticket machines and barriers to reduce fraud.

Rolling stock: 6 three-car emus

Intermodal transport plan
Current situation: An intermodal transport plan for the city covering the period 1995-2007 has been approved by the Andalucia regional government. Pta113 billion has been allocated for infrastructure works (90 per cent) and new rolling stock. Upgrading of RENFE's Fuengirola line will involve four-tracking of the Malaga—Los Prados section and selective double-tracking elsewhere, permitting operation of a 15 minute service. There will be improved access to the airport, and a new intermodal terminal created at Malaga central station. Pta2.2 billion will be spent on new trains. Integrated ticketing is to be introduced.

The plan also calls for development of a four-line light rail network running on reserved track. Initially, Line 1 will be operated by buses sharing reserved lanes with interurban services. Lines 2, 3 and 4 have been accorded priority. Line 2 will run to the north of the city, where demand is put at 94,500 passengers daily. Line 3 will link the hospital and university in the northwest (40,000 daily), while Line 4 will serve the western suburbs (54,000 daily).

Pegaso of EMT on Route 24 to Prados at Arroyo del Cuarto (Bill Luke)   **1999**/0045310

UPDATED

MALMÖ

Population: 234,000

Public transport: Bus services provided by private operator Linjebuss under contract from the regional transport authority, Länstrafiken Malmöhus. Suburban and interurban bus and rail services also operated under contract

Linjebuss

Linjebuss Sverige AB
PO Box 3054, SE-200 22 Malmö, Sweden
Tel: (+46 40) 34 30 00   Fax: (+46 40) 30 32 23
Managing Director: Ragnar Norbäck
Traffic Manager: Bo Fröjd
Staff: 630

Current situation: In 1991 the former municipal operator Malmö Lokaltrafik became a limited company in the ownership of the city. In 1993 the contract for operation of city services was put out to tender and awarded to Linjebuss. As a result, Linjebuss purchased ML, and commenced operations at the beginning of 1994. It continues as the operator of bus services under contract from the transport authority Länstrafiken Malmöhus, which acts as purchaser of all public transport.

Five levels of service are provided — a Head network, linking residential areas, local shopping centres and the city centre; an Express network running mainly at commuting times; a Feeder network providing connections into Head and Express services from sparsely populated areas; Service-Bus operated by low-floor minibuses for elderly and slightly disabled passengers, running on special routes that pass close to main entrances of shops and offices to minimise walking distances; and a Special service for major events and festivals.

Bus

Passenger journeys: (1992) 26 million
(1993) 20.3 million
(1994) 20.3 million
Vehicle-km: (1990) 11 million
(1992) 10.5 million
(1994) 10.3 million

Number of routes: 35
Route length: 566 km

Fleet: 195 vehicles

Scania CR112 (1981)	26
Volvo B10R (1983/84)	33
Scania CR112 CNG-powered (1984)	1
Scania N112 (1984/86)	42
Scania CN113 (1988)	7
Scania CN113 CNG-powered (1988)	9
Neoplan N4007 (1989)	5
Mercedes O405G articulated (1990)	10
Scania CN113 (1991)	8
Mercedes O405G articulated (1992)	7
Scania CN113 (1992)	10
Scania CN113AL articulated (1992)	6
Scania CN113AL articulated (1994)	1
Volvo B10BLE CNG-powered (1995)	30

In peak service: 1,719

Most intensive service: 10 min
One-person operation: All routes
Fare collection: Payment to driver, or prepurchase magnetic cards (also sold on board) and monthly passes
Fare structure: Flat; prepurchase cards
Fares collected on board: 45.3 per cent of journeys, 61 per cent of total fares
Fare evasion control: Inspectors
Operational control: Route inspectors/mobile radio
Arrangements for elderly/disabled: 2 seats with folding arms reserved on each bus for disabled passengers. Buses with 100 mm kneeling capability and low split step arrangement. Low-floor minibus Service-Bus network operates route with stops close to entrances, reducing walking distance
Average peak-hour speed: 19.1 km/h
Average distance between stops: 400 m
Integration with other modes: One route connects with ferry services to Denmark
Operating costs financed by: Fares 50 per cent, other commercial sources 6 per cent, subsidy/grants 44 per cent
Subsidy from: Local taxes

SSK

Sydvästra Skaånes Kommunalförbund
PO Box 2500, SE-200 12 Malmö
Tel: (+46 40) 34 22 49
Transport Manager: Lennert Serder

Type of operation: Suburban heavy rail

Passenger journeys: 4 million (annual)

Current situation: SSK contracts operation to Swedish State Railways (SJ) of suburban services over three routes totalling 130 km from Malmö to Höör, Landskrona and Helsingborg, electrified 15 kV 16⅔ Hz. About hourly off-peak, half-hourly Malmö—Lund (17 km). Zonal and monthly travelcards available for half or all system, monthly cards accepted on buses. Fares contribute 47 per cent of income, local subsidy 53 per cent.

Rolling stock: 18 two-car emus
ASEA X10 (1983/85/88)   M18 T18

Scania 113 of Linjebuss at the Stock Exchange

1996   *VERIFIED*

MANCHESTER

Population: City 451,000, county area 2.6 million
Public transport: Bus services in Greater Manchester metropolitan area are provided by 50 private companies operating about 800 vehicles, alongside the two former GM Buses companies which are now subsidiaries of large UK bus groups. The PTE invites tenders for supply of loss-making and socially desirable bus services which are not provided by commercial operators. Light rail and local rail systems

First Manchester

First Manchester Ltd
Wallshaw Street, Oldham OL1 3TR
Tel: (+44 161) 627 29 29   Fax: (+44 161) 627 58 45
Chair: Robbie Duncan
Managing Director: Mike Mitchell
Commercial Director: Rodney Dickinson
Operations Director: David Kaye
Engineering Director: Richard Noble
Finance Director: Rob Turner
Staff: 2,200

Current situation: Formed by the break-up of GM Buses in 1994, the company was purchased by its staff through an employee share ownership plan. Operates extensive services throughout north Manchester from five depots. The company was acquired by FirstGroup in 1996.
Developments: Over 100 new buses were delivered after take FirstGroup over, including low-floor single-deckers. 'Gold Standard' upgrading, with customer charter and new vehicles, is being introduced on a corridor-by-corridor basis. Operations and 51 vehicles of Timeline Travel of Leigh were acquired in 1998. Articulated buses introduced in 1999.

Bus

Passenger journeys: (1994/95) 96 million
(1996/97) 87.5 million
(1997/98) 82 million

FirstGroup's Volvo low-floor articulated buses entered service with First Manchester in 1999
(Andrew Jarosz)

1999/0045304

Number of routes: 500

Fleet: 887 vehicles

Leyland Lynx	4
Leyland Tiger single-deck	14
Volvo B10M Citybus single-deck	1
Volvo B6 single-deck	38
Volvo B10B single-deck	55
Dennis Dart single-deck	50
Volvo B10L low-floor single-deck	11
Volvo B6LE low-floor single-deck	16
Volvo B10BLE low-floor single-deck	61
Optare Excel low-floor single-deck	10
Dennis Dart SLF low-floor single-deck	110
Leyland Atlantean double-deck	160
Daimler Fleetline double-deck	13
MCW Metrobus double-deck	122
Leyland Olympian double-deck	165
Volvo Citybus double-deck	13
Iveco 59-12 minibus	4
Mercedes minibus	40

On order: 17 Volvo B10BLE low-floor single-deck, 15 Scania L94 low-floor single-deck, 15 Volvo B10LA articulated low-floor single-deck

Most intensive service: 5 min
One-person operation: 100 per cent
Fare collection: Payment on bus with ticket issue by driver
Fare structure: Stage, multijourney ticket; range of prepurchase weekly passes including add-on to rail season tickets and all modes
Fares collected on board: 89 per cent
Fare evasion control: Revenue inspectors charging higher fares

Arrangements for elderly/disabled: On ordinary services low flat fare charged; some single-decks have wheelchair ramps; all new buses are low-floor types
Average peak-hour speed: In bus lanes, 24 km/h; in mixed traffic, 18 km/h
Bus priority: 8 km of bus lanes; turning ban lifted at certain traffic lights; bus-only use of several main streets in city and surrounding town centres, generally during shopping hours
Integration with other modes: Co-ordination with supported rail services and light rail at major interchanges, and smaller feeder schemes.Intergrated ticketing with other bus, train and tram operators.Combined operator telephone enquiry service
Operating costs financed by: Fares 72 per cent, concessionary fares support 16 per cent, other commercial sources 12 per cent

First Manchester Wright-bodied Volvo in Gold Service livery picks up in Piccadilly, Manchester (Andrew Jarosz)   *1999*/0045307

Stagecoach Manchester

Greater Manchester Buses South Limited
Daw Bank, Stockport SK3 0DU
Tel: (+44 161) 273 33 77   Fax: (+44 161) 276 25 95
Managing Director: Mark Threapleton
Engineering Director: Paul Sumner
Finance Director: A Fuller
Operations Director: Chris Bowles
Staff: 1,700

Current situation: GMS was formed when GM Buses was split in 1994. Purchased by staff through an employee share ownership plan, the company was sold in 1996 to Stagecoach. It operates in south and central Manchester.
Developments: Since acquisition by Stagecoach, over 350 new vehicles have entered service. New fare initiatives introduced in 1996/97 included low-fare 'Magic Buses' on the Wilmslow Road and Stockport Road corridors, and a general Megarider weekly ticket valid on all services. Low-floor single-decks and three-axle Dennis Dragon double-decks imported from Kenya were introduced in 1998.

Bus
Passenger journeys: (1995/96) 71.8 million
(1996/97) 79 million
(1997/98) 84 million
Vehicle-km: (1995/96) 35.7 million
(1996/97) 38.5 million
(1997/98) 40.2 million

Number of routes: 200

Fleet: 637 vehicles

Leyland National single-deck	5
Volvo B6 single-deck	19
Volvo B10M single-deck	196
Volvo B6BLE low-floor single-deck	24
Volvo B10BLE low-floor single-deck	5
Leyland Atlantean double-deck	18
MCW Metrobus double-deck	7
Leyland Olympian double-deck	139
Volvo Olympian double-deck	80
Dennis Dragon double-deck	10
Scania double-deck	5
Dennis Dominator double-deck	40
Renault/Dodge minibus	3
Mercedes minibus	83
Dennis Javelin coach	2
Leyland Tiger coach	1

In peak service: 540
On order: 80 MAN/Alexander low-floor single-deck buses

Most intensive service: 3 min
One-person operation: 100 per cent
Fare collection: Payment on bus with ticket issue by driver
Fare structure: Stage, multijourney ticket; range of prepurchase weekly passes including add-on to rail season tickets and all modes
Fares collected on board: 92 per cent
Fare evasion control: Revenue inspectors charging higher fares
Arrangements for elderly/disabled: On ordinary services low flat fare charged. Semi-fixed route accessible services in the Stockport area operate under the 'Localine' identity; vehicles designed for passengers with impaired mobility, with wheelchair lifts
Average peak-hour speed: In bus lanes, 24 km/h; in mixed traffic, 18 km/h
Bus priority: 8 km of bus lanes; turning ban lifted at certain traffic lights; bus-only use of several main streets in city and surrounding town centres, generally during shopping hours
Integration with other modes: Co-ordination with supported rail services and light rail at major interchanges, and smaller feeder schemes. Integrated ticketing with other bus, train and tram operators. Combined operator telephone enquiry service.
Operating costs financed by: Fares 80 per cent, concessionary fares support 18 per cent, other commercial sources 2 per cent

Stagecoach Manchester has imported 20 three-axle Dennis Dragons for Magic Bus services in Manchester (Andrew Jarosz)   *1999*/0045305

Arriva North West

Arriva North West Ltd
73 Ormskirk Road, Aintree, Liverpool L9 5AE
Tel: (+44 151) 522 28 80   Fax: (+44 151) 525 95 56
Managing Director: Bob Hind

Current situation: Merseyside-based company took over operations of Bee Line in Manchester and Star Line of Knutsford. Extensive network of services is operated in Wigan, Leigh and south Manchester from depots in central Manchester, Wythenshawe and Haydock. Some 200 vehicles are operated in the Greater Manchester area.

Stagecoach Ribble

Stagecoach (North West) Ltd
Frenchwood Avenue, Preston PR1 4LU
Tel: (+44 1772) 25 47 54   Fax: (+44 1772) 25 83 14
Managing Director: Michael Chambers
Staff: 900

Current situation: Services are predominantly in Lancashire, operated from six depots, and in north Manchester from a depot in Bolton.

Fleet: 466 vehicles
Double-deck	145
Single-deck	160
Dual-purpose	36
Coach	5
Minibus	120

Mayne

A Mayne & Son Ltd
974 Ashton New Road, Manchester M11 4PD
Tel: (+44 161) 223 20 35   Fax: (+44 161) 231 79 80
Managing Director: Steven Mayne
General Manager: Graydon Thompson
Staff: 98

Current situation: This old-established family firm expanded its services in 1986 and now runs commercial and tendered routes in Manchester, Tameside, Trafford and parts of Derbyshire.

Bus
Passenger journeys: (1993/94) 3.1 million
Vehicle-km: (1993/94) 3.7 million

Number of routes: 9

Fleet: 59 vehicles
Leyland/Daimler Fleetline double-deck	10
Scania double-deck	16
Leyland Leopard coaches	7
Leyland Tiger coach	6
Scania single-deck	2
Dennis Falcon single-deck	1
Dennis Dart single-deck	5

Scania N113 on Mayne's Premier Service route to Mossley   *1997*

Bova coach	4
Dennis Javelin coach	4
DAF coach	2
Volvo B10M coach	2

Finglands

Finglands Coachways Ltd
261 Wilmslow Road, Rusholme, Manchester M14 5JL
Tel: (+44 161) 224 33 41   Fax: (+44 161) 257 31 54
Managing Director: Graham Rayner
Staff: 55

Current situation: Acquired in 1992 by the EYMS Group of Hull and has subsequently upgraded its fleet; 33 routes are operated.

Fleet: 59 vehicles
Leyland Atlantean double-deck	20
MCW Metrobus double-deck	5
Volvo Citybus double-deck	1
Volvo Olympian double-deck	10
Volvo B10M single-deck	6
Leyland Leopard single-deck	3
Leyland Tiger single-deck	2
Minibus	1
Coach	11

Other operators

Current situation: Manchester has around 50 operators running services either commercially or on contract to the PTE from both outside and within the area (see below).

Former National Bus subsidiary which operates into the area is Trent from Buxton and Derby. Urban operators with services in the area include Kingfisher of Huddersfield, Blackburn Transport, Rossendale Transport, and Warrington Transport.

Smaller private companies with stage services include Dennis's Coaches of Ashton, Jim Stones of Leigh, Stevensons of Macclesfield, Bullock of Cheadle, Bluebird of Moston, J P Executive of Middleton, Bu-Val of Rochdale, Vales of Manchester, Pennine of Ashton, Blue Bus of Horwich, Atherton Bus, B&D of Leigh, Checkmate of Ashton, Springfield of Wigan, Pioneer of Littleborough, Glossopdale, UK North of Glossop, Universal Bus of Rochdale and Green Triangle of Leigh.

Greater Manchester PTE

Greater Manchester Passenger Transport Executive
9 Portland Street, Manchester M60 1HX
Tel: (+44 161) 242 60 00   Fax: (+44 161) 228 32 91
Director General: Chris Mulligan
Rail Services Manager: Bob Woolvin

Current situation: The Greater Manchester Passenger Transport Authority is the local government body with responsibility for public transport. It has representatives from 10 district councils. Its policies are implemented by GMPTE.

GMPTE is responsible for contracting socially necessary bus services and supporting the local rail service. It also owns and is responsible for development of the Metrolink light rail system. GMPTE and the Authority are also committed to developing accessible transport, funding fully accessible door-to-door services, as well as providing grants to improve the accessibility of all bus services. GMPTE administers the concessionary fares scheme allowing participants either free or reduced rate travel. It is responsible for bus stations and on-street infrastructure, provision of information, and promotion of public transport.
Developments: A Metrolink extension to Salford Quays and Eccles is under construction (see below), and other lines have been approved. Improvements to the heavy rail network are being promoted, along with high-quality integrated services across all modes.

Contracted bus (GMPTE services)
Current situation: Some 50 operators compete for passengers. GMPTE subsidises services that the Authority deems socially necessary. About 1,000 contracts are issued annually, accounting for 13 per cent of total bus-km. Multi-operator weekly, monthly and annual passes are provided by Greater Manchester Travelcard Ltd, owned by the bus operators and GMPTE. Limited multimodal tickets are also available, and daily multi-modal and multi-operator tickets were introduced in September 1998.
Developments: GMPTE is developing proposals for a guided busway. In partnership with local authorities and operators, a 200 km network of 'quality bus routes' is

Bullock of Cheadle operates the only two low-floor double-deck buses in Manchester. Optare Delta picks up at Greater Manchester town hall (Andrew Jarosz)   *1999*/0045306

Number of stops: 72
Gauge: 1,000 mm
Electrification: 750 V DC, overhead

Service: Peak 5-20 min, off-peak 30-60 min
First/last car: 04.40/01.00
Fare structure: Stage, with single and multiride tickets sold from platform machines

Rolling stock: 44 cars

Duewag 8-axle (1966/88)	M35
LHB/Adtranz Variobahn low-floor (1996/97)	M6
Cycle carriers	T2
Historic tram	M1

On order: 10 Variobahn; plus further 10 unspecified units

Developments: 19.5 km is existing single track and is being converted to double track.

BRN

Busverkehr Rhein-Neckar
PO Box 100564, D-68005 Mannheim
Tel: (+49 621) 12 00 30   Fax: (+49 621) 120 03 60
Directors: Klaus W Teuber
  Werner Ott
Staff: 504

Passenger journeys: (1995) 26.9 million
(1996) 37 million
(1997) 36.8 million
Vehicle-km: (1995) 19.1 million
(1996) 20.2 million
(1997) 20.9 million

Current situation: Regional bus company, owned by DB, providing suburban and regional services over 82 routes with a fleet of 188 buses plus 244 hired. RHB's small bus operation in Bad Dürkheim was taken over in July 1996.

UPDATED

MVV's Mercedes O405GN low-floor articulated, one of three which are CNG-powered   **1997**

MARSEILLE

Population: 808,000, area served 881,000
Public transport: Bus, trolleybus, tramway and metro services provided by municipal undertaking supervised by the city of Marseille and Bouches du Rhône département, with separate metro construction authority. Four bus routes run to adjoining suburbs of Aubagne, La Penne, Allauch and Plan de Cuques. Limited suburban rail services operated by French National Railways (SNCF)

RTM

Régie des Transports de Marseille
PO Box 334, F-13271 Marseille Cedex 8, France
Tel: (+33 4) 91 10 55 55   Fax: (+33 4) 91 10 53 09
Director General: Alain Gille
Staff: 2,706

Refurbished PCC cars at St Pierre   **1996**

Passenger boardings: (All modes)
(1993) 153.1 million
(1994) 150 million
(1995) 148.2 million

Operating costs financed by: (All modes) Fares 57.1 per cent, other commercial sources 6 per cent, subsidy/grants 36.9 per cent
Subsidy from: City council and Bouches du Rhône département

Bus and trolleybus

Passenger journeys: (1992) Bus 87 million, trolleybus 6.4 million
(1993) Bus 83.1 million, trolleybus 6 million
(1995) Bus 85.4 million, trolleybus 6.6 million
Vehicle-km: (1992) Bus 21.4 million, trolleybus 0.8 million
(1993) Bus 19.8 million, trolleybus 0.8 million
(1995) Bus 21.6 million, trolleybus 0.8 million

Number of routes: Bus 77, trolleybus 3, including 13 night
Route length: Bus 575 km, trolleybus 19 km
On priority right-of-way: 24.1 km

Fleet: 542 buses	
Berliet PR100	168
Heuliez GX113	293
Mercedes O405N	37
Heuliez GX77 narrow-body	27
Van Hool AU138 narrow/short wheelbase	16
Renault R312	1

In peak service: 460
Average age of fleet: 9.4 years

Fleet: 47 trolleybuses, all Berliet ER100
In peak service: 41
Average age of fleet: 15.6 years

Most intensive service: 5 min
One-person operation: All routes
Fare collection: Prepurchase passes and multitickets from agencies of metro station ticket machines with validation and cancelling machines on board, or payment to driver
Fare structure: Flat, weekly/monthly passes and multitickets/carnets including transfers; single tickets do not allow interchange
Fares collected on board: 17 per cent
Fare evasion control: Roving inspectors
Arrangements for elderly/disabled: Reduced fares or free travel for over-65s and invalids
Bus priority: Two main corridors into city centre from north and south equipped with bus-activated traffic lights; also some bus lanes on busiest route, Line 21
Operational control: Electronic bus monitoring; all buses, trams and metro cars equipped with radio
Average peak-hour speed: Bus 15.5 km/h, trolleybus 10.1 km/h

Developments: The 10 busiest stops of Route 21 are equipped with Alphabus displays, showing next bus waiting times. Five bus/metro interchanges are equipped with Topbus displays giving next bus departure times; a buzzer warns passengers of imminent departure.

In 1996 RTM introduced the Carte Réseau Libertés, a magnetic card which can be used to pay for all modes of public transport, plus car parks, parking meters and tolls. The ticket allows a one-hour journey including transfers and, unusually, a return journey if required. There are three versions: single journey, fixed-value and rechargeable.

Metro

Operated by: RTM
Construction authority: Société du Métro de Marseille (SMM)
44 avenue Alexandre Dumas, F-13272 Marseille Cedex 8
Tel: (+33 4) 91 23 25 25   Fax: (+33 4) 91 71 05 87
Director General: Michel Croc

Type of operation: Rubber-tyred full metro, initial route opened 1978

Passenger boardings: (1992) 54.7 million
(1993) 56.1 million
(1994) 53.8 million
Car-km: (1993) 9 million
(1995) 9.1 million

Route length: 19.5 km
Number of lines: 2
Number of stations: 24
Track: 2 steel guideways (2,000 mm gauge) for train's pneumatic tyres; 2 steel guidance rails fixed outside running guideways; 2 conventional rails for running in case of tyre punctures and guiding through sections without guidance rails
Tunnel: Bored or blasted
Electrification: 750 V DC, collected by side shoe from guidance rail

Service: Peak 3 min, off-peak 5-10 min
First/last train: 05.00/21.00
Fare structure: Flat
Integration with other modes: Ticket integration with bus services. Monthly ticket for unlimited travel on metro, tramway, trolleybus and bus; also monthly 'Carte Azur' ticket allowing in addition travel on SNCF trains within RTM area
Fare collection: Automatic ticket machines
Signalling: Cab signalling; continuous speed display to drivers; automatic operation with monitored manual drive
Centralised control: Traffic control station or computer ensures regulation of traffic by modifying inter-station speeds and calculating stopping times at stations
Surveillance: CCTV on stations

Rolling stock: 144 cars, in four-car sets
CIMT Series A (1977)   M42 T21
CIMT Series B (1984)   M30 T15
CIMT Series N (1985/86)   M36
In peak service: 116 cars

Current situation: 1.5 km Line 1 extension between Castellane and Hôpital La Timone opened 1992; extensions under study.

Tramway

Type of operation: Conventional tramway

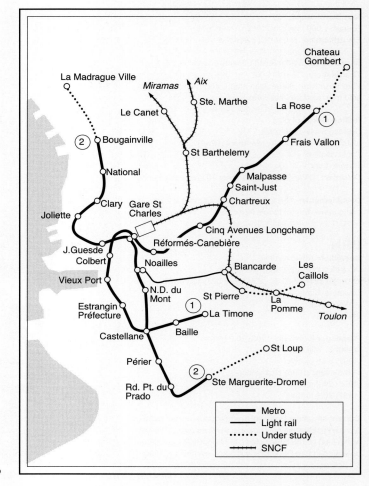

Marseille metro

Passenger journeys: (1992) 5.1 million
(1993) 4.9 million
(1995) 4.6 million
Car-km: (1992) 0.6 million
(1993) 0.6 million
(1995) 0.5 million

Current situation: A 3 km tram line (Route 68) with 14 stops links Noailles Line 2 metro station with St Pierre; 3 min peak service.
Developments: A 1994 study proposed four new tram lines and extension of the existing route to Les Caillols, totalling 20 km, to be in operation by 2015. The 3 km Les Caillols extension has been approved, as has a 5 km westwards route from Noailles to La Canebière for opening in 2006.

Rolling stock: 19 cars, operated as 9 two-car sets
PCC   M16
BN (1984)   M3
In peak service: 16 cars

SNCF

French National Railways (SNCF), Marseille Division
Esplanade St-Charles, F-13232 Marseille
Tel: (+33 4) 91 95 11 10   Fax: (+33 4) 91 95 10 01

Current situation: Limited suburban services are provided on SNCF lines out of Marseille St Charles station. Busiest routes are to Aix-en-Provence (37 km) and Toulon (67 km), each with about 18 return trips daily.

A project has existed for some years to create an RER-style network on the lines to Aix, Aubagne and Marignane airport, near Vitrolles. Plans to double the Aix line have come up against financial and construction problems in an area of dense development and difficult terrain.

VERIFIED

MEDELLÍN

Population: 2.5 million
Public transport: Bus, minibus and metro services provided by private companies

Private bus/minibus

Supervised by:
Ministry of Transport
Calle 26 No 25-50, Piso 3, Apartado Aero 1978, Bogotá DE, Colombia

Passenger boardings: (1993) 2.5 million daily

Line 1 train at Poblado
1997

Current situation: Bus services are operated by private companies and co-operatives on concessions awarded by the Ministry of Transport, initially for a year and then for progressively longer periods after review.

A fleet of more than 4,200 vehicles runs 209 routes.

Metro de Medellín

Empresa de Transporte Masivo del Valle de Aburrá — Metro de Medellín
Calle 44 Nro 46-001, Bello, Antioquia
Tel: (+57 4) 452 60 00   Fax: (+57 4) 452 44 50
e-mail: emetro@col3.telecom.com.co
General Manager: Alberto Valencia Ramirez
Staff: 815

Type of operation: Full metro, opened 1995

Passenger journeys: (1995) 55 million
(1996) 62 million

Route length: 29 km
   elevated: 9 km

Number of lines: 2
Number of stations: 25
Gauge: 1,435 mm
Electrification: 1.5 kV DC, overhead

Service: Peak 5 min, off-peak 10 min
First/last train: 05.00/23.00
Fare structure: Flat; tickets for 1, 2 and 10 trips
Fare collection: Turnstiles
Operating costs financed by: Fares 92 per cent, other commercial sources 8 per cent

Rolling stock: 126 cars, in three-car sets
MAN/Ateinsa/Siemens   M84 T42

Current situation: The metro was opened in three stages in 1995/96.
Developments: Operation of the metro is to be offered on concession; bids were to be adjudicated in early 1998.

A proposed Line C has been considered, possibly as a trolleybus route running on 6 km of exclusive right-of-way.

VERIFIED

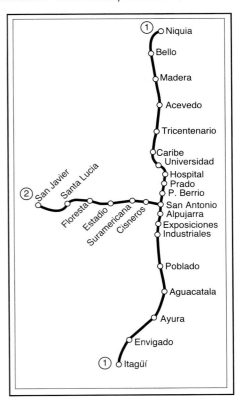

Medellín metro

MELBOURNE

Population: 2.9 million
Public transport: Four corporations, Bayside Trains, Hillside Trains, Swanston Trams and Yarra Trams, operate all heavy rail, light rail and trams in the metropolitan area; extensive private bus operations

PTC

Public Transport Corporation
589 Collins Street, Melbourne 3000, Australia
Tel: (+61 3) 96 19 11 11   Fax: (+61 3) 96 19 23 43
Chief Executive: Andrew Neal
Managing Director, Swanston Trams: Russell Nathan
Managing Director, Yarra Trams: John Wilson
Managing Director, Bayside Rail: Simon Lane
Managing Director, Hillside Rail: Roger Mendes
Staff: 7,045 (total PTC)

Passenger boardings: (All modes, excluding private bus)
(1995/96) 229.5 million
(1996/97) 234.1 million
(1997/98) 234.3 million

Current situation: The PTC was formed in 1989 when the Metropolitan Transit (The Met) and State Transport authorities were merged. Most of the bus network was sold into the private sector in 1994. In 1997 the Victoria government announced privatisation plans for Melbourne's trains and trams, and the remaining eight bus routes operated by the PTC. Bids were sought in early 1998 with the aim of having all services in private hands by mid-1999.

In preparation for privatisation, four new business units were set up to replace the former Met Tram and Met Train divisions. Yarra Trams comprises Routes 11, 12, 48, 70, 75, 86, 96 and 109, while Swanston Trams runs the remaining 20 routes. Met Train was similarly split, with Hillside Trains operating the Lilydale, Belgrave, Alamein, Glen Waverley, Epping and Hurstbridge lines, and Bayside Trains the others. The new corporations have all taken over responsibility for maintenance of their track, infrastructure and rolling stock.

Implementation of an automatic fare collection system covering all modes has been completed.

Tramway
Staff: 1,988

Type of operation: Conventional tramway and light rail

Passenger journeys: (1995/96) 114.1 million
(1996/97) 115.4 million
(1997/98) 116.8 million

Vehicle-km: (1994/95) 21.7 million
(1996/97) 21.9 million
(1997/98) 22.1 million

Route length: 240 km
Number of routes: 28
Gauge: 1,435 mm
Track: 43 kg/m rail; some tram rail also used, weight 43/50.6 kg/m
Electrification: 600 V DC, overhead

Service: Peak 4-8 min, off-peak 6-12-20 min
First/last car: 05.30/00.30
Fare collection: Retail outlets or from onboard ticket machines
Fare structure: Time-based multimodal system operating within 3 zones; discount for prepurchase
One-person operation: All services
Centralised control: Vehicle monitoring system being extended to whole tram network

Rolling stock: 537 cars
W5/SW5/SW6/W6/W7   M108
Comeng/ASEA Z1/Z2 (1975/79)   M115
Comeng/Duewag/AEG Z3 (1979)   M115
Comeng/Duewag/AEG A1/A2 (1984)   M69
Comeng LRV (1986/88/90/91/93)   M130

Developments: In 1996/97, the network recorded its highest level of patronage since 1968/69. February 1997 saw opening of a new tram depot at Southbank, replacing life-expired facilities at South Melbourne Kingsway.

Suburban rail
Staff: 1,943

Type of operation: Suburban heavy rail

Passenger journeys: (1995/96) 109.2 million
(1996/97) 112.6 million
(1997/98) 113 million

Current situation: Suburban services operate over a total of 338 km on 15 routes with 197 stations, linked in the city centre by an underground loop line, all electrified at 1.5 kV DC overhead; track gauge is 1,600 mm. Fare structure is as tram.
Developments: Work has started on an A$123 million project to rationalise Jolimont yard, at the edge of the central business district, to free more than 10 ha of land to become a park. A total of 41 storage sidings will be replaced by new facilities at suburban depots. In addition,

Tram patronage has risen to levels not seen since the late 1960s

1998/0009503

the city's main station, Flinders Street, is being refurbished.

Rolling stock: 904 emu cars
Comeng Harris-type (1961/71)
Martin & King Hitachi-type (1972/81)
Comeng Harris-type (rebuilt 1982)
Comeng (1982/89)

Private bus
Passenger journeys: (1992/93) 69.5 million
(1993/94) 74.7 million
(1994/95) 85.8 million

Number of routes: 225
Fleet: 1,023 vehicles
In peak service: 795

Current situation: Some 50 private companies using their own names and liveries operate in suburban areas; integrated multimodal fares system applies. The National Bus Co operates about two-thirds of the former government bus network in Melbourne, from depots at Doncaster and North Fitzroy.

UPDATED

MEMPHIS
Population: 702,000
Public transport: Bus services managed under contract for city-owned Transit Authority, governed by representative board; city-centre tramway

MATA
Memphis Area Transit Authority (MATA)
1370 Levee Road, Memphis, Tennessee 38108, USA
Tel: (+1 901) 722 71 00   Fax: (+1 901) 722 71 23
President and General Manager: William Hudson Jr
Chairman, MATA Board of Commissioners: M P Carter
Vice Chairman, MATA Board of Commissioners: Roy Holt
Staff: 470

Current situation: MATA was established as a publicly owned transit system in 1960, providing fixed-route and demand-responsive service in the Memphis metropolitan area. The historic tramway route opened on Main Street in 1993, intended as the nucleus of a future light rail network. Initial ridership exceeded expectations by a substantial margin, and funding was granted in 1994 for an extension.

Studies have been made of proposed commuter rail service in two corridors using existing track to link central Memphis with Colliersville and Cordova.

Bus
Passenger boardings: (1991/92) 13.2 million
(1992/93) 12.8 million
(1993/94) 12.1 million
Vehicle-km: (1991/92) 11.9 million
(1992/93) 12.9 million
(1993/94) 17.7 million

Number of routes: 33
Route length: 1,238 km

Fleet: 230 vehicles
GMC RTS (1985/86)	93
MAN articulated (1983/87)	11
TMC (1988/89/94)	39
Chance Coach (1990/91/92)	10
General Coach America vans (1997)	28
NovaBUS LFS low-floor (1997/98)	39
Others	10
In peak service: 156	
On order: 20 buses	

Most intensive service: 15 min
Fare collection: Electronic farebox
Fare structure: Zonal
Arrangements for elderly/disabled: MATAPlus paratransit service carries 500 passengers daily; reduced fare on fixed-route services

This W2 tram imported from Melbourne is operating on the new Riverfront Loop; track closest to the camera is used by Amtrak and an occasional freight (Van Wilkins)   *1999*/0038888

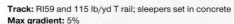

Integration with other modes: Park-and-ride on many routes
Operating costs financed by: Fares 37 per cent, other commercial sources 5 per cent, subsidy/grants 58 per cent
Subsidy from: FTA 21 per cent, state 17 per cent, city 62 per cent

Tramway
Type of operation: Conventional tramway

Passenger boardings: (1994/95) 512,000
(1995/96) 520,000
(1996/97) 556,000

Route length: 7.4 km
Number of routes: 2
Number of stops: 26
Gauge: 1,435 mm

Track: RI59 and 115 lb/yd T rail; sleepers set in concrete
Max gradient: 5%
Minumum curve radius: 8.5 m
Electrification: 600 V DC, overhead

Service: Peak 8 min, off-peak 13 min
First/last car: 06.38/24.00
Fare structure: Flat, reduced rate 'Lunch Fare'
Revenue collection equipment: 13 ticket vending machines
Integration with other modes: Free transfer to bus

Rolling stock: 14 cars
Brill-type 2-axle ex-Oporto	M7
Ex-Melbourne W2 (1924/29)	M7
In peak service: 12 cars	

Current situation: Initial 3 km section of tramway along Main Street in the Mid-America Mall redevelopment area opened 1993, designed as a downtown distributor and intended to become the core route of a future light rail network.
Developments: A 4 km loop to and along the riverfront area opened in 1997. This makes use of little-used rail track running north-south and parallel to the existing tramway, with which it has been connected by new east-west links to form a loop. Four ex-Melbourne W2 cars have been restored to operate the new service.

Proposed is a 3.5 km eastern extension to Medical Center. In 1994 a $4 million grant was made available towards the cost of the Medical Center line, but indecision over its routeing and whether it should be built for light rail operation has delayed design work.

UPDATED

A new NovaBUS low-floor contrasts with a tram built in Oporto, Portugal in the 1930s (Van Wilkins)
1999/0038889

MENDOZA

Population: 475,000
Public transport: 'Colectivo' bus and minibus services provided by private operators and groups operating through an association, and supervised by Provincial transport department. Trolleybus services run by Province-owned corporation

Private bus/minibus/shared taxi

Supervised by:
Departamento Provincial de Transportes (DPT)
Mendoza, Argentina

Current situation: The Provincial DPT is in charge of co-ordinating and regulating the colectivo bus operations of the city's 10 main groupings of private operators and co-operatives, each franchised for one or more specific routes. There are about 50 routes, many of which started as branches of the original 10-route core network but are now numbered and operated separately. The principal operators are: El Trapiche, El Plumerillo, Antartida Argentina, Paso de los Andes and TAC.

In 1990 consultants BVC carried out traffic management studies, which were expected to lead to improved operating conditions for buses.

The DPT is also in charge of regulating city and regional taxi services, as well as the Taxi-Flet public-hire freight pick-ups which charge by the hour.

Passenger journeys: Approx 70 million (annual)
Vehicle-km: Approx 20 million (annual)

Private Mercedes midibus on Maipu route
(Bill Luke) **1999**/0038891

Refurbished ex-Solingen trolleybus on Pellegrini route (Bill Luke) **1999**/0038890

Number of routes: 40
Route length: 560 km
Fleet: Approx 500 vehicles, including Mercedes LO1114, OF1214, OH1314 and OH1419 types, El Detalle OA101 and Zanello, many bodied by local companies
Fare structure: Urban, flat; suburban, distance-related
Fare collection: Payment to driver

EPTM

Empresa Provincial de Transportes de Mendoza (EPTM)
Calle Peru 2592, Mendoza 5500
Tel: (+54 61) 25 17 33   Fax: (+54 61) 38 06 50

Trolleybus

Passenger journeys: Approx 6.5 million (annual)

Number of routes: 5
Route length: 50 km

Fleet: 95 trolleybuses
Tokyu/Nissan/Toshiba (1962, refurbished 1996)   1
Uritsky ZIU9 (1984)   16
Krupp (ex-Solingen) some stored   78
In peak service: 34

Most intensive service: 5-8 min
One-person operation: 100 per cent
Fare structure: Flat, higher in late evening
Fare collection: Payment to driver

Current situation: A phased expansion of the network has begun but progress has been slowed by shortage of funds. The first two new sections opened in 1986, with a third stage following in 1987. Route 4 to Barrio San Martin opened 1989. Further wiring has been completed under a scheme approved in 1991 for elimination of diesel buses from the city centre on environmental grounds. This is a new 17 km north-south cross-city route connecting Las Heras with Godoy Cruz.

One 1962 Toshiba trolleybus was rebuilt with a new rear-end in 1996, but the project was deemed uneconomic and others of the type withdrawn in 1995 will now be scrapped. Twenty-three of the ex-Solingen vehicles have been refurbished for the new north-south line. The operation is expected to remain commercially self-sufficient.

UPDATED

MEXICO CITY

Population: 20 million
Public transport: Trolleybus/tramway and metro services operated for urban area by separate public authorities, and bus services largely run by concessionaires under overall control of co-ordinating body. Extensive private 'colectivo' shared taxi operation and privately run suburban bus services

STV

Secretaría de Transportes y Vialidad
Lerma 62, Mexico City DF 06500, Mexico
Tel: (+52 5) 207 68 15
Director General: Jorge Martínez y Almaraz

Current situation: STV came into being at the beginning of 1995 as successor to the Coordinacíon General de Transporte. It is responsible for regulation of the city's public transport, and for control of roads, streets and parking. One of its first tasks was to cope with the shut-down of the state-owned city bus operator Ruta 100.

Bus services were provided by numerous private firms and paratransit modes until the early 1980s, when urban bus operations were taken over by the government. Now, services are once again provided largely by private operators on concession. Extensive shared taxi 'colectivo' operations continue, with about 60,000 vehicles, and suburban bus services remain in private hands.

Considerable problems are faced in catering for the massive demands of the world's fastest-growing urban area. A further complication is the pressure created by the high levels of atmospheric pollution. Transport provision, in particular the metro, has been expanded rapidly to handle some 30 million daily journeys in the city region. Government environmental regulations stipulate that the

Concarril LRV pulling up to the loading platform at Tasqueña station, to begin a trip to Xochimilco on STE's light rail line (Steve Morgan) **1999**/0038892

city's 2.8 million cars and commercial vehicles must not be used on one day each week, and taxis and 'colectivo' minibuses must be fitted with catalytic converters.

Amongst many proposals for public transport improvements have been schemes to expand trolleybus and light rail, though the existing trolleybus network has been cut back since 1991. Longstanding plans to create a high-speed regional rail network based on poorly used national railways routes have made little progress.

STE

Servicio de Transportes Eléctricos del Distrito Federal (STE)
Av Municipio Libre 402 Ote, Col San Andrés Tetepilco, Mexico City 09440, DF
Tel: (+52 5) 539 65 00/65 09   Fax: (+52 5) 539 26 49
Director General: Joel Ortega Cuevas
Director of Operations: Hugo J Nieto de la Torre
Staff: 2,700

MASA trolleybuses of STE turning at San Lorenzo Tezonco, the east end of trolleybus route K1 where the wiring makes a U-turn in the wide Avenida Tlahuac (Steve Morgan) **1999**/0038893

Current situation: STE is responsible for operation of trolleybus routes, a light rail line, and from November 1997 some bus routes. A major programme of renovation and expansion of the trolleybus network was under way, and in 1990 the system extended to 30 routes. Subsequently there have been several closures, some on account of metro construction, but 5 km Route LL was opened in 1995 and extended 0.5 km in 1996, as was a 1.4 km extension of Route A.

Current policy is to concentrate operations on the busiest routes as a prelude to possible expansion in the future. The first vehicles were delivered in late 1997 of an order for 200 MASA/Mitsubishi AC-powered trolleybuses.

The tram route has been modernised similarly to light rail standard, and the ancient PCC cars replaced by new vehicles.

Developments: STE had been asked to take over all the former Ruta 100 diesel bus routes and vehicles that had not otherwise been concessioned, but declined to take on more than a small number of busy routes, which it started operating in November 1997. These are worked by 170 articulated buses (the entire city fleet of such vehicles). STE also took over the batch of 20 standard buses converted in 1997 for use by wheelchair passengers, and runs them with four similarly converted trolleybuses on three routes providing city-wide coverage.

Trolleybus

Passenger journeys: (1989) 225.2 million
(1991) 120 million
(1993) 99.3 million

Number of routes: 17
Route length: About 200 km

Fleet: 513 trolleybuses

MASA/Toshiba (1984/85)	248
MASA/Melco (1988)	45
MASA/Kiepe (1991)	30
Flyer/GE E800 (ex-Edmonton 1974/76)	22
Flyer/GE E800 (ex-Edmonton, lift-equipped)	4
Flyer/GE E800A (ex-Hamilton 1978)	1
Marmon Herrington (rebuilt Moyada 1984/87)	104
Mitsubishi (ex-Kurobe Dam, 1966/71, in store)	9
MASA/Mitsubishi (1997)	50

In peak service: 323 trolleybuses
On order: 200 MASA/Mitsubishi being delivered 1997/99
Trolleybus electrification: 600 V DC

Fleet: 190 motor buses

MASA articulated (1995/97)	170
MASA two-axle lift-equipped	20

Most intensive service: 2 min
One-person operation: All routes
Fare collection: Payment to driver or sheet of 30 discounted tickets
Fare structure: Flat, no transfers
Fare evasion control: Driver's check

Light rail
Passenger journeys: (1989) 6.8 million
(1991) 5.5 million
(1993) 10.5 million

Route length: 12.7 km
Number of routes: 1
Number of stations: 17
Max gradient: 1%
Min curve radius: 30 m
Electrification: 600 V DC, overhead

Service: Peak 4 min, off-peak 6 min
First/last car: 06.00/23.00
Fare structure: Flat, single and two-weekly tickets
Fare collection: Ticket machines at all stations; magnetic ticket activates turnstile access

Rolling stock: 16 cars

Concarril/Siemens (1991)	M12
Bombardier/Siemens (1995)	M4

In peak service: 10

Current situation: Links metro Line 2 terminus at Tasqueña with Xochimilco. The short on-street branch to Tlalpan, which reopened in 1990 after closure since 1984, was closed and reopened in 1991, and closed yet again in 1993 because of poor patronage.

STC Metro

Sistema de Transporte Colectivo
Organismo Público Decentralizado
Delicias 67, Mexico City 06070 DF
Telephone: (+52 5) 510 05 29   Fax: (+52 5) 512 36 01
Director General: Pedro Benítez
Director of Administration: Antonio Garcia Rojas Barbosa
Director of Operations: Miguel Gerardo Requis Bustos
Director of Planning: Juan Manuel Gutiérrez Arrieta
Staff: 13,196

Type of operation: Full metro, first line opened 1969

Passenger journeys: (1994) 1,422 million
(1995) 1,474 million
(1996) 1,425 million
Car-km: (1994) 291 million
(1995) 308 million
(1996) 301 million

Route length: 178 km
  in tunnel: 107.9 km
  elevated: 14.3 km
Number of lines: 10
Number of stations: 154
Gauge: 1,436 mm (auxiliary guide rails, except Line A)
Track: Guideway for rubber tyres, security rail (39.6 kg/m); Line A is steel-wheel (56.9 kg/m rail)
Max gradient: 7%
Min curve radius: 105 m
Tunnel: Concrete caisson or bored tunnel with double-track
Electrification: 750 V DC, collected from two lateral guide bars; Line A, overhead

Mexico City's metro

▬▬▬	Metro
▪▪▪▪▪	Under construction
───	Light rail

Service: Peak 1 min 55 s
First/last train: 05.00/24.00
Fare structure: Flat; single-trip and sheet of 25 discounted tickets
Revenue control: Turnstiles
Operating costs financed by: Fares 60.1 per cent, other commercial sources 6.1 per cent, subsidy/grants 30.9 per cent, balance as deficit
Integration with other modes: None
One-person operation: All services
Signalling: Automatic block and interlocking; ATO; 3 control centres

Rolling stock: 2,559 cars

Alsthom MP68 (1969/73)	M352 T176
CNCF NM73A-B-C (1975/79)	M231 T114
CNCF NM79 (1980/83)	M350 T177
Alsthom MP82 (1982/83)	M150 T75
Bombardier NC82 (1982/83)	M120 T60
CNCF NM83A (1984/85)	M184 T91
CNCF NM83B (1986/89)	M150 T74
CNCF MF86 (1990/92)	M80 T40
CAF NE92 (1994/95)	M90 T45

On order: 278 cars required for opening of Line B in 1999; bidding for this order was suspended in August 1997 as none of the tenders met STC's requirements

Developments: Construction of east-west Line B (21.8 km, 21 stations) is in progress for mid-1999 opening. This links Cd Azteca in the northeast with Buenavista main line railway station in the city centre. This will be the first rubber-tyred line to extend beyond the Distrito Federal boundary.

Despite the rapid pace of construction, metro development still fails to keep pace with the prodigious growth of the city. STC's master plan, revised in 1996, envisages expansion to 17 lines with 342 route-km by 2020, when 10.2 million daily journeys are expected.

A big rolling stock rehabilitation project is in progress, covering almost the entire fleet of MP68 and NM73B cars. The first batch of 236 MP68 cars was completed in 1996 by Bombardier-Concarril, which is also refurbishing 236 cars in the second stage. The remaining 36 cars are being dealt with by CAF. The aim is to achieve a further 20 years' life at a cost of some 56 per cent of replacement vehicles.

Private buses/minibuses/shared taxis
Current situation: Licensed private operators run a total of some 65,000 vehicles, including 30,000 vans, 15,000 minibuses and 4,000 'colectivo' minibuses/shared taxis. There are in addition about 60,000 conventional taxis, while a further 28,000 vehicles of various types operate services in outer suburban areas beyond the DF boundary. These services are estimated to carry between 8 and 10 million passengers daily.

Regional rail (planned)
Developments: The government has long planned that lines of the National Railway (NdeM), now privatised, should be used for suburban services which might help alleviate the city's chronic traffic problems, but all proposals have failed to progress (see earlier editions for background).

UPDATED

MIAMI

Population: 1.9 million
Public transport: Bus, metro, downtown people mover and paratransit services provided by department of county authority, responsible to board of county commissioners; commuter rail service; extensive unlicensed jitney operations

Miami-Dade

Miami-Dade Transit Agency
111 NW 1st Street, Miami, Florida 33128, USA
Tel: (+1 305) 375 57 65   Fax: (+1 305) 375 46 05
Executive Director: Danny Alvarez
Staff: 2,517

Current situation: In 1991, voters again rejected a proposed additional 1 cent sales tax dedicated to transit operations and improvements, leading to an immediate reduction in service levels and the number of routes, and forcing a 25 per cent rise in fares. Miami-Dade continues to press for the tax increase, which would be used to fund implementation of the 'Year 2010 Plan' to expand bus service and extend the metro.

Bus

3300 NW 32nd Avenue, Miami, Florida 33142
Tel: (+1 305) 637 38 09
Assistant Director, Bus Operations: Roosevelt Bradley
Staff: 1,867

Passenger boardings: (1994/95) 63.8 million
(1995/96) 62.2 million
(1996/97) 62 million
Vehicle-km: (1994/95) 42.5 million
(1995/96) 41.9 million
(1996/97) 44.1 million

Number of routes: 69
Route length: (One way) 1,134 km

Fleet: 795 vehicles, including contracted, of which 723 active

GMC RTS-II (1980)	99
Flxible (1987/88/90)	307
Flxible alternative fuel (1992)	15
FRD (1992/93)	3
MCI (1981/82)	3
DTD vans (1992)	15
FRD (1996/97)	45
Flxible (1993/94)	103
Ikarus articulated (1994/95)	66
NABI (1997)	50
Others	89

In peak service: 519

Most intensive service: 6 min
One-person operation: All routes
Fare collection: Exact fare to farebox or prepurchase pass/token
Fare structure: Flat; drivers issue 25 cent transfer; monthly passes

MDTA articulated bus (Carmona Crichton)
1999/0045316

Arrangements for elderly/disabled: Special Transportation Services ($2.50 fare) and Medicaid ($1) services carried around 1.2 million passengers in 1996/97; reduced ordinary fares and discount passes on fixed routes to those eligible
Operating costs financed by: Fares 39 per cent, subsidy/grants 61 per cent
Subsidy from: Local government 70 per cent, state government 19 per cent, FTA 11 per cent
New vehicles financed by: FTA grants 80 per cent, state 10 per cent, local 10 per cent

Developments: A 13.4 km busway opened in South Dade in 1997, using former rail right-of-way; conversion to metro is proposed (see below).

Metro

Operations Director, Rail: Frank Martin
Staff: 462

Type of operation: Full metro, initial section opened 1984

Passenger journeys: (1994/95) 14.3 million
(1995/96) 14.2 million
(1996/97) 14 million

Route length: 33 km, mostly elevated
   at surface level: 1 km
Number of lines: 1
Number of stations: 21
Gauge: 1,435 mm
Track: Direct fixation fasteners with resilient pads
Electrification: 700 V DC, third rail

Service: Peak 6 min, off-peak 15 min
First/last train: 05.30/24.00
Fare structure: Flat
Fare collection: Exact fare to turnstile; prepurchase pass/token
Arrangements for elderly/disabled: Reduced fare and discount passes
Integration with other modes: Transfers to bus at extra fare, free transfer to people mover; monthly pass; interchange with commuter rail; park-and-ride at some stations
One-person operation: All trains

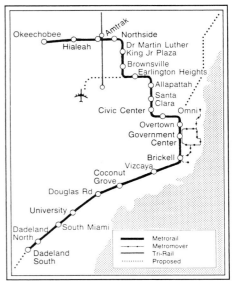

Miami's metro and people mover

Automatic control: Partial, with full operator over-ride
Surveillance: CCTV for passenger/train control
Operating costs financed by: Fares 27 per cent, subsidy/grants 73 per cent

Rolling stock: 136 cars

Transit America (Budd) (1983/84)	M136

In peak service: 86

Developments: Plans for Line 2 have been abandoned after the poor ridership results of Line 1, but two extensions have been discussed. Funding was agreed in 1993 for studies of a 15.3 km extension along Northwest 27 Avenue to serve several educational and leisure facilities, while a proposed 32 km line (also canvassed as a busway, see above) southwards to Cutler Ridge, Homestead and Florida City is seen as an important means of boosting the economy of an area devasted by the 1992 hurricane. Federal funding is to be sought on this basis.

Meanwhile a 1.8 km extension is in design from Okeechobee to NW 74th Street/826 (Palmetto Expressway) where a 2,000-car parking garage is to be built. This is scheduled to open in 2002.

People mover
Staff: 136

Passenger journeys: (1994/95) 3.6 million
(1995/96) 4.3 million
(1996/97) 4.1 million

Current situation: Metromover, a downtown people mover opened 1986, extended 1994, links with metro and bus services for central area passenger distribution; 7.1 km, 21 stations. Unmanned cars carrying up to 120

Metromover people mover (Carmona Crichton)   *1999*/0045318

Cypress Creek station — Tri-Rail's first double-tracked station   *1999*/0045317

passengers run at 90 sec intervals on mostly elevated guideway using right-of-way integrated into a number of commercial developments. Fares cover 4 per cent of operating costs.

Fleet: 29 cars
In peak service: 15

Tri-Rail

Tri-County Commuter Rail Authority
305 S Andrews Avenue, Suite 200, Fort Lauderdale, Florida 33301
Tel: (+1 954) 728 85 12   Fax: (+1 954) 763 13 45
Chair: David Rush
Executive Director: Linda Bohlinger
Director of Operations: W Simmons

Suburban rail
Passenger journeys: (1995) 2.7 million
(1996) 2.3 million
(1997) 2.5 million

Current situation: Commuter trains between Miami, Fort Lauderdale and West Palm Beach (114 km, 19 stations), serving Dade, Broward and Palm Beach counties, inaugurated 1989 over tracks now owned by the state of Florida. Fare-free Tri-Rail feeder buses serve each station, and transfer to local buses of each county's transit system and the Miami metro is also free. Shuttle buses

also link Miami terminal with the city's international airport (3 km).

Trains run hourly at commuting times; all-day service totals 30 trains; all trains and stations wheelchair accessible; zonal fares. Operation is contracted to Herzog Transit Services.

Developments: Main elements in a five-year capital plan to 2000 are double-tracking and upgrading of signalling, station improvements and an increase in park-and-ride spaces from 1,100 to over 7,000. In the south, a 3 km extension is planned to a new Miami airport station, while an 8 km northern extension would extend service to Riviera Beach.

The first 13 km of double-tracking was completed in early 1997, but disruption caused by the work has contributed to a decline in ridership of some 2,000 passengers daily.

Rolling stock: 10 diesel locomotives, 20 coaches

UPDATED

Tri-Rail's Sheridan Street station with Tri-Rail train   *1999*/0045319

MIDDLESBROUGH-TEESSIDE

Population: Teesside urban area 500,000
Public transport: Most bus services in Teesside urban area provided by two operators, both subsidiaries of large UK bus groups. Local rail services; guided busway proposed

Stagecoach Transit

Cleveland Transit Ltd
Church Road, Stockton TS18 2HW, England
Tel: (+44 1642) 60 21 12   Fax: (+44 1642) 61 77 33
Managing Director: Ken Clarke
Engineering Director: Wilson Clark
Finance Director: David Reay
Operations Director: Paul de Santis
Staff: 415

Current situation: The company was purchased by its employees in 1991 from a consortium of local authorities. It purchased Kingston upon Hull City Transport in 1993, and was itself sold to Stagecoach in 1994. The company is also responsible for Stagecoach operations in Darlington and Hartlepool.

Bus
Passenger journeys: (1993/94) 17.3 million
(1995/96) 22.5 million
(1996/97) 22.5 million

Stagecoach Transit operates Alexander-bodied low-floor Dennis Darts on the Salters Lane corridor (Andrew Jarosz)   *1999*/0045302

Vehicle-km: (1993/94) 8.3 million
(1995/96) 10.6 million
(1996/97) 10.5 million

Number of routes: 84
Route length: (One way) 593 km

Fleet: 117 vehicles
Volvo B10M single-deck	13
Volvo B10B single-deck	12
Volvo B6 single-deck	2
Leyland Lynx single-deck	22
Dennis Dart/Alexander low-floor single-deck	11
Leyland Fleetline double-deck	7
Dennis Dominator double-deck	8
Leyland Titan double-deck	16
Leyland PD2 open-top double-deck	1
Volvo Olympian double-deck	8
Volvo/Alexander double-deck	10
Mercedes 811/Alexander minibus	4
Mercedes 811/Wright minibus	3

In peak service: 92

Most intensive service: 5 min
One-person operation: 100 per cent
Fare collection: By driver; Wayfarer machine with change-giving
Fare structure: Stage, monthly passes
Fare evasion control: Inspectors
Operational control: Route inspectors; most vehicles with mobile radio
Arrangements for elderly/disabled: Reduced fares financed by council; low-floor vehicles operate in Stockton
Average distance between stops: 400 m
Average peak-hour speed: In bus lanes, 22.5 km/h; in mixed traffic, 21 km/h
Subsidy from: Borough councils for tendered routes

Mainstay of the Arriva fleet is the Plaxton-bodied low-floor DAF SB220L seen on Stockton High Street (Andrew Jarosz) **1999**/0045301

Arriva North East

North East Bus Ltd
United House, Morton Road, Yarm Road Industrial Estate, Darlington DL1 4PT
Tel: (+44 1325) 35 54 15   Fax: (+44 1325) 28 37 52
Managing Director: Stephen Noble
Commercial Director: Stephen Burd
Subsidiaries: Arriva Durham County Ltd
Arriva Tees & District
Arriva Teesside
Eden Bus, Darlington

Current situation: Both Arriva Tees & District and Arriva Teesside operate local and interurban services in the Middlesbrough area, with 85 single-deck vehicles. Other services are operated on a regional basis. The company was owned by West Midlands Travel, but was sold to the Arriva group in 1996, which merged management with that of Northumbria Motor Services of Newcastle.

Other operators
Current situation: Go-Ahead Northern, and Hartlepool Transport run services into Teesside. Other independents include Robson and Leven Valley.

Northern Spirit

Northern Spirit Ltd

Type of operation: Local railway

Current situation: Local diesel trains run hourly/half-hourly on four routes radiating from Middlesbrough.

Guided bus (proposed)
Current situation: Light rail plans were scrapped in 1993 when Cleveland County Council approved the concept of guided busways and a package of measures to improve frequency of local rail services. A new programme of bus priority over a 'green route' with linked traffic lights and bus-only lanes was introduced in Middlesbrough in 1994.

UPDATED

MILAN

Population: 1.5 million, metropolitan area 4 million
Public transport: Bus, trolleybus, tramway and metro services provided by municipal undertaking now serving neighbouring communities and also operating suburban and interurban services. Suburban rail services operated by national and regionally owned railways, being upgraded to regional metro

ATM

Azienda Trasporti Municipali
Foro Buonaparte 61, I-20121 Milan, Italy
Tel: (+39 02) 86 20 41   Fax: (+39 02) 86 46 37 95
Director General: Roberto Massetti

Director, Personnel: Giuseppe Pinna
Director, Commercial: Pierluigi Silvestri
Director, Logistics: Francesco Lipari
Director, Finance: Dr C di Nella
Manager, Surface Routes: Bruno Decio
Manager, Metro & Tram: Valerio Cocucci
Staff: 9,580

Current situation: ATM is responsible for bus, trolleybus, tram and metro services within the Milan city boundaries, and for metro, bus and tram routes in area extending to about 30 km from the city centre. In this suburban region there are three extensions of metro in the northeast, tram routes to Limbiate and Carate, and 45 bus routes.

Since 1985 ATM has staffed parking areas at metro park-and-ride stations, and in 1988 took over control of many city-centre parking meters. Area-wide integrated fares structure implemented in 1991 covering ATM and private operators' services, based on urban and interurban zones.

Developments: Plans to extend metro further into suburbs have been temporarily halted, but tramway upgrading and segregation is continuing. In an attempt to curb traffic congestion, park-and-ride sites are planned with a total of 35,000 spaces.

Passenger boardings: (All modes)
(1993) 950.3 million
(1994) 891.9 million
(1996) 868.2 million

Operating costs financed by: (Bus and trolleybus) Fares 37.3 per cent, other commercial sources 3.3 per cent, subsidy/grants 59.4 per cent
Subsidy from: Regional and local government

Bus and trolleybus
Passenger boardings: (1993) Bus 299.2 million urban; 47.6 million suburban; trolleybus 54.3 million
(1994) Bus 266 million urban, 45.5 million suburban; trolleybus 49.7 million
(1996) Bus 253.5 million urban, 44.2 million suburban; trolleybus 47.4 million
(1997) Bus 251.4 million urban, 43.4 million suburban; trolleybus 44.5 million
Vehicle-km: (1993) Bus 31.9 million urban, 19.9 million suburban; trolleybus 4.7 million
(1994) Bus 31.9 million urban, 20 million suburban; trolleybus 4.6 million
(1996) Bus 34.8 million urban, 20.3 million suburban; trolleybus 4.7 million

Number of routes: Bus 55 urban, 43 suburban; trolleybus 3
Route length: Bus 428.8 km urban, 649 km suburban; trolleybus 40.4 km

Fiat/Iveco bus and Peter Witt tram of 1928 on Via Galvani **1996**

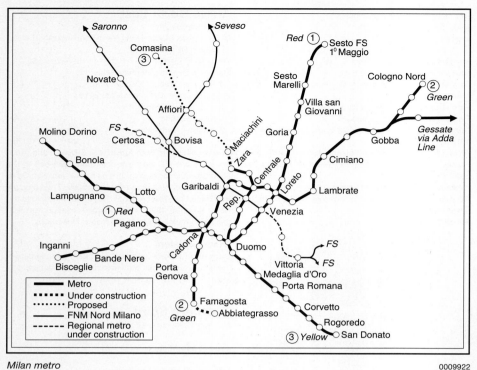

Milan metro   0009922

Map legend:
■■■■ Metro
■■■■ Under construction
······ Proposed
──── FNM Nord Milano
─ ─ ─ Regional metro
        under construction

Fleet: 1,603 buses	
Standard Fiat 421/418/INBUS 210	800
Fiat 471 Effeuno (1984/88)	266
Fiat 571-12 (1982)	5
Iveco Turbocity (1990)	92
Iveco-Macchi 580 (1989)	80
Iveco	50
Bredabus (1991)	71
Menarini NU201/1 (1981)	62
Lancia 718-441 (1973)	2
Lancia 703-08 (1962)	3
Mauri Turbo 5500-5529 (1991)	2
Others	140
Disabled service	30
In peak service: 715 urban, 471 suburban	

Fleet: 165 trolleybuses	
Fiat 2472F (1958/59)	29
Fiat 2470/Socimi (1983)	70
Bredabus 200-232 articulated (1991)	33
Socimi/Macchi articulated (1994/95)	33
In peak service: 120	
Trolleybus electrification: 600 V DC	

Most intensive service: 5 min
One-person operation: All routes

Fare collection: Prepurchase with cancellation on board, or passes
Fare structure: Urban, flat; interurban, zonal; multitickets; prepurchase tickets and multitickets sold through machines and shops; weekly, monthly and annual passes
Fares collected on board: None
Fare evasion control: Random inspection with penalty
Operational control: Inspectors; computerised monitoring system being evaluated on 1 route
Arrangements for elderly/disabled: Fleet of lift-equipped midibuses
Average distance between stops: Interurban 580 m, urban 288 m
Average peak-hour speed: Bus urban 12.9 km/h, suburban 18.4 km/h; trolleybus 12.2 km/h
Bus priority: Reserved trolleybus lanes provided for part of city circular route (6.9 km) on central reserved alignment originally intended for tramway operation; priority measures to be completed for whole route
New vehicles financed by: Regional grants

Metro
Operated by ATM
Construction authority: Metropolitana Milanese SpA

Type of operation: Full metro, first line opened 1964

Passenger boardings: (1993) 343.8 million
(1994) 344.7 million
(1996) 345.7 million
(1997) 307.1 million urban, 31.9 million suburban
Car-km: (1993) 50.6 million
(1994) 51.1 million
(1996) 52.7 million

Route length: 69.3 km
   in tunnel: 48 km
Number of lines: 3
Number of stations: 84
   in tunnel: 68
Gauge: 1,435 mm
Track: 50 kg/m UNI rail; ballasted and slab-track
Electrification: Red line: 750 V DC, third-rail collection and fourth-rail return, conversion to 1.5 kV overhead planned; Green and Yellow lines: 1.5 kV DC, overhead

Service: Peak Red line 2-2½ min, off-peak 5 min
First/last train: 05.56/00.20
Fare structure: Flat, integrated with surface transport systems for urban lines; zonal for interurban line
Revenue control: Automatic entry barriers
Automatic control: Wayside and cab signalling, automatic block with automatic train stop, and CTC; ATO, ATP and ATS on Line 3 from new computerised control centre
Surveillance: Remote control of all stations by CCTV with voice/video datalinks

Rolling stock: 714 cars

Marelli Line 1 (1962-89)	M126
Asgen Line 1 (1962-88)	M122 T82
Ansaldo/Breda/OMS Line 2 (1970-87)	M176 T88
Socimi/Fiat/Breda/OMS Line 3 (1989/90)	M80 T40
In peak service: 558	

Developments: The only projects currently active are the next stage of Line 3 from Zara to Maciachini (0.9 km), and extension of Line 2 from Famagosta to P le Abbiategrasso (1.3 km). Work was scheduled to start on both in early 1998 following approval of grants towards the cost in 1996. A further Line 3 extension (12.6 km) to Comasina in the northern suburbs is also proposed.

Tramway
Type of operation: Conventional tramway

Passenger boardings: (1993) 205.4 million
(1994) 186 million
(1996) 177.4 million
(1997) 172.3 million urban, 4.3 million suburban
Car-km: (1993) 22.1 million
(1994) 22.6 million
(1996) 24 million

Route length: 168.4 km urban, 40.4 km suburban
Number of lines: 16 urban, 2 suburban
Number of stops: 600 urban, 55 suburban
Gauge: 1,445 mm
Track: 52 kg/m grooved and 50 kg/m standard rail, conventional sleepers on ballast
Max gradient: 5%
Min curve radius: 20 m
Electrification: 600 V DC, overhead

Service: Peak 2-5 min, off-peak 5-12 min
First/last car: 05.00/01.30
Fare structure: Flat
Fare evasion control: Travelling inspectors
One-person operation: All routes

Rolling stock: 609 cars

M4X 1500 (1928)	M320
6X 4200 articulated (1955/56/84)	M34
M8X 4800 (1973)	M44
Marelli/Asgen M8X 4900 (1976)	M100
Suburban fleet	M38 T73
In peak service: 367	

Current situation: Also operated are two remaining suburban tram lines totalling 40.4 km.
Developments: Current policy is for modernisation and strengthening of the electrification equipment, along with construction of two extensions and three new light rail lines. Line 24 is being extended from Via Noto to the municipal boundary at Via Selvanesco, for completion in 1999. The light rail schemes are from the city centre to Parco Nord (7.1 km) and to P le Abbiategrasso and

ATM BredaMenarinibus articulated bus   *1999*/0045321

Rozzano (4.2 km), and from P Garibaldi to Cinisello (8.3 km) with a deviation to Precotto. Of the 19.6 km total, 14.9 km comprises new or rehabilitated infrastructure. Construction was scheduled to start in the second half of 1998 for opening between 2000 and 2002.

Orders were placed with Adtranz in 1996 for 20 low-floor trams based on the Strasbourg Eurotram design, with options for further batches.

SFR

Servizio Ferroviario Regionale (SFR)
Director General: Giannantonio Cesi

Current situation: At the end of 1997, all regional and suburban rail services of FS and FNM (see below) in Lombardy became the responsibility of the new regional rail authority SFR. Staff from both railways will be transferred eventually to SFR, which will co-ordinate all commercial aspects of the services but will not own trains.

The integration process started in 1995 with a move towards joint tariffs, and rail fares throughout the region were harmonised by September 1998. Within five years the common tariff willl be extended to include urban bus and tram services, as well as interurban buses.

FS

Italian Railways (FS)
Piazza Croce della Rossa, Roma
Tel: (+39 06) 849 01 Fax: (+39 06) 883 11 08

Type of operation: Suburban heavy rail

Current situation: Services provided on routes into four city terminals, electrified 3 kV DC; 20 minute interval service to Malpensa airport. These are being linked by a cross-city railway (see below) to provide better distribution of passengers in the city centre, improve metro interchange, and create a regional metro serving districts between 30 and 60 km from the city centre.
Developments: Quadrupling started in 1995 of a 22 km section of the Milan–Venice main line between Pioltello and Treviglio. With the doubling already in place between Lambrate and Pioltello, this will complete segregation of the new cross-city services from main line trains. Capacity will thus be raised by over 50 per cent. Stations at Lambrate, Rogoredo and Certosa are being rebuilt.

Iveco CityClass of ATM **1998**/0009504

Famagosta park-and-ride facility at southern terminus of Line 2 of Milan metro **1999**/0045320

FNM

Ferrovie Nord Milano Esercizio SpA
Piazzale Cadorna 14, I-20123 Milan
Tel: (+39 02) 851 11 Fax: (+39 02) 851 15 51
General Manager: Arnaldo Siena
Operations Manager: Luigi Legnani
Staff: 2,096

Type of operation: Interurban railway

Passenger journeys: (1994) 42.4 million
(1995) 41.1 million
(1996) 43 million

Current situation: FNM, largely owned by the Lombardy region, operates 184 km of 1,435 mm gauge route out of Piazza Cadorna terminal to Saronno, Como and Laveno, with branches, electrified at 3 kV DC. A subsidiary operates local bus services. Fares cover 17.7 per cent of operating costs.

Rolling stock: 24 electric locomotives, 86 driving trailers (of which 18 bi-level) and 147 intermediate cars (of which 42 bi-level)
OM/TIBB Class 700 (1928/33)	M22
Class 730/40 (1929/30/32/53/55/57)	M27
Breda Class 750 (1982/94)	M24

Developments: Quadrupling completed of 17 km between Milan and Saronno and a third track commissioned between Bovisa and Seveso (1.9 km). A new connection at Bovisa gives access to the Passante cross-city tunnel (see below), which will carry a service of six trains per hour through to the city centre and so provide relief to the congested approaches to the existing terminal at Cadorna.

Also proposed is a further 15 km of track-doubling beyond Saronno to Busto Arsizio. A 12 km link from the

Busto Arsizio–Novara line into Malpensa airport was scheduled to open in 1998. A dedicated 20 minute airport service will run from central Milan.

A fleet of electric locomotives from Skoda has been commissioned for use with bilevel coaches on Passante services; FNM's share of the order for bilevel emus (see below) is 12.

Regional metro
Under construction
Construction authority: MM Strutture ed Infrastrutture del Territorio SpA
Via del Vecchio Politecnico 8, I-20121 Milan
Tel: (+39 02) 774 71 Fax: (+39 02) 78 00 33

Current situation: A 9 km underground line opened at the beginning of 1998, bringing FNM and FS lines from the north into a new city-centre station at Porta Venezia. This forms the first stage of a cross-city link which will see the line extended to Porta Vittoria in 2002, allowing through running to several FS routes in the east and south. All lines are or will be electrified at 3 kV DC.

The first section comprises a link from FNM lines at Bovisa, through new stations at Lancetti, P Garibaldi and Repubblica, to Venice. All four stations are major bus and/or metro interchanges. At Lancetti, a link comes in from FS lines at Certosa, allowing all suburban trains from the north and west to use the cross-city line.

For the start of services, a joint FS/FNM fleet of 50 four-car double-deck has been supplied by a consortium of Ansaldo, Breda, Firema and Adtranz. When the entire route is completed, a further batch of some 120 trains will be needed to operate eight routes and provide a 3 minute service through the cross-city tunnel.

UPDATED

MILWAUKEE

Population: City 623,000; county 965,000
Public transport: Bus services provided throughout Milwaukee County by undertaking responsible to board of supervisors, managed under contract. Light rail proposed

MCTS

Milwaukee County Transit System
1942 N 17th Street, Milwaukee, Wisconsin 53205, USA
Tel: (+1 414) 344 45 50 Fax: (+1 414) 931 83 42
Managing Director: Thomas P Kujawa
Deputy Managing Director: Kenneth J Warren
Operated by: Milwaukee Transport Services Inc (MTS)
Staff: 1,424 (including 911 drivers)

Current situation: County operation of public transport

began in 1975, MCTS being the main provider in Milwaukee County. The system is directed by the Transportation, Public Works & Mass Transit Committee of the County Board of Supervisors, along with the County Executive. Milwaukee Transport Services, a locally owned not-for-profit firm, has been the successful bidder for the operating contract since 1975.

Service is provided on a grid system including local, express, feeder and park-and-ride flyer routes, designed so that passengers should need change no more than once to reach the central business district or most other destinations. MCTS has put much effort into services designed to link developing suburbs where most new jobs are based. The MetroLink Northwest Express, launched in 1992, links the city centre with the industrialised area in northwest Milwaukee. On weekdays, feeder shuttles serve industrial and business parks, as

well as retail developments, and the concept has been extended to link several areas previously unserved by public transport.

An innovation on the revenue side has been development of the UPASS scheme in which students at Milwaukee's two largest universities must pay $31 per term for an unlimited travel pass. In 1998 some 20,000 passes were taken up. The Commuter Check employee-incentive programme was revised in 1998, becoming a voucher system called Commuter Value Certificate. Tax law permits employers to give up to $65 per month tax free to their employees as a subsidy towards use of public transport.

Developments: Wisconsin DoT concluded its studies of transport options for the busy east-west corridor between Milwaukee and Waukesha. A number of recommendations were made, including light rail, expanded regional bus routes, and road improvements, but the state legislature has refused to fund additional planning and preliminary engineering and so progress is delayed indefinitely.

Almost a million additional bus-km were run in 1997, paid for by state funding offered in conjunction with construction work on the I-94 highway. This, together with introduction of low-floor buses and the increase in passholders, helped raise patronage by 4 per cent.

Bus
Passenger journeys: (1995) 48.9 million
(1996) 48.7 million
(1997) 51.7 million
Vehicle-km: (1995) 31.2 million
(1996) 30.3 million
(1997) 31.2 million

Number of routes: 72
Route length: 1,165 km

Fleet: 536 vehicles

GM New Look rehabilitated (1966/67-1984/87)	78
GMC RTS-II (1980, rehabilitated 1987)	18
Neoplan AN440 Transliner (1985)	72
Neoplan AN440 (1986)	55
Crown-Ikarus articulated (1985)	26
Chance tramcar replica (1985)	3 (non-revenue)
Orion V (1990)	117
Gillig minibus (1991)	12
New Flyer DL40F (1995/96/97)	146
New Flyer D30LF low-floor (1997)	9

In peak service: 438 (am), 417 (pm)

Most intensive service: 4-8 min
One-person operation: All routes
Fare collection: Ready Fare, exact fare to electronic farebox, prepurchase tickets or passes
Fare structure: Flat, according to type of service; free 1 h transfer; weekly passes; prepurchase 10-ride tickets; student passes
Fares collected on board: 36 per cent (49 per cent of

New Flyer low-floor bus with ramp access   **1997**

passengers hold passes, 15 per cent prepurchase tickets)
Fare evasion control: Check by driver; electronic fareboxes
Operational control: Satellite-based vehicle management system
Bus priority: Two routes have limited-access lanes; one route has traffic light priority at two intersections
Arrangements for elderly/disabled: Half fare for disabled and those over 65; user subsidy for van and taxi service; all buses except GM New Look rehabs have kneeling facility or ramps

Integration with other modes: 11 Flyer routes serve 17 outlying parking lots, of which 12 are fully developed park-and-ride sites; reverse-flow Flyer service provided
Average distance between stops: Central business district 1 block, other areas 2 blocks
Average peak-hour speed: 20 km/h
Operating costs financed by: Fares 41.7 per cent, subsidy/grants 58.3 per cent
Subsidy from: State funds 43.6 per cent, FTA funds 5.1 per cent, local funds 9.6 per cent
New vehicles financed by: FTA grants with local share
UPDATED

MINNEAPOLIS/ST PAUL
Population: 600,000, metropolitan area 2.5 million
Public transport: Bus services provided by municipally owned operators and private operators, under overall control of Metropolitan Council responsible for transport planning, policy and day-to-day operations. Services for suburban areas are increasingly being provided independently by local communities. Ride-sharing and car- and vanpooling schemes encouraged

Metropolitan Council
Metropolitan Council
230 East 5th Street, St Paul, Minnesota 55101, USA
Tel: (+1 612) 291 63 59
Chair: Curtis Johnson

Passenger boardings: (1995) 64 million
(1996) 62 million

Operating costs financed by: Fares 33 per cent, state appropriation 27 per cent, federal and other sources 6 per cent, property tax 41 per cent

Current situation: The 17-member Metropolitan Council is responsible for public transport planning and policy-making, and for the day-to-day operations of the largest transport operator Metro Transit. In addition, the council contracts with 24 private operators or communities to provide fixed-route and paratransit services throughout the Twin Cities area.

Twelve suburban cities are served by 'opt-out' transport systems. These cities do not participate in the regional property tax funding formula, but instead choose to levy a local property tax to support their own transport arrangements. Ride-sharing and travel demand management programmes are managed by Metro Commuter Services.

The Metropolitan Council also contracts with operators to provide the Metro Mobility demand-response door-to-door paratransit service, which carries about 1 million passengers a year. All fixed-route services are planned to be fully accessible by 2003.
Developments: In 1994 the council began a review of the

Twin Cities transport provision, and in 1996 approved a Transit Redesign plan that addressed changing travel patterns, stagnant property tax levies and increasingly diverse market areas. A major restructuring of the network was carried out in 1996/97, based on elimination of service duplication, introduction of smaller buses or dial-a-ride in areas of low demand, and improvement of timed-transfers and interchange between routes. This has resulted in a small number of routes being opened to tender. The council is also seeking a more predictable source of funding.

Metro Transit
Metro Transit
560 Sixth Avenue North, Minneapolis, Minnesota 55411-4398
Tel: (+1 612) 349 74 00   Fax: (+1 612) 349 76 12
General Manager: Arthur T Leahy
Operations Manager: William Foster
Staff: 2,369

Current situation: In 1995, Metro Transit became a solely bus-operating subsidiary of the Metropolitan Council. It operates 95 per cent of regular routes in the region. Its service area covers Minneapolis, St Paul and the majority of surrounding inner suburbs.

Bus
Passenger journeys: (1995) 61.1 million
(1996) 61.9 million
(1997) 62.1 million
Vehicle-km: (1996) 22.9 million
(1997) 23.5 million

Number of routes: 114
Route length: (One way) 2,280 km
On priority right-of-way: 6.2 km

Fleet: 963 vehicles

MAN Americana (1984/85/87/88)	148
MAN articulated (1983/84)	65
Gillig Phantom (1989/90/92/93/94/95/96)	630
New Flyer articulated (1991/94)	110

In peak service: 744

Most intensive service: 5 min
One-person operation: All routes
Fare collection: Registering farebox, generally pay-as-you-enter; prepurchase magnetic-strip passes
Fare structure: Local and Express flat fares with peak surcharge; free transfer within 2½ h
Integration with other modes: Service to international airport and intercity bus terminal; van- and carpools encouraged, over 5,000 registered; park-and-ride schemes
Arrangements for elderly/disabled: Metro Mobility special bus services operated under contract; 14 county paratransit operations and 13 local community schemes
Bus priority: City-centre transit mall in Minneapolis provides exclusive bus access for most routes
Average distance between stops: 180 m
Average peak-hour speed: In mixed traffic, 21 km/h; in bus lanes (central business area), 13 km/h
Operating costs financed by: Fares 37.2 per cent, other commercial sources 2.6 per cent, subsidy/grants 18.9 per cent, tax levy 41.3 per cent
Subsidy from: FTA grants 10 per cent, RTB grants 90 per cent

Other operators
Current situation: There are five opt-out programmes under which communities operate their own services. These are: Maple Grove Transit System (peak period express service), Minnesota Valley Transit Authority (peak period express service), City of Plymouth (commuter express, reverse commute and dial-a-ride), City of Shakopee (dial-a-ride and vanpool/ride-share), and Southwest Metro Transit Commission (commuter express, reverse commute and dial-a-ride).

Light rail/transitway (proposed)
Current situation: The Metropolitan Council is supporting development of transitways for bus or rail operation. Initial plans are for a light rail line linking downtown Minneapolis with the international airport, which will open in 2003 at a cost of $448 million.
UPDATED

MONTREAL

Population: 1.8 million

Public transport: Bus and metro services on Montreal island operated by urban transport corporation responsible to Montreal Urban Community, overseen by regional transport authority (AMT) which also operates suburban rail services. Other bus operators STL and STRSM serve north and south shore areas respectively

AMT

L'Agence métropolitain de Transport
500 Place d'Armes, Suite 2525, Montreal, Quebec H2Y 2W2, Canada
Tel: (+1 514) 287 24 64   Fax: (+1 514) 287 24 60
President: Florence Junca-Adenot
Director, Suburban Trains: Pierre Dorval
Rolling Stock Manager: Gerald Lauzé

Current situation: AMT replaced the co-ordinating regional transport office CMTC in 1996. It has wider powers than its predecessor, with a remit to support, develop, co-ordinate and promote public transport in an area extending to 5,000 km², covering 12 regional county municipalities and 94 local municipalities with a population of 3.1 million. Some 800,000 public transport journeys per day are made within the region.

AMT has taken over Montreal's remaining commuter rail operations (along with their deficit), and is empowered to improve, develop and extend suburban train services. It has become the planning authority for bus and metro services, and agrees the tariff for multimodal regional passes valid with one or more of the three major operators STCUM, STL and STRSM. The agency aims to introduce common ticketing throughout its area, embracing in addition all regional and suburban operators.

AMT also owns and operates certain infrastructure deemed as strategic to the development of transport corridors — seven reserved bus lanes, seven regional bus terminals and five parking lots. Operators have free access to these facilities. As patronage grows in these corridors, AMT may consider funding infrastructure improvements to provide increased capacity.

Funding for AMT's activities comes from various taxes — on fuel (1.5 per cent), on non-residential parking, and on real estate (0.1 per cent) — plus a levy on transit providers. In its first year of operation, AMT had a budget of C$158.4 million, almost one-third of which (C$52.9 million) was paid to STCUM, STL and STRSM in the form of a 20 cent subsidy per metro journey and a 50 cent subsidy per bus-lane journey.

Suburban rail

Passenger journeys: (1994) 7 million
(1995) 8 million
(1997) 8.4 million

Montreal suburban rail service on the Deux-Montagnes line   ***1999**/0038895*

Current situation: Canada's only electrified (25 kV DC) commuter railway, the CN line from Montreal Central to Deux-Montagnes (27 km, 12 stations), and the CP suburban line from Windsor station to Dorion and Rigaud (64 km, 18 stations), both formerly controlled by STCUM, are now owned by AMT. Both routes have been rehabilitated. A third route (27 km, 7 stations), from Jean-Talon metro interchange to Blainville, was started in May 1997 as a mitigation measure during temporary closure of a Northshore road bridge. All three services are operated under contract by SNC-Gesproex.

Developments: Since the start of 1996, municipal funding of some 30 per cent of operating costs has supplemented support from national government and AMT, allowing fares to be reduced.

A joint CP/CN study of 1995 recommended extension of commuter service over six routes totalling 227 km.

Rolling stock: 29 two-car emus, 122 diesel-hauled cars, 13 diesel locomotives

Bombardier emu (1995)	M58
Diesel-hauled cars	T122

STCUM

Société de transport de la Communauté urbaine de Montréal (STCUM)
PO BOX 2000, 800 rue de la Gauchetiere Quest, Bureau F2100, Montreal, Quebec H5A 1J6
Tel: (+1 514) 280 55 00   Fax: (+1 514) 280 51 93
www: www.stcum.qc.ca
General Manager: Jacques Fortin

Executive Director, Metro: Carl Desrosiers
Executive Director, Bus: Serge Mathieu
Staff: 7,307

Passenger journeys: (Bus and metro)
(1995) 335.6 million
(1996) 336.5 million
(1997) 338.8 million

Operating costs financed by: Fares 38 per cent, other commercial sources 1.9 per cent, subsidy/grants 55.1 per cent, tax levy 4.2 per cent

Subsidy from: Quebec provincial government 10 per cent, municipalities served 40 per cent

Current situation: The Commission de transport de la Communauté urbaine de Montréal (CTCUM) was established in 1970 to widen the role of its predecessor. In 1980 it became responsible for bus services in the West Island and an extensive regional area, acquiring assets from private firms. In 1983 some of these routes were relinquished following decisions of the communities served, and in 1984 regional routes were returned to private ownership. In 1982 the city's two remaining suburban rail services were taken over from CN and CP, and these were transferred to AMT (see above) in 1996.

In 1985 the authority was restyled as STCUM, and as a public corporation made directly responsible to the metropolitan authority, the Montreal Urban Community. Now STCUM provides services in 29 municipalities with a total population of 2 million.

Developments: A new way to generate bus schedules has been developed by STCUM. It is called Interligne and was introduced in June 1997 as a new bus schedule management system. Interligne is an aid to the planning of bus schedules by adjusting frequency to peak-hour ridership influx. A bus driver will now work on an average of two to three bus routes grouped in the same area of the island instead of only one line, as before. This measure allows for a more productive network management and brings in an annual recurrent saving of $6 million.

During the first months of implementation, some of the schedules had to be adjusted following customers' comments and suggestions. Among these was an increase of service hours in some areas. After the summer recess, in September, more adjustments were made to increase bus frequency where demands were justified.

A large-scale project called Réno-Métro was started in 1997. The project is for renovation (hence the name Réno-Métro) of the 26 initial stations, repair of Line 1-Green tunnels and replacement of the first-generation Westinghouse escalators. The cost is estimated at $100 miliion, to be largely subsidised by the Quebec government and AMT.

Two long-planned metro extensions are to go ahead (see below), and three alignments are being studied as possible routes for light rail.

Bus

Vehicle-km: (1995) 77.3 million
(1996) 73.7 million
(1997) 72.9 million

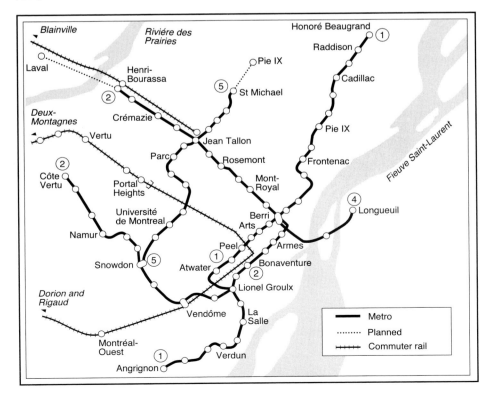

Montreal metro
0045721

NovaBUS LFS ultra-low-floor with STL Laval   *1998*/0009506

Number of routes: 151, plus 20 night only
Route length: 3,150 km
On priority right-of-way: 44 km

Fleet: 1,575 vehicles
GMC TH6-5307 (1979/81)   211
GMC TC40-102 (1983/86)   247
MCI TC40-102N (1989/92)   338
Novabus Classic (1993/94)   419
Novabus LFS low-floor (1996/97)   360
In peak service: 1,291

Most intensive service: 3-15 min
One-person operation: All routes
Fare collection: Exact fare; monthly pass, ticket or cash to driver, or transfer; ticket machines issue transfer from metro
Fare structure: Flat, with 1½ h free transfer; monthly passes and 6-ticket strips sold through over 700 outlets; monthly regional all-modes travelcard also valid on STL and STRSM
Fares collected on board: 9 per cent
Integration with other modes: Fully integrated with metro; Metrobus peak-hour express feeder services, also integrated fares with commuter services and suburban buses
Operational control: Route operations chiefs/mobile radio with central control room
Arrangements for elderly/disabled: Fleet of 79 minibuses and special arrangements with taxi firms provide services within the standard fare structure,

carrying about 1.1 million passengers in 1995; reduced fares on ordinary services
Average distance between stops: 225 m
Average peak-hour speed: In mixed traffic 16-20 km/h
New vehicles financed by: Subsidy from provincial government (50 per cent); STCUM (50 per cent)

Metro
Type of operation: Rubber-tyred full metro, first line opened 1966

Passenger journeys: (1995) 195 million
(1996) 195 million
(1997) 197 million
Car-km (1995) 64.2 million
(1996) 59.9 million
(1997) 57.5 million

Route length: 65 km
Number of lines: 4
Number of stations: 65
Gauge: 1,435 mm
Track: 35 kg/m security rails flanked by 254 mm wide concrete running tracks and lateral guide bars
Max gradient: 6.5%
Min curve radius: 140 m
Tunnel: About 30 per cent cut-and-cover
Electrification: 750 V DC

Service: Peak 3-5 min, off-peak 7-10 min
First/last train: 05.30/01.00

One-person operation: On Lines 1, 2 and 5
Stations: No pavement entrances to stations: access through small off-street structures and through commercial buildings
Revenue collection: Magnetic pass readers installed at all stations
Signalling: Cab signalling with ATC and ATO

Rolling stock: 750 cars, 500 powered, 250 non-powered

Current situation: Two long-planned extensions were confirmed in late 1998. Line 2 is to be extended from Henri-Bourassa across the river to Laval (2 stations), while a 1 km extension of Line 5 from St Michael will serve a new interchange at Pie IX. Both projects are scheduled for completion in 2004.

STL

Société de Transport de la Ville de Laval (STL)
2250 Francis-Hughes Avenue, Laval, Quebec H7S 2C3
Tel: (+1 514) 662 54 01   Fax: (+1 514) 662 54 59
General Manager: Francis Therrien
Staff: 654

Passenger journeys: (1991) 21.4 million
(1992) 18.9 million
(1996) 16 million

Current situation: STL, which was created in 1984, runs buses in the city of Laval on Montreal's north shore, serving an area of 245 m² with a population of 350,000. Its 32 routes extend to 624 km, operated with a fleet of 205 buses. Accessible service provided with 11 minibuses (operated under contract by Autobus R Audet Inc) and Coop-Taxi vehicles.
Developments: A major route revision was under way at the end of 1997.

STRSM

Société de Transport de la Rive Sud de Montreal (STRSM)
1150 Marie-Victorin, Longueuil, Quebec J4G 2M4
Tel: (+1 450) 442 86 00   Fax: (+1 450) 463 10 43
President: Claude Gladu
General Manager: Pierre Vandelac
Staff: 857

Passenger journeys: (1997) 26.9 million
Vehicle-km: (1991) 18.6 million

Current situation: STRSM provides services on 67 routes in the Montreal south shore area, including 23 cross-river routes to central Montreal, with a fleet of 350 buses and minibuses.

UPDATED

MOSCOW
Population: 8.8 million
Public transport: Bus, trolleybus and tramway services provided by unified state undertaking. Metro, responsibility of government ministry, being extended. Some 50 routes of fixed-route shared taxis also operate. Suburban rail services

Mosgortrans

State Company for Passenger Transport
Raushskaya Naberezhnaya 22, Moscow 113035, Russia
Tel: (+7 095) 208 80 31   Fax: (+7 095) 208 80 86
President: A M Uljanov
Staff: 35,763

Current situation: Moscow's substantial surface transport operation provides some 560 routes totalling 6,054 km with a fleet of 10,100 buses, trolleybuses and trams. Some 3.1 billion journeys are made annually, but use of the metro dominates with 47 per cent, and trolleybuses rather than buses are prevalent in the central area. Tramways mainly serve the eastern part of the city. The three modes achieved some 10,018 million passenger-km in 1993, though all services were under pressure from private car ownership which grew 40 per cent between 1992 and 1994.
There is a standard flat fare on all urban routes with

Two ZIU trolleybuses at the terminus of Moscow Route 34 in front of Kyjevskaja station (Milan Šrámek)
1999/0038896

season tickets valid for the surface network alone or plus the metro. Fares are collected by cancelling prepurchase tickets on board.
Proposals for handling the estimated total of 15.2 billion annual public transport journeys in 2010 include major expansion of the electrified surface networks.

Several new metro lines had been planned, but construction ceased on cost grounds in September 1998.

Operating costs financed by: Fares 11 per cent, subsidy/grants 89 per cent

Bus and trolleybus

Passenger journeys: (1991) 2,721 million; bus 1,904 million, trolleybus 817 million

Vehicle-km: (1991) 481 million; bus 394 million, trolleybus 87 million

(1992) 453 million; bus 312 million, trolleybus 85 million

Number of routes: Bus 458 (32 suburban), trolleybus 82

Route length: Bus 4,828 km, trolleybus 877 km

Fleet: 5,627 buses, including Ikarus 280 articulated, Ikarus 435, LIAZ 677, Mercedes Türk 0325

Fleet: Approx 1,700 trolleybuses

Uritsky ZIU9	about 1,150
Uritsky ZIU10	about 520
Ikarus 280 articulated	35

One-person operation: All routes

Fare collection: Prepurchase with cancelling machines on board

Fare structure: Flat. Monthly seasons for surface network or plus metro

Arrangements for elderly/disabled: War and industrial invalids and elderly travel free

Average peak-hour speed: Bus 18.2 km/h, trolleybus 16.1 km/h

Tramway

Type of operation: Conventional tramway

Passenger journeys: (1991) 405 million

Route length: 386 km
Number of lines: 32
Gauge: 1,524 mm
Electrification: 600 V DC, overhead

Service: Frequent
Fare structure: Flat
Fare collection: Cancelling machines on board
Average speed: 14.5 km/h

Moscow Metro prototype 81720/721 Yauza stock

Rolling stock: 934 cars

ČKD Tatra T3/T3M (1980-87)	M618
ČKD Tatra T7 (1990/93)	M6
Kirov KTM8 (1990-96)	M169
Kirov KTM8M	M139
Kirov CTM16	M2

In peak service: 750

Moscow Metro

41 Prospekt Mira, Moscow 129100
Tel: (+7 095) 288 09 91   Fax: (+7 095) 971 37 55
Chief Executive: Dimitry V Gaev
First Deputy Chief Executive: Igor K Yermolenko
Chief Engineer: Aleksandr V Yershov
Staff: 29,003

Type of operation: Full metro, first line opened 1935

Passenger journeys: (1995) 3,188 million
(1996) 3,241 million
(1997) 3,208 million

Car-km: (1995) 588 million
(1996) 615 million
(1997)

Route length: 262 km (17 km surface)
Number of lines: 11
   in tunnel: 244.9 km
Number of stations: 160
Gauge: 1,520 mm
Max gradient: 4%
Min curve radius: 196 m
Electrification: 825 V DC, third rail

Service: Peak 1 min 30 s, off-peak 2-4½ min
First/last train: 06.00/01.00
Fare structure: Flat, by plastic token; magnetic monthly ticket, plastic smartcard; children and students travel at 70 per cent discount; industrial and war invalids, and some other categories, travel free
Revenue control: Open access, but barriers actuated by photo-electric cell if token is not inserted; access lanes for ticket holders
Signalling: Central control; radio-telephone communication with all trains; cab signalling with automatic speed control and driver-only operation on 8 lines

Rolling stock: 4,192 cars, all motored, built by Metrovagonmash Mytischi (Moscow) and Yegorov (St Petersburg) works

E/EM/E*/E*3	M1,675
81714/81714.5/81714.5M	M1,825
81717/81717.5/81717.5M	M535
81720/721	
Others	M157

Current situation: The metro is the city's principal mode of transport, accounting for more than half of all journeys, and its prodigious traffic load has required constant capacity increases. Installation of ATC on two lines has reduced headway to 90 sec, and further resignalling work is in progress to raise capacity on other routes.

Developments: Purchase of new cars is planned at 200 annually. These are based on the Class 81720/721 'Yauza' prototype which started running trials on the Lyublinskaya line in mid-1998.

Under the twelfth five-year plan of 1986/90 there were proposals for new construction totalling 45 km, but little of this has come to fruition. Construction of Line 12 had already ceased well before the economic situation brought all other work to a halt in September 1998.

A modern fare collection system is being installed by Australia's AES Prodata under a contract awarded in 1997. Existing token-operated turnstiles will be fitted with ticket readers having both magnetic-strip and smartcard capability. Initially, the system will use only magnetic tickets, with smartcards being tested prior to eventual adoption.

Russian Railways

Russian Railways (RZhD), Moscow Region
Krasnoprudnaya ul 20, 107040 Moscow
Tel: (+7 095) 262 51 65   Fax: (+7 095) 264 51 77

Suburban rail

Type of operation: Suburban heavy rail

Current situation: As well as suburban services sharing main line tracks there are lines serving commuter areas

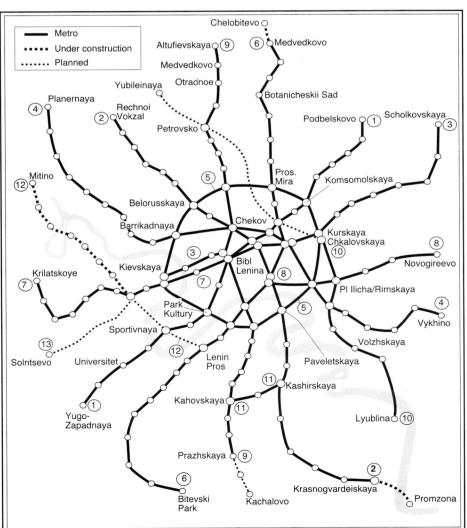

Moscow metro

and a rail link to Domodedovo airport. Total of 10 routes or groups of routes, 1,524 mm gauge. Most of the system is electrified.

Rolling stock: Mostly Class ER911 trains

Shared taxi

Current situation: A system of shared taxis, operated principally by minibuses, serves about 50 fixed routes. Vehicles stop on demand. Employment of drivers and operation is the responsibility of the same department as conventional taxis, but there is said to be co-ordination with the other public transport modes, the routes of which the shared taxis largely duplicate. A fleet of over 500 minibuses carries some 50 million passengers a year.

UPDATED

KTM8M tramcar in Moscow's 850th jubilee livery at Metro Semyonovskaya (Aare Olander)
1999/0038898

MUNICH

Population: 1.2 million, metropolitan area 2.6 million
Public transport: Bus, tramway and metro services provided by city undertaking also responsible for other public utilities, under policy of Münchner Verkehrs- und Tarifverbund. Suburban rail services (S-Bahn) operated by German Railway (DB) and suburban bus services by 47 operators under MVV

MVV

Münchner Verkehrs- und Tarifverbund GmbH (MVV)
PO Box 260154, D-80058 Munich, Germany
Tel: (+49 89) 21 03 30   Fax: (+49 89) 21 03 32 82
www: www.mvv-muenchen.de
Directors: Klaus Wergles
  Alexander Freitag

Passenger journeys: (All modes, linked trips)
(1994) 529.7 million
(1995) 528.6 million
(1996) 533 million

Fare structure: Zonal, free intermodal transfers
Fare collection: Single tickets; multiride tickets; season tickets and passes; transferable pass for off-peak travel; day ticket
Fares collected on board: 14 per cent (vending machines 57 per cent, booking offices 5 per cent, commission agents 24 per cent)
Operating costs financed by: Fares 59 per cent, subsidy/grants 41 per cent

Scheidplatz metro station on Line U2
1996

Subsidy from: State 7 per cent and federal 30 per cent (for S-Bahn only) governments, city of Munich 63 per cent

Current situation: All public transport in Munich and surrounding area of 5,500 km² is co-ordinated by the regional transport authority MVV, and fully integrated. MVV is responsible for future transport planning, marketing, tariffs and recommendations concerning headways and capacity.

A total of 18,800 park-and-ride spaces and 27,800 cycle racks are available at S-Bahn and metro stations.

Stadtwerke München

Stadtwerke München Werkbereich Verkehrs
Einsteinstrasse 28, D-81675 Munich
Tel: (+49 89) 219 11   Fax: (+49 89) 21 91 21 55
www: www.swm.de
Director: Dieter Buhmann
General Manager: Dipl-oec Herbert Koenig
Deputy General Manager: Manfred Hiemer
Operating Manager: Dieter Buhmann
Chief Engineer, Equipment: Dipl-Ing Helmut Schemmel
Chief Engineer, Vehicles: Dipl-Ing Günter Pedall
Chief Engineer, Traffic Management:
  Hans Joachim Kroetz
Staff: 3,973

Passenger journeys: (1995) 420.8 million
(1996) 423.4 million
(1997) 422.6 million

Operating costs financed by: Fares 51 per cent, subsidy/grants 49 per cent
Subsidy from: Contributions made through cross-subsidy from other municipal enterprises, city of Munich, state and federal government

Current situation: Planners are working on Transit 2000, a scheme for fully integrated transport throughout the city. Options range from further metro construction to light rail extensions of existing tram routes.
Developments: Computer-based system planned to secure connections, initially at 15 junctions, affecting 5 tramway and 19 bus routes. Later to be extended.

Bus
Vehicle-km: (1994) 32.2 million
(1995) 31.5 million
(1996) 31.7 million

Lift-equipped MAN NL202 by metro access lift at Scheidplatz
1996

Kansai line (Nagoya—Kameyama, 59.9 km). Rapid service trains which omit some stations are operated on the Chuo and Tokaido lines.

Developments: Since its formation in 1987, Tokai has increased ridership on all lines in the Nagoya area through introduction of new air conditioned cars (Series 211, 213, 311 emus and Kiha 75 dmus), increasing the number of trains and speeding-up services. Other developments include modernisation of stations, elevation of tracks to eliminate level crossings, installation of CTC, and introduction of high-quality reserved seat 'Home Liner' commuter services on the Chuo and Tokaido lines.

Tokai Kotsu Jigyo

Tokai Transport Services Company
8-1, Yasuji-cho, Nishi-ku, Nagoya-shi 452-0815
Tel: (+81 52) 504 30 02   Fax: (+81 52) 452 08 15

Suburban railway

Current situation: The 11.2 km Johoku line provides an east-west suburban link between JR's Tokaido and Chuo lines. The largely elevated line was planned as part of a JNR loop connecting radial routes around Nagoya, but this project was abandoned and the line is run as a self-contained operation with an hourly local service provided by four diesel railcars. It opened in 1991 and was extended by 1.9 km in 1993. TKJ is a JR Tokai subsidiary.

New railways (planned)

Current situation: Further investment in rail transit is planned in recommendations put forward by the Council for Transport Policy in 1992 for completion by 2008. The proposals include: a third east-west metro line; extensions to existing metro lines; upgrading and extension of Meitetsu's Komaki line into central Nagoya via a new metro connection; construction of a new West Nagoya Port line between central Nagoya and the waterfront area; upgrading of several suburban lines; and construction of two new ICTS lines. Beyond 2008 further metro extensions and another ICTS are envisaged.

UPDATED

The outward spread of suburban housing is generating commuter traffic on lines such as JR Central's non-electrified Taketoyo line (Andrew Phipps) *1999*/0038900

NAGPUR

Population: 1.7 million
Public transport: Bus services operated by State Road Transport Corporation; some rail services by Central Railway

Maharashtra State Road Transport

Maharashtra State Road Transport Corporation
Regional office, near Main Bus Stand, Nagpur 440018, India
Tel: (+91 712) 72 04 74   Telex: 0715316
Regional Manager: S S Rathod

Current situation: SRTC has an almost complete monopoly of bus services in Maharashtra State, carrying 2,637 million passengers in 1995/96 with a fleet of 15,832 vehicles. Apart from Bombay, Nagpur is the largest city operation. Three central workshops, including one at Nagpur (Hingana), produce bus bodywork to the tune of some 2,000 units annually.

Bus (Nagpur city operations)
Staff: 1,369

Passenger journeys: (1991/92) 35.1 million
(1992/93) 44.5 million
Vehicle-km: (1990/91) 7.5 million
(1991/92) 8.2 million
(1992/93) 10.9 million

Number of routes: 152
Route length: 2,019 km
Fleet: 212 buses

Most intensive service: 10 min
Fare structure: Graduated (flat up to 4 km)
Fare evasion control: Inspectors
Arrangements for elderly/disabled: Blind persons charged 75 per cent, other concessions granted to those suffering from certain illnesses, journalists and students
Operating costs financed by: Fares 75 per cent

CR

Central Railway
Divisional Offices, Nagpur
Tel: (+91 712) 52 46 22/53 84 80

Current situation: Some commuting on lines into Nagpur Junction from nearby towns such as Wardha and Amla. Electric push-pull commuter service between Nagpur and Badnera.
Developments: With the population expected to grow further to 2.5 million by 2001, the Nagpur Improvement Trust is examining proposals for electrified commuter service over an east-west route that would be created by building new links to existing CR and South Central Railway lines. A commuter service of push-pull electric trains was planned to start in 1997 between Nagpur and Badnera.

In the meantime, a study is to be made of road traffic problems in preparation for a traffic management system.

UPDATED

NAIROBI

Population: 3 million
Public transport: Main bus services provided by independent company operating under franchise from city council, which holds 25 per cent stake. Private 'Matatu' minibus and van services also operate, along with some peak suburban rail services by Kenya Railways

Kenya Bus Services

Kenya Bus Services Ltd
1st Avenue, Eastleigh, PO Box 30563, Nairobi, Kenya
Tel: (+254 2) 22 97 07   Fax: (+254 2) 76 22 30/24 09 39
Managing Director: Malcolm Stewart
Operations Director: W Mwangi
Staff: 3,095

Developments: Stagecoach Holdings plc has sold its entire shareholding in Kenya Bus Services to a management consortium, though property interests have been retained by Stagecoach.

Nairobi's infrastructure has deteriorated over the past few years, with roads being poorly maintained, leading to difficult operating conditions and increased bus maintenance costs. With the cost of living in Kenya, and Nairobi in particular, running at a very high rate, the company has experienced considerable resistance to its fares. As envisaged, the number of Matatus has increased substantially due to economic liberalisation. These vehicles are largely imports of second-hand minibuses; with the widespread availability of counterfeit spare parts, the Matatu is an attractive investment. This and their attempt to offer lower fares has resulted in strong competition for Stagecoach, as well as worsening traffic congestion and so making conventional services less attractive.

On the other hand, the government-owned service Nyayo Bus, inaugurated in 1986, which had at first competed strongly with KBS, was closed down in 1996.

Bus
Passenger journeys: (1993/94) 121 million
(1994/95) 131 million
(1995/96) 135 million
Vehicle-km: (1993/94) 28 million
(1994/95) 28 million
(1995/96) 31 million

Number of routes: 62
Route length: 2,345 km

Fleet: 422 vehicles
Leyland Victory
ERF Trailblazer
DAF TB2100
Dennis Dragon double-deck
In peak service: 368
New vehicles required each year: 30

Most intensive service: On major corridors, 9 sec
Fare collection: On-bus conductors with Setright machines; peak periods 2 conductors on bus
Fare structure: Graduated (zonal scale); single tickets only with monthly passes for students; prepaid seasonal passes
Fare evasion control: Double-conducting system and multi-inspector checking teams
Fares collected on board: 90 per cent
Operational control: Inspectors/patrol cars
Arrangements for elderly/disabled: Bus passes for blind and disabled

Kenya Bus ERF Trailblazers picking up in City Hall Way (Andrew Jarosz) **1999**/0045404

Average distance between stops: City centre 200 m, outside 300-500 m
Average peak-hour speed: In mixed traffic, 13 km/h
Operating costs financed by: Fares 100 per cent
New vehicles financed from: Revenue

Minibus
Current situation: Matatu 12-25 seat light pick-up and minibus operations have developed informally and an estimated 2,500 vehicles carry around 0.5 million passengers daily.
Developments: Shortages of spare parts and frequent accidents combined to reduced the number of Matatus in service in the early 1990s, but they have since grown in number thanks to economic liberalisation and the availability of cheap second-hand imported vehicles.

There are two operators' associations and 35 individual route associations.

KR
Kenya Railways

Current situation: Some peak-hour services are operated to help relieve overcrowded bus services.

UPDATED

NANCY
Population: 250,000, conurbation 315,000
Public transport: Bus and dual-mode trolleybus services operated as franchise on behalf of local authority

CGFTE
Compagnie Générale Française de Transports et d'Entreprises (CGFTE)
11 avenue de Boufflers, BP 3683, F-54097 Nancy Cédex, France
Tel: (+33 3) 83 40 29 65   Fax: (+33 3) 83 27 09 20
Director: Michel Laramée
Staff: 602

Current situation: CGFTE holds the franchise for operation of the urban bus and trolleybus network, and is also responsible for operating three suburban routes totalling 59 km for a consortium of 19 suburban local authorities, the District de l'Agglomération Nancéienne, and 11 others. Traffic figures for these are included in the totals below.

Three trolleybus routes are operated, serving 30 per cent of the population and 40 per cent of the public transport demand. Outer sections of route are served by off-wire running, with the vehicles using their diesel engines.

Taxibus service operates in three areas, allowing passengers to start or finish their journeys by taxi without payment of extra fare. 'Carte Jonquille' allows season ticket holders on local TER Lorraine train to transfer to bus. A government-backed 'Rytmobus' experiment on Route 5 in 1991 abandoned a timetable in favour of regular (every 8 min) non-scheduled buses at peak times.
Developments: Grand Nancy Urban Community has

ordered 25 GLT LRVs from Bombardier Transportation and they will be built by its French-based facility ANF-Industrie. The vehicles, which run on rubber tyres but are guided by a central rail, are expected to be running by 2000.

Bus and trolleybus
Passenger journeys: (1993) Bus 15.3 million, trolleybus 11.5 million
(1994) Bus 13.5 million, trolleybus 10.7 million
(1995) Bus 13.3 million, trolleybus 10.1 million
Vehicle-km: (1993) Bus 4.3 million, trolleybus 2.1 million
(1994) Bus 4.2 million, trolleybus 2.1 million
(1995) Bus 4.8 million, trolleybus 2 million

Number of routes: Bus 16, trolleybus 3, taxibus 3
Route length: Bus 203 km, trolleybus 30 km
On priority right-of-way: 9.3 km

Fleet: 182 buses	
Saviem SC10	25
Berliet PR100	8
Renault R312	64
Renault PR118 articulated	8
Renault PR180 articulated	2
Renault PR180-2 articulated	24
Renault A500	1
Renault PR100-2	2

Average age of fleet: 8 years

Fleet: 48 trolleybuses, all articulated Renault PR180H dual-mode
Trolleybus electrification: 750 V DC

Most intensive service: 5 min

One-person operation: All routes
Fare structure: Flat in urban area central zone, plus three outer zones for suburban routes; reduced rate for 10- and 20-trip ticket; higher fares for journeys after 21.35 on 3 routes; weekly and monthly passes; one-way unlimited transfer within 1 h; bus/rail pass
Fare collection: Payment to driver or prepurchase multijourney tickets or passes; magnetic tickets and passes must be validated on every boarding
Operational control: Computerised vehicle monitoring system based on monitoring of distance run/stops made by vehicles and display of this information to both drivers and central controllers, as well as analysis by computer
Bus priority: Traffic signal control gives bus priority. Pedestrianised bus-only precinct along 1 km of central area street served by trolleybus routes; original 5.8 km of bus lanes extended to 9 km
Average peak-hour speed: In mixed traffic, 13.2 km/h
Operating costs financed by: Fares 47.5 per cent, other commercial sources 5.7 per cent, subsidy/grants 46.8 per cent
Subsidy from: District

SNCF
French National Railways, Nancy/Metz Division
1 rue Henry Maret, F-75010 Metz
Tel: (+33 3) 87 38 81 10   Fax: (+33 3) 87 38 86 00

Current situation: Limited service on seven routes. Hourly 'Metrolor' interurban service to Metz and Thionville; about hourly service to Epinal.

UPDATED

NANJING
Population: 2.2 million
Public transport: Bus and trolleybus services provided by municipal authority; metro in design

Nanjing City Transport Company
Nanjing, Jiangsu Province, People's Republic of China

Bus
Passenger journeys: Approx 300 million (annual)

Number of routes: Approx 20

Fleet: Approx 500 buses, including articulated, mostly locally built

Fare collection: Payment of stage fare to seated conductor; monthly passes

Trolleybus
Passenger journeys: Approx 100 million (annual)

Number of routes: At least 4

Fleet: Over 100 vehicles, mostly articulated

Fare collection: Payment of stage fare to seated conductor; monthly passes

Metro (planned)
Current situation: Plans for a north-south metro line were put forward in 1990. This is Line 1 of what is now proposed as a four-line network totalling 121 km. Approval was granted in late 1994 for construction to start in 1997, and Line 1 is expected to open by 2002.

The initial route will run 16.8 km from Maigaoqiao in the north via an interchange with the city's main railway station to Xiaohang in the southwest; there will be 13 stations. Some 10.2 km in the city centre will be in cut-and-cover tunnel, with the remainder elevated. A fleet of four-car trains will take power from a bottom contact 750 V DC third rail.

VERIFIED

NANTES

Population: City 244,000, conurbation 546,000
Public transport: Bus services provided in conurbation and environs by Semitan, a semi-public undertaking controlled (and 65 per cent owned) by 'Le District' consortium of 21 regional local authorities through representative board and supervised by Transport Commission of the member authorities. Private firms operate+15 routes under contract. Light rail

TAN

Société d'Economie Mixte des Transports en Commun de l'Agglomération Nantaise (Semitan)
PO Box 64605, 3 rue Bellier, F-44046 Nantes Cedex 1, France
Tel: (+33 2) 51 81 77 00   Fax: (+33 2) 51 81 77 70
President: Alain Chénard
Director General: Maudez Guillossou
Staff: 1,050

Passenger journeys: (1995) 62 million
(1996) 62.4 million
(1997) 63.9 million

Operating costs financed by: Fares 41.1 per cent, other commercial sources 5.8 per cent, subsidy/grants 53.1 per cent

Current situation: Passenger traffic on the routes of Semitan (marketed as TAN) and its contract operators has increased substantially under a pro-public transport policy established by the controlling district local authority consortium.
The tramway had a striking effect on the city's public transport (see earlier editions of *JUTS*), accounting for more than half of the 165,000 daily journeys by public transport in 1995. The bus network has been restructured to act largely as a feeder to the tramway; 80 per cent of bus routes serve at least one tram stop.
Developments: 'Le District' adopted a 10-year public transport plan in 1994 which would see construction of tramway Line 3 and extensions to the existing lines bringing the network to 45 km by 2005 (see below).

Bus (Semitan direct operations)
Vehicle-km: (1995) 12.4 million
(1996) 12.7 million
(1997) 12.7 million

Number of routes: 49 (plus 7 night)
Route length: 405 km

Fleet: 287 vehicles
Heuliez	21
Mercedes-Heuliez GX44	149
Heuliez articulated	73
Mercedes-Heuliez O305G articulated	30
Citroën-Gruau C35 midibus	2
Minibuses for disabled service	9
CMB	3
In peak service: 237

Most intensive service: 10 min
One-person operation: All routes
Fare collection: Payment to driver, or prepurchase multitickets or passes with cancellation on board; single tickets valid 1 h
Fare structure: Flat. Various passes/multitickets
Fares collected on board: 15 per cent
Arrangements for elderly/disabled: Minibuses adapted

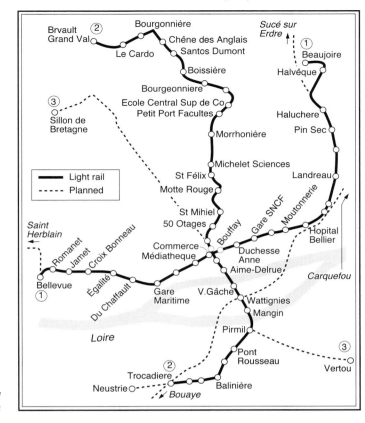

Nantes light rail
0045422

to take wheelchairs. System administered for Semitan by a local disablement research body. Free travel for blind people and escorts, free/reduced for persons over 65 provided by communities participating in Semitan
Average speed: 20 km/h

Bus (contracted)
Services operated under contract by Cariane, FAST, Transports Gautier, CTA, CFIT and Voyages Brounais

Vehicle-km: (1993) 2.9 million
(1996) 3.4 million
(1997) 3.4 million

Current situation: Contract operators run 14 routes in suburban areas with a fleet of 70 buses, plus 49 school buses; they carried 5.3 million passengers in 1992.

Light rail
Type of operation: Light rail, initial route opened 1985

Passenger journeys: (1992) 16.6 million
(1993) 25.8 million
(1995) 35 million
Car-km: (1995) 2.5 million
(1996) 2.5 million
(1997) 2.5 million

Route length: 27 km
Number of routes: 2
Number of stops: 54
Gauge: 1,435 mm
Track: Ri60 grooved rail on street sections, conventional ballasted track with UIC50 rail elsewhere
Electrification: 750 V DC, overhead

Service: Peak 2½-6 min, off-peak 7-8 min
First/last car: 04.30/00.30
Fare structure: As bus
Revenue collection: Automatic ticket vending machines, validators on board
Integration with other modes: Six park-and-ride sites have a total of 905 spaces

Rolling stock: 46 cars
Alsthom articulated (1984/88/94)	M46

Developments: Northwest to southeast Line 3 (9 km) from Sillon de Bretagne to Gare de Vertou is proposed for opening in stages between 2000 and 2005, as well as extensions to both the existing lines. Line 1 would be extended 3 km from Bellevue to Saint Herblain Charron (opening January 2000) and Line 2 from Trocadière to La Neustrie (2 km, opening 2001). A further 29 cars would be required.

SNCF
French National Railways, Nantes Division
2 boulevard de Stalingrad, F-44401 Nantes
Tel: (+33 2) 40 74 45 94   Fax: (+33 2) 40 08 16 03

Current situation: Local trains, mostly dmus refurbished with funds from the Pays de la Loire region, serve four routes.
Developments: LRT services over SNCF lines are planned for an extension of tram line 1 from Haluchere to Sucé-sur-Erdre and a cross-city line from Carquefou to Bouaye.

UPDATED

NAPLES

Population: City 1.2 million, metropolitan area 2 million
Public transport: Bus, trolleybus, tramway and funicular services provided by municipal undertaking with further suburban bus, trolleybus and local railway undertaking, and private suburban bus operators. Suburban trains on Circumvesuviana and other local railways, and on Italian Railways (FS) providing underground cross-city connection. Short metro line

ANM
Azienda Napoletana Mobilità (ANM)
Via GB Marino 1, I-80125 Naples, Italy
Tel: (+39 081) 763 11 11   Fax: (+39 081) 763 20 70

President: Prof Francesco Testa
Board members: Dott Stefano Consiglio, Arch Carla Majorano, Prof Mario Rusciano, Prof Mario Sforza
Staff: 4,165

Passenger boardings: (1996) 129 million

Operating costs financed by: Fares 13 per cent, other commercial sources 2 per cent, subsidy/grants 85 per cent

Current situation: ANM is an independent subsidiary of the municipality of Naples.
Introduction of the all-modes 'Napolipass' in 1994 has stimulated a recovery in patronage of some 20 per cent

Iveco articulated bus on Naples route R2 between the funicular station at Trento and Naples Central station
1999/0038901

Battery-powered Technobus on Naples route E1 providing a circular service   *1999*/0038902

across all operators. Two suburban rail operators, SEPSA and Circumvesuviana, have not joined the pass scheme, but are considering doing so. The intention is to introduce standard ticket issuing and control equipment throughout the region, with the aim of eliminating fare anomalies between operators and cutting the estimated 40 per cent fraudulent travel.

Developments: A fleet of hybrid buses has been introduced as part of the the European Union Centaur/THERMIE programme. Other facets of the Centaur programme include AVIT (Automatic Vehicles Identification Technology) and introductions of wheelchair lifts for disabled people.

Bus and trolleybus
Passenger boardings: (1996) Bus 132.2 million, trolleybus 5.6 million
Vehicle-km: (1997) Bus 27.9 million, trolleybus 1.2 million

Number of routes: Bus 143, trolleybus 4
Route length: (One way) bus 1,796 km, trolleybus 54 km

Fleet: 1,016 buses
In peak service: 485

Fleet: 65 trolleybuses
Alfa 1000AF (1962/63)   65
In peak service: 20

Fare collection: Multiride tickets and passes with validation and cancelling machines on board, or payment to driver or farebox
Fare structure: Stages (3 rates); monthly passes, multiride all-mode and all-operator tickets
Fare evasion control: Roving inspectors
Average peak-hour speed: Bus 13.6 km/h, trolleybus 11.8 km/h

Tramway
Type of operation: Conventional tramway

Passenger boardings: (1997) 8.8 million
Vehicle-km: (1997) 1.9 million

Route length: 51 km
Number of routes: 5

Rolling stock: 72 cars
In peak service: 30

Current situation: 21 km light rail Line 2 under construction, partly incorporating existing rail alignment between Mergellina and Piazza Garibaldi. Part of this line is complete, but it has not been opened.

Funicular
Current situation: Three funiculars are operated (total 2.6 km) with 14 cars, carrying about 1.5 million passengers a year. Annual vehicle-km in 1997 was 42,500.

Developments: A modernisation programme has been carried out and is now almost completed.

CTP

Consorzio Trasporti Pubblici (CTP)
Via Sabbio 19, I-80146 Naples
Tel: (+39 081) 700 11 11   Fax: (+39 081) 700 51 01
President: Claudio Cicatiello
Director General: Marcello Turrini
Director of Finance: Alberto Salvatore
Director of Planning & Quality: Giuseppe Fiorentino
Staff: 2,436

Passenger journeys: (1996) 5.7 million

Current situation: CTP was created in a 1988 reorganisation of public transport; its members are the municipality and province of Naples. It operates a network of suburban and interurban bus services, a self-contained trolleybus system from Naples to Aversa, serving Secondigliano, on a former tramway route, and a local railway.

At least one new trolleybus route is proposed in the Secondigliano area. This would be a branch off Route M15 to act as a feeder to the metro and would use the trackbed of a former narrow-gauge railway line as a segregated 'trolleybusway'.

Bus and trolleybus
Vehicle-km: 27.2 million (annual)

Number of routes: Bus 152, trolleybus 2
Route length: 9,789 km

Fleet: 492 buses
Urban   91
Suburban   130
Interurban   271

Fleet: 22 trolleybuses
Alfa-Romeo/Aerfer/Ocren 1000 (1962)   22

Local railway
Current situation: A fleet of 11 emus is operated on the Alifana railway between Naples and Piedemonte Matese.

FS

Italian Railways (FS), Naples Division

Suburban railway
Current situation: Suburban rail services run on a number of lines into Centrale and Piazza Garibaldi stations. A cross-city connection marketed as 'Metropolitano' links Pozzuoli with P Garibaldi and Gianturco, serving 11 stations and including an underground section through the city centre.

MetroNapoli

MetroNapoli SpA

Current situation: Initial section between Vanvitelli and Colli Aminei opened 1992/93, and extended to Secondigliano in 1995. The central section, 5 km from Vanvitelli to Dante with 5 stations, was held up awaiting further finance, which was eventually granted in late 1995. This section incorporates a dramatic underground spiral loop to descend to the city centre. A further portion, from Dante to Garibaldi (3 km, 5 stations), was at the planning stage in 1997.
Developments: The construction concession for the metro is held by a group of civil engineering companies known as Metropolitane Napoletane.

An extension to the present line, three other lines and two funiculars have been proposed for construction.

Route length: 9.5 km
Number of lines: 1
Number of stations: 9

Naples tram on route 1   *1999*/0038903

Optare Delta on coastal service of Arriva at Haymarket (Andrew Jarosz)   ***1999*/0045408**

Commercial Director: Martin Hams
Finance Director: Colin McPherson
Staff: 2,200

Current situation: Operates services in Tyne & Wear, County Durham and parts of Cleveland, Northumberland and North Yorkshire. Also operates a network of limited-stop, regional and commuter services, local minibus networks, bus and coach hire, coaching holidays and long-distance coach contracts.

The company comprises a number of operating subsidiaries — Go Coastline, Go Gateshead, Go Wear Buses, Go Northern.

Developments: Considerable commercial expansion of the network operated by low-floor buses took place in 1996, with involvement in quality partnerships with local authorities.

Vehicle-tracking and real-time information displays introduced in 1996 on one group of routes in the Gateshead area.

Bus
Passenger journeys: (1994/95) 86 million
(1996/97) 81 million
(1997/98) 84.5 million
Vehicle-km: (1994/95) 54 million
(1996/97) 46 million
(1997/98) 44 million

Fleet: 738 vehicles
Leyland Atlantean/Olympian, Metrobus double-deck	254
Dennis Dart/Lance/Javelin, Volvo B6/B10B/B10M, Leyland Leopard/Lynx/National, DAF, Optare Delta, Optare Excel, Scania, Bristol LH single-deck	351
Iveco, Renault, Mercedes, Metrorider minibus	105
Bova, DAF, Dennis, Leyland, Scania, Volvo coach	28

In peak service: 620
On order: 20 Optare Excel, 15 DAF and 22 Optare Solo single-deck low-floor buses, and 16 Volvo Olympian double-deck buses

One-person operation: 100 per cent
Fare collection: Payment to driver or prepurchase. Conversion to Wayfarer 3 system with magnetic card reader capability in progress; stored-value magnetic tickets
Operational control: Radio
Integration with other modes: Extensive integration continues with metro
Operating costs financed by: Fares 97.5 per cent, subsidy/grants 2.5 per cent
New vehicles financed by: Internal resources and leasing

Arriva North East
Northumbria Motor Services Ltd
6 Portland Terrace, Jesmond, Newcastle upon Tyne NE2 1QQ
Tel: (+44 191) 281 13 13   Fax: (+44 191) 281 46 34
Managing Director: Stephen Noble
Engineering Director: John Greaves

Current situation: Formed as Northumbria Motor Services in 1986 when the United Automobile Company was split. Most routes run into Newcastle from outside the city, but a sizeable network has been developed in the northern suburbs and new developing areas. The company became part of the Arriva group in 1996.

Fleet: 366 vehicles
Volvo Olympian/Scania/Leyland Olympian/ Bristol VR double-deck	130
Leyland National/Scania/Optare Delta single-deck	86
Mercedes/MCW/Optare minibus	110
Leyland/Volvo coach	40

Other operators
Current situation: A few smaller companies operate both commercial and secured routes in Newcastle and the surrounding Tyne & Wear County. These include Amberline, Classic Buses, ERB, Kingsley's North Rider, Redby, Snaiths, Welco and Wrights.

Nexus
Tyne & Wear Passenger Transport Executive
Cuthbert House, All Saints, Newcastle upon Tyne NE1 2DA
Tel: (+44 191) 203 33 33   Fax: (+44 191) 203 31 80
Director General: Michael Parker
Head of Operations: Ian Clayton

Current situation: Following the local government changes, a joint board of district council nominees — the Passenger Transport Authority — determines policy within a budget established by the levying district councils, whose total spending is constrained by government limits. The Passenger Transport Executive, which adopted the marketing name Nexus in 1996, carries out these policies and remains directly responsible for metro and ferry services. It is empowered to subsidise bus services not operated on a commercial basis, and also to provide travel information and administer concessionary fares schemes in on behalf of PTA.

Since deregulation, the former policy of integration between bus and metro has had to be promoted on a commercial basis with additional metro feeder services secured by Nexus. There remains a high level of bus/metro interchange, with 23 per cent of passengers arriving at stations by bus; 29 per cent of passengers use Travelcards.

Although Nexus no longer operates buses, it secures socially necessary services not provided by commercial operators, and is involved in management of some bus stations on behalf of the local authorities which own them.
Developments: In their policy document called Towards 2010 published in 1997, the PTA and Nexus put forward a range of improvements thought necessary if the drift away from public transport was to be stemmed. Since bus deregulation in 1986, there has been a decline of 27 per cent in public transport patronage in the region, though metro patronage showed signs of recovery at the end of 1997. Amongst the suggestions is a network of busways to be run as metro feeders.

Metro
Type of operation: Full metro, first line opened 1980

Passenger journeys: (1994/95) 37.2 million
(1995/96) 36.5 million
(1996/97) 35.3 million

Route length: 59.1 km
   in tunnel: 6.4 km
Number of lines: 2
Number of stations: 46
Gauge: 1,435 mm
Track: BS113A rail laid on tied concrete sleepers in tunnels; on concrete and timber sleepers with ballast on surface; PACT slab track on Byker Viaduct
Max gradient: 3.3%
Minimum curve radius: 210 m
Electrification: 1.5 kV DC, overhead

Service: 7/8-10-15 min
First/last train: 05.22/00.14
Fare structure: Zonal
Integration with other modes: High level of integration;

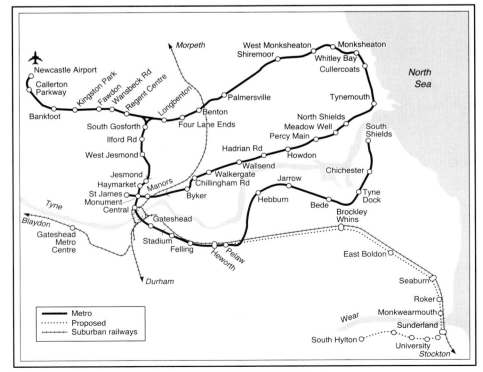

Tyne & Wear metro   0045918

county-wide Travelticket, plus substantial multimodal single through-ticket network (Metrolink Transfares); through-ticketing to airport from rail stations nationwide
Fare collection: Crouzet automatic ticket vending machines; roving inspectors
Signalling: Two-aspect lineside signals with repeaters; inductive train stop equipment to prevent over-running signals; Philips Vetag vehicle identification system
Operating costs financed by: Fares 84 per cent, grants

from central and local government, and European Social Fund 16 per cent

Rolling stock: 90 cars
Metro-Cammell (1979/80)   M90

Developments: Various options were considered for extending the metro to Sunderland, and in 1993 it was decided to adopt a 19 km route involving sharing existing

tracks with local trains between Pelaw and Sunderland. Beyond Sunderland station a short extension would run over disused rail alignment to Sunderland University and South Hylton. Parliamentary approval was given early in 1999.

A proposal for a northern extension to Cramlington was rejected in a study carried out for Northumberland County Council in 1996, but a link to Ashington was deemed worthy of further study. Nexus is also involved in the East Coast main line study into ways of improving local services on the route, which runs north and south of Newcastle.

Ferry

Current situation: Cross-Tyne ferry operations by Nexus between North and South Shields carried 598,000 passengers in 1996/97. There is half-hourly service; journey time is 7 min; two vessels.

Northern Spirit

Northern Spirit Ltd
Station Rise, York YO1 1HT
Tel: (+44 1904) 65 30 22   Fax: (+44 1904) 52 37 91
Managing Director: Paul Davison

Type of operation: Local railway

Current situation: Diesel service operated on three routes totalling 82 km. Newcastle—Sunderland line (every 15 minutes) receives Section 20 grant payments from Nexus, carrying 2.1 million passengers in 1997. Services also run to Gateshead Metro Centre (every 15 minutes), and to Hexham on the line to Carlisle (about half-hourly), and to Morpeth (irregular).

Metro train in red livery   *1996*   **UPDATED**

NEW ORLEANS

Population: City 497,000, city-region 1.2 million
Public transport: Regional Transit Authority controls and operates bus services and tramway. Authority also supervises other bus operations including routes contracted out to private sector. River ferries operated by Bridge Authority

Regional Transit Authority

New Orleans Regional Transit Authority
6700 Plaza Drive, New Orleans, Louisiana 70127, USA
Tel: (+1 504) 242 26 00   Fax: (+1 504) 248 36 37
General Manager: John F Potts Jr
Assistant General Manager, Operations:
    W Lee Burner II
Staff: 1,414

Passenger boardings: (1993) 48.9 million
(1994) 50.7 million
(1995) 70.5 million

Operating costs financed by: Fares 45 per cent, other commercial sources 4 per cent, subsidy/grants 10 per cent, tax levy 41 per cent
Subsidy from: FTA 19.7 per cent, local sales tax 80 per cent

Current situation: The RTA, controlled by a board appointed by the City of New Orleans and Jefferson Parish Council, was created in 1979 and took over transit operations in 1983. In 1985 the RTA took over transit operations in the neighbouring city of Kenner. Contracted operations ended in 1989, when a local management team, Transit Management of Southeast Louisiana, took over.

An increase in the sales tax allocated to the RTA from ½ cent to 1 cent was approved in 1985 and is used to fund capital improvements (25 per cent) and operations (75 per cent). The RTA demands that 45 per cent of operating costs be covered from fares.

The tramway plays a modest part in the city's transit. Several proposals exist for modern light rail routes, in particular in the former tram right-of-way in the median of busy Canal Street from the Waterfront to City Park Avenue (6.4 km), on which construction is expected to start in late 1999, to link the airport with downtown (21 km) using mostly existing rail right-of-way, and several extensions. A new fleet of 35 cars would be required (see below).

The 1988-built Riverfront line has been converted to 1,586 mm gauge to standardise the rolling stock fleet.

Bus

Passenger boardings: (1993) 42.9 million
(1994) 44.3 million
(1995) 63.4 million
Vehicle-km: (1995) 20.5 million

Number of routes: 62
Route length: 936 km
On priority right-of-way: 3.5 km

Fleet: 553 vehicles
Blue Bird (1986/87)   36
GMC (1979)   173
MAN 792 (1985/86)   165
Orion V (1990)   13
Boyerville trolley replicas (1989)   8
New Flyer D40 (1994)   73
Orion (1996)   85
In peak service: 420

Most intensive service: 2-3 min
One-person operation: All routes
Fare collection: Cash or token to GFI electronic farebox; monthly or visitor pass
Fare structure: Flat base ordinary and express fares;

In New Orleans, trams newly built in the Authority's workshops will replace these buses in a restored Canal Street rail service by 2001 (Van Wilkins)
1999/0038904

prepurchase tokens; 10 cent coupon for multitransfers; monthly pass (not valid in Kenner); 1- and 3-day visitor passes
Operational control: Route inspectors; on-bus radio
Integration between modes: Park-and-ride
Arrangements for elderly/disabled: 'The Lift' special door-to-door lift service operated under contract carried 214,000 passengers in 1994; some fixed-route buses lift-equipped; dial-a-ride; reduced fare
Average peak-hour speed: 16.9 km/h

Tramway

Type of operation: Conventional tramway, opened 1835

Passenger boardings: (1993) 5.9 million
(1994) 6.1 million
(1995) 7.1 million
Car-km: (Annual) 1.1 million

Route length: 26 km
Number of lines: 2
Gauge: 1,586 mm
Electrification: 600 V DC, overhead

Service: Peak 4-5 min, off-peak 7 min; 24 h service on St Charles route
Fare structure: Flat (as bus)
One-person operation: All cars

Rolling stock: 54 cars
Perley Thomas Car Co (1923)   M37
W2 (ex-Melbourne)   M2
PCC (ex-SEPTA Philadelphia)   M12
Others   M3

Current situation: The St Charles route runs along a median strip in St Charles Avenue and is the last remaining US tram line to run pre-PCC cars. It is designated a national monument. A three-year refurbishment was completed in 1990. Unconnected Riverfront route opened 1988 and extended in 1990.
Developments: Refurbishment of 1923-vintage cars was completed in 1995, and the Riverfront line was converted from 1,435 mm to 1,586 mm gauge in 1997. Further extensions planned (see above).

RTA has bought 12 PCC tramcars from SEPTA Philadelphia. Three are to be rebuilt with Perley Thomas replica bodies and wheelchair access for use on the Riverfront line. Further replica cars based on the Perley

Thomas veterans have been built in RTA's shops for the Canal Street line.

Other operators

Current situation: Services in Jefferson Parish are provided by two operators — Louisiana Transit (east bank), and Westside Transit (west bank). There are 13 routes, five of which run to central New Orleans. Jefferson Parish itself owns the fleet of 29 Flxible buses which operates the east bank service; a further 33 Flxibles serve the west bank.

Mississippi River Bridge Authority
2001 Behrman Avenue, New Orleans, Louisiana 70114

Ferry

Current situation: Operates a single ferry route across the Mississippi river, with three vessels, carrying foot passengers and vehicles.

UPDATED

The transit authority at New Orleans is building new trams using a 1923 design but equipped with new bogies and controls from ČKD of the Czech Republic (Van Wilkins) **1999**/0038905

NEW YORK

Population: 7.3 million, metropolitan area 13.2 million
Public transport: Bus, metro (subway) and two suburban rail networks operated by various subsidiaries of the Metropolitan Transportation Authority including suburban bus operations contracted for Nassau County. MTA, also responsible for seven bridges and two tunnels, is governed by a board representing city and suburban communities served. A regional metro (PATH) is operated between New York and New Jersey by the Port Authority. A number of private bus lines provide substantial additional suburban and commuter services from and within New York under City Department of Transportation, and other commuter bus services operate from New Jersey (see also Newark/New Jersey). There are also some private door-to-door minibus pick-up services and express routes to Manhattan. A private bus operation is contracted for the Westchester County area. Ferries operate to Staten Island, New Jersey and Long Island leisure areas

MTA

Metropolitan Transportation Authority (MTA)
347 Madison Avenue, New York, New York 10017, USA
Tel: (+1 212) 878 70 00   Fax: (+1 212) 878 70 30/70 31
www: http://www.mya.nyc.ny.us
Chair: E Virgil Conway
Executive Director: Marc V Shaw
Chief Financial Officer: Stephen V Reitano
Headquarters staff: 294

Passenger journeys: (All modes)
(1995) 1,711 million
(1996) 1,657 million
(1997) 1,718 million

Operating costs covered by: Fares 50.9 per cent, toll income 15.4 per cent, other commercial sources 2.2 per cent, subsidy/grants 31.4 per cent

Current situation: Created in 1965 by New York State as the Metropolitan Commuter Transportation Authority, it was initially given responsibility for purchase and rehabilitation of the Long Island Rail Road. In 1968 it was renamed MTA and its powers expanded to include additional agencies. These include the MTA Long Island Rail Road, MTA NYC Transit, MTA Metro-North Railroad, MTA Bridges & Tunnels, MTA Staten Island Railway, MTA Card Company, and MTA Long Island Bus. Some 13.2 million people in 14 counties are served.

Over 750,000 vehicles daily use the seven bridges and two tunnels operated by MTA Bridges & Tunnels. Surplus revenue from bridge and tunnel tolls helps support the other MTA operations, amounting to $611 million in 1996.
Developments: In 1995, the new Chairman, E Virgil Conway, announced a revised $11.9 billion five-year capital programme, of which the principal feature is expenditure of $1.9 billion on 840 metro cars, $888 million

on refurbishment of 70 metro stations, $610 million on new and refurbished emus for Long Island Rail Road, and $282 million emus for Metro-North. In addition, $700 million was allocated for purchase of 2,300 new buses for NYCTA.

In 1996 these plans were further revised and confirmed, together with increased financial support from the city, state and federal governments designed to eliminate MTA's deficit and ensure financial stability through to the end of the century. MTA's costs were to be reduced by $3 billion over the 1995/99 period, $2 billion of which had been achieved by the end of 1996. This stabilisation in its finances allowed MTA to introduce the all-modes MetroCard in 1997 and multiride discounts in 1998, made possible by introduction of automated fare collection systems throughout the network. By the end of 1997, MetroCard accounted for almost 60 per cent of ticket sales, and ridership was up significantly on both bus and metro. Over time, the new fares policies are expected to generate between 90 and 100 million additional journeys.

MTA New York City Transit

New York City Transit Authority (NYCTA)
370 Jay Street, Brooklyn, New York 11201
Tel: (+1 718) 330 30 00   Fax: (+1 718) 243 45 66
President: Lawrence G Reuter
Executive Vice President: Barbara R Spencer

Senior Vice Presidents
 Subways: Joseph E Hofmann
 Buses: Millard L Seay
 Operations Support: George A Carrano
 Capital Program Management: Mysore Nagaraja
 Customer Services: David Goldenberg (Acting)
Staff: 42,617 (excludes Staten Island Railway)

Passenger journeys: (Bus and metro)
(1995) 1,559 million
(1996) 1,551 million
(1997) 1,560 million

Operating costs financed by: Fares 71.8 per cent, other commercial sources including tolls 4.1 per cent, subsidy/grants 7.8 per cent, tax levy 16.3 per cent
Subsidy from: Federal, state and local government, and bridge subsidy

Current situation: Almost all surface public transport in the five boroughs of New York City is provided by the TA and its subsidiaries.
Developments: Free bus/metro transfers for MetroCard customers introduced 1997, followed by 10 per cent discount on MetroCard purchase over $15 in 1998. 7-day and monthly passes for unlimited travel on both modes introduced July 1998. These measures appear to have reversed the long-term decline in bus ridership in particular, with preliminary 1998 figures showing significant increases.

MTA New York City Bus RTS buses (George Bennet) **1999**/0045411

Train departing Smith-9th station in Brooklyn with lower Manhattan in the background (Van Wilkins)

1999/0038908

Type of operation: Full metro, initial underground route opened 1904

Passenger journeys: (1995) 1,093 million
(1996) 1,109 million
(1997) 1,132 million
Car-km: (1995) 487 million
(1996) 498 million
(1997) 592 million

Route length: 371 km
  in tunnel: 223 km
Number of lines: 25
Number of stations: 468
  in tunnel: 277
  elevated: 153
Gauge: 1,435 mm
Track: Timber sleepers on ballast or embedded in concrete, or concrete with resilient pads
Tunnel: Cut-and-cover, under-river bored tunnel, cast-iron with concrete liners, some concrete horse-shoe
Electrification: 625 V DC, third rail

Service: Peak 2-10 min, off-peak 5-15 min, late night 20 min; 24 h service at most stations
Fare structure: Flat; MetroCard availability as bus, with one free transfer to Staten island metro or any local bus of NYCTA or contracted private operators
Fare collection: Automatic turnstiles accessed by token or electronic fare card (MetroCard)
Operating costs financed by: Fares 85.4 per cent, other commercial sources 2.1 per cent, FTA, state and local government subsidies 3.9 per cent, tax levy 8.5 per cent
One-person operation: On five shuttles and Line G only; may be extended to other routes at night and weekends during 1999
Signalling: Wayside signals/train control

Rolling stock: 5,799 cars
51 ft cars
AC&F R26 (1959/60)   M110
AC&F R28 (1960/61)   M100
St Louis Car R29 (1962)   M236

MTA New York City Bus

Staff: 11,696

Passenger journeys: (1995) 460 million
(1996) 436 million
(1997) 423 million
Vehicle-km: (1995) 143 million
(1996) 138 million
(1997) 156 million

Number of routes: 234
Route length: (One way) 2,695 km

Fleet: 4,037 vehicles, all air conditioned
GMC RTS 04 (1981/85)   1,156
TMC RTS 06 (1986/87)   589
TMC RTS 06 (1990)   396
TMC RTS 06 (1993)   167
BIA Orion V (1993)   211
TMC RTS 06 (1994)   104
BIA Orion V (1995)   231
Nova RTS 06 (1996)   600
Remanufactured (1996)   24
BIA Orion V (1996)   50
Remanufactured (1997)   63
New Flyer articulated (1997)   70
Nova RTS 06 (1998)   348
Remanufactured (1998)   3
MCI (1998)   16
Nova RTS 06 (1998/99)   5
Orion hybrid-electric   4
In peak service: 3,507
On order: 1,322 from various builders

Most intensive service: 1½ min
One-person operation: All routes
Fare collection: Prepurchase token, electronic fare card (MetroCard) or cash to farebox (exact fare in coins); tokens and MetroCards sold at metro stations and retail outlets
Fare structure: Flat, higher for express routes; pay-per-ride MetroCard with 10 per cent bonus on cards value $15 or more; 7- or 30-day unlimited-ride MetroCard (higher charge for express); one free transfer to any NYCTA bus or Jamaica Buses, Green Bus, Command Bus and Queens Surface services; one free transfer to metro with MetroCard
Operational control: Mobile radio link to central dispatch
Arrangements for elderly/disabled: A half-fare pass is offered in co-operation with the NY City Department for the Aging, the NY City DoT and MTA; seniors' fare concessions partially financed by reimbursement from the City of New York; bus fleet entirely lift-equipped; Access-A-Ride contracted demand-response service provides door-to-door transport for ADA eligible persons at standard bus fares, carried 0.7 million passengers in 1997; this is provided by three private contractors using 237 vehicles
Operating costs financed by: Fares 51 per cent, other commercial sources 7.1 per cent, subsidy/grants 13.1 per cent, tax levy 28.7 per cent
Source of subsidy: City and State of New York, FTA grants, MTA Bridge & Tunnel Authority surplus
New vehicles financed by: Capital programme funds

Developments: Building on the initial success of MetroCard, further variants were introduced in 1998,

including 7- and 30-day passes. A 10 per cent bonus was added to MetroCards valued at $15 or over, and Express fares were cut by 25 per cent.

In 1998, a total of 1,695 buses were on order for delivery through to 2002, including standard buses, articulateds for high-volume routes, express coaches for premium fare passengers, and low-floor types. CNG-powered buses are included, along with some hybrid-electric types following trials in 1998.

An automatic vehicle location and control system was commissioned for pilot testing during 1998 at the 126th Street depot in Manhattan. With real-time tracking of bus location, the system is expected to improve service reliability, whilst it will also provide real-time information to electronic signs at bus stops on two routes under the 'ITS about Time' demonstration programme of intelligent transport systems technologies.

MTA New York City Subway

Staff: 25,078

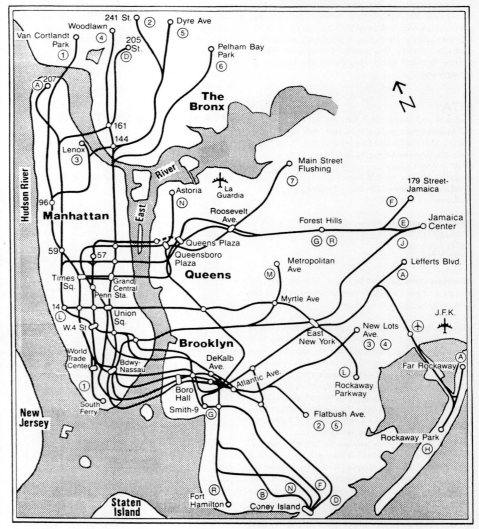

New York's metro

NIZHNY NOVGOROD
Population: 1.4 million
Public transport: Bus and trolleybus/tramway services operated by municipal undertakings; metro

Upravlenie Automobil'novo Transporta
Upravlenie Automobil'novo Transporta
Nizhny Novgorod, Russia

Bus
Passenger journeys: 119 million (annual)

Current situation: Bus, express bus and fixed-route taxibus services are operated.

Fare collection: Prepurchase tickets; day tickets for bus only or combinations of other modes

Fleet: Comprises Ikarus 260/280, LIAZ 677/5256, LAZ 695, MAN and others ex-German cities, and PAZ 3205 taxis

Munitsipal'noe Tramvaino-Trolleibusnoe Predpriyatie
Munitsipal'noe Tramvaino-Trolleibusnoe Predpriyatie
Yaroslavskaya ul 25, Nizhny Novgorod 603000
Tel: (+7 8312) 33 23 15
Director: Pyotr Ruzavin

Trolleybus
Passenger journeys: 175 million (annual)

Current situation: A fleet of about 250 Uritsky ZIU9 trolleybuses is operated over 21 routes extending to some 300 route-km. The system comprises three portions, of which one on the right bank of the Oka river is physically separate.
Developments: The World Bank has funded purchase of 40 ZIU9 trolleybuses (modernised ZIU 52642).

Tramway
Current situation: There are 15 routes, many on segregated right-of-way, extending to some 183 route-km.

Rolling stock: Approx 380 cars
ČKD Tatra T3	About M190
ČKD Tatra T3m	M32
Kirov KTM5	About M130
Riga RVZ6	M10
KTM8/KTM8M	M21

Upravlenie Metropolitena
Type of operation: Full metro, initial route opened 1985

Passenger journeys: 66 million (annual)

Route length: 13 km
Number of lines: 2
Number of stations: 12
Gauge: 1,524 mm
Electrification: 825 V DC, third rail

Service: Peak 2 min, off-peak 6 min
Fare structure: Flat
Fare collection: Token to turnstile

Rolling stock: 50 cars
Mytischy G-1	M50

Current situation: Line 1 opened 1985, linking suburban industrial area with the main railway station; extended 1986. Further 15.1 km Line 2 with nine stations under construction, of which portion with two stations opened 1994.

UPDATED

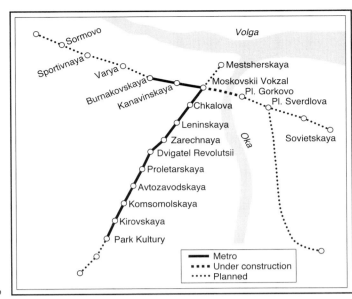

Nizhny Novgorod metro

Tramway at Avtozavod (GAZ automobile factory) with KTM5 cars (Aare Olander) **1999**/0038914

Nizhny Novgorod metro station (Aare Olander) **1999**/0038915

NORFOLK

Population: City 260,000, area served 1 million
Public transport: Bus and ferry services provided by public authority controlled by representative board; paratransit and vanpool schemes operated; light rail planned

Tidewater Regional Transit

Tidewater Transportation District Commission
PO Box 2096, 1500 Monticello Avenue, Norfolk, Virginia 23501, USA
Tel: (+1 757) 640 62 00   Fax: (+1 757) 640 63 03
Chair: Cameron Pitts
Executive Director: L A Kimball
Operating Manager: Milton Woodhouse
Staff: 430

Current situation: Established in 1973, TTDC is a regional transportation authority covering five cities in southeastern Virginia — Portsmouth, Norfolk, Virginia Beach, Suffolk and Chesapeake — with a service area of some 1,600 km². TTDC is responsible for planning, regulation, acquisition, operation or provision of public transport. It does not have taxing authority so relies on annual contributions from the state and cities served.

In the many low-density areas not served by fixed routes, contracted on-demand services, paratransit and vanpool schemes (called Maxi-Ride) are available on prior reservation. Paratransit carried 194,000 passengers in 1994/95.

Vanpooling was launched in 1977 with vehicles leased by TRT to employees. The number of leasings has declined from a peak of 103 vehicles carrying 455,000 passengers in 1981, to 13 carrying 109,000 in 1994/95. TRT also leases vehicles to communities and private-interest groups.

Developments: TRT has implemented the multicentred timed transfer system (known as Direct Transfer) which brings all fixed-route and paratransit services together in a unified network. Services have timed connections with each other on a 30 min (sometimes 60 min) interval basis at a number of transfer centres. All transport services, including taxis, have been encouraged to participate.

Merger of TRT with neighbouring Peninsula Transportation District Commission is under consideration; the two organisations would form a regional transportation authority covering the entire seven-city Hampton Roads region. Executive Director Kim Kimball was appointed in 1996 to take the merger forward.

Bus

Passenger boardings: (Including ferry)
(1993/94) 8.4 million
(1994/95) 8.2 million
(1995/96) 8.7 million
Vehicle-km: (1993/94) 9 million
(1994/95) 9.8 million
(1995/96)

Number of routes: 30
Route length: (One way) 472 km

Fleet: 163 vehicles, plus 85 vans on contract operations
Grumman Flxible (1973)	3
GMC/TRS (1980)	15
Flxible Metro (1989/90)	62
Boyertown replica trolley (1983-88)	28
BIA 02501 (1992)	6
BIA 05501 (1993/95)	49
Dodge B350 van (contract)	85
Chance replica trams (1996)	15
In peak service: 125	

Most intensive service: 15 min
One-person operation: All services
Fare collection: Payment to driver or prepurchase ticket, token or pass
Fare structure: Flat; free transfer; 10-ticket carnets
Arrangements for elderly/disabled: Fleet of Handi-Ride vans and minibuses, 60 lift-equipped; network of accessible fixed-route services; paratransit services carried 254,000 passengers in 1995/96
Integration with other modes: Carpools, lease of vans to vanpool participants; park-and-ride
Operating costs financed by: Fares 39 per cent, subsidy/grants 61 per cent
Subsidy from: FTA 12 per cent, state 24 per cent, local 25 per cent

Ferry

Current situation: Service across the Elizabeth river between Norfolk and Portsmouth is aimed at both residents and visitors, but most use is for leisure purposes. The three vessels carry about 0.5 million passengers annually.

Light rail (planned)

Current situation: A 28 km light rail line with 13 stations to link Norfolk and Virginia Beach, utilising the alignment of an under-utilised main line railway, is at the planning stage. Light rail was selected as the preferred choice of mode to serve the Norfolk—Virginia Beach corridor in 1996, and preliminary engineering and environmental impact studies began in 1997. Construction is not expected to start before 2001.

Also under study is a link to the Norfolk naval base, the airport and other cities in the region.

VERIFIED

NOTTINGHAM

Population: 272,000
Public transport: Most bus services in city and suburbs provided by municipally owned company, with others operated by private firms. Local rail service; light rail proposed

Nottingham City Transport

Nottingham City Transport Ltd
Lower Parliament Street, Nottingham NG1 1GG, England
Tel: (+44 115) 950 57 45   Fax: (+44 115) 950 44 25
Managing Director: John Pope
Engineering Director: John Lowrie
Staff: 1,109

Current situation: The city established its bus undertaking as a separate company in 1986. The fleet of

Erewash Valley Services of Ilkeston, acquired in 1988, was integrated in 1990. South Notts of Gotham was acquired and integrated in 1991. Pathfinder (Newcastle) was acquired in 1991.

Bus
Number of routes: 100
Route length: (One way) 284 km

Fleet: 421 vehicles
Leyland Atlantean AN68 double-deck	53
Leyland Lion double-deck	18
Scania double-deck	34
Volvo Citybus double-deck	47
Leyland Olympian double-deck	2
Volvo Olympian double-deck	28
Dennis Arrow double-deck	4
Leyland National single-deck	14

Leyland Lynx single-deck	28
Scania single-deck	10
Volvo B6 single-deck	13
Volvo B10B single-deck	20
Volvo B10M single-deck	5
Scania L113 low-floor single-deck	9
Dennis Dart SLF low-floor single-deck	1
Optare Excel low-floor single-deck	5
Leyland Atlantean single-deck	1
Leyland Tiger/Royal Tiger/Bova coach	8
Renault midibus	27
Mercedes minibus	51
Optare Metrorider minibus	33
Optare Solo low-floor midibus	10

Most intensive service: 2½-5 min
One-person operation: 100 per cent
Fare collection: Farebox and Eurofare
Fare structure: Stage; 1-, 2- and 4-week network passes
Fare evasion control: Uniformed inspectors
Operational control: Route inspectors/mobile radio
Arrangements for elderly/disabled: Free travel in city and half rate in county area, financed by rate fund grants
Average distance between stops: 200-250 m
Average peak-hour speed: 15 km/h
Bus priority: City-centre access priority by sections of bus-only road

Barton

Barton Buses
Mansfield Road, Heanor DE75 7BG
Tel: (+44 1773) 53 63 13
Managing Director: Brian King
Operations Director: Ian Morgan

Current situation: Barton operates rural and interurban routes with coaches adapted for local services. In 1989 the company was taken over by the holding company which owns Trent Motor Traction. The fleet profile has been improved by replacement of 20-year-old coaches with new and second-hand buses. Low-floor Rainbow buses were added in 1998.

Fleet: 109 vehicles
Leyland National/Optare Delta/Optare Excel/ Dennis Lance/Dennis Dart single-deck	103
Coaches	6

Nottingham City Transport Dennis Arrow on Forest park-and-ride service (Andrew Jarosz)   **1999**/0045409

Other operators

Current situation: Two operators, Camm's (10 buses) and Dunn Line (24), run competitive local services, while Trent and East Midland run long-distance services.

Central Trains

Central Trains Limited
PO Box 4323, Birmingham B1 1TH
Tel: (+44 121) 643 44 44   Fax: (+44 121) 644 44 61
Managing Director: Nick Brown

Type of operation: Local railway

Current situation: Services run into Nottingham from stations on lines to Derby (26 km), Grantham (35 km), Newark (28 km) and Worksop (51 km); diesel-worked, about hourly service.
Developments: Reopening of the local railway to Mansfield and Worksop was completed in 1998.

Light rail (planned)

Greater Nottingham Rapid Transit Ltd
4-8 Regent Street, Nottingham NG1 5BQ
Tel: (+44 115) 950 22 33   Fax: (+44 115) 950 03 20
General Manager: Pat Armstrong

Current situation: Construction is expected to start in 1999 on a light rail route, Nottingham Express Transit (NET), linking the city's Midland station with Hucknall and Cinderhill to the north. The 14 km route will run 4 km on-street from the city centre to Wilkinson Street where it will join the reopened railway to Mansfield and Worksop (see above), over which it is proposed to share the alignment to Hucknall. A short branch runs to Cinderhill and Phoenix Park. There will be 23 stops, five of them with park-and-ride spaces for a total of 3,000 cars. A fleet of 15 cars will be required.

Barton Buses low-floor Optare Excel on Rainbow 5 service (Andrew Jarosz)   *1999*/0045410

This is the initial route of a proposed network of six lines extending to 45 km. It is being promoted by GNRT, which is a joint venture between Nottingham City Council, Nottinghamshire County Council, and Nottingham Development Enterprise, representing 13 private-sector investors.
Developments: Parliamentary approval for Line 1 to Hucknall was granted in 1994, and government approval came in December 1998. Construction begins in 1999 with services operating in 2002.

In 1995 a private-sector consortium, consisting of manufacturer Adtranz, civil contractor Tarmac and operators Transdev and Nottingham City Transport, joined the promoters to develop the project. Now known as Arrow Light Rail, this group was awarded the 30-year concession to design, build and operate the line in 1997.

UPDATED

NOVOSIBIRSK

Population: 1.5 million
Public transport: Bus and trolleybus/tramway services provided by separate municipal undertakings. Metro; suburban rail

Avtotrans

Avtotrans
Novosibirsk, Russia

Bus

Passenger journeys: 90 million (annual)

Route length: 637 km
Fleet: About 400 vehicles, including Ikarus 260/280, LIAZ 677 and LAZ 695

One-person operation: All routes
Fare collection: Cash to conductor
Fare structure: Flat
Average peak-hour speed: 19 km/h

Urban Electric Transport

Urban Electric Passenger Transport Executive
Lenina ul 59, Novosibirsk 630004
Tel: (+7 3832) 22 08 44
General Manager: B Y Ten

Trolleybus

Passenger journeys: (1990) 121.2 million

Number of routes: 30
Route length: 500 km
Fleet: Approx 250 vehicles
Uritsky ZIU9	About 240
ZIU10	8

One-person operation: All routes
Fare collection: As bus
Fare structure: Flat
Average peak-hour speed: 19 km/h

Tramway

Staff: 639

Type of operation: Conventional tramway

Passenger journeys: (1990) 119.4 million

Number of routes: 18
Route length: 353.7 km
Electrification: 550 V DC, overhead

Rolling stock: 260 cars
Riga RVZ6	M30
Ust-Katav KTM5	M230

Current situation: Changes took place in 1990 on opening of the metro spur from Sibirskaya to Vokzalnaya (main station), when the network was split into two separate systems. Elimination of all but one route from the

Novosibirsk metro

ZIU9 trolleybus at the central market   *1997*

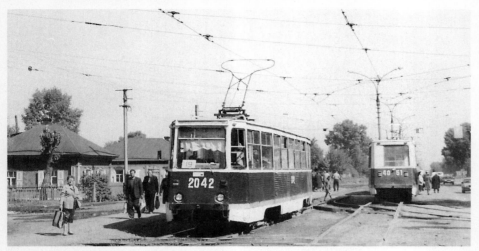

KTM5 cars on Route 19 in the southwestern suburbs   *1997*

Route length: 13 km
Number of lines: 2
Number of stations: 10
Gauge: 1,520 mm
Electrification: 825 V DC, third rail

Service: Peak 3-5 min, off-peak 4-10 min
Fare structure: Flat
Signalling: Full ATC with first Russian application of computers to train control

Rolling stock: 76 cars

Current situation: Initial section of Line 1 opened 1985 along with short section of Line 2 to the main railway station opened 1990. Line 1 extended north from Sibirskaya to Pl Kalinina in 1992.

Planned four-line system totalling 52 km with 36 stations now augmented by proposed orbital Line 5. Construction of Kirov Line 2 (4.2 km with five stations) started 1987.

city centre has been balanced by new construction in the western suburbs.

Novosibirsk Metropolitan

Novosibirsk Metropolitan Municipal Enterprise
Ul Serebrennikovskaya 34, 630099 Novosibirsk
Tel: (+7 3832) 22 31 70
General Manager: V I Demin

First Deputy Director: V A Lokhmatov
Chief Engineer: N P Balakleevskiy
Staff: 1,500

Type of operation: Full metro, initial route opened 1985

Passenger journeys: (1991) 62.4 million
(1992) 82 million
(1993) 90.9 million

Suburban rail
Passenger journeys: (1990) 53.9 million

Current situation: Suburban trains operate over several routes extending to some 550 km, electrified 3 kV DC; fleet of 378 emu cars.

VERIFIED

NUREMBURG

Population: 492,000, region 2.1 million
Public transport: Bus, tramway and metro services operated in Nürnberg and on behalf of the municipalities of Erlangen and Fürth by VAG, a subsidiary of municipally owned utilities holding company Städtische Werke Nürnberg GmbH. Regional metro (S-Bahn) services operated by German Railway (DB). All public transport in area around Nuremburg, including local bus services in Schwabach and regional bus services, are co-ordinated by the regional transit authority VGN

VGN

Verkehrsverbund Grossraum Nürnberg GmbH
Rothenburger Strasse 9, D-90443 Nuremburg, Germany
Tel: (+49 911) 27 07 50   Fax: (+49 911) 270 75 50
www:www.vgn.de
Directors: Norbert Mahr
  Dr Willi Weisskopf

Passenger journeys: (All modes and operators)
(1995) 180 million
(1996) 168.8 million
(1997) 187.2 million

Fare structure: Zonal, free transfer between all modes and operators
Fare collection: Season tickets (62 per cent), multiride tickets (24 per cent), single tickets (10 per cent), others

(4 per cent); vending machines at metro stations and all tram stops, sales by driver only on buses
Operating costs financed by: Fares 33 per cent, subsidy/grants 67 per cent
Subsidy from: State 65 per cent, local 35 per cent

Current situation: Regional transit authority founded by city of Nuremburg and 14 other local authorities, with the Bavarian state government, to co-ordinate public transport in Nuremburg and the surrounding area. Federal government participation ended in 1996. Fare structures have been standardised, allowing free transfer between modes and operators. Schedules have been co-ordinated to reduce travelling time. Revenues are pooled between operators and local authorities provide subsidy. All planning and marketing is undertaken by VGN.
Developments: VGN's area was enlarged in June 1997 by addition of five rural districts, bringing the area covered to 11,000 km² with a population of almost 2.1 million.

VAG

Verkehrs-Aktiengesellschaft
Südliche Fürther Strasse 5, D-90338 Nuremburg
Tel: (+49 911) 28 30   Fax: (+49 911) 283 46 41
Chair: Herbert Dombrowsky
Directors: Dr Friedrich König
  Dr Rainer Müller (Manager, Bus)
Manager, Metro & Tram: Ernst Wentzel
Staff: 2,025

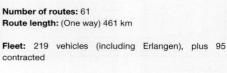

U-Bahn train at Rathenauplatz   *1997*

Passenger journeys: (All modes, including Fürth and Erlangen)
(1994) 143 million
(1995) 144 million
(1996) 148 million

Current situation: Operations are conducted jointly with those of Stadtwerke Fürth, which operates a fleet of 76 buses, and incorporating local services for the town of Erlangen.

The future of the tramway network appears assured, though the city council elected in 1996 favours extension of the metro rather than the tramway. Some of the statistics given below have been restated and so differ from those previously published.
Developments: VAG has formed a joint venture with Würzburg transport operator WVV to operate local rail services formerly run by DB which are being put out to tender by local authorities. Frankenbahn GmbH will initially run four local lines, one of which links Nuremburg with Gräfenberg.

Bus
Pssenger journeys: (1995) 39.1 million
(1996) 39.6 million
(1997) 40 million
Vehicle-km: (1995) 20 million
(1996) 20.4 million
(1997) 20.3 million

Number of routes: 61
Route length: (One way) 461 km

Fleet: 219 vehicles (including Erlangen), plus 95 contracted

CNG-powered low-floor MAN NL202 kneeling at a street-level stop   *1997*

Volvo B10MA articulated bus of STCP (Bill Luke)   **1999**/0038934

There are also plans for reopening closed routes to create a modern network alongside the light rail system being developed by Metro do Porto (see below).

The last trolleybus routes were converted to bus operation in January 1998.

Operating costs financed by: Fares 64 per cent, other commercial sources 3 per cent, government grants 13 per cent, remainder as deficit

Bus

Vehicle-km (including trolleybus, now closed):
(1995) 33.9 million
(1996) 34.8 million
(1997) 35.6 million

Number of routes: 66
Route length: 412 km

Fleet: 562 buses

Volvo B58 (1973(c)82)	249
Volvo B10R (1984/86/87)	83
Volvo B10M (1985)	20
Volvo B10M articulated (1983-89)	65
Mercedes O405 (1991-95)	135
Renault PS150 minibus (1995)	10

Average age of fleet: 13.6 years
On order: Proposes to purchase 50 vehicles a year to 2001

Most intensive service: 5 min
One-person operation: All routes
Fare collection: To driver or conductor or prepurchase
Fare structure: Zonal; carnets, monthly passes for various groups of services
Fares collected on board: 10 per cent
Fare evasion control: Roving/route inspectors
Integration between modes: A few common passes with one private operator and CP
Operational control: Control centre; some route inspectors
Arrangements for elderly/disabled: Reduced rate passes for city or total network valid at all times
Average peak-hour speed: 15.9 km/h
Bus priority: Some bus access to pedestrianised areas; traffic signal control allows bus priority over Luis I bridge from Vila Nova de Gaia

New vehicles financed by: Government/bank loans

Tramway

Passenger journeys: (1995) 5 million
(1996) 3 million
(1997) 1 million

Current situation: Only Route 18 remains in operation, extending to 28.3 km and operated by 16 Brill cars.
Developments: A 3.4 km extension from São Bento to Matosinhos is to open in 1999.

Bus (contracted operations)

Current situation: Several city routes are operated under contract to STCP by a number of private companies, including Valpi Bus, A Nogueira da Costa, A Martins Soares and Empresa de Transported Gondomarense.

CP

Caminhos de Ferro Portugueses (CP)
Calcada do Duque 20-1, P-1294 Lisbon

Type of operation: Suburban heavy rail

Current situation: Commuter services operate into three city-centre terminals. From São Bento trains run to São Romao (19 km) and Braga (57 km); from Trinidade a frequent diesel service operates to Vilar do Pinheiro (17 km) and Póvoa (30 km), carrying about 6.5 million passengers a year, while hourly trains run to Guimaraes (62 km); lastly, from São Bento and Campanha stations there is a combined suburban/regional service to Aveiro (67 km).

Oporto Railway Development Board

Gabinete de Nó Ferroviário do Porto
President: José Espinho
Director of Planning & Studies: Duarte Pereira

Current situation: This quango was set up by the Ministry of Transport to undertake all rail infrastructure improvements in the Oporto metropolitan area. It is to be merged with the new national rail infrastructure authority set up in 1997.

Developments: The Oporto—Braga line is being double-tracked and electrified to raise line speed to 170 km/h, and so reduce journey times to stimulate a 68 per cent growth in patronage by 1999. Between Trofa and Guimaraes the existing metre-gauge track is being replaced by 1,668 mm gauge; after conversion, trains will be diverted from Trinadade to São Bento station in Oporto. Campanha station is being replaced, and that at São Bento extensively remodelled for its future role as terminus for all services on the Northern and Minho lines.

Private bus

Current situation: Services on 190 suburban and commuter routes are provided by 39 operators, 37 privately owned and two owned by the government. Plans have been considered (see above) for integration of private routes into the STCP network.

Passes are available providing travel on privately operated, CP, and STCP services.

Light rail

Metro do Porto SA
Av dos Aliados 133, 3°, P-4000 Oporto
Tel: (+351 2) 208 80 28/88 13   Fax: (+351 2) 208 88 14
General Manager: João Lopes Porto

Current situation: Oporto will be Cultural European Capital in 2001 and the Oporto Light Rail Transit System project idea is seen as desirable for the Oporto Metropolitan Area constituted by nine municipalities, with 1.2 million inhabitants. Metro do Porto SA was set up in 1993 to implement proposals to build a light rail network. Its share capital is held by: Metropolitana do Porto 80 per cent and Metropolitano de Lisboa (Lisbon Subway) 5 per cent.

The network, with four lines, will have a route length of 70 km with 7 km underground. The North-South line will run 9 km from Santo Ovidio, in Vila Nova de Gaia, to São Joao hospital, crossing the Douro River on the upper deck of the existing Luis I road bridge, and serving the city centre by a tunnel section. The East-West line (15.5 km) will start at CP's Campanha station and run in a tunnel via São Bento to Trindade, where it will take over CP's alignment to the north, through Senhora da Hora, until Matosinhos. This line will branch in Senhora da Hora to serve Póvoa (24 km) and Trofa (21.5 km). The contest was won by the consortium Normetro, which is formed by eight companies (Soares da Costa, Adtranz Italy, Adtranz Portugal, ABB Sae, Soconstroi, Impregilo, Transdev and Semaly).

The project, under the responsibility of the consortium Normetro, comprises a turnkey LRT system, with 5 years' operation and maintenance. The vehicles — Eurotrams — will be produced by Adtranz. The capacity of each LRV will be 216 passengers, the fleet will include 72 vehicles, with 100 per cent low floor, air conditioning and modularity. EIB, the Portuguese State, EU funds and the financial market will finance the project.

Construction was expected to begin at the end of 1998. The first line in operation will be Trindade—Senhora da Hora—Matosinhos in 2001. All of the system is expected to be in operation in 2003.

UPDATED

ORLANDO

Population: City 173,000, Tri-county area 1.3 million
Public transport: Fixed-route bus, demand-responsive services and commuter assistance programmes provided by authority governed by nine-member board; extensive private operations

LYNX

Central Florida Regional Transportation Authority
225 East Robinson Street, Suite 300, Orlando, Florida 32801, USA
Tel: (+1 407) 841 22 79   Fax: (+1 407) 245 03 27
Chair: Daryl McLain
Executive Director: Leo P Auger
Director of Operations: W William Schneeman
Staff: 735

Current situation: The former Orange-Seminole-Osceola Transportation Authority was formed by inter-local agreement in 1972 to serve Orange, Seminole and Osceola counties. It adopted the trading name LYNX in 1992, and was merged with the Central Florida RTA in 1994 to create the Central Florida Regional Transportation Authority.

Fixed-route bus service is provided in a 6,573 km² area, with 'Lymmo' fixed-route downtown circulator providing a fares-free link with parking, employment and entertainment centres on a 5 km route operated by CNG-powered buses. LYNX also operates a mobility assistance programme that co-ordinates van- and carpools and a ride-matching service throughout central Florida.

LYNX has no dedicated funding source and is hoping to gain voter approval for a local sales, property or petrol tax.

Developments: Civil engineering and design consultants were appointed in February 1998 for development of the initial 24 km route of a proposed 84 km light rail network, planned for the first decade of the new century. Line 1, with 17 stations, will link Central Florida Parkway and Livingston Street in Orlando, serving major leisure attractions and the central business district. Construction could start in late 1999 for opening two years later.

Express bus services from outlying residential areas were launched in 1997.

A novel approach to reducing traffic congestion, the motorist's assistance patrol, came into operation in early 1998. The patrol will offer minor mechanical help to cars which break down in the busiest traffic corridors.

'Lymmo' service was upgraded and extended in 1997 with new bus priority sections, vehicles and street furniture. A second depot was opened in 1997 at West Colonian Drive.

Bus

Passenger journeys: (1994) 11.9 million
(1995) 13.5 million
(1996) 15 million
Vehicle-km: (Annual) 15.8 million

Number of routes: 53
Route length: (One way) 1,142 km

Fleet: 240 vehicles

Flxible 35 ft (1987)	24
Flxible 40 ft (1987)	13
Gillig 40 ft (1994/95/96)	72
Gillig 40 ft Suburban (1996)	7
Neoplan 35 ft (1985/90/91)	27
Orion II minibus (1993)	12
Orion V 31 ft (1994)	20
Orion V 31 ft CNG-powered (1993/94)	6
Orion V 40 ft (1994)	17
Orion V 40 ft Suburban (1994)	4
Gillig 35 ft (1997)	11
Gillig 40 ft (1997)	17
New Flyer low-floor CNG-powered (1997)	10
In peak service: 166	

Most intensive service: 5 min
One-person operation: All routes
Fare structure: Flat; weekly and monthly passes; discount for scholars and seniors
Arrangements for elderly/disabled: Demand-responsive door-to-door service for those who cannot use fixed routes; reduced fare on fixed-route services for others
Operating costs financed by: Fares 31.8 per cent, other commercial sources 4.1 per cent, subsidy/grants 64.1 per cent
Subsidy from: Orange County, Seminole County, City of Orlando, Osceola County/City of Kissimmee, City of Altamonte Springs, International Drive Transit District total 63 per cent, state 16 per cent, FTA 21 per cent
New vehicles financed by: Local 10 per cent, state 10 per cent, FTA 80 per cent

Walt Disney World

WED Transportation Services
Tel: (+1 305) 824 44 57

Gillig Phantom of Central Florida Regional Transit departing from the Lynx downtown terminal in Orlando (Bill Luke)   **1999**/0038919

CNG-powered New Flyer of LYNX pauses at the downtown terminus of the free Lymmo service (Andrew Jarosz)   **1999**/0045401

Current situation: Bus transport is provided within the Disney World complex and from the Buena Vista area of Orlando on 28 routes. Some operate until 02.00; most buses lift-equipped. Two circular monorail routes operate within the complex.

Fleet: 160 buses

GMC RTS III	43
TMC RTS III	115
Ford van	2
	UPDATED

OSAKA

Population: 2.6 million
Public transport: Bus, metro and elevated automated guided transport system operated by municipal authority. Several private commuter and interurban rail lines provide suburban services along with Japan Railways (JR), with through running to the metro from four lines. Rail-based travel is dominant, with a 60 per cent share, compared with only 3 per cent by bus, 3 per cent by taxi and 34 per cent by private car. Private railways handle about 25 per cent, the municipal metro some 19 per cent and JR lines about 15 per cent. Some privately operated buses, monorail, tramway and ferry service on the Yodo river.

Major expansion of the rail network in the Kansai metropolitan region (Osaka, Kyoto, Kobe) has been proposed by the Council for Transport Policy, involving 27 new lines totalling 220 km, with a further 110 km of additional tracks alongside existing lines to be built by 2005.

The 'Surutto Kansai' stored-fare card system, introduced in 1996, covers seven rail and bus operators including the Hankyu, Hanshin, Nose and Kita Osaka railways and all Osaka's municipal operations. A further 18 Kansai region rail and bus operators are to join the system in 1999, including the Kobe and Kyoto municipal operators and the Keihan, Nankai, Kobe Electric and Sanyo railways.

Osaka-shi Kotsu Kyoku

Osaka Municipal Transportation Bureau
Kujo Minami-1, Nishi-ku, Osaka 550-0025 Japan
Tel: (+81 6) 65 82 11 01   Fax: (+81 6) 65 82 79 97
General Manager: Katsutada Sasakura
Staff: 9,581

Passenger journeys: (All modes)
(1995) 1,120 million
(1996) 1,111 million
(1997) 1,094 million

Current situation: The metro carries the vast majority of city travellers, being one of the most intensively used in the world, with 508,000 a day passing through the busiest station at Umeda.

A 'ride-and-ride' system operates by division of the city into 18 zones, with public transport reorganised around area transport for each zone, with trunk services interconnecting them and serving the city centre. Local zone bus services connect with rail trunk routes supplemented by high-frequency bus corridors. Some 25 transfer terminal points have been identified for interchange between trunk and local routes.

Bus

Staff: 2,078

Passenger journeys: (1995) 120.5 million
(1996) 117.4 million
(1997) 111.6 million

Buses of Osaka-shi Kotsu Kyoku at Osaka JR station   **1998**/0009510

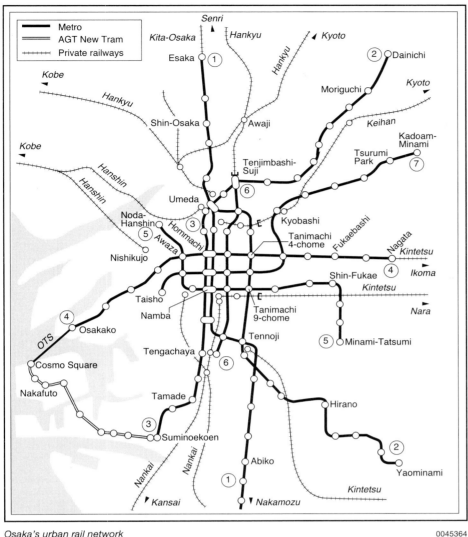

Osaka's urban rail network

0045364

Metro (map legend)

- ▬▬ Metro
- ═══ AGT New Tram
- ┼┼┼┼ Private railways

Vehicle-km: (1995) 29.6 million
(1996) 29.5 million
(1997) 28.9 million

Number of routes: 107
Route length: (One way) 449 km
On priority right-of-way: 106.2 km

Fleet: 980 vehicles, all air conditioned

Mitsubishi	296
Isuzu	224
Hino	270
Nissan Diesel	187
Neoplan	3

In peak service: 854
New vehicles required each year: 100

Most intensive service: 3 min
One-person operation: All routes
Fare collection: Payment on alighting to farebox by driver, ticket or pass; fareboxes have cancellation facility for stored-value discount multiride Kaisuken Card (bus/metro/tram) also valid on metro and New Tram
Fare structure: Flat, with transfer without charge between trunk and local routes; multiride tickets, 1- or 3-monthly passes (student, commuter, all routes), monthly daytime (10.00-16.00) discount passes: day, 1-, 3- and 6-month multimode tickets (bus/metro/New Tram); stored-fare 'Rainbow' cards introduced 1996 valid on bus/metro/New Tram, and private rail and bus companies within the Surutto Kansai card network. Other stored-value cards issued by companies within Surutto Kansai are also valid for all municipal operations; 'No-My-Car-Day' discount tickets (bus/metro) available every Friday and on 20th of every month to promote the use of public transport
Fare evasion control: None
Operational control: Computerised operational control with real-time bus location displays at 606 stops
Arrangements for elderly/disabled: Free passes and concessionary fares financed by city welfare bureau; newer buses have wheelchair space; 69 lift-equipped buses and 8 low-floor 'non-step' buses.

Integration with other modes: All routes integrated with metro; zonal interchange system; unified bus/rail fare scale; reduced fare bus/metro, New Tram transfer tickets
Average distance between stops: 427 m
Average speed: In mixed traffic, 12.8 km/h
Bus priority: 82.9 km bus-only lanes; 7.9 km bus-only roads; 22.8 km bus priority lanes; 167 bus priority signals. Staff on duty during rush hours to ensure observance of lane discipline
Operating costs financed by: Fares 57 per cent, other commercial sources 26.5 per cent, subsidy/grants 16.5 per cent
Subsidy from: City's general account (98.5 per cent), prefectural government (0.2 per cent) and national government (1.3 per cent)

Developments: New Urban Bus System concept adopted, involving bus priority measures, computerised operational control, bus shelters and real-time travel information displays.

Metro

Staff: 7,503 (including New Tram)

Type of operation: Full metro, initial route opened 1933

Passenger journeys: (1995) 974.5 million
(1996) 968.6 million
(1997) 957.2 million
Car-km: (1995) 97.1 million
(1996) 101.5 million
(1997) 106.3 million

Route length: 115.6 km
Number of lines: 7
Number of stations: 92
  in tunnel: 83
Gauge: 1,435 mm
Track: 50 kg/m flat-bottom rail
Max gradient: 3.5%
Minimum curve radius: 100 m
Electrification: 750 V DC, third rail; 1.5 kV DC, overhead (Line 6 and 7)

Service: Peak 2 min, off-peak 4-7 min
First/last train: 05.00/24.00
Fare structure: Five-section distance-based fare scale; multiride tickets; 1-, 3- and 6-month commuter and student passes; day, 1-, 3- and 6-month multimode tickets (bus/metro/New Tram); 'Rainbow' stored-fare cards and 'No-My-Car-Day' tickets (as bus)
Fare collection: Ticket machines and automatic barriers at all stations; with introduction of stored-value multiride tickets, almost all tickets are magnetically encoded for use in automatic barriers
Arrangements for elderly/disabled: Concessionary fares; 766 cars have wheelchair space; lifts at 67 stations; planned to equip all stations with lifts or escalators by 2001
Operating costs financed by: (including New Tram) Fares 90 per cent, other commercial sources 8.1 per cent; subsidy/grants 1.9 per cent
Subsidy from: National government 15.2 per cent, city 83.5 per cent, prefecture 1.4 per cent (includes New Tram)
Integration with other modes: Free interchange with New Tram (see below) and reduced fare bus/metro transfer tickets and passes; reduced fare single tickets for short-distance travel from/to reciprocal running sections of private railways
Signalling: ATC, CTC, and automatic block; cab signalling and ATC (Line 7)
Surveillance: CCTV at some stations

Rolling stock: 1,200 cars, Hitachi, Kawasaki, Kinki, Tokyu and Alna Koki; all air conditioned

Series 10 Line 1	M138 T92
Series 20 Lines 1/2/3/4/5	M328 T328
Series 30 Lines 2/3	M55 T23
Series 60 Line 6	M30 T10
Series 66 Line 6	M48 T48
Series 70 Line 7	M100

Current situation: Reciprocal through running services operate between Line 1 and North Osaka Express Electric Railway, between Line 6 and the Hankyu Senri and Kyoto lines, and between Line 4 and Kintetsu's Higashi—Osaka line and Osaka Port Transport System's Technoport line. Line 7 is built to a small profile, with trains powered by linear motor.
Developments: Small-profile Line 7 was extended 5.7 km from Kyobashi to Shinsaibashi in 1996, and further extended at both ends in 1997. The line now totals 15 km running from Taisho (interchange with JR Osaka Loop line) to Kadoma-minami via central Osaka, providing interchange with all six other metro lines.

Reciprocal through running between Line 4 Osaka Port Transport System's 2.4 km Technoport line started in December 1997.

ICTS

Type of operation: New Tram Intermediate Capacity Transit System (ICTS) opened 1981, fully automatic operation, rubber-tyred cars on concrete guideway

Passenger journeys: (1995) 24.7 million
(1996) 24.9 million
(1997) 25.5 million
Car-km: (1995) 4.3 million
(1996) 4.4 million
(1997) 4.3 million

Route length: 6.6 km (trains also run over 1.3 km OTS line)
Number of stations: 8 (plus 2 OTS)
Electrification: 600 V AC, third rail

Service: Peak 2 min, off-peak 7½ min
First/last train: 05.17/24.00
Fare structure: As metro
Operating costs financed by: (see metro)
Revenue control: Ticket machines and automatic barriers
Train control: Fully automated operation; no driver, but some trains have an attendant to provide customer information and deal with emergencies
Signalling: Fixed block (continuous transmission and receiving with check-in and check-out system); ATC, CTC
Surveillance: CCTV on all platforms

Rolling stock: 18 four-car trains, air conditioned
Niigata Iron Works Series 100   M72

Current situation: Under the same management as the

Tsurumi-ryokuchi station on small-profile Line 7   ***1998**/0009511*

metro, the elevated New Tram serves new residential and commercial development on land reclaimed from Osaka Bay.

Developments: Reciprocal through-running to Osaka Port Transport System's 1.3 km Technoport New Tram line started in December 1997.

Osaka Port Transport System (OTS)

Tel: (+81 6) 65 69 71 82

Current situation: OTS, a third sector company, was established to construct and operate extensions of metro line 4 and New Tram to serve the Port Town commercial development area built on an artificial island in Osaka bay.

The 2.4 km Technoport metro line (2 stations, 1,435 mm gauge, electrified at 750 V DC third rail) runs from the Osakako terminus of Line 4 via a cross-harbour tunnel to Cosmo Square, where it connects with the 1.3 km Technoport New Tram line (1 station, 600 V AC third rail).

Reciprocal through-running services to the municipal metro and New Tram lines commenced in December 1997, with a fleet of two six-car metro trains and three four-car New Tram sets.

Hankyu Dentetsu

Hankyu Corporation
16-1, Shibata 1-chome, Kita-ku, Osaka 530-8389
Tel: (+81 6) 63 73 50 92   Fax: (+81 6) 63 73 56 70
President: M Sugai
Staff: 4,841

Interurban railway

Passenger journeys: (1995/96) 715 milllion
(1996/97) 740 million
(1997/98) 710 million
Car-km: (1997/98) 168 million

Current situation: Operates nine lines with 90 stations over 147 km of 1,435 mm gauge route, electrified 1.5 kV DC. Interurban routes run to Kobe, Kitasenri, Kyoto and Takarazuka, through running from Kitasenri and Kyoto line stations to metro Line 6.
Developments: A stored-fare card system was introduced in 1992 and its validity was extended in 1996 to other operators within the Surutto Kansai card network including Hanshin, Nose, Kita Osaka and Osaka municipal bus and rail services.

Rolling stock: 1,334 emu cars   M746 T588

Bus

Tel: (+81 6) 68 66 31 12   Fax: (+81 6) 68 66 31 42
Passenger journeys: (Whole conurbation)
(1991/92) 118.6 million
(1992/93) 115.8 million
Vehicle-km: (1992/93) 28 million

Current situation: Hankyu Bus operates 733 buses on

services linked to rail operations, including suburban bus routes in Osaka. A computer-controlled bus terminal/route information system is in operation between Osaka international airport and Hankyu Hotarugaike terminals.

Kita Osaka Kyuko Dentetsu

North Osaka Express Electric Railway
2-4-1, Terauchi, Toyonaka-shi, Osaka 560-0872
Tel: (+81 6) 68 65 06 01   Fax: (+81 6) 68 66 02 54
President: J Konishiike
Staff: 161

Passenger journeys: (1991/92) 66.8 million
(1992/93) 67.8 million
Car-km: (1991/92) 6.1 million
(1992/93) 6.1 million

Number of lines: 1
Route length: 5.9 km
Number of stations: 4
Electrification: 750 V DC, third rail

Rolling stock: 70 emu cars in 10-car sets
8000 series Alna Koki (1986-96)   M35 T35

Current situation: This expressway median line extends from Esaka to Senri-Chuo serving residential development north of Osaka (Senri New Town). A reciprocal through running service is operated to Line 1 of the metro; trains were lengthened from nine to 10 cars in 1995 to provide extra capacity on this intensively used line.

The company is part owned by the prefectural government and the Hankyu Electric Railway; operations are on a wholly commercial basis.
Developments: Surutto Kansai stored-fare card system introduced 1996, also valid on the Hanshin, Hankyu, Nose and Osaka municipal bus and rail services.

Hanshin Denki Tetsudo

Hanshin Electric Railway
1-24, Ebie 1-chome, Fukushima-ku, Osaka 553
Tel: (+81 6) 64 57 21 23
President: M Tezuka
Staff: 2,322

Interurban railway

Staff: 1,201

Passenger journeys: (1992/93) 246 million
(1994/95) 229 million
(1995/96) 191 million
Car-km: (1992/93) 36.6 million

Current situation: Operates 40.1 km of 1,435 mm gauge route with 42 stations, comprising Osaka—Kobe main line and two branches, electrified 1.5 kV DC. Reciprocal through services operate on the Sanyo Railway via the underground Kobe Rapid Railway.
Developments: A 1.6 km extension of the Nishi-Osaka

line is under construction from Nishi-kujo to Kujo; this is the first stage of a planned link through to the Nankai Railway terminus at Namba.

Surutto Kansai stored-fare card system introduced 1996, also valid on Hankyu, Nose, Kita Osaka and Osaka municipal bus and rail services.

Rolling stock: 314 emu cars   M235 T79

Bus

Passenger journeys: (1991/92) 21.9 million
(1992/93) 24.4 million
Vehicle-km: (1991/92) 7.8 million
(1992/93) 7.9 million

Current situation: Operates 165 buses on 15 local routes extending to 153 km, consisting of Osaka—Kobe and Osaka—Takarazuka trunk routes, and feeder services to rail stations. Bus lanes and computer-aided bus location system introduced. Also operates sightseeing, long-distance express and airport services.

Keihan Denki Tetsudo

Keihan Electric Railway
2-27, Shiromi 1-chome, Chuo-ku, Osaka 540-6034
Tel: (+81 6) 69 44 25 21   Fax: (+81 6) 69 44 25 01
www: http://www.keihan.co.jp/
Chair: M Miyashita
President: A Kimba
Staff: 3,424

Interurban railway

Staff: 2,656

Passenger journeys: (Including Kyoto light rail)
(1995/96) 401 million
(1996/97) 390 million
(1997/98) 361 million
Car-km: (1996/97) 95.5 million
(1997/98) 97.2 million

Current situation: Operates 66.1 km of 1,435 mm gauge route, electrified at 1.5 kV DC. Main line, 51.6 km with 42 stations, runs from underground terminal in Osaka (Yodoyabashi station) to Kyoto, with two branches. Frequent service of limited-express, express and local trains on main line, where all stations have automatic ticket barriers which accept multiple-ride cards.

Also operates 21.6 km light rail system in Kyoto and Otsu (see under Kyoto).
Developments: Plans exist for a 2.7 km underground link in central Osaka (Nakanoshima line) to provide a connection with the proposed Naniwa-suji line to Kansai international airport (see JR West entry). A programme of grade-separation continues, with construction under way of a 1.7 km section of the main line including Neyagawashi station. The company is to join the Surutto Kansai stored-fare network in 1999.

Rolling stock: 702 emu cars, M379 T323, all air conditioned; limited-express trains have a car with television, and one double-deck car

Bus

Passenger journeys: (including Kyoto)
(1996/97) 67.6 million
(1997/98) 64.8 million
Vehicle-km: (including Kyoto)
(1996/97) 22 million
(1997/98) 22 million

Current situation: Keihan Bus, a railway subsidiary, operates approximately 350 of its 516 buses on services in Osaka Prefecture, including routes in Osaka's northeastern suburbs (see Kyoto entry).

Ferry

Current situation: Osaka Aqua-Bus, a subsidiary of the Keihan Electric Railway, offers a limited peak-hour service with five stops on a 5.1 km section of the Yodo river running through central Osaka.

Kinki Nippon Tetsudo 'Kintetsu'

Kinki Nippon Railway
6-1-55, Uehommachi, Tennoji-ku, Osaka 543-8585
Tel: (+81 6) 67 75 34 44   Fax: (+81 6) 67 75 34 68
President: W Tashiro
Staff: 11,907

Interurban railway

Passenger journeys: (1994/95) 791 million
(1995/96) 788 million
(1996/97) 742 million
Car-km: (1992/93) 324 million
(1996/97) 339 million

Current situation: Operates express and local services over main line of 190 km from Osaka to Nagoya, and over several other routes totalling 595 km on 1,435, 1,067 and 762 mm gauges, electrified at 1.5 kV DC and 750 V DC. A reciprocal through-running service operates between the Higashi—Osaka line and Line 4 of the Osaka metro. This is the largest private railway in Japan.

Rolling stock: 2,115 emu cars   M1,173 T942

Developments: Plans exist for a future link between Kintetsu's Nara line at Ikoma and its Kyoto line at Takanohara, to provide a through service between west Osaka and south Kyoto.

Bus

Passenger journeys: (1992/93) 32.3 million
(1996/97) 27.6 million

Current situation: 381 buses run on 49 routes related to rail operations in the Osaka region, extending to 3,467 km.

JR West

West Japan Railway Company
Nishi Nihon Ryokaku Tetsudo
4-24, Shibata 2-chome, Kita-ku, Osaka 530-0012
Tel: (+81 6) 63 75 89 81   Fax: (+81 6) 63 75 89 19
Chair: T Tsunoda
President: M Ide

Type of operation: Interurban/suburban railway

Passenger journeys: (Urban Network only)
(1993/94) 966 million
(1994/95) 963 million
(1995/96) 1,012 million

Current situation: JR West's Urban Network comprises 12 lines (about 600 km) serving Kobe, Osaka and Kyoto. Osaka is the hub of the network, with frequent local and rapid service emus colour-coded according to line of operation on eight routes including the 21.7 km Osaka loop around the central area.

Faster and more frequent services and new rolling stock on urban lines have led to increased passenger-km. Further growth is expected from large development projects such as the new Kansai international airport and Kansai Science City, and from the continuing movement of population to suburban areas.

Developments: The 12.3 km Katafuku line with seven stations opened in March 1997, providing an east-west link through central Osaka connecting two important commuter routes, the Gakkentoshi line serving Kansai Science City, and JR's Takarazuka line. The line was built by Kansai Rapid Railway, a third sector company whose shareholders include JR West, Osaka prefecture and Osaka city.

JR West operates a rapid service from central Osaka to Kansai international airport using Series 223 emus and an express service 'Haruka' from Kyoto and Shin-Osaka using purpose-built five-car Series 281 emus. Access to the airport is via a new 11.2 km link from JR's Hanwa line, 6.9 km of which is shared by competing Nankai airport services. Plans exist for through airport services to Kobe and Nara via existing freight connections on to the Sanyo and Kansai systems respectively.

Plans also exist for a new link through central Osaka, the Naniwa-suji line, to connect Minato-machi and Shiomibashi and provide direct access for JR and Nankai trains from Kansai airport to the central business districts. Connecting links between the Naniwa-suji line and the Hanshin and Hankyu systems are also planned.

Work is in progress for start-up of passenger service on JR's 18.6 km Joto freight line. An outer orbital service will be provided through Osaka's eastern suburbs linking Shin-Osaka, Shigino, Hanaten and Kami. JR West, Osaka prefecture and Osaka city have set up a third sector company to undertake the ¥140 billion project, which includes double-tracking, electrification, new stations and new trains. Opening is scheduled for 2005.

Through-running Semboku emu on the Nankai main line, Osaka (Andrew Phipps)   ***1999**/0038921*

Automatic gates are being introduced at Urban Network stations in connection with introduction of the Surutto Kansai stored-fare system.

Nankai Denki Tetsudo

Nankai Electric Railway
1-60 Namba 5-chome, Chuo-ku, Osaka 542-0076
Tel: (+81 6) 66 44 71 21
President: S Yoshimura
Staff: 3,207

Interurban railway

Passenger journeys: (1992/93) 305 million
(1994/95) 304 million
(1995/96) 302 million
Car-km: (1992/93) 79.7 million

Current situation: Operates 163.5 km of 1,067 mm gauge lines of which 149.2 km electrified 1.5 kV DC and 14.3 km at 600 V DC.

Main routes Osaka—Wakayama (Nankai main line) and Osaka—Gokurakubashi (Koya line) served by frequent local and express services. Also through service using Nankai and Semboku cars from Namba to the Semboku Rapid Railway to serve suburban housing.

Rolling stock: 718 emu cars   M417 T301

Developments: In 1994 new services were introduced between Nankai's Namba terminal in central Osaka and Kansai international airport, a distance of 43 km. The express 'Rapi:t' service, operated by distinctively styled purpose-built Series 50000 units, is supplemented by local services, both of which compete with JR services for airport traffic. Access to the airport is via an 8.8 km branch line from Izumi-Sano, part of which is shared with JR. To further compete with JR, Nankai proposes to lay mixed-gauge track along its existing 1,067 mm main line to enable airport services to operate through central Osaka via the 1,435 mm gauge Sakaisuji line metro and on to Kyoto and Nara via the Hankyu, Keihan and Kintetsu systems. A 4 km link between the Nankai and Hanshin terminals in Osaka would also permit through running to Kobe.

The company is to join the Surutto Kansai stored-fare card network in 1999.

Bus

Passenger journeys: (1992/93) 62.6 million

Current situation: Approximately 570 vehicles run on routes related to rail services in southern half of Osaka Prefecture.

Semboku Kosoku Tetsudo

Semboku Rapid Railway
Osaka Prefectural Urban Development Company
5-7, Kawaramachi 3-chome, Chuo-ku, Osaka 541
Tel: (+81 6) 62 01 97 71   Fax: (+81 6) 62 01 97 88

Suburban railway

Passenger journeys: (1991/92) 58.1 million
(1992/93) 57.8 million
(1993/94) 58.1 million
Car-km: (1991/92) 6.9 million
(1992/93) 7.3 million
(1993/94) 7.5 million

Current situation: This 12.1 km line (1,067 mm gauge, electrified 1.5 kV DC), constructed and operated by Osaka Prefectural Urban Development Company, serves Semboku New Town (population 160,000) to the south of Osaka. A reciprocal through-running service is operated to central Osaka via the Nankai Railway.

Rolling stock: 134 emu cars   M73 T61

JR West urban network services at Amagasaki station (Andrew Phipps)   ***1999**/0038920*

'Rapi:t' airport express emu (left) and local service (right) at Nankai's Namba terminal (Andrew Phipps)
1999/0038922

Fare structure: Stage; transfer tickets available between routes; prepurchase coupon tickets, 1- and 3-month passes
One-person operation: All cars

Rolling stock: 48 cars
Kawasaki Ship Building (1927)	M4
Kawasaki Rolling Stock (1928)	M9
Fuji Nagata Ship Building (ex-Osaka) (1929)	M3
Osaka Iron Works (1930)	M2
Tanaka Sharyo (1930)	M3
Teikoku Sharyo (1957/62/63)	M10
Tokyu Car (1987/93/94/95)	M11
Type 601 (rebuilt 1996/97)	M6

Osaka Kosoku Tetsudo
Osaka Rapid Railway (Osaka Monorail)
5-1-1, Higashi-machi, Shin-Senri, Toyonaka-shi, Osaka-fu 565
Tel: (+81 6) 68 71 82 80   Fax: (+81 6) 68 71 82 84
Staff: 153

Type of operation: Straddle monorail, opened 1990

Passenger journeys: (1992/93) 7.8 million
(1993/94) 8.4 million
Car-km: (1992/93) 1.4 million
(1993/94) 3.6 million

Current situation: This orbital monorail line round north-east Osaka links Osaka airport and Kadoma-shi providing interchange with the North Osaka Express Electric Railway, the Hankyu Senri, Kyoto and Takarazuka lines, and the Keihan main line.

Route length: 23.9 km
Number of lines: 1
Number of stations: 16
Electrification: 1.5 kV DC

Service: 5-12 min
One-person operation: All trains
Fare collection: Full AFC
Signalling: Cab signalling, ATP
Surveillance: CCTV
Operating costs financed by: Fares 100 per cent

Rolling stock: 12 four-car sets
Hitachi/Kawasaki Type 1000   M48

Developments: The initial 6.7 km line was extended by 3.5 km in 1994, and further extended from Shibahara to Osaka airport (3.1 km) and from Minami-Ibaraki to Kadoma-shi (7.9 km) in 1997. A 2.7 km northwards branch to Osaka University Hospital opened in 1998 and it is planned to extend this line a further 6.3 km to serve Kokusai Bunka garden city.
The line is designed for eventual operation by six-car trains running at 3 min headways.

Private bus
Current situation: A number of private bus operators, mainly private railway subsidiaries, provide suburban and commuter services, carrying around 170 million passengers a year and catering for about 6 per cent of Osaka's travel demand.

Hankai Denki Kido
Hankai Electric Tramway
3-14-72 Shimizuoka, Sumiyoshi-ku, Osaka 558-0033
Tel: (+81 6) 66 71 30 80
President: N Hiramatsu
Staff: 261

Current situation: 100 per cent owned by the Nankai Electric Railway, this tramway became a separate operation in 1980. Serves the southern part of Osaka and Sakai City from two terminals in Osaka.

Tramway
Number of lines: 2
Number of routes: 3
Route length: 18.7 km
Number of stops: 40
Gauge: 1,435 mm
Electrification: 600 V DC, overhead

Service: 2-15 min
First/last car: 05.16/23.32
Fare collection: Farebox or prepurchase

Osaka monorail running alongside the Kinki Expressway   **1996**   *UPDATED*

OSLO
Population: 500,000, metropolitan area 800,000
Public transport: Bus, metro, light rail and tramway services operated by authority governed by nominated board (including employee representatives) under overall control of city council, and which also contracts private ferry and bus lines, and provides support for common overall fare structure within city area, extending to local rail journeys on State Railway (NSB BA). Agreements with Stor Oslo Lokaltrafikk A/S (responsible for public transport within the county surrounding Oslo and services into Oslo) give an integrated fare structure and transfer system for the whole region. Road pricing in force

Strømmens Verkstad/Duewag LRV on Aker Brygge waterfront service (Tony Pattison)
1999/0038923

Oslo Sporveier

AS Oslo Sporveier
Økernveien 9, Postbox 2857-Tøen, N-0608 Oslo 6, Norway
Tel: (+47) 22 08 40 00   Fax: (+47) 22 08 40 30
Managing Director: Trond Bi{os}rgan
Director, Metro Division: Rolf Gillebo
Director, Tramway Division: Rolf Bergstrand
Director, Commercial Affairs Division:
   Viggo Johannessen
Staff: 1,695 (excluding employees of subsidiary companies)

Passenger boardings: (All modes, including contracted operations)
(1995) 147 million
(1996) 150 million
(1997) 153 million

Operating costs financed by: Fares 63 per cent, other commercial sources 7 per cent, subsidy/grants and special agreements 30 per cent
Subsidy from: City of Oslo 95 per cent (financed by municipal income and property taxes), special agreements (Akershus/Baerum counties) 5 per cent; concessions to pensioners financed by operator
New vehicles financed by: Loans through Municipality of Oslo

Current situation: OS, popularly named Sporveien, has overall responsibility for public transport provision in the Oslo area and contracts with its own and three private bus operators, boat services and about 100 km of State Railway lines. For these Sporveien collects all the revenue and pays the contractors a set rate, assuming responsibility for any deficits except those of the State Railway. Contracted services carried about 60 million passengers in 1997 (including subsidiary AS Sporveisbussene).
Developments: A 2 per cent increase in patronage was recorded in 1996 and again in 1997, the fifth consecutive year of traffic growth. This confirms Sporveien's strategy which presupposes annual growth of between 2 and 2.5 per cent.
   Operating revenues for 1997 rose by 5 per cent, mainly on account of a NKr51 million increase in traffic receipts. The city of Oslo's purchase of service (as subsidy/grant) rose by NKr5 million to NKr447 million, but this did not match the increase in operating costs, resulting in a net decrease in subsidy from 31 per cent in 1996 to 30 per cent in 1997.
   All bus service is now contracted out, following establishment of Sporveien's bus operations as a subsidiary company AS Sporveisbussene, competing on equal terms with private operators.

Bus

Passenger boardings: (Figures not comparable with previous years)
(1995) 51.8 million
(1996) 52.8 million
(1997) 53 million
Vehicle-km: (1995) 16.7 million
(1996) 16.6 million
(1997) 16.6 million

Number of routes: 34
Route length: (One way) 1,454 km

Fleet: 280 buses (total fleet operated by the four contractors)

One-person operation: All routes
Fare collection: Coupon cards cancelled on board; driver sells single tickets and various types of card, but not season tickets or passes
Fare structure: Flat, single zone covers the whole city; single ticket and 8-ticket Flexicard permit free transfer on all modes within 1 h, other seasons/passes unrestricted; 24-h, 7-day, monthly and 6-monthly passes; children, elderly and those on municipal pensions travel free
Operational control: Mobile radio; two-way radio on all vehicles
Arrangements for elderly/disabled: Five routes operated by low-entry midibuses with wheelchair lifts link residential areas with local bus stations; door-to-door service for mobility impaired transferred in 1997 to the city's Department of Transport & Communications
Average peak-hour speed: 16 km/h
Bus priority: Buses and trams equipped to gain priority at

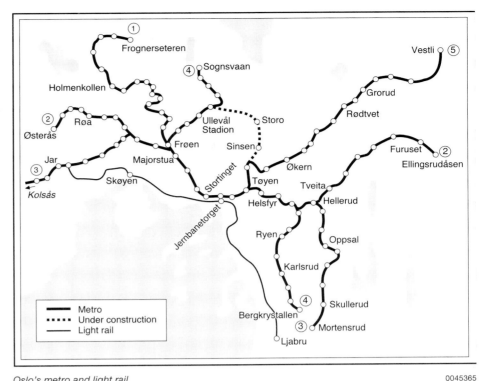

Oslo's metro and light rail   0045365

some 120 signal-controlled intersections under plan for general adoption of system
Integration with other modes: Full integration between modes with free transfers (see above)

Metro

Type of operation: Full metro, initial route opened 1966; suburban rail upgraded to metro standards

Passenger boardings: (1995) 56 million
(1996) 57 million
(1997) 59 million
Car-km: (1995) 15.5 million
(1996) 16.7 million
(1997) 16.8 million

Route length: 80.2 km (corrects previous figure)
   in tunnel: 16.5 km
Number of lines: 5
Number of stations: 101
   in tunnel: 13
Gauge: 1,435 mm
Max gradient: 5%
Minimum curve radius: 200 m
Electrification: 750 V DC, third rail; Frognerseteren line 750 V DC overhead, Kolsås line 680 V DC overhead

Service: 15 min all day on branches; peak 1¾ min, off-peak 3¾ min in central area
Fare structure: Flat, as bus

Integration with other modes: Full fare integration with all other modes within the city boundaries
Signalling: Cab signalling

Rolling stock: 207 cars
Strømmens Vaerksted
Single-cab cars	M120
Dual-cab cars	M26
Single-cab cars dual-system	M34
Dual-cab cars dual-system	M15
ABB T2000 dual-system (1994)	M12

Developments: Through cross-city service on all lines was completed in 1995. Through service from the Frognerseteren line (1) to Helsfyr runs with the new T2000 dual-system cars, while the Kolsås line uses existing cars converted for dual third-rail and overhead current collection. The other two Western lines, to Sognsvann and Østerås, are fully upgraded to the standards of the Eastern lines.
   An extension from Skullerud to Mortensrud opened in 1997; it was built and financed by the State Highway Administration. A preferred alignment through urban renewal areas at Nydalen and Storo has been selected for the link between Lines 4 and 5, planned to create a circular route known as T-baneringen.

Tramway/light rail
Type of operation: Conventional tramway and light rail
Lines 10 and 19

T2000 dual-system car alongside original Western metro stock (right) at Majorstua   **1998**/0009512

Passenger journeys: (1995) 31.5 million
(1996) 32 million
(1997) 33 million
Car-km: (1995) 3.9 million
(1996) 3.8 million
(1997) 3.7 million

Route length: 38.3 km (corrects previous figure)
Number of lines: 8
Electrification: 600 V DC, overhead

Service interval: Peak 15 min
One-person operation: All cars

Rolling stock: 57 cars plus 40 LRVs for Lines 10 and 19

MBO (1952/58)	M26
MBO rebuilt (1983)	M11
M25 ex-Göteborg	M20
Strømmens Verksted/Duewag LRV (1979-I)	M25
Strømmens Verkstad/Duewag LRV (1979-II)	M15

Developments: Zoning plans for a tramway extension to the Aker hospital have been approved, and a further extension to Tonsehagen is planned. A 1.4 km extension from John Colletts plass to the new state hospital (Rikshospitalet) is scheduled to open in September 1999.

A new fleet of 30 low-floor air conditioned cars is on order from Italy's Ansaldo, with an option for a further 15, for delivery in 1998/99.

Ferry
Current situation: Operated under contract by Skibs A/S Bygdøfergene from Rådhusplassen to Bygdø and by Oslo Fergene to islands in the Oslofjord. The four routes (22 km) carry about 0.8 million passengers annually.

NSB
Norges Statsbaner
Prinsens gate 7-9, N-0048 Oslo
Tel: (+47) 23 15 00 00   Fax: (+47) 23 15 31 46

Type of operation: Suburban heavy rail

Passenger journeys: (1995) 25.5 million
(1996) 24 million
(1997) 24 million

Current situation: NSB's suburban lines link Oslo Central with Moss, Mysen, Kongsvinger, Jaren, Eidsvoll, Kongsberg and Spikkestad, totalling 568 km, electrified 15 kV 16⅔ Hz. Trains run hourly or half-hourly. Services within the city boundaries extend to about 100 km.
Developments: The line to the new airport at Gardermoen opened in October 1998.

Rolling stock: 182 emu cars plus 16 three-car trainsets for airport service

UPDATED

OSTRAVA
Population: 330,000
Public transport: Bus, trolleybus and tramway services operated by municipal authority

Dopravní podnik Ostrava AS
Dopravní podnik Ostrava AS
Podebradova 2, CZ-70171 Ostrava 1, Czech Republic
Tel: (+420 69) 248 81 11   Fax: (+420 69) 23 68 63
Director: František Vaštik
Staff: 2,900

Passenger journeys: (All modes)
(1993) 269 million
(1994) 252 million
(1996) 232 million

Developments: Tramway extension to Mistecka (2.1 km) under construction; modernisation and enlargement of Moravska-Ostrava tram depot in progress.

Fare collection: Prepurchase with validation/cancelling machines on board

Fare structure: Flat fare for each route
Fare evasion control: Roving inspectors
Operating costs financed by: Fares 33.8 per cent, other commercial sources 5 per cent, subsidy/grants 60.7 per cent, tax levy 0.6 per cent

Bus and trolleybus
Passenger journeys: (1993) Bus 120.4 million, trolleybus 16.4 million
(1994) Bus 112 million, trolleybus 16 million
(1996) Bus 102.9 million, trolleybus 15.2 million
Vehicle-km: (1993) Bus 20.7 million, trolleybus 2.8 million
(1994) Bus 20.8 million, trolleybus 3.1 million
(1996) Bus 20.8 million, trolleybus 3.1 million

Number of routes: Bus 49, trolleybus 9
Route length: Bus 670 km, trolleybus 69 km

Fleet: 409 buses	
Karosa B731	94
Karosa B732	182
Karosa C734	11
Karosa C735	1
Karosa LC	1

Ikarus 280 twin-set	42
Karosa C744 twin-set	8
Karosa B741 twin-set	29
Karosa/Renault low-floor (1997)	6
Skoda 21Ab low-floor (1997)	2
Karosa B932 (1997)	23
Karosa B941 (1997)	9
Karosa LC936 (1997)	1
Others	9
In peak service: 313	

Fleet: 54 trolleybuses, some 14Tr second-hand ex-Potsdam	
Skoda 14Tr	39
Skoda 15Tr twin-set	11
Skoda 21Tr low-floor (1997)	4
In peak service: 52	

Most intensive service: 1-2 min
One-person operation: All routes
Average peak-hour speed: In mixed traffic, bus 26.6 km/h, trolleybus 18.5 km/h

Tramway
Type of operation: Conventional tramway

Passenger journeys: (1993) 133 million
(1994) 124 million
(1996) 114.4 million
Car-km: (1993) 15.6 million
(1994) 15.4 million
(1996) 15.6 million

Route length: 254 km
Number of lines: 19
Number of stops: 98
Gauge: 1,435 mm
Electrification: 600 V DC, overhead

Service: Peak 10 min
First/last car: 24 h service

Rolling stock: 295 cars	
ČKD Tatra Tr	M18
ČKD Tatra T3	M221
ČKD Tatra K2	10
ČKD Tatra KT8 articulated	M16
ČKD Tatra T6A5	M30
In peak service: 247	

UPDATED

Type 21Tr Škoda trolleybus built in 1996 for Dopravní podnik Ostrava AS (Milán Šrámek)   **1999**/0038924

OTTAWA
Population: 654,000
Public transport: Bus services in Ottawa and surrounding urban area are the responsibility of a Regional Transit Commission governed by a board of commissioners drawn from the Regional Municipal Council

OC Transpo
Ottawa-Carleton Regional Transit Commission
1500 St-Laurent Boulevard, Ottawa K1G 0Z8, Canada
Tel: (+1 613) 741 64 40   Fax: (+1 613) 741 73 59
www: www.octranspo.com
Chair: Al Loney
General Manager: Mike Sheflin
Staff: 1,966

Current situation: Established in 1972, OC Transpo has exclusive rights to operate within the area of the 741,000 population Regional Municipality of Ottawa-Carleton. The Council of the Regional Municipality appoints the controlling board of the commission from amongst its members. In practice the Regional Council has established a designated Urban Transit Area with some 654,000 inhabitants within which OC Transpo is the sole

Bus priority: HOV lanes on Interstate 10 through city and Red Mountain Freeway; priority bus and carpool entrance ramps at 5 freeway locations; reserved lanes on 2 downtown approach streets

Average distance between stops: 400 m

Average peak-hour speed: Local 22 km/h

Operating costs financed by: Fares 30 per cent, subsidy/grants 70 per cent

Subsidy from: RPTA 10 per cent, FTA and other 7 per cent, LTAF 21 per cent, city general funds 32 per cent (state lottery, RPTA and other cities purchasing service)

New vehicles financed by: FTA grants 80 per cent, RPTA and Phoenix general fund revenues 20 per cent

UPDATED

LNG-powered New Flyer low-floor of Valley Metro
1997

PITTSBURGH

Population: City 370,000, metropolitan area 1.4 million

Public transport: Bus, reserved busway, tramway/light rail and funicular services provided by transport authority serving county area controlled by representative board

Port Authority Transit (PAT)

Port Authority of Allegheny County
2235 Beaver Avenue, Pittsburgh, Pennysylvania 15233, USA
Tel: (+1 412) 237 70 00   Fax: (+1 412) 237 71 01
Executive Director: Paul Skoutelas
Director, Transit Operations: Don Bell (Acting)
Staff: 2,868

Passenger boardings: (All modes)
(1993) 76.2 million
(1994) 75.4 million
(1996) 71.5 million

Operating costs financed by: Fares 38.2 per cent, other commercial sources 7.3 per cent, subsidy/grants 44 per cent, tax levy 10.5 per cent

Current situation: Pittsburgh's high level of transit usage, its extensive system of exclusive rights-of-way and the survival of its tramway are all due to its extreme topography, located in hilly terrain where the Allegheny and Monongahela rivers join to form the Ohio.

Partial upgrading of the tramway has been carried out, with new alignments and conversion to light rail standards of the 17 km route to South Hills. There are two busways, two contraflow bus lanes, and a high-occupancy vehicle lane.

Developments: Construction started in 1994 on the Airport Busway—Wabash HOV lane (see below), and a 4 km extension of the Martin Luther King Jr East Busway is proposed.

A Pennsylvania Public Transportation Assistance Fund created in 1991 has generated up to $38.2 million a year in dedicated funding for PAT; for details see Philadelphia entry. Despite this, reduced state funding and lower revenues as a result of declining ridership have led to service cuts.

Purchase of 170 buses, previously approved by the PAT Board, is being financed by a bond issue agreed in 1996.

Bus

Staff: 2,469 (operational)

Passenger boardings: (1993) 67.3 million
(1994) 64.7 million
(1996) 64.1 million

Vehicle-km: (1993) 49.9 million
(1996) 50.3 million

Number of routes: 195
Route length: 3,996 km
On priority right-of-way: 18.7 km

Fleet: 1,058 vehicles

MCI MC9 (1980/83)	32
Neoplan (1983/86)	290
MAN SG310 articulated (1983)	29
Ikarus articulated (1991)	25
Orion/Bus Industries (1991/92)	263
Flxible (1994)	250
Novabus Classic (1996)	169
In peak service: 784	

Most intensive service: 3 min

One-person operation: All routes

Fare collection: Exact fare to electronic fareboxes; fare collected on entry for in-bound trips, on leaving for outbound; passes

Fare structure: Zonal (central area plus 5 zones); 10-trip tickets; annual, weekly and monthly passes from 181 outlets

Average speed: 21.6 km/h

Bus priority: 7 km two-lane purpose-built exclusive busway (South Busway) and 11 km Martin Luther King Jr East Busway; both on own right-of-way, with sheltered passenger stations (see below); exclusive right-of-way on two contraflow bus lanes in downtown Pittsburgh and Oakland; also 8 km of HOV lanes on I-279 expressway, used by 7 routes at peak hours

Integration with other modes: Tramway shares portion of South Busway track and connects with Martin Luther King Jr East Busway; park-and-ride extensively developed

Arrangements for elderly/disabled: ACCESS door-to-door service with lift-equipped vehicles provided by 10 contractors carried 2 million passengers in 1994. Senior citizens free on all regular services off-peak, funded by Pennsylvania lottery proceeds

New vehicles financed by: Dedicated funding sources

Busway

Current situation: The South Busway, opened in 1977, carries some 19 bus routes with 470 movements and more than 13,000 riders on an average weekday. Certain portions share a pre-existing tramway alignment and the route is available for emergency police, ambulance or fire

An articulated bus from North American Bus Industries loads at the terminal of Pittsburgh's East Busway (Van Wilkins)   *1999*/0038931

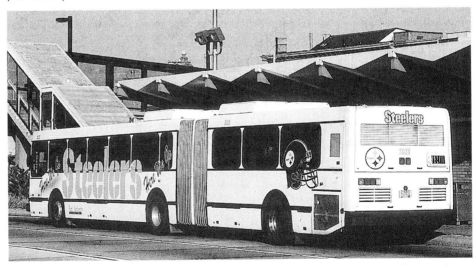

A NABI bus decorated in honour of the Pittsburgh Steelers football team pauses at East Liberty station on the East Busway (Van Wilkins)   *1999*/0038932

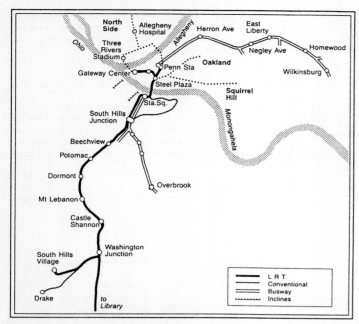

Pittsburgh's light rail and busways

Type of operation: Conventional tramway partially reconstructed to light rail standards

Passenger boardings: (1993) 8.8 million
(1994) 8.1 million
(1996) 7.4 million
Car-km: (1992) 3.4 million
(1993) 3.5 million
(1996) 2.7 million

Route length: 17.2 km
  in tunnel: 3.9 km
Number of lines: 3
Gauge: 1,588 mm
Track: 57.5 kg/m RE standard rail; ballasted track at grade, ballasted track bridges, open deck bridges, direct fixation subway, direct fixation bridges
Electrification: 650 V DC, overhead

Service: Peak 3 min, off-peak minimum 15 min
Integration with other modes: Connections with local bus routes at 9 stations
Fare collection: Fareboxes on vehicles, peak-hour platform collection at 7 stations

Rolling stock: 68 cars

PCC 4000 series (1981/90 to 1949 style)	M13
Siemens-Duewag SD400 LRV (1984/85)	M55

In peak service: 41 cars

service use. The second exclusive busway, Martin Luther King Jr East Busway, from Wilkinsburg to the edge of the city centre at Penn Park station, opened in 1983, is 11 km and has six stations for walk-on riders. With buses originating from 12 suburban communities it is served by 27 Express and Flyer routes as well as an end-to-end shuttle. More than 25,000 riders per day are carried. Some 35 park-and-ride facilities with 3,461 spaces are provided on bus and tram routes, including those serving the busway.
Developments: Extension of the East Busway to

Swissvale was planned for 1998 completion, but construction has been stalled by opposition from residents. The Airport Busway and Wabash HOV lane, originally planned as a 13 km route with a new HOV-only bridge over the Monongahela river, has now been cut back to 9 km and will make use of existing streets and river crossings to reach downtown. It will have eight stations; estimated ridership is 53,000 daily.

Tramway/light rail
Staff: 390

Developments: In 1993 the Overbrook line was closed until the long-discussed rebuilding under Stage II of the LRT upgrading had been carried out. This includes the Overbrook line and the Drake and Library routes which continue to operate, totalling 19 km. Funding for this scheme has now been approved and two of the seven contracts were expected to be awarded in 1998.

Extension of the city-centre underground section has been proposed to Northside and Oakland, the city's university and medical centre district and the third largest generator of transit trips in the state. Study of the Oakland route have been suspended, but several routeing options are being considered for the Northside–Downtown segment.

A further 27 cars are likely to be ordered for delivery in 2000.

Funicular
Current situation: The 200 m 71 per cent incline Monongahela Incline funicular was reopened in 1983 after rehabilitation which coincided with its integration into the PAT system and the Station Square commercial redevelopment project adjacent to the lower station. Built in 1870 it is the oldest inclined plane in the USA. It carries about 1 million passengers a year.

The neighbouring Duquesne Incline carries around 500,000 passengers a year. It is owned by PAT but operated by a non-profit-making historic society.

Cars pass on a short section of street running in Beechview

1997   *UPDATED*

POONA

Population: 2.6 million
Public transport: Bus services provided by municipal undertaking operating within the urban and suburban area, with some longer-distance routes running into the service area of a second municipal operator serving the twin city of Pimpri-Chinchwad (population 516,000). Extensive taxi and autorickshaw services; interdistrict and state routes operated by the Maharasthra State Road Transport Corporation

Poona Municipal Transport

Poona Municipal Transport
Swargate, Poona 411037, India
Tel: (+91 212) 44 04 17/44 11 89
Fax: (+91 212) 44 54 90
General Manager: Mahesh Shukla
Staff: 6,952

Ashok Leyland bus of PMT
1996

Bus

Passenger journeys: (1992/93) 226.2 million
(1993/94) 214.1 million
(1994/95) 225.9 million
Vehicle-km: (1992/93) 52.2 million
(1993/94) 56.9 million
(1994/95) 62 million

Number of routes: 221
Route length: 3,442 km

Fleet: 806 vehicles
Tata	136
Ashok Leyland single-deck	665
Ashok Leyland double-deck	5

In peak service: 642
On order: 674 buses
Average age of fleet: 7 years

Most intensive service: 5 min
One-person operation: None
Fare collection: Conductors
Fare structure: Stage; higher fare for night and express services; monthly passes

Fares collected on board: 92 per cent
Arrangements for elderly/disabled: Concessional fare
Average peak-hour speed: 20 km/h
Operating costs financed by: Fares 95.7 per cent, tax levy 3.6 per cent, subsidy/grants 0.6 per cent

Developments: Study for a high-capacity mass transit for the city has been carried out by RITES.

PCMT

Pimpri-Chinchwad Municipal Transport
Nigdi, Poona 411044
Tel: (+91 212) 78 36 82
General Manager: S M A Kazi
Transport Manager: N N Bothe
Staff: 2,120

Current situation: Competes with PMT on some busy routes, but is the sole provider in some areas of Poona's twin city Pimpri-Chinchwad. Has introduced high-quality minibus services at premium fares.

Bus

Passenger journeys: (1994/95) 48 million
(1995/96) 49 million
(1997/98) 34.9 million
Vehicle-km: (1994/95) 15.5 million
(1995/96) 16.8 million
(1997/98) 15.3 million

Number of routes: 53
Route length: 1,463 km

Fleet: 228 vehicles
Ashok Leyland single-deck	151
Ashok Leyland double-deck	11
Tata	57
Others	9

Average age of fleet: 7.3 years

Operating costs financed by: Fares 85.3 per cent, other commercial sources 9.7 per cent

UPDATED

PORT ELIZABETH

Population: 1.5 million
Public transport: Bus services across most of metropolitan area provided by subsidiary of industry-owned trust company. Suburban rail services. Shared taxi 'Kombi' minibuses. Transport policy gradually being formalised under a Metropolitan Transport Advisory Board. Light rail plans abandoned, suburban rail extensions proposed

Algoa Bus

Algoa Bus Company (Pty) Ltd
PO Box 225, Port Elizabeth 6000, South Africa
Tel: (+27 41) 41 42 41   Fax: (+27 41) 43 74 37
Managing Director: Gerald Botha
Staff: 648

Current situation: Algoa Bus was formed in 1991 to take over the assets of the former operating company PE Tramways, and was later incorporated as a non-profit utility company.

It is planned to replace or refurbish about 65 per cent of the fleet by 2000.

The company is currently operating in terms of an interim contract with the National Department of Transport in preparation for the Route Tender System to be introduced in 2000.

Bus

Passenger boardings: (1994/95) 13.8 million
(1996/97) 17.2 million
(1997/98) 14.6 million
Vehicle-km: (1994/95) 12.6 million
(1996/97) 12.2 million
(1997/98) 11.5 million

Number of routes: 70
Route length: 900 km

Fleet: 274 vehicles
AEC Regent	1
Leyland 680	10
ERF Super Trailblazer	30
Leyland Victory Mk II	154
Guy Big J Mk I	40
ERF Trailblazer single-deck	56
Mercedes 811/Busaf Speedliner midibus (1992/94)	8
Mercedes 812	1
AAD 320D minibus (1996)	5

In peak service: 248
On order: none

Most intensive service: 1 min
Fare collection: Wayfarer Mk III ETMs with integral smart-card readers; mobile ticket offices at major loading points; shops acting as agents for prepurchase multijourney coupons, exchanged for tickets on board
Fare structure: Flat and zonal, discount coupons
Fare evasion control: On-bus inspection
Bus priority: On certain main arterials, extreme left lane demarcated 'no stopping, except buses' in direction of peak flow for duration of peak period. New bus lanes in long-range planning stage by Metropolitan Transport Advisory Board
Average distance between stops: 400 m
Average peak-hour speed: In mixed traffic, 20 km/h
Operating costs financed by: Fares 45 per cent, other commercial sources 20 per cent, subsidy/grants 51 per cent
Subsidy from: National government 100 per cent

Metro Rail

South African Rail Commuter Corporation Ltd
Port Elizabeth Metropolitan Area
Private Bag X2, Sunninghill, Johannesburg 2157
Tel: (+27 11) 804 29 00   Fax: (+27 11) 804 38 52

Type of operation: Suburban heavy rail

Passenger journeys: (1994/95) 2.6 million
(1995/96) 2.7 million
(1996/97) 3 million

Current situation: Operates 18 return weekday journeys between Port Elizabeth and Uitenhage (33 km), serving 11 stations, with a fleet of 51 diesel-hauled cars. Fares cover 19 per cent of operating costs.

Extension to Motherwell proposed using existing trackage plus a new short branch.

Minibus/shared taxi

Current situation: There are extensive operations by private minibuses known locally as 'Kombi-taxis', licensed as taxis but operating as shared taxis. They have been responsible for substantial poaching of passengers from conventional bus routes and the suburban railway.

UPDATED

PORTLAND

Population: City 509,000, metropolitan area 1.3 million
Public transport: Bus and light rail services provided by Tri-Met, a public agency responsible to the state and governed by a local volunteer representative board of directors appointed by the state governor. Service area is 1,533 km² covering three Oregon counties and Clark County, Washington, the latter mainly served by a separate transit authority that integrates fares and co-ordinates services with Tri-Met

Tri-Met

Tri-County Metropolitan Transportation District of Oregon
4012 SE 17th Avenue, Portland, Oregon 97202-3993, USA
Tel: (+1 503) 238 49 10   Fax: (+1 503) 239 64 69
Board President: George Passadore
General Manager: Fred Hansen
Director, Bus Transportation: Clyde Earl
Director, Bus Maintenance: Tony Bryant
Director, Rail Operations: Dan Caufield

Manager, Rail Maintenance: Bruce Miller
Staff: 2,321

Current situation: Tri-Met was established in 1969 to serve the Portland metropolitan area, replacing private operations. Since 1979 the bus route network has been restructured in accordance with the dual concept of suburban timed-transfer and urban grid; there are now eight timed-transfer centres (for description see *JUTS 1990*). The grid plan was implemented in the city area in 1982, and both it and the suburban timed-transfer trunk-feeder system have led to significant increases in ridership and productivity.

Service hours have been increased each year since 1992, the 1997 rise being one of the largest at 3.5 per cent. The increased service has been rewarded with growing patronage.

Passenger journeys: (Both modes)
(1995/96) 49.3 million
(1996/97) 51.4 million
(1997/98) 53.1 million

New low-floor cars allow 100 per cent level access for wheelchairs   **1998**/0009709

New low-floor LRV on Portland's Westside extension   *1999*/0038933

Operating costs financed by: Fares 18 per cent, local employee payroll and other taxes 66 per cent, federal sources 2.7 per cent, state sources (cigarette tax 1 per cent, interest 2 per cent, miscellaneous 13 per cent)
New vehicles financed by: FTA grants 75 per cent, with local match from Tri-Met funds

Bus

Vehicle-km: (1995/96) 39.5 million
(1996/97) 39.7 million
(1997/98) 40.5 million

Number of routes: 101
Route length: 1,217 km (one way)

Fleet: 680 vehicles

GMC RTS-II (1982)	18
GMC RTS-II (1982) in store	20
Flxible Metro 40 ft (1988/89)	138
Gillig Phantom 30 ft (1990/91)	43
Gillig Phantom 40 ft (1990)	63
Gillig 40 ft LNG-powered (1992)	2
Flxible Metro 40 ft (1992)	108
Flxible Metro 30 ft (1992)	10
Flxible Metro 40 ft LNG-powered (1993)	8
Flxible Metro 40 ft (1994)	37
El Dorado minibus (1997)	10
Gillig Phantom 40 ft (1997)	65
Flyer 40 ft low-floor (1997)	40
World Trans 3000 midibus (1998/99)	18

In peak service: 547
On order: 118 New Flyer 40 ft low-floor for late 1998 delivery
Average age of fleet: 5.8 years

Most intensive service: Peak 5-20 min, off-peak 15-60 min
Fare collection: Cash or discount ticket to farebox, day, monthly and annual passes
Fare structure: Zonal (3 radial zones); 1 h free transfer; free travel in 12 × 25 block city centre 'Fareless Square' area; discount fares for youth, elderly and disabled; 10-ride discount multitickets
Fare evasion control: Driver monitoring and random inspection
Arrangements for elderly/disabled: Door-to-door LIFT van service (156 vans) caters for some 650,000 trips annually; fixed routes 100 per cent accessible; elderly and disabled travel at discounted fare at all times
Bus priority: 18-block city-centre transit mall; two adjacent one-way bus-priority streets offer improved passenger waiting facilities, information kiosks, and TV monitors with real-time information; intersection queue and signal priority at several locations
Integration with other modes: 61 park-and-ride lots; 21 are purpose-built, the rest are shared-use mainly church parking areas. Connections with light rail at 27 stations

outside the city centre, including timed-transfer at 7 suburban transit centres on the rail line; carpooling encouraged and assistance provided; cycles carried on all bus routes using front-mounted racks

Light rail

Type of operation: Light rail, opened 1986

Passenger boardings: (1995/96) 8.9 million
(1996/97) 9.7 million
(1997/98) 10.4 million
Car-km: (1995/96) 2.5 million
(1996/97) 2.6 million
(1997/98) 2.8 million

Route length: 52.6 km
Number of lines: 1
Number of stations: 50 (8 are unidirectional)
Gauge: 1,435 mm
Track: Continuously welded rail on timber or concrete sleepers in ballast
Max gradient: 7%
Electrification: 750 V DC, overhead

Service: Peak 7-10 min, off-peak 10 min, evenings and Sundays 15 min, 12 min summer Saturdays
First/last car: 03.59/01.34
Fare structure: Zonal, as bus
Fare collection: Honour system with random inspectors. Change-giving ticket vending machines and prepaid ticket cancellers at all stations; monthly passes, free transfer to and from bus
Integration with other modes: Bus connections at 27 stations, including timed transfers at 7 transit centres; 15 park-and-ride lots providing 6,900 spaces, and kiss-and-ride; cycle racks at most stations outside the city centre and storage bins at 22 transit centres; up to 12 cycles allowed on two-car train with some peak-hour restrictions
Arrangements for elderly/disabled: 100 per cent accessible with at least one low-floor car in every train
Signalling: Automatic block on private right-of-way sections and 7.2 km Banfield freeway portion; traffic light priority on most other sections; driver-controlled signals in downtown

Rolling stock: 76 cars

Bombardier/BBC (1983/86)	M26
Gomaco Brill replica cars (1991/92)	M4
Siemens-Duewag SD660 low-floor (1997)	M46

In peak service: 54
On order: A further 6 SD660 cars for early 2000 delivery

Developments: A 750 m westward extension from the city centre to 18th Avenue & Salmon Street opened in 1997. This was the initial section of the 28.4 km Westside line including the 9.8 km Hillsboro extension approved later. The full route opened September 1998 and includes

a 4.5 km tunnel and underground station serving Washington Park zoo. Delays in tunnelling meant that this opening date was a year later than originally planned for the section to 185th Avenue, though the delay enabled the Hillsboro extension to open at the same time. Patronage on the newly expanded system averaged about 60,000 per weekday during late 1998, 20 per cent higher than expected.

The first of a new fleet of low-floor cars entered service in 1997. These are the first low-floor cars in North America, and pairing them with existing cars has given all trains a low-floor section, so permitting elimination of wheelchair lifts at stations. Of the 52 cars being delivered, 36 were required for the Westside line, while 10 have been used to raise capacity on the Eastside line. The last six, a supplementary order placed in October 1997, will be used either for a further capacity increase in 1999/2000, or for the proposed airport line, if built.

Plans for a 19.3 km route running from the northeast business district through the city-centre transit mall to suburbs in the southeast, the so-called South/North line, received a major setback in November 1998 when local voters narrowly rejected a request to issue bonds backed by property taxes to provide the local share of the project's funding. The project cannot now proceed, but discussions were under way in early 1999 as to whether it might be feasible to still pursue a short, north-only line from the city centre to Kenton district.

Construction of an 8.9 km branch from Gateway on the existing Eastside line to Portland international airport will begin in 1999, pending the approval of the Federal Aviation Administration. Under an agreement signed in October 1998, the project would be financed without any Federal funds, using a combination of private money and funding from Tri-Met and other local governments. The bulk of the construction cost would be paid by the airport's operator, the Port of Portland, and by the developer of a large vacant site adjacent to the airport.

Vintage Trolley

Current situation: A fares-free vintage tram service funded by local businesses and other non-Tri-Met sources, inaugurated 1991, shares city-centre tracks, complementing regular services at off-peak times in summer and autumn. Operated under contract by Tri-Met, the service is managed by a non-profit-making body, Vintage Trolley Inc, which also owns the four replica trams used (included in Tri-Met rolling stock list). The service is a significant player in transit provision between the city centre and Lloyd District.

Tramway (under construction)

Central City Streetcar

City of Portland, Office of Transportation
1120 SW 5th Ave, Room 802, Portland, Oregon 97204, USA
Tel: (+1 503) 823 70 04   Fax: (+1 503) 823 73 71
Transportation Commissioner: Charlie Hales
Project Co-ordinator: Vicky Diede

Current situation: Under discussion since 1988, the Central City Streetcar Project has been developed independently of Tri-Met by the City of Portland, and a non-profit body, Portland Streetcar Inc, has been formed to design and build the line.

An initial 3.7 km on-street city-centre circulator route extending from the Good Samaritan Hospital to Portland State University could form the nucleus of a network of on-street routes extending to various parts of the city.

A major impetus for this project was the desire by the city and regional planning authority Metro to foster new high-density (multistorey) 'transit-friendly' housing development in the areas immediately north of the city centre known as the Pearl District and River District, to gradually replace old industrial development.

Financing for the $42 million project, which received final approval in September 1998, is coming from several sources including a 20-year municipal bond to be repaid by rate increases at city-owned car parks and a special temporary tax to be imposed on property owners along the route (a 'local improvement' district).

In January 1999 five articulated air conditioned low-floor cars were to be supplied by Skoda, The fleet will be supplemented (on an as-needed basis) by one or two of the Gomaco-built Brill replica trams currently operating on the Tri-Met light rail line.

Construction was due to begin in April 1999 and

inauguration of the service is targeted for September 2000.

C-Tran

Clark County Public Transportation Benefit Area Authority
PO Box 2529, 2425 NE 65th Avenue, Vancouver, Washington 98668-2529
Tel: (+1 360) 696 44 94   Fax: (+1 360) 696 16 02
Executive Director: Les White
Director of Operations: Thomas G Hartley

Current situation: C-Tran operations began in 1981 after voter endorsement of a plan to develop services for the fast-growing Clark County area with a total population that had grown to 300,000 by 1996, and including the city of Vancouver. Based on a private operation run by Vancouver city since 1969, C-Tran is now a Public Transportation Benefit Area Authority under a representative board. C-Tran and Tri-Met co-operate to provide a regional network for the Portland/Vancouver

metropolitan area, including express commuter routes between the towns. Four per cent of km is operated under contract to Tri-Met. Vanpool service inaugurated 1988, carpools in 1995.

Bus

Passenger journeys: (1993) 3.5 million
(1994) 3.8 million
(1995) 4.3 million
Vehicle-km: (1993) 5.9 million
(1994) 5.5 million
(1995) 7 million

Number of routes: 29
Route length: 980 km

Fleet: 139 vehicles

GM RTS-II (1982)	34
Gillig Phantom (1991/95)	60
Diamond minibus (1991)	3
GMC 'New Look' (1981)	10
Champion minibus (1986)	2
Collins Diplomat 25 ft	7
Escort 20 ft	7
El Dorado 25 ft	10
Dodge vans	6

In peak service: 116

Arrangements for elderly/disabled: C-VAN paratransit service with 13 lift-equipped vehicles carried 78,600 passengers in 1992. Contract staff are employed. It covers only 4 per cent of costs from fares
Operating costs financed by: Fares 16.8 per cent, other commercial sources 5.9 per cent, subsidy/grants 77.3 per cent
Subsidy from: A ⅕ per cent sales tax is dedicated to transit and matched from annual Motor Vehicle Excise tax collected by Washington state and FTA grants

UPDATED

PORTO ALEGRE

Population: 1.3 million, metropolitan area 2.7 million
Public transport: Bus and minibus services provided by private operators holding concessions, and fixed-route shared taxi system, supervised by municipal administration which has established busway system. Suburban rail

Secretaria Municipal dos Transportes

Secretaria Municipal dos Transportes (SMT)
Prefeitura Municipal de Porto Alegre
Av Ipiranga 1138, 9000 Porto Alegre, RS, Brazil
Tel: (+55 512) 23 70 00
Secretary of Transport: Jarbas Luiz Macedo Haag
Director of Operations: Luiz Mário Magalhães Sá

Current situation: SMT was established in 1976. It has overall responsibility for co-ordination of public transport provided by private operators, highway provision and management, pedestrianisation, road safety and area traffic control. Pursuit of an integrated policy led to establishment of a five-route central area bus system run by a designated private firm and seven corridors segregating buses on radial services from all other traffic in busways. Longer-distance commuting is regulated by the Department of Road Transport (DAER).

Urban services are provided by 15 operators, plus the state-owned Cia Carris Porto-Alegrense, with a total fleet of 1,476 buses, carrying about 1.2 million passengers daily. Carris also operates a fleet of seven vehicles adapted to carry disabled passengers.

There is also a fleet of some 400 21-seater minibuses which are permitted to carry seated passengers only. These cater for 100,000 daily journeys.

Busway

Current situation: Bus-only lanes in the centre of major roads on seven radial corridors are used by both urban

services and those originating outside the city, and some bus flows exceed 350 per hour. The Comonor convoy system is used to maximise the capacity of the lanes which are up to 4.9 km long. Buses to/from various destinations are held at lane entry points to travel as a unit halting in unison at each stop, enabling volumes of up to 20,000 passengers/h to be carried at speeds of more than 20 km/h including stops. Buses serve protected 'stations', though passengers generally must cross the outer (general) traffic lanes to reach them. SMT staff assist in this by undertaking traffic control.

Some vehicles are operated with trailers to increase capacity, though articulated buses have been introduced by SMT on one corridor, with an alternative operating system based on a single trunk route using the dedicated bus lane run by express buses serving interchanges, with local feeder bus connections as in Curitiba (qv).

Trensurb

Empresa de Trens Urbanos de Porto Alegre SA
Rua Ernesto Neugebauer 1985, Bairro Dona Teodora, 90250-140 Porto Alegre, RS
Tel: (+55 51) 337 35 33   Fax: (+55 51) 337 12 19
www: www.trensurb.com.br
President: Adeo Dornelles Faraco
Director, Operations: R Guimarães
Director, Administration & Finance: N Soares
Superintendent, Development: N L Nunes
Staff: 1,100

Type of operation: Regional metro, opened 1985

Passenger journeys: (1993) 33.1 million
(1994) 31.4 million
(1995) 29.7 million

Route length: 31.4 km
Number of routes: 1
Number of stations: 16

Gauge: 1,600 mm
Track: Conventional ballasted, twin-block concrete sleepers with 57 kg/m welded rail
Electrification: 3 kV DC, overhead

Service: Peak 5 min, off-peak 12 min
First/last train: 05.15/23.20
Fare structure: Flat

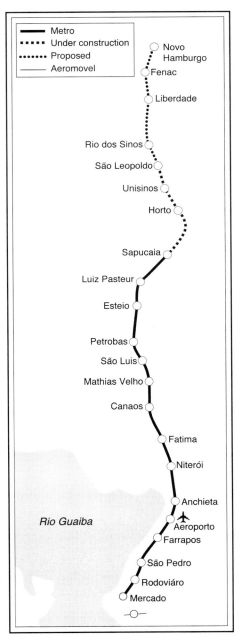

Porto Alegre metro

Trensurb metro train on elevated section in Porto Alegre

1999/0038935

Integration with other modes: Transfer to some bus routes at higher charge; 60 bus routes feed Trensurb stations

Operating costs financed by: Fares 25 per cent, other commercial sources 6 per cent, subsidy/grants 69 per cent

Rolling stock: 25 four-car trains
Nippon Sharyo/Hitachi/Kawasaki (1984)   M100
In peak service: 14 trains

Current situation: Trensurb was established in 1980 to develop a high-capacity regional metro from the existing RFFSA suburban line north from the city centre to Novo Hamburgo, an important development corridor. The service currently links Mercado and Unisinos.

Developments: Following opening in late 1997 of a 3.9 km extension from Sapucaia to Unisinos, a further 2.4 km to São Leopoldo is scheduled for completion in 1999. Adtranz is supplying overhead, power supply and communications equipment for the extension, and is also upgrading the existing CTC system.

Though not part of the state commuter railway operation CBTU, Trensurb is managed directly by the federal government; transfer to local state control has been discussed. This would involve the federal government assuming responsibility for the line's accumulated debt.

Several proposals have been canvassed for a second route. That currently favoured is a 17.3 km mostly underground alignment from Sarandi to Azenha, with 18 stations. A 3.1 km branch is also planned to link

Aeropuerto station on Line 1 with Cairu on Line 2 to provide access to the existing rolling stock maintenance depot.

Aeromovel
Coester SA

Type of operation: Demonstration people mover, powered by compressed air

Current situation: Porto Alegre firm Coester developed the Aeromovel system in the 1970s, and a 600 m demonstration track was built in 1979-81 with financial assistance from EBTU; later extended to 1.1 km. The elevated route lies in the median of the Avenida Loureiro da Silva.

UPDATED

PORT OF SPAIN
Population: 400,000
Public transport: Bus services in Port of Spain and other areas of Trinidad operated by state corporation which also operates busway; extensive private shared taxi operations

PTSC
Public Transport Service Corporation (PTSC)
Railway Building, South Quay, PO Box 391, Port of Spain, Trinidad
Tel: (+1 809) 623 23 41
e-mail: ptsc@wow.nwt
General Manager: Dr Trevor Townsend
Staff: 250

Current situation: Though PTSC services operate throughout Trinidad and Tobago, its market share has declined substantially due to strong competition from shared taxis.
Developments: Long-standing government subsidies were phased out in 1994, and PTSC implemented a restructuring which reduced costs by cutting staff and services. PTSC's market share rose from about 10 per

cent to 14 per cent in 1996, while its private hire business grew by 100 per cent.

Two new business units have been established to boost income. The Engineering Services Division will provide contract maintenance to private vehicle operators, and the Property Development unit will maximise revenues from PTSC-owned property.

Bus
Number of routes: 19
On priority right-of-way: 24.8 km

Fleet: 100 vehicles

Most intensive service: Priority busway 10-15 min, other heavily used routes 15-30 min
One-person operation: All routes
Fare collection: Prepurchase tickets
Fare structure: Graduated (telescopic)
Fare evasion control: Inspectors
Operational control: Inspectors
Arrangements for elderly/disabled: Pensioners and persons receiving public assistance carried free
Average peak-hour speed: In bus lanes 40 km/h; in mixed traffic 15-20 km/h

Bus priority: 24.8 km busway links Port of Spain with Arima (see below), also used by maxi-taxis to which a controlled number of passes are issued for a fee
Operating costs financed by: Fares 95 per cent, other commercial sources 5 per cent

Busway
Current situation: The Port of Spain to Arima busway is a two-lane 7.3 m wide single-carriageway reserved route using former railway trackbed with four major 'stations' and 27 stops. The route is shared with 700 privately owned minibuses (maxi-taxis) and over 600 private cars with special passes.

Shared taxi
Current situation: Shared taxis carry some four times as many passengers as buses, amounting to over 150 million journeys a year. There are about 20,000 sedan taxis and 4,600 12-25 seater minibuses (maxi-taxis). They operate fixed routes and make pick-ups at central points according to the areas served.

VERIFIED

POZNAN
Population: 582,000
Public transport: Bus and tramway services provided by municipal authority, with some contracted bus operations. Suburban rail services by State Railway (PKP)

MPK
Miejskie Przedsiębiorstwo Komunikacyjne (MPK)
ul Glogowska 131, PL-60244 Poznan, Poland
Tel: (+48 61) 69 93 61   Fax: (+48 61) 66 37 08
General Manager: Wojciech Tulibacki
Financial Manager: Lidia Bartosiak
Tramway Manager: Jan Firlik
Bus Manager: Krzysztof Ksiazyk
Staff: 3,007

Passenger journeys: (All modes)
(1995) 194.5 million
(1996) 205.8 million
(1997) 225.6 million

Operating costs financed by: Fares 48.9 per cent, subsidy/grants 51.1 per cent
Subsidy from: Municipal budget

Developments: MPK's computer-based traffic control system, commissioned in late 1998, provides operational control with radio data links, passenger information, demand-control of buses and tram movements, timetable database, and financial data.

In March 1998, MPK introduced a new ticketing system based upon distance travelled.

Bus
Passenger journeys: (1995) 83.6 million
(1996) 88 million
(1997) 101.5 million
Vehicle-km: (1995)16 million
(1996) 16.7 million
(1997) 16.6 million

Number of routes: 47 (plus 11 night routes)
Route length: (One way) 465 km

Fleet: 294 vehicles	
Ikarus 260 (1985)	18
Jelcz M11 (1984/90)	36
Den Oudsten (1982)	14
Jelcz M121M low-floor (1985)	1
MAN NL202 low-floor (1996)	40
Neoplan N4016 low-floor (1996/97)	31
Neoplan N4009 low-floor (1996/97)	22
Ikarus 280 articulated (1983/94)	88
Ikarus (Yu) IK160P articulated (1992)	14
Ikarus 435 articulated (1994)	1
MAN NG272 low-floor articulated (1996)	10
Neoplan N4020 Megatrans low-floor articulated (1996/97)	19
In peak service: 230	

One-person operation: All routes
Fare collection: Prepurchase day passes, carnets or single tickets; validation/cancelling machines on board
Fare structure: Timed tickets, 10, 30, 60 min, 24 h, 7 days; free transfer
Fares collected on board: Nil; 47 per cent of passengers hold prepurchase tickets, 53 per cent passes
Fare evasion control: Inspectors
Operational control: Route inspectors
Arrangements for elderly/disabled: Invalids and over-75s travel free, pensioners pay reduced fare; seats allocated for disabled

Neoplan N4016 low-floor at the International Fairground   *1998*/0009705

Average distance between stops: 603 m
Average peak-hour speed: 19.2 km/h
New vehicles financed by: City Council

Tramway
Type of operation: Conventional tramway

Passenger boardings: (1995) 110.9 million
(1996) 117.3 million
(1997) 124.1 million

Car-km: (1995) 14 million
(1996) 14.1 million
(1997) 15.7 million

Route length: 150 km
Number of lines: 15
Number of stops: 237
Gauge: 1,435 mm
Max gradient: 5.6%
Min curve radius: 25 m

Electrification: 600 V DC, overhead

Service: 15 min, evenings 20 min
First/last car: 04.49/22.49
Fare structure: As bus
One-person operation: All routes

Rolling stock: 316 cars
LHB 1G ex-Amsterdam (1956-59)   M14
Duewag GT6 ex-Düsseldorf (1956/57)   M10
Duewag GT8 ex-Düsseldorf (1956/59)   M12
Konstal 105N (1970-90)   M240
Konstal 102N articulated (1975-90)   M29
HCP Cegielski 105N/2 low-floor articulated (1995)   M1
ČKD Tatra RT6N low-floor articulated (1997/98)   M10
In peak service: 234

Developments: A section of rapid tramway (PST) running from the city centre to the northern suburbs, including 7 km fully segregated, opened in 1997. Lines 12, 14 and 15 have been diverted to the new alignment, operated by a dedicated fleet of 10 low-floor and 15 standard cars. Line 14 was extended southwest to Górczyn as rapid tramway in January 1999.

Several extensions have been approved but work is halted due to funding difficulties. Through running to the main tram network is to be introduced, using a new fleet of 10 Tatra eight-axle cars.

PKP

Polish State Railways
ul Chalubinskiego 4, PL-00-918 Warsaw

Type of operation: Suburban heavy rail

Current situation: Services operate irregularly (about every 2 h, more frequently at commuting times) over nine routes into Poznan's main and inner suburban stations.

ČKD Tatra RT6N low-floor articulated LRV (Marcel Vleugels)   **1999**/0045400   *UPDATED*

PRAGUE

Population: 1.2 million
Public transport: Bus, tramway and metro services provided by municipally owned corporation, some bus services contracted from private operators. Suburban services by State Railway and private bus operators

Dopravní podnik hlavního města Prahy

Dopravní podnik hlavního města Prahy a s
Bubenská 1, CZ-17026 Prague 7, Czech Republic
Tel: (+420 2) 96 19 20 00   Fax: (+420 2) 96 19 20 03
Director General: Milan Houfek
Director, Metro: Ladislav Houdek
Director, Tramway: Milan Pokorný
Director, Bus: Jiri Machač
Staff: 12,364

Passenger journeys: (1995) 1,074 million
(1996) 1,078 million
(1997) 1,076 million

Current situation: As the metro network has expanded, the role of the tramway has been reduced. Tramway construction was suspended for a time in the 1980s, but resumed in 1988. Buses provide a supplementary network to the rail-based modes, mainly serving outer areas. Public transport usage, though declining, is still high, accounting for 65 per cent of weekday journeys.
Developments: Current fares policy is driven by the need to improve the farebox ratio to between 30 and 50 per cent, but rapidly rising operating costs have absorbed the quite substantial fares increases implemented since 1991.

Fare structure: Flat rate for single tickets valid for 15 (no transfer) and 90 min (with transfer) within Prague inner and outer zones P and 0; 24 h, 3-, 7- and 15-day, monthly, 3-monthly and yearly passes; concessions for children, students, elderly and military
Fare collection: Prepurchase tickets with mechanical validation on buses and trams, electronic validation on metro; most passengers use passes

Fare evasion control: Inspectors on board and in paid station areas
Arrangements for elderly/disabled: Some special bus services
Operating costs financed by: Fares 25 per cent, other sources 6 per cent, subsidy/grants 69 per cent

Bus
Staff: 3,919

Passenger journeys: (1995) 327 million
(1996) 331 million
(1997) 330 million
Vehicle-km: (1995) 63.3 million
(1996) 65 million
(1997) 63.5 million

Number of routes: 208 (10 night routes)
Route length: 2,108 km

Fleet: 1,353 vehicles
Karosa B731/B732/E734/LC735   818
Karosa B741 articulated   174
Karosa B931   169
Karias citybus   16
Ikarus 280 articulated   109
Neoplan   3
Karosa B941 articulated   55
Long-distance bus   9
In peak service: 1,004

Most intensive service: Peak 2.4 min
One-person operation: All routes
Average peak-hour speed: 23.3 km/h

Metro
Staff: 4,191

Type of operation: Full metro, initial route opened 1974

Passenger journeys: (1995) 413 million
(1996) 406 million
(1997) 407 million

Karosa standard in suburban Prague   **1997**

Route length: 43.6 km
Number of lines: 3
Number of stations: 43
Gauge: 1,435 mm

Tunnel: Cut-and-cover and bored; over the Nusle valley metro tunnel incorporated beneath highway on Nusle bridge, 43 m above ground
Electrification: 750 V DC, bottom-contact third rail

Service: Peak 1 min 50 s
First/last train: 05.00/24.00
Signalling: Automatic block; ATP
Centralised control: Radio communication with trains individually or en masse

Rolling stock: 504 cars in five-car sets
Mytischy T 81717 cab cars (1978 on)   202
Mytischy T 81714 non-driving cars   302
In peak service: 79 trains

Current situation: Eastern extension of Line B to Černý Most (6.4 km, five stations) opened in November 1998.

Construction is expected to start in 1999 of a northern extension of Line C to Ládví (4 km, 3 stations) to serve satellite housing developments, which could open in 2002, and Line D is proposed to link Namesti Miru and Nové Dvory.

Developments: A fleet of 110 new-generation cars is being delivered from a consortium of builders comprising ČKD, Adtranz, Siemens and SGP, with delivery starting in 1998.

In 1994 a contract was awarded to Matra Transport for modernisation of Line C with the PA135 automatic train control system. This work was completed in 1999.

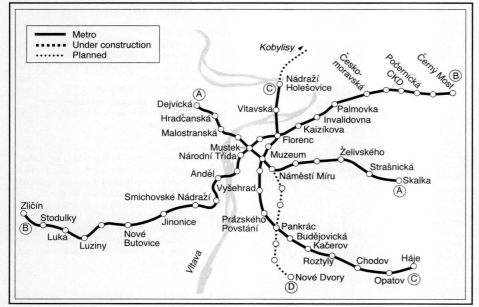

Prague metro   0045720

Prague new-generation metro train built by ČKD, Adtranz and Siemens (Marcel Vleugels)   *1999*/0045399

Tramway
Staff: 3,819

Type of operation: Conventional tramway, with new light rail sections

Passenger journeys: (1995) 333 million
(1996) 341 million
(1997) 339 million
Car-km: (1995) 44 million
(1996) 45.7 million
(1997) 45.5 million

Route length: 494 km
Number of lines: 31 (8 night)
Number of stops: 606
Gauge: 1,435 mm
Electrification: 600 V DC, overhead

Service: Peak 4-12 min
First/last car: 04.30/24.00 (day service); night service runs every 40 min with timed transfers at interchanges
One-person operation: All cars

Rolling stock: 977 cars
Tatra T3 standard (1961/76)   M675
Tatra T3M (thyristor control)   M101
Tatra KT8D5 (1990)   M47
Tatra T6A5 (1995/96/97)   M150
Tatra RT6N   M4
In peak service: 647

Developments: After a period of suspension in favour of metro construction, tramway construction resumed in 1988 and two extensions have opened since. In 1995 a 5.8 km extension with light rail characteristics opened from Braník to Modřany.

Future plans include an extension to the Barrandov housing estate in the southwestern suburbs, while new routes are planned to feed the metro Line C extension in the north.

Funicular
Current situation: The 510 m funicular which climbs Petřín Hill carries 1.1 million passengers annually.

ČD
Česky Drahy
Na přikopě 33, CZ-11005 Prague 1

Type of operation: Suburban heavy rail

Current situation: Services provided on eight routes, partially electrified, to a distance of about 60 km. Approximately hourly on three routes, irregular services elsewhere.
Developments: Improved service is to be offered on the line to Kladno (37.5 km), which is to be upgraded and electrified by a new private company PRAK. Two branches are proposed for construction, to Ruzyne international airport and Kladno town centre.

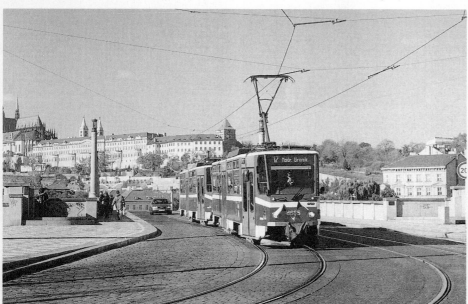

Between 1995 and 1997 Prague Transport Authority acquired 150 Type T6A5 four-axle trams from ČKD Dopravní Systémy (Milan Šrámek)   *1999*/0038936

UPDATED

PRETORIA

Population: 1 million
Public transport: City bus services provided by transport department of the city council. Extensive longer-distance commuter bus services operated by private companies and suburban rail services by Rail Commuter Corp

Pretoria City Transport

City Council of Pretoria
Logistic Services Department, Transportation Services
PO Box 890, 1 Schoeman Street, Pretoria 0001, South Africa
Tel: (+27 12) 308 02 00   Fax: (+27 12) 308 02 13
Executive Director, Logistic Services: C Bosch
Staff: 437

Current situation: Public transport policy is being revised and competitive tendering was expected to be introduced in 1998 covering all operators, with the aim of reducing costs and improving service quality.

Bus

Passenger journeys: (1994/95) 16 million
(1995/96) 13.8 million
(1996/97) 13 million
Vehicle-km: (1994/95) 11.5 million
(1995/96) 11.3 million
(1996/97) 11 million

Number of routes: 245, including school and contract routes
Route length: (One way) timetabled routes 685 km

Fleet: 300 vehicles

MAN City Bus	20
MAN semi-luxury	15
MAN double-deck	20
Mercedes O305 city bus	87
Mercedes O305 semi-luxury coach	50
Mercedes O305 double-deck	108
In peak service: 267	

Most intensive service: 5 min
One-person operation: All services
Fare collection: Cash to driver or prepurchase
Fare structure: Stage; multiticket books (coupons); trip tickets valid 1 month for 1, 2, 3 or 4 stages allowing 4 trips per day, 2 on any route within the municipal boundary and 2 within the central area. Monthly tickets allowing 6 trips per day on any routes within the municipal boundary
Fares collected on board: 26.7 per cent; 9.9 million passengers took prepurchase tickets in 1994/95
Fare evasion control: Ticket inspectors
Operational control: Route inspectors
Arrangements for elderly/disabled: Disabled and over-68s free; low-price senior citizens' monthly pass for unlimited off-peak travel
Average peak-hour speed: In bus lanes, 23.5 km/h; in mixed traffic, 20.5 km/h
Bus priority: 7.5 km of bus lanes
Operating costs financed by: Fares 49 per cent, other commercial sources 1 per cent, subsidy/grants 50 per cent
Subsidy from: City tax funds
New vehicles financed by: Loans/tax fund

Other operators

Current situation: PUTCO provides mostly longer-distance bus services to bring commuters to work (see Johannesburg entry). Its Pretoria area operations carry more than 50 million passengers annually. A second private operator Northwest Star (formerly BTH) also runs services.

Metro Rail

South African Rail Commuter Corporation Ltd
Pretoria Metropolitan Area
Private Bag X2, Sunninghill, Johannesburg 2157
Tel: (+27 11) 804 29 00   Fax: (+27 11) 804 38 52

Type of operation: Suburban heavy rail

Passenger journeys: (1994/95) 72.6 million
(1995/96) 74.6 million
(1996/97) 75.8 million

Current situation: Suburban rail serving whole of Pretoria (Northern Transvaal area, population 1.5 million); seven routes totalling 146 km with 78 stations, 1,065 mm gauge, electrified 3 kV DC; links with Johannesburg area services. Peak service 10 trains per hour, off-peak every 20 min. Fares cover 30 per cent of operating costs.
Developments: An 18 km extension is proposed in Metro Rail's 10-year capital development programme.

Rolling stock: 589 emu cars

Union Carriage & Wagon	M163 T426

VERIFIED

PROVIDENCE

Population: 596,000
Public transport: Bus services in Providence and in 35 of the other 38 towns in the state of Rhode Island provided by public transit authority controlled by representative board; commuter rail link to Boston

RIPTA

Rhode Island Public Transit Authority (RIPTA)
PO Box 2816, 265 Melrose Street, Providence, Rhode Island 02907, USA
Tel: (+1 401) 781 94 50   Fax: (+1 401) 784 95 95
Director of Transit Administration: Edward Scott
Director of Transit Operations: William Dame
General Manager: Beverly A Scott
Staff: 520

Current situation: Established in 1966 to take over residual private bus operations. A 10-year development programme expanded services throughout the state.

Bus

Passenger journeys: (1993) 16.4 million
(1994) 17.4 million
Vehicle-km: (1990/91) 12.2 million

Number of routes: 73

Route length: 580 km

Fleet: 242 vehicles	
GMC RTS-II (1981)	15
Neoplan AN460 articulated (1984)	5
Volvo B10M (1985)	55
Neoplan AN440 (1988)	64
TMC RTS T80 (1990)	28
TMC RTS T80 (1992)	48
Boyertown trolley replicas (1984)	2
Eldorado Aerotech (1993)	25
In peak service: 196	

Most intensive service: 30 min
One-person operation: All routes
Fare collection: Registering fareboxes
Fare structure: Zonal (4 zones); transfers (15-60 min dependent on frequency); 10-ticket books; monthly passes; free downtown loop service
Fares collected on board: 85 per cent
Operational control: Route inspectors; radio
Arrangements for elderly/disabled: 179 buses lift-equipped; free off-peak travel
Bus priority: Buses use 300 m former tram tunnel under College Hill in central Providence
Integration with other modes: 14 park-and-ride sites served by 9 commuter bus routes
Average peak-hour speed: 16 km/h
Operating costs financed by: Fares 27 per cent, subsidy/grants 73 per cent
Subsidy from: FTA 74 per cent, state 26 per cent
New vehicles financed by: Voter-approved bonding and federal grants

Suburban rail

Current situation: About 10 Amtrak trains daily link Providence with Boston (69 km), plus commuter-hour services operated by MBTA Boston under auspices of Rhode Island DoT.
Developments: Electrification of the Amtrak route is in progress for 1999 completion.

Rhode Island Public Transit Authority RTS bus at Kennedy Plaza in Providence (Bill Luke) **1999**/0038937

UPDATED

PUSAN

Population: 3.9 million
Public transport: Bus services provided by private companies organised into statutory associations. Urban transit authority operates metro; light rail planned

Private bus

Current situation: Buses carry over 1,000 million passengers a year, accounting for around 45 per cent of public transport, with a further 14 per cent handled by taxis and smaller vehicles. Each bus company typically operates up to five routes. Frequencies and fares (flat, with a premium for seat buses) are set by government agency.

Fleet: About 2,500, including mostly standard locally built 72-capacity and some smaller 'seat buses' providing premium all-seated services

PUTA

Pusan Urban Transit Authority
861-1 Bum Chun-dong, Pusan-Jin-ku 614-021, Republic of Korea
Tel: (+82 51) 463 42 06
President: Kim Chang-Gap
Staff: 1,667

Type of operation: Full metro, opened 1985

Passenger journeys: (1991) 181.5 million
(1992) 192 million

Route length: 32.5 km
Number of routes: 1
Number of stations: 30
Gauge: 1,435 mm
Min curve radius: 180 m
Electrification: 1.5 kV DC, overhead

Service: Peak 3½ min
Fare structure: 3 zones
Fare collection: Ticket or stored-value pass
Signalling: ATO-equipped, but currently operating in manual mode
Operating costs financed by: Fares 11 per cent

Rolling stock: 216 cars formed into 6 six-car sets
Marubeni/Hyundai (1984/85)   M216

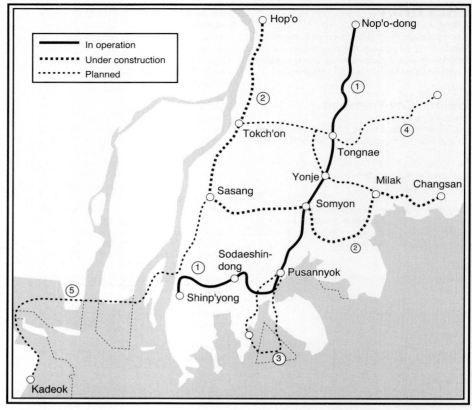

Pusan metro

On order: 336 cars being built by Hanjin for opening of Line 2 in 1998

Current situation: Initial 16.1 km section of Line 1 opened 1985, further 5.2 km in 1987, and the remainder a year later.
Developments: Line 1 extension to Shinp'yong (6.4 km) opened June 1994. The 22.4 km Phase I of east-west Line 2 from Hop'o to Somyon was due to open in 1995 but completion was delayed until 1998. Phase II, from Somyon to Changsan (16.6 km), should open in 1999.

A network of five lines totalling 138 km had been scheduled for completion by 2001, but work on Lines 3, 4 and 5, totalling 67 km, is unlikely to start before the end of the century.

Light rail (proposed)

Current situation: A light rail link to Kimhae airport has been proposed.

VERIFIED

PYONGYANG

Population: 2.5 million
Public transport: Bus, trolleybus and tram services provided by People's Assembly of city under government supervision. Metro operated by government department

Pyongyang People's Assembly

Pyongyang People's Assembly Transport Committee
Pyongyang, Democratic People's Republic of Korea

Bus and trolleybus

Passenger journeys: Approx 150 million (annual)

Number of routes: 50

Fleet: Approx 500 buses, including Ikarus 260 and 280 articulated; Karosa SM and B731

Fleet: There are about 1,000 locally built trolleybuses, both two-axle and articulated

One-person operation: None
Fare structure: Flat, prepaid tickets deposited in box at rear of vehicle
Fare collection: Conductors

Current situation: The trolleybus operation acts mainly as a feeder to the metro, though there are signs that the system is to be run down as the tramway develops. There are 10 routes.

Tramway

Current situation: The first tramway route was opened in 1991 and extended in 1992 and 1994. There are three routes extending to at least 50 km, operated by a fleet of ČKD Tatra and Chinese-built cars, plus second-hand vehicles. An extensive network is planned, including a circular route.

Rolling stock: Approx 300 cars
ČKD Tatra KT8 articulated   M45
ČKD Tatra T6B5   M129
Shenfeng Trolleybus Works KT4 articulated   M60
Ex-Zürich
Ex-Leipzig

Pyongyang Metro

City Metro Unit, Railway Section, Transport & Communication Commission

Type of operation: Full metro, initial route opened 1973

Passenger journeys: (1990) 42 million
(1994) 35 million

Route length: 22.5 km
Number of routes: 2
Number of stations: 17
Gauge: 1,435 mm
Track: Concrete trackbed
Tunnel: Bored and blasted to maximum depth of 150 m; mostly single-bore
Electrification: 825 V DC, third rail

Service: Peak 2 min, off-peak 5-7 min
First/last train: 05.00/23.00
Fare structure: Flat

Tram and trolleybus outside Pyongyang's main station   1997

Fare collection: Automatic entry barriers, coin in slot, no tickets; manual surveillance
Signalling: Colourlights; CTC

Rolling stock: 168 cars
Kim Chong The works (1973)	M48
Ex-BVG Berlin	M120

Current situation: Line 1 opened 1973, Line 2 in 1978. The two lines are not connected but interchange is provided in the city centre between Chonu station on Line 1 and Chongsing station on Line 2.
Developments: An east-west route through the city centre is planned in connection with a major residential development in the eastern suburbs, but progress has been hampered by shortage of funds.

Pressure on the rolling stock fleet was eased during 1997 by delivery of 120 cars of 1960s vintage second-hand from the Berlin U-Bahn.

VERIFIED

Yonggwang metro station
1997

QUEBEC
Population: 480,000
Public transport: Bus services provided by transport commission responsible to urban municipal authority

STCUQ
Société de Transport de la Communauté Urbaine de Québec (STCUQ)
720 rue des Rocailles, Quebec G2J 1A5, Canada
Tel: (+1 418) 627 23 51   Fax: (+1 418) 627 72 28
President: Claude Larose
General Manager: Steve Cameron
Director of Operations: Robert Chassé
Director of Research & Marketing: Raymond Paquin (Acting)
Staff: 1,100

Current situation: STCUQ was created in 1969 and acquired the buses and services of seven companies which had previously served the 400 km² area and 13 municipalities in and around the city.
Developments: Following a major reorganisation in 1992, STCUQ implemented the second phase of its transit development programme in 1995. At the heart of the plan is the Metrobus system of high-frequency limited-stop routes using designated bus lanes, designed to provide metro-like service quality.

These and other measures implemented in 1997 led to a 5 per cent increase in journeys. More bus lanes were introduced, along with many new shelters and provision of improved information on several sections of route. The year also saw introduction of STCUQ's first low-floor buses, but they did not match up to expectations and it was decided that future fleet policy should be based on second-hand purchases and refurbishment of existing vehicles on economic grounds.

In 1998 a further step was taken in development of a regional transport network, with integration of fares on both sides of the St Lawrence river.

Bus
Passenger journeys: (1993) 37.2 million
(1994) 32.5 million
(1997) 38.7 million
Vehicle-km: (Annual) 22 million

Number of routes: 93

Route length: 600 km
Number of stops: 4,280

Fleet: 450 vehicles
GM Canada New Look (1971-82)	117
GM/MCI/NovaBUS Classic (1983-95)	282
MCI Classic articulated (1992)	2
Orion II 24 ft (1994)	4
NovaBUS LFS low-floor (1996-98)	45

In peak service: 400
Average age of fleet: 10.7 years

Most intensive service: 5 min
One-person operation: All services
Fare collection: Payment to driver or prepurchase pass
Fare structure: Flat; exact fare; monthly passes
Operational control: Inspectors, radio
Bus priority: 30 km peak-hour bus lanes
Average peak-hour speed: 20 km/h
Operating costs financed by: Fares 36 per cent, subsidy/grants 64 per cent
Subsidy from: Province and 13 municipalities

UPDATED

QUITO
Population: 800,000, metropolitan area 1.3 million
Public transport: Bus and minibus services mostly provided by independent operators forming route or area associations and co-operatives, supervised by the municipality. Municipal services also operate some routes; trolleybus route

Municipality of Quito
Municipio de Quito
PO Box 17-17-484, Quito, Ecuador
Tel: (+593 2) 51 35 18   Fax: (+593 2) 46 03 41
Director of Planning: Cesar Arias

Current situation: The municipality is the overall planning and licensing authority for the city's transport services. It also built the trolleybus route opened in 1995 and owns the vehicles. Bus services are being progressively franchised to private operators.
Developments: All bus routes serving the north-south Villa Flora/El Recreo to La Y corridor through the city centre were cut back to the new interchanges built at the northern and southern terminals of the trolleybus line. In total, 110 bus routes were revised.

Nearly all operations are contracted to private companies, though Empresa Metropolitana del Transporte (EMT) runs some of the secondary routes feeding its trolleybus line.

Private bus/minibus
Passenger journeys: (1995) 1 million daily
Vehicle-km: 55 million (annual)

Number of routes: 50
Route length: 700 km
Fleet: 1,500, including 500 buses and 1,000 minibuses; types include Ford, Dodge, Mercedes, Bedford. Thomas locally built bodywork is widely used

One-person operation: All services
Fare collection: Payment to driver; some vehicles with turnstiles
Fare structure: Flat
Fares collected on board: 100 per cent
Average peak-hour speed: 18 km/h

Trolleybus
Passenger journeys: (1996) 150,000 daily
(1997) 180,000 daily

Current situation: An 11.2 km route constructed on new

Trolleybus equipped for high-platform loading only enters the northern terminal of Quito's trolleybus trunk line (Steve Morgan)
1999/0038938

bus-only lanes throughout opened in 1995/96, along with two other parallel busways which are diesel bus operated. Built by the municipality, the system is being managed by the Empresa Metropolitana del Transporte prior to seeking a private-sector concessionaire. Two short routes have been introduced, overlapping with the through route on the busy Av Colón—Plaza Grande section.

This unique system has been described as a rubber-tyred light rail line; light rail was rejected only on the grounds that vibration might harm historic buildings in the city centre. The route is entirely segregated and forms the city's central trunk route. All bus routes in the north-south corridor have been cut back to act as feeders; 70 routes now run to huge interchanges built at the Villa Flora/El

Recreo and La Y trolleybus terminals. Some of the feeders are operated by EMT using Ikarus articulated buses.

All passenger boarding and alighting is at high-platform enclosed 'stations' (20 southbound, 19 northbound), which give stepless access to the vehicles. New traffic signals have been installed at 140 intersections along the route, with detectors beneath the road surface. All fare collection takes place off the vehicles, tickets being issued either on board the feeder buses or from vending machines and sales staff at the stations, which also have security personnel. Access to the 'platforms' is by turnstiles which accept the prepurchased tokens, tickets or stored-fare cards.

Developments: The immediate success of the trolleybuses has led to proposals for extensions at each end of the route, southwards to Chillogallo and northwards to Cotocollao, both about 6 km. Planning is well advanced, and finance is reported to have been arranged.

Fleet: 54 trolleybuses with auxiliary diesel engines
Mercedes/Hispano Carrocera/AEG articulated
(1995/96) 54

UPDATED

RAWALPINDI-ISLAMABAD

Population: Rawalpindi 800,000, Islamabad 200,000
Public transport: Bus services in Rawalpindi provided by provincial government-owned Road Transport Corporation, also operating intercity routes and urban services in Lahore and Faisalabad. Between Rawalpindi and Islamabad there are frequent services of private

buses known as 'Flying Coaches'. Extensive paratransit operations

PRTC
Punjab Road Transport Corporation
Rawalpindi, Pakistan

Current situation: PRTC operates urban services in Rawalpindi with a fleet of Fiat 331A, Volvo B57 and Isuzu buses, this fleet being distinct from that used on long-distance routes. Older buses have perimeter seating but transverse seats are fitted to newer vehicles. Buses have separate compartments for men and women and carry two conductors.

Other operators
Current situation: Most of the demand in Rawalpindi and the neighbouring new capital city Islamabad is satisfied by 10-seat microbuses based on Suzuki pick-ups, Morris Minor taxis, Vespa autorickshaws and horse-drawn 'tongas'.

Rapid transit (planned)
Current situation: A mass transit network for the twin cities has been proposed by the Capital Area Development Authority which, in 1995, sought bids from parties interested in developing detailed proposals.

VERIFIED

Micros touting for business in central Rawalpindi (John Bamforth)
1996

RECIFE

Population: 1.5 million, metropolitan area 3 million
Public transport: Bus services provided by private companies, with trolleybus network and some bus routes run by municipally owned undertakings. System of reserved route trolleybusways being established; suburban railway

EMTU
Empresa Metropolitana de Transportes Urbanos (EMTU)
Cais de Santa Rita s/n São José, 50020-360 Recife, Brazil
Tel: (+55 81) 424 13 22 Fax: (+55 81) 224 06 10
President: Oswaldo C Lima Neto
Head of Planning: Maurício Renato Pina Moreira

Current situation: EMTU was created in 1980 to eliminate conflict between public transport operators licensed by the federal, state and municipal authorities. EMTU supervises a network of 341 bus and 3 trolleybus routes operated by 20 private companies. The operators are no longer paid subsidy according to the number of passengers carried; instead they must achieve an agreed set of objectives. There is a flat-fare regime throughout the city.

Private bus/minibus
Current situation: Operations of some 20 private companies carry over 500 million passengers annually with a total fleet of about 2,600 buses.

CTU
Companhia de Transportes Urbanos
Recife

Current situation: CTU is a mixed-capital company linked

to the municipality of Recife. It started operations in the early 1960s and by the mid-1970s was providing four-fifths of the city's public transport. After creation of EMTU, CTU's role was drastically reduced and today it operates only 23 routes, including the three trolleybus lines. Productivity is low, with 7.9 employees per bus, 57 per cent more than in private companies.

Trolleybus
Current situation: A mid-1970s study led to recommendations for encouragement of public transport journeys into the restricted city centre by integrated trunk services based, in the northwest quarter of the city, on concentrated trolleybus services operating on dedicated lanes of five highway corridors, and in the southwest by buses feeding an upgraded suburban railway.

The operation is complemented by provision of exclusive trolleybus right-of-way on a distribution loop around the central business district, which is only open to trolleybuses, buses, taxis and vehicles requiring access, and by control over bridges crossing the water which surrounds the city centre on three sides, thus effectively ensuring public transport priority.

The trolleybusway system involves provision of exclusive lanes on three-lane dual carriageways serving five radial corridors. Trolleybuses are allocated to the outer lanes adjacent to the central reservations of the dual carriageways, separated from the main traffic flow by road markings and served by 'stations' built on the median strip. Access to the stations, provided at about 1 km intervals, is by overbridges or light-controlled crossings. Hourly one-direction passenger flow capacity for the system is intended to be 25,000, with a potential of 40,000 achievable with a guided bus system. Buses may also use the reserved lane system and stations.

A system of bus feeders is provided with free interchange to trolleybuses for journeys to the city centre.

There are also connections with private bus services, but these require payment of an additional fare. The trolleybusways incorporate turnround points for short workings and interchange. Eventually 42.5 km of segregated trolleybus route will be operated, and plans call for a fleet of 300 trolleybuses to carry 30 per cent of city traffic.

Number of routes: 3
Route length: Approx 28 km

Fleet: 48 trolleybuses
Scania/Marmon-H/Villares (1958/59 rebuilt 1981/84) 48

Metrorec
CBTU STU/REC, Companhia Brasileira de Trens Urbanos, Recife Division
Rua José Natario 478, 50900-000 Recife
Tel: (+55 81) 251 09 33 Fax: (+55 81) 251 48 44
President: J Dias Fernandes
Superintendent: Fernando Antonio Caminha Dueire
Staff: 1,612

Type of operation: Regional metro, first line opened 1985

Passenger journeys: (1994) 36 million
(1995) 37.2 million
(1997) 38.5 million

Route length: 52.5 km
Number of routes: 2
Number of stations: 27
Gauge: 1,600 mm
Track: Conventional ballasted
Electrification: 3 kV DC, overhead (20.5 km Metrorec line)

The trolleybus network has expanded in the past decade, in particular to routes across two new bridges over the Daugava river.

Fare structure: Flat
Fare collection: Roving conductors on all but lightly used routes; prepurchase monthly and semi-monthly tickets

Bus
Operated by:
Imanta, Kleistu iela 29, 1067 Riga

Talava, Vestienas iela 35, 1039 Riga

Passenger boardings: (1994) 108 million
(1995) 105.8 million
(1996) 88.3 million

Number of routes: 37
Route length: 489 km

Fleet: 367 vehicles
Ikarus 280 articulated	207
Ikarus 260/263	81
Volvo ex-København	27
MAN ex-Braunschweig	10
Scania CR111 ex-Uppsala	7
DAF/Den Oudsten	at least 10
Mercedes Turk O345 (1997)	20
Mercedes Turk O345G articulated (1997)	5
In peak service: 207	

Operating costs financed by: Fares 77.5 per cent, subsidy/grants 22.5

Taxi/shared taxi/minibus
Current situation: Shared taxis operate on seven urban and four suburban routes totalling 360 km; over 4,000 ordinary taxis also ply for hire.

Fleet: 850 vehicles, including 50 AF2203 Latvia microbuses and a number of former Danish and Swedish city buses on two routes

TTP
Tramway & Trolleybus Board
Brivibas iela 191, 1012 Riga
Tel: (+371 7) 37 13 49   Fax: (+371 7) 54 17 48
Staff: 1,800

Skoda 9Tr in double traction in Riga city centre (Aare Olander)   *1999*/0038941

Trolleybus
Passenger journeys: (1994) 110.6 million
(1995) 98.7 million
(1996) 137.3 million (with tramway)
Vehicle-km: (Annual) 17 million

Number of routes: 23
Route length: 348 km

Fleet: 350 trolleybuses, some 9Tr run in multiple
Skoda 9Tr	100
Skoda 14Tr	226
Skoda 15Tr articulated	24
In peak service: 271	

On order: 20 Skoda for 1998 delivery

Operating costs financed by: Fares 68.2 per cent, subsidy/grants 7.1 per cent, remainder as deficit

Tramway
Type of operation: Conventional tramway

Passenger journeys: (1994) 88.1 million
(1995) 79.7 million
(1996) 137.3 million (with trolleybus)
Vehicle-km: (Annual) 15 million

Route length: 167 km
Number of routes: 8
Gauge: 1,524 mm
Electrification: 600 V DC, collection by trolley pole

Rolling stock: 271 cars
ČKD Tatra T3 (1975/87)	M209
ČKD Tatra T3M (1988/90)	M62
In peak service: 171	

Latvian Railway (LDZ)
Latvijas dzelzcels
Turgeneva iela 14, 1018 Riga
Director: V Hristins
Fax: (+371 7) 22 50 77

Type of operations: Suburban heavy rail

Passenger journeys: (1992) 70 million
(1993) 50 million
(1996) 35 million

Current situation: Suburban services are operated over six routes totalling 828 km, partly electrified at 3 kV DC, fleet of 45 emus and 33 dmus.

Metro (planned)
Current situation: Approval granted 1982 for construction of a 19.9 km line with 16 stations linking the city centre with housing and industrial areas on the opposite bank of the Daugava river; 1,524 mm gauge, electrified 825 V DC. Construction started 1986 on the initial section of Line 1, with eight stations, but was suspended in 1990 pending re-examination of the 1975 plans for tramway expansion. This reflected loss of metro expertise and rolling stock supply following independence, and no early resumption of work is likely.

Tatra T3M tramcar in Riga city centre (Aare Olander)   *1999*/0038942   ***UPDATED***

RIO DE JANEIRO
Population: 5.8 million, metropolitan area (including Niterói and 13 other cities) 10.2 million
Public transport: Bus services (and also residual tramway) provided in part by state-controlled public company and in part by more than 60 independent operators and co-operatives, which provide all services in adjoining city of Niterói and also operate a number of premium express services across conurbation. Metro franchised to private-sector company; ferries across

Guanabara Bay; suburban railways controlled by regional authority; extensive illegal bus and van services

Private bus
Licensed and supervised by:
Superintêndencia Municipal de Transportes Urbanos (SMTU)

Current situation: Following collapse of the municipally owned bus company CTC-RJ, services are provided by 33

independent bus operators under licences issued by the municipality for the operation of defined services at set fares levels, though the level of supervision is low. Services include all-seated premium express commuter links with air conditioned coaches aimed particularly at private car commuters, and microbuses. SMTU also licenses the city's 20,000 legal taxis.
Developments: In 1996, Rio municipality issued tenders for operation of 12 new bus routes, the first time this had been done for 22 years. This implied acquisition of 150

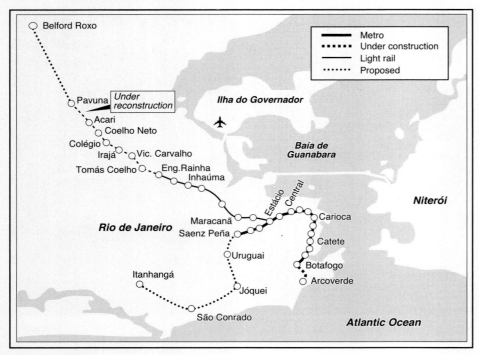

Rio de Janeiro metro

run regular commuter services to the north and west of the city, and also to Niterói. Vehicles range from Kombis to imported 14-seater Topics with air conditioning, music and reclining seats. Some operators offer free drinks and sweets.

Some vans shadow regular bus routes, calling at the same stops and poaching passengers, while others demand references from prospective passengers to avoid police surveillance. SMTU's tiny staff cannot keep pace with the spread of illegal operations, and in any case attempts to close them down have led to violent confrontations between passengers and the authorities. Surveys by the illegal operators apparently show that 85 per cent of their passengers are car owners attracted by the fast and comfortable services, even though fares are higher than on regular routes.

Tramway
Type of operation: Conventional tramway

Current situation: Two routes totalling 8.2 km survive to serve the hilly suburb of Santa Teresa, operated with vintage rolling stock, partly as a tourist attraction. The Carioca tramway has survived due to its unique central area access across a broad valley on a single track atop an arched stone aqueduct. Trams run half-hourly from 06.00 to 23.30; fares revenue covers only the cost of the electricity required to run the service.

Rolling stock: 17 cars
St Louis Car/General Electric (1909)   M17

Cia do Metropolitano
Companhia do Metropolitano do Rio de Janeiro
Av NS de Copacabana 493, CEP 22020-000 Rio de Janeiro
Tel: (+55 21) 255 92 92   Fax: (+55 21) 235 45 46
President: Alvaro José Martins Santos
Director of Operations: Luiz de Lucca e Silva
Staff: 2,700

Type of operation: Full metro and light rail, first line opened 1979

Passenger journeys: (1992) 87 million
(1993) 86.8 million
(1995) 85 million

Route length: Metro (Line 1) 11.6 km, all in tunnel; light rail/pre-metro (Line 2) 13.9 km
Number of lines: 2
Number of stations: 24
Gauge: 1,600 mm
Max gradient: 4%
Minimum curve radius: 500 m
Tunnel: Mainly cut-and-cover; various techniques, including diaphragm walls up to 1.2 m thick, used to prevent soil subsidence and property damage due to high water table
Electrification: 750 V DC, third rail

Service: 3 min 45 s Line 1, 5 min Line 2; Sunday service operates only on special occasions
First/last train: 06.00/23.00
Fare structure: Flat, with combined bus/rail and rail/ferry ticket for some journeys
Revenue control: Automatic fare collection
Integration with other modes: Suburban rail, ferries, and some bus
Automatic control: Automatic pilot system

Rolling stock: 146 metro and 30 LRVs, of which 76 metro and 12 LRVs in serviceable condition
Mafersa A cab cars   M46
Cobrasma B   M100
Cobrasma/BN LRV   M30
On order: Six trains; a further 44 existing cars being refurbished

Current situation: Development of Rio's metro has not met with the success recorded in São Paulo. Funding problems and lack of commitment on the part of city and state government led to difficulties in getting the first sections into operation. These problems were compounded by the city's bankruptcy in 1988. Only part of the metro and pre-metro car fleets had been delivered when the money was cut, so services are limited by shortages.

In a reversal of the state government's previous stance,

new buses, with concessions being awarded to the companies promising most investment (in terminals and signalling), as well as the most modern and comfortable buses. The new routes were needed because the existing network is saturated. SMTU no longer requires operators to have a minimum fleet of 120 buses.

Fare collection: Payment to conductor seated at turnstile near rear entrance
Fare structure: Flat in city

Operating costs financed by: Fares 100 per cent; Vale Transporte tickets subsidised by employers up to 6 per cent of wage levels

Other bus operators
Current situation: In addition to the licensed operations described above, there are estimated to be some 2,000 buses and 5,000 vans which operate illegally. Unlicensed paratransit vans originally provided late-evening shuttle services from the city centre to the suburbs, but they now

Buses of two private operators on Av President Vargas   *1998*/0009712

Daimler-Benz midibus of BrasoLis at Copacabana   *1998*/0009713

a plan was approved in 1987 for a 4 km extension from Botafago through the Copacabana area to General Osório, and for rehabilitation and completion of the truncated Line 2. A further 22 metro cars were supplied, but deliveries were stopped during a further financial crisis in 1990.

Line 1 is in operation from Botafago to Saenz Peña, while Line 2 from Estácio to Inhaúma (reopened from Maria da Gracia in 1987) is worked by pre-metro cars powered from a third rail following dismantling of the overhead current collection system. The extension to Pavuna, closed in 1985, has suffered from vandalism and looting of equipment, but the section from Inhaúma to Engenho da Rainha was reopened as light rail in 1990.

Developments: Operation was franchised in December 1997 to the Opportrans consortium on a 20-year concession following the municipality's decision not to assume managerial control of the metro; although it has shown a willingness to provide operating funds, it has not so far done so. The metro authority continues to seek further loans from the World Bank, but Brazil's national development bank BNDES agreed funding of R$171 million to enable construction to continue. Work on Line 1, paralysed for more than six years, started again in 1995 on the Botafago—Arcoverde section, along with construction of a new turnback facility at Saenz Peña. The extension to Arcoverde was scheduled to open in October 1997. Still under discussion is a 12 km extension of this line from Saenz Peña to Itanhangá.

Line 2 construction also recommenced in 1995 between Engenho da Rainha and Pavuna, although more ambitious suggestions have been proposed for an eventual extension to Belford Roxo where there would be connections with Flumitrens suburban services. These two extensions will add 12 km to the network and are expected to boost patronage from the current 400,000 daily to around 1 million. On completion, operational changes are planned for Line 2, with a heavy metro service between Estácio and Irajá and light rail vehicles running from there to Pavuna; 6.5 min headways would apply on both sections.

Rio de Janeiro's state government is seeking US$1.6 billion to finance an intermodal public transport project in the metropolitan region; half of the money would come from the World Bank and the balance from the state. Some $400 million would go to the metro, with a further $100 million earmarked for the proposed Niterói—São Gonçalo light rail line.

The Barra consortium is building the Tijuca—Barra Line 4.

Flumitrens

Companhia Fluminense de Trens Urbanos
Edificio da Estacão Dom Pedro II, Praca Cristiano Ottoni, s/no Centro, Rio de Janeiro, CEP 20221-250
Tel: (+55 21) 233 85 94   Fax: (+55 21) 253 30 89
President: Murilo Siqueira Junqueira
Staff: 4,228

Type of operation: Suburban heavy rail

Passenger journeys: (1994) 111 million
(1996) 93 million
(1997) 71 million

Current situation: Flumitrens operates frequent suburban services (peak hours every 7-15 min) over some 264 km of route on 1,600 mm gauge (172 km, of which 163 km electrified 3 kV DC overhead) and 1,000 mm gauge (92 km), operated as eight routes with 127 stations. Fares cover 23 per cent of operating expenditure.

Developments: Rio's suburban railways came under the control of a new regional (state) company in 1994. Funding shortages had brought the network to near-

Méier station on Flumitrens' stopping service to Deodoro   **1998**/0009711

collapse; the accumulated debt has been retained by the federal government, but all assets passed to Flumitrens. As a condition of the agreement with the World Bank (see below), a concession for operation, management and maintenance of the network began in November 1998, for a period of 25 years.

The decentralisation project included an investment component to complete the modernisation programme begun more than a decade ago, but which had made little progress, and a further element to fund implementation of a modernised management strategy. An agreement with the World Bank was signed in 1994, under which a US$272 million investment programme was approved, and a further scheme valued at US$372.5 million is being negotiated. This forms part of a state programme of transport improvements for the Rio metropolitan area, involving both public and private operators. Among other aims, this master plan would increase private sector participation in urban transport provision, encourage integration, and develop new funding policies.

Rolling stock: 244 emu sets, normally operated as six- or eight-car trains, of which 70 serviceable; 65 loco-hauled coaches, 39 diesel locomotives

Metro-Vick Series 200 (1957)	M90 T180
GE Series 400 (1964)	M90 T180
Nippon Sharyo S-500 (1977)	M60 T60
Mafersa Series 700 (1980)	M60 T60
Santa Matilde Series 800 (1980)	M120 T120
Cobrasma Series 900 (1980)	M120 T120
Series 1000	

In peak service: 58 emu sets, 6 diesel-hauled trains

CONERJ

Companhia de Navigação do Estado do Rio de Janeiro
Praça 15 de Novembro 21, Rio de Janeiro, CEP 20010-010
Tel: (+55 21) 231 03 98
President: J Washington Lobo
Staff: 930

Ferry
Passenger journeys: (1991) 33 million

Current situation: CONERJ is the Rio de Janeiro government-owned ferry operator, providing services between Rio and Niterói, Paquetá Island and Governador

Island across Guanabara Bay, plus Mangaratiba—Grande Island and Grande Island—Angra dos Reis; total five routes. On the Niterói route (5 km) a fleet of 2,000-passenger vessels provides departures every 7 min during peak hours, 15-30 min off-peak.

On the longer routes to Paquetá Island (18.8 km) and Governador Island (11.5 km) there are eight journeys daily taking about 1 h 40 min, using vessels of 1,000-passenger capacity.

Total fleet of 18 vessels; fares cover about one-third of costs with Rio state funding the difference.

Transtur

Aerobarcos do Brasil, Transportes Maritimos e Turismo
Praça Iaia Garcia 03, Ribeira, Rio de Janeiro 21930-040
Tel: (+55 21) 396 35 67/594   Fax: (+55 21) 396 39 65
Director of Administration: Hamilton Amarante Carvalho
Staff: 207

Ferry
Passenger journeys: (1994) 5.2 million

Current situation: Operates between Rio and Niterói, every 10 min from 06.15 to 20.15, and between Rio and Paquetá Island every 2 h weekdays and hourly at weekends and holidays. The fleet includes hydrofoils and catamarans. Fares cover 100 per cent of costs.

Light rail (planned)
Current situation: Attempts to build a 25 km light rail line in the western suburbs were abandoned in 1995. Despite extending the concession period from 10 to 30 years, no private sector companies entered compliant bids of sufficient standing. The project is now being taken forward by the municipality as a busway, or possibly a trolleybusway.

Monorail
Current situation: An Intamin straddle monorail (1.9 km, 3 stations) opened in 1996 serving the Barra shopping retail development in the west of the city. Two 10-car trains provide capacity of 7,000 passengers/day. Extensions have been proposed to serve the Barra residential district and, later, to the Alvorada bus terminal.

UPDATED

ROCHESTER

Population: 690,000
Public transport: Bus services provided in Rochester and surrounding areas by operating agency of regional transport authority controlled by representative board

Regional Transit Service

Rochester-Genesee Regional Transportation Authority
PO Box 90629, 1372 E Main Street, Rochester, New York 14609, USA

Tel: (+1 716) 654 02 00   Fax: (+1 716) 654 02 93
Chairman: Andrew F Caverly
Chief Executive Officer: Donald J Riley
Director of Special Services: Robert Finke
Director of Urban Service: Ellen Cicero
Staff: 500

Current situation: As well as a fixed-route urban network in Rochester and surrounding areas of Monroe County, supplemented by peak-hour express routes, RTS operates rural bus services in Livingston County (LATS),

the city of Batavia (B-Line) in Genesee County, Wayne County (WATS) and Wyoming County (WYTS) — all operated by small buses, some on dial-a-bus basis. It also operates Lift Line Inc, a fully accessible paratransit service. Figures below cover all operations; rural services carried some 350,000 passengers in 1994/95.

Bus
Passenger boardings: (1991/92) 15 million
(1993/94) 13.2 million
(1994/95) 14.2 million

Vehicle-km: (1991/92) 9.4 million
(1993/94) 9.1 million
(1994/95) 12.6 million

Number of routes: 31
Route length: (One way) 960 km

Fleet: 337 vehicles

GMC RTS (1982/83)	75
Flxible Metro (1986)	17
Gillig Phantom (1988/91)	33
MAN SG310 articulated (1984)	10
Orion V (1990/93)	48
Orion V CNG-powered (1992)	5
Thomas/BIA/other midi/minibus	80
NovaBus Classic (1995/96)	69

In peak service: 244

Most intensive service: 15 min
Fare structure: Flat; prepurchase 10-ride tickets and monthly pass; transfers 10 cents; free service 11.00-14.00 in downtown Rochester
Fare collection: Coin to farebox
Arrangements for elderly/disabled: 100 lift-equipped buses; Lift Line is demand-responsive accessible service provided throughout RTS area using 21 low-floor buses; carried 132,000 passengers in 1994/95.
Integration with other modes: Peak-hour express buses

RTS bus in downtown Rochester   *1999*/0038943

serve 31 suburban park-and-ride sites; Park-and-Ride Plus express routes provide suburb-to-suburb commuter service
Operating costs financed by: Fares 39 per cent, other commercial sources 6 per cent, subsidy/grants 45 per cent, tax levy 10 per cent
Subsidy from: FTA, state and county funds

UPDATED

ROME

Population: 2.8 million
Public transport: Bus, tramway, metro, suburban railway and suburban bus services operated by municipal authority. Other suburban rail services by State Railway (FS)

ATAC-Cotral

Azienda Tranvie e Autobus del Comune di Roma (ATAC)
Via Volturno 65, 00185 Rome, Italy
Tel: (+39 06) 46 95 20 27   Fax: (+39 06) 46 95 22 84
President: Mario di Carlo
General Manager: Domenico Mazzamurro
Operating Manager: Ottavio Mirabelli
Staff: 12,691

Passenger journeys: (All modes)
(1991) 817 million
(1992) 811 million
(1994) 821 million

Operating costs financed by: Fares 23 per cent, other commercial sources 2.5 per cent, subsidy/grants 74.5 per cent

Current situation: ATAC-Cotral is responsible for urban bus and tramway services, the metro, three suburban rail networks and an extensive bus operation extending throughout Lazio Province. Creation of new connections and extension of existing routes has been an objective, but increases in fares to improve on the very low farebox recovery rate led to significant passenger losses. Some recovery has been evident since 1991, with growth in bus traffic particularly strong.

A new city government elected in 1993 had as one of its principal aims a dramatic improvement in public transport provision, and several new tram routes in the historic city centre and extensions have been proposed. There are to be more interchanges and park-and-ride, designed to encourage more drivers to leave their cars at home.
Developments: The two operators ATAC and Cotral came under common management in 1994. A new transport authority is planned for the region. It will comprise Rome municipality (51 per cent), Lazio region (30 per cent) and FS (20 per cent), and will take responsibility for all modes including FS trains, though assets would be retained by members. The debts of ATAC and Cotral would pass to the municipality.

Merger of the two undertakings has been proposed, but apparently is not now to go ahead. Nevertheless, an integrated management structure has been established. This has seen staffing levels cut by 17.5 per cent, with more redundancies planned. Nevertheless, the deficits for 1995 and 1996, at Lit65 billion for each year, were much higher than budget.

An all-modes integrated tariff system known as Metrebus was introduced throughout the Lazio region in

ATAC Autodromo low-floor bus in Piazza Giovanni XXIII (Andrew Jarosz)   *1999*/0045396

1994, covering some 378 municipalities and believed to be the largest scheme of its type in Europe. ATAC, Cotral and FS bus and train services are involved in the system, which is based on zones. A 5 per cent increase in patronage was recorded in the first few months; the ultimate goal is to raise public transport's market share by 25 per cent by the end of the century.

Bus (ATAC network)
Passenger journeys: (1991) 696 million
(1992) 740 million
(1994) 749.3 million
Vehicle-km: (1991) 120 million
(1992) 121.4 million
(1994) 120.4 million

ATAC Autodromo low-floor bus passes PCC tram at Piazza del Risorgimento (Andrew Jarosz)

1999/0045395

Operating costs financed by: Fares 29.8 per cent, other commercial sources 4 per cent, subsidy/grants 66.2 per cent

Bus

Passenger boardings (unlinked): (1995) 22.3 million
(1996) 23 million
(1997) 22 million
Vehicle-km: (1995) 11.1 million
(1996) 11.4 million
(1997) 11.2 million

Number of routes: 40
Route length: 481 km
On priority right-of-way: 5.2 km

Fleet: TCAR 186 vehicles, SATAR 35 vehicles
TCAR
Renault SC10	56
Heuliez GX107	29
Kassborer Setra S300NC low-floor	32
Mercedes-Benz O405G articulated	7
Mercedes-Benz O405N	39
Heuliez GX187 articulated	7
Kassborer 215SL	16

SATAR
CBM/Renault/Heuliez midibus	15
Renault SC10	10
Setra 215SL	7
Others	3

Average age of fleet: 8.3 years
Most intensive service: 3 min
One-person operation: All routes
Fare structure: Flat, 1 h unlimited travel; 10-journey tickets for single journeys; monthly and 1-, 2-, 3- and 7-day passes
Fare collection: Magnetic tickets sold by approved vendors, bus drivers sell only single tickets; validators on board
Fare evasion control: Inspectors
Arrangements for elderly/disabled: Reduced fares; taxi or minibus provision by appointment
Subsidy from: District
New vehicles financed by: District

Light rail

Type of operation: Light rail, first line opened 1994

Passenger journeys (unlinked): (1995) 10.5 million
(1996) 11.1 million
(1997) 11.9 million
Car-km: (1995) 1.1 million
(1996) 1 million
(1997) 1.1 million

Route length: 15.1 km
in tunnel: 2.2 km
Number of lines: 2
Number of stops: 31
in tunnel: 4
Gauge: 1,435 mm
Max gradient: 7%
Minimum curve radius: 25 m
Electrification: 750 V DC, overhead

Average commercial speed: 19.1 km/h
Service: Daytime 6-9 min (3 min in peak on central trunk), evening 15-20 min
First/last car: 05.00/23.30
Fare structure: As bus
Fare collection: No onboard sales, change-giving machines at stops; validators on board

Rouen tram at the underground Palais de Justice station, departing towards the newly opened St Etienne de Rouvray station
1999/0038947

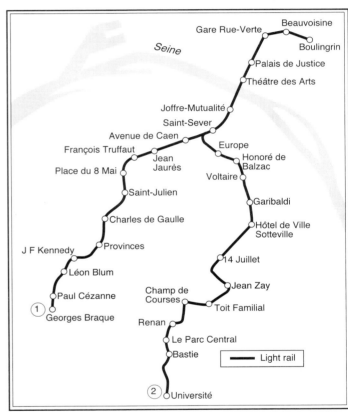

Rouen's light rail line

Rolling stock: 28 cars
GEC Alsthom (1993/94)   M28

Developments: A 4.6 km extension of Line 2 with eight stations from Sotteville to St Etienne de Rouvray (Université) opened in September 1997. At the same time, an underground station was opened at Palais de Justice in the city centre.

A decision is awaited on construction of a Line 1 extension from Georges Braque to Grand Couronne. The district decided in December 1997 to create an East-West reserved track route to be operational in late 2000. The route will be operated by new-generation buses.

UPDATED

SACRAMENTO

Population: 1 million
Public transport: Bus and light rail services in city and regional area provided by transit authority controlled by appointed board. Some commuter services and contracted bus operations in Yolo County and cities of Roseville and Folsom provided by private operator

Regional Transit

Sacramento Regional Transit District (RT)
PO Box 2110, Sacramento, California 95812-2110, USA
Tel: (+1 916) 321 28 00   Fax: (+1 916) 444 21 56

Chair: Lauren Hammond
General Manager: Pilka Robinson
Chief Operating Officer: Cameron Beach
Light Rail Manager: Alan Storey
Bus Transportation Manager: Diedre Brown
Staff: 750

Current situation: RT came into operation in 1973 and gradually enlarged its service area to cover most urbanised portions of the city and county.

The light rail line was funded in part from Interstate Transfer funds originally earmarked for road construction. The northeast section from Watt/I-80 follows an alignment

originally reserved for highway construction, while the eastern section follows R Street and abandoned rail right-of-way.

Developments: A 20-year transit master plan was adopted in 1993, calling for light rail extensions to Sunrise Boulevard and Antelope Road as well as a new line serving South Sacramento, all to be built within 10 years. The full 20-year plan envisages further extensions of these lines, provision of light rail service along three new corridors, and major bus service increases throughout the region. County and city land-use plans have adopted these transit corridors for increased density of development. Light rail expansion was confirmed in 1995

RT Siemens/Duewag just after the opening of Mather Field/Mills LRT station ***1999**/0043936*

Gauge: 1,435 mm
Electrification: 750 V DC, overhead

Service: 15 min
First/last car: 04.59/23.57
Fare structure: Flat, as bus
Fare collection: Vending machines at all stations; prepurchase tickets, monthly passes
Fare evasion control: Proof-of-payment enforced by RT fare inspection staff and police/sheriff officers
One-person operation: All trains
Integration with other modes: 10 stations have parking space and 12 provide bus interchange

Rolling stock: 36 cars
Siemens/Duewag U2-A (1985/86)   M26
 (1990/91)   M10
In peak service: 32

Developments: Extensions north to Antelope Road and east to Sunrise Boulevard and Folsom were approved by the RT board in 1991, along with a proposed 20 km line to South Sacramento. Construction of the initial section of this latter route (10.4 km, 6 stations), from the city centre to Meadowview Road, is expected to start in late 1999 for opening in 2003 following the award of FTA funding in 1997. The line will parallel existing Union Pacific tracks.

The first new line is a 3.7 km extension from Butterfield on the eastern leg of the line to Mather Field Road, opened in September 1998. The 5 km from there to Sunrise Boulevard is funded, as is a 1 km extension to the Amtrak station at 4th and I Street. The 12 km from Sunrise Boulevard to Folsom is awaiting funding, following a decision by the City of Folsom not to proceed with plans for a diesel-operated commuter link to RTD. Bids were sought in late 1998 for a further 40 cars (with option for another 14) required for the four extensions.

Other operators
Current situation: Contracted 'Yolobus' services are provided on eight routes in Yolo County into central Sacramento from Davis and West Sacramento by Yolo County Transit Authority (27 buses). Unitrans (40 buses) operates in Davis only. These two operators together carry some 2 million passengers annually.

Other local door-to-door services are provided in Roseville, Folsom, Marysville/Yuba City and El Dorado County.

when an eight-year construction programme for four extensions was approved (see below).

Passenger boardings: (All modes)
(1994) 22.5 million
(1996) 24.7 million
(1997) 25.2 million

Operating costs financed by: Fares 27.8 per cent, other commercial sources 5.2 per cent, subsidy/grants 4.6 per cent, tax levy 67.4 per cent
Subsidy from: FTA, state and local sources (sales tax)

Bus
Passenger boardings: (1995) 16 million
(1996) 17.1 million
(1997) 18.2 million
Vehicle-km: (1995) 10.5 million
(1996) 10.6 million
(1997) 10.9 million

Number of routes: 65
Route length: (One way) 674 km

Fleet: 208 vehicles
Gillig Phantom (1985/90)   73
BIA Orion 05.501 CNG-powered (1993/94)   95
OBI Orion 05.501 40 ft CNG-powered (1996)   25
OBI Orion 05.501 31 ft CNG-powered (1996)   15
In peak service: 176
Average age of fleet: 5.9 years

Most intensive service: 15 min
One-person operation: All routes
Fare collection: GFI electronic fareboxes; exact fare only
Fare structure: Flat, with free one-way intermodal transfer, low fare in city centre; prepurchase tickets, daily and monthly passes
Fares collected on board: 49 per cent
Fare evasion control: Driver supervision and police/sheriff inspection
Operational control: Road supervisors, all buses equipped with mobile radio
Arrangements for elderly/disabled: Lifts fitted to all vehicles, all services accessible; half fare and reduced rate passes for persons over 62 or disabled; free life-time pass for over-80s. Paratransit service with 50 minibuses for those unable to use fixed routes

Average distance between stops: 270 m
Average peak-hour speed: In mixed traffic, 23.2 km/h
Integration with other modes: Park-and-ride sites; 38 bus routes serve light rail stations; cycle lockers at some stations; 2 bus routes serve Amtrak station
New vehicles financed by: FTA and local sales tax funds

Light rail
Staff: 110 (operational)

Type of operation: Light rail, initial route opened 1987

Passenger boardings: (1995) 7.1 million
(1996) 7.6 million
(1997) 7.9 million
Car-km: (1995) 5.6 million
(1996) 5.8 million
(1997) 6 million

Route length: 32.8 km
Number of routes: 1
Number of stops: 34 (10 are uni-directional)

UPDATED

RT 1997 OBI bus powered by CNG at Archives Plaza LRT stop ***1999**/0038948*

SALT LAKE CITY

Population: 1,600,000 (Utah service area)
Public transport: Bus services provided by regional transit authority for city and surrounding areas of Salt Lake, Utah, Davis, Weber and Tooele counties. Light rail under construction

UTA

Utah Transit Authority
3600 South 700 West, PO Box 30810, Salt Lake City, Utah 84130-0810, USA
Tel: (+1 801) 262 56 26   Fax: (+1 801) 287 46 14/46 22
President: Steven Randall
General Manager: John M Inglish
Staff: 1,050

Current situation: UTA started operations in Salt Lake

County in 1970, and operations in Davis and Weber counties were annexed by voter approval in 1973. All private transit operations in the three-county area were incorporated into UTA in 1975.

In 1974, voters in Salt Lake and Weber counties approved a ¼ per cent sales tax to fund public transport, and Davis County followed suit a year later. In 1985, UTA expanded service into the Provo and Orem city areas of Utah County. In 1989, four cities in northern Utah County agreed to join the transit district and impose the ¼ per cent tax. The following year, elections brought one more Utah County city, plus Tooele and Grantsville in Tooele County, into the district. Operations were extended to the cities of Alpine, Cedar Hills and Highland in 1994, and to Mapleton, Payson, Salem, Spanish Fork and Sundance in 1995.

Of 133 regular routes, 78 run in the Salt Lake area, 33 in Ogden, and 15 serve Utah and Tooele counties. There is a summer-only downtown circulator in Salt Lake City operated by replica trolleys. During the winter months, UTA operates seven busy routes to four nearby skiing areas.

Developments: In 1992, Salt Lake County voters rejected imposition of a further ¼ per cent sales tax to fund the local share of a transit expansion programme. Three-quarters of the money raised would have been used to finance a greatly expanded bus system and an initial 24 km light rail line. Despite the election result, preliminary engineering work on the expansion programme continued, and construction of the light rail route started in April 1997 (see below) following final approval by the UTA board in 1996.

Heavily discounted passes introduced for large employers and the University of Utah have proved successful in reducing parking demands and costs, as well as increasing ridership.

After community-wide consultation, a comprehensive transit plan has been developed for the coming 20 years. Planned improvements include expansion of Flextrans service, and extension of service to developing suburban communities.

Bus
Passenger journeys: (1993) 22.8 million
(1994) 23.3 million
(1997) 24.1 million
Vehicle-km: (1993) 31.2 million
(1994) 32.5 million
(1997) 31.4 million

Number of routes: 153

Fleet: 446 vehicles, plus 48 inactive
GMC Classic (1983/84)	77
Gillig Phantom (1984/87)	89
Orion II (1988/89)	52
MCI TAC40102N (1990)	66
Orion I (1991)	9
Orion V (1992/93)	128
Chance replica trolleys (1984/85)	8
Ford vans (paratransit)	15
Classic (1991)	2
In peak service: 377, plus 33 for ski service

Most intensive service: 10 min
One-person operation: All routes
Fare collection: Manual drop fareboxes; tokens
Fare structure: Flat, free in Salt Lake city-centre and state capitol zone; Express, worker and ski bus services have higher fare; discount passes for large employers, university students, faculty and staff

UTA bus on downtown service　　　　*1999*/0038950

Fares collected on board: 50 per cent
Fare evasion control: Periodic observation of operators by outside security firm
Integration with other modes: Park-and-ride service to local ski resorts; Utah LIFT regional ride-sharing programme encourages car- and vanpools, 77 operating in 1994; 43 park-and-ride lots used for ride-sharing, with several also served by buses
Operational control: Route supervisors/mobile radio
Arrangements for elderly/disabled: Reduced fares; accessible fixed-route service offered on several main corridors in Salt Lake City; over 300 buses lift-equipped; Flextrans demand-responsive and accessible fixed-route service with low flat fare; separate demand-responsive service in other counties; customer services for persons with disabilities, eg Braille timetables; all fixed routes to be fully accessible by 1998
Operating costs financed by: Fares 16.5 per cent, other commercial sources 4.8 per cent, FTA subsidy 6.2 per cent, sales tax 72.5 per cent

Light rail
Under construction

Current situation: Construction started in April 1997 on the TRAX light rail line linking the centre of Salt Lake City with 10,000 South Street in Sandy City (24 km, 21 stations) utilising Union Pacific rail right-of-way. This will form the initial stage of a corridor route linking Ogden, Salt Lake City and Provo.

The FTA had originally accorded the scheme low priority on account of its undue reliance (75 per cent) on traffic mitigation funds likely to be provided for reconstruction of highway I-15. But this situation changed in 1995 following selection of Salt Lake City to host the 2002 Winter Olympics. Federal funding amounting to $241 million was approved in 1995, and is being supplemented by $70 million raised locally. A fleet of 23 cars is on order from Siemens Transportation. The line is expected to open in March 2000.

The line will take over a single-track UP route purchased by UTA in 1993, and over which freight trains are run by a short line operator. The route will be doubled for its new role as a passenger carrier, but freight trains will still run during night hours.

East-west Line 2 (17.5 km), linking the university with the airport through the city centre, is likely to be built to an accelerated schedule so that it too will be ready in time for the Winter Olympics. Construction is expected to start in late 1999 for opening in late 2001. Studies have also been made for extensions to Draper and West Jordan, and a third extension to West Valley City is being examined.

UPDATED

SALVADOR
Population: 2.2 million
Public transport: Bus services in the city and 17 administrative areas are provided by franchised private groups supervised by municipal organisation. Suburban rail services operated by Brazilian Urban Railways Company (CBTU). Ferry service, funiculars and public elevator; mass transit proposed

STP
Superintendência de Transporte Público
Avenida Tancredo Neves 2.681, 41820-021 Salvador, Bahia, Brazil
Tel: (+55 71) 340 78 00　Fax: (+55 71) 340 78 01/78 02
Superintendent: Aristides Amorim de Cerqueira
Staff: 535

Current situation: Organising provision of bus services is the responsibility of STP, set up in 1992 as successor to the former SETRAM organisation. STP co-ordinates and supervises the services of 18 private bus operators (for which SMTU is the holding company) working under franchises issued by the municipality (see below for list of private operators and their fleets). It also operates the

Exclusive road for buses in Salvador (Ascom/SMTU)　　　　*1999*/0038951

major Lapa and Pirajá bus stations and plans bus priority and promotional measures. STP oversees planning of bus services, sets fares levels and supervises the franchisees.
Developments: Studies are taking place into possible introduction of a high-capacity mass transit system over a 25 km corridor, probably on existing surface rights-of-way. The technology has yet to be chosen.

Passenger journeys: (All operators)
(1995) 533 million
(1996) 511 million
(1997) 477 million
Vehicle-km: (1995) 212 million
(1996) 211 million
(1997) 213 million

Number of routes: 400 (including 9 executive, 6 semi-express and 15 night)
Route length: Roads covered 1,345 km
Operating costs financed by: Fares 100 per cent

Private bus
Current situation: There are 18 franchised companies: Axé Transportes (143 buses), Bahia (184), Barramar (60), Boa Viagem (135), Farol da Barra (154), Itapoan Transportes Triunfo (212), Joevanza (76), Lapa (156), Mont Serrat (145), Ondina (216), Praia Grande (214), Rio Vermelho (161), São Cristovo (110), São Pedro (133), Transol (131), Verdemar (126), União (170), and Vitral (113).

Fleet: 2,639 buses, mainly long-wheelbase conventional types and Volvo Padron two-door; average age is 4 years
In peak service: 2,296

Funiculars
Current situation: The Plano Inclinado Liberdade—Calçada carries 2.8 million passengers a year, and a second funicular, the Gonçalves, 2 million.

Elevator
Current situation: The Elevador Lacerda provides a lift service of four cars between the upper and lower town areas, used by about 9 million passengers a year.

Ferry
Current situation: Cross-harbour ferries and catamarans operated by the Consórcio Maritimo da Bahia carry about 6 million passengers a year and 700,000 motor vehicles.

CBTU
Companhia Brasileira de Trens Urbanos (CBTU)
Largo de Calçada 1, 40410-360 Salvador, Bahia
Tel: (+55 71) 313 87 60
General Manager: A Mello
Staff: 221

Type of operation: Suburban heavy rail

Passenger journeys: (1991) 4.6 million
(1995) 1.5 million

Current situation: CBTU operates a 13.7 km 3 kV DC electrified line with nine stations; four emus run a 20 min interval peak-hour service. Fares cover 4.5 per cent of operating costs. Plans for further electrification and upgrading of 69 route-km to form a regional metro have been delayed by the country's poor economic conditions.
Developments: Transfer of this system to Bahia state control is under discussion. A group of local businesses has put forward a proposal to rehabilitate the line and operate a service over a further 24 km of RFFSA route, with the aim of carrying 22,000 passengers daily. The idea

is to replace the 2,000 daily bus movements carrying workers to the Camaçari petrochemical and Aratu industrial complexes.

An initial approach to the Brazilian Development Bank was rejected, but a new proposal involving a 30-year operating concession and a US$65 million loan is being considered. A fleet of 20 coaches and 10 RFFSA diesel locomotives would be refurbished, and 71 bilevel cars purchased. A protocol has been signed between the project manager Enefer, civil engineering contractor Mendes Junior and the rolling stock builder Cobrasma.

Two projects have emerged. The first would add 8 km to the existing line, from Calsçada to Paripe, at a cost of US$110 million. The second envisages a 12 km extension with 14 stations from Retiro to Cajazeiras. Half of the US$172 million cost of this proposal would come from the private sector, which would also furnish the operator; the remainder would come from the state. Traffic projections for the two schemes are respectively 133,000 and 243,000 passengers daily.

UPDATED

Bus for disabled people   **1999**/0038952

SAMARA
Population: 1.3 million
Public transport: Bus and trolleybus/tramway services provided by separate municipal undertakings; metro

Upravlenie Automobil'novo Transporta
Upravlenie Automobil'novo Transporta
Samara, Russia

Bus
Passenger journeys: Approx 26 million (annual)

Number of routes: 56
Route length: 216 km

Fleet: Includes LIAZ 677, Ikarus 260/280, Autosan and about 200 Mercedes Türk O345/O345G (financed by the World Bank)

Tramvaino-Trolleibusnoe Upravlenie
Tramvaino-Trolleibusnoe Upravlenie
Kommunisticheskaya ul 8, Samara 443030
Tel: (+7 8462) 32 12 03
Director: V N Vodolazov

Trolleybus
Passenger journeys: Approx 55 million (annual)

Number of routes: 19
Route length: 125 km

Fleet: Approx 250 vehicles

ZIU9, some in double-traction	About 240
ZIU10	5
SZTM Works using ZIU9 parts	2

Tramway
Type of operation: Conventional tramway

Passenger journeys: Approx 127 million (annual)

Route length: 171 km
Number of routes: 24
Gauge: 1,524 mm

Rolling stock: 450 cars

ČKD Tatra T3SU (1972/87)	About M360
ČKD Tatra T3SU ex-Moskva	M40
ČKD Tatra T3M (1988/93)	M48

On the short surface section of the metro, a four-car train approaches Yungorodok station   **1998**/0009716

Track: 57 kg/m rail on continuous concrete beams in tunnels and on elevated sections; concrete sleepers on surface
Max gradient: 4%
Minimum curve radius: 300 m
Tunnel: Double-track cut-and-cover; single-track shield-driven bore
Electrification: 750 V DC, third rail

Service: Peak 1 min 40 s, off-peak 2 min 45 s
First/last train: 05.00/24.00
Fare structure: Flat, combined tickets available for through journeys by bus or suburban rail; 'Vale Transporte' passes; 6 months free travel for the unemployed
Integration with other modes: CMSP has taken a lead in integration through development of feeder suburban rail, bus and trolleybus services
Revenue control: Microprocessor-controlled electronic turnstiles
Signalling: ATS available, ATO throughout, being adapted to cut headway to 90 s. All lines controlled from central control room at Paraíso
Operating costs financed by: Fares 81.3 per cent, other commercial sources 4.5 per cent, government grants 7.8 per cent, tax levy 2.6 per cent

Rolling stock: 654 cars, formed into six-car trains
Mafersa Line 1 (1974) M306
Mafersa/Cobrasma Line 2 (1982 onwards) M276
GEC Alsthom/Adtranz Spain (1996) M6
Alstom Transporte/Adtranz Spain (1998/99) M66
In peak service: 528
On order: 30 four-car trains from Alstom Transporte and Adtranz Spain, delivery stated late 1998

Developments: Fleet expansion, headway reduction and line extensions are in progress to raise capacity of one of the most heavily utilised metros in the world from 3.5 to 5.5 million daily journeys. After delays due to funding problems, two extensions opened in 1998, Santana–Tucuruvi (3.5 km, three stations) and Clinicas–Vila Madalena (2.9 km, two stations). Work also resumed on the eastern extension from Itaqueira and Pessego to Guaianazes (6.3 km, three stations), though this is to be transferred to CPTM on completion and will be operated as part of the suburban rail network.

New metro construction proposals have been revised to give priority to areas poorly served by public transport. Now being constructed is Line 4 linking Luz with Vila Sônia in the southwest of the city. The initial section (9.8 km, 8 stations) will run from Paulista to Vila Sônia, serving en route a major interchange with CPTM suburban trains at Pinheiros. Scheduled to open in 2002, it is expected to attract 660,000 passengers daily. About half the US$1.46 billion cost will be financed by the World Bank (US$300 million) and BNDES (US$400 million), with the remainder coming from the private sector.

This will be followed by the first portion of Line 5 – an isolated section from Santa Amaro to Capão Redondo (9.3 km, six stations), which will become Line G of the suburban network (see above).

Line A train of CPTM at Barra Funda **1998**/0009724

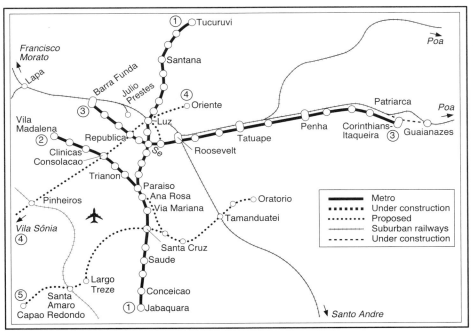

São Paulo metro 0010337

The northern extension of Line 1 has three new stations – Jardim São Paulo, Parada Inglesa and Tucuruvi. Line 2 western extension has two new stations – Sumaré and Vila Madalena, where there will be a bus interchange terminal.

EMTU
Empresa Metropolitana de Transportes Urbana
194-196 Av Juruce, São Paulo 04080-010, SP
Tel: (+55 11) 240 92 08 Fax: (+55 11) 531 38 44

Passenger journeys: 350,000 daily

Current situation: CMSP was authorised to build and operate a feeder trolleybus network outside the city's boundaries. EMTU later took over operations, but CMSP remains as the construction authority. Four routes in the southern suburbs were opened in 1988/90, known as the Medium Capacity Network. These total 37 km and run from Ferrazopolis and Piraporinha to Jabaquara metro station, Santo André station on the suburban rail system and the São Mateus terminal of the SPTrans trolleybus operation, and five other interchanges, on routes provided with segregated trolleybus lanes. The trolleybuses are in use operating alongside motor buses.
Developments: Operation and maintenance of EMTU's system was transferred to private-sector operator Metra in 1997. Other similar metro feeder routes were planned, but are now in doubt following withdrawal of government subsidies for electrically powered vehicles. An extension from Diadema to Brooklin on CPTM's Jurubatuba line is the only one currently under construction.

Fleet: 68 trolleybuses
Cobrasma/Tectronic (1986/90) 46
Scania/Marcopolo/Powertronics ex-Belo Horizonte 22

Santana-bound metro train at Armênia **1998**/0009725 **UPDATED**

SAPPORO

Population: 1.7 million
Public transport: Bus, metro, and tramway operated by municipal authority. Suburban services provided by private bus companies and JR

Sapporo-shi Kotsu Kyoku

Sapporo City Transportation Bureau
Higashi 2-4-1 Oyachi, Atsubetsu-ku, Sapporo,
Hokkaido 004-0041, Japan
Tel: (+81 11) 896 27 08   Fax: (+81 11) 896 27 90
Managing Director: T Ikegami

Current situation: The three-line metro forms the nucleus of the city's transport system under the Long-Term Comprehensive Development Plan, with bus services seen increasingly as feeding the metro.

Bus

Staff: 1,447

Passenger journeys: (1991/92) 82 million
(1992/93) 80 million
(1993/94) 78 million
Vehicle-km: (1991/92) 19.6 million
(1992/93) 19 million
(1993/94) 18.3 million

Number of routes: 70
Route length: 409 km

Fleet: 555 vehicles, including Hino, Nissan, Mitsubishi-Fuso and Isuzu

One-person operation: All routes
Fare collection: Payment to farebox on exit, pass, stored-fare card
Fare structure: Zonal; metro transfer system; 'coupon tickets'; commuter passes; day tickets (metro/bus/tram); one-day Eco-Ticket gives reduced-rate travel on designated 'no car days' twice a month, when car drivers are encouraged to use public transport; stored-fare cards, 'With You Card' valid on metro/bus/tram, 'Common Card' valid on metro/tram/city bus/JR Bus/Chuo Bus
Fares collected on board: 62.9 per cent
Operational control: Radio
Arrangements for elderly/disabled: Pass for free travel covered by subsidy; wheelchair-accessible vehicles
Integration with other modes: Bus and metro systems closely integrated with many feeders and interchanges; transfer ticket system
Bus priority: 11 bus-only lanes (46.1 km); 5 bus priority lanes (13.2 km)
Operating costs financed by: Fares 80 per cent, other commercial sources 0.7 per cent, subsidy/grants 19.3 per cent
Subsidy from: City
New vehicles financed by: Internal resources

Developments: Bus position indication system indicates time of arrival of next bus to passengers at stops. Hail-and-Ride introduced on one suburban route. 'Factory Line' service connects industrial zone with metro stations. Latest vehicles feature air conditioning and lower floors. A Nissan Diesel CNG-powered bus entered service in 1997, the first low-pollution bus in Hokkaido.

Metro

Staff: 1,225

Type of operation: Full metro, rubber-tyred system, initial route opened 1971

Passenger journeys: (1991/92) 223 million
(1992/93) 219 million
(1993/94) 216 million
Car-km: (1991/92) 32.4 million
(1992/93) 31.8 million
(1993/94) 30.9 million

Route length: 48 km
  in tunnel: 43.3 km
Number of lines: 3
Number of stations: 49
Gauge: Rubber-tyred trains on concrete guideway, Line 1 spacing 2,180 mm; Line 2, 2,150 mm
Track: Line 1 concrete slab track without sleepers, surface paved with epoxy-resin plastic; centre-guide steel I-beam. Line 2 similar but running track surface

Car 254 on Sapporo's remaining tram line   1997

paved with steel plates; Line 3 track on concrete sleepers
Max gradient: 4.3%
Minimum curve radius: 200 m
Tunnel: Generally double-track, cut-and-cover; beneath the Toyohira river the section has been built by the caisson method. Elevated section has a circular aluminium shelter to prevent heavy snowfall affecting operations
Electrification: 750 V DC, third rail on Line 1; 1.5 kV DC, RS-AFB overhead conductor system on Lines 2 and 3

Service: Peak 3½-4 min, off-peak 6-7 min
First/last train: 06.15/23.30
Fare structure: 6 sections; AFC handles interchange between metro and bus and provides 25 per cent discount on each fare; commuter passes; metro/bus/tram day tickets; one-day Eco-Tickets (see under bus); stored-fare 'With You Card' valid on metro/bus/tram, and 'Common Card', valid additionally on JR Bus and Chuo Bus services
Revenue control: Central processor, automatic ticket vending and fare adjusting machines, coin collecting unit and automatic gates with stored-fare card readers; automatic commuter pass vendor at main stations
Arrangements for elderly/disabled: Lifts at 24 stations
Operating costs financed by: Fares 92 per cent, other commercial sources 1 per cent, subsidy/grants 7 per cent
Signalling: Full ATC and CTC. Linked to the signalling is the Subway Total System, whose main subsystems comprise: optical total transmission line control; related operating control equipment; power control; automatic operations control; fire-control system; automatic inspection of rolling stock; ticket vending and inspection equipment; public address and surveillance. The system also allows automated driverless operation of empty trains over the 1.3 km link to Higashi depot

Rolling stock: 378 cars

Kawasaki 2000 Line 1	M48
Kawasaki 3000 Line 1	M40
Kawasaki 5000 Line 1	M33 T33
Kawasaki 6000 Line 2	M72 T72
Kawasaki 7000 Line 3	M40 T40

On order: Series 5000 – 24 cars; Series 6000 – 24 cars; Series 8000 – 14 cars

Developments: A 2.8 km extension of Line 2 from Kotoni to Teine Higashi opened in February 1999. Extension planned of Line 3 from Fukuzumi to Kitano (3.2 km).

Tramway

Staff: 135

Type of operation: Conventional tramway

Passenger journeys: (1991/92) 9.7 million
(1992/93) 9.5 million
(1993/94) 9.3 million
Car-km: (1993/94) 1.1 million

Number of routes: 1, retained as metro feeder
Route length: 8.4 km
Number of stops: 23
Gauge: 1,067 mm
Electrification: 600 V DC, overhead

Service: 3-10 min
First/last car: 06.18/23.18
Fare collection: Farebox or prepurchase
Fare structure: Flat; tram/metro transfer tickets, day ticket (bus/metro/tram), one-day Eco-Ticket (see under bus); prepurchase coupon tickets, 1- and 3-monthly passes; stored-fare 'With You Card' valid on metro/bus/

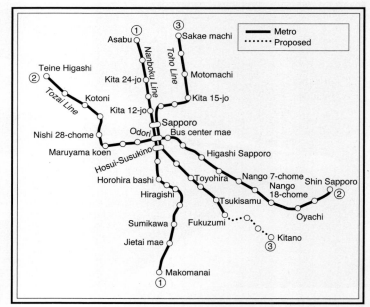

Sapporo's metro
0045370

tram, and 'Common Card' valid additionally on JR Bus and Chuo Bus services

Rolling stock: 30 cars

Sapporo Sogo Tekko Kumiai (1958/61)	M18
Hitachi (1958)	M5
Nippon Sharyo (1961)	M1
Kawasaki (1985/87/88)	M6
Alna Koki (1998)	M1

Current situation: Audio/visual 'tram approaching' indicators installed at nine stops. All passenger shelters are equipped with footway and roof heating to prevent snow accumulation.

Developments: Alna Koki has delivered the first Type 3300 car which incorporates trucks and electrical equipment from Hitachi car 334. A second Hitachi car is to be rebuilt in 1999. The City Council is investigating a possible extension of the tramway.

JR Hokkaido

Hokkaido Railway Company
Hokkaido Ryokaku Tetsudo
Nishi 15-chome, Kita 11-jo, Chuo-ku, Sapporo 060-8644
Tel: (+81 11) 700 57 17   Fax: (+81 11) 700 57 19

e-mail: jrhokkaido@hjsd.co.jp
www: http//www.hjsd.co.jp/jrhokkaido
Chair: Y Omori
President: S Sakamoto

Suburban/interurban rail
Passenger journeys: (1990/91) 49.5 million (Sapporo city)

Current situation: All-stations emu services operate Sapporo—Otaru (34 km) and Sapporo—Iwamizawa (40 km) on the Hakodate main line and Sapporo—Chitose airport (44 km) on the Chitose line. Some trains continue over longer distances. Local dmu service operates Sapporo—Daigaku-mae (30.5 km) on the Sassho line.
Developments: New Series 731 three-car emus have been introduced on Sapporo suburban services to provide capacity for ridership which is increasing by up to 10 per cent a year.

Bus
Current situation: JR buses run 44 routes serving the northwest and southeast suburbs in association with rail services, and as feeders to the metro. Transfers available to metro. Stored-fare 'Common Card' accepted on all routes in Sapporo.

Hokkaido Chuo Bus

Hokkaido Chuo Bus Company (Chuo Bus)
1-8-6 Ironai, Otaru-shi, Hokkaido 047-0031
Tel: (+81 134) 24 11 11

Current situation: Provides 61 suburban services in the Sapporo area, with transfer fare system to metro. Fleet of 965 buses and 161 coaches. Stored-fare 'Common Card' accepted on selected routes in Sapporo.

Jotetsu Bus

Jotetsu Bus Company
9-1-1 Toyahira-shijo, Toyohira-ku, Sapporo-shi 062-0904
Tel: (+81 11) 811 61 41

Current situation: Provides six suburban services in the Sapporo area with 60 buses and 25 coaches. Jotetsu is a subsidiary of the Tokyu Corp which has extensive bus and rail interests in the Tokyo area.

UPDATED

SEATTLE

Population: City 535,000, King County area 1.6 million
Public transport: Bus, trolleybus and waterfront vintage tramway provided in metropolitan Seattle and King County by metropolitan agency responsible to county government. City operates monorail; state ferries. Other operators provide bus service in adjacent Snohomish and Pierce counties, which have joined with King County in forming a regional transit authority. Light rail and commuter rail proposed

Sound Transit

Central Puget Sound Regional Transit Authority
1100 Second Avenue, Suite 500, Seattle, Washington 98101-3423, USA
Tel: (+1 206) 684 67 76   Fax: (+1 206) 684 35 21
e-mail: main@soundtransit.org
www: http://www.soundtransit.org/
Chair: Paul Miller
Executive Director: Robert K White
Director, Light Rail: Paul Bay
Director, Commuter Rail: Paul Price
Director, Regional Express: Agnes Govern

Current situation: Sound Transit is a public agency created in 1993 to plan and provide a regional transport system for the urban areas of King, Pierce and Snohomish counties. It covers an area with a population of about 2.4 million, which is expected to more than double by 2020. ST is governed by an 18-member board, of whom 17 are local city and county elected, appointed by the County Executive of each county; the eighteenth member is the state transport department Secretary. Three standing board committees assist in policy-making, and an independent Citizen Oversight Panel monitors ST's performance in meeting its public commitments.

The three-county area is served by four local public transport agencies — King County Metro, Pierce Transit, Community Transit and Everett Transit.
Developments: In 1996 ST's board adopted Sound Move, a ten-year plan for a high-capacity regional public transport network, to be integrated with local bus services and using a common fare structure. Its major features are: construction of a light rail line from the university through central Seattle to Seattle/Tacoma airport, and central Tacoma to Tacoma Dome (40 km); development of a cross-city commuter rail line between South Tacoma and Everett using existing rights-of-way (130 km); and introduction of up to 20 regional express bus routes running mainly on HOV lanes.

First to open, in late 1999, will be the initial 55 km segment of the 'Sounder' commuter rail service, linking Seattle and Tacoma, for which 12 diesel locomotives and 60 bilevel cars are on order. A year later, the line will be extended northwards to Everett.

The first section of light rail line will open in 2001, linking Tacoma Dome station on the commuter line with downtown Tacoma (2.6 km, five stops). This starter line will not initially be connected to the main Seattle spine

Both articulated buses and electric trolleybuses are important elements of transit in Seattle (Van Wilkins)
1999/0038959

route, scheduled to open by 2006. The total cost of Sound Move is $3.9 billion at 1995 prices. In late 1996, voters approved local sales and motor vehicle excise tax increases to help fund the scheme, and these came into effect in April 1997.

Metro

King County Department of Transportation
Exchange Building, 821 Second Avenue, Seattle, Washington 98104
Tel: (+1 206) 684 14 41
County Executive: Ron Sims
Director, Department of Transportation: Paul Toliver
General Manager, Transit: Rick Walsh
Staff: 3,854

Passenger boardings: (All modes)
(1995) 83.5 million
(1996) 86.8 million
(1997) 92.5 million

Operating costs financed by: Fares 20.9 per cent, other commercial sources 9.5 per cent, tax levy 69.6 per cent
Subsidy from: 51.5 per cent from 0.6 per cent local sales tax, 36.6 per cent from 1 per cent motor vehicle excise tax

Current situation: In 1973 public transport for Seattle and King County was brought under the control of the Metro authority, created in 1957 for water pollution control. A dedicated 0.3 per cent sales tax was increased to 0.6 per cent in 1982. One-half of the 1 per cent Washington State motor vehicle excise tax collected in Metro's service area is allocated to public transit.

A 2 km tunnel in the city centre opened in 1990 for use by dual-mode buses; it is designed for light rail use and will carry LRVs when Seattle's spine route opens in 2004 (see above). There are three underground stations, and a combined station and bus staging area at each end. The

tunnel is served by 27 routes carrying about 35,000 passengers a day.

In 1994, voters in King County elected to merge the Municipality of Metropolitan Seattle and the existing government of King County. Full integration of the two entities was accomplished in 1996, with a separate Transit Division created within the Department of Transportation.
Developments: Recent rapid expansion of population and employment growth in areas outside central Seattle has required new approaches to meet changed public transport demand. A transit development plan inaugurated in 1996 has added over 400,000 service-hours and reoriented the network towards a hub-and-spoke system, connecting new centres of population and employment in King County as well as maintaining links to downtown Seattle.

After a demonstration, the seven public transport authorities in central Puget Sound have completed the planning phase for a common area-wide fare collection system using smartcard technology. Proposals were to be sought from suppliers at the beginning of 1999.

Washington State's Commute Trip Reduction law requires employers with 100 or more staff arriving during peak hours to implement schemes that promote the use of high-occupancy transport modes, as well as walking, cycling and telecommuting. The intention is to improve air quality, reduce traffic congestion and cut fuel consumption. With state grant funding, Metro assists employers to develop alternative commute plans as incentives for their employees.

Bus and trolleybus
Passenger journeys: (1995) 73.4 million
(1996) 76.3 million
(1997) 79.1 million
Vehicle-km: (1995) 63.2 million
(1996) 63.9 million
(1997) 66.8 million

Former Melbourne tram 518 approaching Pike Street on the Waterfront Streetcar service (Peter Newman)
1999/0038960

Number of routes: Bus 241, trolleybus 14
Route length: (One way) 6,081 km
Trolleybus overhead: 199 km

Fleet: 886 buses
MAN articulated (1978/82)	274
MAN Americana standard 40 ft (1987)	157
Flyer 35 ft and 40 ft	2
Transit van (1994/95/96)	95
Gillig 35 ft and 40 ft (1996)	358

Fleet: 384 trolleybuses
AM General (1979)	102
MAN articulated (1987)	46
Breda dual-mode (1990)	236

Average age of fleet: 7.9 years
In peak service: 1,036

Most intensive service: 6 min
One-person operation: All routes
Fare collection: Payment to farebox; prepurchase tickets and 1- and 3-month/annual passes
Fare structure: Zonal (2 zones, covering Seattle and rest of area, with free central area travel); peak surcharge. Prepurchase monthly, quarterly and annual passes; multiticket books; free transfers, all-day passes at weekends. Subsidised employer-purchased pass scheme
Fares collected on board: 23 per cent
Operational control: Route inspectors/mobile radio; computerised radio communication; vehicle location system
Arrangements for elderly/disabled: 94 per cent of vehicles and 212 routes (91 per cent) accessible, average 480 daily passengers; reduced fares and passes; half-price subscription taxi scheme; demand-response services carried 940,000 passengers in 1997
Average peak-hour speed: Bus 23.8 km/h, trolleybus 10.8 km/h
Bus priority: 217 km of HOV lanes, with city-centre penetration for trolleybus services
Integration with other modes: Cycle racks offered for free cycle carriage all routes; park-and-ride lots with space for 17,472 cars
New vehicles financed by: Sales tax and motor vehicle tax with FTA grants

Tramway

Type of operation: Conventional tramway, mainly as tourist attraction, serving waterfront area

Passenger journeys: (1995) 311,000
(1996) 467,000
(1997) 482,000

Current situation: Five vintage tramcars acquired from

Melbourne provide a 20 min service on this 3.4 km route with 10 stops.

Monorail

Seattle Monorail Services Inc

Type of operation: Elevated monorail, opened 1962

Current situation: 2 km two-track route, built in 1962 to serve the World's Fair site, links Westlake Mall in the downtown area with the Seattle Center cultural and pleasure facility; it carries about 2 million passengers a year. Two cars provide a frequent service at up to 80 km/h. Conductors are carried. The monorail is owned by the City of Seattle and operated under contract by Seattle Monorail services.
Developments: Proposals to extend the line to form a 65 km network at a cost of $1 billion, promoted by private citizens, were approved by voters in November 1997.

Ferry

Washington State DoT, Marine Division
Colman Dock, Seattle, Washington 98104
Tel: (+1 206) 464 72 34   Fax: (+1 206) 587 51 60

Current situation: Puget Sound ferry services are provided by Washington State as an integral part of the highway system. A fleet of 25 vessels carries about 23 million passengers and 10 million vehicles annually.

CT

Community Transit (CT)
Snohomish County Public Transport Benefit Area Corporation
7100 Hardeson Road, Everett, Washington 98203-5834
Tel: (+1 425) 348 71 00   Fax: (+1 425) 438 61 41
Chair: Jeanne Edwards
Executive Director: Joyce Olson
Staff: 462

Current situation: CT was created in 1975 to provide public transport in Snohomish County, immediately north of Seattle. The County Public Transportation Benefit Area Corp was the first such authority in Washington state. Voters initially approved a 0.3 per cent sales tax; in 1990 an additional 0.3 per cent was approved to fund service expansion, bringing the tax to the legal maximum of 0.6 per cent. Other funding for operating costs comes from a motor vehicle excise tax.

This is a rapidly growing area, and service is provided to a population of over 500,000. Express commuter services run to downtown Seattle (contracted to Grosvenor Bus Lines), to the University of Washington, and to the growing employment centres of Bellevue and Overlake east of Seattle.
Developments: Two new areas — Tulalip reservation and Eastmont/Silver Firs — were incorporated into CT's service area in 1997, with services provided from 1998. Increased service provision continued in 1997, with the additional 11 per cent of vehicle-km bringing a 10 per cent rise in patronage. The vanpool fleet was augmented by 45 vehicles to cope with a 49 per cent increase in ridership to 562,000, making it the fourth-largest such fleet in the USA.

The new Merrill Creek operations and maintenance centre opened in 1997, after which private contract operator Grosvenor moved into CT's former facility at Kasch Park. Grosvenor won the contract for operation of CT's commuter service to Seattle. Another new building was added to the Merrill Creek facilities in 1998.

Under the 1996/2001 six-year plan, CT raised service levels by 11.6 per cent in 1998, and the fleet was augmented by 16 buses and 25 vans. New routes are planned to serve growing employment areas and to cater for reverse-flow commuting. A 1,000-space park-and-ride lot at I-5/164th Street Southwest was scheduled for late 1998 opening.

Bus

Passenger journeys: (1995) 6 million
(1996) 7 million
(1997) 7.3 million
Vehicle-km: (1995) 11.9 million
(1996) 14.1 million
(1997) 14.9 million

Number of routes: 65
Fleet: 301 buses, plus vans
In peak service: 218 buses

Most intensive service: 15 min
Fare structure: Flat, double fare for inter-county journeys; higher for university and commuter services; mostly free transfers
Fare collection: Exact fare to farebox; monthly and annual passes, ticket books

Breda dual-mode vehicle (running as a trolleybus) about to enter the city-centre bus tunnel (Peter Newman)
1999/0038961

demand; low-floor buses and trams; stops specially designed for ease of access

Current situation: STAS holds the franchise for operation of urban transport from the Syndicat Intercommunal pour l'Organisation des Transports de l'Agglomération Stéphanoise (Siotas), which is a grouping of St Etienne and 14 neighbouring towns. Eight routes are operated under contract by three operators.

The short tramway Route 4 carries 37 per cent of all STAS passenger-km, and is the only route to produce a financial surplus. Trolleybus Route 9 handles 10 per cent of passenger-km.

Developments: Delivery of 20 low-floor cars in 1998 has allowed withdrawal of all old PCC cars.

Studies are in progress to assess the feasibility of tramway extensions, including a route linking the SNCF station at Châteaucreux with Le Clapier. A report was scheduled for publication in late 1998.

A new fleet of 60 trolleybuses is planned for commissioning in 1999/2000, of which 50 per cent would be articulated.

Bus and trolleybus

Vehicle-km: (1995) Bus 4.1 million, trolleybus 1.8 million (1996) Bus 4.3 million, trolleybus 1.9 million (1997) Bus 4.2 million, trolleybus 1.9 million

Number of routes: 26 bus, 7 trolleybus
Route length: 183 km
On private right-of-way: 10 km

Fleet: 126 buses	
Renault Agora	20
Renault PR100	20
Renault PR102	29
Renault PR312	40
Renault PR180 articulated	7
Mercedes O405GN articulated	2

Low-floor tram of STAS (David Haydock) ***1999**/0038968*

CBM/Renault midibus	5
Heuliez midibus	3
In peak service: 81	
Average age of fleet: 8 years	

Fleet: 51 trolleybuses	
Renault ER100R	16
Renault ER100H	25
Renault PER180H articulated	10
In peak service: 50	
Average age of fleet: 16 years	
New vehicles financed by: Siotas	

Contracted bus
Vehicle-km: (1994) 1.2 million
(1995) 1.2 million
(1997) 1.2 million

Current situation: Eight routes totalling 81.6 km are operated under contract by three companies.

Tramway
Type of operation: Conventional tramway

Car-km: (1995) 1.5 million
(1996) 1.5 million
(1997) 1.5 million

Route length: 9.3 km
Number of routes: 1
Number of stops: 26
Gauge: 1,000 mm
Electrification: 600 V DC, overhead

Service interval: Peak 2 min

Rolling stock: 35 tramcars	
GEC Alsthom articulated (1994)	M15
GEC Alsthom/Vevey articulated (1997/98)	M20
In peak service: 31 cars	

SNCF
Address as for Lyon region
Type of operation: Suburban heavy rail

Current situation: Limited service on three lines, almost hourly or better to Lyon.
Developments: Electrification of St Etienne–Firminy line is planned.

St Etienne centre with STAS low-floor tram on grassed reservation (David Haydock) ***1999**/0038969*

UPDATED

ST LOUIS
Population: City 453,000, metropolitan area 2.1 million
Public transport: Bus, light rail and paratransit service provided by regional authority serving St Louis and surrounding parts of Missouri and Illinois, controlled by representative board. Vanpool schemes

Bi-State Transit System
The Bi-State Development Agency
707 North First Street, St Louis, Missouri 63102, USA
Tel: (+1 314) 982 14 00   Fax: (+1 314) 982 14 70
Chair: Betty Van Uum
Executive Director: Thomas J Irwin
Director of Communications: Linda Hancock
Staff: 1,900

Siemens-Duewag SD400 St Louis light rail cars
***1999**/0038970*

Current situation: Bus, light rail and paratransit van service provision is the responsibility of the transport division of the Bi-State Development Agency. Created in 1949, the agency purchased and consolidated the region's 15 private bus operators in 1963. The service area covers St Louis and three county areas in each of Missouri and Illinois. Bi-State has responsibility for other transport and industrial development functions, and operates local bus operations (CitiLine) in St Clair County, Illinois. It also owns St Louis Downtown Parks airport and operates the Gateway Arch revenue collection centre and Arch Tram system.

Fixed-route buses are supplemented by Call-a-Ride demand-responsive van operations serving passengers with disabilities and residents in low-population density areas.

Developments: A 15-year public transport improvement plan was unveiled in 1992, with US$3.7 billion spending proposed on bus service upgrades, three new rail routes extending to 92 km and improved suburban bus service and paratransit. In 1994, a state contribution towards operating deficits was agreed, and voters approved a ¼ per cent increase in sales tax to fund transit improvements. This tax was at first subject to periodic review, so prohibiting the undertaking from borrowing against future tax revenue, but in 1995 it was made permanent and thus gave Bi-State its first dedicated source of funding for transit improvements.

First project likely to benefit is the proposed light rail extension from Forest Park to Clayton, Maplewood and Shrewsbury. This is Phase I of the Cross-Country Corridor, running north-south through the city's western suburbs. Conceptual design studies are in progress for completion in mid-1999.

One-third of the bus fleet will be CNG-powered by 2000; 36 CNG buses were acquired in 1997.

Bus

Passenger boardings: (1995/96) 37.4 million
(1996/97) 38.5 million
(1997/98) 39.6 million
Vehicle-km: (1995/96) 30.6 million
(1996/97) 30.6 million
(1997/98) 29.4 million

Number of routes: 111
Route length: (One-way) 3,631 km
On priority right-of-way: 8 km

Fleet: 578 vehicles

GMC T8H (1981)	61
Neoplan articulated (1988)	40
Flxible 40 ft (1988/89/90/91)	233
Gillig Phantom (1992)	54
Flxible CNG-powered (1992)	2
Orion II (1993)	18
Goshen Sentry (1993)	13
Gillig Phantom (1995)	49
Eldorado Aerotech (1995)	48
Gillig Phantom (1996)	24
Neoplan AN440 articulated CNG-powered (1997)	36
In peak service: 496	

Most intensive service: 3-15 min
One-person operation: All routes
Fare collection: Exact fare to farebox; multitickets, passes
Fare structure: Flat; express supplement; transfer supplement; weekly passes; fares-free area in downtown
Fares collected on board: 100 per cent
Fare evasion control: Undercover police surveillance system
Operational control: Route inspectors/mobile radio
Arrangements for elderly/disabled: Reduced fares and lift-equipped buses; 377,000 passengers carried in 1997/98 on Call-A-Ride demand-responsive services, partially contracted out to private operators
Integration with other modes: Extensive park-and-ride provision; carpooling scheme
Average distance between stops: 1 city block
Average peak-hour speed: In mixed traffic, 8.3 km/h
Operating costs financed by: Fares 24 per cent, other commercial sources 1 per cent, subsidy/grants 75 per cent
Subsidy from: FTA and Illinois state grants; dedicated transport sales tax in St Louis city, St Louis County, Madison County and St Clair County
New vehicles financed by: FTA capital grants and local matching funds

MetroLink

General Manager: Thomas Sehr

Type of operation: Light rail, initial route opened 1993

Passenger boardings: (1995/96) 12.9 million
(1996/97) 14.5 million
(1997/98) 14.6 million

Route length: 29 km
  in tunnel: 1.8 km
Number of lines: 1
Number of stations: 19
Gauge: 1,435 mm
Track: 57 kg/m RE rail on timber sleepers, on concrete slab in tunnels
Electrification: 750 V DC, overhead

Service: Peak 7½ min, off-peak 20 min
First/last car: 05.30/00.30
Fare structure: Flat
Fare collection: Prepurchase; proof-of-payment
Integration with other modes: Park-and-ride at 8 stations; 90 bus feeders have timed transfers
Arrangements for elderly/disabled: All stations accessible

Rolling stock: 37 cars

Siemens-Duewag SD400 (1992/93)	M31
Siemens-Duewag SD400 (1997/98)	M6
In peak service: 30	

Developments: Construction started in March 1998 of a 28 km extension with 8 stations running southeast from the existing terminal at 5th & Missouri to Belleville Area College, scheduled to open in mid-2001. A further 14.2 km thence to Mid America airport is in final design. Up to 15 cars will be ordered to serve the new route.

Other proposed extensions, approved for further studies in 1997, run into St Louis County, south to Oakville and southwest to Valley Park. These are included in the 15-year plan (see above).

Gillig Phantom of Bi-State in St Louis

1999/0038971

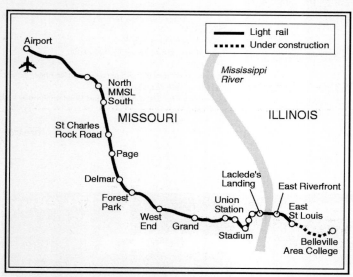

St Louis light rail
0045369

UPDATED

STOCKHOLM

Population: City 727,000, Greater Stockholm county 1.8 million

Public transport: Bus, suburban rail, local rail, tramway and metro services provided under contract to company owned by Stockholm County Council and controlled by nominated board, with subsidiaries operating metro, local rail and bus services, and also contracting bus and local train services from private operators and suburban rail operations of Swedish State Railways (SJ); county-owned ferries

Storstockholms Lokaltrafik

AB Storstockholms Lokaltrafik (SL)
Arenavägen 27, 120 80 Stockholm, Sweden
Tel: (+46 8) 686 10 00   Fax: (+46 8) 686 15 03
General Manager: Kjell Nilsson
Staff (SL Group of Companies): (1997) 6,016 (full year employees)

Passenger boardings: (All modes)
(1995) 570 million
(1996) 585 million
(1997) 600 million

Scania Omnicity articulated bus for city trunk network   *1999*/0038974

Operating costs financed by: Fares 43 per cent, other commercial sources 5 per cent, subsidy/grants 52 per cent
Subsidy from: County Council

Current situation: Greater Stockholm was one of the first West European cities to establish a fully integrated public transport system. The arrangements, agreed in 1964, brought together bus, metro and tramway services operated in the 25 county municipalities by AB Stockholms Spårvägar (SS) (based on former tramway companies), Swedish State Railways (SJ), two municipal bus companies and 10 private operators. As a result of the agreement SS was reorganised as AB Storstockholms Lokaltrafik (SL) which began operations in 1967.

A uniform fares system is based on a common distance-related tariff with the region divided into five zones. Fares are based on cash coupons offered at a one-third discount when purchased in strips of 20. Basic fare for one zone is two coupons with one per zone thereafter, up to a maximum of five coupons. Period tickets are also available for frequent travellers, and they are not confined to use by one person. About 70 per cent use some sort of period ticket for their journeys.

Municipal environmental regulations could force SL to abandon diesel-engined buses older than eight years, and various options for electric traction or gas-powered vehicles are being considered. 220 out of the inner-city fleet of 250 buses are already methanol-powered, and six electric duobuses are in revenue service.

Developments: Management reorganisation in 1991 saw SL split into operating and planning divisions, the latter specifying service levels and contracting with the operators for provision of service. The bus, metro and local railways have been reorganised as subsidiaries, and the aim is for their operations to be put out to tender. The first package of bids in 1993 involved the three local railways, whose existing SL operators won the franchises.

Tenders for operation of metro Line 3 and certain bus routes, sought in 1993, were won mainly by SL subsidiaries, as were those for metro Lines 2 and 1 in late 1994 and 1996 respectively.

Bus service is contracted mainly from three companies, SL-owned SL Buss, Linjebuss and Swebus, owned by the UK company Stagecoach Holdings, which took over five SL garages in 1993. AB Linjebuss became a contractor in a fresh round of tendering at the beginning of 1995, and in 1997 also took on operation of the Roslagsbanan local railway, while the tendered bus lines went to SL Buss.

Approval was given in 1991 for a package of public transport improvements over the period to 2005. Included were better quality service on the metro and construction of an orbital light rail line linking Gullmarsplan, Liljeholmen and Alvik metro stations with the suburban railway. This would help SL cater for the rapidly increasing number of non-radial and cross-city journeys. Other improvements now centre on a core network of clean-air buses running over reserved rights-of-way and with traffic light priority.

A dedicated trunk network for buses in the inner city

and the new suburban light rail line are together expected to improve the street environment and cut journey times by more than one-third. The aim is to provide an attractive bus service for the city centre. One of the five planned trunk lines is already in service.

Passenger boardings: (1995) 242 million
(1996) 254 million
(1997) 258 million
Vehicle-km: (1995) 87 million
(1996) 88 million
(1997) 89 million

Number of routes: 2,604
Route length: (One way) 45,400 km

Fleet: 1,676 vehicles

One-person operation: All routes
Fare collection: Prepurchase multitickets (coupons) or passes, or single coupons bought from driver
Fare structure: Zonal, based on coupon system with coupons sold separately or in booklets; monthly and annual season tickets for unlimited travel
Fares collected on board: 9 per cent; 65 per cent use monthly seasons, 20 per cent prepaid discount tickets; 6 per cent other
Operational control: Route inspectors/mobile radio with centralised radio control
Average distance between stops: City area, 350 m; outer zones, 700 m
Average peak-hour speed: In city; 15 km/h; in mixed traffic, 20 km/h; in bus lanes, 30 km/h
Bus priority: System for bus priority by means of on-board traffic light control in place for 80 buses. These buses are also equipped with a system to announce the destination/next stop; bus lanes provided and continuing programme for extensions; major traffic light priority scheme in city centre
Integration with other modes: All services and ticketing fully integrated; special bus services connect with Arlanda airport and ferries to Gotland and Finland
New vehicles financed by: County council loans

Metro
Type of operation: Full metro (T-Banan)

Passenger boardings: (1995) 256 million
(1996) 257 million
(1997) 263 million
Car-km: (1995) 84 million
(1996) 85 million
(1997) 85 million

Route length: 110 km
   in tunnel: 64 km
Number of lines: 3 with branches
Number of stations: 100
   in tunnel: 55
Gauge: 1,435 mm
Track: Flat-bottom 50 kg/m rail
Max gradient: 4.8%
Minimum curve radius: 200 m
Tunnel: Concrete, rock and steel

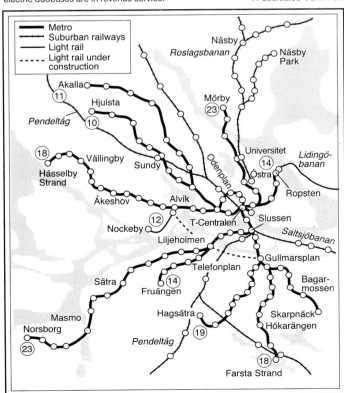

Map legend:
— Metro
—+— Suburban railways
— Light rail
- - - - Light rail under construction

Näsby
Roslagsbanan
Näsby Park
Akalla (11)
Hjulsta
Pendeltåg (10)
Mörby (23)
(18) Vällingby Sundby
Hässelby Strand
Universitet (14) Lidingö-banan
Östra
Åkeshov Alvik
Ropsten
Nockeby (12) T-Centralen
Slussen
Liljeholmen Saltsjöbanan
Gullmarsplan
Telefonplan
Sätra (14) Bagar-mossen
Fruängen
Masmo Hagsätra Skarpnäck
Norsborg (19) Hökarängen
(23) Pendeltåg
(18)
Farsta Strand

Stockholm's metro and local rail system
0010340

Car-2000 metro trainset in centre of Stockholm   *1999*/0038973

Car-2000 metro trainset on SL T-Banan service
1999/0010340

Electrification: 650-750 V DC, third rail

Service: Peak 2-5 min, off-peak 3-15 min
First/last train: 05.00/01.00
Fare structure: As bus
Revenue control: Barriers in all ticket halls, automatic gates for monthly passes in most stations; spot checks
One-person operation: All trains
Signalling: Cab signalling with fixed lineside signals installed only at junctions; central control office linked to all trains by radio
Surveillance: CCTV at 31 stations for passenger/train control

Rolling stock: 896 cars

C2/C3	M34
ASJ/ASEA C4 (1960/67)	M200
ASJ/ASEA/Hägglunds	
C6 (1971/74)	M158
C7 (1973)	M8
ASEA/Hägglunds	
C8 (1974/75)	M44
C9 (1976/77)	M20
C12 (rebuilt 1977/82)	M165
C13 (rebuilt 1982/84)	M94
C14 (rebuilt 1986/90)	M126
C15 (1985/86)	M14
C14Z (1987/88)	M4
Adtranz Car-2000 (1998/99)	M29

On order: A new fleet of 75 cars was ordered from Adtranz in 1998, and the order has since been doubled. Twenty-nine cars are already in service and the number will be successively increased to 150 before the end of 2001

Tramway
Passenger boardings: (1995) 2 million
(1996) 2 million
(1997) 1 million (line closed for repair for substantial part of year)

Current situation: One former tram route remains, the 5.7 km Line 12 from Alvik to Nockeby. Following a decision to retain and upgrade the line, the rolling stock is being extensively rebuilt. There is also a short tourist tramway, the Djurgårdslinjen, in the city centre.

Light rail
Under construction
Current situation: A light rail line from Alvik to Gullmarsplan metro station via Liljeholmen metro station (11 km, 12 stations) is under construction as the first stage of an orbital route for which 12 LRVs have been ordered from Bombardier Transportation. Opening is scheduled for 1999.

Local railway
Passenger boardings: (1995) 14 million
(1996) 14 million
(1997) 16 million

Current situation: SL's subsidiary SL Tunnelbana AB operates two of the three local railways under contract. They are the Saltsjöbanan (19 km, 1,435 mm gauge, electrified 750 kV DC, 28 cars, 18 stations) and the Lidingöbanan (9 km, 1,435 mm gauge, electrified 700 V DC, 20 cars). The third local railway, the Roslagsbanan (65 km, 891 mm gauge, electrified 1.5 kV DC, 101 cars, 39 stations) is operated under contract by Linjebuss.

The Saltsjöbanan links Stockholm Slussen with Saltsjöbaden, with a branch to Solsidan. It is being equipped with ATC by Adtranz as part of its contract to signal the new light rail line (see above). The Lidingöbanan serves the island of Lidingö, with a bridge link to the metro at Ropsten, and the Roslagsbanan runs northwards from Stockholm Östra station to Kårsta with branches to Näsby Park and Österskär. Modern cars replaced the entire rolling stock early in 1995.

Suburban railway
Operated under contract by: Swedish State Railways (SJ)

Type of operation: Suburban heavy rail

Passenger journeys: (1995) 56 million
(1996) 58 million
(1997) 62 million
Car-km: (1995) 35 million
(1996) 36 million
(1997) 36 million

Current situation: Services on three routes totalling 186 km with 48 stations; 1,435 mm gauge; electrified 15 kV 16⅔ Hz. Trains run half-hourly, with extras during peak hours.

Under an agreement between SJ, the government and Stockholm county council, SL and the county council made a major financial commitment to raising capacity and improving standards on the lines into Stockholm Central station. Further double-tracking and other capacity improvements were approved in 1991 for the period through to 2005.
Developments: SJ is contracted to operate these lines until the end of 1999, when a new operator takes over. VIA-GTI was awarded a five-year contract.

Rolling stock: 318 cars

Waxholms Ångfartygs
Waxholms Ångfartygs AB
PO Box 7422, 10391 Stockholm
Tel: (+46 8) 614 64 50   Fax: (+46 8) 611 84 07
Managing Director: Ewa Steinberg Sundqvist
Staff: 25

Ferry
Passenger journeys: (1995) 3.9 million
(1996) 3.9 million
(1997) 3.8 million

Operating costs financed by: Fares 35 per cent, other commercial sources 5 per cent, county council subsidy 65 per cent

Current situation: The 25 ships of WÅ, directly owned by Stockholm county council, form an integral part of the passenger services in the greater Stockholm area. There are 19 vessels operating in the sea inlets and to the islands of the archipelago, and six ply two routes in Stockholm harbour, Djurgården—Nybroplan and Slussen—Djurgården, at frequent intervals.

Arlanda Express
A-Train AB
PO Box 935, 19505 Arlandstad
Tel: (+46 8) 59 51 14 40   Fax: (+46 8) 59 51 14 50
e-mail: arlandaexpress@atrain.se
Website: www.arlandaexpress.se
Chief Executive Officer: Göran Lundgren
Marketing Executive: Tomas Kreij
Information: Inger Fjordgren
Sales: Maria Bohman

Current situation: The Arlanda Link consortium is building a 22 km loop off the Stockholm—Uppsala main line to serve Arlanda international airport, for opening in 1999. The consortium has a 45-year concession to build the loop and operate a dedicated airport service. The line voltage is 15 kV 16 ⅔ Hz and a service of four trains an hour will serve three stations. The trainsets are being built by Alstom Transport, UK.

Street running on the Alvik-Nockeby line (Andrew Jarosz)   *1999*/0043897

UPDATED

STOKE-ON-TRENT

Population: Conurbation 340,000
Public transport: Bus services in 'Potteries' six-town conurbation mainly provided by private company. Local routes also operated by some private companies; local rail services

First PMT

PMT Limited
Hobson Street, Burslem, Stoke-on-Trent ST6 2AQ, England
Tel: (+44 1782) 52 44 44 Fax: (+44 1782) 52 44 99
Managing Director: Steven Ellis
Operations Director: Ian Mackintosh

Current situation: Until 1986 PMT was a subsidiary of state-owned National Bus but as part of the break-up and sale of the group it was sold to its managers. In 1990, the company purchased Chester-based Crosville from Drawlane Holdings; the acquisition operates as a separate branded unit. PMT was purchased by Badgerline in 1994, and became a subsidiary of the FirstBus group in 1995. The company also trades as Red Rider in Merseyside and Pennine in Greater Manchester. **Developments:** PMT has installed a bus identification, communication and control system in its Stoke operating area, using satellite technology. The city's first permanent park-and-ride opened in Hanley in 1996. Branded services introduced 1997 on some corridors.

Bus

Number of routes: 153
Route length: 907 km

Plaxton-bodied Dennis Lance on First PMT's Crewe—Hanley 'Silver Service' leaving Hanley bus station
(Andrew Jarosz)
1999/0043890

Fleet: 505 vehicles

Bristol/Leyland double-deck	88
Leyland National/Lynx/Optare Delta/Dart/Swift/ Lance single-deck	151
Mercedes/Dodge/MCW/Optare minibus	260
Coaches	6

One-person operation: All routes
Fare collection: Payment to driver or passes
Fare structure: Distance-related and market-priced; passes
Average peak-hour speed: 18.7 km/h

Other commercial operators

Current situation: Procters, Stevensons, Arriva Midlands, Moorland, Knotty Bus, County Bus, Green Line, Matthews Motors and Scraggs all operate in the area.

Central Trains

Central Trains Limited
PO Box 4323, Birmingham B1 1TH
Tel: (+44 121) 643 44 44 Fax: (+44 121) 654 44 61
Managing Director: Nick Brown

Type of operation: Local rail

Current situation: Services provided about two-hourly to Stafford and peak-hours only to Manchester (both 25 kV AC), also to Crewe and Derby (diesel), serving local stations.

Light rail (proposed)

Current situation: The city council has authorised studies of proposed light rail systems both for the immediate Stoke area and for the conurbation.

UPDATED

ST PETERSBURG

Population: 3.2 million
Public transport: Bus, and trolleybus/tramway services operated by separate municipal undertakings. Metro. Suburban rail services

Upravlenie Automobil'novo Transporta

Upravlenie Automobil'novo Transporta
St Petersburg, Russia

Bus

Passenger journeys: Approx 225 million (annual)
Vehicle-km: Approx 60 million (annual)

Number of routes: 150
Route length: 1,100 km

Fleet: Approx 2,000 vehicles, comprising LAZ 699R, LIAZ 677, Ikarus 280 articulated, Ikarus 250 and a few Ikarus 260. The LAZ 699R and Ikarus 250s operate limited-stop express routes

One-person operation: All services
Fare collection: Payment to driver/conductor
Fare structure: Flat, higher on express routes
Fare evasion control: Random inspection

Current situation: Most of the money available from the city government for public transport improvements is earmarked for renewal of the bus fleet. During 1997 a further 500 or so new buses were delivered, mainly of old models such as Ikarus 280 and LIAZ 677, but it is hoped

Ikarus 280 bus by the Winter Palace (Norman Griffiths)
1999/0043896

ZIU9 trolleybuses at Nevsky Prospekt
(Aare Olander)
1999/0038975

that modern designs can be built locally at lower cost. Breda, Iveco, Volvo, Ikarus and Hyundai were bidders in a competition for establishment of a local production facility.

LenElektro Trans

LenElektro Trans
Ul ZodChego Rossi 1/3, St Petersburg 190011
Tel: (+7 812) 311 32 20

Trolleybus
Passenger journeys: Approx 500 million (annual)
Vehicle-km: 65 million (annual)

Number of routes: 48
Route length: 550 km

Fleet: 1,050 vehicles
Uritsky ZIU9
Uritsky ZIU10

Fare collection: Conductors
Fare structure: Flat; monthly seasons
Fare evasion control: Random inspection
Average peak-hour speed: 16 km/h

Tramway
Type of operation: Conventional tramway

Route length: 678 km
Number of lines: 65
Number of stops: 1,215
Gauge: 1,524 mm

Fare structure: Flat
Fare collection: Conductors

Rolling stock: About 1,900 cars
LM68M (1975/88)	About M1,200
KTM5 (1982/85)	M180
LVS86 articulated (1987/97)	About M480

Current situation: With the majority of city transport funding going towards renewal of the bus fleet, the tramway is in a steep decline. There are numerous temporary closures of track including reconstruction of the Liteyny bridge and street using expensive western technology. Movement in the city centre is severely restricted by traffic congestion. Renewal of the fleet has ceased (22 new LVS97 cars in 1996, only five in 1997), and series-production of the three-section LVS93 has not started as planned. A new two-section articulated variant of LVS97 was produced in 1997, but with no real improvement over the LM68M of 1973 vintage.

Developments: Track has been removed from some streets in the city centre, and further restriction of tram routes in the centre is planned, initially on the Kirov bridge.

A major new depot is under construction to house 300 trams, and there are plans for new central maintenance works to replace various sites around the city.

Petersburg Metro

Petersburg Metropoliten
Moskovskii Prospekt No 28, St Petersburg 198013
Tel: (+7 812) 251 66 68   Fax: (+7 812) 316 14 41
Chief Executive: Vladimir A Garuigin
Chief Engineer: Vladimir D Ocheret
Staff: 12,000

Type of operation: Full metro, first line opened 1955

Passenger journeys: (1989) 850 million
(1993) 623 million
(1996) 721 million

Route length: 94.3 km
Number of lines: 4
Number of stations: 56
Gauge: 1,520 mm
Max gradient: 4%
Minimum curve radius: 400 m
Electrification: 825 V DC, third rail

Service: Peak 1 min 35 s, off-peak 4 min
First/last train: 05.40/01.00
Fare structure: Flat

LVS89 articulated car at Liteinyi Prospekt in the city centre (Aare Olander)   *1999*/0038976

St Petersburg metro   0009925

Revenue control: Prepurchase token to barrier; open access with photoelectric cell control
Stations: At many stations 'platforms' replaced by open halls with doors at either side, opened automatically to correspond with the train doors when the train has stopped. Platform doors close again before the train leaves
Signalling: Automatic train stop; radio-telephone communication with trains; ATO

Rolling stock: 1,343 cars, formed into five- and six-car sets
Mytischy D/E/EJ	M1,343

Current situation: Further 14 km under construction, including northwest Line 4 extension with six stations, the initial portion of which from Pl Mira to Chkalovskaya opened in 1997.

LM68M cars at Moskovsky Vokzal, crossing the Nevsky Prospekt (Aare Olander)
***1999**/0038977*

RZD

Russian Railways (RZD), October Railway
Ostrovskogo pl 2, 191011 St Petersburg
Tel: (+7 812) 168 60 40   Fax: (+7 812) 311 83 39

Type of operation: Suburban heavy rail

Current situation: Electrified (3 kV DC) commuter services operate on routes extending from the city's five terminals.

UPDATED

STRASBOURG

Population: City 252,000, conurbation 450,000
Public transport: Bus and light rail services provided by franchised company CTS, owned mainly by the Communauté Urbaine de Strasbourg (CUS) (52 per cent) and Bas-Rhin Département (26 per cent), also operating regional routes. CTS is administered by a board which includes representatives from the city and CUS

CTS

Compagnie des Transports Strasbourgeois
14 rue de la Gare aux Marchandises, BP2, 67035 Strasbourg Cedex 2, France
Tel: (+33 3) 88 77 70 11   Fax: (+33 3) 88 77 70 99
President: Roland Ries
Director General: Marc Le Tourneur
Operating Manager: J-P Basset
Project Director, LRT: Alain Giesi
Project Manager, LRT: Georges Müller
Staff: 1,214

Passenger boardings: (both modes, unlinked trips)
(1995) 54.1 million
(1996) 55.9 million
(1997) 56.8 million

Current situation: Service started on the first tram route (Line A) in 1994, when parallel bus routes were restructured to avoid duplication and act as feeders, principally at Baggersee and Rotonde. Traffic levels have surpassed all forecasts, running at between 65,000 and 70,000 passengers daily in 1997 and reaching more than 110,000 on some Saturdays.
Strasbourg has enforced severe restrictions on car traffic;

Strasbourg Eurotram at Baggersee on Route A (Norman Griffiths)   ***1999**/0043893*

the city centre is pedestrianised and cars cannot drive from one side to the other. Their only access is to four 'loops' which extend to the edge of the central area.

Bus
Vehicle-km: (1995) 12.6 million
(1996) 12.8 million
(1997) 12.8 million

Number of routes: 26 urban, 286 interurban
Route length: Urban 288 km, interurban 316 km
On priority right-of-way: 7 km

Fleet: 381 vehicles
Urban fleet

Renault SC10	85
Renault R312	69
Heuliez GX317	8
Mercedes/Heuliez articulated	9
Van Hool low-floor articulated	56
Renault S53	6
Interurban fleet	
Renault Tracer	9
Renault S53	80
Volvo/Heuliez	7
Volvo/Heuliez articulated	9
Renault Agora	20
Renault Agora articulated	20
Mercedes-Benz Sprinter	1
Neoplan Electric Shuttle	2

In peak service: Urban 252, interurban 98
Average age of fleet: 7 years

Most intensive service: 4 min
One-person operation: All routes
Fare structure: Urban, flat; interurban, zonal
Fare collection: 'Unipass' ticket from driver, valid up to 1 h, with free transfer, or prepurchase carnets with validation on board; daily, weekly and monthly passes; car or cycle parking plus return tram tickets issued at Etoile and Rotonde; Alsaplus pass for CTS/SNCF journeys

New Renault Tracer on interurban service   ***1998**/0010022*

Arrangements for elderly/disabled: Special minibus services; reduced rate tickets and monthly passes for over-65s and invalids

Operating costs financed by: Fares 53 per cent, other commercial sources 4 per cent, subsidy/grants 43 per cent

Subsidy from: CUS (urban) and Bas-Rhin Département (interurban)

Light rail

Type of operation: Light rail, initial route opened 1994

Passenger journeys: (1995) 63,000 daily
(1996) 65,000 daily
(1997) 70,000 daily
Car-km: (1995) 1.1 million
(1996) 1.3 million
(1996) 1.3 million

Route length: 12.6 km
Number of lines: 1
Number of stations: 23

Gauge: 1,345 mm
Electrification: 750 V DC, overhead

Service: Peak 3 min
First/last car: 04.30/00.30
Fare structure/collection: As bus
Integration with other modes: Several park-and-ride sites account for some 10 per cent of daily journeys

Rolling stock: 26 cars
ABB (1993/94)   M26
In peak service: 20
On order: Further 27 cars from Adtranz Derby; 17 will be 43 m long on five bogies, making them the world's longest LRVs

Developments: Extension of Line A from Baggersee to Illkirch Graffstaden (3 km) opened in July 1998. After construction of turn-back facilities at Etoile, Line D was introduced as a city-centre shuttle, providing a three-minute frequency 07.00–19.00 Mondays to Saturdays. Work started in 1998 on two east-west alignments. Line B

will link Elsau with the city centre and Rond-Point Esplanade in the east, while Line C branches off at Republic to serve Foire Exposition and Hoenheim. Both should be in operation by the end of 2000.

Route D will be extended to Kehl in Germany by 2010. It is also proposed to extend Line B to Neudorf and Neuhof, and to introduce tram service over some existing suburban rail alignments, for example to Molsheim (26 km).

SNCF

French National Railways (SNCF), Strasbourg Region
3 boulevard du Président Wilson, 67803 Strasbourg
Tel: (+33 3) 88 32 56 33   Fax: (+33 3) 88 75 41 39

Current situation: Limited local services operate on five routes. The Alsace region has financed a half-hourly peak, hourly off-peak 200 km/h local services to Mulhouse using Corail stock and Sybic electric locomotives.

UPDATED

STUTTGART

Population: City 586,000, metropolitan area 2.3 million
Public transport: Bus, tramway/light rail, rack railway and funicular services provided by company with majority ownership by the city of Stuttgart, developing S-Bahn and associated feeder buses operated by German Railway (DB), other bus services by WEG/KVG and independent operators, all co-ordinated under Stuttgart Verkehrs- und Tarifverbund (VVS)

VVS

Verkehrs- und Tarifverbund Stuttgart GmbH (VVS)
Rotebühlstrasse 121, 70178 Stuttgart, Germany
Tel: (+49 711) 660 60   Fax: (+49 711) 660 62 57
Directors: Dipl-Ing Wolfgang Wörner
    Günter Mötsch
    Thomas Porombka

Current situation: Regional bus and rail developments, fares and services, publicity and planning in an area of 3,012 km² surrounding Stuttgart are co-ordinated by a Verkehrsverbund formed in 1978 by Stuttgarter Strassenbahnen and DB to provide finance for and co-ordination of the developing 14-line Stadtbahn and urban bus network operated by SSB and the six-line regional metro (S-Bahn) and associated feeder bus services operated by DB. The area includes the city of Stuttgart and 141 other towns and neighbourhoods, including Esslingen, Böblingen, Ludwigsburg and Waiblingen, with a total population of some 2.3 million. The only partners in VVS are SSB and DB, though 38 other transport operators are now associated with VVS.

The Verkehrsverbund is controlled by a board of representatives of SSB, DB and local authorities, including the Baden-Württemberg Land government.

Stuttgarter Strassenbahn MAN rack tram with cycle carrier at front (Norman Griffiths)   *1999*/0043891

Tariff standardisation applies to an inner area centred on Stuttgart comprising four zones.

Passenger boardings: (All modes)
(1995) 281 million
(1996) 277 million
(1997) 273 million

Number of routes: Rail 30, bus 304

Fare structure: Zonal, single and multiride tickets; daily, weekly and monthly passes; annual subscription, discounted sales to employers who buy passes for all their staff; off-peak passes at reduced fares; first class available on S-Bahn; free transfers between modes and operators

Operating costs financed by: Fares 46 per cent, subsidy/grants 54 per cent

Subsidy from: Federal and state governments, city of Stuttgart, four surrounding counties

SSB

Stuttgarter Strassenbahnen AG (SSB)
PO Box 801006, 70510 Stuttgart
Tel: (+49 711) 788 50   Fax: (+49 711) 78 85 28 91
www: www.ssb-ag.de
Chair: Manfred Bonz
Managing Directors: Peter Höflinger
    Reinhold Bauer
Staff: 2,759

Passenger journeys: (All modes)
(1995) 169.7 million
(1996) 169.2 million
(1997) 171.4 million

Operating costs financed by: Fares 50.5 per cent, grants 29.2 per cent, subsidy 20.3 per cent
Subsidy from: Local authority subsidy; federal and state grants for new investment

Current situation: SSB's majority shareholder is the city

Stuttgarter Strassenbahn newest U-Bahn route at Ruhbank (Norman Griffiths)   *1999*/0043894

Stuttgarter Strassenbahn low-floor Mercedes-Benz O405GN CNG bus at Heidehof Strasse (Norman Griffiths)   **1999**/0043895

of Stuttgart. Operations extend outside the city to serve a total population of 900,000, with co-ordination on a regional level with DB under VVS.

Fare collection: Prepurchase from offboard ticket-issuing machines and ticket offices, or driver on buses only; cancellation/validation machines on board

Fare structure: Zonal; single, day and multiride tickets, weekly, monthly and annual passes; 69 per cent use passes

Integration with other modes: Free transfer in VVS areas with tramway, S-Bahn and private rail and bus services

Bus
Vehicle-km: (1995) 14.1 million
(1996) 13.3 million
(1997) 14.1 million

Number of routes: 56
Route length: (One way) 476 km
On priority right-of-way: 13.9 km

Fleet: 250 vehicles, plus 81 contracted
Mercedes O405 (1985/92/96)	100
Mercedes O405G articulated (1986/95)	127
Mercedes O405GNDE (1997)	17
Neoplan N4114DE (1997)	2
Coaches	4

Average age of fleet: 5.5 years

Most intensive service: Peak 7½ min
One-person operation: All routes
Average distance between stops: 618 m
Average speed: 20 km/h

Developments: In accordance with the INVK (Integrated Local Transport Planning) strategy, bus services in parts of the city and region are being restructured. Parallel with development of the LRT network, buses act mainly as feeders for the light rail and S-Bahn lines, and duplication of rail services is avoided.

Bus flow improvements in progress include provision of more bus lanes, projecting kerbs at stops, traffic signal priority and integration in computer-based monitoring. Special service of nine routes operates on Friday and Saturday nights.

A fleet of 17 Mercedes O405GNDE low-floor articulated buses with diesel-electric propulsion were introduced on busy Route 42 in 1997. At the same time, a real-time passenger information system came into operation on

this route, which won for SSB the UITP award for innovation.

Tramway/light rail
Type of operation: Conventional metre-gauge tramway being upgraded to 1,435 mm gauge Stadtbahn (LRT), with mixed 1,435/1,000 mm gauge operation on some sections

Car-km: (1995) LRV 8.5 million, tram 6.6 million
(1996) LRV 8.9 million, tram 6.6 million
(1997) LRV 9.5 million, tram 6 million

Route length: 108.5 km (LRT 86.6 km)
  reserved track: 95.7 km
  in tunnel: 19 km
Number of lines: LRT 19, tram 2
Number of stops: 176
Gauge: 1,000 mm and 1,435 mm
Max gradient: 7%, tramway 8.5%
Minimum curve radius: 50 m, tramway 25 m
Electrification: 750 V DC, overhead

Service: Peak 6-7½-10 min, off-peak 10-12 min
First/last car: 04.45/00.15
Arrangements for elderly/disabled: 112 of the 128 high-platform stations are accessible by ramp or lift
One-person operation: All routes
Operational control: Computer-based monitoring also provides passenger information

Rolling stock: 191 cars
Maschinenfabrik Esslingen GT4 metre-gauge (1961/64)	M72
Duewag DT8 LRV (1985/93/96)	M114
MAN/SLM rack-LRV (1982)	M3
Funicular	2

On order: 23 cars of a new DT8.10 design from Adtranz/Siemens for 1999 delivery, with an option for a further 27

Current situation: SSB has in progress a multistage conversion of metre-gauge tramway to standard-gauge light rail (Stadtbahn), now scheduled to be completed by 2005 with the conversion of Route 15. Most of the route (88 per cent) is already segregated and there is 18.9 km of tunnel in the city centre; dual-gauge tracks have been laid on some routes.

U6 was extended to Gerlingen in May 1997, conversion of Route 13 was completed in September 1997 and is

being followed by conversion of much of Route 2 for completion in 2000.

A 4.9 km extension of U14 from Mühlhausen to Remseck-Neckargröningen was scheduled for May 1999 opening. Work started in 1997 on the tunnel for the future U7 extension to Nellingen, although the routeing in Nellingen has yet to be decided. The first section to Ruhbank opened in May 1998, with the next stage to Heumaden (replacing part of tram Route 15) due for 1999 opening. Also U5 to be extended to Mühlhausen to give access to the new depot to be built at Remseck-Aldingen.
Developments: In connection with DB's 'Stuttgart 21' project, which will convert the present surface terminal Hbf into an underground through station, changes to both tram (Route 2) and Stadtbahn will be necessary. SSB has started planning for a new route U12 from Degerloch to Hbf and Münster (13 km), with services to start in 2001.

Rack railway/funicular
Current situation: A 2.2 km rack line on the Riggenbach-Lamelle system links Marienplatz with Degerloch, metre-gauge, 18 per cent maximum gradient, 680 V DC overhead, three cars. SSB also operates a 600 m funicular from Südheimer Platz to Waldfriedhof on a 27 per cent maximum gradient.

DB
Deutsche Bahn AG, DB Regio
Regionalbereich Württemberg
Heilbronner Str 7, 70174 Stuttgart
Tel: (+49 711) 209 20   Fax: (+49 711) 20 92 34 95
Managers: Karl Jürgen Sabban (Controller)
  Wolfgang Seidemann (Technical)
  Theodor Schneider (Marketing)
Staff: 797

Regional metro
Type of operation: Regional metro (S-Bahn)

Passenger journeys: (1996) 46 million

Current situation: S-Bahn trains run over six routes with a total length of 174 km serving 70 stations, electrified 15 kV 16⅔ Hz overhead. Peak-hour trains every 15 min, off-peak 30 min; being extended to Bernhausen. Suburban trains also run on 12 non-S-Bahn routes with a route length of 148 km. Operations co-ordinated under VVS.

Rolling stock: 134 ET 420 and ET 423 three-car trains
On order: First deliveries due in May 1999 of 23 sets of ET 423 emu for Route S1

RBS
Regional Bus Stuttgart GmbH
PO Box 103937, 70034 Stuttgart
Tel: (+49 711) 66 60 70   Fax: (+49 711) 666 07 99
Managing Directors: Peter Müller
  Rudolf Schmidt
  Theodor Schneider
Staff: 442

Current situation: Regional bus company owned by DB runs a network of 41 routes as feeders to the S-Bahn, carrying about 15 million passengers a year on services within the VVS area. Also operates outside the VVS area.

Fleet: 275 buses, plus 333 contracted

Other operators
Current situation: Other bus services are provided by WEG Kraftverkehrsgesellschaft (KVG), and several independent operators within the framework of VVS.

UPDATED

SURABAYA
Population: 4 million
Public transport: Bus services operated by government-owned company and private operators of buses and minibuses, with substantial numbers of Bemo shared minibuses and Becak tricycle pedicabs. Ferries link Surabaya and Madura Island; metro planned

DAMRI
Djawatan Angkutan Motor Republik Indonesia
Proyek Biskota, Jl Jend Basoki Rakhmat 80, Surabaya, Java Timor, Indonesia
Tel: (+62 31) 439 20

Passenger journeys: (1989) 13 million
(1990) 12.8 million
(1991) 13 million

Bus
Current situation: The government-owned bus operations account for only a limited part of the public transport provision, with 10 routes, parts of which are contracted out to other operators. Separate flat fares for local and express services.
Fleet: 215 buses, mostly Mercedes OH306 and OH408 types, plus some Leyland Atlantean double-deck and Tata

Private bus/minibus
Supervised by: Urban Road Traffic Board
Jl Jend a Yani 268, Surabaya

Current situation: About 30 per cent of public transport journeys are accounted for by a fleet of some 3,200 Bemo 10-seater minibuses, mostly Mitsubishi L300 Colt and Daihatsu models, operating on 37 routes. An estimated 38,000 Becak tricycle pedicabs handle an even larger proportion. There are also a few independent operators of full-size buses, known as Bis Kota.

Metro (planned)
Current situation: A two-line metro is in design, with a 19 km north-south route likely to be built first. A consortium will take the project forward to the stage where a bidding process for a build-operate-transfer contract can be started. The three consortium members, who signed an agreement in October 1996, are the Indonesian railway operator Perumka, GEC Alsthom Transport and a local development and finance company.

Line 1 would run from the Tanjung Perak ferry terminal in the north to Purubaya bus station in the south, serving Perumka's main station and the city centre. In a later phase, Line 2 would link Laguna Indah in the east with residential developments at Kota Baru to the west. There would be interchange with Line 1 at New Kota.

VERIFIED

SYDNEY

Population: 3.6 million
Public transport: Bus and ferry/catamaran services serving central urban area and Sydney harbour provided by State Transit Authority. The Department of Transport exercises overall responsibility for planning and co-ordination of all public transport including privately run bus, ferry, taxi and hire car services. State Rail Authority provides extensive suburban rail services over routes owned by the state Rail Access Corporation. Private bus operators serve suburban and outer areas. Monorail serves the Darling Harbour redevelopment; light rail

State Transit

State Transit Authority of New South Wales
PO Box 1327, North Sydney, New South Wales 2059, Australia
Tel: (+61 2) 92 45 57 77   Fax: (+61 2) 92 45 57 10
Chief Executive: John Stott
Staff: 4,100

Passenger journeys: (1993/94) 197.7 million
(1994/95) 194.9 million
(1995/96) 190.2 million

Current situation: State Transit's structure was reorganised at the start of 1993 to meet the government's requirement for a new and accountable business-like culture in the public sector, capable of meeting minimum service levels set by the Department of Transport. A smaller corporate head office now oversees eight major business units and three satellite depots, plus Sydney Ferries and a further business unit responsible for operations in Newcastle (180 km north). There are 25 operating contracts within ST's area.

The Sydney bus system serves a population of 1.7 million and covers an area of 645 km². Separate bus and ferry networks run in Newcastle. Details below refer only to Sydney.

Sydney Buses

(Sydney city and inner metropolitan area operations only)
Chief Executive Officer: John Scott
Address above
Tel: (+61 2) 92 45 56 06   Fax: (+61 2) 92 45 56 11
Staff: 3,225

Passenger journeys: (1993/94) 165 million
(1994/95) 168.1 million
(1995/96) 177.1 million

Scania ultra-low-floor bus of Sydney Buses
1999/0038978

Vehicle-km: (1993/94) 60.5 million
(1994/95) 61.4 million
(1995/96) 65.7 million

Number of routes: 250
Route length: 946 km

Fleet: 1,721 vehicles

Mercedes O305 Mk II to V	1,218
Mercedes O305G articulated	30
MAN SL202	50
Renault PR100-2	2
Mercedes O405 Mk VI	18
Mercedes O405N low-floor	2
Scania L113CRB CNG-powered	102
Scania L113RBL	50
Scania L11CRL	156
MAN 11-220 HOCL/RNM	30
Volvo B10LBLE ultra-low-floor (1997/98)	52
Mercedes-Benz 814D	11

In peak service: 1,350
Average age of fleet: 11.5 years

On order: 30 MAN 11-220 HOCL/R NM 10.2 m ultra-low-floor for delivery through to 1999; 300 ultra-low-floor CNG-powered from Mercedes-Benz Australia, first delivery due in January 1999; also 11 Mercedes Benz Vario midibuses (100 vehicles renewed each year)

Most intensive service: 3 min
One-person operation: All routes
Fare collection: Payment to driver, or cancellation of prepurchase multitrip tickets or pass
Fare structure: Stage; multitrip tickets; quarterly and annual 'Travelpass' intermodal passes; off-bus multitrip tickets for use with onboard cancelling machines
Fares collected on board: 25 per cent
Integration with other modes: Timed interchange with suburban rail services and ferries; intermodal 'Travelpass'; airport express bus
Bus priority: Peak-hour bus lanes and priority when joining traffic flow; priority traffic signals
Operational control: Route inspectors/mobile radio; two-way radio in all vehicles; central radio control room
Arrangements for elderly/disabled: Ultra-low-floor buses have ramp and space for two wheelchairs; half fare for elderly, with low-cost day tickets for unlimited bus/train/ferry travel after 09.00. Ministry of Transport subsidises taxi service for disabled; wheelchair users have specially modified vehicles, others use standard taxis and all pay half metered fare, state government subsidising remainder
Operating costs financed by: Fares 55 per cent, other commercial sources 4.6 per cent, subsidy/grants 40.4 per cent
Subsidy from: State government contract payment
New vehicles financed by: Internal funds

Sydney Ferries

Staff: 408

Passenger journeys: (1995/96) 13.1 million
Vehicle-km: 70 million (annual)

Number of routes: 11
Fleet: 27 vessels

Operating costs financed by: Fares 64 per cent, other commercial sources 10 per cent, subsidy/grants 26 per cent

Current situation: Ferries provide an important link between Sydney Harbour residential suburbs and the major bus/rail interchange at Circular Quay. Extensive cruise services also operate.

Private bus

Represented by: Bus & Coach Association
27 Villiers Street, North Parramatta, NSW 2151
Tel: (+61 2) 96 30 86 55   Fax: (+61 2) 96 83 14 65
President: S J J Bosnjak

Current situation: Around 50 per cent of suburban services are operated by private firms with a fleet of 3,000 buses in the Sydney/Newcastle/Wollongong urban areas. Operators are given five-year performance-based contracts stipulating minimum service levels and standard fares.

CityRail

Division of the State Rail Authority of New South Wales
PO Box K349, Haymarket, NSW 1238
Tel: (+61 2) 93 79 30 00   Fax: (+61 2) 93 79 15 50
Chief Executive, SRANSW: Simon Lane
Staff: 5,429

Light rail comes to the streets of Sydney
1998/0010346

Type of operation: Suburban and interurban rail

Passenger journeys: (1995/96) 256.4 million
(1996/97) 264.7 million
(1997/98) 266.5 million

Current situation: CityRail operates an extensive suburban and intercity rail network totalling 1,700 km with 301 stations, mostly electrified 1.5 kV DC. The network extends well beyond the Sydney suburban area and includes intercity trains to Hunter Valley, Central Coast, Blue Mountains, South Coast and Southern Highlands. Statistics given here cover the entire network. CityRail pays annual access charges to the state-owned infrastructure authority Rail Access Corporation to operate its services.

Fares cover 36 per cent of operating costs, other commercial sources 2 per cent, with the remainder being a state government payment to cover concession fares and for operating non-commercial services.

Developments: February 1998 saw opening of a 6 km loop and station to serve the Olympic 2000 stadium at Homebush Bay. Construction is also in progress of a direct underground link to the airport (10 km, four stations), for opening in 2000. This is a joint venture between the NSW government, Transfield Construction and project manager CRI Ltd, and is the first such scheme to allow private-sector operation of a railway.

A further project is at the environmental impact assessment stage — a 3 km extension from Bondi Junction to Bondi Beach.

More double-deck cars are to be purchased. An order was signed in December 1998 for supply of an initial batch of 80, to be followed by two more batches of 60.

An environmental impact study is under way into the building of the new Parramatta line to run between Parramatta and Chatswood via Epping.

Rolling stock: 1,457 emu cars and 46 diesel cars

Suburban double-deck	770
Tangara suburban double-deck	367
Intercity double-deck	240
Tangara outer-suburban (1994/95)	80
Endeavour diesel railcar	30
Class 620 diesel railcar	16
In peak service: 1,312	

Sydney Monorail
CGEA Transport
220 Pyrmont Street, Darling Harbour, NSW 2000
Tel: (+61 2) 96 60 52 88   Fax: (+61 2) 96 60 09 55
General Manager: Kevin Warrell

Newly opened Homebush Bay station to serve the Sydney 2000 Olympics. The running tracks are to the left of the picture, below the main concourse (Pauline Cain)   **1999**/0038979

Operations Director: Eddie Croft
Staff: 85

Type of operation: Straddle monorail, opened 1988

Current situation: A 3.6 km automated loop line with seven stations connects the city centre with Darling Harbour; electrified 500 V AC. Privately developed by TNT, the link is a fully commercial operation. The company was acquired by CGEA in 1998. Cars run every 4 min.

CGEA has been contracted to operate the light rail line (see below), opened in August 1997.

Rolling stock: 6 seven-car trainsets

Sydney Light Rail
CGEA Transport
220 Pyrmont Street, Darling Harbour, NSW 2000
Tel: (+61 2) 96 60 52 88   Fax: (+61 2) 96 60 09 55
General Manager: Kevin Warrell
Operations Director: Eddie Croft

Current situation: A 3.5 km light rail link from Central station to the Darling Harbour and City West (Ultimo) development areas opened in August 1997. TNT operates the line under contract.

Developments: Two extensions have been proposed and are under consideration by the NSW government. These would extend the line to the central business district and westwards, adding a further 12 km of route and 15 cars.

Light rail
Type of operation: Light rail, initial route opened 1997

Route length: 3.5 km
Number of routes: 1
Gauge: 1,435 mm
Electrification: 750 V DC overhead

Service: 15 min

Rolling stock: 7 cars
Adtranz Variotram LRV (1997)   M7

UPDATED

SZCZECIN
Population: 413,000
Public transport: Bus and tramway services provided by municipal authority. Suburban rail services by State Railway (PKP)

MZK
Miĕjskie Zaklady Komunikacyjne (MZK)
ul Klonowicza 5, 712-41 Szczecin, Poland
Tel: (+48 91) 744 11   Fax: (+48 91) 389 93
Staff: 3,689

Passenger journeys: (All modes) (1990) 248.2 million

Operating costs financed by: Fares 37 per cent, subsidy from city 73 per cent

Current situation: In 1991 the former operating authority WPKM, which had provided public transport services in the cities of Szczecin, Stargard Szczecinski and Swinoujscie, was split into three organisations. The Szczecin operation came under the control of the local authority and took a new name. An annual grant towards operating costs comes from central government, allocated by the Administrator of the province of Szczecin.

Bus
Passenger journeys: (1990) 151.2 million
Vehicle-km: (1990) 23.9 million

Number of routes: 66
Route length: 719 km

Fleet: 440 vehicles
Jelcz PR110M
Jelcz M11
Ikarus 280 articulated
Volvo/Carrus articulated
In peak service: 278

Volvo/Carrus articulated of MZK   **1998**/0010025

One-person operation: All routes

Fare collection: Prepurchase ticket or pass with validation and cancelling machines on board
Fare structure: Flat
Fare evasion control: Random inspectors
Average peak-hour speed: 19.6 km/h

Tramway
Type of operation: Conventional tramway with sections upgraded to light rail

Passenger journeys: (1990) 97 million
Car-km: (1990) 14.8 million

Route length: 110 km
Number of lines: 12

Gauge: 1,435 mm

Service: Peak 5 min; 24 h service
Fare structure: As bus
Average peak-hour speed: 14.6 km/h

Rolling stock: 353 cars
Konstal Chorzow
N (1952-62)	M93
102N (1971/72)	M24
105N (1975/79)	M94
105Na (1981-90)	M49
ND	T93

In peak service: 239

PKP
Polish State Railways (PKP)
ul Chalubinskiego 4, 009-28 Warsaw
Tel: (+48 22) 624 40 00   Fax: (+48 22) 621 27 04

Type of operation: Suburban heavy rail

Current situation: Services on several lines in Szczecin urban area and on routes to Trzebiez Szczecinski (37 km), Kostrzyn (104 km) and Choszczno (75 km); irregular, but about hourly.

VERIFIED

TAIPEI

Population: City 2.5 million, metropolitan area 5 million
Public transport: Integrated bus services for designated urban area provided by City Bus Administration and nine private groups and companies regulated by Taipei City government, which also licenses the single ferry operation. Suburban rail services provided by Taiwan Railway Administration being upgraded. Metro; automated light metro

Taipei City Bus

Taipei City Bus Administration
5 Peiping East Road, Taipei City, Taiwan
Chief Administrator: Wua-Hsiung Lee
Staff: 3,087

Current situation: Publicly owned Taipei City Bus is responsible to the Reconstruction Bureau of Taipei municipal government which also regulates nine other private bus undertakings working in the United Operating System (see earlier editions of *JUTS* for history).

Taipei City Bus is the largest single operator, carrying about 1 million passengers daily. Three levels of service are offered: conventional and air conditioned buses, and minibuses.

Bus

Passenger journeys: (1992/93) 293.7 million
Vehicle-km: (1992/93) 50.8 million

Number of routes: Total 157; ordinary services 54, air conditioned 89, minibus 14
Route length: (One way) 1,520 km

Fleet: Total 1,356 buses; ordinary 238, air conditioned 1,075, minibuses 43; including locally bodied Hino, Isuzu, Volvo 6FA buses and Toyota and Mercedes (L508D) mini/midibus
In peak service: 1,216

Most intensive service: 3 min
Fare structure: 2 zones
Fare collection: Cash or prepurchase 10-zone tickets; additional tokens required for air conditioned services
Arrangements for elderly/disabled: Free with multijourney tickets clipped by drivers; clippings counted for reimbursement of operator by government
Operating costs financed by: Fares 77.3 per cent, other commercial sources 2.8 per cent, subsidy/grants 17.7 per cent, tax levy 1.8 per cent
Subsidy from: Taipei municipal government (if received)

Taiwan Railway Administration Nippon Sharyo dmu   **1999**/0038998

Red line metro trials   **1996**

Private bus
Regulated by: DoT, Taipei City Government
17th Floor, No 222 Sec 5, Chung-hsiao E Road, Taipei
Director General of Transport: Robert S F Tang
Staff: 8,065

Current situation: Nine private companies participating in the United Operating System (see above): Hsin Hsin, Kuan Hua, Tayo, Ta Nan, Chi Nan, Taipei, Chung Shin, San Chung and Shoudu bus companies.

Fares and concessions are standardised between the independent operators and TCBA working within the UOS area, including prepurchase zone tickets and concessionary multijourney tickets. Most of the private operators run services from outside the city and in the outer suburbs as well as within the designated UOS area.

Another 10 long-distance bus operators carry some passengers within the Taipei metropolitan area.
Developments: Plans for ordering a new fleet of 636 buses in 1994 were abandoned after the city government refused to raise fares to the level requested by the operators.

Passenger journeys: (1990) 768 million
(1992) 768 million
Vehicle-km: (1990) 176 million
(1992) 183 million

Number of routes: 176
Route length: 3,852 km

Fleet: Total 3,422 (UOS commitment), including Isuzu, Hino, Mercedes, Mitsubishi, Renault, International, and Volvo. Fleets by operator are as follows (UOS only): Hsin Hsin (355), Kuan Hua (220), Tayo (375), Ta Nan (230), Chi Nan (84), Taipei (267), Chung Shin (205), San Chung (174), Shoudu (156).
In peak service: 2,080

One-person operation: All routes
Fare collection: Cash

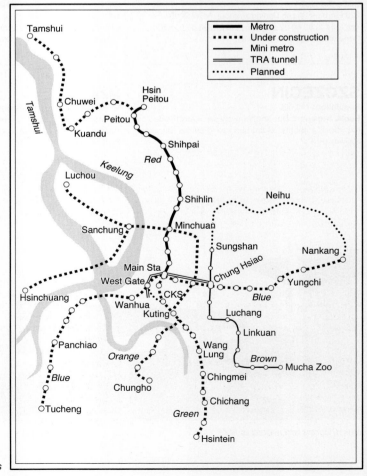
Taipei's metro routes

TEHRAN

Population: 10 million
Public transport: Bus and trolleybus services provided by government authority, which also supervises private minibus operations. Metro and suburban railway under construction

UBCT

United Bus Company of Tehran
Narmak Avenue, Tehran, Iran
Tel: (+98 21) 744 59 00/75 97   Fax: (+98 21) 70 13 26
Managing Director: M A Taraffo
Staff: 11,731

Current situation: As well as operating the extensive bus network and the new trolleybus route, UBCT supervises the declining minibus service.
Developments: As part of a nationwide environmental movement, UBCT has started conversion from diesel to LPG- and CNG-powered engines, with 250 buses re-equipped initially. UBCT is buying a further 300 buses, which are being built in Iran.

Bus

Passenger journeys: (1994) 939 million
(1995) 910 million
(1997/98) 819 million
Vehicle-km: (1994) 154 million
(1995) 155 million
(1997/98) 141 million

Number of routes: 207
Route length: 1,774 km

Fleet: 4,505 buses	
Mercedes O302	2,187
Mercedes O305	579
Mercedes O355	660
Mercedes O305G articulated	14
Mercedes O400	1
Leyland Atlantean double-deck	187
Ikarus 260	181
Ikarus 280 articulated	461
MAN standard	3
MAN articulated	1
Volvo B10M	230
Renault 350	1

In peak service: 2,700 vehicles
Average age of fleet: 12.8 years

One-person operation: all routes
Fare collection: Prepurchase at ticket booths
Fare structure: Flat, (in some cases cash fares are paid)
Operational control: Route inspectors
Bus priority: Bus lanes extend to 66 km
Operating costs financed by: Fares 34 per cent, subsidy/grants 66 per cent

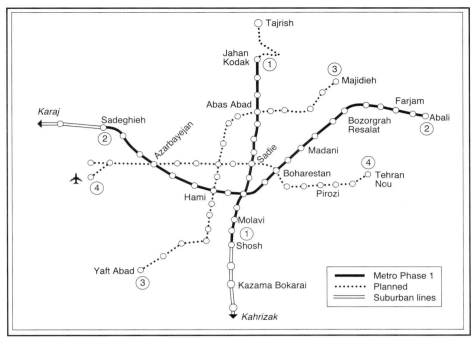

Tehran metro and regional metro

Subsidy from: National government and municipality of Tehran

Trolleybus
Current situation: A 7 km trolleybus route opened in the west of the city in 1992 following an agreement under which Skoda installed the infrastructure and supplied vehicles. A fleet of 25 articulated bi-mode trolleybuses was delivered for the start of service, with a further 40 supplied later. Trolleybuses carry about 75,000 passengers daily.
The network is currently made up of three routes with a total length of 14.1 km.

Passenger journeys: (1997/98) 22.7 million
Vehicle-km: (1997/98) 1.7 million

Fleet: 90 trolleybuses	
Mercedes O302	10
Volvo B10M	15
Skoda (articulated)	65

Minibus
Current situation: Private operators run minibus services on 114 routes. There has been, in recent years, a noticeable increase in the number of minibus operations due to the growth in public demand which, in turn, is the

consequence of rapid population growth in the suburbs of Tehran. The minibuses are privately owned and operate under special contract between each individual owner and UBCT.
In addition to minibuses, there are 571 buses operating under similar conditions on 113 routes carrying around 2 million passsengers annually.

Fleet: 4,343	
Fiat	2,538
Mercedes	1,242
Iveco	553
Other	10

Metro/Regional metro
Under construction
Tehran Urban & Suburban Railway Company
PO Box 4661, 37 Miramad Avenue, Tehran 15875
Tel: (+98 21) 874 01 11/01 12
Fax: (+98 21) 874 01 14/01 15
Managing Director: M Hashemi

Current situation: Construction in progress of Lines 1 and 2 of four-line metro, 1,435 mm gauge, electrified 750 V DC third rail. Lines 1 and 2 extend to 55 km with 45 stations, the initial phase of which is scheduled to open in 2000.
Line 1 connects the north of Tehran with the southern part of the city, while Line 2 connects the east and west areas. The metro is expected to carry some 30 per cent of all daily journeys in Tehran and the suburbs.
Also under construction is a 42 km regional metro link with nine stations running west from the Line 2 terminal at Ayatollah Kashani to the satellite cities of Karaj and Mehrshahr.
Developments: Financial assistance agreed with Australia in 1993 funded further progress on the regional metro, whilst a contract for supply of the urban metro rolling stock (217 cars in seven-car sets) was awarded to Changchun Car for delivery starting in 1997.
Fitting-out of the metro is in progress, with fixed installations also being supplied by Chinese contractors, though Line 1 is being signalled by Alcatel SEL. A Chinese consortium headed by China North Industries is building the regional metro.

Mercedes O305 on park-and-ride service   *1996*   *UPDATED*

TEL AVIV - JAFFA (YAFO)

Population: 350,000, conurbation 2 million
Public transport: Bus services provided by two co-operative groups. Suburban rail services; light rail proposed

A national outline plan has been approved for the construction of an urban mass transit network in the Dan area. The plan includes an integrated system of

underground and surface alignments and covers the territory between Netanya and Ashdod.

DAN

DAN-Cooperative Society for Public Transport Ltd
39 Shaul Hamelech Blvd, PO Box 33038, Tel Aviv, Israel
Tel: (+972 3) 693 32 16   Fax: (+972 3) 693 35 11

Chair: Drori Yeshayhu
Executive Traffic Director: Barkochva Yimini
Staff: 3,500

Current situation: The DAN bus co-operative is the largest provider of bus services in Tel Aviv and its metropolitan area. Its operating territory covers the most densely populated areas, comprising the Tel Aviv metropolitan area and seven surrounding cities, with a population of 2 million, of which DAN services reach some 617,000.

Bus
Passenger journeys: (1997) 195 million

Number of routes: 112
Bus priority: 43 km bus lanes
Route length: (One way) 2,820 km

Fleet: 1,340 vehicles
MAN SL200   973
MAN articulated   244
Coaches   96
Minibuses   27
In peak service: 1,138
New vehicles required each year: 95
On order: 15 minibuses and 80 standard MAN buses per year

Most intensive service: 5 min
One-person operation: 100 per cent
Fare collection: Payment to driver
Fare structure: Zonal
Average peak-hour speed: 17.0 km/h
Operating costs financed by: Fares 72 per cent, government subsidy/grants 28 per cent

EGGED

EGGED-Israel Transport Cooperative Society Ltd
Bet 'EGGED' Derech Petach-Tiqwa 142, Tel Aviv 64921
PO Box 33091, Tel Aviv 61330
Tel: (+972 3) 43 22 11   Fax: (+972 3) 696 53 54
Chair: Shlomo Levin
Staff: 8,400 (national total)

Current situation: EGGED's Northern Region provides part of the Tel Aviv area bus services. It also runs services in most other parts of Israel, including city areas, and at regional and interurban level. The co-operative has about 5,800 members and some 3,200 additional hired staff. The total passenger carryings are about 1.5 million daily, with a 4,000 vehicle fleet operating more than 1,200 routes. The figures for Tel Aviv are approximations and reflect some regional as well as city services.

Bus
Passenger journeys: Approx 100 million (annual)
Vehicle-km: Approx 40 million (annual)

Number of routes: 25
Fleet: 400 buses, including Leyland and Mercedes

Most intensive service: 5-10 min
One-person operation: All routes
Fare collection: Tickets sold by driver from rack or prepurchased with cancellation by driver. Manual machines
Fare structure: Zonal
Fare evasion control: Inspectors
Average peak-hour speed: 17.2 km/h
Bus priority: 15.4 km of bus lanes in 7 sections in central area

TAMAR

Tel Aviv-Yafo Metropolitan Area Rapid Transit

Current situation: Formed in 1995, this organisation is responsible for developing plans for a rapid transit system for the region.

Following a consultant's report which recommended construction of a 50 km four-line light rail network as the basis for the city's public transport in the 21st century, the municipal authorities commissioned feasibility studies in 1995 from Parsons Brinckerhoff and Sofrétu in joint venture. TAMAR sought bids at the end of 1995 for a 30-year concession to design and build a 20 km light metro system at a cost of US$1 billion.

The two lines would comprise a loop linking IR's Central station with the city centre, university and coastal strip, with branches northeast to the Petah Tiqwa housing development, south to Bat Yam and Rishon le Zion, and to the central bus station. Some tunnelling would be required beneath city-centre streets. Trial bores for the tunnel sections were started in August 1996 and opening is planned for 2000.

Light rail is still envisaged as the mode for routes to Kiryat Ono and Tel-Hashomer.

Railway 2000

Israel Railways
PO Box 18085, Tel Aviv 61180
Director: Yitzahak Ben-Dov

Current situation: Cross-city service was inaugurated by Israel Railways in 1993 with completion of a 4.5 km double-track connection between IR's South and Central stations. Diesel-hauled suburban trains link Herzliyya in the north with Lod in the south. Two new stations on the cross-city line opened in late 1995.
Developments: Under IR's Railway 2000 plans, two new suburban lines are to be built, to Kfar-Sava and Ben Gurion international airport, the latter as the first stage of a new high-speed alignment between Tel Aviv and Jerusalem. The projects involve upgrading some 28 km of existing freight-only lines and 22 km new construction; electrification is planned. Initially, services will be provided by a fleet of four-car double-deck push-pull trains, the power car being designed for later conversion to electric traction.

In 1996, Railway 2000 was launched as a subsidiary of IR to carry the project forward. Funding has been approved for reconstruction of the first 4 km to Bene Berak of the route to Kfar-Sava, along with some double-tracking.

UPDATED

TIANJIN

Population: 5.4 million, municipal area 8 million
Public transport: Bus services operated by municipal company and metro run by separate agency in limited operation; trolleybus network closed; metro of long-term future significance only

Tianjin City Transport

Tianjin City Transport Corporation
Tianjin, People's Republic of China

Bus
Number of routes: 59

Fleet: 1,400 buses, most locally built at Tianjin factory

Fare collection: Fixed conductor
Fare structure: Flat

Tianjin Metro

Tianjin Metro Administration
97 Jie-Fang-Bei Road, He-ping, 300041 Tianjin
Tel: (+86 22) 23 99 45 42   Fax: (+86 22) 23 39 61 94
General Manager: Wang Yu-ji

Type of operation: Full metro, initial route opened 1980

Passenger journeys: (1993) 15 million

Route length: 7.4 km
Number of lines: 1
Number of stations: 8
Gauge: 1,435 mm
Track: 50 kg/m rail laid on concrete sleepers
Max gradient: 3%
Minimum curve radius: 300 m
Tunnel: Cut-and-cover
Electrification: 750 V DC, third rail

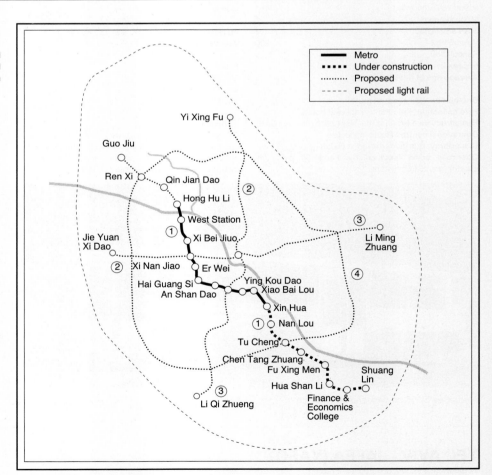

Tianjin metro

Service frequency: 12 min peak, 15–20 min off-peak
First/last train: 05.30/22.30
Fare structure: Flat
Fare collection: Manual sale from booking offices
Integration with other modes: Because of limited rolling stock, passengers are not yet encouraged to use the metro instead of other public transport
Signalling: Automatic block

Rolling stock: 24 cars, former Beijing prototypes
Changchun BJ-111 M24
On order: A fleet of cars similar to those running in Beijing is being built

Current situation: An 11.1 km southern extension from Xinhualu to Shuang Lin is being started, with completion estimated for 2002.

Seven lines are planned, with a total length of 154 km.

UPDATED

TIJUANA

Population: 1.5 million
Public transport: Extensive bus services provided by private operators; light rail planned

Bus
Main operators:
Auto Transportes Baja California Azul y Blanco J Magellanes

Linea Transportes Urbanos y Sub Urbanos de Baja California
Transportes Passajeros Urbanos y Sub Urbanos

Current situation: This fast-growing city across the Mexican border from San Diego is served exclusively by private operators. Because of the duty-free status of the area, equipment is usually US-built and ranges from second-hand transit buses to vans and schoolbus-derived types.

Mexicoach inaugurated an upmarket service from the US border at San Ysidro to downtown Tijuana in 1989, provoking violent protests from taxi drivers. In 1990 a further cross-border service was introduced jointly by Mexicoach and MTDB of San Diego, linking the light rail station at San Ysidro with central Tijuana.

Light rail (planned)
Current situation: The city authorities have considered light rail plans following studies made by Siemens for a route to the US border at San Ysidro, terminus of San Diego's light rail network.

VERIFIED

Ex-US GMC of Auto Transportes Baja California Azul y Blanco J Magellanes crosses Revolution Avenue on its return to the city centre (Andrew Jarosz)
1999/0043907

TIMIŞOARA

Population: 500,000
Public transport: Bus, trolleybus, tramway and some taxi services operated by municipal undertaking

RATT

Regie Autonomă de Transport Timişoara
Bdul Take Ionescu 56,1900 Timişoara, Romania
Tel: (+40 56) 13 32 15   Fax: (+40 56) 13 33 54
General Manager: Nicolae Marcu
Staff: 2,134

Passenger journeys: (All modes)
(1991) 160 million
(1992) 199 million
(1996) 91.9 million

Operating costs financed by: Fares 48.9 per cent, other commercial sources 6 per cent, subsidy/grants 45.1 per cent

Current situation: RATT's area of operation has been reduced by splitting off outer-suburban and regional bus services to a separate company, with a loss of about 30 buses from the fleet. RATT also operates taxis, a fleet of small vans for local goods delivery, and a vessel carrying tourists on the River Bega.

Major works have continued to repair worn out and damaged tram tracks, with reconstruction in progress on four busy streets in 1997/98. Trolleybus routes 15 and 16 are being extended to Lidia Str. Proximity to the Banat (Timiş) tramcar works has ensured good maintenance of the tram fleet, and both tram and trolleybus networks are in better condition than in most other Romanian cities.

Bus and trolleybus
Passenger journeys: (1991) Bus 19.2 million, trolleybus 35.3 million
(1992) Bus 31 million, trolleybus 36.7 million
(1996) Bus 14.1 million, trolleybus 25.5 million
Vehicle-km: (1991) Bus 2.8 million, trolleybus 2.3 million
(1992) Bus 2.4 million, trolleybus 2.2 million
(1996) Bus 2.3 million, trolleybus 2.7 million

Tram and trolleybus meet at Str Brediceanu

1996

Number of routes: Bus 18, trolleybus 7
Route length: Bus 182 km, trolleybus 59.6 km

Fleet: 83 buses, mostly DAC and including 19 articulated, plus Van Hool/Fiat ex-Brussels
In peak service: 50

Fleet: 81 trolleybuses
Gräf & Stift 3
Ikarus 280T ex-Eberswalde 9
DAC 117E/217E articulated
Rocar 317E articulated About 10
In peak service: 49

Most intensive service: 10 min
Fare collection: Prepurchase, with validation/cancellation on board; some drivers sell tickets
Fare structure: Flat

Tramway
Passenger journeys: (1991) 105.4 million
(1992) 131.4 million
(1996) 52.3 million

Car-km: (1991) 8.5 million
(1992) 9.4 million
(1996) 4.5 million

Number of routes: 10
Route length: 139.5 km
Gauge: 1,435 mm

Rolling stock: 123 cars
Timiş
Timiş trailers
Hansa ex-Bremen (1963) M20
In peak service: 59

CFR
Caile Ferate Romane

Current situation: The passenger company CFR-Calafori of state railway CFR operates suburban service over several routes.

UPDATED

TIRANA

Population: 250,000
Public transport: Until 1991, bus services provided by state-owned authority had a virtual monopoly of motorised passenger transport as there were no private cars and few other passenger-carrying vehicles such as taxis in Albania. Changed political circumstances have led to a rapid influx of privately owned vehicles, though most journeys are still made by cycle or on foot

Drejtoria Transport Tiranë

Ministry of Communications
Rruge Myslym Shyri 41, Tirana, Albania

Bus
Passenger journeys: Approx 30 million (annual)

Number of routes: 20
Route length: 175 km

Fleet: About 100 Saviem SC10, Mercedes-Benz O305

(some articulated) and MAN SG192 (articulated). Also Škoda buses rebodied by Shkodër (many articulated). A further 50 ex-Paris buses delivered 1991

Fare structure: Flat within city, outside distance-related; monthly passes
Fare collection: Tickets prepurchased from kiosks, cancelled on vehicle

Current situation: Since 1987 Albania has imported a large number of second-hand city buses from France and Germany, which has enabled introduction of modern services with one-person operation and prepurchased tickets cancelled on board by machine. The French buses, all Saviem SC10s, are said to number 73 and previously ran in Lyon, Paris, Strasbourg, Nice and Clermont Ferrand. These generally work very frequent radial services from on-street terminals east and west of the central Skanderbeg Square, and east-west cross-city services.

Standard and articulated Mercedes-Benz O305s from Lübeck and Pinneberg, and more recently articulated

MAN SG192s from Mainz, Osnabrück and Bremerhaven, have also been acquired. The articulated buses work similar routes to the SC10s, while the rigid O305s work a north-south route whose northern terminus is Tirana railway station at a 5 min daytime service interval. A few Dutch-bodied O305s from Dordrecht are also used on the latter service.

All second-hand buses are still in the liveries of their former operators, though advertisements and insignia have been removed. These buses are generally about 15 years old. Other services are still worked by articulated buses which have Albanian Shkodër bodywork on what are thought to be old Škoda chassis, but trailers appear to be no longer in use. Most rigid buses in Tirana, apart from the Saviem and Mercedes-Benz, are believed to operate suburban and long-distance routes.

VERIFIED

TOKYO

Population: City (23 wards) 8 million, metropolitan area 11.8 million, conurbation 30 million (including Chiba, Kawasaki and Yokohama)
Public transport: Bus, tramway and metro services provided by municipal authority, with second metro system operated by rapid transit authority. Extensive suburban rail services operated by several private railways and JR, with through running to metro system from many lines; monorail and two automated guideway systems. Additional bus services by 12 independent operators licensed by Transport Ministry. Majority of travel is by rail modes with approx 80 per cent share of total passenger trips in the conurbation; suburban systems of JR and private railways account for about 32 per cent each, with the remainder by the metros.

Further major rail investment is planned under proposals put forward in 1985 by the Council for Transport Policy, affecting the metro, JR and private railways. Under the plans, some 530 km of route would be constructed within 50 km of central Tokyo to serve expanding suburban areas and to disperse traffic and development from the congested central area to existing subcentres at Shibuya, Shinjuku and Ikebukuro and new ones at Ueno-Asakusa, Kinshicho-Kameido and Ohsaki

Hino HIMR diesel-electric hybrid of Toei at Shinjuku (Andrew Phipps)   **1998**/0010030

Tokyo-to Kotsu Kyoku 'Toei'

Transportation Bureau of Tokyo Metropolitan Government
2-8-1, Nishi-Shinjuku, Shinjuku-ku, Tokyo 163-8001, Japan
Tel: (+81 3) 53 20 60 06   Fax: (+81 3) 53 88 16 50
General Manager: K Yokomizo
Staff: 8,287

Passenger journeys: (All modes)
(1995/96) 895 million
(1996/97) 872 million
(1997/98) 875 million

Current situation: Toei operates four of Tokyo's 12 metro lines, 117 bus routes, a tram route and a 0.3 km monorail (in Ueno Park).

Bus
Director, Bus Department: K Ito
Staff: 4,093

Passenger journeys: (1994/95) 318 million
(1995/96) 308 million
(1996/97) 293 million
Vehicle-km: (1994/95) 66 million
(1995/96) 65.7 million
(1996/97) 63 million

Number of routes: 117
Route length: 970 km (unduplicated 768 km)
On priority right-of-way: 219 km

Fleet: 1,829 vehicles, all air conditioned

Isuzu	617
Hino	516
Nissan	306
Mitsubishi-Fuso	390

Additional 80 lift-equipped school buses used to transport disabled children
In peak service: 1,706
New vehicles required each year: 100

Most intensive service: 2 min
One-person operation: All routes
Fare collection: Farebox at entrance or prepurchase
Fare structure: Flat; 1 and 3 month commuter passes, coupon tickets, Bus Mutual Card and day tickets (Toei metro/Toei bus/tram and Toei metro/bus/tram/JR/Eidan); Bus Mutual Card valid on Toei and private operators' buses within Tokyo and adjoining Kanagawa and Saitama prefectures

Fares collected on board: Flat, including day tickets 39 per cent, coupon tickets 7 per cent, Bus Mutual Card 17 per cent, commuter passes 37 per cent
Operational control: Bus location system in use on 64 routes
Arrangements for elderly/disabled: Fares concession compensated for by city; fleet includes wheelchair-accessible vehicles
Average distance between stops: 395 m
Average peak-hour speed: 11.3 km/h
Operating costs financed by: Fares 86 per cent, other commercial sources 10 per cent (including interest income and dividends received), subsidy/grants 4 per cent

Keio (left) and Toei Shinjuku line trains at Sasazuka (Andrew Phipps)   **1998**/0010031

Subsidy from: Metropolitan government (central government contributes only to metro)
New vehicles financed by: Business bonds

Current situation: Within Tokyo's 23 urban wards buses account for a mere 6.5 per cent of the total number of public transport journeys of which Toei carries 45 per cent, with the remainder split between nine private operators — Keihin Kyuko, Keio, Keisei, Odakyu, Seibu, Tobu, Tokyu, Kanto Bus and Kokusai Kogyo. Toei has a virtual monopoly in the central and inner areas while the majority of services in the outer wards are operated by the private companies with a few routes operated jointly with Toei.

Services in the outer metropolitan area are operated by the private railways and three other companies — Kanagawa Chuo Kotsu, Nishi Tokyo Bus and Tachikawa Bus.

Developments: New Urban Bus System concept adopted on eight routes, involving bus priority measures, computerised operational control and real-time travel information displays at bus stops.

Low-floor buses have been introduced on 24 routes and lift-equipped buses on 20 routes; kneeling 'non-step' buses introduced 1997. Buses using LPG-blend and CNG fuel, diesel-electric hybrids, and dust-particle-free buses are being tried out to assess their ability to reduce pollution.

Tram replica buses operate a distributor route serving Ginza shopping district in central Tokyo, and double-deck tourist routes run in the Asakusa and Edogawa areas.

Metro

Chief Engineer: R Sasano
Staff: 3,764

Type of operation: Full metro, initial line opened 1960

Passenger journeys: (1995/96) 564.2 million
(1996/97) 556 million
(1997/98) 557 million
Car-km: (1995/96) 67.2 million
(1996/97) 67 million
(1997/98) 70 million

Route length: 77.2 km
in tunnel: 69.6 km
Number of lines: 4
Number of stations: 77
in tunnel: 69
Gauge: Mita line 1,067 mm, Shinjuku line 1,372 mm, Asakusa line and Line 12 1,435 mm
Track: 50 kg/m N-rail; conventional sleepers on ballast, sleepers on concrete and slab track
Max gradient: 3.5%
Minimum curve radius: 161 m
Tunnel: Cut-and-cover, shield driven and concrete caisson
Electrification: 1.5 kV DC, overhead

Service: Peak 2½-4 min, off-peak 5-8 min; some trains run through to other railways

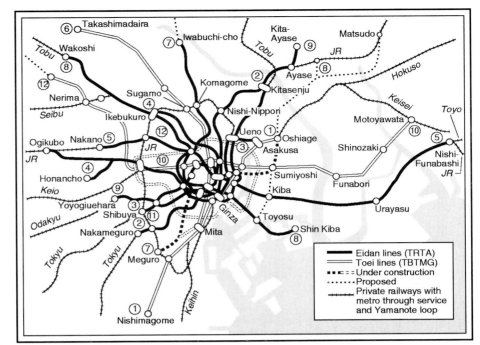

Tokyo's complex urban rail system   0045371

First/last train: 05.00/00.30
Fare structure: Graduated, multiticket books, 1, 3 and 6 month commuter passes, day tickets (Toei metro/bus/tram and Toei metro/bus/tram/JR/Eidan), discount on single and season tickets for combined Toei/Eidan and Toei/private railway travel; stored-fare card Toei/Eidan
Arrangements for elderly/disabled: All Line 12 stations wheelchair accessible
Operating costs financed by: Fares 82.9 per cent, other commercial sources 6.4 per cent, subsidy/grants 10.7 per cent
Subsidy from: National government 10 per cent, metropolitan government 90.3 per cent
Signalling: Automatic block with three-aspect colourlight signalling and ATS, cab signalling and ATC
Surveillance: CCTV on platforms

Rolling stock: 736 cars, all air conditioned

5200, Asakusa Line 1 (1976)	M8
5300, Asakusa Line 1 (1990/95/98)	M108 T108
6000, Mita Line 6 (1968/76)	M96
6300, Mita Line 6 (1993/94)	M39 T39
10-000, Shinjuku Line 10 (1978/91/97)	M168 T56
12-000, Line 12 (1991/94/97)	M120

Current situation: Through services operate between the Asakusa Line 1 and the Keisei, Hokuso and Keihin Kyuko systems, and between the Shinjuku line and the Keio Railway.

The first 4.8 km section of small-profile Line 12 between Nerima and Hikarigaoka opened 1991, and a further 9.1 km between Nerima and Shinjuku opened in 1997 to complete the radial section between the northwestern suburbs and central Tokyo. The remainder of the line is under construction and will extend from Shinjuku via a 29 km loop around central Tokyo back to Shinjuku. On completion in 2000, the line will provide interchange with JR and private railways at 22 of its 38 stations.

Developments: The Council for Transport Policy's proposals include extension of the Shinjuku Line 10 from Motoyawata to Shin-Kamagaya on the Hokuso Railway. A 1.6 km extension of the Mita Line 6 from Mita to connect with Eidan's new Line 7, allowing through running to Meguro and on to Tokyu tracks, is under construction for 1999 opening.

A 4 km westward extension of Line 12 to Oizumi-Gakuen, and a 9.7 km new transit system line to serve Adachi ward (north Tokyo), are at the planning stage.

Tramway

Staff: 155

Type of operation: Conventional tramway

Passenger journeys: (1995/96) 22.6 million
(1996/97) 22.5 million
(1997/98) 22.4 million
Car-km: (Annual) 1.8 million

Route length: 12.2 km
Number of lines: 1
Number of stops: 29
Gauge: 1,372 mm
Track: 50 kg/m PS rail; conventional sleepers on ballast, and sleepers on concrete with resilient pads
Electrification: 600 V DC, overhead

Service: Peak 2½ min, off-peak 5 min
First/last car: 05.30/23.30
Fare structure: Flat; multiticket books, 1-, 3- and 6-month passes, day tickets (Toei metro/bus/tram and Toei metro/bus/tram/JR/Eidan)
Fare collection: Farebox or prepurchase
Operating costs financed by: Fares 64.5 per cent, other commercial sources 3.1 per cent, subsidy/grants from metropolitan government 29.9 per cent

Rolling stock: 42 cars

Nippon Sharyo 6000 (1949)	M1
Alna Koki 7000 (1955/56 cars rebodied 1977)	M23
Alna Koki 7500 (1962 cars rebodied)	M13
Alna Koki 8500 (1990/93)	M5
In peak service: 37 cars	

Current situation: Toei's remaining tram line provides an orbital link through Tokyo's northwest suburbs from Minowabashi to Waseda. The line is mostly on reserved track with high platforms.

Toei tramcars at Machiya Eki-mae (Colin Brown)   *1999*/0043902

TRTA 'Eidan'

Teito Rapid Transit Authority
Teito Kosokudo Kotsu Eidan
3-19-6, Higashi Ueno 3-chome, Taito-ku, Tokyo 110-0015
Tel: (+81 3) 38 37 70 46   Fax: (+81 3) 38 37 70 48
President: K Terashima
Staff: 10,397

Type of operation: Full metro, initial line opened 1927

Passenger journeys: (1995) 2,090 million
(1996) 2,095 million
(1997) 2,082 million
Car-km: (1995) 230 million
(1996) 236 million
(1997) 236 million

Route length: 171.5 km
   in tunnel: 145 km
   elevated: 26.5 km
Number of lines: 8
Number of stations: 158
Gauge: 1,435 mm (Ginza and Marunouchi lines), others 1,067 mm
Track: 50 and 60 kg/m rail; in tunnel, solid bed; at surface level, sleepers on ballast
Tunnel: Shield driven and cut-and-cover
Electrification: 600 V DC, third rail (Ginza and Marunouchi lines); others 1.5 kV DC, overhead

Service: Peak 1 min 50 s, off-peak 3-8 min; some trains on 5 lines run through to other private railways or JR lines
First/last train: 05.00/00.30
Fare structure: Graduated (kilometric-sectional); multitickets (Eidan/Toei metro, Eidan/JR East, Eidan/ private rail), passes, day tickets (Eidan only and Eidan/ JR/Toei metro/bus/tram); stored-fare SF Metrocard (Eidan/Toei metro)
Revenue control: AFC at all stations
Operating costs financed by: Fares 85.8 per cent, other commercial sources 11 per cent
One-person operation: Nambuku line only
Signalling: Wayside signals on 3 lines, cab signalling on 5
Surveillance: CCTV on curved platforms

Rolling stock: 2,419 cars

01 Ginza Line 3 (1983 on)	M114 T114
02 Marunouchi Line 4 (1988 on)	M171 T165
03 Hibiya Line 2 (1988 on)	M168 T168
05 Tozai Line 5 (1988 on)	M104 T136
06 Chiyoda Line 9 (1993)	M4 T6
07 Yurakucho Line 8 (1993)	M24 T36
5000 Tozai (5) & Chiyoda (9) lines (1964 on)	M188 T48
6000 Chiyoda Line 9 (1971 on)	M194 T159
7000 Yurakucho Line 8 (1974 on)	M204 T136
8000 Hanzomon Line 11 (1980 on)	M114 T76
9000 Nambuku Line 7 (1991 on)	M60 T30

In peak service: 2,197

Current situation: Eidan lines account for 80 per cent of metro journeys. The Hibiya (2), Tozai (5), Chiyoda (9), Yurakucho (8) and Hanzomon (11) lines run through to JR and/or private railways.

Initial 6.3 km section of the Nambuku line (7) opened 1991 from Akabane-Iwabuchi to Komagome, with one-person operation and platform screen doors. It was extended 7.1 km to Yotsuya in 1996, and a further 2.2 km to Tameike-Sanno in 1997. The final 5.3 km from Tameike-Sanno to Meguro is under construction for opening in 2000. At its southern end the line will have through running to Tokyu's Mekama line; at its northern end the third-sector Saitama Rapid Railway is constructing a 14.6 km extension from Akabane-Iwabuchi to Urawa-Daimon with seven stations for opening by 2000.

In 1996, Toyo Rapid Railway completed a 16.2 km line which extends from the eastern end of the Tozai line (5) at Nishi-Funabashi to Keisei's Katsutadai station. A reciprocal through service is operated between the Tozai and Toyo lines. Toyo rolling stock comprises 10 ex-Eidan Series 5000 trains.
Developments: The Council for Transport Policy's proposals include extensions to the Yurakucho (8) and Hanzomon (11) lines, totalling 26.4 km. A branch of the Yurakucho line would extend from Toyosu northwards to reach JR's Joban line at Kameari. Also the Hanzomon line would be projected east to Sumiyoshi then north, partly sharing the Yurakucho line extension, diverging to reach Matsudo. Line 13 is planned to run on new track from Shibuya to Kotake-Mukaihara, then take over the existing section of the Yurakucho line to Wakoshi and run through

to Shiki on Tobu's Tojo line, a total of 25.5 km. The 3.2 km section between Ikebukuro and Kotake-Mukaihara opened in late 1994.

The first 5.9 km of the Hanzomon line extension from Suitengumae to Oshiage is under construction. This will provide interchange with Toei's Shinjuku line at Sumiyoshi, JR's Sobu line at Kinshicho and Tobu's Isesaki line at Oshiage, with opening due by 2000.

JR East

East Japan Railway Company
Higashi Nihon Ryokaku Tetsudo
2-2-2 Yoyogi, Shibuya-ku, Tokyo 151-8578
Tel: (+81 3) 53 34 11 51   Fax: (+81 3) 53 34 11 10
Chair: S Yamanouchi
President: M Matsuda
Staff: 79,100 (whole company)

Type of operation: Inner and outer suburban heavy rail

Passenger journeys: (Metropolitan area)
(1995) 5,076 million
(1996) 5,307 million
(1997) 5,451 million

Current situation: JR East's Tokyo metropolitan area network comprises 21 lines extending to 1,096 route-km, located within a radius of approximately 100 km from Tokyo station and including Chiba, Kawasaki and Yokohama. All are 1,067 mm gauge, almost all are electrified, most are equipped with ATC or ATS-P (automatic train stop-pattern), and all trains are air conditioned. Trains on some JR lines run through to metro destinations and on to private lines. The 16 high-frequency inner-suburban services known as 'E-den' are operated by a large standardised fleet of emus, colour-coded according to line of operation. Headway on the Chuo line (rapid service) is 2 min 10 sec and on the Yamanote and Keihin-Tohoku lines 2½ min. ATS of an improved type is being introduced throughout the Tokyo area to reduce headways further. Automatic fare collection gates have been installed at most metropolitan area stations, and a stored-fare card system introduced.

Rolling stock: 6,767 cars and locos (Tokyo area)

Electric locos	76
Diesel locos	30
Emu cars	6,392
Dmu cars	8
Coaches	261

Developments: Through its 'Tokyo New Network 21' project, JR East is investing to reduce the serious problems of overcrowding and lack of capacity on Tokyo commuter services. Additional tracks are proposed for the Chuo line between Mitaka and Tachikawa and freight lines are being upgraded for passenger use.

Longer trains are to be run at higher speeds and rolling stock capacity increased; Series 205 Yamanote line trains have one car with six doors per side and fold-away seats to increase peak capacity; Series 211 sets include double-deck cars, and 10-car Shonan Liner all double-deck emus operate commuter services on the Tokaido line.

Series 209 'disposable' commuter emus with a planned service life of 10 years, built at a cost of only 60 per cent of conventional units, have been introduced on the Keihin-Tohoku inner-suburban service, and short-life E217 outer-suburban trains, each including two double-deck cars, operate on the Yokosuka and Sobu lines. Double-deck Shinkansen trains have also been introduced to cater for increased long-distance commuting into Tokyo on the Joetsu and Tohoku lines.

Construction of the 58.3 km Joban new line between Akihabara in central Tokyo and Tsukuba in Ibaraki prefecture has started, with opening scheduled for 2005.

Keihin Kyuko Dentetsu 'Keikyu'

Keihin Express Electric Railway
20-20 Takanawa 2-chome, Minato-ku, Tokyo 108-0074
Tel: (+81 3) 32 80 91 22   Fax: (+81 3) 32 80 91 93
President: I Hiramatsu

Interurban rail

Staff: 2,634

Passenger journeys: (1991/92) 445 million
(1992/93) 439 million
(1993/94) 438 million
Car-km: (1992/93) 89 million
(1993/94) 91 million

Current situation: More of a Yokohama commuting line, but runs through trains to central Tokyo (Shinagawa) and over Asakusa metro line and on to Keisei Railway tracks; 83.6 km, 1,435 mm gauge, electrified 1.5 kV DC.
Developments: The Kuko branch was extended in 1993 to a new interchange with the Tokyo monorail at Haneda in connection with expansion of Haneda airport and a 3.2 km underground extension to the new airport terminal building opened in 1998. A through service operates to central Tokyo via the Toei Asakusa line metro and a limited number of trains continue via the Keisei Railway to Narita airport.

Rolling stock: 758 emu cars   M644 T114

Bus

Staff: 1,792

Passenger journeys: (1992/93) 120.5 million
(1993/94) 117 million
Vehicle-km: (1992/93) 35.9 million
(1993/94) 37.6 million

Current situation: Keihin Kyuko also owns a fleet of 773 buses and 112 coaches; 349 routes are operated in southern Tokyo, Kawasaki, Yokohama and Kanagawa prefecture. Bus services account for 16 per cent of the company's revenue.

Keio Teito Dentetsu

Keio Teito Electric Railway
9-1, Sekido 1-chome, Tama City, Tokyo 206
Tel: (+81 423) 37 31 41
President: K Kuwayama

JR East suburban trains at Veno station (Colin Brown)

Interurban rail
Staff: 2,472

Passenger journeys: (1991/92) 586 million
(1992/93) 587 million
(1993/94) 588 million
Car-km: (1992/93) 98 million
(1993/94) 102 million

Route length: 84.8 km
Number of lines: 7
Operating costs financed by: Fares 88.7 per cent, other commercial sources 11.3 per cent

Current situation: Operates the main Keio line out of an underground terminal below the Keio department store at Shinjuku, with four branches totalling 72 km, 1,372 mm gauge, electrified 1.5 kV DC.
The 3.6 km underground Keio new line links the main line with the Toei Shinjuku line metro, enabling trains to run through to central Tokyo (Iwamoto-cho). Also 12.8 km 1,067 mm gauge Inokashira line, electrified 1.5 kV DC, runs from a terminal at Shibuya to Kichijoji.
Developments: Larger cars with five doors have been introduced to increase capacity; platforms have been lengthened to handle 10-car trains (Keio line) or large five-car trains (Inokashira line); track elevation is in progress to eliminate level crossings.

Rolling stock: 848 emu cars   M515 T333
On order: 16 cars

Bus
Passenger journeys: (1993/94) 113 million
Vehicle-km: (1993/94) 34 million

Current situation: The Bus Division was reconstituted as a separate company called Keio Bus in April 1997. It operates 244 local bus routes extending to 4,032 km, carrying an average of 310,000 passengers a day. Fleet comprises 560 buses and 42 coaches, all air conditioned and including wheelchair-accessible vehicles.

Keisei Dentetsu
Keisei Electric Railway
10-3, Oshiage 1-chome, Sumida-ku, Tokyo 131-0045
Tel: (+81 3) 36 21 22 31

Interurban rail
Managing Director: H Hosokawa
Staff: 2,169

Passenger journeys: (1991/92) 276 million
(1992/93) 279 million
(1993/94) 281 million
Car-km: (1992/93) 76 million
(1993/94) 76 million

Current situation: Operates main line from Ueno station in Tokyo to Narita airport, and four branches totalling 102.4 km, 1,435 mm gauge, electrified 1.5 kV DC. Through running to Toei Asakusa metro line, the Hokuso Railway and the Keihin Kyuko Railway.

Keio Series 6000 train on Keio service to Hashimoto (Makato Ashizawa)   *1999*/0043901

Keio wheelchair-accessible bus in central Tokyo (Andrew Phipps)   *1998*/0010032

Developments: The 10.9 km Chiba Express Railway was taken over in 1998, becoming the Chihara Line.

Rolling stock: 502 emu cars   M440 T62

Bus
Managing Director: K Sato
Staff: 2,200

Passenger journeys: (Conurbation, including Chiba)
(1991/92) 138.8 million
(1992/93) 135.3 million
(1993/94) 136.5 million
Vehicle-km: (1992/93) 32.6 million

Current situation: Keisei's bus division runs 980 buses of which about 250 are operated on routes in Tokyo's northeastern wards and the rest in adjoining Chiba prefecture. The fleet comprises Isuzu, Hino and Mitsubishi types; 50 coaches are also operated. Bus services account for 30 per cent of revenue.

Hokuso Kaihatsu Tetsudo
Hokuso Development Railway
14-5, 2-chome, Narihira, Sumida-ku, Tokyo 130-0002
Tel: (+81 3) 36 26 33 10
President: K Sugiyama

Suburban rail
Passenger journeys: (1991/92) 16.5 million
(1992/93) 19.5 million
Car-km: (1992/93) 8.8 million

Current situation: This Keisei subsidiary operates a 19.8 km line, 1,435 mm gauge, electrified 1.5 kV DC, connecting with the Keisei Railway at Takasago and with the 4 km Housing & Urban Development Railway, which serves Chiba New Town, at Komoro. A through running service is operated between Chiba New Town-Chuo and central Tokyo via the HUD railway, the Hokuso and Keisei railways, and the Toei Asakusa metro line.
Developments: An 8.5 km eastward extension beyond Chiba New Town-Chuo is under construction to serve new residential development areas.

Rolling stock: 7 eight-car emus   M46 T10

Odakyu Dentetsu
Odakyu Electric Railway
8-3 Nishi-Shinjuku 1-chome, Shinjuku-ku, Tokyo 160-8309
Tel: (+81 3) 33 49 21 51   Fax: (+81 3) 33 46 18 99
President: M Kitanaka
Staff: 4,410

Odakyu Series 1000 train at Shinjuku terminus (Makato Ashizawa)   *1999*/0043900

Interurban rail

Passenger journeys: (1992/93) 711 million
(1993/94) 711 million
(1996/97) 704 million
Car-km: (1992/93) 137 million
(1993/94) 140 million
(1996/97) 144 million

Current situation: Operates main line from Tokyo Shinjuku to Odawara, with two branches, totalling 120.5 km, 1,067 mm gauge, electrified 1.5 kV DC. Some trains run through to Eidan's Chiyoda metro line and on to JR's Joban line, also onward from Odawara over mixed-gauge track on 1,435 mm gauge Hakone Tozan Railway to Hakone-Yumoto (6.1 km), and from Matsuda to Nomazu over JR's Gotemba line (50 km).
Developments: Elevated multiple double tracks were completed in 1997 between Kitami and Izumi-Tamagawa (2.4 km), allowing reduced journey times. Construction for 10-car express train operation on all lines was completed in August 1998. Installation of ATS and OTC (Odakyu Traffic Control) has also been completed on all lines.

Rolling stock: 1,042 emu cars   M664 T378
In peak service: 969

Odakyu Bus

Odakyu Bus
2-19-5 Senkawa-cho, Chofu-shi, Tokyo 182
Tel: (+81 3) 53 13 82 11
President: K Kinoshita

Passenger journeys: (Conurbation including Kawasaki and Yokohama)
(1991/92) 78.5 million
(1992/93) 77.7 million
(1993/94) 76.3 million
Vehicle-km: (1992/93) 17.8 million

Current situation: A fleet of 396 buses and 65 coaches is operated by Odakyu Electric Railway's associate company Odakyu Bus, about 275 of them used on services in the Tokyo metropolitan area.

Seibu Tetsudo

Seibu Railway
1-11-1 Kusunokidai, Tokorozawa-shi, Saitama 359-0037
Tel: (+81 429) 26 20 35   Fax: (+81 429) 26 22 37
President: Y Tsutsumi

Suburban rail
Staff: 4,089

Passenger journeys: (1991/92) 674 million
(1992/93) 672 million
(1993/94) 667 million
Car-km: (1992/93) 139 million
(1993/94) 146 million

Current situation: Operates two busy suburban routes west from Ikebukuro and Shinjuku, with branches, totalling 172 km, 1,067 mm gauge, electrified 1.5 kV DC. These are particularly busy lines, with Ikebukuro terminal handling some 700 trains daily.
Developments: Through running between the Ikebukuro line and the Eidan Yurakucho metro line started in 1998 following the acquisition of elevated quadruple tracks.To increase capacity and reduce overcrowding of peak trains from 200 to 150 per cent, Seibu plans to build an additional 13 km underground line beneath its existing Shinjuku line to speed up express trains running non-stop into Shinjuku terminal. Local trains would continue to serve stations on the existing line.

Rolling stock: 1,203 emu cars   M766 T437
All air conditioned

ICTS

Type of operation: Intermediate capacity transit system, rubber-tyred guideway

Passenger journeys: (1991/92) 4,200 daily

Current situation: The 2.8 km Yamaguchi line rubber-tyred guideway, opened 1985, links two Seibu outer termini, Kyojomae and Yuenchi, about 25 km to the west

of central Tokyo. Electrified at 750 V DC. Manual operation with driver on board.

Rolling stock: 12 cars in four-car sets
Niigata (1984/85)   M12

Bus

Passenger journeys: (Conurbation)
(1990/91) 130.8 million
(1991/92) 138.8 million
(1992/93) 135.4 million

Current situation: Seibu's associated bus company owns a fleet of 709 buses and 98 coaches, about 400 of which are employed on services in the Tokyo metropolitan area, including Nissan/Fuji buses. The fleet includes lift-equipped vehicles.

Tobu Tetsudo

Tobu Railway
1-2-2 Oshiage, Sumida-ku, Tokyo 131-0045
Tel: (+81 3) 36 21 51 44
President: T Uchida

Interurban rail
Staff: 7,158

Passenger journeys: (1993/94) 950 million
(1994/95) 945 million
(1996/97) 927 million
Car-km: (1992/93) 240 million
(1993/94) 244 million
(1994/95) 251 million

Current situation: Tokyo's largest interurban railway operates 13 lines totalling 464 km, 202 stations, 1,067 mm gauge, electrified 1.5 kV DC. Main lines link Asakusa and Ikebukuro with Nikko and Yorii. Some trains on the Isesaki and Tojo lines run through to central Tokyo over metro lines.
Developments: Through running services to the extended Hanzomon metro line (11) are to start in 2000; the first of 14 Series 30000 emus for this service was delivered in 1997.

Rolling stock: 1,886 emu cars   M1,057 T829

Bus

Staff: 3,031

Passenger journeys: (Conurbation)
(1990/91) 122.3 million
(1991/92) 125.9 million
(1992/93) 116.3 million

Current situation: Tobu Railway's bus operation has a fleet of 1,130 buses and 306 coaches, about 100 of which are used on Tokyo metropolitan area services. Recent deliveries include lift-equipped wheelchair-accessible vehicles. Bus services account for 13 per cent of revenue.

Tokyo Kyuko Dentetsu 'Tokyu'

Tokyo Express Electric Railway
Tokyu Corporation
5-6, Nanpeidai-cho, Shibuya-ku, Tokyo 150-0036
Tel: (+81 3) 34 77 61 81   Fax: (+81 3) 34 96 29 65
President: S Shimizu

Current situation: In addition to important Tokyo-based rail and bus operations, the Tokyu Group has interests in other railways, bus companies and rolling stock manufacture (Tokyu Car).

Interurban rail
Staff: 3,221

Passenger journeys: (Including tramway)
(1991/92) 974 million
(1992/93) 967 million
(1993/94) 961 million
Car-km: (Including tramway)
(1992/93) 107 million
(1993/94) 107 million

Current situation: Operates seven lines totalling 95.6 km, 1,067 mm gauge, electrified 1.5 kV DC. Principal route is from Shibuya (Tokyo) to Sakuragicho in Yokohama, with

through trains over Eidan's Hibiya metro line from central Tokyo. Also underground metro-style route out of Shibuya to Futako-Tamagawaen and Chuo-Rinkan, with through trains from the Hanzomon metro line. A new line paralleling Tokyu's main line is planned in recommendations put forward by the Council for Transport Policy. The Tokyu also serves Yokohama commuters.
Developments: A major quadruple-tracking project on the Toyoko line was completed in 1997. In addition, a 3.3 km portion of the Mekama line is to be replaced by a new tunnel section to facilitate through running with the extended Namboku and Mita metro lines.

Rolling stock: 1,036 emu cars   M735 T301

Tramway
Staff: 91

Passenger journeys: (1991) 20 million
(1993) 19 million
Car-km: (1991) 1 million
(1993) 1 million

Current situation: Tokyu also operates the 5 km reserved track Setagaya tramway, 1,372 mm gauge, electrified 600 V DC, which feeds Tokyu's Shin-Tamagawa line and Keio Railway's Keio line.

Rolling stock: 9 two-car sets

Tokyu Bus

Tokyu Bus Corporation
1-5-3 Ohashi, Meguro-ku, Tokyo 153-0044
Tel: (+81 3) 54 58 01 09   Fax: (+81 3) 54 58 20 21
President: T Momose

Bus

Staff: 2,225

Passenger journeys: (1990) 164 million
(1993) 160 million
(1994) 153 million
Vehicle-km: (1993) 39 million
(1994) 38 million

Current situation: Tokyu Bus Corp is an independent company in the Tokyu group. A fleet of 822 buses carries 419,000 passengers per day on 165 routes in southwest Tokyo, Kawasaki and Yokohama with a total route length of 2,028 km. About 500 vehicles are used on the routes operated in Tokyo. Services include five 'Tokyu Coach' demand-responsive routes, 'Midnight' routes which operate after last-train times, and upgraded urban routes featuring computerised bus location and passenger information systems. Fleet includes lift-equipped vehicles.
Developments: During 1997, 21 Mitsubishi KC-MP747M non-step buses were introduced on two routes serving Meguro station.

Tokyo Monorail

Tokyo Monorail
4-12, Hamamatsu-cho 2-chome, Minato-ku, Tokyo 105-0013
Tel: (+81 3) 34 34 31 71   Fax: (+81 3) 34 33 43 13
President: A Takeishi
Staff: 442

Type of operation: Monorail on the Alweg system, opened 1964

Passenger journeys: (1995) 62 million
(1996) 64.7 million
(1997) 65.2 million
Car-km: (1993/94) 14.2 million
(1995/96) 18.1 million
(1996/97) 18 million

Current situation: 16.9 km straddle-monorail links Hamamatsu-cho in Tokyo with Haneda airport, formerly the main airport but now only handling domestic flights. Electrified 750 V DC; 9 stations; service every 3.5-5 min.
Developments: A 6.1 km extension from Haneda-Seibijo to the new airport terminal at Haneda-Kuko opened in 1993, when the existing section from Haneda-Seibijo to Haneda was closed. An intermediate station provides

New Series 2000 train on the Tokyo monorail (Andrew Phipps)　　　**1998**/0010036

interchange with the Keihin Kyuko Kuko line. A further 0.9 km extension to the new east terminal building scheduled to open 2005.

Rolling stock: 19 six-car trains
Series 1000 (1989/94)	M96
Series 2000 (1997/98)	M12 T6

On order: 12 cars

Tama Urban Monorail
Type of operation: Straddle monorail

Current situation: This third-sector company is building a 16 km north-south monorail line (straddle type) with 19 stations to serve Tama New Town in Tokyo's western suburbs. Shareholders comprise the metropolitan government (25 per cent), local government (12.2 per cent) and other undertakings, including the Seibu, Keio and Odakyu railways (62.8 per cent).

The line will link Tama Center with Tachikawa and Kamikitadai, providing connections with several radial rail routes into central Tokyo. The first section, from Tachikawa to Kamikitadai (5.5 km, eight stations) opened in December 1998 with the remainder scheduled to open in 1999.

Tokyo Rinkai Shin Kotsu
Tokyo Waterfront New Transit
Tel: (+81 3) 35 29 77 77

Type of operation: Rubber-tyred guideway system 'Yurikamome' (Seagull)

Passenger journeys:
(1995) 27,000 daily
(1996) 65,000 daily
(1997) 75,000 daily

Current situation: This third-sector company, 67 per cent owned by the Tokyo metropolitan government, opened the Yurikamome automated elevated rubber-tyred transit system (11.9 km, 12 stations) in 1995. It links central Tokyo with Tokyo Teleport Town, a commercial development area being built on land reclaimed from Tokyo Bay. The line runs from Shimbashi on the JR Yamanote line to Ariake, crossing Tokyo Bay via the 918 m Rainbow Bridge which also carries a road.

Interchange with a branch of JR's Keiyo line is planned, and in the longer term the line may be extended beyond Ariake to Toyosu and Harumi. Service is provided by a fleet of six-car trains with full ATO. Some 100,000 passengers a day are expected to use the line on completion of Teleport Town in 2010.

Rolling stock: 13 six-car trains
Series 7000 (1995)	M78

Tokyo Rinkai Kosoku Tetsudo
Tokyo Waterfront Rapid Railway
Ariake Frontier Building B4, 3-1-25 Ariake, Tokyo-to 135
Tel: (+81 3) 55 64 23 61

Type of operation: Urban rail

Current situation: This third-sector company, owned by the Tokyo metropolitan government (85.6 per cent) and JR East (5 per cent), is constructing the 12.2 km mainly underground Rinkai Fukutoshin line to serve new development areas built on land reclaimed from Tokyo Bay. The first 4.9 km section from Shin-Kiba on JR East's Keiyo line to Tokyo Teleport Town (4 stations) opened in 1996. The remaining 7.3 km section from Tokyo Teleport Town to Osaki on the Yamanote line is due to open in 2000. Rolling stock currently comprises four four-car Series 70-000 sets based on JR East's Series 209 design.

Kanagawa Chuo Kotsu
Kanagawa Chuo Transport
6-18 Yaezaki-cho, Hiratsuka-shi, Kanagawa-ken 254-0811
Tel: (+81 463) 22 88 00
Staff: 3,250

Bus
Passenger journeys: (Conurbation, including Yokohama)
(1990/91) 257.9 million
(1991/92) 256.2 million
(1992/93) 253 million

Current situation: This Odakyu Group company operates a fleet of 1,784 buses in the region, providing services based on Machida City in Tokyo metropolitan area with about 150 buses. The company's main operating area is in adjoining Kanagawa prefecture including some routes in Yokohama. Also operates 31 coaches.

Kanto Bus
Kanto Bus Co Ltd
5-23-14 Higashi-Nakano, Nakano-ku, Tokyo 164-0003
Tel: (+81 3) 33 71 71 11

Bus
Passenger journeys: (1990/91) 72.4 million
(1991/92) 73.8 million
(1992/93) 73.5 million
Vehicle-km: (1992/93) 15.8 million

Current situation: Runs a fleet of 374 buses on Tokyo metropolitan area services, extending to 167 route-km. Also operates 48 coaches.

Kokusai Kogyo
Kokusai Kogyo
2-10-3 Yaesu, Chuo-ku, Tokyo 104-0028
Tel: (+81 3) 32 73 11 25　Fax: (+81 3) 32 73 10 15
Senior Vice President, Bus: Teruaki Goto
Staff: 1,800 (Bus division)

Bus
Passenger journeys: (1991/92) 113.5 million
(1992/93) 112.7 million
(1993/94) 111.9 million
Vehicle-km: (1990/91) 30.8 million
(1993/93) 31.7 million

Number of routes: 269
Route length: 2,491 km
Fleet: 779 buses
In peak service: 686

Current situation: Around 250 of the fleet are committed to Tokyo metropolitan area services. The operating area covers part of northwest Tokyo, with several routes terminating at Ikebukuro, and extends into outer suburban areas in adjoining Saitama prefecture. Fleet includes lift-equipped vehicles.

Nishi Tokyo Bus
Nishi Tokyo Bus
4-9-7 Miyojin-cho, Hachioji-shi, Tokyo 192-0046
Tel: (+81 426) 45 12 11

Bus
Passenger journeys: (1990/91) 32 million
(1991/92) 33.5 million
(1992/93) 33.3 million
Vehicle-km: (1992/93) 12.4 million

Current situation: Runs 271 buses on services based on Hachioji City in the Tokyo metropolitan area, total route length 316 km. Also operates coaches.

Tachikawa Bus
Tachikawa Bus
2-27-27 Takamatsu-cho, Tachikawa-shi, Tokyo 190-0011
Tel: (+81 425) 24 31 11

Bus
Passenger journeys: (1990/91) 28.7 million
(1991/92) 29.1 million
(1992/93) 28.2 million
Vehicle-km: (1992/93) 8.5 million

Current situation: This Odakyu Group company operates 197 buses on services at Tachikawa City in the Tokyo metropolitan area, total route length 186 km. Also operates coaches.

UPDATED

Kanto Bus service at Shinjuku (Andrew Phipps)　　　**1998**/0010035

TORONTO

Population: Conurbation 2.3 million
Public transport: Bus, metro, tramway and advanced light rail services provided by Transit Commission, responsible to the City of Toronto (formed in 1998 by the amalgamation of Metropolitan Toronto Council. Metropolitan and Greater Toronto) area bus and rail regional commuter services run by GO Transit

TTC

Toronto Transit Commission
1900 Yonge Street, Toronto M4S 1Z2, Canada
Tel: (+1 416) 393 40 00   Fax: (+1 416) 488 61 98
Chair: Paul Christie
Chief General Manager: David L Gunn
General Managers
  Operations: Gary Webster
  Engineering & Construction: Dennis Callan
  Executive & General Secretary: Vincent Rodo
  Corporate: Lynn Hilborn
Staff: 9,491

Passenger journeys: (1994) 388 million
(1995) 388 million
(1996) 372.4 million

Operating costs financed by: Fares 75 per cent, subsidy/grants 25 per cent
Subsidy from: City of Toronto Council and Province of Ontario

Current situation: Constituted in its present form in 1954, TTC serves the 630 km² City of Toronto area in co-ordination with a number of neighbouring systems including Markham Transit, Richmond Hill Transit, Vaughan Transit, Brampton Transit, Mississauga Transit, and the GO Transit commuter system (see below).
Developments: Construction is in progress at a cost of $875 million of the Sheppard Avenue East extension (6.4 km, five stations), forecast to add 30 million journeys annually. This is the only metro construction project following shelving of the Eglinton West line in 1995 (see previous editions for background).

Bus

Passenger journeys: (1994) 191 million
(1995) 192.5 million
(1996) 188 million
Vehicle-km: (1994) 100.4 million
(1995) 100.9 million
(1996) 93.6 million

Number of routes: 134
Route length: (One-way) 2,956 km

Fleet: 1,611 buses
GM/MCI New Look/Classic T6H-53707N (1975/83) 558
Flyer various models (1977/81/85/86) 552
OBI Orion II low-floor 139
OBI Orion V 40 ft 241
OBI Orion V CNG-powered 75
OBI Orion 60 ft 45
Overland Custom Coach Elf (Wheeltrans) 1
In peak service: 1,210
Average age of fleet: 9 years
On order: 100 low-floor CNG-powered buses from OBI

Most intensive service: 2-4 min
One-person operation: All routes
Fare collection: Pay-as-you-enter, exact fare or token to farebox; or prepurchase
Fare structure: Flat; free transfers; prepurchase multitickets and tokens; daily and monthly passes
Fare evasion control: Visual check by drivers, route supervisors and security staff
Integration with other modes: 226 timed connections at metro/ICTS stations during the morning peak; connections with GO Transit trains; numerous connections with other local transit authorities, without fare integration; 22 park-and-ride lots
Operational control: AVLC via computerised communications and information system, with control from seven divisions through onboard communications and data exchange system (TRUMP) fitted to all vehicles
Arrangements for elderly/disabled: 16 fixed routes accessible; Wheel-Trans door-to-door service uses 139 low-floor buses, plus 125 sedan/taxis and 25 wheelchair-accessible taxis operated by private contractors. Wheel-Trans staff handle reservations, despatching and

TTC GM bus at Kennedy Interchange (Andrew Jarosz) ***1999**/0043911*

scheduling; fares match regular TTC, except for a discounted adult cash fare. Four community bus routes link seniors' centres, shopping areas, medical and community facilities
New vehicles financed by: Subsidy: Province 75 per cent, City of Toronto 25 per cent

Metro

Type of operation: Full metro, first line opened 1954

Passenger journeys: (1994) 151.2 million
(1995) 148.4 million
(1996) 142.1 million
Car-km: (1994) 63.8 million
(1995) 62.8 million
(1996) 63.9 million

Route length: 56.4 km
Number of lines: 2
Number of stations: 61
Gauge: 1,495 mm
Track: 57.5 kg/m T-rail; open cut, conventional sleepers on ballast and concrete sleepers (on new sections) on ballast; bored tunnel, rail laid on concrete bed; and rail laid on double concrete sleepers on resilient rubber pads
Tunnel: Cut-and-cover sections, steel-reinforced poured concrete box structures; bored tunnels, shield driven precast concrete or cast-iron linings
Electrification: 600 V DC, third rail

Service: Peak 2½ min, off-peak 4-7 min
First/last train: 05.47/01.34
Fare structure: Flat with free transfers to surface system
Revenue control: Conventional and wheelchair-accessible turnstiles; token and monthly pass activate turnstiles; high-gate turnstiles at automatic entry areas
Integration with other modes: Free transfer with surface systems at 36 stations; free paper transfer at 29 stations
Arrangements for elderly/disabled: Programme under way to improve access at 23 stations (see below)

One-person operation: None
Signalling: Automatic block and interlocking signals and wayside signals
Centralised control: Centralised train despatch and control system; similar system installed on Scarborough ICTS line (see below)
Surveillance: Designated waiting areas at all stations consisting of well-lit location monitored by CCTV cameras and with voice intercom system

Rolling stock: 806 cars
MIW M1 (1962/63)	M36
Hawker Siddeley Canada H1 (1965/66)	M136
Hawker Siddeley Canada H2 (1971)	M76
Hawker Siddeley Canada H4 (1974/75)	M88
Hawker Siddeley Canada H5 (1976/79)	M134
UTDC/Can-Car Rail H6 (1986/89)	M126
Bombardier T1 (1995/1999)	M210

In peak service: 498

Developments: Easier access to 23 major stations is being achieved by installation of lifts, with five completed by late 1997. The new T1 cars are fully accessible, with wider doors, clear centre aisles and lock-in positions for wheelchairs.
Sheppard Avenue East line under construction for opening in 2002 (see above).

Tramway/light rail

Type of operation: Conventional tramway, light rail Harbourfront line

Passenger journeys: (1994) 43.1 million
(1995) 44.7 million
(1996) 40 million
Car-km: (1994) 11.2 million
(1995) 11.1 million
(1996) 10.9 million

Route length: 79.6 km

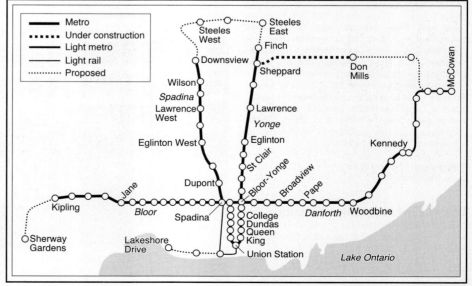

Toronto's metro

0010339

Number of lines: 10
Gauge: 1,495 mm
Track: 50 kg/m T-rail
Electrification: 580 V DC, overhead

Service: Peak 3-12 min, off-peak 5-16.5 min
Fare structure: As bus
Fare collection: As bus; proof-of-payment on Queen Street line
One-person operation: All cars

Rolling stock: 248 cars
UTDC/Swiss Industrial L1 (1977/78)	M6
UTDC/Hawker Siddeley Canada L2 (1979/81)	M190
UTDC/Can-Car Rail L3 (1987/89)	M52

In peak service: 162

Developments: A 3.6 km northwards extension of the Harbourfront line along Spadina Avenue, linking the central waterfront area with the Bloor—Danforth metro line at Spadina, opened in 1997.

ALRT (Scarborough line)

Type of operation: Intermediate capacity advanced light metro transit system, opened 1985

Passenger journeys: (1994) 3 million
(1995) 2.6 million
(1996) 2.3 million
Car-km: (1994) 3.6 million
(1995) 3.7 million
(1996) 3.6 million

Route length: 6.5 km
    elevated: 2.3 km
Number of routes: 1
Number of stations: 6
Gauge: 1,435 mm
Track: 115 lb/yd continuously welded T-rail fixed to concrete base with rubber insulation pads
Max gradient: 5.2%
Minimum curve radius: 35 m normal, 18 m minimum
Electrification: 600 V DC, ungrounded, collection from two power rails and reaction rail

Service: Peak 4 min, off-peak 8 min
Fare structure: Flat, free transfers
Revenue collection: Conventional and token and monthly pass-activated turnstiles; visual inspection
Integration with other modes: Fully integrated with rest of TTC system
One-person operation: None
Automatic control: Fully automatic with manual over-ride, manual door operation
Signalling: Moving block; centralised control and dispatch

Rolling stock: 28 cars
UTDC/VentureTrans S1 (1984/85)	M28

In peak service: 24

Current situation: This fully automated system linking Scarborough with Kennedy metro station has cars powered by linear induction motors (LIMs) running on conventional steel-rail track.

TTC Rocket tramcar picks up on Front Street/Yonge Street intersection (Andrew Jarosz)   **1999**/0043908

Ancient and modern on the opening day of the Spadina tramway extension   **1998**/0010038

GO Transit

GO Transit
20 Bay Street, Suite 600, Toronto M5J 3W3
Tel: (+1 416) 869 36 00   Fax: (+1 416) 869 35 25
Chairman: E R King
Managing Director: R C Ducharme
Staff: 1,000

Current situation: GO Transit was established in 1967, funded by the Ontario provincial government, to provide services to attract commuter motorists off the highways and reduce the need for new road investment. A comprehensive rail and bus network has been built up serving a population of 4.5 million in an area up to 90 km from Toronto.

Since 1974 the operation has been run by the Toronto Area Transit Operating Authority, a provincial crown agency with representation from the regional municipalities served, including Toronto. In January 1998, funding responsibility for GO Transit was transferred to Toronto-area municipalities. A Greater Toronto Services Board was due to be established at the beginning of 1999 which would have overall responsibility.

GO Transit sets service levels and fares and contracts train operations. CN and CP (StL&H) are the rail contractors. GO provides over 30,000 spaces for park-and-ride cars and manages several major bus terminals.
Developments: Wheelchair-accessible train service started in 1995, with 30 out of 49 stations now accessible, including Toronto Union. Hamilton GO Centre opened 1996, combining separate bus and rail stations into a single interchange located in the former Toronto, Hamilton & Buffalo station.

Passenger journeys: (Both modes)
(1995/96) 32.5 million
(1996/97) 33.5 million
(1997/98) 36.2 million

Operating costs financed by: Revenue (mostly fares) 77.8 per cent

Suburban rail
Passenger journeys: (1995/96) 23.8 million
(1996/97) 24.9 million
(1997/98) 27.2 million

Current situation: Diesel-hauled suburban service operated under contract. Lakeshore route Oakville—Toronto—Pickering runs all day, with peak hour extension from Oakville to Hamilton and Pickering to Oshawa. Other

ALRT train at Scarborough Centre station (Andrew Jarosz)   **1999**/0043910

routes to Stouffville, Richmond Hill, Milton, Bradford and Georgetown run peak hours only (two to five return journeys daily). Total 361 km, 1,435 mm gauge, zonal fares.

Rolling stock: 45 diesel locomotives, 315 double-deck coaches

Bus

Passenger journeys: (1995/96) 8.7 million
(1996/97) 8.6 million
(1997/98) 9 million

Route length: (One way) 1,315 km

Fleet: 198 buses
GMC (1974/77)	17
OBI Orion 01.508 (1985/87)	17
MCI MC9 (1981)	20
MCI 102A2 (1986/87/89/90)	69
New Flyer D40 (1991)	51
MCI 102A3 (1990)	15
MCI 102C3 (1983)	9

Current situation: Launched in 1970 as an extension of the Lakeshore rail route, the bus operation now provides service on seven corridors, mainly feeding the rail lines.

UPDATED

GO Transit MCI and New Flyer buses at Downtown Transit Terminus (Andrew Jarosz) **1999**/0043909

TOULOUSE

Population: City 350,000, conurbation 650,000
Public transport: Urban and interurban bus services and metro organised in the conurbation and its environs by the Syndicat Mixte des Transports en Commun de l'Agglomération Toulousaine (SMTC), which comprises Toulouse, 52 surrounding towns and the département of Haute Garonne. SMTC grants concessions for bus and metro operations, and decides transport policy and fares levels. Limited suburban services provided by French National Railways (SNCF)

Semvat

SA d'Economie Mixte des Transports Publics de Voyageurs de l'Agglomération Toulousaine (Semvat)
49 rue de Gironis, 31081 Toulouse Cedex, France
Tel: (+33 5) 62 11 26 11   Fax: (+33 5) 62 11 26 20
Director General: Francis Grass
Deputy Director General: Daniel Audibert
Staff: 1,550

Current situation: Semvat is the concessionaire appointed by SMTC to operate bus services in the city and conurbation. While the metro is operated under a concession by a separate company, MTD, both modes are marketed as a single network by Semvat.

Fare collection: Ticket sales by approved vendors on bus and from change-giving machines on metro stations; cancellers on board buses and in metro stations
Fare structure: Flat in each of 2 zones, inner covering Toulouse, Balma and Blagnac, and outer extending to 50 neighbouring towns; day, weekly and monthly passes; 10- and 12-journey tickets
Fare evasion control: Penalty payment

Bus

Passenger journeys: (1993) 44.2 million
(1994) 28.4 million
(1995) 30 million
Vehicle-km: (1993) Urban 16.7 million, interurban 3.3 million
(1994) Urban 16 million, interurban 3.2 million

Number of routes: Urban 53, interurban 22
Route length: Urban 607 km, interurban 1,363 km
On priority right-of-way: 9 km

Fleet: 561 vehicles
Saviem SC10	284
Heuliez 0305 articulated	10
Saviem S53/E7	80
Renault FRI	19
Heuliez GX107	123
Renault Tracer	27
Heuliez GX17	5
Others	13

In peak service: Urban 345
Average age of fleet: 7.1 years

Most intensive service: 3-4 min
One-person operation: All routes
Average distance between stops: 300-400 m
Average peak-hour speed: In mixed traffic, 8 km/h; in bus lanes (city-centre only), 14 km/h
Bus priority: Bus lanes, dedicated traffic signals, bus priority at intersections; 9 km reserved
Operational control: All buses have radios
Arrangements for elderly/disabled: 5 buses equipped for disabled riders; on-demand service in co-operation with city authorities and SETRAS (Service de Transport Spécialisé); free transer
Operating costs financed by: Urban — fares 47 per cent, other commercial sources 3 per cent, subsidy/grants 50 per cent
Interurban — fares 74 per cent, other commercial sources 3.5 per cent, subsidy/grants 3.5 per cent
Subsidy from: Employers' payroll tax (versement) 28 per cent, local councils 22 per cent; interurban, Haute Garonne département
New vehicles financed by: Loans and proceeds of employers' tax

Metro

Operated by: Métropole Transport Développement (MTD)
Staff: 120

Type of operation: Fully automated (unmanned) rubber-tyred metro, VAL system, opened 1993

Passenger journeys: (1993/94) 22.4 million
(1995) 21.5 million

Route length: 10 km
 in tunnel: 9 km
Number of lines: 1

Number of stations: 15
Gauge: 2,060 mm between H-type guide bars
Electrification: 750 V DC, collection by shoes from guide bars

Service: Peak 1 min 40 sec
First/last train: 05.00/00.12
Integration with other modes: Feeder buses serve 5 stations

Rolling stock: 29 two-car trains
GEC Alsthom (1993)	M58

Developments: Approval of north-south Line B was confirmed in 1996, though construction will not start until 2000. This 17 km line with 20 stations will link Les Minimes with Rangeuil university campus, providing interchange with Line A at Jean-Jaurès in the city centre. The route is not yet fully defined, and may include a loop near St Agne SNCF station to serve the Empalot district. Northwards extensions to Fondeyre and Borde-Rouge have also been agreed, as has a Line A extension eastwards to Gramont.

SNCF

French National Railways (SNCF), Toulouse Region
rue Marengo 9, 31079 Toulouse
Tel: (+33 5) 61 10 11 10   Fax: (+33 5) 61 10 15 45

Type of operation: Suburban heavy rail

Current situation: Limited suburban services provided on six routes into Toulouse Matabiau station, with seven stations within the city limits and a further eight in the conurbation.
Developments: With opening of metro Line A, the suburban station at St Cyprien was renamed Arènes and Semvat tickets became valid over the SNCF line thence to Colomiers, which is knows as metro Line C. This portion of the Toulouse—Auch line, which is single-track and diesel-operated, is to be doubled to allow operation of a much-improved service.

VERIFIED

TRIVANDRUM

Population: 825,000
Public transport: Bus services provided by state road transport corporation

Kerala State Road Transport

Kerala State Road Transport Corporation
Transport Bhawan, Fort Thiruvananthapuram 65023, India
Tel: (+91 471) 46 28 29   Fax: (+91 471) 462 26 79
Managing Director: M N Krishnamoorthy
Staff: (State-wide total) 26,393

Current situation: The State Road Transport Corporation provides services throughout most of Kerala State with a fleet of 3,783 buses. The Corporation as a whole carried some 936 million passengers in 1997/98.

Bus

(Trivandrum city operations)
Staff: 3,646

Passenger journeys: (1990/91) 163.3 million
(1991/92) 175 million
(1992/93) 182.3 million
Vehicle-km: (1990/91) 25 million
(1992/93) 26.8 million

Number of routes: 60
Route length: 650 km

Trivandrum Leyland double-deck bus (Malcolm Chase)   ***1999**/0043912*

Fleet: 471 buses
Ashok Leyland and Mercedes single-deck   469
Ashok Leyland double-deck   2

Most intensive service: 10 min
Fare collection: Roving conductors
Fare structure: Stage

Operating costs financed by: Fares 90 per cent, subsidy/grants 10 per cent

UPDATED

TUCUMÁN

Population: 503,000
Public transport: Bus services provided by private operators under contract to state and municipal authorities

Bus

Current situation: At the centre of this conurbation is the city of San Miguel de Tucumán which, with neighbouring towns of Yerba Buena, Banda del Rio Sali, Tafi Viejo and Lules, has a population of some 700,000. Current bus provision dates from 1959 when private contractors were authorised to supplement operations of the ailing municipal undertaking.

San Miguel city is served by two distinct operations.

One comprises 13 urban routes each run by a different operator under contract to the municipality; seven of these routes extend into the suburbs. The remaining area is covered by six companies licensed by the provincial authorities. The city council, traffic police and urban development authorities are also involved in decisions regarding route changes, fares and parking.

There is constant friction between the two groups, as the growing suburban operations compete increasingly (and illegally) with those restricted to the area within the city boundaries. Merger of the city services, forbidden under the 1959 legislation, has been authorised by the city council but not carried out, and there has also been no progress with a 1990 transport plan which proposed the reintroduction of trolleybuses, a suburban rail service

and bus priority measures. Nevertheless, light rail proposals were canvassed in 1995.

Severe recession and unemployment, coupled with increased car ownership, caused a 30 per cent decline in patronage in 1992/93 as well as encouraging growth in the number of taxis. These do not operate as shared taxis, but nevertheless tout illegally at bus stops. No new route has been introduced since 1986, though there have been some extensions of existing lines. A proposed orbital Route 19 was rejected by the mayor in 1995.

Passenger journeys: (1994) Urban 100 million, suburban 50 million
Vehicle-km: (1994) Urban 37 million, suburban 18 million

Number of routes: Urban 13, suburban 23, plus many branches
Route length: Urban 313 km, suburban over 300 km

Fleet: 658 buses
Mercedes LO1114 (1980/88)   59
Mercedes OF1214/1315 (1987/1993)   325
Mercedes OH1314/1318/OHL1316
  (1990/91/93/95)   154
El Detalle OA101 (1988/95)   120
New vehicles required each year: 20 per cent of fleet

Most intensive service: 3 min
One person operations: All routes
Fare collection: Token to driver on urban routes, cash to driver on suburban routes; conversion to electronic fareboxes in progress
Fare structure: Flat in urban area, sectional in suburbs; double fare on weekend nights
Operational control: Inspectors
Integration with other modes: None

A 10.37 m version of El Detalle's OA101 on El Ranchilleño's suburban route to Lastenia   ***1996***

VERIFIED

TUNIS

Population: 1.4 million
Public transport: Bus services in Tunis and suburbs provided by central government corporation and some private operators. Light rail system run by another similar corporation, also responsible for suburban rail service. Both corporations directly responsible to Ministry of Transport & Communications. Other suburban rail services provided by national railway (SNCFT)

SNT

Société Nationale des Transports
PO Box 660, 1 avenue Habib Bourguiba, Tunis 1001, Tunisia
Tel: (+216 1) 25 94 22   Fax: (+216 1) 34 27 27
President/Director General: M Moncer el Kafsi
Operating Manager: Ridha Essefi
Information & Publicity Manager: H Houa
Staff: 5,193

Current situation: In 1981 state-owned SNT was divided into three autonomous companies covering bus services in Tunis and its suburbs (SNT), the light rail system then under construction and the existing suburban rail line (SMLT — Société du Métro Léger de Tunis), and rural and interurban transport (SNTRI — Société de Transport Rural et Interurbain). Private operators were permitted from 1990.

Bus

Passenger boardings: (1991) 263 million
(1992) 280.6 million
(1993) 294 million
Vehicle-km: (1991) 46.7 million
(1992) 50 million
(1993) 51.7 million

Number of routes: 163
Route length: (One way) 2,597 km
On priority right-of-way: 10 km

Fleet: 855 vehicles
Fiat 418	505
Volvo B10M	74
Volvo articulated	3
Fiat 418 articulated	94
Ikarus IK280 articulated	36
Iveco AP160	45
STIA AP160 (1994/95)	44
Others	54

In peak service: 678

Most intensive service: 5 min
One-person operation: None
Fare collection: Season tickets, and onboard sales by seated conductor; some prepurchase, being extended
Fare structure: Stage; weekly and annual passes and season tickets; through ticketing to SMLT
Fares collected on board: 41 per cent
Fare evasion control: Penalty payment
Average peak-hour speed: 10 km/h
Operating costs financed by: Fares 65.6 per cent, other commercial sources 3.1 per cent, subsidy/compensation 21.5 per cent, deficit 9.8 per cent
Subsidy from: Government; payments made to preserve financial equilibrium

Private operators

Current situation: The first privately operated bus services began in 1991. Amongst them is TCV which established a route from the city centre to La Marsa in direct competition with the TGM railway, which experienced a decline in first-class traffic in particular.

SMLT

Société du Métro Léger de Tunis (SMLT)
Incorporating Tunis-Goulette-Marsa Railway (TGM)
6 rue Khartoum, Tunis 1002
Tel: (+216 1) 34 85 55   Fax: (+216 1) 33 81 00
Director General: Habib Allegue
Finance Director: H Zaatour
Infrastructure Director: B Hammami
Head of Information: R Kazdaghli
Staff: 1,470

Suburban railway (TGM)

Passenger journeys: (1993) 18.3 million
(1994) 18 million
(1995) 19.1 million

Current situation: 19.5 km suburban railway with 18 stations, 1,440 mm gauge, electrified 750 V DC overhead, linking Tunis, La Goulette and La Marsa; off-peak service of five trains/h.

Rolling stock: 36 cars
Duewag/MAN/Siemens (1977)   M18 T18
On order: 18 two-car sets

Light rail

Type of operation: Light rail, initial route opened 1985

Passenger journeys: (1993) 71 million
(1994) 82 million
(1995) 88.3 million
Car-km: (Annual) 4.3 million

Route length: 32 km
Number of lines: 5
Number of stations: 36
Gauge: 1,440 mm
Electrification: 750 V DC, overhead

Iveco AP160 on SNT's Route 10 at Place Barcelone station   *1996*

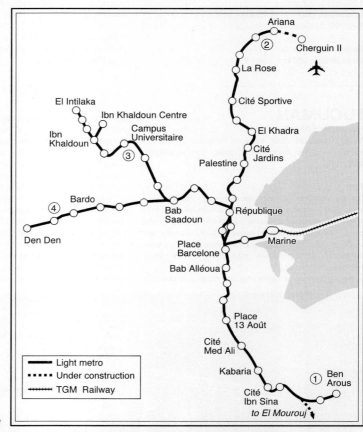

Tunis light rail

Line 3 LRV approaching République
1996

Service: Peak 4 min, off-peak 12 min
Fare structure: 2 zones per route; through fares to bus

Rolling stock: 135 cars
Siemens-Duewag (1984/85)	M78
(1991/92)	M43
(1997)	M14

In peak service: 104 cars

Developments: Extension of Line 2 by 1.4 km under construction from Ariana to the Cherguin II industrial development. The alignment of the southwards extension from Ben Arous to the new town of El Mourouj has been revised. It will now be built as a branch of Line 1 running 6.5 km from Cité Ibn Sina.

SNCFT
Société Nationale des Chemins de Fer Tunisiens
67 avenue Farhat Hached, Tunis 1001
Tel: (+216 1) 24 99 99   Fax: (+216 1) 34 85 40

Type of operation: Suburban heavy rail

Current situation: SNCFT operates suburban services on four routes totalling 142 km, carrying about 2 million passengers annually.

Rolling stock: Diesel-hauled push-pull trainsets and dmus

VERIFIED

TURIN
Population: 923,000, conurbation 1.5 million
Public transport: Public transport services operated by three public companies, ATM, Satti and FS. ATM operates the urban and suburban bus and tramway networks, while Satti provides transport for Turin and 220 neighbouring towns by bus and local railways. Some 50 private companies run interurban bus routes. Suburban rail services provided by Italian Railways (FS)

Trasporti Torinesi-ATM
Consorzio Trasporti Torinesi/Azienda Tranvie Municipali (TT/ATM)
Corso Turati 19/6,I-10128 Turin, Italy
Tel: (+39 011) 576 41   Fax: (+39 011) 576 42 91
President: Gianni Guerra
General Director: Giovanni Fava (Commercial)
Operating Director: Antonio Ardissone
Staff: 4,270

Passenger journeys: (All modes)
(1993) 204 million
(1994) 194 million
(1995) 194 million

Operating costs financed by: Fares 25 per cent, other commercial sources 5 per cent, subsidy/grants 70 per cent
Subsidy from: Regional government 81 per cent, municipalities of Turin and surrounding area 19 per cent

Current situation: ATM operates the urban and suburban bus networks and tram routes, two of which are on segregated right-of-way. It serves the city of Turin and 24 municipalities with a total population of 1.5 million.

Bus
Vehicle-km: (1993) 40.5 million
(1994) 41.6 million
(1995) 41 million

Number of routes: 68, plus some special routes
Route length: 774 km
On priority right-of-way: (Tram and bus) 62 km

Fleet: 1,006 vehicles
Iveco 471 Viberti (1985/88)	47
Iveco 580 TurboCity-S (1990)	30
Iveco 571 S-Euffeno (1988)	15
Bredabus 3001.12LL (1989)	20
Iveco 471 U-Euffeno (1985/88)	100
Iveco 480 TurboCity-U (1989/91)	118
Iveco 480 Viberti (1989/91)	152
Fiat 421 (1973/83)	302
Bredabus BB3001 08AC (1992)	5
Inbus AU280FT De Simon (1991)	30
Iveco 490 Altrobus dual-mode (1994)	2
Iveco 490 Viberti (1994)	45
Iveco 490 (1994)	19
Iveco 490E TurboCity UR-Green (1994)	100
Iveco 480 18.29 Viberti (1994)	21

In peak service: 790

Most intensive service: Peak 4-7 min, off-peak 6-13 min
One-person operation: All routes
Fare collection: Prepurchase passes and multitickets from automatic machines and shops
Fare structure: Flat within urban and suburban zones; tickets with time validity, passes and 10-journey multitickets (urban only); integrated 'Formula' weekly/ monthly passes allow all modes travel within specified zones
Fare evasion control: Roving inspectors
Average peak-hour speed: 17.8 km/h

Series 5000 LRV on Line 9 at Porta Nuova station   *1996*

Integration with other modes: Bus and tram services integrated and connect with rail stations and outer-suburban termini; fares integration between ATM, Satti and FS started in 1996 (passes only)

Tramway/light rail
Type of operation: Conventional tramway/light rail

Car-km: (1993) 9.8 million
(1994) 8.9 million
(1995) 9 million

Route length: 104.8 km, plus light rail 19.2 km
Number of lines: 9 tramway, 2 light rail
Gauge: 1,445 mm
Track: Part conventional sleepers on ballast
Max gradient: 5.8%
Minimum curve radius: 15 m
Electrification: 580 V DC, overhead

Service: Peak 4-7 min, off-peak 6-10 min
First/last car: 04.30/01.00

Fare structure: As bus
Fare collection: As bus
One-person operation: All cars
Signalling: Centralised control; priority at traffic lights in operation on Routes 3, 4, 9, 10, 16

Rolling stock: 299 cars
3100 (1949/58, rebuilt 1975/78)	M92
2800 (1958/60, rebuilt 1979/82)	M102
Fiat/Ansaldo/OMS 7000 LRV (1982/86)	M51
Fiat/Ansaldo/OMS 5000 LRV low-floor (1989/92)	M53
Restaurant tram (1958, rebuilt 1968)	M1

In peak service: 198

Light metro (proposed)
Current situation: In 1991 the city council approved construction of a two-route automated light metro using VAL technology. In 1995, Phase I of Line 1 (Collegno—Turin Central FS station, 9.5 km, 15 stations) received preliminary approval for funding under Law 211.

Line 1 will run east-west from Campo Volo to Porta Nuova station in central Turin, and then turn south

Iveco Turbocity on Via S Secondo   *1996*

Satti emus (second-hand from Belgium's SNCB) at Turin Dora   *1998*/0010037

Current situation: Satti operates local trains from Rivarolo to Settimo (40 km, 1,435 mm gauge) and thence over FS tracks to Turin Porta Susa, and from Ceres to Turin Dora (44 km, 1,435 mm gauge, electrified 3 kV DC over the 34 km between Germagnano and Dora).

Developments: A new joint through service with FS was introduced in 1997, linking Rivarolo with Chieri; enhanced to hourly in May 1998.

The project to build an underground link to the FS station at Porta Nuova (see *JUTS 1994/95*) has been abandoned, but Satti services will eventually be linked to the Passante (see below) for through running to Lingotto. The Ceres line is being modernised, with seven two-car low-floor emus delivered from Fiat, and a branch is planned to serve Caselle airport.

Rolling stock: 4 electric locomotives, 4 diesel locomotives, 20 diesel railcars, 8 two-car emus, 27 coaches and trailers

FS
Italian Railways (FS)
Piazza della Croce Rossa, Rome

Type of operation: Suburban heavy rail

Current situation: Frequent service provided on five routes, electrified 3 kV DC.

Developments: Construction continues of the first stage of the Passante cross-city line. A 6 km line with two stations, partly underground, will link Porta Susa with Lingotto, avoiding the main Porta Nuova terminus. Most suburban trains will be diverted over the new route when it is completed. An intermediate station will be built later at Zappata to allow interchange with the Turin—Bussoleno—Modane line.

In the long term, a second pair of tracks will be built alongside the Turin—Milan main line from Porta Susa to Stura, and Satti trains will be extended from Dora to Porta Susa and beyond. Interchange is planned with pre-metro lines (see above) at several points.

VERIFIED

---

towards Nichelino. A second line, to be known as Line 4, runs north-south with a city-centre interchange with Line 1 and other rail services at Porta Nuova.

Satti
Satti SpA, Torinese Trasporti Intercomunali
Address as ATM above
e-mail: satti-torino@iol.it
President: Giancarlo Guiati
General Manager: Rodolfo Notaro
Staff: 8,680

Passenger journeys: (All modes)
(1996) 16.3 million
(1997) 3 million

Current situation: Satti has responsibility for outer suburban and commuter bus services, serving Turin and the towns of Asti, Cuneo, Alessandria, Vercelli and the urban area of Ivrea, as well as two rail lines.

Bus
Passenger journeys: (1996) 13.7 million
Vehicle-km: (1996) 13.9 million

Number of routes: 73
Route length: (One way) 3,370 km
Fleet: 338 buses, mostly Fiat

Local railways
Passenger journeys: (1996) 2.6 million
(1997) 3 million

UFA
Population: 1.1 million
Public transport: Bus and trolleybus/tramway services provided by separate municipal undertakings

Bus
Number of routes: 40, plus 15 express
Fleet: Includes Mercedes Türk O325, Chavdar articulated and Ikarus 260/280
Fare collection: Conductors

Tramvaino-Trolleibusnoe Upravlenie
Tramvaino-Trolleibusnoe Upravlenie
Revolutsionnaya ul 98, 400005 Ufa, Russia
Tel: (+7 3472) 23 44 03   Fax: (+7 3472) 22 72 90
General Manager: V A Belyayev
Staff: 2,550

Current situation: Both tram and trolleybus networks are in a poor state; half the fleet stands near-derelict in the depots and service is irregular with no effective scheduling. No fares are collected. Some large industrial concerns now operate their own buses to transport staff to and from work, thereby further undermining the network.

Trolleybus
Number of routes: 17
Fleet: Approx 180 trolleybuses, ZIU9 and ZIU10

Tramway
Passenger journeys: (1996) 98 million

Number of routes: 20
Route length: 156 km

Rolling stock: 342 cars
ČKD Tatra T3 (1977/87)   About M100
RVZ6 (1980/87)   About M60

KTM5 (1992)	M15
KTM8 (1992/95)	M75
LM93 (1995/96)	About M10
Others	M80

VERIFIED

RVZ6 trams and a Mercedes Türk city bus on Oktyabrski Prospekt   *1997*

UJUNG PANDANG

Population: 709,000
Public transport: Government-owned transport corporation provides part of public transport services, supplemented by independent minibuses

DAMRI

Djawatan Angkutan Motor Republik Indonesia
Jalan G Latimojong 21, Ujung Pandang, Sulawesi Selatan, Indonesia
Tel: (+62 411) 242 26

Current situation: Public corporation operates several cross-city bus routes extending up to 20 km into suburban communities.

Fleet: Mercedes O306 and OH408 single-deck, Volvo double-deck

One-person operation: None
Fare collection: Conductor
Fare structure: Flat

Private bus
Current situation: A large fleet of 'Mikrolet' Daihatsu, Suzuki and Mitsubishi 10-seaters, radiating over several routes from the central market, supplements the government bus services. Most of these vehicles are one-man operated. Fares are usually 25 per cent (on longer routes 100 per cent) higher than those charged by government buses.

VERIFIED

ULAAN BAATAR

Population: 600,000
Public transport: Bus and trolleybus services provided by municipal undertaking responsible to Ministry of Transport

Municipal Motor Transport Commitee

Municipal Workers' Council
Ulaan Baatar, Mongolian People's Republic

Current situation: Services are provided by the local municipal committee under overall control of the Ministry

of Transport & Communications. Figures for public transport in Mongolia's major urban centres indicate some 120 million passengers are carried annually.

Bus
Passenger journeys: Approx 35 million (annual)
Vehicle-km: Approx 5 million (annual)

Number of routes: 8

Fleet: Approx 150 buses, including LIAZ 677 and 697, Karosa SM, B731 and PAZ 672

Fare collection: By conductress, seated at rear

Fare structure: Flat

Trolleybus
Current situation: Operation commenced in 1987 of an initial 13 km trolleybus route. Ultimately a 40 km system with 150 trolleybuses is planned.

Fleet: 36 trolleybuses
ZIU 682B   27
Trolza 52642   9

VERIFIED

UTRECHT

Population: 250,000
Public transport: Most bus services provided by municipal undertaking with some additional suburban routes operated by private regional bus companies; separate company responsible for operation of light rail line. Suburban/interurban services by Netherlands Railways (NS)

GVU

Gemeentelijk Vervoerbedrijf Utrecht (GVU)
PO Box 8222, 3503 RE Utrecht, Netherlands
Tel: (+31 30) 236 36 36   Fax: (+31 30) 231 65 40
Chief Officer: J J P Kunst
Staff: 721

Current situation: GVU operates most urban and some suburban bus services in and around Utrecht. Other operators run interurban services into the city.
Developments: Planning for new high-quality bus services is going well. Starting in 1999, a network of routes will be introduced utilising dedicated right-of-way and a fleet of advanced buses. Also due for 1999 start-up is service to a new suburb of 30,000 homes called Heidsche Rijn.

Feasibility studies are being made of proposals to integrate urban and regional services.

Bus
Passenger boardings: (1994) 35.5 million
(1995) 32.2 million
(1996) 32.4 million
Vehicle-km: (1994) 8 million
(1996) 8 million

Number of routes: 22
Route length: (One way) 223 km
On priority right-of-way: 25 km

Fleet: 220 vehicles
DAF/Hainje standard   93
Volvo/Den Oudsten articulated   74
Van Hool AG300 LPG-powered (1997/1998)   40
Hainje midibus   9
Fiat Ducato minibus   4
In peak service: 152

Most intensive service: 3 min
One-person operation: All routes
Fare structure: Zonal; prepurchase nationally available 'Strippenkaart' tickets, also available on vehicle (see Amsterdam for details); passes; student ticket
Average distance between stops: 300-400 m
Average peak-hour speed: In mixed traffic, 16 km/h; in bus lanes, 25 km/h
Arrangements for elderly/disabled: Reduced fares

Integration with other modes: Services co-ordinated with those of neighbouring regional public transport authority and NS. National 'Strippenkaart' gives standard tram, bus and metro fares throughout the Netherlands
Operating costs financed by: Fares 41%, other commercial sources 4%, subsidy/grants 55%
Subsidy from: Regional council, drawing 100% government contribution

Sneltram

Midnet Groep NV, Sneltram Utrecht
Huis ter Heideweg 8, 3705 LZ Zeist
Tel: (+31 340) 42 65 00   Fax: (+31 340) 41 79 47
Director: A F M Hilhorst

Current situation: The Sneltram light rail line was built by Netherlands Railways (NS) and is now controlled by the Midnet bus group.
Developments: A 2.5 km extension is being built to serve the Zenderpark housing development in IJsselstein, for 2000 opening. Midnet is developing an automatic vehicle location and control system for the Sneltram, which is also undergoing rehabilitation.

Studies are being made to assess whether the Sneltram can play a part in the Randstad 2000 scheme for S-Bahn style train service throughout the region.

Buses and Sneltram at Utrecht CS interchange (Tony Pattison)

1999/0038999

Utrecht's Sneltram

Light rail (Sneltram)

Type of operation: Light rail, opened 1983

Passenger journeys: (1998) 36,000 daily
Car-km: (1998) 1.8 million

Route length: 21.5 km
Number of stops: 23
Number of lines: 1, with branches
Gauge: 1,435 mm
Track: 46 kg/m rail on concrete sleepers
Electrification: 750 V DC, overhead

Service: 5 min peak, 7½ min day, 10 min evening/weekend
Signalling: Only on 1.5 km section, otherwise ordinary street traffic lights

Rolling stock: 27 cars
SIG/Holec/BBC (1983)   M27

Bus

Current situation: Operates suburban and regional bus routes in the provinces of Utrecht, Gelderland and Flevoland, and urban routes in 10 medium-size cities.

NS

Netherlands Railways
PO Box 2025, 3500 HA Utrecht
Tel: (+31 30) 235 91 11   Fax: (+31 30) 233 24 58

Type of operation: Suburban heavy rail

Current situation: Only Centraal and two suburban stations lie within the city boundaries, and are not heavily used for local trips, though there is much longer-distance commuting. Service of 2 to 34 trains per hour according to time of day.

UPDATED

VALENCIA (Spain)

Population: 852,000
Public transport: Urban bus services provided by municipal transport company, suburban services by Consorcio Municipal de Transportes and other private companies. Rail services operated by FGV regional railway upgraded with cross-city link. Other suburban services by State Railway

EMT

Empresa Municipal de Transportes de Valencia SA (EMT)
Aben al Abbar 2, 46021 Valencia, Spain
Tel: (+34 96) 369 69 00/64 40   Fax: (+34 96) 360 74 05
Director General: Ramón Ruiz Hernández
Staff: 1,511

Current situation: In 1986 EMT replaced the former municipal operator Saltuv, becoming the licensee for city bus operations. Since then almost complete fleet renewal has been carried out, together with some expansion of routes into developing areas.
Developments: All buses are now equipped with air conditioning, and the first steps have been taken towards fitting the fleet with an electronic monitoring and management system. Sensors have been installed in an experimental batch of buses to monitor the state of major components.

A new depot is to be built in the north of the city to complement the existing installation at San Isidro in the south. A programme of fleet renewal has started with acquisition of 160 vehicles; the first 76 are low-floor types. Initial deliveries comprise 21 Mercedes O405N2 with ramps and kneeling capability. Trials are also in progress with a bio-diesel fuel, a mixture of conventional diesel and sunflower oil.

Tariffs are to be integrated with those of RENFE and FGV, following installation of new ticket-issuing machines.

Bus

Passenger journeys: (1995) 117.9 million
(1996) 117.1 million
(1997) 115.5 million
Vehicle-km: (1995) 21.9 million
(1996) 21.9 million
(1997) 21.8 million

Pegaso EMT bus on Carrier de Xativa Street (Bill Luke)   *1999*/0043914

Number of routes: 52
Number of stops: 1,291
Route length: 770 km

Fleet: 480 vehicles
Pegaso 6038	123
Pegaso 6420	56
Renault PR100-2	158
Renault R312 (1993)	62
Mercedes O405 N2 (1996)	21
Renault Citybus (1997)	55
Pegaso 5081	1
MAN	4

In peak service: 426
On order: 40–50 a year
Average age of fleet: 7 years

Most intensive service: 4 min
One-person operation: All routes
Fare collection: Payment to driver or prepurchase
Fares collected on board: 18.1 per cent
Fare structure: Flat; prepurchase 'bonobus' 10-journey tickets; monthly passes

Arrangements for elderly/disabled: Discount annual passes for unlimited travel; special door-to-door service at normal fares
Operating costs financed by: Fares 55.2 per cent, other commercial sources 3 per cent, subsidy/grants 41.8 per cent
Subsidy from: City council

FGV

Ferrocarrils de la Generalitat Valenciana
Partida de Xirivelleta, B de S Isidro, 46014 Valencia
Tel: (+34 96) 357 81 03   Fax: (+34 96) 357 55 61
President: Eugenio Burriel de Orueta
Managing Director: Jorge Garcia Bernia
Commercial Director: Jorge Beltrán
Staff: 1,100

Passenger journeys: (1993) 18.4 million
(1994) 19.6 million
(1997) 22.5 million

Current situation: FGV took over two groups of Valencia local lines from FEVE, the state narrow-gauge railway operator, in 1987. Lines 1 and 2 from Lliria and Bétera in the north are now linked through a 6.8 km city-centre tunnel with eight stations to the Villanueva de Castellón line in the south, providing a metro-style service. Former Line 4 was converted to reserved track tramway operation in 1994, while Line 3 was diverted away from the former Pont de Fusta terminus in 1995 and now runs through Alameda via a 3 km tunnel.

The network extends to 219 km of metre-gauge; Lines 1, 2 and 3 are electrified at 1.5 kV DC overhead, Line 4 at 750 V DC overhead.
Developments: Running east-west across the city centre, the 8.6 km Line 5 with 12 stations is under construction to link Nuevo Cauce and Cabanyal, making connection with all four existing lines. The planned city-centre tunnel section from Alameda to Cabanyal may now be built as street-running tramway, following studies made by the Valencia regional government. The Pta18 million saved could be used to fund construction of other light rail lines.

Despite considerable opposition to the plans to reopen Line 4 as a tramway, the service has been received enthusiastically by residents and nearly 5 million passengers were carried in its first year of operation. Two extensions are to go ahead, from Ademúz to Burjassot (3 km) and Grao to the Balearic Islands ferryport at

Valencia Metro Line 4 LRV at El Grau terminus (D Trevor-Rowe)   *1999*/0043916

Valencia Metro Line 3 train (D Trevor-Rowe)   **1999**/0043913

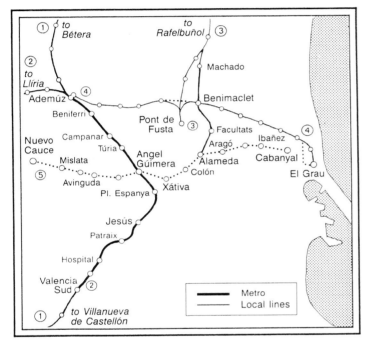

Valencia's FGV lines

Nazaret. Line 3 was extended to Avenida del Cid in September 1998.

Rolling stock: 145 cars

Babcock & Wilcox three-car sets Lines 1 and 2	M10 T20
CAF two-car sets Lines 1 and 2	M40
GEC Alsthom Series 3900 Lines 3 and 5 (1994/96)	M36 T18
Siemens articulated LRV (1994)	M21

On order: A further 8 LRVs from Siemens

RENFE

Spanish National Railways (RENFE)
Avenida Ciudad de Barcelona 8, 28007 Madrid
Tel: (+34 91) 506 62 15   Fax: (+34 91) 506 73 26
Director, Valencia: Juan José Cholvi Puig
Staff: 414 (Valencia area)

Type of operation: Suburban heavy rail

Passenger journeys: (1995) 21.2 million
(1996) 21.2 million
(1997) 21.2 million

Current situation: An intensive service is operated out of Norte station on six routes totalling 372 km, with 68 stations. Trains run to Gandia, Xàtiva and Castelló every 15 min during the peak, to Utiel and Riba-Roja every 30 min, and to Caudiel every hour. Four lines electrified, the others diesel-worked.
Developments: Accelerated service brand-named 'Civis' introduced in 1997 on the Castellón line, with a 23 min journey time. New combined car parking and travel introduced.

More emphasis is being placed on good interchange between modes, in a plan which also proposes electrification of one of the diesel-worked lines. The dmu fleet is being modernised.

Rolling stock: 117 emu cars and 39 dmu cars

Class 440 emu	M2 T1
Class 470 emu	M20 T10
Class 447 emu	M56 T28
Class 592 dmu	39

UPDATED

VALENCIA (Venezuela)

Population: 900,000, conurbation 1.2 million
Public transport: Bus services provided by private operators. Light rail under construction

Private bus

Current situation: About 12 private companies serve 12 routes with a total of some 250 buses. Vehicles in general are of relatively recent origin, supplied by various of the Valencia-based Venezuelan bus builders and assemblers, including Blue Bird.

Having initially resisted incursion by 'Por Puesto' minibuses, by 1993 the city had 34 associations serving 90 routes with a fleet of over 1,900 vehicles. Buses and minibuses carry about 805,000 passengers daily.

Light rail

Under construction
CA Metro de Valencia

Current situation: Construction started in mid-1997 on the initial 6.2 km section of a 23 km light rail line. Siemens Transportation is supplying electrical and mechanical equipment, as well as a fleet of 8 cars.

VERIFIED

VALPARAÍSO

Population: 300,000
Public transport: Bus and trolleybus services operated by private firms; some 20 municipal and privately owned funiculars and elevators; commuter rail

Private bus

Current situation: Bus services in Valparaíso and adjacent resort of Viña del Mar, as elsewhere in Chile, are wholly operated by private firms. No details are available for private bus vehicles and passenger volumes in Valparaíso.

Merval emu calls at Bellavista in Valparaíso
1997

ETCE

Empresa de Transportes Colectivos Eléctricos Ltda
Victoria No 3022, Av Independencia, Valparaíso, Chile
Tel: (+56 32) 21 48 64
President: Pedro Massai B

Current situation: The former government-owned trolleybus system was closed in 1980/81, but was purchased by a private company in 1982 and operations resumed. Following closure of the Av Pedro Montt route in 1993, the remaining line serves the busy Av Colón. At last report, some 5 million passengers were carried annually.

ETCE extended operations to Santiago (qv) in 1991, but this operation was closed in 1994. Though ETCE hopes to resume services in Santiago, the fleet was transferred to storage in Valparaíso in 1996.

Trolleybus
Number of routes: 1
Route length: 5 km

Fleet: 47 trolleybuses

Pullman (1952)	6
Pullman (1947/48, rebodied 1987/88)	4
Pullman (1947/48, 3 slightly rebuilt 1988/89)	4
Pullman (in store)	4
FBW/SWS/MFO articulated (1959, ex-Zürich)	2
FBW/R&J/BBC articulated (1974, ex-Zürich)	1
Berna/SWS/SAAS articulated (1965, ex-Geneva)	16
FBW/Hess/BBC articulated (1975, ex-Geneva)	2
Berna 2-axle (1966, ex-Schaffhausen)	1
Berna articulated (1966, ex-Schaffhausen)	2
Saurer/Hess/BBC (1970/75, ex-St Gallen, in store)	5
In peak service: 20	

Most intensive service: 3 min
One-person operation: All vehicles
Fare collection: Payment to driver
Fare structure: Flat
Operating costs financed by: Fares 100 per cent

Municipalidad de Valparaíso

Municipalidad de Valparaíso
Calle Condell 1490, Valparaíso

Funiculars/Elevators

Current situation: There are 24 ancient funiculars (Ascensors), of which 16 are currently in operation, serving the many hills which ring Valparaíso Bay. Five are municipally owned; the remainder are private, but with fares and service levels regulated by the city. They carry about 500,000 passengers annually. There are also a number of public lifts, of which three are believed to be working.

Suburban railway

Current situation: A frequent service is operated by Chilean State Railways subsidiary Merval between Valparaíso and Limache (43 km, 17 stations), electrified at 3 kV DC. Four trains daily run through to Los Andes. Merval (Metro Regional de Valparaíso) was set up in 1988 with a remit to create a regional commuter railway based on the existing route.

UPDATED

Berna-built ex-Geneva trolleybus of ETCE (Bill Luke)

1999/0039000

VANCOUVER

Population: 1.8 million
Public transport: Bus, trolleybus and ferry services operated by or for provincial crown corporation BC Transit. Automated rapid transit (SkyTrain) and commuter rail owned by BC Transit and operated by associated companies. BC Transit is responsible for management and operation of public transport in the Vancouver region. Policy and planning is determined by the Vancouver Regional Transit Commission, composed of locally elected officials appointed by the provincial government. Funding comes from provincial government and the Commission

BC Transit

British Columbia Transit
13401 108 Avenue, Surrey, BC V3T 5T4, Canada
Tel: (+1 604) 540 30 00   Fax: (+1 604) 540 32 30
Website: www.bctransit.com
Chief Executive Officer: R G Lingwood
Chief Financial officer: R Krowchuk
Staff: 3,955 (Vancouver operations only)

Current situation: BC Transit is a provincial crown corporation responsible for planning, policy, funding and operating either directly or indirectly public transit systems throughout the Province of British Columbia.

In Vancouver, BC Transit operates bus, trolleybus and ferry services as well as providing through associated companies automated rapid transit and commuter rail services. The planning and funding of public transport is a shared responsibility between BC Transit and the Vancouver Regional Transit Commission, which comprises the 20 municipalities and two electoral areas making up the Greater Vancouver Regional District.

BC Transit has a similar arrangement to provide bus services in Victoria with the Victoria Regional Transit Commission. Outside Vancouver and Victoria, BC Transit contracts with public and private operators for bus, paratransit and transport for the disabled services through the Municipal Systems Program. Under the co-operative arrangement with smaller municipalities, BC Transit provides centralised planning, marketing and financial services with a strong component of local decision making. Private sector companies provide most

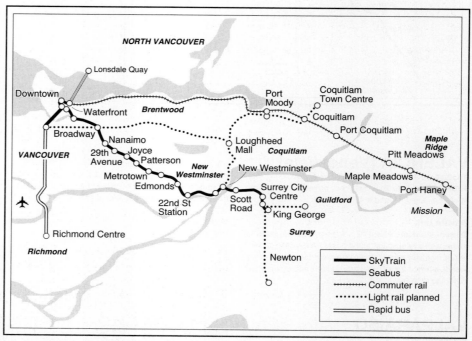

BC Transit's metro

0009926

of the service through transport operating and supply contracts which are tendered every three to five years. Vehicles are leased to the private operators from a provincial fleet, with uniform design and livery standards. In four cities, the municipality operates the transport service directly under contract to BC Transit.

Developments: In 1995, the provincial government approved a 10-year transport development plan. Included were two conventional light rail lines, introduction of rapid bus services and a major expansion of conventional bus services. In June 1998, the Province approved an accelerated rapid transit plan which will see development of an expanded SkyTrain system in place of the two conventional light rail lines. Completion of the Skytrain extension from New Westminster to Lougheed town

centre is now scheduled for the end of 2000. Construction is due to start in early 1999.

Completion of the remaining 27.5 km from Broadway and Granville in Vancouver to Lougheed and Coquitlam city centre is proposed for 2005. A rapid bus route using new low-floor articulated buses has been introduced along the Broadway–Lougheed corridor from UBC to Lougheed town centre as an interim high-quality service prior to the opening of SkyTrain. A second rapid bus route between downtown Vancouver and Richmond city centre is proposed for implementation in 2000, as is a third route between Lougheed and Coquitlam.

Other components of the plan include expansion of the SkyTrain fleet from 150 to 190 cars, and of the bus fleet to over 1,200 vehicles. Replacement of 530 older buses with

New Flyer low-floor at Simon Frazer University on Route 135   **1999**/0043275

New Flyer D60 low-floor articulated buses on rapid bus B-Line Route 99   **1999**/0043277

low-floor types will make the entire fleet accessible by 2006. Improved infrastructure includes a new operating and maintenance centre in Richmond (completion in 2000) and construction of public transport interchanges and park-and-ride lots in suburban areas.

A heritage streetcar, using one restored vehicle, is operating along a short section of former railway alignment on the south side of False Creek. The service, which is provided by the City of Vancouver, operates weekends only and is proposed as the first leg of a more extensive downtown streetcar system.

In July 1998, the provincial government approved new legislation that will create a Greater Vancouver Transportation Authority (GVTA). The new Authority came into being on April 1 1999 and is responsible for planning, policy and funding of the region's public transport system, a network of major roads, transport demand management initiatives and the region's Air Care system.

Bus, trolleybus and ferry services now operated by BC Transit and SkyTrain and commuter rail, operated by its associate companies, BC Rapid Transit Company and West Coast Express, will become subsidiary companies of GVTA. The new Authority will be given dedicated funding to finance its operations directly or through contracted suppliers.

BC Transit will continue to be a crown corporation responsible for public transport services outside the Vancouver region.

Passenger journeys: (all modes)
(1995/96) 117.9 million
(1996/97) 122.4 million
(1997/98) 124.2 million

Operating costs financed by: Fares 50 per cent, local tax sources 18 per cent, provincial subsidy/ grants 32 per cent
Subsidy from: General provincial revenue and local taxes (property, motive fuel and hydro levy) collected by Vancouver Regional Transit Commission; total costs of the system include debt service costs on capital assets

Bus and Trolleybus
Staff: 3,521

Passenger journeys: (bus and trolleybus)
(1995/96) 90.3 million
(1996/97) 91.8 million
(1997/98) 92.9 million
Vehicle-km: (bus and trolleybus)
(1995/96) 58.7 million
(1996/97) 59.9 million
(1997/98) 61.8 million

Number of routes: 157 bus and 13 trolleybus
On priority right-of way: 37.6 km
Trolleybus electrification: 600 V DC

Fleet: 1,032 buses
GM (1969)	5
GMC (1970s)	112
GMC New Look (1982)	15
GMC Classic (1987)	28
MCI Classic (1989/90)	134
Flyer D902 (1982)	35
Flyer D40 (1991/92)	156

Flyer D60 articulated (1991)	21
New Flyer CNG-powered (1995/96)	25
New Flyer G40 low-floor (1996/97/98)	192
New Flyer G40 low-floor CNG-powered (1998)	25
New Flyer D60 low-floor articulated (1998)	21
Orion II minibus	19

In peak service: 873
On order: 26 New Flyer low-floor articulated and 83 New Flyer low-floor D40s for 1999. Also one NovaBUS low-floor

Fleet: 244 trolleybuses
Flyer E901/902 (1982/83)	244

Most intensive service: 3 min
One-person operation: all routes
Fare collection: Duncan farebox; exact fare integrated with proof of payment system on SkyTrain, SeaBus and West Coast Express
Fare structure: Time and distance based; three zones apply on weekdays before 18.30; free transfers, valid for 90 minutes multidirectional; low-cost annual passes for low-income residents provided by Government of BC; monthly passes (FareCards), discount tickets (FareSavers) in books of 10; daypasses
Fare evasion control: Scrutiny by driver; random inspection on SeaBus, SkyTrain and West Coast Express
Operational control: All vehicles radio-equipped; automated vehicle location being tried out on 9 vehicles
Integration with other modes: All modes totally integrated, including fares; 18 park-and-ride lots, some with cycle lockers; four bus routes bicycle rack-equipped
Average distance between stops: Two city blocks
Average peak hour speed: In mixed traffic 20 km/h
Arrangements for elderly/ disabled: Dial-a-ride system (handyDART) provides door-to-door service using computerised registration and management information system; SeaBus, SkyTrain and West Coast Express are accessible; over 40 per cent of buses lift-equipped
New vehicles financed by: Debt, private-sector lease whenever possible

Developments: Introduction of 21 new low articulated buses dedicated to B-Line rapid service between University of BC and Lougheed town centre. Buses painted in new rapid bus livery and all equipped with exterior bike racks.

Nine buses testing new automated vehicle location (AVL) system with transit signal priority. Richmond operating and maintenance centre under construction for completion in mid-2000. Feasibility study under way of median busway corridor on King George Highway from King George SkyTrain Station to Newton and South Surrey.

Ferry
Staff: 76

Passenger journeys: (ferry)
(1995/96) 2.5 million
(1996/97) 2.8 million
(1997/98) 2.8 million

Current situation: Two SeaBus catamarans operate cross-inlet ferry services (2.1 km); fares and schedules integrated with buses, SkyTrain and West Coast Express.

SkyTrain
Operated under contract by British Columbia Rapid Transit Company
President: Larry Ward
Staff: 349

Type of operation: Automated intermediate-capacity metro (light rail transit), opened in 1986 with extensions in 1990 and 1994

Passenger journeys: (1995/96) 22.2 million
(1996/97) 23.9 million
(1997/98) 24.1 million
Car-km: (1995/96) 23.4 million
(1996/97) 23.8 million
(1997/98) 24.5 million

Route length: 28.9 km
  in tunnel: 1.6 km
  elevated: 23.8 km
Number of stations: 20
Gauge: 1,435 mm
Track: mainly lightweight, prestressed elevated concrete

Flyer trolleybus in the centre of Vancouver (Peter Newman)   **1999**/0043276

SkyTrain heading east towards Broadway station, Vancouver   **1999**/0043273

SeaBus catamaran operating cross-inlet ferry service between Lonsdale Quay and Waterfront station   **1999**/0043278

guideways; 47.7 kg/m rail fixed direct to concrete track bed

Electrification: 600 V DC collected by brushes from side rails (2 in vertical series) and fed to linear induction motors through variable-voltage variable-frequency converter

Service: 2-5 min
Integration with other modes: Many bus routes serve stations; city-centre station with SeaBus and West Coast Express
Revenue collection: Self-ticketing proof of payment system; roving inspectors also responsible for security and information
Signalling: Seltrac system with central computer control; all trains are driverless, with roving staff on trains and stations

Rolling stock: 150 cars

Metro Canada (1985)	M114
UTDC (1990/91)	M 16
Bombardier (1995/96)	M20

On order: Bombardier Transportation is building 60 cars for delivery starting in late 2000, with option to supply a further 60.

Current situation: The automated light rail transit system (SkyTrain) was developed as an intermediate capacity transit system by the Urban Transportation Development Corporation (UTDC). Lightweight cars are powered by linear induction motors, and have steerable bogies to reduce noise and vibration and wheel and track wear.

The line serves the city centre in the former CP Rail Dunsmuir tunnel, converted to accommodate two single tracks one above the other. There are two stations on the underground section. Elsewhere, much of the route is elevated. A 6.5 km branch line from Columbia Station (New Westminster) to Lougheed town centre is under construction for completion in 2000 as part of the Rapid Transit Expansion programme.

Suburban rail

Operated under contract by West Coast Express; service operated by CP Rail
President: Jan Pezarro
Staff: 28

Passenger journeys: (1995/96) 469,000
(1996/97) 1.3 million
(1997/98) 1.5 million

Current situation: West Coast Express commuter service between Mission and Vancouver (65 km) was inaugurated in 1995, using CP Rail tracks. There are eight stations with a total of 2,500 park-and-ride spaces, also served by feeder buses. Five peak-hour peak-direction trips are operated daily; CP Rail provides train crew, while VIA Rail maintains the rolling stock.

Rolling stock: 5 diesel locomotives, 28 bilevel cars. An additional 3 second-hand bilevel cars are being leased.

West Vancouver Municipal Transit

Manager of Transportation: A Lorage
Staff: 76

Passenger journeys: (West Vancouver Bus)
(1995/96) 2.5 million
(1996/97) 2.6 million
(1997/98) 2.8 million

Current situation: Provides bus service under contract to BC Transit on eight routes connecting West Vancouver and Lions Bay with Vancouver and the University of BC. BC Transit owns the buses and maintenance facility and determines routes, service levels and fares. Buses are identified by a blue motif which is different from the livery used elsewhere.

Fleet: 27 buses

Orion I (1992)	9
Flyer G40 low-floor (1995)	17
GMC (1974)	1
In peak service: 25	

UPDATED

VENICE
Population: 320,000
Public transport: Bus and boat services in city, Lido and surrounding areas provided by authority owned by consortium of Province of Venice and 21 local authorities. Suburban rail services operated by state railways (FS)

ACTV

Azienda Consorzio Trasporti Veneziano (ACTV)
Corte dell'Albero 3880, PO Box 688, 30124 Venice, Italy
Tel: (+39 041) 272 21 11   Fax: (+39 041) 520 71 3 5
Managing Director: Dr Antonio Stifanelli
Staff: 3,000

Operating costs financed by: Fares 43.3 per cent, other commercial sources 7.2 per cent, regional and national subsidies 49.5 per cent

Developments: From April 1997, the ferry routes linking San Marco with Lido, Murano and the airport, and Piazzale Roma with Murano, have been contracted to a private operator. Fares and timetables are integrated with ACTV services.

Bus
Passenger journeys: (1992) 90.6 million
(1995) 91.7 million
(1996) 93 million
Vehicle-km: (1992) 32.6 million
(1995) 32 million
(1996) 31.9 million

Number of routes: Urban 49, suburban 35
Route length: 707 km

Fleet: 570 vehicles
In peak service: Urban 256, suburban 223
On order: 28 buses for delivery during 1998

Most intensive service: 10 min
One-person operation: All routes
Fare collection: Payment to farebox or prepurchase with validation and cancelling machines on board
Fare structure: Urban, stage or flat rate for each hour's travel, day and 3-day tickets; suburban/interurban, stage
Fare evasion control: Random inspection
Average peak-hour speed: Urban 21.6 km/h

Three-door Iveco urban bus of ACTV   **1998**/0010040

Autosan H9 of private operator Bus-City on Legionowo—Warsaw suburban service   **1998**/0010045

Current situation: The transport authority ZTM was established at the end of 1992 to oversee all urban transport planning and operations, ticket sales and marketing. It purchases services mainly from three city-owned operators — MZA (bus), TW (tramway), and MW (metro). Some bus services are now contracted to private operators by ZTM, and their number is increasing.

The initial metro route opened in 1995. The metro is intended to become the main transport system for the city, connecting the new suburban housing estates of Natolin, Ursynow, and Stuzew nad Dolinka with the central area, and bringing much-needed relief to the city's congested surface transport.

Tramways will form the basic transport system for districts not served by the metro, as well as serving secondary routes. Buses are seen as providing direct connections from distant estates to the city centre as well as feeding the metro and railway terminals.

Plans exist for creation of several more bus lanes to speed peak-hour journeys. A location and communication system for the tram network, introduced in 1996, is being extended to buses starting in 1998.

Fare collection: Prepurchase at kiosk with validation and cancelling machines on board
Fare structure: Flat, no transfer; prepurchase single tickets, monthly, quarterly and semi-annual passes
Arrangements for elderly/disabled: Half-price single tickets and monthly passes for pensioners and retired persons. Free travel for those over 75, war and army invalids, blind persons and their guides, disabled schoolchildren. Financed from budgeted subsidies
Operating costs financed by: (All modes) Fares 71.6 per cent, subsidy/grants from city 28.4 per cent

MZA

Miejskie Zaklady Autobusowe
(address above)
Principal Officers: Roman Podsiadly,
Wlodzimierz Wojciechowski, Roman Wawrowski
Staff: 5,923

Bus
Vehicle-km: (1997) 93.5 million

Number of routes: 158
Route length: 777 km
Priority right-of way: On three streets

Fleet: 2,171 buses

Ikarus 260 (1979/97)	597
Ikarus 405 midibus (1979/94)	429
Jelcz L11 (1994)	5
Jelcz 120M (1989)	5
Dennis Lance (1992/94)	3
DAB 1200 (1979/85)	4
Ikarus 411 (1995)	2
Jelcz M121M (1995/97)	79
Ikarus 280 articulated	996
Ikarus 435 articulated (1992)	5
Ikarus 417 low-floor (1995)	2
Jelcz Volvo articulated (1993)	1
Jelcz M181MB articulated (1996)	11
Neoplan N4020 15 m low-floor (1994/97)	32

In peak service: 1,224
Average age of fleet: 8.4 years

Most intensive service: 5 min
One-person operation: All routes
Fare evasion control: Roving inspectors
Operational control: Permanent supervisors at terminal points on approx 60 per cent of routes; other terminals and route operations subject to spot checks by inspectors in radio-controlled cars; introduction of computerised monitoring and control in progress
Average peak-hour speed: 17.6 km/h
New vehicles financed by: Central fund (70 per cent of depreciation cost transferred to budget account)

Contracted bus
Current situation: Eleven routes totalling 121 km were contracted out in 1994, with more following in 1995. Statistics for these services are included in the MZA figures above.

Suburban bus
Current situation: The suburban communities of Józefów, Legionowo, Lominaki and Wolomin run their own municipal bus services, connecting with MZA buses and/or TW trams. In addition, private operators Albatros, Arka, DJ Cars, Ekspress, Ekspress-Nowa Linia, Mini Bus, Mustang, Okuniew, Pasmo, Raj Bus, Rapid, Toro, Translud and Transwar run through services from the suburbs to central Warsaw.

TW

Tramwaje Warszawskie (TW)
(address above)
Tel: (+48 22) 827 28 13   Fax: (+48 22) 827 05 43
Principal officer: Krysztof Karos
Staff: 3,241

Tramway
Type of operation: Conventional tramway

Car-km: (1992) 39.7 million
(1994) 42.2 million
(1996) 43.5 million

Route length: 122 km
   reserved track: 86 km
Number of routes: 28
Number of stops: 500
Gauge: 1,435 mm
Electrification: 600 V DC, overhead

Rolling stock: 880 cars

Konstal 13N (1964 on)	407
105N (1974 on)	464
106N	M8
112N	M1

In peak service: 650

On order: Alstom Konstal: 24 single cars and 15 articulated (three-unit, low-floor), delivery 1998/99; 20 single cars and 10 articulated (three-unit, low-floor), delivery 1999

First/last service: 04.00/00.20

MW

Metro Warszawskie (MW)
ul Marszalkowska 77/79, 016-83 Warsaw
Tel: (+48 22) 826 82 11   Fax: (+48 22) 727 22 42
Principal officers: Kazimierz Kulig, Bogdan Bator, Leszek Nowak
Staff: 754

Type of operation: Full metro, opened 1995

Passenger journeys: (1996) 27 million
(1997) 29.5 million

Route length: 10.9 km
Number of lines: 1
Number of stations: 11
Gauge: 1,435 mm
Track: Concrete slab
Max gradient: 3.1%
Minimum curve radius: 300 m
Signalling: Automatic speed control with cab signalling
Surveillance: Automatic fire-control system; CCTV at stations
Electrification: 750 V DC, third rail

Service: Peak 4 min
Fare structure: Flat; free transfer to other modes

Rolling stock: 60 cars

Mytischi	M10
Wagonmash	M32
Wagonmash (1997)	M18

In peak service: 36
On order: 108 cars from Alstom Poland (Konstal) for delivery 2000–2004

Current situation: Construction started in 1983 on north-south Line 1 of the long-planned 105 km four-line system, and was dogged by financial problems. The first section links Politechnika in the city centre with Kabaty in the south. The remainder of Line 1, running 13.5 km to a northern terminus at the Warsaw steelworks at Mlociny, is under construction in two phases, with a total of 11 stations.

Plans for the other three metro lines are under study. These are Line II, from Wola through Śródmieście, central Prague to Tarchomin and Nowodwory; and Line III, from Ochota through Śródmieście, South Praga to Goclaw.

PKP

Polish State Railways (PKP)
ul Chalubinskiego 4, 009-28 Warsaw
Tel: (+48 22) 624 40 00   Fax: (+48 22) 621 27 05

Suburban rail
Current situation: Operates extensive suburban services (some electrified) on routes to Skierniewice (71 km, at least every hour), Czachowek (42 km, hourly), Lowicz (87 km, hourly), Nasielsk (56 km, at least hourly), Tiuszcz (34 km, half-hourly), Minsk Mazowiecki (45 km, half-hourly), Otwock (32 km, half-hourly) and Milanowek/Grodzisk (32 km, half-hourly to each). Frequent cross-city service provided by these and other trains between Warsaw Wlochy/Zachodnia and Wschodnia stations, about nine trains per hour. Also at less regular intervals on other routes.

Light rail
Current situation: 29 km suburban light rail line runs southwest to Grodzisk, with a short branch to Milanówek, carrying about 5 million passengers annually; electrified 600 V DC overhead.

Rolling stock: 40 six-axle articulated cars

UPDATED

WASHINGTON

Population: City 607,000, metropolitan area 3.2 million
Public transport: Bus and metro services in city of Washington, and parts of suburban Maryland, Virginia and District of Columbia provided by Area Transit Authority governed by representative board. Separate local bus services feeding metro provided by county agencies for Montgomery County suburban area, city of Alexandria and Fairfax and Prince George's counties. MARC commuter rail service supported by Maryland state; Virginia commuter rail service supported by local transportation commissions; commuter buses run by private companies. Shared taxi system based on zonal tariff operates in city

WMATA

Washington Metropolitan Area Transit Authority (WMATA)
600 Fifth Street NW, Washington, DC 20001, USA
Tel: (+1 202) 962 12 34   Fax: (+1 202) 962 28 97
Chair: Cleatus E Barnett
General Manager: Richard A White
Deputy General Manager, Operations: Charles W Thomas
Staff: 8,632

Passenger journeys: (Both modes)
(1995/96) 211.2 million
(1996/97) 210.8 million

Operating costs financed by: Fares 47.2 per cent, other commercial sources 3.4 per cent, local subsidy/grants 48.2 per cent, FTA subsidy 1.2 per cent

Current situation: A major programme of metro construction and bus fleet renewal and service development has taken place since WMATA was created in 1967. The metro plan adopted called for a 166 km 83-station network, of which 150 km is in service.
Developments: LS Transit Systems Inc (LSTS) is supplying Rail Operations Simulation System software to WMATA. LSTS is serving as a sub-contractor to Alstom Signalling Inc (formerly General Railway Signal Corporation) as part of Alstom's contract to provide a train control system for the Green Line extension.

During FY98, WMATA reported record ridership of approximately 536,000 passengers on its rail network each weekday.

One hundred additional cars are on order to accommodate ridership growth and the Green Line extension. Line extensions for the remaining seven Metrorail stations in the funded WMATA system are scheduled to be completed by early 2001. The inner Green Line connection between U Street-Cardozo and Fort Totten is scheduled to open in December 1999. The outer Green Line extension, extending from Anacostia to Branch Avenue in Price George's County, Maryland, is due to open in the spring of 2001.

Cubic Transportation Systems (CTS) is installing smartcard systems and will retrofit smartcard readers to existing gates as the project unfolds. However, implementation will start with the installation of electric paddle gates at those stations which are not already gated.

Bus

Passenger boardings: (1994) 168 million
(1995) 147 million
(1996) 123 million
Vehicle-km: (1995) 70.9 million
(1996) 67.6 million

Number of routes: 365
Route length: (One way) 2,118 km
On priority right-of-way: 79.3 km

Fleet: 1,557 vehicles, plus 182 in reserve
GMC RTS (1979)	115
Gillig Phantom (1988)	20
Flxible 'New Look'	99
GMC/Blitz refurbished	163
Flxible Metro (1986/95)	761
MAN articulated (1983)	32
Orion V (1992)	60
Ikarus 436 articulated (1995)	45
Orion V (1997/98)	262
In peak service:	**1,155**

Most intensive service: 5-6 min
One-person operation: All routes

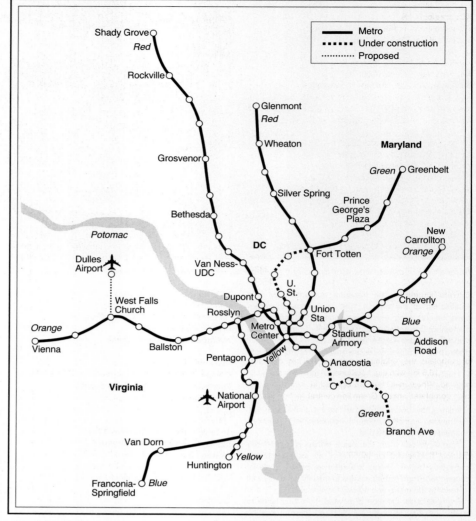

Washington metro

Fare collection: Exact fare; GFI registering fareboxes
Fare structure: Zonal, 10 cent transfer; area monthly/2-weekly pass, monthly bus/rail pass; off-peak pass
Fare evasion control: Non-uniformed police officers; registering fareboxes
Integration with other modes: Buses feed metro stations; transfer from metro for journeys continued by bus
Operational control: Street supervisors/central radio
Arrangements for elderly/disabled: Half fare, subsidised from local budgets; on call bus service; fleet of 35 vans; MetroAccess paratransit service
Average peak-hour speed: In mixed traffic, 11 km/h; in bus lanes, 25-27 km/h
Bus priority: I-66 road from Beltway into Washington open to buses and carpools only during peak hours in peak direction; I-395 has reversible-flow HOV lanes
Operating costs financed by: Fares 31.1 per cent, other commercial sources 2.8 per cent, subsidy/grants 66.1 per cent

New vehicles financed by: FTA grants 80 per cent, local funds 20 per cent

Metro

Type of operation: Full metro, initial route opened 1976

Passenger boardings: (1994) 198 million
(1995) 198.4 million
(1996) 194 million
Car-km: (1994) 68.6 million
(1995) 67.6 million
(1996) 69.7 million

Route length: 150 km
  in tunnel: 52.8 km
  elevated: 10.4 km
Number of lines: 5
Number of stations: 75
  in tunnel: 41
Gauge: 1,435 mm

Up to 10,000 passengers a day are using Franconia-Springfield metro station, opened in 1997

Fare structure: Zonal; multitickets; passes
Fare evasion control: Roving inspectors
Operational control: Computer-based system (RBL)
Average distance between stops: 390 m
Average peak-hour speed: 19.5 km/h
Integration with other modes: Free transfers between monorail/bus and regional rail services of DB
Operating costs financed by: Fares 33 per cent, other commercial sources 53 per cent, subsidy/grants 14 per cent
Subsidy from: City council
New vehicles financed by: Transport undertaking and partly by grants

Developments: Two CNG-powered buses were evaluated in a two-year trial started in 1995. WSW runs its own gas filling station which is also available to other users of CNG.

Suspended monorail 'Schwebebahn'
Staff: 260

Type of operation: Monorail on Langen system, opened 1901

Car-km: (Annual) 1.8 million

Route length: 13.3 km
Number of routes: 1
Number of stations: 19
Max gradient: 4%
Electrification: 600 V DC

Service: 3 min
Integration with other modes: Bus and rail
One-person operation: With CCTV surveillance of platforms
Operating costs financed by: Fares 44 per cent, other sources 38 per cent, subsidy/grants 18 per cent

Rolling stock: 29 cars
MAN (1972/75)   M28
Historic car (1901)   M1
In peak service: 22
On order: 36 cars required for delivery 2005

DB
Deutsche Bahn AG

Type of operation: Suburban heavy rail

Current situation: Extensive suburban services including express routes (SB) link Wuppertal with other cities in the Rhein-Ruhr. The city's first S-Bahn route is the east-west line from Hagen through Wuppertal to Düsseldorf, Neuss and Mönchengladbach, opened in 1988 as S8 (see Rhein-Ruhr entry).

Regional bus
Current situation: Joint or connecting services provided by WSW with neighbouring municipal operators in Solingen, Remscheid, Ennepe-Ruhrkreis, Bochum, Essen and Düsseldorf. Certain routes operated by Busverkehr Rheinland (BVR).

UPDATED

New Schwebebahn station Kluse under construction   **1999**/0043918

XI'AN
Population: 2.5 million
Public transport: An extensive network of bus and trolleybus services provided by municipal agencies covers the city and inner suburbs. The trolleybus system includes an interurban route to a satellite town. Minibuses. A few suburban trains are run by Chinese Railways

Xi'an City Transport
Xi'an City Transport Company
Xi'an, Shaanxi Province, People's Republic of China

Bus
Current situation: The bus fleet was progressively

modernised throughout the 1980s, with buses built locally and in Beijing. The two administrative divisions have been reorganised into three to cope with expanding operations.

Most bus routes also support minibus services run in parallel, providing more comfort for a higher fare.

Number of routes: 40

Fleet: Approx 500 buses, including many articulated. Types are mainly Xi'an two-axle and articulated, and Beijing BK663 articulated, but there are also small batches of Chengdu, Siping, Jianyu and Tianjin buses, and Daimler Fleetline double-deck ex-KMB of Hong Kong

Fare collection: Stage fares paid to seated conductor, two conductors on articulated vehicles; monthly passes

Trolleybus
Current situation: Large-scale renewal of the obsolete trolleybus fleet took place in 1982 and 1985. Many more new trolleybuses have been delivered since 1986.

Number of routes: 5
Fleet: Over 100, all articulated. Most are type Shanghai SK561, but latest deliveries are Beijing BD562

VERIFIED

YANGON (RANGOON)
Population: 1.5 million
Public transport: Bus services provided by private operators; suburban services operated by state railway

Bus
Current situation: Apart from limited diesel-powered suburban rail services, public transport is entirely road-based, the vehicles ranging from full-size single-deck

buses down to small pick-ups. Intensive bus services exist in the downtown area, the density reducing towards the edge of the city, which gives way to open countryside and limited interurban sevices.

It is understood, but not confirmed, that the former Road Transport Corporation has been abolished, and that all bus service is now provided by private enterprise. The present organisational structure of the network is not known and it is not possible for foreign visitors to obtain meaningful understanding of it on sight because all names and numerals are displayed only in Burmese script.

For many years the backbone of bus operations was a large fleet of medium-size buses built on Chevrolet and Dodge military truck chassis of North American origin, assumed to date back to the Second World War. Many such buses, which must have been rebuilt for right-hand running in 1970, remain in service.

From 1987 a number of Saviem SC10 and at least two Berliet PR100 city buses from several French cities were imported. It is assumed that they were used in Yangon and were not very successful in local conditions, as few Saviems were to be seen in the Yangon area and none elsewhere in 1995. The Berliets were still in use at Yangon airport.

More recently, second-hand buses have been obtained

Toyota Dyna pick-up minibus awaits passengers   **1996**

Saviem SC10 on Yangon city service   **1996**

from other Asian countries, notably Japan and South Korea. Many city buses from Tokyo were in service in 1995, along with some from the Ryukyu Islands and others from unidentified operators. Former operators' liveries were retained.

Korean buses are probably preferred because, unlike Japanese and Thai vehicles, they do not need to be converted for right-hand running. Examples of Daewoo BF101 and Hyundai FB485 models were numerous and a fresh shipload of Korean buses arrived in 1995.

Paratransit

Current situation: Paratransit vehicles (in descending order of size) include Toyota Dyna, HiLux and Publica types and locally built Mazda B600 and related types. All these are small truck or pick-up chassis with rudimentary bodywork.

MR

Myanmar Railways
Bogyoke Aung San Street, PO Box 118, Yangon, Myanmar
Tel: (+95 1) 29 60 96   Fax: (+95 1) 29 85 80

Type of operation: Suburban heavy rail

Passenger journeys: (1991) 35 million
(1992) 19.1 million
(1993) 18.3 million

Current situation: Suburban services run on seven routes around Yangon totalling 179 km, including a circular service, part of which has been proposed for electrification in feasibility studies carried out by Japanese engineers. Resignalling and other rehabilitation works started on part of the circular route in 1992.

Rolling stock: 11 diesel locomotives, 63 coaches

VERIFIED

YEKATERINBURG

Population: 1.4 million
Public transport: Bus and trolleybus/tramway services provided by separate municipal undertakings. Metro under construction.

Upravlenie Automobil'novo Transporta

Upravlenie Automobil'novo Transporta
Yekaterinburg, Russia

Bus

Passenger journeys: Approx 50 million (annual)

Number of routes: About 40
Route length: 350 km

Fleet: Includes Ikarus 260/263/280 and second-hand vehicles from Sweden and Germany

Tramvaino-Trolleibusnoe Upravlenie

Tramvaino-Trolleibusnoe Upravlenie
Shartashskaya ul 4, Yekaterinburg 620038
Tel: (+7 3432) 51 57 83
Director: G S Sergeyev
Staff: 5,000

Trolleybus

Passenger journeys: (1994) 120 million

Current situation: A trolleybus network of some 65 km is operated over 17 routes.

Fleet: 260 trolleybuses	
Uritsky ZIU9	239
Uritsky ZIU10	21
In peak service: 210	

Tramway

Passenger journeys: (1994) 240 million
(1996) 193.5 million

Current situation: A 1,524 mm gauge tramway network of 185 km is operated over 32 routes. Modernisation of the fleet started in 1995 with delivery of the first locally built Tatra-based T3M.

Rolling stock: 471 cars	
ČKD Tatra T3	M404
ČKD Tatra T3M	M67
In peak service: 360	

Metro

Current situation: Initial section of Line 1 now reported as in operation, 12 km with six stations, 1,524 mm gauge, electrified 825 V DC, fleet of 54 cars.

VERIFIED

ZIU9 trolleybus and ex-Swedish Scania near the railway station   **1998**/0010050

YOKOHAMA

Population: 3.2 million
Public transport: Bus and metro services operated by divisions of Municipal Transport Bureau. Commuter rail services run by JR and three private railway companies. Additional bus services provided by the three private railways and four private bus operators. Ferry service across Yokohama port. Automated guideway system

Yokohama-shi Kotsu Kyoku

Yokohama Municipal Transportation Bureau
1-1 Minato-cho, Naka-ku, Yokohama 231-0017, Japan
Tel: (+81 45) 671 31 60   Fax: (+81 45) 664 32 66

Current situation: Serves part of the Yokohama conurbation with a population of about 1 million.

Over half of Yokohama's bus routes are provided by this municipal operator with the remainder, serving mainly outer suburbs, run by seven private companies. All operators charge a common fare within the flat fare area which covers much of the city.

A computer-controlled bus location system which relays information about approaching buses to bus stop panels has been installed.

Late evening 'Midnight' services operate on 21 routes, and lift-equipped vehicles on four routes.

Bus

Staff: 2,412

Passenger journeys: (1990/91) 175.4 million
(1991/92) 180.3 million
(1992/93) 179.6 million
Vehicle-km: (1990/91) 40.7 million
(1991/92) 41.7 million
(1992/93) 42.1 million

Route length: 557 km
On priority right-of-way: 59 km
Number of routes: 138

Fleet: 1,038 vehicles, all air conditioned	
Hino	322
Isuzu	202
Mitsubishi	282
Nissan Diesel	232
In peak service: 908	

One-person operation: All vehicles
Fare collection: Farebox at entrance or prepurchase
Operational control: Inspectors; computerised 'bus operation improvement system' (see below)
Fare structure: Flat except for 9 stage fare routes which extend beyond flat fare zone; prepurchase coupon

tickets, 1- and 3-month passes (bus, bus/metro), day tickets (bus, bus/metro). Prepurchase coupon tickets valid on buses of all 8 companies operating in Yokohama
Bus priority: Exclusive bus lanes (25 km), bus priority lanes (33 km), 6 bus priority traffic signal installations and one section of road with movable centre line allowing contraflow bus lane
Average peak hour speed: 13.7 km/h
Operating costs financed by: Fares 91.2 per cent, other commercial sources 3.2 per cent, subsidy/grants 5.6 per cent
Subsidy from: City 100 per cent

Metro

Staff: 788

Type of operation: Full metro, first line opened 1972

Passenger journeys: (1990/91) 91.3 million
(1991/92) 94 million
(1993/94) 113 million
Car-km: (1990/91) 13.8 million
(1991/92) 13.9 million
(1992/93) 14.1 million

Route length: 32.9 km
  in tunnel: 26.8 km

Number of lines: 2, operated as a single through route
Number of stations: 27
Gauge: 1,435 mm
Max gradient: 3.5%
Minimum curve radius: 125 m
Tunnel: Box
Electrification: 750 V DC, third rail

Service: Peak 4½ min, off-peak 8 min
First/last train: 05.20/00.17
Signalling: Full ATC with cab signalling and CTC
Operating costs financed by: Fares 36.9 per cent, other commercial sources 29.8 per cent, subsidy/grants 33.3 per cent
Subsidy from: National government 46.9 per cent, city 49.1 per cent, region 4 per cent

Rolling stock: 186 cars, in six-car sets
1000 series (1972/76/77/84)	M56 T28
2000 series (1986)	M36 T18
3000 series (1992/93)	M32 T16

Current situation: 10.8 km extension from Shin-Yokohama via Kohoku New Town to an interchange with the Tokyu Denentoshi line at Azamino opened in 1993. A further extension from Totsuka to Shonandai (7.4 km 5 stations), providing interchange with the Odaku Enoshima line and extended Sagami Izumino line at Shonandai, is under construction for 1999 opening.
Developments: 67.8 km network with four lines planned. Powers have been sought to build 16 km Line 4 from Hiyoshi (on Tokyu's Toyoko line) via Kohoku New Town to Nakayama (on JR East's Yokohama line) for opening in 2004.

Yokohama New Transit
Yokohama Shin Toshi Kotsu
1-1 Sachiura 2-chome, Kanazawa-ku, Yokohama 236-0003
Tel: (+81 45) 787 70 02   Fax: (+81 45) 787 70 19

Type of operation: Rubber-tyred automated guideway system 'Kanazawa Seaside Line'

Passenger journeys: (1990) 34,000 daily
(1991) 40,000 daily
(1992) 41,000 daily
Car-km: (1992) 2,700 daily

Route length: 10.6 km
Number of lines: 1
Number of stations: 14
Track: Elevated with side guidance
Gauge: 2,900 mm between guide bars
Max gradient: 4%
Minimum curve radius: 50 m
Electrification: 750 V DC

Service: Peak 5 min, off-peak 10 min
First/last train: 05.55/23.47
Train operation: Driverless, ATO

Rolling stock: 17 five-car trains

Current situation: The Kanazawa Seaside Line, opened in 1989, serves new development areas built on land reclaimed from the sea and connects with JR's Negishi line at Shin-Sugita and with Keihin Kyuko at Kanazawa-Hakkei. Yokohama New Transit is a third-sector company half-owned by Yokohama municipality.
Developments: A 0.2 km extension from the current provisional terminus at Kanazawa-Hakkei is planned to improve interchange with the Keihin-Kyuko Railway.

Sagami Tetsudo 'Sotetsu'
Sagami Railway
2-9-14 Kitasaiwai, Nishi-ku, Yokohama 220-0004
Tel: (+81 45) 319 21 11
President: K Tsushima

Suburban railway
Staff: 1,133

Passenger journeys: (1991/92) 247 million
(1992/93) 247 million
(1993/94) 248 million
Car-km: (1992/93) 41 million
(1993/94) 42 million

Current situation: Main line totalling 24.6 km runs from Yokohama to Ebina, with 8.2 km branch from Futamatagawa to Izumi-chuo, total 23 stations, 1,067 mm gauge, electrified 1.5 kV DC. Connects with Odakyu Railway trains at Ebina.

Rolling stock: 432 emu cars   M242 T190

Developments: A 3.1 km extension of the Izumino line is to open in 1999 and will connect with the Odakyu Enoshima line and the extended Yokohama metro at Shonandai. A further 14.5 km extension is planned from Shonandai to Hiratsuka. A deep-level line to run 8 km from central Yokohama westwards to Futamatagawa is also proposed.

Bus
Passenger journeys: (1990/91) 45 million
(1991/92) 45.4 million
(1992/93) 44.7 million
Vehicle-km: (1992/93) 10.3 million

Current situation: Sagami Tetsudo operates 286 buses on Yokohama area services, totalling 243 route-km.

Keihin Kyuko Dentetsu 'Keikyu'
Keihin Express Electric Railway
20-20 Takanawa 2-chome, Minato-ku, Tokyo 108-0074
Tel: (+81 3) 32 80 91 22   Fax: (+81 3) 32 80 91 93
President: K Hiramatsu

Interurban rail
Current situation: Main line links Shinagawa (Tokyo) with Kawasaki/Yokohama and Misaki-guchi, with three branches totalling 83.6 km, 1,435 mm gauge, electrified 1.5 kV DC. In Tokyo some trains run through to Keisei tracks via Toei Asakusa line metro, but the heaviest traffic is from the southern suburbs into Yokohama.

Rolling stock: 758 emu cars   M640 T118

Bus
Current situation: Keikyu Bus operates Yokohama area services as well as services in Tokyo, Kawasaki and other parts of Kanagawa Prefecture.

Tokyo Kyuko Dentetsu 'Tokyu'
Tokyo Express Electric Railway — Tokyu Corp
5-6, Nanpeidai-cho, Shibuya-ku, Tokyo 150-0036
Tel: (+81 3) 34 77 61 81   Fax: (+81 3) 34 96 29 65
President: S Shimizu

Interurban rail
Current situation: Main Toyoko line (26.3 km) links Tokyo (Shibuya) and Yokohama's Sakuragi-cho station, with through service from Hiyoshi, just within Yokohama,

to central Tokyo via Eidan Hibiya line metro. The Denentoshi line provides a direct link from eight stations in Yokohama's northwest suburbs to central Tokyo via Tokyu's underground Shin-Tamagawa line and the Eidan Hanzomon line metro. Additional hourly shuttle service operated on 3.4 km branch to Kodomo-no-kuni (Children's World) Park, 1,067 mm gauge, electrified 1.5 kV DC.
Developments: The third sector Yokohama Rapid Railway (builder of the Minato Mirai 21 line, see below) has assumed control of the Kodomo-no-kuni line and will upgrade it to cater for increasing commuter traffic from new residential developments. The scheme, due for 2000 completion, includes a new intermediate station.

Rolling stock: 1,036 cars   M735 T301

Bus
Current situation: Tokyu Bus Corp operates 41 Yokohama area routes including two 'Tokyu Coach' demand-responsive services.

JR East
East Japan Railway Company
Higashi Nihon Ryokaku Tetsudo
2-2-2 Yoyogi, Shibuya-ku, Tokyo 151-8578
Tel: (+81 3) 53 34 11 51   Fax: (+81 3) 53 34 11 10
Website: www.jreast.co.jp/
Chair: S Yamanouchi
President: M Matsuda

Type of operation: Inner and outer suburban heavy rail

Passenger journeys: (1995/96) 481.3 million (Yokohama city)

Current situation: Frequent trains between Tokyo and suburban areas to the south of Yokohama carry commuters to both cities. All-stations inner suburban service is provided on the Keihin-Tohoku line (Ofuna–Yokohama–Kawasaki–Tokyo–Omiya, 81 km), and rapid service outer suburban service on the Tokaido line (Tokyo–Yokohama–Odawara) and Yokosuka line (Tokyo–Yokohama–Kurihama). Local suburban service on 43 km Yokohama line from Hachioji to Higashi-Kanagawa via Shin-Yokohama with some trains continuing to Isogo and Ofuna on the Negishi line. Also 7 km Tsurumi line from Tsurumi to Ogimachi.

Yokohama Kosoku Tetsudo
Yokohama Rapid Railway

Current situation: This third sector company is building a 4.1 km underground line from Yokohama along the waterfront to Motomachi to serve the new Minato Mirai 21 commercial development area. The line is due for

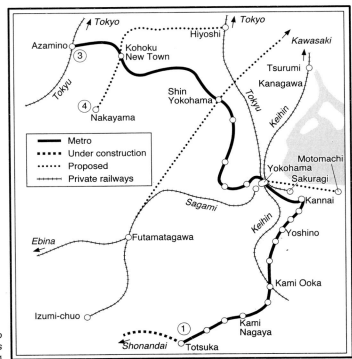

Yokohama metro and private railways
0010344

JR East Yokohama line train at Sakuragi-cho (Colin Brown)   **1999**/0043917

completion in 2001. Longer-term plans exist for a 7 km extension to Negishi, with a possible connection from there via Kami-Ooka and Higashi-Totsuka to Tsurugamine, so creating a Yokohama loop line. Shareholders include Yokohama city, Kanagawa prefecture and the Tokyu Railway.

Developments: The company has taken over responsibility for the Tokyu Kodomo-no-kuni (Children's World) line, which it will upgrade and build an intermediate station, ready to run a full commuter service in 2000.

Other bus operators
Current situation: Yokohama area services are also provided by Kanagawa Chuo Kotsu and Odakyu Bus (see Tokyo entry), Kawasaki Tsurumi Rinko Bus (see Kawasaki entry) and Enoshima Dentetsu.

Railway developments (planned)
Current situation: Further investment in rail transit is planned in recommendations put forward by the Council for Transport Policy in 1985.

North of Yokohama, a 19 km line would connect the Sagami Railway at Futamatagawa with Shin-Yokohama and Kawasaki, joining Tokyu's Toyoko line at Okurayama. This would allow trains off Tokyo's new metro Line 7 to reach Shin-Yokohama and beyond. A further joint service would tie in with another planned extension to the Yokohama metro.

Also a new direct service would connect the JR Yokosuka line with Shinjuku and Ikebukuro in Tokyo.

UPDATED

ZAGREB
Population: 775,000, conurbation 1 million
Public transport: Bus, tramway, funicular and cable car services provided by municipal undertaking. Suburban services provided by state railway, with some other bus operators

ZET
Javno Poduzeće Zagrebački električni tramvaj (JP ZET)
Ozaljska 105, 10000 Zagreb, Croatia
Tel: (+385 1) 33 35 15   Fax: (+385 1) 34 05 20
General Manager: Julius Pevalek
Deputy General Manager, Traffic: Branko Mikinac
Staff: 4,637

Passenger journeys: (All modes)
(1995) 268.8 million
(1996) 252.7 million
(1997) 260.5 million

Operating costs financed by: Fares 47.8 per cent, other commercial sources 32.4 per cent, subsidy/grants 22.9 per cent

Current situation: Following a restructuring, the municipal area of Zagreb was reduced somewhat to 610 km². ZET operates within this area and neighbouring municipalities, having separately contracted arrangements with each in regard to service levels and fares. Trams provide the main city-centre penetration, with buses generally acting as feeders. Many suburban bus routes now terminate at interchange points with trams or articulated buses providing frequent trunk services to the city centre, with express journeys operating in peak hours.
Developments: At the end of 1994 ZET ceased to operate bus services outside the city limits, these operations being tendered for by private companies. Tendering for city services started in 1995, with the aim of reducing operating costs.

ZET MAN low-floor bus   **1999**/0043287

ZET's funicular service   **1999**/0043285

Bus
Passenger journeys: (1995) 101.4 milion
(1996) 95 million
(1997) 97.8 million
Vehicle-km: (1995) 25.9 million
(1996) 26.5 million
(1997) 26.8 million

Number of routes: 118 plus 4 night
Route length: (One way) 1,240 km
On priority right-of-way: 3.9 km

Fleet: 332 buses

TAM standard	78
MAN standard	78
MAN low-floor	6
MAN articulated	73
MAN NG272/312 low-floor articulated	33
Mercedes standard	23
Mercedes articulated	41
In peak service: 272	

Most intensive service: 5 min
One-person operation: All routes
Fare collection: Prepurchase or payment to driver, with cancelling machines on board
Fare structure: Zones covering Zagreb and each neighbouring municipality; 20-trip carnets, single tickets; monthly and yearly passes valid in Zagreb only, or individual municipalities plus Zagreb Zone 1; free transfer between bus and tram in direction of journey
Fare evasion control: Ticket inspectors
Operational control: Mobile route inspectors in radio contact with supervisors at terminal points and with central control on UKW system
Arrangements for elderly/disabled: Monthly passes for retired persons at half rate funded by retired and disabled insurance fund; annual passes for disabled financed by ZET; free travel for over-65s; 2 buses equipped to carry wheelchairs

ZET's refurbished trams with chopper control
1999/0043286

Average peak-hour speed: 24 km/h

Tramway
Type of operation: Conventional tramway

Passenger journeys: (1995) 167.4 million
(1996) 157.7 million
(1997) 162.1 million
Car-km: (1995) 23.1 million
(1996) 22.3 million
(1997) 22.5 million

Route length: 187 km
Number of lines: 15, plus 4 night
Number of stops: 212
Gauge: 1,000 mm
Max gradient: 4.5%
Minimum curve radius: 18 m
Electrification: 600 V DC, overhead

Service: Peak 6-7 min, off-peak 8-9 min
First/last car: (Day service) 04.45/23.58
Fare structure: Monthly and yearly passes, single tickets, 20-trip carnets, day tickets
One-person operation: On all routes except three-car trains on Lines 11 and 12, when conductors in rear cars issue tickets for cancelling on board
Fare evasion control: Roving inspectors
Centralised control: UKW system

Rolling stock: 416 cars

Duro Dakovic 101 two-axle	M50
2101 articulated (refurbished)	M6
201 four-axle	M22
TP1Z trailer	T90
ČKD Tatra 301 articulated	M51
401 four-axle	M87
B4 trailer	T77
TMK900	M1

Duewag ex-Mannheim   M32
In peak service: 289

Developments: Local builder Končar is rebuilding old Djuro Djakovic tramcars as the 2101 class with chopper-controlled traction equipment supplied by Adtranz.

Two extensions are under Construction-Dubrava to Culinecka (3 km) and Jarun to Precko (1.5 km).

Cable car/funicular
Current situation: A 4 km tourist cable car runs to the summit of Mount Medvednica, carrying 80,000 passengers in 1997. A 66 m funicular links the upper old town with the city centre. It carried 594,000 passengers in 1997.

UPDATED

ZARAGOZA
Population: 630,000
Public transport: Bus services provided by franchised municipal undertaking responsible to city council; light rail proposed

Transportes Urbanos
Transportes Urbanos de Zaragoza SA
Miguel Servet 199, Apartado 534, Zaragoza 50013, Spain
Tel: (+34 976) 41 39 00   Fax: (+34 976) 41 93 72
Director General: Antonio Gonzalez de Zulueta
Staff: 804

Bus
Passenger boardings: (1994) 99.4 million
(1996) 102.7 million
Vehicle-km: (1994) 15.5 million

Number of routes: 26
Route length: (One way) 237 km

Fleet: 273 vehicles
Mercedes O405	64
Mercedes O305	43
Mercedes O405 GN2	12
Renault PR100	50
Renault PR100-2	56
Renault R312	25
Renault Citybus	18
Renault PS160.09 (disabled service)	5
In peak service: 228

Most intensive service: 15 min
Fare structure: Flat
Arrangements for elderly/disabled: Several fixed-route services equipped with specially adapted vehicles

Operating costs financed by: Fares 80.4 per cent, other commercial sources 0.5 per cent, subsidy/grants 19.1 per cent
Subsidy from: Local government

Light rail (proposed)
Current situation: The Ministry of Transport agreed to finance studies initiated by the regional government for a three-line light rail network in this city, which was the last in Spain to close its tramways. No progress has been reported.

VERIFIED

ZÜRICH
Population: City 342,000, urban area 556,000, canton 1.2 million
Public transport: Bus, trolleybus, tramway, funicular, rack and local railway services provided by municipal undertaking also running a privately owned rack railway for its owners and responsible for regional bus services. S-Bahn, including airport link, run by Swiss Federal Railways (SBB). Also two private railways. Lake ferries. Verkehrsverbund (ZVV) co-ordinates these and other operations

ZVV
Zürcher Verkehrsverbund (ZVV)
Hofwiesenstrasse 370, 8090 Zürich, Switzerland
Tel: (+41 1) 311 39 39   Fax: (+41 1) 313 00 18
President: Georg Elser

Passenger journeys: (All modes)
(1994) 971,000 daily
(1995) 970,000 daily

Current situation: ZVV was established in 1990 to co-ordinate and promote all forms of public transport in the Canton of Zürich, with a total population of 1.2 million. Services are provided by 43 operators over a network extending to some 2,700 km. With nearly 1 million daily journeys in the urban area, Zürich claims to have the highest use of public transport per head of population in the western world. There is a fully integrated ticketing system based on nine fare stages (45 zones).

All fares income is remitted to ZVV, which compensates individual operators in proportion to service provision and communal tax base.
Developments: A light rail network is proposed for the Mittleren Glattal area east of Zürich, linking Oerlikon with Dübendorf, Wallisellen, Opfikon, the airport and Kloten. Light rail was selected in mid-1996 following evaluation of several unconventional systems, including elevated monorail. The 13 km initial route is unlikely to be in operation before 2005.

VBZ
Verkehrs-Betriebe Zürich (VBZ)
Luggeswegstrasse 65, 8048 Zürich
Tel: (+41 1) 43 44 11   Fax: (+41 1) 434 47 49
Managing Director: Rolf A Künzle
Staff: 2,234

Passenger journeys: (All modes)
(1995) 283 million
(1996) 277 million
(1997) 269 million

Current situation: As the leading member of ZVV, VBZ has achieved spectacular success in promoting its

VBZ Zurich MAN low-floor bus on Route 383 (D Trevor-Rowe)   **1999**/0043288

Class Be4/6 tram of VBZ in front of Zürich Hbf (Milan Šrámek)   **1999**/0043289

Tram at new terminus Hallenstadion Messe on Route 11   *1999*/0043921

'Züri mobile' short-term car rental service with Renault minibus on Route 45 and tram on Route 7
1999/0043929

services to non-users, in particular by sales of annual tickets through major employers. It also encourages walking and greater use of cycles. Also 'Züri mobile' car rental (short term – by the hour).

Developments: Extensions to the tramway are being evaluated, in West-Zürich (Langstrasse), west of the Hardbrücke and to the Zollikerberg. Each would serve large residential or commercial developments, and would complement S-Bahn services. New trams will be required in large numbers after 2000; six prototypes are being evaluated.

Fare collection: Prepurchase of single tickets from 839 vending/validation machines
Fare structure: Zonal (2 city, 3 suburban), covers VBZ and 6 other operators in the Zürich region; weekly, monthly and annual passes
Fares collected on board: Nil
Fare evasion control: Random inspection; penalty fare
Operational control: Computerised online monitoring
Arrangements for elderly/disabled: Reduced-rate weekly, monthly and annual passes
Operating costs financed by: Fares sold by ZVV 45.1 per cent, other commercial sources 11.9 per cent, Federal support for regional lines 0.2 per cent, deficit nil

Bus and trolleybus
Vehicle-km: (1996) Bus 9.9 million, trolleybus 4.8 million
(1997) Bus 9.2 million, trolleybus 5.1 million

Number of routes: Bus 23, trolleybus 7
Route length: (One way) bus 111.9 km, trolleybus 41 km
On priority right-of-way: 12.5 km

Fleet: 173 buses including Saurer and MAN-Büssing
Standard	107
Articulated	41
15-seat minibus	25

Fleet: 85 trolleybuses
FBW and Mercedes	85

On order: 15 Mercedes O405GTZ

Most intensive service: 5 min
One-person operation: All routes
Average peak-hour speed: Bus 16.5 km/h, trolleybus 15.5 km/h
Bus priority: Extensive system of bus lanes, including traffic light controlled dual-direction lane in narrow Langstrasse used by trolleybuses

Developments: There are long-term plans to convert a further four routes to trolleybus operation. Route 46 converted to trolleybus operation in May 1995.

Tramway
Type of operation: Conventional tramway

Car-km: (1995) 18 million
(1996) 17.9 million
(1997) 17.9 million

Route length: 108.9 km
Number of lines: 13
Number of stops: 168
Gauge: 1,000 mm
Electrification: 600 V DC, overhead

Service: Peak 6.7 min, off-peak 8, 10 and 12 min
First/last car: 05.00/00.30

Rolling stock: 355 cars
SWS/MFO Be4/4 (1940/60)	M18
SIG/FFA B4 (1946/63)	T39
SWS/SIG/MFO/BBC Be4/6 (1960/66/68/69)	M127
SWS/SWP/BBC Be4/6 (1976/78)	M60
SWP/BBC Be4/6 (1985/87)	M73
ABB (1992)	M38

On order: Six Cobra five-section low-floor trams from the Züri-Tram consortium of Adtranz and Fiat-SIG. There is an option for supply of a further 11 cars after test running of the six in 2000

Local railway (Forchbahn)
Current situation: 16.4 km metre-gauge line links Zürich (Stadelhofen) and Esslingen, electrified 1.2 kV DC, carries about 4.3 million passengers annually.

Rolling stock: 31 cars SWS/MFO BDe4/4×4 (1959/
1966)	M6
SWS/MFO B+4/4 (1981)	T7
SWS/SWP/SIG/BBC Be8/8×4 (1976/1988)	M6
SWS/SWP/BBC B+4×4 (1981)	T4
SWS/SIG/ABB Be4/4×4 (1983)	M8

Funicular/rack railway
Current situation: VBZ operates a fully automated and unmanned 0.4 km funicular, the Seilbahn Rigiblick (SRB), with two cars. There is a VBZ-operated rack line, the Dolderbahn, a former funicular.

Funicular (Polybahn)
Current situation: A privately owned funicular railway, the Polybahn, is operated by VBZ on behalf of the owner with sponsorship from a local bank.

SBB
Swiss Federal Railways, Zürich & North Eastern Division
PO Box, 8021 Zürich
Tel: (+41 51) 222 11 11   Fax: (+41 51) 222 38 80
Divisional Manager: Erwin Rutishauser

Type of operation: Regional metro (S-Bahn)

Passenger journeys: (1992) 220,000 daily
(1993) 240,000 daily

Current situation: S-Bahn trains serve network of 23 lines extending to 380 route-km with 144 stations, 1,435 mm gauge, electrified 15 kV 16⅔ Hz, including airport link. Services are based on a cross-city tunnel opened in 1990 giving suburban lines on the east side of the city direct access to the city centre at a new underground station at Hbf.

Half-hourly trains run on all routes but one, from about 06.00 to 24.00. Some 40 local bus operators run feeders to S-Bahn stations, where there are timed connections. Zonal fares scheme extends to all modes.

Rolling stock: 110 four-car sets of double-deck stock plus conventional trainsets.

SZU
Sihltal-Zürich-Uetliberg-Bahn
Manessestrasse 152, 8045 Zürich
Tel: (+41 1) 206 45 11   Fax: (+41 1) 206 45 10
Chief Executive Officer: Mrs Christiane Weibel
Staff: 158

Type of operation: Local railway

Passenger journeys: (1995) 7.5 million
(1996) 7.6 million
(1997) 7.5 million

Current situation: Routes link Zürich Hbf with Sihlbrugg (electrified 15 kV 16⅔ Hz) and Uetliberg (1.2 kV DC); total 30 km with 22 stations; trains run every 10 min peak, 20-30 min off-peak. Fare structure integrated with other operators. Also runs one bus route (7 km, one vehicle).
Developments: Buses replace trains at times of low demand.

Rolling stock: 52 emu cars, 6 electric locomotives

UPDATED

MANUFACTURERS

Rail Vehicles and Traction Equipment
Rail and Bus Components and Subassemblies
Electrification — Project Contractors and Equipment Suppliers
New Technology/Innovative Transit Systems
Buses — Chassis, Integrals and Bodies
Trolleybus Traction Equipment
Road Vehicle Chassis Components
Signalling, Communications and Traffic Control Equipment
Revenue Collection Equipment
Vehicle Maintenance Equipment and Services
Track Components and Maintenance Equipment

RAIL VEHICLES AND TRACTION EQUIPMENT

(*Manufacturer of traction equipment)

Company Listing by Country

AUSTRALIA
Adtranz*
Clyde*
Goninan
Walkers

AUSTRIA
Adtranz
Bombardier Transportation
ELIN*
Siemens SGP

BELGIUM
ALSTOM
Bombardier Transportation
CMI

BRAZIL
Adtranz*
ALSTOM*
Gevisa*
Santa Matilde

CANADA
Bombardier Transportation

CHINA, PEOPLE'S REPUBLIC
CCC

CROATIA
Djuro Djaković

CZECH REPUBLIC
ČKD
MSV
Škoda

DENMARK
Adtranz

EGYPT
SEMAF

FINLAND
Adtranz*
Rautaruukki

FRANCE
ALSTOM*
Bombardier Transportation
De Dietrich

GERMANY
Adtranz*
ALSTOM
Bombardier Transportation
Duewag
Kiepe*
Siemens*

HUNGARY
Ganz Ansaldo*
Ganz-Hunslet

INDIA
Bharat
Crompton Greaves
ICF

ITALY
Adtranz*
Ansaldo*
Breda
Costaferroviaria
Fiat
Firema*
Sofer

JAPAN
Alna Koki
Fuji Electric*
Hitachi
Kawasaki
Kinki Sharyo
Mitsubishi Electric*
Niigata Engineering Co
Nippon Sharyo
Tokyu
Toshiba*

KOREA, REPUBLIC
Daewoo
Hanjin
Hyundai
Korea Shipbuilding & Engineering

LATVIA
RVR

MEXICO
Bombardier Transportation

NETHERLANDS
Adtranz
Traxis*

NORWAY
Adtranz*

PORTUGAL
Adtranz

ROMANIA
Astra

RUSSIA
Mytischi*
Ust-Katav

SOUTH AFRICA
Union Carriage

SPAIN
Adtranz*
ALSTOM
CAF

SWEDEN
Adtranz*

SWITZERLAND
Adtranz*
Alusuisse Road & Rail
FIAT-SIG
Schindler Technik

UK
Adtranz
ALSTOM*
Bombardier Transportation
Brush*
Railcare
RFS(E)

USA
Adtranz
Delaware Car
GE Transportation Systems*
Kawasaki Rail Car
Siemens Transportation Systems

Classified Listing

BODYSHELLS
Adtranz
Alusuisse Road & Rail
Bombardier Transportation
Schindler Technik
Siemens Transportation Systems

BOGIES (see also Rail and Bus Components section)
Adtranz
ALSTOM
Bombardier Transportation
Duewag
Fiat
FIAT-SIG
Ganz-Hunslet
Nippon Sharyo
Santa Matilde
SEMAF
Siemens
Siemens SGP Bogie Division
Siemens Transportation Systems
Sofer

COMMUTER/SUBURBAN CARS (unpowered)
Adtranz
ALSTOM

Bombardier Transportation
ČKD Praha
Daewoo
Delaware Car
Firema
Ganz-Hunslet
Goninan
Hitachi
Hyundai
Kawasaki
Kinki Sharyo
Niigata Engineering Co, Japan
Nippon Sharyo
Santa Matilde
Siemens Transportation Systems

COMPLETE ELECTRICAL TRACTION EQUIPMENT
Adtranz
ALSTOM
Ansaldo
Bharat
Bombardier Transportation
Brush
Crompton Greaves
ELIN*
Fiat

Firema
Fuji Electric
Ganz Ansaldo
GE Transportation Systems
Gevisa
Hitachi
Kiepe
Mitsubishi
Siemens
Škoda
Toshiba
Traxis

CONTRACT MAINTENANCE
Adtranz
ALSTOM
Bombardier Transportation
Firema
Goninan
Railcare
RFS(E)
Siemens

DMU/DIESEL RAILCARS
Adtranz
ALSTOM

Bharat
Bombardier Transportation
CAF
Clyde
Daewoo
De Dietrich
Djuro Djaković
Duewag
Ganz-Hunslet
Goninan
Hanjin
Hitachi
Hyundai
ICF
Korea Shipbuilding & Engineering
MSV
Niigata Engineering Co
Nippon Sharyo
RVR
Siemens
Siemens Transportation Systems
Sofer
Tokyu
Toshiba
Traxis
Union Carriage

DOUBLE-DECK CARS
Adtranz
ALSTOM
Bombardier Transportation
Firema
Goninan
Hitachi
Kinki Sharyo
MSV
Rautaruukki

EMUS
Adtranz
Alna Koki
ALSTOM
Ansaldo
Astra
Bharat
Bombardier Transportation
CAF
CCC
Clyde
Daewoo
Firema
Ganz Ansaldo
Ganz-Hunslet
Goninan
Hanjin
Hitachi
ICF
Kawasaki Rail Car
Kinki Sharyo
MSV

Nippon Sharyo
RVR
Santa Matilde
SEMAF
Siemens
Siemens SGP
Siemens Transportation Systems
Sofer
Tokyu
Toshiba
Union Carriage
Walkers

LOW-FLOOR TRAMCARS/LRVs
Adtranz
ALSTOM
Astra
Bombardier Transportation
Breda
CAF
ČKD Praha
De Dietrich
Djuro Djaković
Duewag
Fiat
Firema
Ganz-Hunslet
Hyundai
Kiepe
MSV
Niigata Engineering Co
Schindler Technik
Siemens
Siemens SGP
Siemens Transportation Systems

METRO CARS
Adtranz
Alna Koki
ALSTOM
Astra
Bharat
Bombardier Transportation
Breda
CAF
CCC
ČKD Praha
Costaferroviaria
Daewoo
Duewag
Fiat
Firema
Ganz Ansaldo
Ganz-Hunslet
Hitachi
Hyundai
ICF
Kawasaki
Kawasaki Rail Car
Kinki Sharyo

Korea Shipbuilding & Engineering
MSV
Mytischi
Niigata Engineering Co
Nippon Sharyo
Rautaruukki
SEMAF
Siemens SGP
Škoda

REFURBISHMENT
Adtranz
ALSTOM
Bombardier Transportation
Breda
ČKD Praha
Delaware Car
Firema
Gevisa
Goninan
Railcare
Santa Matilde
Schindler Technik
SEMAF

TRAMCARS/LRVs
Adtranz
ALSTOM
Alna Koki
Astra
Bombardier Transportation
Breda
CCC
ČKD Praha
Costaferroviaria
De Dietrich
Djuro Djaković
Duewag
FIAT-SIG
Firema
Ganz Ansaldo
Ganz-Hunslet
Kinki Sharyo
Mitsubishi Electric
Niigata Engineering Co
Nippon Sharyo
Railcare
Rautaruukki
RVR
Santa Matilde
SEMAF
Siemens
Siemens SGP
Siemens Transportation Systems
Skoda
Toshiba
Union Carriage
Ust-Katav
Walkers

Adtranz

DaimlerChrysler Railsystems
Group Holding Headquarters and Group Corporate Centre
PO Box 130127, D-13601 Berlin, Germany
Tel: (+49 30) 383 20   Fax: (+49 30) 38 32 20 00

Berlin office: Saatwinkler Damm 43, D-13627 Berlin
Group Executive Board
President and Chief Executive Officer (CEO):
　Rolf Eckrodt
Group Advisor: Sir Alastair Morton

EVP, Mass Transit Business Segment (MT):
　Christer Bådholm
EVP, Main Line Business Segment (ML):
　Jürgen Lochmann
EVP, Systems and Components Business Segment (SC):
　Joachim Gaissert
Chief Technical Officer: Åke Wennberg
Chief Financial Officer: Rainer Schmückle
Integration of the Organistion by end 1999:
　Heinz Cronimund
President Marketing and Services (M+S) Product Unit
　(PU) Customer Support: Chris Sheppard
Transition Support: Ruben Ornstein

Product Unit Chief Executives
Marketing and Services (M+S) (NTC – National Transportation Company Executive)
Customer Support: C Sheppard, NTC UK
Fixed Installations: M Leger, NTC Germany

Mass Transit
Innovia People Movers: R Betler, NTC North America
TRS Total Rail Systems: K Rands, NTC UK

Main Line (ML)
Crusaris Inter-City, Inter-Regional & High-Speed Trains:
　J Vinberg, NTC Sweden
Octéon and Blue Tiger Locomotives: B Müller, NTC
　Switzerland
Signalling: P Nottrodt, NTC UK

Systems and Components (S+C)
Converters: H Strasser, NTC Switzerland

Fixed Installations (Electrification) Group (FIX)
Headquarters (see Electrification section)
DaimlerChrysler Railsystems (Deutschland) GmbH
Mainzer Landstrasse 349-351, D-60326 Frankfurt am Main
Tel: (+49 69) 750 75 51   Fax: (+49 69) 750 75 84
Executive: Manfred Lager

UK
Signal Group (SIG) (see Signalling and Communications)
DaimlerChrysler Railsystems Signal Group
Holybrook House, 63 Castle Street, Reading RG1 7SN
Tel: (+44 118) 952 48 00   Fax: (+44 118) 952 48 10
Executive: Lars Afzelius
(For changes to Adtranz structure see Developments)

Adtranz Classic emu car jointly developed with Angel Train Contracts **1998**/0010276

Regional Transportation Companies, Regional and Branch Offices
RTC — Regional Transportation Company; BO — Branch Office; Regional Office, with its RM (Regional Manager), is the contact for countries where Adtranz has no own office. Regional offices are usually attached to an RTC or BO.

Albania: see Yugoslavia

Algeria
Adtranz
General Agent for Algeria/Bureau de liaison en Algérie
Cité des PTT, Rue A/16035 Hydra, Malki, Algiers
Tel: (+213 2) 269 12 68/11 24   Fax: (+213 2) 269 11 06
Executive: Alessandro Baiocci

Argentina (BO and Regional Office)
DaimlerChrysler Railsystems (Argentina)
Av del Libertator 2424, Piso 11a, RA 1425 Buenos Aires
Tel: (+54 1) 808 87 99   Fax: (+54 1) 808 87 01 (808 87 00
+ extension 84 88 for countries with tone-phone system,
USA and Brazil)
Executive: Eugenio-Jorge Vago (also RM for Argentina
　and Chile)
RM, Latin America: Lutz Elsner (see Latin America)

Australia (RTC and Regional Office)
DaimlerChrysler Railsystems (Australia) Pty Ltd
PO Box 1387, Milton, Queensland 4034
Tel: (+61 7) 38 58 24 00   Fax: (+61 7) 33 67 24 22
Executive: Lars Brodin (also RM for Australia, New
　Zealand, Oceania, Indonesia)

Other plants in Dandenong (Vic), Maryborough (Qld),
ABB Engineering Construction Pty Ltd, Sydney (NSW)

Austria (RTC)
DaimlerChrysler Railsystems Austria GmbH
PO Box 57, A-2351 Wiener Neudorf
Tel: (+43 22) 36 40 40   Fax: (+43 22) 36 40 42 05
Executive: Manfred Fischer

Baltic States: see Sweden

Bangladesh (AG)
Aziz & Company Ltd, General Agent for Bangladesh
20 Kemal Atatürk Avenue, Safura Tower 8th-9th floor,
Banani C/A, Dhaka 1213
Tel (+880 2) 988 65 89/872 228   Fax: (+880 2) 87 23 37
Executive: Mosharaf H Khan

Belgium (AG)
AGE Belgium SA, General Agent for Belgium
Rue Verheyden 39, B-1070 Brussels
Tel: (+32 2) 529 62 11   Fax: (+32 2) 529 66 30
Executive: Karl Johnen

Bhutan: Contact South-West Asia Region Office,
Switzerland

Bosnia/Herzegovina (AG)
Adtranz, General Agent for Bosnia
Zmaja od Bosne 44, 71000 Sarajevo
Tel: (+387 71) 65 72 05   Fax: (+387 71) 65 72 06
Executive: Namik Hadziibrahimovic

Brazil (RTC)
DaimlerChrysler Railsystems (Brasil) Ltda
Av dos Autonomistas 1496, 06020-902 Osaco SP
Tel: (+55 11) 704 84 01   Fax: (+55 11) 702 91 08
Executive: Albert Blum
RM, Latin America: Lutz Elsner (see Latin America)

Bulgaria (BO)
DaimlerChrysler Railsystems (Bulgaria)
5 Triadica Street, 1040 Sofia
Executive: Ivan Botev
Tel: (+359 2) 980 76 96   Fax: (+359 2) 981 45 44
RM: John Kapala (see Poland)

Burma (Myanmar): see Malaysia

Cambodia: see Thailand

Canada: see USA

Chile (AG)
BMV Industrias Electricas SA, Agent for Chile
Ave Vicuna Mackenna 1540, Santiago de Chile
Tel: (+56 2) 555 88 06   Fax: (+56 2) 555 88 07
Executive: Ms Soledad Padovani

China (RTC)
DaimlerChrysler Railsystems (China) Ltd
Beijing Liaison Office (also Regional Office)
Unit 2501, Landmark Building, 8 North Dongsanhuan Bei
Rd, Chaoyang District, Beijing 100004
Tel: (+86 10) 65 06 62 14
Fax: (+86 10) 65 06 62 18/62 19
County Manager and RTC Executive: Wilhelm Buckwar

Ghuangzhou Office
Room 1-8 & 16, 21/F Guangzhou Metro Plaza, 183 Tian
He Bei Road, Ghuangzhou 510620
Tel: (+86 20) 87 55 08 73   Fax: (+86 20) 87 55 05 62

Hong Kong Office
Room 1301/2, Houston Centre, 63 Mody Rd, Tsimshatsui
East, Kowloon, Hong Kong
Tel: (+852) 23 68 01 55   Fax: (+852) 23 69 18 74
Executive: Cyril Moore

Chiltern Railways Adtranz dmu on commuter service to London **1999**/0043213

Adtranz Class 365 Networker Express with Connex South East   **1998**/0010278

Shanghai Liaison Office
Room 1701, Hua Ting Guest House, 2525 Zhong Shan Xi
Lu, Shanghai 200030
Tel: (+86 21) 64 39 50 05   Fax: (+86 21) 64 39 50 11
Executive: Andrew Lezala

Other plant in Shenyang (see Signalling section)

CIS: see Russia and Ukraine

Colombia (AG)
Adtranz
Carrerea 100, No 45A-11, Santa fe de Bogota DC
Tel: (+57 1) 415 65 66/47 47   Fax: (+57 1) 413 40 86
Executive: Roberto Yepes

Croatia (AG)
Adtranz
Trg. J F Kennedya 7, HR-1000 Zagreb
Tel: (+385 1) 233 53 55   Fax: (385 1) 22 88 36
Executive: Darko Eisenhuth

Cyprus: see Greece

Czech Republic (BO)
DaimlerChrysler Railsystems (Czech)
Sokolovska 73, CZ-186 00 Praha 8
Tel: (+420 2) 283 22 50   Fax: (+420 2) 283 22 51
Executive: Josef Schorm

Denmark (RTC)
DaimlerChrysler Railsystems (Denmark) a/s
Toldbodgade 39, DK-8900 Randers
Tel: (+45) 86 42 53 00   Fax: (+45) 86 41 57 00
RM: Henrik Mortensen (for Israel)
Executive: Per Noerret

Other plant in Hvidovre (see Signalling section)

Egypt (BO and Regional Office)
DaimlerChrysler Railsystems (Egypt)
Commercial Center-Office No. 33, Nile Hilton Hotel, Tahrir
Square, Cairo
Tel: (+20 2) 579 01 97/01 98   Fax: (+20 2) 579 01 96
Executive and RM, Middle East: Rudi Stoecker

Ecuador (AG)
Empresa Tecnica Comercial CA General Agent for
Ecuador
Ave Amazona 6017 y rio Coca, CP 17-17-589,
Commutator 468600 Quito
Tel: (+593) 246 86 00   Fax: (+593) 246 91 15
Executive: Ricardo Zeller

Estonia (AG)
Adtranz
Tondi 17, EE-0013 Tallinn
Tel: (+372) 671 18 00   Fax: (+372) 671 18 10
Executive: Bo Henriksson

Finland (RTC)
DaimlerChrysler Railsystems (Finland) Oy
Atmitie 5c, FIN-00370 Helsinki
Tel: (+358) 10 22 20 60/22 22 11
Fax: (+358) 10 22 20 66
Executive: Markku Tanttu

France (BO)
Adtranz France
Tel: (+33 1) 46 69 79 47

La Défense (France) (BO)
5 bis, Place de la Défense, F-92974 Paris la Défense
Cedex
Tel: (+33 1) 41 97 59 00   Fax: (+33 1) 41 97 59 05
Executive: Fabien-Ghislain Arveux

Germany (RTC)
DaimlerChrysler Railsystems (Deutschland) GmbH
Am Rathenau-Park, D-16761 Hennigsdorf
German Adtranz Company HQ
Tel: (+49 330) 28 90   Fax: (+49 330) 289 20 88
Executive: Wolfgang Toelsner

DaimlerChrysler Railsystems (Deutschland) GmbH
PO Box 100351, D-68128 Mannheim
Tel: (+49 621) 38 10   Fax: (+49 621) 381 87 88
Business Area Systems and Components, Executive:
    Uwe Stohwasser

DaimlerChrysler Railsystems (Deutschland) GmbH
Frankenstrasse 140, D-90461 Nuremburg
Tel: (+49 911) 945 60   Fax: (+49 911) 94 56/14 07
Business Area Mass Transit Executive: Werner Rauer

Other plants in Berlin, Braunschweig Kassel and Siegen

DaimlerChrysler Railsystems (Deutschland) GmbH
Mainzer Landstr 3490351, D-60326 Frankfurt am Main
Tel: (+49 69) 750 75 50   Fax: (+49 69) 750 75 84

Ghana (AG)
Holtrade GmbH, General Agent for Ghana
Am Wehrhahn 86, D-40211 Düsseldorf, Germany
Tel: (+49 211) 16 21 08   Fax: (+49 211) 16 27 29
Executive: Hagen Riehl

Greece (AG)
Adtranz
15, Messogion Ave, GR-115 26 Athens
Tel: (+30 1) 775 15 01   Fax: (+30 1) 775 30 72
Executive: Andreas Mamalis

Hungary (RTC)
DaimlerChrysler Railsystems (Hungary) Kft
PO Box 52, H-1554 Budapest
Tel: (+36 1) 270 54 99   Fax: (+36 1) 270 54 90
Executive: Matyas Racz
Holding company of MAV Dunakeszi Wagon
Manufacturing & Repair Ltd
Allomaf Setany 19, H-2120 Dunakeszi
Tel: (+36 27) 341 95 17   Fax: (+36 27) 34 19 97
Executive: Lajos Varga
RM: John Kapala (see Poland)

India (RTC)
DaimlerChrysler Railsystems (India) Ltd
3rd floor, B-wing, Som Dutt Chambers 1, 5 Bhikaji Place,
New Delhi 110 066
Guru Nanak Foundation Bldg, 15-16 Quatab Institutional
Area, New Delhi 110 067
Tel: (+91 11) 618 03 40 44   Fax: (+91 11) 618 66 51
Executive: Viren P Srivastava

Other plant in Baruda

Indonesia (BO)
DaimlerChrysler Railsystems (Indonesia)
Plaza Exim 31st floor, Jl Jend Gatot Subroto Kav 36-38,
Jakarta 12190
Tel: (+62 21) 527 54 04   Fax: (+62 21) 527 53 54
Executive: Inpaulus Tandiah

Ireland (BO)
DaimlerChrysler Railsystems (Ireland)
Belgard Rd, Tallaght, Dublin 24
Tel: (+353 1) 405 73 68   Fax: (+353) 405 73 70
Executive: Colin Blackwood

Israel (AG)
Adbin Ltd, General Agent for Israel
PO Box 3349, IL-31333 Haifa
Tel: (+972 4) 853 32 84   Fax: (+972 4) 85 24 28 24 78
Executive: Alex Greenshlag

Italy (RTC)
DaimlerChrysler Railsystems (Italy) SpA
Centro Direzionale Milano, Oltre 2, Palazzo Cedri, V le
Europa, I-20090 Segrate MI
Tel: (+39 02) 29 60 61   Fax: (+39 02) 26 90 65 55
Executive: Roland Kitten

Other plant in Vado Ligure, Rome

Japan (BO and Regional Office)
DaimlerChrysler Railsystems (Japan)
Roppongi First Bldg, 1-9-9 Rop, Minato Ku, Tokyo 106
Tel: (+81 3) 55 62 08 21   Fax: (+81 3) 55 62 08 81
Executive: Gert Andersson (also RM for North East Asia-
Pacific — Korea, Japan, Taiwan)

Adtranz Flexliner front modules attached to AM96 emu   **1998**/0010279

Korea (RTC)
DaimlerChrysler Systems (Korea) Ltd
143-42 Samsung-dong Kangnam-ku, Wonbang Bldg,
10th floor, 135-090 Seoul
Tel: (+82 2) 569 19 91   Fax: (+82 2) 50 82 44 84
Executive: Gert Andersson

Laos: see Thailand

Libya
Adtranz
That El Imad, Tower No 3, Floor 9, PO Box 91492, Tripoli
GSP LAJ
Tel: (+218 21) 360 11 78   Fax: (+218 21) 333 76 95
Executive: Hans-Peter Schaub

Luxembourg (AG)
Adtranz
Zone Industrielle, Grasbusch, L-3370 Leudelange
Tel: (+352) 49 31 16   Fax: (+352) 49 28 59
Executive: Jos Grass

Macao: see China

Macedonia: see Yugoslavia

Malaysia: (RTC)
DaimlerChrysler Railsystems Malaysia SDN BHD
Suite 27-02, Menara Lion, 165 Jalan Ampang, 50450
Kuala Lumpur
Tel: (+60 3) 262 73 66   Fax: (+60 3) 262 73 35
Executive: Rauno Boga (also RM for South East Asia-
Pacific (Cambodia, Laos, Malaysia, Myanmar, Singapore,
Thailand, Vietnam))

Mauritania (AG)
AMAMI Nouakchott, General Agent for Mauritania
Zone Industrielle, PO Box 154, Nouakchott
Tel: (+222) 262 73 66   Fax: (+222) 23 35
Executive: Friederich Mensing

Mexico BO
DaimlerChrysler Railsystems (Mexico)
Rubén Dario 281, Piso 8, 11580 Mexico City
Tel: (+52 5) 280 53 50   Fax: (+52 5) 280 29 54
Executive: Guillermo Carrion

Middle East: see Egypt

Mongolia: see Russia

Morocco (AG)
Adtranz
1198 Blvd Emile Zola, 9th floor, 20300 Casablanca
Tel: (+212 2) 31 08 99/311 187   Fax: (+212 2) 31 11 21
Executive: Jean-Claude Lancy

Netherlands (AG)
Adtranz
Marten Meesweg 5, PO Box 2714, NL-3000 CS Rotterdam
Tel: (+31 10) 407 82 84   Fax: (+31 10) 407 83 57
Executive: Henri van Woezik

Nigeria (AG)
Adtranz
Industrial Ave Plot C, Block 1, PO Box 21055, Ikeja
(Lagos)
Tel: (+234 1) 493 73 47/48   Fax: (+234 1) 493 73 29
Executive: Wolfgang Pfeiffer

North Africa Region: see Egypt

Crusaris high-speed metro on Oslo—Gardermoen airport link at Oslo S station   *1998*/0015896

North America (USA and Canada)
DaimlerChrysler Railsystems USA: (North America) Inc,
(RTC)
1501 Lebanon Church Rd, Pittsburgh, Pennsylvania
15236-1491
Tel: (+1 412) 655 57 00   Fax: (+1 412) 655 58 50
Executive: Ray Betler

Other plants in: West Mifflin, Elmira Heights, Pittsburg

Norway (RTC)
DaimlerChrysler Railsystems (Norway) AS
Stasjonsveien 1, N-2011 Stroemmen
Tel: (+47) 63 80 96 00   Fax: (+47) 63 80 96 01
Executive: Ronny Solberg

Pakistan (AG)
Adtranz
7-D Kashmir-Egerton Road, Paaf Bldg 3rd floor, PO Box
2353, Lahore 54000
Tel: (+92 42) 636 61 84   Fax: (+92 42) 696 85 65
Executive: Alexander Roentgen

Panama (AG)
Adtranz
Ave Balboa, Edificio Banco Exterior, Piso 14, 1655
Panama City, Panama 5039, zone 5
Tel: (+507) 335 54 90   Fax: (+507) 225 44 91
Executive: Alvaro Malviero

Philippines (RTC)
DaimlerChrysler Railsystems (Philippines) Inc
19th floor, JMT Bldg, ADB Ave, Ortigas center, 1655 Pasig
City
Tel: (+63 2) 634 16 33   Fax: (+63 2) 634 16 45
Executive: Lino P Pangan

Poland (RTC)
DaimlerChrysler Railsystems (Poland) Ltd
ul Bitwy Warszawskiej 1920r nr 18, PL-023-66 Warsaw
Tel: (+48 22) 608 07 60   Fax: (+48 22) 608 07 66
Country Manager & RTC Executive: Czeslaw Soltysiak

Other sites: Lodz, Katowice (see Signalling)

Portugal (RTC)
DaimlerChrysler Railsystems (Portugal) SA
Rua Vice-Almirante Azevedo Cout, PO Box 60005, P-2701
Amadora Codex
Tel: (+351 1) 496 91 00   Fax: (+351 1) 499 10 52
Executive: Manuel Norton

Other plant: Sines

Romania (BO)
DaimlerChrysler Railsystems (Romania)
16 I Cimpineau, 5th floor, R-70100 Bucharest
Tel: (+40 1) 310 43 85   Fax: (40 1) 310 43 84
Executive: Mircea Marian
Regional Manager: John Kapala (see Poland)

Russia (BO and RO)
DaimlerChrysler Railsystems (Russia)
Pokrovskij Boulevard, Korpus 3, 1st floor, 10100 Moscow
Tel: (+7 095) 207 29 59   Fax: (+7 095) 230 23 13
Executive and Regional Manager for Russian Federation
   & Associated States and Mongolia: Franz Weber

Singapore (RTC)
DaimlerChrysler Railsystems (Singapore) Pty Ltd
2 Ayer Rajah Crescent, 4th floor, Singapore 139935
Tel: (+65) 773 82 77   Fax: (+65) 775 68 61
Executive: Kjell Karsen

Adtranz GTW 2/6 demu   *1998*/0010280

Strasbourg LRV on Adtranz test track at Derby, UK (Tony Pattison)   *1999*/0043938

Slovakia (BO)
DaimlerChrysler railsystems (Slovakia)
Nam SNP 15B, SK-811 06 Bratislava
Tel: (+421 7) 32 30 50   Fax: (+421 7) 32 65 67
Executive: Rudolf Kvetan
Regional Manager: John Kapala (see Poland)

Slovenia (AG)
Adtranz
Dunajska 22, SI-1000 Ljubljana
Tel: (+386 61) 131 51 26   Fax: (+386 61) 131 50 67
Executives: Victor Hribar & Velimir Ruzicka

Spain (RTC)
DaimlerChrysler Railsystems (España) SA
Complejo Triada—Torre A, planta 4 a, Avenida de Burgos
17, E-28036 Madrid
Tel: (+34 91) 383 62 00   Fax: (+34 91) 383 61 99
Holding Company, Country Manager and RTC
   Executive: Jose Capparros

DaimlerChrysler Railsystems (España) SA
San Jos, Artesano 12-14, E-48510 Alcobendas-Madrid
Tel: (+34 91) 657 91 00   Fax: (+34 91) 657 91 25
Customer Support (CUS) Executive: Eusebio Mora

Other plants: 48510 Trapagaran, Vizcaya; E-28100
Alcobendas, Madrid (see Signalling and Electrification
sections)

South Africa (RTC and RO)
DaimlerChrysler Railsystems South Africa (Pty) Ltd
PO Box 857, Johannesburg 2000
Tel: (+27 11) 806 91 11   Fax: (+27 11) 887 05 65
Executive and Regional Manager for Sub-Sahara Africa:
   Gert Kruger

Sri Lanka (AG)
UTE United Tractor & Equipment Ltd, General Agent for
Sri Lanka
447 Union Place, Colombo 2
Tel: (+94 1) 169 30 08   Fax: (+94 1) 169 91 43
Executive: W Priath Fernando

Sweden: (RTC and RO)
DaimlerChrysler Railsystems (Sweden) AB
Ostra Ringväigen, SE-72183 Västerås
Tel: (+46 21) 32 20 00   Fax: (+46 21) 14 82 71
Executive and Regional Manager for Nordic Countries
   and Turkey: Staffan Hakanson

Other plants in: Helsingborg, Kalmar, Surahammar,
Hässleholm, Stockholm (see Signalling section)

Switzerland (RTC and RO)
DaimlerChrysler Railsystems (Switzerland) Ltd
PO Box 8384, CH-8050 Zurich
Tel: (+41 1) 318 33 33   Fax: (+41 1) 312 61 59
Executive: Beat Müller
Regional Manager, North Africa Region (Algeria, Libya,
Mauritania, Morocco, Tunisia) and South West Asia
Region (Bangladesh, Bhutan, Pakistan, Nepal, Sri Lanka):
   Werner Bohli

Other plants in: Geneva, Turgi

Fully low-floor GT8N LRV in Nuremburg **1997**

Syria (AG)
Tcheleby Bros (Sy), General Agent for Syria
PO Box 1264, Damascus
Tel: (+963 11) 224 89 93   Fax: (+963 11) 221 90 54
Executive: Said and Ali Tcheleby

Tcheleby Bros (Sy), Germany Liaison Office
Frankfurt Airport Centre, B9-64, D-60549 Frankfurt/M
Tel: (+49 69) 69 38 23   Fax: (+49 69) 69 38 42
Executives: Said and Ali Tcheleby

Taiwan (RTC)
DaimlerChrysler Railsystems (Taiwan) Ltd
6th F 1, 8 Min-Chuan 2nd Rd, Kaohsiung
Tel: (+886 7) 330 40 61   Fax: (+886 7) 330 53 59
Executive: Charles Chen

Other plant: Taipei

Tanzania (AG)
Thyssen, Henschel Export, General Agent for Tanzania
Baobab Village Gate No 4, Plot No 1259R, Msasani
Peninsula, PO Box 6279, Dar Es Salaam
Tel: (+255 51) 60 22 46/22 81   Fax:(255 51) 60 22 45
Executive: Karl-Heinz Liebchen

Thailand (RTC and RO)
DaimlerChrysler Railsystems (Thailand) Ltd
3354/16-19 Manorom Bldg, 6th floor, Rama 4 Rd,
Klongton, Klongtrey, 10110 Bangkok
Tel: (+66 2) 672 82 90   Fax: (+66 2) 249 85 22
(See also Signalling)
Country Manager and RTC Executive:
   Hans-Olof Hoferberg

Tunisia (AG)
Adtranz Maghreb Services SA, General Agent for Tunisia
Immeuble El Badr, Berges du Lac, BP 381, Tunis 1080
Tel: (+216 1) 186 00 03   Fax: (+216 1) 186 02 25
Executive: Rachid D Menebhi

*Nottingham has selected Adtranz to supply LRVs
similar to those supplied for Strasbourg for its new
LRT system (Tony Pattison)* **1999**/0043940

Turkey (BO)
DaimlerChrysler Railsystems (Turkey)
Özden Konak Ishani, Kat 9, Kasap Sokak No. 2, TR-80280
Esentepe-Istanbul
Tel: (+90 212) 275 28 15   Fax: (+90 212) 275 83 93
Executive: Ali Savci
Regional Manager: Staffan Hakanson (see Sweden)

Uganda (BO)
DaimlerChrysler Railsystems (Uganda)
PO Box 21821, Kampala
Tel: (+256 41) 20 04 19   Fax: (+256 41) 20 04 19
Executive: Tom Barrow

Ukraine
DaimlerChrysler Railsystems, General Agent for Ukraine
wul I Klimenko 5/2, 252680 Kiev 37
Tel: (+380 44) 271 78 42   Fax: (+380 44) 271 85 55

United Kingdom (RTC)
DaimlerChrysler Railsystems (UK Holdings & Ireland) Ltd
Litchurch Lane, Derby DE24 8AD
Tel: (+44 1332) 34 46 66   Fax: (+44 1332) 26 64 72
Country Manager and Executive: Per Staehr

DaimlerChrysler Railsystems (UK and Ireland) Ltd
Litchurch Lane, Derby DE24 8AD
Tel: (+44 1332) 34 46 66   Fax: (+44 1332) 26 62 89

DaimlerChrysler Railsystems (Rolling Stock) Ltd
Litchurch Lane, Derby DE24 8AD
Tel: (+44 1332) 38 37 37   Fax: (+44 1332) 25 19 62
Executive: Per Staehr

DaimlerChrysler Railsystems (Customer support) Ltd
Litchurch Lane, Derby DE24 8AD
Tel: (+44 1332) 34 46 66   Fax: (+44 1332) 25 18 84
Executive: John Morgan

Other plants: Crewe, Chart Leacon, Doncaster, Ilford,
London, Manchester, Swindon

DaimlerChrysler Railsystems (Total Rail Systems) Ltd
St Dunstan's, Osmaston Rd, Derby DE24 8BZ
Tel: (+44 1332) 26 60 01   Fax: (+44 1332) 26 63 15
Executive: Keith Rands

Other plants: Reading, Plymouth, Birmingham (see also
Signalling section)

USA: see North America

Vietnam (BO)
Representative office of DaimlerChrysler Railsystems in
Hanoi
HITC Building, 6th floor, Cau Giay Street, Tu Liem District,
Hanoi
Tel: (+84 4) 833 38 26/38 25   Fax: (+84 4) 833 38 83
Executive: Ernst Bening
Regional Manager: Rauno Boga (see Malaysia)

Yugoslavia (AG)
Adtranz, General Agent for Yugoslavia, Albania,
Macedonia
E Josimovica 4, 11000 Belgrade
Tel: (+381 11) 32 43 43 41   Fax: (+381 11) 324 16 23
Executives: Predrag Antic, Ivan Kokeza

Products
Development, design, engineering, sales, production,
installation, maintenance and after-sales service of rolling
stock, systems, components and equipment for urban
transport.

Adtranz lightweight RS1 diesel railcar **1997**

received an order for 14 three-car diesel-electric Talent diesel multiple-units from Deutsche Bahn AG, Germany. This followed an original order for 75 three-car diesel-mechanical and 45 three-car diesel-electric units awarded in 1996.

In November 1997, Bombardier Transportation received an order for 11 two-car Talent diesel multiple-units from Norwegian State Railways. These will feature Bombardier's tilting system. In the same month the company was awarded a contract to supply 24 two-car metro trainsets to HKL, Helsinki. In October 1997, EVAG, Essen, Germany awarded an order to Bombardier Transportation supply of 12 low-floor Street-Trams. In September 1997, the company received an order to supply 18 Type LVT/S lightweight diesel-mechanical railcars from the Kastorfer Eisenbahn-Gesellschaft mbH (KEG), Germany.

In May 1997, Deutsche Bahn AG awarded an order to Bombardier Transportation to supply 151 bilevel coaches, brings to 571 the total number of bilevel coaches purchased by DB AG since 1994. In April 1997, the company was selected by MTA NYCTA, New York, to

design and supply 680 R142 rapid transit cars. The contract includes an option for up to 200 additional vehicles. In April 1997, Bombardier Transportation received an order to supply a third batch of 40 City-Trams to Cologne, bringing the total ordered to 120.

In March 1997, STIB, Brussels awarded a contract to Bombardier Transportation for supply of 25 metro cars. In the same month the company received an order for supply of 12 low-floor Street-Trams from KVG Kassel, Germany, while in February 1997, a contract was placed for 15 Type GTW 2/6 articulated diesel-electric multiple-units by Hessische Landesbahn GmbH, Germany.

In December 1996, GO Transit, Canada, selected Bombardier Transportation for a seven-year maintenance contract of its fleet of rolling stock, consisting of 39 General Motors locomotives and 49 Bombardier bilevel commuter cars. In November 1996, the company received a contract for supply and maintenance of 24 City-Trams from Croydon Tramlink, London. In August, June and May 1996, Bombardier Transportation received orders from Deutsche Bahn AG, Germany to supply a total of 49 bilevel coaches.

In July 1996, Bombardier, in partnership with Traxis, received an order for delivery of eight three-car NINA trainsets for BLS, Switzerland. In March 1995, the company was awarded a contract by Deutsche Bahn AG, Germany for 470 Type ET 481/482 electric multiple-units for the Berlin S-Bahn. The order followed an original December 1994 order for 146 similar units, and brought to 616 the total number cars ordered.

Developments: In October 1998, Bombardier Transportation and US Federal Railroad Administration (FRA) signed an agreement to initiate the development of a prototype high-speed non-electric passenger locomotive.

Bombardier Transportation finalised a joint agreement with Greenbrier Companies to build freight wagons at Bombardier's existing manufacturing facility in Sahagun, Mexico. The new company is called Gunderson-Concarril.

UPDATED

Breda

Breda Costruzioni Ferroviarie SpA
110B Via Ciliegiole, I-51100 Pistoia, Italy
Tel: (+39 0573) 37 01   Fax: (+39 0573) 37 02 92
Chairman: Dr Luigi Roth
Group General Manager: Corrado Fici
Deputy General Manager: Fausto Cutuli
Director, Business Development: Claudio Mannucci
Business Development, Mass Transit: Claudio Fumagalli

Works
Via Ciliegiole 110b, I-51100 Pistoia, Italy
Via Appia Antica Km 13, I-75100 Matera, Italy
Contrada Olivelli Platone, I-9044 Carini, Italy
Via Gebbione, Torre Lupo, I-89100 Reggio Calabria, Italy
Via Miliscola 37, I-80078 Pozzuoli, Italy
Via San Donato 190, I-40127 Bologna, Italy
1000 Frank E Rodgers Boulevard, Harrison, New Jersey 07029, USA

Background: The company dates from 1886, when Ernesto Breda took over the steam locomotive manufacturer L'Elvetica. In 1997 the transfer was completed of Breda Costruzione Ferroviarie and BredaMenarinibus to the Finmeccanica Group, forming a conglomerate made up of Ansaldo (qv) and Breda.

Products: Metro cars and light rail vehicles, dual-mode buses, trolleybuses (qv).

Contracts: The first of 52 articulated LRVs for Muni San Francisco entered service in 1996. They have stainless steel bodywork, two motor bogies, inverter propulsion system, eight passenger doors, air conditioning and automatic couplers

Firema and Ansaldo (qv) are building the 19 three-section articulated cars for the automated mini-metro in Copenhagen. Each car is 39 m in length, has 96 seats and space for 252 standing.

MTA Los Angeles took delivery of 42 double-deck Metrolink cars in 1996/97.

Thirty-three single-ended articulated LRVs for Ankara have been built, with two motor bogies, chopper control, eight doors and driver's cab.

A fleet of 60 double-deck emu power cars and 90 double-deck trailer cars is being delivered to FS Italy during 1997/98; seven diesel railcars were supplied to the Apulo—Lucane Railway in 1996.

VERIFIED

Breda-built Muni LRV in San Francisco **1997**

Breda-built single-ended LRV for Ankara **1997**

Brush

Brush Traction
A member of the FKI Group
PO Box 17, Loughborough LE11 1HS, UK
Tel: (+44 1509) 61 70 00   Fax: (+44 1509) 61 70 01

Traction Director: Oliver R Lewy
Sales Manager: Peter L Needham

Background: Brush Electrical Engineering was founded in 1889. Today the company is a major supplier of electric

propulsion equipment and is able to undertake refurbishment of complete vehicles or components.

Products: Battery electric service locomotives for metro systems; complete AC and DC propulsion packages,

including traction motors and control equipment, locomotive servicing and refurbishment.

Contracts: Twenty-one battery-electric locomotives have been supplied to MTRC Hong Kong.

Brush has supplied traction equipment for London Docklands cars built in Belgium by BN. Also involved in supply of traction equipment based on GTO technology for London Underground's Central line cars, built by ABB Transportation.

VERIFIED

Brush dual-mode battery electric service locomotive supplied to MTRC Hong Kong
1998/0010289

CAF

Construcciones y Auxiliar de Ferrocarriles SA
J M Iturrioz 26, E-20200 Beasain-Guipuzcoa, Spain
Tel: (+34 943) 88 01 00   Fax: (+34 943) 88 14 20
President: José María Baztarrica Garijo
Chairman & Chief Executive Officer:
José María Baztarrica Garijo
General Managing Directors: Alejandro Legarda
Andrés Arizcorreta

Products: Electric and diesel-electric multiple-units, metro cars, passenger coaches, light rail vehicles, powered and trailing bogies.

Contracts: CAF has delivered 16 dmus for RENFE regional services. These air conditioned units have a top speed of 160 km/h and have been built using Flexliner technology.

A further 20 Series 447 air conditioned three-car emus are being supplied for RENFE suburban services, and orders have been placed for a further 46 similar units for delivery from 2000.

Deliveries have been completed of 72 Series 2000 two-car emus for Metro de Madrid. They consist of motor and trailer cars and have air conditioning, CCTV, a central diagnostic system and vandal-resistant materials. Deliveries have also commenced to Metro de Madrid of 44 S/600 trainsets with IGBT traction equipment, air conditioning, gangways, onboard computer system for train control and diagnostics, data-recorder and CCTV. Seven of these units are intended for service on the new Arganda Corridor.

Also recently completed are deliveries of five Series 2100 trainsets for Metro de Barcelona.

CAF is supplying 20 Series 213 three-car emus to FGC Barcelona. Each air conditioned set consists of two motor

IGBT-powered Series S/6000 two-car emu for Metro de Madrid   **1999**/0043502

cars and a trailer built in aluminium; the design is derived from the recently delivered Series 112 but built to metre gauge.

In collaboration with Adtranz, a total of 184 aluminium-bodied emu cars has been supplied to MTRC Hong Kong, comprising 11 eight-car trains for Airport Express service and 12 eight-car sets for Lantau Line commuter services.

In collaboration with ALSTOM, construction is in progress of 36 cars of an order for 18 four-car double-deck emus for the Lisbon cross-Tagus service.

A consortium led by CAF, and including Adtranz and ALSTOM, has commenced delivery of 30 four-car emus for CPTM São Paulo.

Construction is in progress of 10 two-car suburban emus for VR-Group in Finland. Contracts have also been received for 16 Class 333 three-car emus for Northern Spirit in the UK, and for 110 metro cars for the Washington metro.

UPDATED

CCC

Changchun Car Company
5 Qingyin Road, Changchun, Jilin 130062, People's Republic of China
Tel: (+86 431) 790 11 14   Fax: (+86 431) 293 87 40
General Manager: Ma Shu-kun
Deputy Managing Director: Teng Mao-gen
Technical Director: Guang Ming-quan

Background: CCC is the largest Chinese manufacturer of passenger coaches and urban transit vehicles. At the end

of 1996, Adtranz (qv) and Changchun Car Company, China signed a joint venture to produce rolling stock for urban transport applications. CCC is owned by the Chinese Railway Ministry and manufactures 1,200 passenger cars a year. From the beginning of 1997, a new company, Changchun Adtranz Railway, was formed, with 51 per cent of shares owned by Adtranz and 41 per cent owned by CCC. Planned production is 160 cars a year.

Products: Passenger coaches, metro cars.

Contracts: CCC supplied the rolling stock for the Beijing

and Tianjin metros, and also exported a batch of cars for the Pyongyang metro, North Korea. The works is currently supplying further orders for 174 cars for Beijing and a fleet of 217 cars for Line 2 of the Tehran metro, the first of which arrived in Iran at the end of January 1999.

The latest metro design is the DK20 wide-body set, consisting of two driving motor cars and four non-driving trailer cars, for 750 V DC third-rail operation; each car is 19 m long, 3.51 m high and 2.8 m wide.

UPDATED

Kawasaki

Kawasaki Heavy Industries Ltd
Rolling Stock Group
World Trade Center Building, 4-1 Hamamatsu-cho
2-chome, Minato-ku, Tokyo 105, Japan
Tel: (+81 3) 34 35 25 88
Fax: (+81 3) 34 35 21 57/34 36 30 37
President: Hiroshi Ohba
Executive Vice-Presidents: Yoshiro Manabe,
  Junji Hayashi, Yukihiro Hirata, Tetsuro Takahashi
Senior General Manager, Rolling Stock Group:
  Sotaro Yamada

Subsidiary company
Kawasaki Rail Car Inc, USA (qv)

Works
1-18 Wadayama-dori 2-chome, Hyogo-ku, Kobe 652,
Japan
Tel: (+81 78) 682 31 33
Fax: (+81 78) 682 31 34/671 57 84

Products: Electric multiple-units and rapid transit cars
(including rubber-tyred).

Contracts: Kawasaki, in association with Sumitomo, has
supplied the Keihan Railway with 10 Series 800 double-
deck cars.

Kawasaki led the consortium which built 66 trains for
Singapore Mass Rapid Transit Corporation. Contracts in
the domestic market include stainless steel and
aluminium alloy commuter, long-distance and suburban
electric cars for Japan Railways Group and private
railways.

UPDATED

Kawasaki Rail Car

Kawasaki Rail Car Inc
One Larkin Plaza, Yonkers, New York 10701, USA
Tel: (+1 914) 376 47 00   Fax : (+1 914) 376 47 79
President: Masashi Oka

Products: Electric multiple-units, rapid transit cars,
passenger coaches.

Contracts: Include assembly of 53 double-deck cars for
MTA Maryland's MARC commuter service and 13 similar
cars for the neighbouring Virginia Railway Express
(delivery late 1999); 114 double-deck cars for Long Island
Rail Road, New York; and 17 double-deck cars for MBTA
Boston.

On order are 50 bilevel commuter cars for delivery by
the end of 2000. In December 1998, MTA New York
ordered 100 metro cars for the large-profile L-Carnasie
line of NYCTA.

UPDATED

Kiepe

Kiepe Elektrik GmbH & Co KG
PO Box 130540, D-40555 Düsseldorf, Germany
Tel: (+49 211) 74 971   Fax: (+49 211) 749 73 00
e-mail: info@kiepe-elektrik.com
www: www.kiepe-elektrik.com
Chairman: T Weber
General Manager, Marketing Sales: W Huober

Background: Kiepe was established in 1906. Formerly a
subsidiary of ACEC, the company became part of GEC
Alstom in 1988 along with its Austrian subsidiary Kiepe
Electric in Vienna. In 1993, Kiepe became a subsidiary of
AEG Rail Systems and in 1996, following the merger of
AEG and ABB, Kiepe became a member of the Schaltbau
Group, Munich.

Products: Traction control equipment for 600/750 V DC
traction systems; three-phase AC and DC chopper power
electronics for LRVs and trolleybuses, with regenerative
braking in IGBT or GTO technology. Control electronics in
microprocessor technology. See also entry under
Trolleybus Traction Equipment.

Contracts: Include equipment for 78 four-section low-
floor trams for Bremen (1992/96), which includes three-
phase PWM inverter drives, databus and onboard
diagnostics systems. The same equipment has been
delivered for 68 low-floor trams for Vienna, 120 low-floor

Kiepe-equipped dual-voltage LRV delivered to Saarbrücken　　　　　**1997**

trams for Cologne, and 48 low-floor trams for Düsseldorf.
Recent contracts include equipment for 22 trams for
Kassel, 18 for Düsseldorf, 24 for Croydon, 14 for Krakow,
10 for Vienna and 12 for Graz. For Saarbrücken, 23 dual-
voltage LRVs, with an option for a further five, are being
supplied, that can operate on 750 V DC in the city and on
15 kV AC DB interurban lines.

Kiepe supplies components and subassemblies for
most metro and LRV systems in Germany, and
undertakes installation and wiring of electrical equipment
in manufacturers' works.

UPDATED

Kinki Sharyo

The Kinki Sharyo Co Ltd
Subsidiary of the Kinki Nippon Railway
3-9-60, Inada-Shinmachi, Higashi-Osaka City 577, Japan
Tel: (+81 6) 67 46 52 40   Fax: (+81 6) 67 45 51 35
President: Junro Ono
Executive Vice President: Shunji Matsumoto
Senior Managing Director: Hirokazu Iyota
Managing Director: Masahiro Hotta
Director, Manufacturing: Hiroyuki Seki
Director, Sales: Yosuke Saida
General Manager, Rolling Stock Management:
  Atsushi Tokutake
Export General Manager: Hitoshi Tomoda

Kinki Sharyo LRV for DART, Dallas
1999/0043511

Products: Electric multiple-units for main line, commuter, rapid transit, metro and light rail vehicles, double-deck passenger coaches.

Contracts: Recent orders include Series 653 AC/DC emus for JR East; Series 313 suburban emus for JR Central; Series 700 Shinkansen and Series 223 commuter emus for JR West; Series 787 express emus for JR Kyushu; commuter emus for Kinki Nippon Railway; metro cars for NAT Cairo; LRVs for Denver; and 43 low-floor LRVs for New Jersey Transit.

UPDATED

Kinki Sharyo Series 285 emu for JR Central
1999/0043512

Korea Shipbuilding & Engineering

Korea Shipbuilding & Engineering Corp
1-1 ka Jongro, Jongro-ku, Seoul, Republic of Korea
Tel: (+82 2) 739 55 77   Fax: (+82 2) 733 81 13

Chair: Ryun Namkoong
President: Ho Namkoong
Managing Director: Jong-Chul Mun
Sales Director: Jun Kil Suh
Main works: Pusan

Products: Diesel and electric multiple-units.

VERIFIED

Mitsubishi Electric

Mitsubishi Electric Corporation
Mitsubishi Denki Building, 2-3 Marunouchi 2-chome, Chiyoda-ku, Tokyo 100, Japan
Tel: (+81 3) 32 18 34 30   Fax: (+81 3) 32 18 28 95
President: Takashi Kitaoka
Deputy General Manager, Public Use & Building Systems Group: Kenji Kimura
Products: Electrical equipment for multiple-units, electric locomotives and light rail vehicles, including VVVF inverter control, chopper control equipment, AC and DC traction motors, main transformers and main rectifiers.

Contracts: Supplied over 100 GTO VVVF inverter AC drive systems for Series 209 emus for East Japan Railway. Also supply of 100 IGBT three-level VVVF AC inverters for Teito Rapid Transit Railway. Supplied six VVVF inverter sets with IGBT technology for Odakyu Railway.

GTO VVVF inverter AC drive systems have been supplied for 90 cars for Line 4 of the Seoul metro, and also for 70 cars for the Il-san line of Korean National Railroad, along with GTO/PWM converter/VVVF inverter equipment for 128 dual-voltage cars for Seoul metro cross-city services operated jointly with KNR.

GT and VVVF inverters for Malaysian Railways and IGBT inverters for KCRC Hong Kong have been supplied.

In November 1998, Mitsubishi, in consortium with Hyundai, won a contract from MTR Corporation in Hong Kong, to design and supply 13 eight-car metro train sets equipped with automatic train operation for the Tseung Kwan O extension. Delivery of the first train is scheduled for 2001.

UPDATED

MSV

Moravian Silesian Wagon Works
Butovicka Stra, CZ-74213 Studénka, Czech Republic
Tel: (+420 655) 47 11 11/47 22 01
Fax: (+420 655) 47 20 00/47 22 04
e-mail: jvyoralek@oasanet.cz
General Manager: Ivan Heczko
Managing Director: Ivan Heczko
Production Manager: Dipl Ing Tomáš Hrabal
Commercial Manager: Pavel Kožuch

Products: Diesel-electric and diesel-hydraulic railcars and multiple-units, railcar trailers, double-deck electric multiple-units including double-deck Class 471 emus and Class 843 diesel railcars.

Contracts: Orders have been received for dmus for ČD, comprising 30 Class 843 power cars (a later version of the 842), 20 Class 043 non-driving trailers and 11 Class 943 driving trailers. The Class 843 railcar is powered by two LIAZ M1.2C engines and has seating for 60.

VERIFIED

MSV Class 843 diesel railcar
1998/0002166

Mytischi

Metrowagonmash Joint Stock Company
4 Kolontsov Str, Mytischi 141009, Moscow Region, Russia
Tel: (+7 095) 582 56 51   Fax: (+7 095) 581 12 56
President & General Director: J A Goulko
Vice President & Technical Director: P Soldatov
Foreign Relations: A Andreyev

Products: Metro cars.

Contracts: Mytischi has built cars for all metro systems in the former USSR, and for the Prague, Sofia, Budapest and Warsaw metros. Standard designs are the 81-717 driving and 81-714 intermediate car, built for both 1,520 mm and 1,435 mm gauges.

The N5 trainset was developed by the Avtovaz Institute for Moscow metro Line 9 with 750 V third-rail current collection and power equipment from the Dynamo works

(qv, Trolleybus Traction Equipment section). The cars have stainless steel bodyshells, double-glazed windows, fold-down emergency door at the front, microprocessor traction control and disc brakes.

An air conditioned railcar prototype for low-density secondary routes has been developed with a Cummins underfloor diesel engine and Voith transmission, seating 64 with 160 standing.

VERIFIED

Niigata

Niigata Engineering Co Ltd
9-3 Kamatahoncho 1-chome, Ohta-ku, Tokyo 144, Japan
Tel: (+81 3) 37 39 89 31   Fax: (+81 3) 37 39 81 19
President: Yoshihiro Muramatsu
General Manager: Toshio Sato
Sales Manager, Trans-Con Systems Division:
   Eiichi Kobayashi
Manager, International Sales Department: Hideki Mori

Works
Ohyama Works, 1-2-1, Akiba, Niigata City, 950 Japan

Products: Diesel and electric railcars; LRVs; passenger coaches.

Contracts: Following delivery in 1997 of a low-floor LRV with Adtranz running gear to Kumamoto, Japan, an order for two similar vehicles was received in 1998. The floor height is 360 mm above street level (200 mm at stops) and the two-section vehicle is 18.5 m long.

UPDATED

Niigata LRV for Kumamoto   *1998*/0010309

Nippon Sharyo

Nippon Sharyo Ltd
Head office: 1-1 Sanbonmatsu-cho, Atsuta-ku, Nagoya 456-8691, Japan
Overseas contact: Riverside Yomiuri Bldg, 11th Floor, 36-2 Nihombashi-Hakozaki-cho, Chuo-ku, Tokyo 103-0015
Tel: (+81 3) 36 68 33 30   Fax: (+81 3) 36 69 02 38
President: Yasuo Shimizu
Director & General Manager, Rolling Stock Division:
   Isao Kiuchi
General Manager, Overseas Department:
   Masataka Nakajima

Main works
2-20 Honohara, Toyokawa, Aichi 442-8502

Products: Electric and diesel multiple-unit cars, LRVs, automated guideway transit cars, monorail cars, bogies for urban and suburban trainsets, high-speed trains.

Contracts: Over 300 cars were delivered in 1996/97 for urban and suburban operation, to domestic and international markets.

TRA Taiwan has ordered 66 dmu cars from Sumitomo (qv) and Nippon Sharyo.

An order for an additional fleet of linear induction motor (LIM) powered emus for Tokyo Metropolitan Transportation Bureau was in production during 1998.

UPDATED

Nippon Sharyo LRV for Nagoya Railroad service in Gifu   *1998*/0010310

Nippon Sharyo LIM emu for Tokyo Metropolitan Transportation Bureau
1998/0010311

Railcare

Railcare Limited
3 Ibstock Road, Coventry CV6 6NL, UK
Tel: (+44 1203) 36 48 97   Fax: (+44 1203) 36 53 15
e-mail: marketing.railcare@dial.pipex.com
Managing Director: Barry Turnbull
Business Development Director: Paul Robinson
Engineering Director: Dave Furlong
Finance Director: Eric McDonnell

Works
Wolverton Depot, Stratford Road, Wolverton, Milton Keynes MK12 5NT

Springburn Depot, 79 Charles Street, Glasgow G21 2PS

3 Ibstock Road, Coventry CV6 6NL

Background: Railcare Ltd, a joint venture of Babcock International and Siemens, was formed in 1995 to purchase heavy maintenance facilities from British Rail. Railcare acquired the former BR works at Wolverton and Glasgow in 1995. Tickford Rail, the interior design and supply business, is part of the Railcare Group.

Products: Rail vehicle maintenance, refurbishment, modification and overhaul; painting, crash and damage repairs, including bogies, wheelsets, brake cylinders and AC modules; diesel engine and equipment overhaul including in-field support; vehicle exterior and interior design, including design and supply of seats, toilets, lighting systems and partitions; light rail vehicles; specialist conversions.

Contracts: Include design and refurbishment of seven four-car Class 319 emus for Connex South Central; similar work on 40 four-car Class 319 emus for Thameslink;

London   Underground   Victoria   line   train refurbished by Railcare   **1996**

repair and overhaul of 22 three-car Class 320 emus for Eversholt Leasing; and design and refurbishment of 24 Class 317/2 emus for West Anglia Great Northern.

UPDATED

Rautaruukki

Rautaruukki Oy
Engineering Division
Transtech
PO Box 217, FIN-90101 Oulu, Finland
Tel: (+358 8) 883 60   Fax: (+358 8) 883 69 70

Managing Director: Tapani Tapaninaho
Executive Manager, Sales: Matti Haapakangas

Products: Electric trainsets, tramcars, passenger coaches, locomotives.

Contracts: Supply of 42 double-deck aluminium-bodied

passenger coaches to VR Limited, Finland. Delivery began 1998, with completion by 2000.
Rautaruukki is building the bodyshells and carrying out final assembly of 20 Adtranz Variotrams for HKL Helsinki. Delivery began 1998, with completion by 2000.

UPDATED

RFS(E)

RFS(E) Ltd
PO Box 400, Hexthorpe Road, Doncaster DN1 1SL, UK
Tel: (+44 1302) 79 00 37   Fax: (+44 1302) 79 00 58
Commercial Director: John Meehan
Fleetcare Director: Martin Pridmore
Operations Director: Mick Bostock
Finance Director: Robert Johnson

Background: Formed from the privatisation of British Rail Engineering Ltd's Doncaster works in 1987, RFS(E) was bought out by its management in 1994. It was acquired by Westinghouse Air Brake Company (WABCO) in 1998.

Products: Vehicle conversion/overhaul/new construction; bogie and wheelsets overhaul and maintenance; fleetcare maintenance management service; equipment overhaul.

Contracts: RFS(E) is refurbishing 87 six-car trains for the Piccadilly line, London Underground. Work started in 1995 and was expected to continue until 1999.
In 1998, Class 158 dmu overhauls were being carried out for Porterbrook Leasing, and dmu bogie overhauls were underway for Central Trains, North Western Trains and Northern Ireland Railways.

UPDATED

RVR

Riga Carriage Building Works
201 Brivibas Street, LV-1039 Riga, Latvia
Tel: (+371) 36 54 40   Fax: (+371) 55 52 19/82 83 96
President: Janis Anderson
Vice President, Financial Director: Velerij Novarro
Vice President, Technical Director: Robert Reingardt
Commercial Director: Sergey Chigorin
Sales & Marketing Manager: Vadim Maximov

Products: 1,435 mm and 1,520 mm gauge diesel and electric (AC and DC) multiple-units for local services.

Contracts: 1,520 mm gauge dmu production includes the Type DR1B, comprising two power cars (modified Type M62 Co-Co diesel-electric locomotives) and 10 trailers, and the Type DR8. A development of the Type DR1A, the DR8 comprises two power cars with cabs and four trailers. Each power car has two 736 kW M787BR diesel engines driving GDP1000M hydraulic

transmissions, with a maximum speed of 120 km/h. Driving trailer cars for DR1A and DR1B dmus are also available.
Recent contracts include the supply of Type DR1B dmus to Belarussian Railways.
A new articulated LRV, the TR-2, has been produced in prototype form.

UPDATED

Santa Matilde

Santa Matilde
Cia Industrial Santa Matilde
Rua Frei Caneca 784, São Paulo, CEP 01307-000, Brazil
Tel: (+55 11) 852 24 76   Fax: (+55 11) 30 61 99 15
Marketing & Export Director: Eduardo Hubert K Monteiro

Works
Rua Isaltino Silveira 768, CEP 25804-020, Tres Rios, Rio de Janeiro

Products: Emus; passenger coaches.

Contracts: Include refurbishment of Series 160 and

Series 401/431 stainless steel emus for CPTM São Paulo, and refurbishment of two Series 500 and five Series 800 stainless steel emus for Flumitrens in Rio.
Refurbishment of 12 Series 900 emus is being carried out under contract to Adtranz.

VERIFIED

Schindler Technik

Schindler Technik AG
CH-9423 Altenrhein, Switzerland
Tel: (+41 71) 858 43 53   Fax: (+41 71) 858 44 20

Background: Schindler Technik AG remains within the Schindler Group following the 1998 acquisition by Adtranz of the company's Pratteln-based rail vehicle manufacturing division, Schindler Waggon AG.

Products: Non-powered low-floor intermediate sections for existing tramcars and LRVs. Schindler Technik also produces complete interior modules of composite materials for refurbishment of existing rail vehicles. See also *Rail and Bus Components and Subassemblies.*

Contracts: In collaboration with other suppliers, Schindler Technik has produced low-floor intermediate sections for high-floor vehicles operating in five cities, including Basle and Cottbus.

Developments: Low-floor intermediate sections for tramcars and LRVs are manufactured using bodyshells constructed of composite materials, built up using the company's purpose-designed winding technology.

NEW ENTRY

SEMAF

Société Générale Egyptienne de Matériel des Chemins de Fer
Ein Helwan, Cairo, Egypt
Tel: (+20 2) 78 23 58/78 21 77   Fax: (+20 2) 78 84 13
Chairman: Eng T El-Maghraby
Technical Director: Eng A Rahik
Commercial Manager: A Farid
Works Manager, Coach & Metro: Dr Eng L Melek
Works Manager, Wagons & Bogies: Eng El-Sherbini

Products: Passenger cars, railcars, light rail vehicles, tramcars.

Contracts: Include trams for Cairo, Helwan, Heliopolis and Alexandria. Production capability totals more than 100 tramcars per year.

SEMAF has assembled 72 cars for Line 2 of the Cairo metro, under a contract awarded jointly with Kinki Sharyo. An initial batch of 18 cars was supplied complete from Japan. It has also assembled a further 12 tramcars for Alexandria from parts supplied by Kinki Sharyo.

SEMAF's light rail cars and tramcars have electrical equipment, traction motors, pantographs, wheelsets and axleboxes imported from Japan under an agreement signed in 1979 with Mitsubishi Corporation.

Cairo metro emu   **1997**

UPDATED

Siemens

Siemens AG
Transportation Systems Group (VT)
Mass Transit Rolling Stock Division (VT5)
PO Box 3240, D-91050 Erlangen, Germany
Tel: (+49 9131) 72 11 56   Fax: (+49 9131) 72 05 05
Divisional Executive Management
   Technical: R Kehl
   Commercial: T Rackow

Turnkey Systems Division (VT4)
PO Box 65, Elsenstrasse 87-96, D-12435 Berlin, Germany
Tel: (+49 30) 38 65 14 38   Fax: (+49 30) 38 65 12 75
Executive Management Division
   Technical: R van Ark
   Commercial: K Neuneck

Background: Provides complete railway systems on a turnkey basis worldwide, including manufacture and supply of signalling and control systems, fare collection, telecommunications, electrification and rolling stock, comprising planning, design and construction of both electrical and civil works, project management, installation and commissioning; training, service and maintenance.

UK Representative
Siemens Transportation Systems Ltd
Siemens House, Windmill Road, Sunbury-on-Thames TW16 7HS
Tel: (+44 1932) 75 29 73   Fax: (+44 1932) 75 29 79

USA Representative
Siemens Transportation Systems (qv)

Products: Rolling stock for urban and suburban guided public transport.

Siemens has developed complete LRVs with a floor height down to 150 mm above rail level. They have three-phase AC drives and microcomputer controls. Siemens is also involved in development of ultra-light emus and metro cars. A twin-engined lightweight diesel railcar has been designed for regional operators in Germany.

Contracts: A fleet of 14 Class 332 25 kV four-car emus was delivered for the Heathrow Express Project, England, in 1997/98. ATP and AWS is fitted and other communications facilities include a fault-logging computer, track-to-train and in-train communication, train data recorder and cab secure radio. The seating is 2+2 with tip-up seats in the vestibules. Air conditioning is fitted and there is a public telephone. The luggage stacks and seating are located so that passengers can view their luggage. Wheelchair accommodation is provided and there is a dedicated secure luggage area for checked-in baggage.

Siemens' Mass Transit Rolling Stock Division (VT5) has developed from a supplier of electrical equipment to a builder of complete rolling stock. It has delivered vehicles for urban transport systems of which about half were for the European market, including Sheffield, UK, with the remainder to the USA, Canada, Mexico, Colombia, Tunisia and other countries.

Major contracts have been awarded in Asia (Singapore and Taipei metros) and USA (Los Angeles light rail and Portland low-floor LRVs).

Contracts for construction of a metro for the city of Ghangzhou in southeast China have been signed by the Ghangzhou Metro Corporation and a consortium consisting of the Transportation Systems Group of Siemens AG and Adtranz, under the leadership of

Siemens low-floor Combino prototype LRV   **1998**/0010312

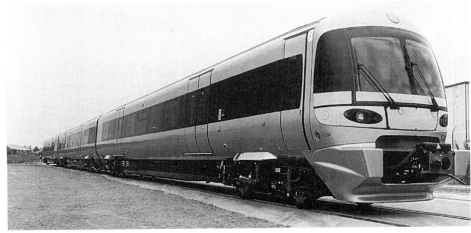

Heathrow Express emu supplied in association with CAF   **1998**/0023006

Siemens LRV of Stagecoach Supertram at Halfway terminus   **1998**/0023007

Siemens. Line 1 is 18.5 km, will have 16 stations and runs mostly underground on an east-west axis. It is expected to open in 1999.

A consortium led by the Transportation Systems Group of Siemens has signed a contract with the municipal authorities in Bursa, Turkey, to build a light metro system on a turnkey basis. Siemens' share of the DM500 million order is more than DM250 million, with consortium members Ansaldo Trasporti receiving DM80 million and Turkish firm Guris receiving DM150 million for the civil works portion of the agreement.

Other major turnkey projects include the project for the San Juan Puerto Rico metro and with Adtranz for BERTS Bangkok.

Ten three-section low-floor LRVs have been delivered to Carris Lisbon, for operation on the Lina de Bélem line. Each car carries 210, with 65 seated.

Indian Railways Rail Coach Factory, Kapurthala, has signed an agreement with Siemens to build LRVs for Indian cities on a technology transfer basis. Electric traction equipment is being supplied by Siemens.

The Combino ultra-low-floor tram was announced in 1996, offering construction costs reduced by 30 per cent through standardisation. Up to five body modules and off-the-shelf seating and door systems can be specified. The first order for Combino came in 1996, when ViP Potsdam ordered 48 cars.

Recent turnkey contracts have been for light rail systems in Tunis, Medellin, Konya and Ankara (Turkey) and Guadalajara; for metro systems in Shanghai and Athens and for the SIPEM people mover at Düsseldorf airport.

VERIFIED

Siemens SGP

Siemens SGP Verkehrstechnik GmbH
Brehmsstrasse 16, A-1110 Vienna, Austria
Tel: (+43 1) 74 06 90   Fax: (+43 1) 70 75 15 17
Managing Directors: Ing Günter Janak
    Mag Manfred Dönz
Sales Director for Austria, Slovenia, Croatia and Slovakia:
    Ing Franz Proksch (Siemens AG, Austria)
Sales Director Worldwide: Rainer Kehl (Siemens AG, Erlangen)

Main works: Vienna; Graz

Background: Siemens took a 74 per cent shareholding in SGP in 1993.

Products: Metro cars, light rail vehicles, ultra-low-floor tramcars, double-deck cars.

Contracts: In 1997, Siemens SGP delivered the last two-car sets of a total of 253 for the Vienna metro. It is also developing a six-car trainset for Vienna.

Siemens SGP is supplying 216 carbody shells and 432 bogies for Taipei metro cars and is supplying 105 metro cars for BTS Bangkok, Thailand, with delivery starting in 1998.

Two prototypes of the ultra-low-floor tramcar for Vienna were delivered in 1995. Called the ULF197, it has a floor height of 197 mm. It is 23.6 m long and is powered by vertically mounted AC motors with SIBAS32 microprocessor-based control technology.

The first 34 of a contract for 150 ULF197 cars is being delivered to Wiener Linien.

Siemens SGP is building 240 double-deck push-pull suburban cars for local services in the Vienna district. Designed by ÖBB, each seats 114, with a higher density on the lower deck for short-distance passengers and a lower density on the upper deck for longer journeys. The formation of each push-pull trainset is five non-driving trailers and one driving trailer.

UPDATED

Siemens SGP's ultra-low-floor tram in Vienna   *1997*

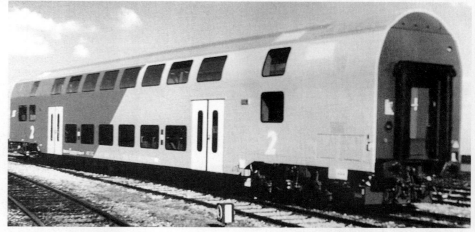

Siemens SGP double-deck suburban car   *1998*/0010313

Siemens Transportation Systems

Siemens Transportation Systems Inc
Head Office, 186 Wood Avenue South, Iselin, New Jersey 08830, USA
Tel: (+1 732) 205 22 00   Fax: (+1 732) 603 73 79
President & Chief Executive Officer: J Morrison
Vice President, Marketing: M Pracht
Vice President & Chief Financial Officer: G Donahue

Mass Transit Division
7464 French Road, Sacramento, California 95828
Tel: (+1 916) 688 50 14   Fax: (+1 916) 688 31 00

Products: Light rail vehicles, heavy rail vehicles, bogies, propulsion systems, diesel and electric multiple-units, AC traction motors and components (See also *Electrification section.*)

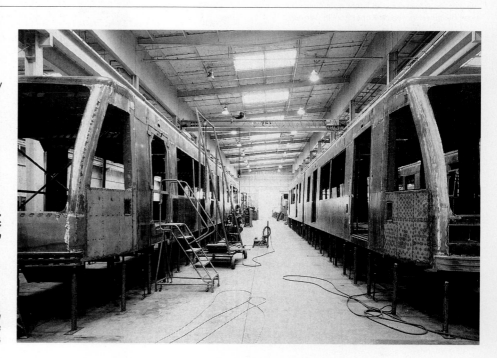

Bodyshells for LRVs for Los Angeles in production at Siemens Carson works
1999/0043514

Siemens SD 460 LRV in service with St Louis MetroLink, which operates 41 of the type
1999/0043513

The first of the Siemens low-floor LRVs for Tri-Met is seen at the new Elmonica depot   **1998**/0010315

Contracts: Siemens Transportation Systems (STS) has over 400 LRVs in operation throughout North America, including Sacramento, San Diego, Pittsburgh, St Louis, Los Angeles, Denver and Portland, USA, and in Edmonton and Calgary in Canada.

Metro de Valencia is taking delivery of eight LRVs from STS. The turnkey order, its first export contract, also covers project management, electrification, train control systems and communications.

STS was also awarded the contract to supply 52 LRVs to MTA Los Angeles for the Green Line.

Additional cars are in course of delivery to St Louis, and 23 LRVs are being built for Salt Lake City. STS is also

supplying 74 heavy-rail vehicles for the San Juan Tren Urbano turnkey rail project and is consortium leader for this project, providing project management, rail and power system for the 17.2 km routes and communications/train-control systems, in addition to the vehicles.

STS is supplying 46 low-floor LRVs to Tri-Met Portland to supplement an existing fleet of 39.

A contract for 14 six-axle SD-100 LRVs for RTD Denver has been announced. The vehicles will be used on the new Southwest Corridor line and are similar to Denver's

existing fleet of 17 LRVs, which were also supplied by STS. The bodyshells are being constructed at its Carson facility, with final assembly at the Sacramento facility. The cars have DC technology, with chopper control and one motor per bogie.

In November 1998, STS received an order for a further 11 high-floor LRVs for Denver, with deliveries scheduled to start in May 2000. Calgary Transit ordered two similar cars in December 1998.

UPDATED

Škoda

Škoda Dopravnı Technika sro
Škoda Transportation Systems
Tylova 57, CZ-316 00 Pilsen, Czech Republic
Tel: (+420 19) 773 50 02   Fax: (+420 19) 773 90 59
Managing Director: Ivo Šindelek
Marketing & Sales Director: Milan Šulák
Technical Director: Ladislav Sobotka

Background: Škoda commenced production of electric locomotives in 1927 and has now moved into production of LRV and metro cars, and associated traction equipment.

Products: Development and manufacture of rolling stock; electric locomotives; metro/commuter cars; LRV manufacture and refurbishment; electric traction drives

and components; turnkey projects including vehicles and electrification.

Developments: The modular low-floor tramcar with asynchronous drive has been awarded a gold medal at the 39th International Engineering Trade Fair, Brno, Czech Republic.

A electric shunting locomotive has been introduced. It has asynchronous motors and GTO thyristor drive.

A high-performance traction motor with IGBT inverter control is being developed.

UPDATED

Prague metro car refurbished by Škoda   **1997**

Škoda low-floor LRV   **1998**/0010316

Sofer

Sofer Officine Ferroviarie SpA
Via Miliscola 37, I-80078 Pozzuoli, Napoli, Italy
Tel: (+39 081) 526 25 22   Fax: (+39 081) 526 22 88
General Manager: Dott Ing Fausto Cutuli

Products: Diesel and electric railcars, multiple-unit trainsets, passenger coaches; powered bogies.

VERIFIED

Tokyu

Tokyu Car Corporation
Head Office and Yokohama plant: 3-1 Ohkawa, Kanazawa-ku, Yokohama 236-0043, Japan
Tel: (+81 45) 785 30 09   Fax: (+81 45) 785 79 62
Sales Department: 1-1 Taishido 4-chome, Satagaya-ku, Tokyo 154-0004
Tel: (+81 3) 54 31 10 91   Fax: (+81 3) 54 31 10 59
Omiya plant: 610-1, Kushibiki-cho 2-chome, Omiya, Saitama-prefecture 331-0051
Hanyu plant: 705-23, Komatsudai 2-chome, Hanyu, Saitama-prefecture 348-0038
Osaka plant: 200, Otoriminami-machi 3-cho, Sakai, Osaka 593-8325
President: Takahisa Tozawa
Vice Presidents: Tetsuo Noguchi, Katsuyoshi Koizumi

Background: Formed in 1948 from the Yokohama works of the Tokyu Corporation, the company built the first all-stainless steel cars in Japan in 1962 following a technical agreement with Budd (USA). Tokyu absorbed the Teikoku Car & Manufacturing Co of Osaka in 1968 to become one of Japan's biggest rolling stock suppliers for domestic railways and those in other countries. Annual capacity is more than 700 emu cars and passenger coaches.

Products: Electric and diesel railcars, passenger cars.

Contracts: JR East has taken delivery of Series E653 emus for Tokyo—Tohoku district commuter services. Each aluminium-bodied seven-car unit features four powered cars employing VVVF inverters for traction purposes and static inverters for auxiliaries. Lightweight bolsterless bogies are employed, with blended air and regenerative braking. Passenger facilities include onboard telephone, vending machines and information displays and provision for travellers in wheelchairs.

The company has also supplied Type 10 'heritage-style' tramcars to the Enoshima Electric Railway for commuter and tourist services in Kamakura. Stainless and corrosion-resistant steel is used for the bodies of the two-car articulated vehicles.

UPDATED

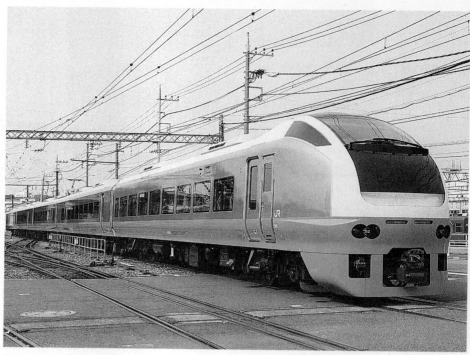

Tokyu Series E653 emu for JR East   **1999**/0043515

Enoshima Electric Railway Type 0 emu
1999/0043939

Toshiba

Toshiba Corporation
Railway Projects Department
1-1 Shibaura 1-chome, Minato-ku, Tokyo 105-800, Japan
Tel: (+81 3) 34 57 49 24   Fax: (+81 3) 54 44 94 22
President: Taizo Nishimuro
General Manager: Shigenori Yamakawa
Senior Manager, Railway Projects Dept: Shunji Uchino

Products: Electric traction equipment, auxiliary power supply; train control/monitoring equipment for emus and LRVs; electric and diesel locomotives.

Contracts: KNR Korea is taking delivery of 60 sets of traction equipment for its Seoul suburban Line 1 in addition to 330 carsets, supplied also by Toshiba.

A further 220 carsets have been received by KNR for the Kwachon and No 1 lines serving suburban regions of Seoul.

The National Authority for Tunnels, Egypt, took delivery of 750 V DC third rail and AC drive systems for 186 carsets on Cairo metro Line 2 between 1993 and 1998. Rheostatic control systems for 90 electric carsets have been supplied to Egyptian National Railways.

UPDATED

Traxis

Traxis BV
PO Box 3021, NL-2980 DA, Ridderkerk, Netherlands
Tel: (+31 180) 44 54 16   Fax: (+31 180) 44 54 43
Managing Director: E C Yntema
Marketing & Sales Director: M C J M Lahmeijer

UK subsidiary
Transys Projects Ltd (qv)

Background: Traxis BV and Transys Projects Ltd are members of the Dutch Royal Begemann Group.

Products: Complete electrical installations for new or refurbished rolling stock and hybrid trolleybuses. These include traction drives, motors, auxiliary power supply and vehicle information systems. Also hub motors for low-floor trams, electronic bogie control, hybrid systems and people mover technology.

Contracts: Amsterdam metro/LRV Ringlijn contract;

refurbishment of Bucharest LRVs; 36 metro cars for Rotterdam; 53 diesel-hydraulic suburban dmus for Netherlands Railways; eight suburban three-car NINA emus for BLS Switzerland; diesel-electric hybrid bus for Rotterdam; two trolleybuses for Arnhem.

UPDATED

One of 12 Helsinki metro cars with complete electrical equipment supplied by Traxis
***1999**/0041198*

Union Carriage

Union Carriage & Wagon (Pty) Ltd
PO Box 335, Nigel 1490, South Africa
Tel: (+27 11) 814 44 11   Fax: (+27 11) 814 20 64
Works: Marievale Road, Vorsterkroon, Nigel 1490
Chief Executive: L Taljaard
Contracts Manager: D Ward
Engineering Manager: P Watts

Products: Electric multiple-units, diesel multiple-units, railcars, passenger coaches, electric and diesel locomotives.

Contracts: 64 push-pull locomotives for Taiwan Railway Administration; 66 emu cars for KTM Malaysia's Kuala Lumpur suburban network; 56 passenger coaches for National Railways of Zimbabwe.

UPDATED

Three-car emu for KTM Malaysia
***1998**/0010319*

Ust-Katav

Ust-Katav Tramway Works
456040 Ust-Katav, Russia
Tel: (+7 351) 672 65 41   Fax: (+7 351) 672 55 48
General Director: Yuri Kirilitchev
Deputy Chief of Marketing Department: V N Mikheev

Background: Ust-Katav was formerly the S M Kirov Works.

Products: Tramcars and light rail vehicles.

Contracts: Has supplied tramcars to the systems in many cities of the former USSR. Among recent orders were KTM-8 cars for Moskva (70), Barnaul (10) and Chelyabinsk.

Ust-Katav has abandoned manufacture of the former Kirov standard 71-605 (KTM-5M3) design which has been in production since the mid-1960s. In its place comes a new range of standard LRVs designed to replace traditional Tatra and Riga-built cars for which spare parts are now unobtainable in Russia. The first design is the KTM-11, a two-car double-ended development of the KTM-8.

The 71-611 tram is suitable for metro operation. It is 15.25 m long and 2.62 m wide and has longitudinal seating for 37 with 110 standing. The trailer car seats 41 with 110 standing.

Ust-Katav 71-611 tram in multiple-unit formation
***1998**/0010320*

Developments: The 71-616 tram, developed jointly with Siemens, is now in operation. It has up to four doors, the two centre ones being double-width, and is 15.25 m long and 2.5 m wide. It seats 32 with 110 standing.

UPDATED

Ust-Katav 71-616 tram
1998/0010321

Walkers

Walkers Limited
23 Bowen Street, Maryborough, Queensland 4650, Australia
Tel: (+61 7) 41 21 81 00   Fax: (+61 7) 41 22 44 00
Group General Manager: Danny Broad
Rolling Stock Design Manager: R Bailey

Background: Founded in 1864, Walkers opened its Maryborough works in 1868. Electric multiple-units are produced in association with Adtranz. Walkers is a subsidiary company of Evans Deakin Industries, Brisbane.

Products: Complete cars for suburban, rapid transit and interurban operations, and light rail vehicles.

Contracts: In a joint venture with Adtranz Australia, Walkers is supplying Westrail Perth with five two-car emus.

The Brisbane silver suburban fleet is being replaced by 18 sets being built by Walkers. Delivery is expected to be complete by 2001.

Walkers built 34 articulated LRVs for the Kuala Lumpur STAR light rail system, with traction equipment supplied by main contractor AEG. A further 56 cars were delivered to operate Phase II of the system.

Queensland Railways has ordered 30 three-car SMU2 suburban emus for delivery April 1999-April 2001.

UPDATED

The perfect drive system for public transport systems.
Economic, ecological, comfortable, safe.

Voith, the specialist for demanding tasks in power transmission technology is particularly committed to developing innovative drive systems for road and rail vehicles.

For citybuses: Voith DIWA.3 automatic transmissions
- suitable for the low pollution EURO-1 and EURO-2 diesel engines
- with the best gear-shifting quality
- with the longest maintenance intervals
- with the unique diagnostic programme.

For electric citybuses: Voith ELVO-Drive system
- high overall economy
- stepless and jolt-free
- flexible installation
- optimised emission output and fuel consumption.

For light rail vehicles in commuter trains with high acceleration: Voith power packs:
- suitable for low-floor applications
- flanged to the engine or in free installation
- proven and cost-effective.

For metros and city rail vehicles: Voith Hydrolock self-locking limited slip differentials for decoupled single-wheel or single axle drives
- sinusoidal running on straight track
- low torque between driving wheels when negotiating curves
- better adhesion utilisation.

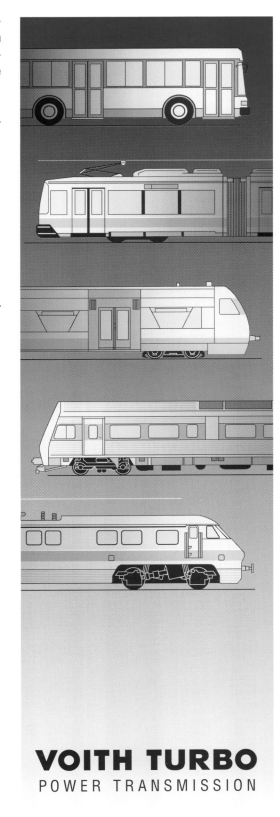

For high-performance diesel railcars with high final speeds, Voith turbo transmissions
- high tractive effort
- high degree of efficiency in the main operating range
- wear-free retarder.

Reference deliveries:

Turbo transmission for diesel railcars
- VT 611 of Deutsche Bahn AG
- X-TER of SNCF France
- DM 90 of Nederlandse Sporwegen
- CDC of Korean National Railways

Automatic transmission for light rail vehicles
Regio Shuttle built by ADtranz, Germany

Cooling units for electrical rail vehicles
- BR 145 of Deutsche Bahn AG
- ICE 3 of Deutsche Bahn AG
- S-Bahn Brisbane Australia

Axle drive gearboxes and self-locking limited slip differential for unterground railways
- E 152 of Deutsche Bahn AG
- Underground Valencia
- Underground Taipeh
- S-Bahn Taiwan
- Underground RATP Paris
- Municipal railway Berlin

More information from:

Voith Turbo GmbH & Co. KG
P.O. Box 1930
D-89509 Heidenheim
Tel. (++) 73 21-37-0
Fax (++) 73 21-37 76 03

VOITH TURBO
POWER TRANSMISSION

at 029.1e

RAIL AND BUS COMPONENTS AND SUBASSEMBLIES

Company Listing by Country

AUSTRALIA
Coachair
Energy Controls
Knorr-Brake Australia
Saydair Commercial Seating
Sigma

AUSTRIA
IFE
Knorr-Bremse

BELGIUM
ALSTOM Belgium
Knorr-Bremse Benelux
Roues et Trains Montes
Twin Disc

BRAZIL
Freios Knorr Sistemas Ferroviários
Knorr-Bremse Sistemas Para Veiculos Commerciais
Mafersa

CANADA
London Mat Industries
Otaco Seating

CHINA, PEOPLE'S REPUBLIC
Knorr-Bremse (Far East)

CZECH REPUBLIC
Knorr-Autobrzdy
ŽDB

FINLAND
Berendsen Pimatic
Rica Seats
Tamware
Teknoware

FRANCE
ALSTOM
Faiveley Transport
Fels
Ferraz
Freinrail
Jarret
Knorr-Dahl Freinage
Métal Déployé
SAFT

GERMANY
Adtranz
Bergische Stahl-Industrie
Bode
Cleff
Dellner Couplers
Deuta Werke
FAG
Freudenberg
Gardner Denver Wittig
GMT
Grammer
Hanning & Kahl
HFG
Hübner
IBG Monforts
Kiel
Kiepe
Klübner
Knorr-Bremse
Konvekta
Lechmotoren
Luwa
MTU
Sanivac
SBF
Scharfenbergkupplung
SÜTRAK
Transtechnik
VAW aluminium

Vogelsitze
Voith
ZF Hurth

HUNGARY
Ganz-David Brown
Knorr-Bremse Hungary

INDIA
Crompton Greaves
Knorrbrakes
Knorr-Bremse Rail Systems

ITALY
Ansaldo
Autoclima
Ellamp Interiors
FISA
FTS
HP
ISAF
Isoclima
Knorr-Bremse Sistemi
LPA Industries
Lucchini
Mediter
Metalnastri
Nuti
Parizzi
POLI
Ruspa
Sguinzi Pietro
Socar
ZF Padova

JAPAN
Alna Koki
Ferraz
Koshin-Knorr
Mitsubishi Electric
Sumitomo
Toshiba

KOREA, REPUBLIC
Knorr-Bremse Rail Systems Korea

MACEDONIA
MZT Hepos

NETHERLANDS
Decostone
Etrometa
Koni
Stork RMO

NORWAY
VBK

SOUTH AFRICA
Dorbyl
Knorr-Bremse
Widney Transport Components

SPAIN
FAINSA
SEPSA
Stone Ibérica
Temoinsa

SWEDEN
Dellner Couplers
EVAC
Knorr-Bremse System
SAB WABCO
SKF
UWE

SWITZERLAND
Airex
EAO

Oerlikon-Knorr
Sécheron
Tibram

TURKEY
Knorr-Orsan Ticari Arad Sistemleri

UK
Air Vehicles
Airscrew Howden
ALSTOM
Altro Floors
Atlas Lighting Components
Bowmonk
Bremskerl
British Furtex Fabrics
Chapman Seating
Clayton
Craig & Derricott
Cromweld
CSPL
David Brown Hygate
Deans Powered Doors
Dellner Couplers
Disc-Lock Europe
Don
Eaton
EBAC
Eberspacher
Engineering Development Unit
Entrelec
European Friction Industries
Ferranti
Firestone
Fleetmaster
Fuchs
The Halo Company
Hepworth Rail
Holdsworth
Hydrovane
Invertec
Knorr-Bremse Systems
KV
Lab Craft
MAC
Metalastik
Mitel Semiconductor
MTB
Multipart
Oleo
Percy Lane
Pilkington Rail Glazing
Powernetics
Proximeter
Raychem
Robert Wagner
Rose Bearings
Sabre
SAB WABCO Davies & Metcalfe
SMC Transit International
Stone International
Stone UK
Tecalemit
Time 24
Timken
Transintech
Transmatic
Twiflex
Webasto
Westinghouse Brakes
Williamson
Woodhead

USA
Air-O-Matic
American Seating
Bostrom
Carrier Transicold
Coach and Car
Crow River

Dellner Couplers
Deutsch Relays
Diesel Power and Controls
EG & G Rotron
Electric Fan Engineering
Ferraz
Firestone
Holland
Johnson Matthey
Knorr-Brake
Lift-U

Microphor
Motor Coils
Nelson
New York Air Brake
Power Parts
Ricon
Q'Straint
Specialty Bulb
Sportworks
Startmaster
Stewart & Stevenson

Stone Safety
Texstar
Thermo King
Timken
Transmatic
Transpec
Unicel
Vapor
Veam
WABCO

Classified Listing

AXLEBOXES/BEARINGS
FAG
Lucchini
Metalastik
Rose Bearings
SKF
Timken

BOGIES
Adtranz
ALSTOM
Knorr-Bremse
Mafersa
Stork RMO
Sumitomo

BODYSHELL CONSTRUCTION
Cromweld
Hübner
Metalnastri

BRAKES AND BRAKE COMPONENTS
Bergische Stahl-Industrie
Bharat
Bowmonk
Bremskerl
Don
Dorbyl
European Friction Industries
Freudenberg
Gardner Denver Wittig
Hanning & Kahl
Hydrovane
Knorr-Bremse
Lucchini
Métal Déployé
MZT Hepos
New York Air Brake
Oerlikon-Knorr
POLI
Sabre
SAB WABCO Davies & Metcalfe
Sumitomo
Time 24
Twiflex
Veam
WABCO
Westinghouse Brakes

CLIMATE CONTROL/HEATING
Adtranz
Airscrew Howden
Autoclima
Carrier Transicold
Clayton
Coachair
Dorbyl
EBAC
Eberspacher
EG & G Rotron
Electric Fan Engineering
Faiveley Transport
FTS
HFG
Konvekta
Luwa
MAC
SAB WABCO
Sigma
SMC Transit International
Startmaster
Stone Ibérica
Stone International

Stone Safety
Stone UK
SÜTRAK
Temoinsa
Thermo King
Toshiba
UWE
Vapor
Veam
Webasto

COUPLERS AND ASSOCIATED EQUIPMENT
Bergische Stahl-Industrie
Dellner Couplers
Dorbyl
Jarret
New York Air Brake
Oleo
SAB WABCO
SAB WABCO Davies & Metcalfe
Scharfenbergkupplung
Sécheron
Sumitomo
Twiflex
WABCO

DOORS AND DOOR EQUIPMENT
Alna Koki
Berendsen Pimatic
Bode
Craig & Derricott
Deans Powered Doors
EAO
Faiveley Transport
HP
Hydrovane
IFE
ISAF
Kiepe
Knorr-Bremse
KV
London Mat Industries
SAB WABCO
Saydair Commercial Seating
Sguinzi Pietro
SMC Transit International
Tamware
Transintech
Vapor
Westinghouse Brakes

INTERIORS
Altro Floors
Ellamp Interiors
Engineering Development Unit
MTB
Robert Wagner
Ruspa
Temoinsa
Transintech
Unicel
VAW
Widney Transport Components

LIGHTING AND ASSOCIATED EQUIPMENT
Adtranz
Atlas Lighting Components
Cleff
Invertec
Lab Craft
Percy Lane
Ruspa
SAB WABCO

SBF
Specialty Bulb
Stone Ibérica
Stone International
Stone UK
Teknoware
Transmatic
Transtechnik
Veam

LIVERY
The Halo Company
Williamson

PANTOGRAPH/THIRD RAIL CURRENT COLLECTORS
Faiveley Transport
Ferraz
Knorr-Bremse
SAB WABCO
Sécheron
WABCO

REFURBISHMENT
Adtranz
Airex
ALSTOM
Coach and Car
Engineering Development Unit
Temoinsa
Texstar
Transintech
Vapor
Voith
WABCO

RESTRAINT/SAFETY SYSTEMS
Air Vehicles
CSPL
Q'Straint
Ricon
Sportworks
Stewart & Stevenson

SEATING
Air Vehicles
American Seating
Bostrom
British Furtex Fabrics
Chapman Seating
Coach and Car
Deans Powered Doors
Decostone
Dorbyl
FAINSA
FISA
Grammer
Holdsworth
Kiel
MTB Equipment
Otaco Seating
Rica Seats
Ruspa
Saydair Commercial Seating
Transintech
VBK
Vogelsitze

SUSPENSION/RUNNING GEAR/LUBRICATION SYSTEMS
Disc-Lock Europe
Etrometa
FAG
Firestone

FTS
Fuchs
GMT
Holland
Hydrovane
IBG Monforts
Klübner
Knorr-Bremse
Koni
KV
Mediter
Metalastik
Nuti
SAB WABCO
Tecalemit
Timken
Woodhead

TESTING EQUIPMENT/DATA RECORDERS
Bowmonk
Deuta Werke
Engineering Development Unit
Ferranti
Knorr-Bremse
Multipart
Powernetics

TOILET EQUIPMENT
EVAC
Faiveley Transport
Microphor
Sanivac
Temoinsa

TRACTION MOTORS AND EQUIPMENT
Adtranz
ALSTOM
Crompton Greaves

Diesel Power and Controls
Eaton
Energy Controls
FAG
Fels
Ferraz
Lechmotoren
Mitel Semiconductor
Mitsubishi Electric
Motor Coils
MTU
Parizzi
Sécheron
SEPSA
Startmaster
Tibram

TRANSMISSIONS AND ELECTRICAL EQUIPMENT
Adtranz
ALSTOM
David Brown Hygate
Deutsch Relays
Diesel Power and Controls
Freudenberg
FTS
Ganz-David Brown
Johnson Matthey
Kiepe
Lechmotoren
LPA Industries
Métal Déployé
MTU
Multipart
Powernetics
Power Parts
Raychem
SAFT
SEPSA

Time 24
Timken
Twin Disc
Voith
ZF Hurth
ZF Padova

VIGILANCE SYSTEMS
Proximeter
SAB WABCO Davies & Metcalfe

WHEELCHAIR EQUIPMENT
American Seating
Crow River
Lift-U
Q'Straint
Stewart & Stevenson

WHEELSETS
Dorbyl
Lucchini
Roues et Trains Montes
Sumitomo
ŽDB

WINDOWS/GLAZING
Alna Koki
Cleff
Hepworth Rail
Isoclima
Nelson
Percy Lane
Pilkington Rail Glazing
Sguinzi Pietro
Socar
Transpec
Widney Transport Components

Adtranz

DaimlerChrysler Railsystems
PO Box 130127, D-13601 Berlin, Germany
Tel: (+49 30) 383 20   Fax: (+49 30) 38 32 20 00
(See main entry under Rail Vehicles and Traction
Equipment)

Products: Development, engineering, design,
production, supply, installation, refurbishment, support
services for systems, subassemblies and components on
rail vehicles. The product range comprises train
communication and control and fault diagnosis, traction
power converters, onboard power supply, auxiliaries,
climate control HVAC (heating, ventilation, air
conditioning) systems.

Product range includes propulsion systems, bogies,
vehicle bodyshells and onboard power supply systems.

Adtranz has established System Lead Centres (SLC)
which manage, worldwide, all design and production
activities for the abovementioned systems, subassemblies and components.

SLC Propulsion delivers complete drive packages
including traction motors, drive systems amd power
converters, nowadays mostly for three-phase traction
applications, but still also for conventional DC traction
drives with chopper control. In the high-power range,
advanced, compact, high-efficiency power conversion
equipment with GTO technology is supplied for
locomotives.

IGBT technology is applied in the medium power range
for heavy mass transit and regional multiple-unit traction
vehicles, and in the low-power range for LRVs.

SLC TCC (traction communication and control)
delivers complete electronic control systems. The
microprocessor-based MITRAC® TCC system operates
in all Adtranz vehicles for control and supervision of train,
motive power, drive control and diagnosis.

SLC Bogies provides products and technology for all
bogie types. Heavy bogies (Fexifloat) for locomotives,
bogies for multiple units, metro cars, LRVs and other rail
applications. Focus is on design and production,
technology development and technology transfer to
partner companies.

SLV Vehicle Bodyshells provides design for all types of
application, fabricated from carbon steel, stainless steel
or aluminium as well as from composite materials.

Onboard power supply systems are available for
vehicle types, in the power output range from 15 to
250 kVA. From 1985 to the end of 1996 over 3,000
vehicles, including motor cars and LRVs for regional or
urban transport services, have been equipped with
Adtranz onboard converters. Most of these vehicles have
been produced by Adtranz companies but also by other
manufacturers.

Adtranz onboard converters have been specified on
over 4,600 vehicles.

UPDATED

Air Vehicles

Air Vehicles
Three Gates Road, Cowes PO31 7UT, UK
Tel: (+44 1983) 29 31 94   Fax: (+44 1983) 29 19 87
Managing Director: Charles Eden
Technical Director: Stuart Edwards

Products: Design, development and manufacture of
lightweight transport seating with emphasis on safe
passenger restraint in the event of a collision.

VERIFIED

Airex Composites

Airex AG
CH-9320 Arbon, Switzerland
Tel: (+41 71) 447 10 10   Fax: (+41 71) 447 10 20
General Manager: Georg Reif
Marketing Manager: Thibault de Kalbermatten

Associated company
Alusuisse Road & Rail (see Rail Vehicles and Buses
sections)

Products: Large composite mouldings for rail vehicles
and buses; complete structures such as driver's cabs with
Airex rigid foam core; aluminium-faced foam sandwich
composite.

Contracts: Include driver's cab in phenolic resin
composite for Berlin metro cars built by Adtranz.

VERIFIED

Air-O-Matic

Air-O-Matic Power Steering
6501 Barberton Avenue, Cleveland, Ohio 44102, USA
Tel: (+1 216) 281 78 10   Fax: (+1 216) 281 11 32
President: Theodore J Berger
Chief Financial Officer: T John Berger
Vice President, Marketing: Christopher Berger

Parent company: Maradyne Inc

Products: Pneumatic steering for heavy duty buses and
trucks.

Developments: Pneumatic steering has been developed
for alternative fuelled and electric buses.

UPDATED

Airscrew Howden

Airscrew Howden Limited
111 Windmill Road, Sunbury TW16 7EF, UK
Tel: (+44 1932) 76 58 22   Fax: (+44 1932) 76 10 98
Senior Sales Manager, Rail: Peter Heapy

Products: Fans and other components for heating and
ventilation.

UPDATED

Alna Koki

Alna Koki
4-5, Higashi Naniwa-cho, 1-chome, Amagasaki 660,
Japan
Tel: (+81 6) 401 72 81   Fax: (+81 6) 401 61 68
President: Masatoyo Uji
Managing Director, Sales & Production:
   Yoshonobu Sugomoto
Engineering Director: Shigeo Ueki

Subsidiary company
Nippon Fukuso Glass Co

Products: Aluminium window sashes for rail vehicles and
buses; honeycomb-sandwich construction doors and
panels for rail vehicles and buses.

VERIFIED

ALSTOM

ALSTOM
48, rue Albert Dhalenne, F-93482 Saint-Ouen Cedex,
France
Tel: (+33 1) 41 66 90 00   Fax: (+33 1) 41 66 96 66
(See main entry under Rail Vehicles and Traction
Equipment)

Products: Basic electrical and mechanical components;
trailer and motor bogies; DC synchronous and
asynchronous traction motors from 100 to 2,800 kW;
choppers and inverters; motor-alternator sets ranging
from 2 to 100 kW; switchgear and motor units; wheelset
brushless generators; contactors and circuit breakers;
static inverters; automatic couplings; onboard computer
systems; completely enclosed fanless equipment.

Microprocessor applications, initially developed for
TGV Atlantique and Line D of the Lyon metro; high-level
language programmable controllers or specific devices to
monitor auxiliaries and to process all functions in both
power and trailer cars, and for both technical and
passenger service purposes.

UPDATED

Altro Floors

Altro Floors
Works Road, Letchworth SG6 1NW, UK
Tel: (+44 1462) 48 04 80   Fax: (+44 1462) 48 00 10

Products: Transflor® flooring for buses and coaches.
The floor material is made of PVC with silicon carbide,
quartz, glass scrim and aluminium oxide chips on a non-
woven backing.

Contracts: Flooring has been supplied to Duewag,
Neoplan, Van Hool, MAN, Aabenraa, Kässbohrer, LHB,
Scania, Säffle and DAB Silkeborg.

VERIFIED

American Seating

American Seating Company
Transportation Products Group
401 American Seating Center, Grand Rapids, Michigan
49504, USA
Tel: (+1 616) 732 64 06   Fax: (+1 616) 732 64 91
President, Transportation Products: Dave McLaughlin
Manager, OEM Sales & Service: Bruce Wright

Products: Passenger seating for bus, metro, rapid transit
and trams; aftermarket service; parts on all American
seating models; seating and securement systems for
special service vehicles.

Developments: Lightweight modular seating has been
introduced with interchangeable parts.

UPDATED

Ansaldo

Ansaldo Trasporti
425 Via Argine, I-80147 Napoli, Italy
Tel: (+39 81) 24 31   Fax: (+39 81) 243 26 98/26 99
(See main entry under Rail Vehicles and Traction
Equipment)

Products: Chopper and inverter electronic drives for rail
vehicles and trolleybuses; AC and DC traction motors;
power supply equipment for onboard auxiliary services.

VERIFIED

Atlas Lighting Components

Atlas Lighting Components
3 King George Close, Eastern Avenue West, Romford
RM7 7PP, UK
Tel: (+44 1708) 77 63 74   Fax: (+44 1708) 77 63 76
Sales & Business Development Manager: Chris Morley

Products: Light fittings, inverters/ballasts for DC and AC
supplies, luminaires and integrated light systems for
heavy and light rail vehicles.

Contracts: Lighting systems have been supplied to MTR
Hong Kong, KCR Hong Kong and SL Stockholm.

Developments: Introduced an extended range of Atlas
brand electronic lighting inverter ballasts to operate at
15 to 40 W, in 26 to 38 mm tubes, and in voltages covering

24 to 110 V DC. They meet RIA, European (EN), French (NF), International (UIC) and associated standards for rolling stock.

A fluorescent reading light has been developed.

UPDATED

Autoclima

Autoclima SpA
Via Rondò Bernardo 11/3, I-10040 Beinasco, Italy
Tel: (+39 011) 358 08 76   Fax: (+39 011) 358 23 88/35 27
Managing Director: Giorgio Moffa
General Manager: Giovanni Mosso
Sales Manager: Mirella Serra

Products: Air conditioning equipment, roof-mounted or in-vehicle.

Contracts: Driver air conditioning equipment has been installed in buses of ATAF Firenze. Air conditioning/ heating units have been installed in ONCF Morocco cars.

VERIFIED

Berendsen Pimatic

Berendsen PMC Oy Ab
PO Box 21, FIN-32701 Hutittinen, Finland
Tel: (+358 2) 560 15 00   Fax: (+358 2) 56 85 01
Director: Marti Pulli
Export Manager: Paul Nikku
Product Manager: Markku Rekioja
A member of Berendsen PMC Group

Products: Automatic door systems; pressure-sealed gangway doors; interior doors; fire barrier doors; electro-pneumatic and electric-powered door gear for rail vehicles; pneumatic bus actuators.

UPDATED

Bergische Stahl-Industrie

BSI-Verkehrstechnik
Papenberger Strasse 38, D-42859 Remscheid, Germany
Tel: (+49 2191) 150   Fax: (+49 2191) 15 22 15
Sales Manager: O Berghaus
Technical Director: W Wiebelhaus

Parent company: Thyssen Guss AG

Products: Complete brake systems and equipment for mass transit vehicles; automatic couplers.

VERIFIED

Bharat

Bharat Brakes and Valves Ltd
A subsidiary of Burn Standard Co Ltd, A Government of India undertaking
26 Raja Santosh Roy Road, Alipore, Calcutta 700027, India
Tel: (+91 33) 244 38 54/17 56   Fax: (+91 33) 244 08 55
Managing Director: B Munshi
Deputy General Manager: R Sinha
Chief Manager, Finance: G C Bardhan
Chief Manager, Design: D Guhathakurta

Works: 22 Gobra Road, Calcutta 700014, India

Products: Air and vacuum brake system components; slack adjusters; northey adjuster; distributor valves; air exhausters; air compressors.

Developments: An air compressor for air brakes for Indian Railways and a load-sensing device for distributor valves have been developed.

UPDATED

Bode

Gebrüder Bode & Co GmbH
Ochshäuser Strasse 14, D-34123 Kassel, Germany
Tel: (+49 561) 500 90   Fax: (+49 561) 559 56
Commercial Director: Rainer Wicke
Technical Director: Dr Jürgen Habermaier
Export Manager: Horst-Dieter Bernhardt
Sales Manager: Jürgen Holz

Products: Sliding doors; plug doors (inswing/outswing, pressure-sealed); pneumatic/electric door drives; ramp systems; step systems; door controls.

Contracts: Main supplier to Mercedes-Benz, MAN, Neoplan and other European bus builders as well as Duewag, LHB, MBB and other European railway car manufacturers.

UPDATED

Bostrom

H O Bostrom
818 Progress Avenue, Waukesha, Wisconsin 53186, USA
Tel: (+1 414) 542 02 22   Fax: (+1 414) 542 37 84
Presidents: John Bostrom, Kurt Bostrom
Sales & Marketing: Dave Parks

Products: Driver seating systems.

VERIFIED

Bowmonk

Bowmonk Limited
Diamond Road, St Faith's Industrial Estate, Norwich NR6 6AW, UK
Tel: (+44 1603) 48 51 53   Fax: (+44 1603) 41 81 50
General Manager: Y Hatcher
Managing Director: Roy J Street

Products: Portable mechanical and electronic vehicle brake testers and calibration.

The Water Eliminator, produced by an associate company, absorbs water in fuel including petrol.

Recently launched is the Bowmonk VI, a portable electronic brake and acceleration tester.

Contracts: Testers have been supplied to leading transport undertakings in the UK and USA.

VERIFIED

Bremskerl

Bremskerl (UK) Ltd
Unit 2, Stable Yard, Windsor Bridge Road, Bath BA2 3AY, UK
Tel: (+44 1225) 44 28 95   Fax: (+44 1225) 44 28 96
General Manager, UK: C Prior

German company
Bremskerl-Reibbelagwerke, Emmerling & Co
PO Box 1860, D-31658 Nienburg/Weser
Tel: (+49 5025) 97 80   Fax: (+49 5025) 97 81 10
Managing Director: R Gramatke
Sales Director: R Wolf

Products: Asbestos-free organic disc brake pads and wheel tread brake blocks.

Contracts: Customers include DB, SNCF, SNCB, FS, ÖBB, SJ, VR, RATP Paris, NSB, SBB, NSWSRA (Tangara) and Los Angeles MTA.

Developments: A new high-speed disc pad material, BK2000, and a new L-type tread block material, BK4938, have been announced.

UPDATED

British Furtex Fabrics

British Furtex Fabrics
Luddenfoot Mills, Luddenfoot HX2 6AQ, UK
Tel: (+44 1422) 88 21 61   Fax: (+44 1422) 88 25 16
Chief Designer: Anthony L Priestly

Products: Upholstery velvets and moquettes for the coach and bus industry.

VERIFIED

Carrier Transicold

Carrier Refrigeration Operations (Division of Carrier Corporation)
PO Box 4805, Carrier Parkway, Building TR20, Syracuse, New York 13221, USA
Tel: (+1 315) 432 64 34   Fax: (+1 315) 432 72 18
President: Nick Pinchuk
Vice President, Transport Air Conditioning:
   Lex van der Weerd

Transport Air Conditioning – Regional Sales Offices:

North America
Carrier Transicold-Transport A/C
715 Willow Springs Lane, York, Pennsylvania 17402, USA
Tel: (+1 717) 767 65 31   Fax: (+1 717) 764 04 01

Latin America
Carrier Transicold-Mexico
Tezoquipa No 142 Col La Joya, Deleg Tlalpan, 14090 Mexico DF
Tel: (+52 5) 573 55 55/655 05 07   Fax: (+52 5) 655 21 02

Europe/Middle East/Africa
Carrier-Sutrak, Heinkelstrasse 5, D-71272 Renningen, Germany
Tel: (+49 7159) 92 31 00   Fax: (+49 7159) 92 31 08

Asia Pacific
Carrier Transicold-APO
12 Gul Road, Singapore 629343
Tel: (+65) 862 00 98   Fax: (+65) 862 32 86

Business Units
Transport Air Conditioning Group
Transport Refrigeration and Air Conditioning

Products: Air conditioning and heating systems for rail and bus applications, roof-mounted, rear-mounted or in-vehicle; air conditioners for small vehicles; components including compressors, evaporators and heater coils, open drive and semi-hermetic compressors; and replacement components.

UPDATED

Chapman Seating

Chapman Seating Ltd
79 Miles Road, Mitcham CR4 3YL, UK
Tel: (+44 181) 640 60 11   Fax (+44 181) 640 10 50
Sales Manager: M Newbold

Products: Driver's, passenger and specialised seating.

VERIFIED

Clayton

Clayton
Hunter Terrace, Fletchworth Gate, Burnsall Road, Coventry CV5 6SP, UK
Tel: (+44 1203) 69 19 16   Fax: (+44 1203) 69 19 69

Products: Design, development and manufacture of demisting, ventilators, convectors and blown heating systems; climate control systems for road and rail vehicles.

Contracts: Major body builders are supplied in UK and other countries including North America and Hong Kong.

Developments: Cab air conditioning for buses and vehicle diagnostics/condition monitoring systems have been introduced.

UPDATED

Cleff

Cleff Fahrzeugteile GmbH
PO Box 260180, D-42243 Wuppertal, Germany
Tel: (+49 202) 64 79 90   Fax: (+49 202) 647 99 88

Products: Ventilation and lighting systems for buses and coaches; windows for rail vehicles.

VERIFIED

Coach and Car

Coach and Car Equipment Corp
1951 Arthur Avenue, Elk Grove Village, Illinois 60007, USA
Tel: (+1 847) 437 57 60   Fax: (+1 847) 437 96 56
President: Gene Germaine

Products: Seating for bus and rail vehicles.

VERIFIED

Coachair

Coachair Manufacturing Australia Pty Ltd
PO Box 60, Archerfield, Queensland 4108, Australia
Tel: (+61 7) 32 77 84 11   Fax: (+61 7) 32 77 30 26

Products: Air conditioning equipment for rail vehicles and buses.

VERIFIED

Craig & Derricott

Craig & Derricott Ltd
Hall Lane, Walsall Wood, Walsall WS9 9DP, UK
Tel: (+44 1543) 37 55 41   Fax: (+44 1543) 45 26 10
e-mail: rail@craigdev.com
Managing Director: Kevin Jones
Rolling Stock Co-ordinator: Lionel Collins
Field Sales Manager: Mike Ingram
Sales & Marketing Manager: Richard Kennedy

Products: Switchgear and control panels, rotary switches and isolators, rotary switches with driver key and other interfaces, passenger alarm switches, mushroom-headed push-buttons, limit reed switches, driver's master controls and talkback passenger alarms.

UPDATED

Crompton Greaves

Crompton Greaves Limited
Rail Projects Division
Vandhna, 11 Tolstoy Marg, New Delhi 110001, India
Tel: (+91 11) 331 70 75/373 04 45
Fax: (+91 11) 332 70 75/332 43 60
Managing Director: K K Nohria
Board Member & President: C P Dusad
Vice President, Rail Transportation: B Banerjee
Deputy General Manager, Rail Transportation:
   M P Singhal

Products: Traction transformers, SF6 gas interrupters and circuit breakers, DC traction motors, AC and DC auxiliary motors, brushless alternators for coaches, static converters/inverters.

VERIFIED

Cromweld

Cromweld Steels Ltd
The Old Vicarage, Tittensor, Stoke-on-Trent ST12 9HY, UK
Tel: (+44 1782) 37 41 39   Fax: (+44 1782) 37 33 88

USA subsidiary
Cromweld Steels, PO Box 1500, Cornelius, North Carolina 28031
Tel: (+1 704) 896 81 14   Fax: (+1 704) 896 81 15
Contact: Chris Beckitt

Products: 3CR12 ferritic stainless steel, available in tube, sheet and plate that can be handled, fabricated, welded, painted and installed by conventional techniques.

VERIFIED

Crow River

Crow River Industries Inc
2800 Northwest Blvd, Minneapolis, Minnesota 55441, USA
Tel: (+1 612) 694 38 80   Fax: (+1 612) 694 38 00
President and General Manager: Jerry K Sirjord

Products: Wheelchair lifts for vehicles and associated equipment.
   An electric variable-speed lift has been developed that fits most full-sized vans.

UPDATED

CSPL

Carstyle Safety Products Ltd
34 Gratton Road, Queens Park, Bedford MK40 4EF, UK
Tel: (+44 1234) 35 22 43   Fax: (+44 1234) 35 42 98
Managing Director: David Lamb
Technical & Sales Manager: Carey Lamb

Products: Seat belts for buses and coaches, made to British Standard specification.

VERIFIED

David Brown Hygate

David Brown Hygate
Park Road, Huddersfield HD4 5DD, UK
Tel: (+44 1484) 46 55 00   Fax: (+44 1484) 46 55 12
e-mail: info.medg@davidbrown/
   sales.hygate@davidbrown.com
Managing Director: Chris Reed
Sales Director: N Crossley
Project Manager: N Antrobus
Part of the David Brown Group

Products: Design and manufacture of gears, gearboxes and associated parts for light rail, multiple-units and main line locomotives.

Contracts: Current orders include the Eurotram for Strasbourg Phase 2 and for Milano and Rome trams.
   Metro gearboxes and couplings are being supplied for Inchcon Line 1 emus.

Developments: A high-speed coupling is being developed.

UPDATED

Ganz-David Brown

Ganz-David Brown Transmissions Kft
Orczy út 46-48, H-1089 Budapest, Hungary
Tel: (+36 1) 210 11 50   Fax: (+36 1) 334 03 64
General Manager: Tamás Fodor
Marketing & Technical Manager: József Fáy

Products: Hydrodynamic transmissions, axle drives and traction gears, fluid couplings; spiral bevel gears, single and double reduction gearbox for LRVs and a hydrodynamic transmission for LRVs and dmus.

Contracts: 1,000 hydrodynamic gearboxes have been delivered to Lithuanian Railways for modernisation of dmus.

Include a 200 to 520 kW underfloor hydrodynamic gearbox family and a special direct drive for 100 per cent low-floor trams.

UPDATED

Gardner Denver Wittig

Gardner Denver Wittig GmbH
PO Box 1311, D-76950 Schopfheim, Germany
Tel: (+49 7622) 39 40   Fax: (+49 7622) 39 42 00

Works
6-8 Johann-Sutter Strasse, D-79650 Schopfheim

Products: Rotary vane compressors for road and rail vehicles, including LRVs, low-floor trams, metro cars and trolleybuses. Compressed air generators are used predominantly for the following vehicle systems: brakes, air suspension, door activating system, current collector, sander and flexible coupling units.

Gardner Denver Wittig rotary vane compressors can be installed either under the floor or on the roof of the vehicle. They are therefore suitable for installation in low-floor chassis/vehicles.

Developments: A new model, the ROL2-6, provides a capacity of between 200 and 600 litres/min at a pressure of up to 11 bar. These units, combined with an oil-cooler, fan, oil separator and a motor, can be attached directly to the vehicle as ready-to-fit units.

UPDATED

GMT

Gummi-Metall-Technik GmbH
Liechtersmatten 5, D-77815 Bühl, Germany
Tel: (+49 7223) 80 40   Fax: (+49 7223) 210 75
Marketing Director: Susanne Engstler

UK office
GMT Rubber-Metal-Technic Ltd
The Sidings, Guiseley LS20 8BX
Tel: (+44 113) 287 06 70   Fax: (+44 113) 287 06 31

Subsidiary companies
GMT International Corporation, Villa Rica, Georgia, USA
GMT Ireland, Clifden, Galway
Gumeta AG, Ebikon, Switzerland
GMT GesmbH, Grödig, Austria
RMT, Perak, Malaysia

Products: Moulded rubber-metal elements for road and rail vehicles, bogies, axles and wheelsets.

Contracts: ICE and ICE II high-speed trains, Germany; DWA railbus project.

VERIFIED

Grammer

Grammer AG
PO Box 1454, D-92204 Amberg, Germany
Tel: (+49 9621) 88 00   Fax: (+49 9621) 88 01 30
Marketing Director: Klaus Kellner

Associate company
Lazzerini & Co Srl
Via Toscana, I-60030 Monsano (AN), Italy
Tel: (+39 0731) 602 61   Fax: (+39 0731) 604 49
e-mail: cml.lazzerini@fastnet.it

Products: Driver and passenger seating and three-point seat belts, tables and interior fittings. The passenger seat range includes the Comfort reclining seat with arm rests and leather trim.

VERIFIED

The Halo Company

The Halo Company (Sussex) Ltd
Osborne House, Station Road, Burgess Hill RH15 9EH, UK
Tel: (+44 1444) 24 77 17   Fax: (+44 1444) 87 02 20
Managing Director: Peter Low
Sales Director: John Veasey
Commercial Manager: Bob King

Products: Graphic sign and plastic products; vehicle livery design.

Contracts: Include new logos and signing for Sheffield Supertram.

UPDATED

Hanning & Kahl

Hanning & Kahl GmbH & Co
Rudolph Diesel Strasse 6, D-33818 Oerlinghausen,
Germany
PO Box 1342, D-33806 Oerlingenhausen
Tel: (+49 5202) 70 76 00   Fax: (+49 5202) 70 76 29
e-mail: HANNING-KAHL@t-online.de
General Manager: Eckart Dümmer
Divisional Manager: Ulrich Bückers

Products: Track brakes, actuators, calipers, hydraulic
power units, electro-hydraulic brake systems, solenoids,
brake electronics with wheel slide protection. Brake
control unit based on a microcomputer with two
independent channels, for maximum safety.

Contracts: Has supplied brake equipment and
components for LRVs and low-floor trams extensively to
German, other European, Australian and North and South
American transit systems.

UPDATED

Hepworth Rail

Hepworth Rail
Brook Street, Redditch B98 8NF, UK
Tel: (+44 1527) 601 46   Fax: (+44 1527) 601 46
Chief Executive: J P Eddy

Subsidiary company
Dudley Screenwipers (address as above)

Products: Heavy-duty screenwiper systems for road and
rail vehicles.

Contracts: Include supply of equipment to CTS
Strasbourg; ALSTOM London Underground; Adtranz,
London Tilbury and Southend line; ALSTOM Gatwick
Express; ALSTOM Arlanda Airport line; Bombardier
Transport Canada and also contracts for Spain, New
Zealand, Hong Kong and China.

UPDATED

HFG

Hagenuk Faiveley GmbH
Industriestrasse 60, D-04435 Schkeuditz, Germany
Tel: (+49 34204) 853 00   Fax: (+49 34204) 853 02
General Manager: K Weiss
Engineering Director: H Schmerler
Sales Director: B Lehman-Maffhaei

Associated company
Faiveley (qv)

Products: Heating and air conditioning systems, oil
burners, oil-fired preheaters and hot-water heaters,
circulating pumps, heat exchangers, valves and fittings.

VERIFIED

Holdsworth

John Holdsworth & Co Ltd
Shaw Lodge Mills, Halifax HX3 9ET, UK
Tel: (+44 1422) 34 99 99   Fax: (+44 1422) 33 01 95
Managing Director: Michael Holdsworth
Sales Director: E Hirsch
Operations Manager: Martin Osin

Subsidiary company
Holdsworth North America

Products: Upholstery fabrics for rail, bus and coach
vehicles; also for side walls, ceilings and luggage racks.

VERIFIED

Holland

Holland Company
1020 Washington Avenue, Chicago Heights, Illinois
60411, USA
Tel: (+1 708) 756 06 50   Fax: (+1 708) 756 26 41
President & General Manager, Emerald: Ray Despres
Executive Vice President, Emerald Product Development:
  Glen Litten

Background: Holland is offering suspension systems
through a financial investment in the restructuring of
Emerald Hydraulics, Springfield, Oregon. The new
company is known as Emerald Rail Technologies though
the product is marketed under the Holland name.

Products: Rail car spring and suspension systems.

VERIFIED

HP

HP Srl
A Westinghouse Air Brake Company
A member of the Vapor Group
Viale Regina Pacis 296, I-41049 Sassuolo, Modena, Italy
Tel: (+39 0536) 80 64 41   Fax: (+39 0536) 80 17 89
e-mail: hpdoors@sirnet.it
Managing Director: Luigi Camellini
Export Manager: Vinicio Mathis

Products: Sliding, bifold, swing and plug doors for bus
and rail vehicles, featuring infra-red sensitive edge and
other passenger protection devices, body-end fire doors,
both pneumatic and electric drive units with control
electronics.

VERIFIED

Hübner

Hübner Gummi- und Kunststoff GmbH
Agathof Strasse 15, D-34123 Kassel, Germany
Tel: (+49 561) 570 10   Fax: (+49 561) 570 11 58

Products: Folding bellows for buses and rail vehicles;
vehicle articulation systems, including low-floor bus
systems with electronically guided angle dampening; rail
vehicle gangways; moulded rubber parts; rubber profiles.

VERIFIED

Hydrovane

The Hydrovane Compressor Co
Claybrook Drive, Washford Industrial Estate, Redditch
B98 0DS, UK
Tel: (+44 1527) 52 55 22   Fax: (+44 1527) 52 11 40
Managing Director: James Blott
Sales & Marketing Director: Mike Harrison
Manager, Railway Compressor Department: Peter L Batty

Products: The TR range of rotary vane air compressors
and associated equipment for brakes, doors and air
suspension systems.

VERIFIED

IBG Monforts

IBG Monforts GmbH
PO Box 200853, D-41208 Mönchengladbach, Germany
Tel: (+49 2166) 868 20   Fax: (+49 2166) 86 82 44
Director: Rudolf Palm

Products: Bearings for bogies.

VERIFIED

IFE

IFE Industrie-Einrichtungen Fertiigungs-AG
Patertal 20, A-3340 Waidhofen/Ybbs, Austria
Tel: (+43 7442) 51 50   Fax: (+43 7442) 51 52 13
e-mail: doors–vk@ife-ag.com
Managing Director: Ferdinand Reich
Sales Director, Export & Marketing for Automatic Door
  Systems: Manfred Teufl

Products: Plug, pocket and sliding door systems for rail
rolling stock and buses; external sliding doors, pocket
doors, inside swing doors; movable steps; door control
equipment including sensitive-edge doors, fire barrier
doors.

Contracts: Orders include doors for LRVs in Mainz,
Debrecen, Saarbrücken, Caen, Nürnberg, Los Angeles;
for metro cars in Bucureşti, Berlin, Frankfurt, Guangzhou
and Indonesia.

VERIFIED

Invertec

Invertec Ltd, Horcott Industrial Estate, Fairford GL7 4DW,
UK
Tel: (+44 1285) 71 35 50   Fax: (+44 1285) 71 35 48
Managing Director: James Valentine

Products: Low-voltage DC lighting for the transport
industry, including trains and buses.
  Manufacturers of fluorescent lighting inverters,
individual luminaires and continuous lighting systems.

Contracts: Preferred suppliers with the UK coach
building industry and to many other European bus and
coach manufacturers including Scania. Specified by large
operators such as Stagecoach and FirstGroup.
  Rail lighting inverters are also supplied to the industry
including Adtranz.

NEW ENTRY

ISAF

ISAF Bus Components srl
Via Stazione 43, I-21020 Mornago (Varese), Italy
Tel: (+39 0331) 90 35 40   Fax: (+39 0331) 90 32 09
Director: Massimo Sessa
Production Manager: Gianni Turcatti

Products: Rotary power systems; electric, hydraulic and
pneumatic door actuators; folding door systems; exterior
and interior door systems; door panels.

VERIFIED

Isoclima

Isoclima SpA
Direzione Commerciale Trasporti, Via degli Scipioni
286A, I-00192 Rome, Italy
Tel: (+39 06) 36 00 01 40   Fax: (+39 06) 36 00 01 70
Director: Filipo Ugolini

Austria/Germany office
Isoclima GmbH
Dauthendeystrasse 2, D-81377 Munich 70, Germany
Tel: (+49 89) 719 20 51   Fax: (+49 89) 719 55 75

UK office
Isoclima (UK) Ltd
Alfred Court, Saxon Business Park, Hanbury Road, Stoke
Prior B60 4AD
Tel: (+44 1527) 57 79 55   Fax: (+44 1527) 57 79 88

Products: Glazing for rail vehicles including curved,
double curved, wire/film heated, polycarbonate core,
tinted and unframed, windscreens and side passenger
windows.

VERIFIED

Jarret

Jarret
198 avenue des Grésillons, F-92600 Asnières, France
Tel: (+33 1) 46 88 46 20   Fax: (+33 1) 47 90 03 57
e-mail: contact@jarret.fr
Chairman & General Manager: Bruno Domange
General and Sales Manager: Antoine Domange

Products: High-performance shock-absorbers for protection of rolling stock during high-speed impact (10-25 km/h), mainly used in central couplers for heavy rail (high-speed trains), rapid transit and LRVs, allowing increased maximum coupling speed; end-of-track stop buffers; side buffers for heavy rail; front and end car bumpers. Also semi-automatic coupler for rapid transit cars.

UPDATED

Johnson Matthey

Johnson Matthey
460 Swedesford Road, Wayne, Pennsylvania 19087-1880, USA
Tel: (+1 610) 971 31 15   Fax: (+1 610) 293 12 84
Sales Manager, Environmental Products:
   Diane McKeon

Products: Catalytic exhaust systems.

VERIFIED

Kiel

Franz Kiel GmbH
PO Box 1228, D-86720 Nördlingen, Germany
Tel: (+49 9081) 210 30   Fax: (+49 9081) 210 31 51

Products: Seating for buses, coaches and light rail vehicles, including mother-and-child seat.

VERIFIED

Kiepe

Kiepe Elektrik GmbH & Co KG
Bublitzer Strasse 28, D-40599 Düsseldorf, Germany
Tel: (+49 211) 749 71   Fax: (+49 211) 749 73 00
e-mail: info@kiepe–elektrik.com
www: www.kiepe–elektrik.com
(See main entry under Rail Vehicles and Traction Equipment)

Products: DC contactors, reversers, switches; electrically driven and electronically controlled camshaft controllers for metro and LRV; crank-operated camshafts for trams; master controllers; braking resistors; AC and DC propulsion electronics; door and step controls; weight, speed and displacement transducers; time delay, light and blinker relays; static converters.

UPDATED

Klübner

Klübner Lubrication München KG
Geisenhausenerstrasse 7, D-81379 Munich, Germany
Tel: (+49 89) 787 60   Fax: (+49 89) 787 63 33

UK subsidiary
Klübner Lubrication Great Britain Ltd
Hough Mills, Northowram, Halifax HX3 7BN, UK

Products: Lubrication systems.

VERIFIED

Knorr-Bremse

Knorr-Bremse AG
Moosacher Strasse 80, D-80809 Munich, Germany
Tel: (+49 89) 354 70   Fax: (+49 89) 35 47 27 67
Chairman: Heinz Hermann Thiele
Executive Board: H H Thiele, Peter Riedlinger

Knorr-Bremse Systeme für Schienenfahrzeuge GmbH
(address above)
Chairman: Dr Eckart Lehmann
General Manager: Heinz Atorn

Works: Berlin and Munich

Subsidiary companies
Knorr-Bremse Electronic GmbH, Munich
Knorr-Bremse GesmbH, Mödling, Austria
Dr Techn Josef Zelisko GesmbH, Mödling, Austria
Oerlikon-Knorr Eisenbahntechnik AG, Zürich, Switzerland
Freinrail SA, Colombes, France
Frensistemi Srl, Florence, Italy
Sociedad Espanola de Frenos, Calefaccion y Senales SA, Pinto/Madrid, Spain
Knorr-Bremse Rail Systems India Pvt Ltd, Faridabad, India
Knorr-Bremse SA (Pty) Ltd, Kempton Park, South Africa
Knorr-Brake Australia Pty Ltd, Sydney, New South Wales, Australia
Koshin-Knorr Ltd, Tokyo, Japan
Knorr-Bremse Rail Systems Korea Ltd, Seoul, South Korea
Knorr-Brake Holding Corp, Watertown, New York, USA
Knorr Brake Corp, PO Box 9300, Westminster, Maryland 21158-9300, USA
   Tel: (+1 410) 875 09 00   Fax: (+1 410) 875 90 53
Knorr-Brake Ltd, Kingston, Canada
New York Air Brake Corporation, Watertown, USA
Knorr-Bremse (Far East) Ltd, Hong Kong, PR China
Freios Knorr Sistemas Ferroviários Ltda, São Paulo, Brazil

Products: Rail-based brake systems for rapid transit, tramcars, LRVs, people mover and metro systems; air supply systems; wheel-slip and wheel-slide protection; auxiliary equipment including windscreen washer and wiper, sanding equipment, air suspension, door control, pantograph control and emergency brake systems; bogie brake equipment including slack adjusters, tread brake units and electromagnetic track brakes.

Knorr-Bremse Systeme für Nutzfahrzeuge GmbH
(address above)
General Management: Dr Rudolph Gerich (Chairman), Oscar Flach, Viktor Kühne

Subsidiary companies
Knorr-Dahl Freinage SA, Lisieux, France
Knorr-Bremse Systems for Commercial Vehicles Ltd, Douglas Road, Kingswood, Bristol BS15 2NL, UK
   Tel: (+44 117) 984 61 00   Fax: (+44 117) 984 61 01
Knorr-Bremse Sistemi per Autoveicoli Commerciali, Milan, Italy
Knorr-Bremse Ungarn GmbH, Kecskemét, Hungary
Knorr-Autobrzdy Sro, Jablonec, Czech Republic
Knorr-Bremse Benelux BVBA, Herentals, Belgium
Knorr-Bremse System för Tunga Fordon AB, Malmö, Sweden
Knorrbrakes Ltd, New Delhi, India
Knorr-Orsan Ticari Arad Sistemleri Ltd, Turkey
Knorr-Bremse Sistemas Para Veiculos Commerciais Brasil Ltda, Brazil
Knorr Brake Truck Systems Co, Watertown, New York, USA
AlliedSignal Truck Brake Systems Co, Elyria, Ohio, USA

Products: Air, hydraulic and electric brake systems and brake equipment for railways, complete brake systems for motor vehicles, including trailers. High-performance energy-saving compressors, air processing and drying, pressure regulation, control devices, air suspension levelling valves, clutch servos and brake boosters, anti-lock systems (ABS) and traction control (ASR). EBS (Electronic Braking Systems) with integrated ABS/ASR electronics.
   Air disc brakes for commercial vehicles, brake actuators for air drum and disc brakes.

UPDATED

Koni

Koni BV
PO Box 1014, NL-3260 AA Oud-Beijerland, Netherlands
Tel: (+31 1860) 355 00   Fax: (+31 1860) 123 22
Sales Director: Pieter A Maarleveld
Technical Director: H J T Medenblik
Associated companies in France, USA and Germany

Products: Shock-absorbers for rail and road vehicles.

Contracts: Shock-absorbers have been supplied for the Heathrow Express (London) and the Lantau Airport Express (Hong Kong) emus.

Developments: Koni shock-absorbers now have electrically controlled damping.

VERIFIED

Konvekta

Konvekta AG
PO Box 2280, D-3578 Schwalmstadt, Germany
Tel: (+49 6691) 760   Fax: (+49 6691) 76 11/76 21

Products: Air conditioning systems for buses and rail vehicles.

VERIFIED

KV

KV Automation Systems
43 Burners Lane South, Kiln Farm, Milton Keynes MK11 3HA, UK
Tel: (+44 1908) 56 15 15   Fax: (+44 1908) 56 12 27
Managing Director: A R Cersell
Technical Services Manager: B Horsler
Product Manager, Systems: M J Sanders

Products: Pneumatic control components and modular systems for control of vehicle doors; anti-lock braking equipment; vehicle suspensions.

UPDATED

Lab Craft

Lab Craft Ltd
Bilton Road, Waterhouse Land, Chelmsford CM1 2UP, UK
Tel: (+44 1245) 35 98 88   Fax: (+44 1245) 49 07 24
e-mail: sales@labcraft.demon.co.uk
Managing Director: Rodney Luscombe

Products: Transport lighting, fire detection and alarm systems.

VERIFIED

Lechmotoren

Lechmotoren GmbH
Suedliche Roemerstrasse 12–16, D-86972 Altenstadt, Germany
Tel: (+49 8861) 710   Fax: (+49 8861) 71 01 80

Products: Converters, generators up to 1.5 kV, internal combustion generator sets, AC motors, asynchronous/synchronous motors, electronic components for urban transport applications.

NEW ENTRY

Lift-U

Lift-U Division of Hogan Mfg Inc
1520 First Street, Escalon, California 95320, USA
Tel: (+1 209) 838 24 00 Fax: (+1 209) 838 86 48
Works: PO Box 398, Escalon, California 95320, USA
President: Mark Hogan
General Manager: Paul Reichmuth
Executive Vice President: Donald R Smith
Vice President: Larry M Green

Products: Wheelchair lifts and associated equipment.

VERIFIED

London Mat Industries

London Mat Industries
635 Newbold Street, London, Ontario, Canada N6E 2T8
Tel: (+1 519) 681 29 80 Fax: (+1 519) 685 93 18
President: Heine Holm
General Manager: James Clare

Products: Treadle switches for automatic door closing, opening and safety applications.

VERIFIED

LPA Industries

LPA Industries plc
PO Box 15, Tudor Works, Debden Road, Saffron Walden
CB11 4AN, UK
Tel: (+44 1799) 51 37 33 Fax: (+44 1799) 51 37 10
Sales Manager: Stephen A Cheek

Products: Cable glands, cleats, trays, plugs, sockets and connectors.

VERIFIED

Lucchini

Lucchini Siderurgica SpA
Via Oberdan 1/A, I-25127 Brescia, Italy
Tel: (+39 030) 399 21 Fax: (+39 030) 30 37 84
President & Managing Director: Luigi Lucchini
Managing Directors: Giuseppe Lucchini
  Michele Bajetti
Commercial Director: Giovanni Bajetti
Sales Manager, Railway Products: Roberto Forcella

Piombino works
Products: Rails, from 27 to 60 kg/m.

Lovere works
Products: Design, manufacture and assembly of wheels, tyres, axles and wheelsets, complete with axleboxes, disc brakes and drive units.

Subsidiary company
Lovere Meccanica Ferroviaria–TMC
Via Georgio Paglia 94, I-24065 Lovere (BG), Italy
Tel: (+39 035) 96 31 11 Fax: (+39 035) 98 36 47
President & Managing Director: Pier Luigi Scetti
Technical Manager: Zaverio Tignonsini
Sales Manager: Roberto Forcella

Products: Overhaul and full refurbishment of wheelsets including axleboxes, bearings, disc brakes and drive units. Production of axleboxes for railway and mass transit systems.

UPDATED

Luwa

Luwa Fahrzeugklimatechnik GmbH
PO Box 101437, D-60014 Frankfurt am Main, Germany
Tel: (+49 69) 403 51 42 00 Fax: (+49 69) 403 51 13 85
Managing Directors: C Hattingberg, K Pokorny

Products: Air conditioning, heating and ventilation equipment.

Contracts: Supply of equipment for Germany's ICE high-speed train as well as for Germany's Maglev Transrapid TR08 train.

UPDATED

MAC

Mobile Air Conditioning Consultants Ltd
Unit 4, Provident Industrial Estate, Pump Lane, Hayes
UB3 3NB, UK
Tel: (+44 181) 569 33 77 Fax: (+44 181) 569 33 48
Director: John Goddard

Products: Air conditioning systems for buses and rail vehicles, including a thermostatically controlled overhead bus heating and ventilation system which can be upgraded to full air conditioning.

Contracts: MAC-Hispacold heating and air conditioning systems have been selected by Daimler-Benz for its Mercedes-Benz Vita coach and O405N bus models, launched in 1997.

Eighty per cent of the Spanish market is supplied by Hispacold and units have been sold to operators in the Middle East, Africa and Asian countries. MAC equipment is standard for Irizar (qv) vehicles.

VERIFIED

Mafersa

Mafersa SA
Avenida Raimundo Pereira de Magalhães 230, Vila
Anastácio, Lapa, São Paulo, SP 05092-901, Brazil
Tel: (+55 11) 261 71 33 Fax: (+55 11) 260 96 97
Directors: Aparecido Nobuo Terazima
  Lilian Aparecida Fava

Main works
Caçapava, SP 12280-000, Rodovia Presidente Dutra, Km
128.6
Tel: (+55 122) 52 14 11 Fax: (+55 122) 52 12 81

Contagem, MG 32341-490, Rua das Indústrias s/no,
Parque São João
Tel: (+55 31) 391 24 11 Fax: (+55 31) 351 28 81

Background: Founded in 1944, Mafersa became part of ALSTOM in 1997. Rail passenger vehicle manufacture continues with the latter company, under the name ALSTOM Transporte do Brazil SA, while the present Mafersa company produces vehicle running components as listed below.

Products: Rail vehicle wheels, axles and bogies.

UPDATED

Mediter

Mediter Shock-Absorbers srl
Via Torino 46, I-14015 San Damiano d'Asti, Italy
Tel: (+39 0934) 57 53 60 Fax: (+39 0934) 57 53 73

Products: Shock-absorbers for rail and road vehicles, including specialised applications.

VERIFIED

Métal Déployé

Métal Déployé SA Resistance Department
Route de Semur, F-21500 Montbard, France
Tel: (+33 3) 80 89 58 72 Fax: (+33 3) 80 92 24 33
Managing Director: X de Froment
Sales Manager: H El Assad

Products: High-power resistors for starting, braking and shunt applications; snubbers; auxiliary resistors; snubber resistors for high-speed trains, braking resistors for urban transport applications, static braking load banks.

UPDATED

Metalastik

Metalastik Vibration Control Systems, Dunlop Ltd
Evington Valley Road, Leicester LE5 5LY, UK
Tel: (+44 116) 273 02 81 Fax: (+44 116) 273 56 98
Managing Director: A D Burton
Sales & Marketing Director: Jonathon O'Donnell

Products: Rubber-bonded-to-metal springs for primary and secondary suspension systems; air spring systems; anti-vibration mountings; flexible bearings.

Contracts: Products have been supplied for both the London Underground Northern and Jubilee line rolling stock projects.

UPDATED

Metalnastri

Metalnastri srl
Via Magenta 1/c, I-20053 Muggio (Mi), Italy
Tel: (+39 039) 214 47 33 Fax: (+39 0397) 963 67
e-mail: Metal@tin.it
General Manager: Dr Cocucci Vincenzo
Sales Director: Sem Massimo

Products: Design and manufacture of zinc, copper and aluminium anti-corrosive foil.

Contracts: Held with Adtranz, Breda, Dellner Couplers, Evobus, Fiat Ferroviaria, Firema, Rautaruukki and Scania.

VERIFIED

Microphor

Microphor Inc
PO Box 1460, 452 East Hill Road, Willits, California 95490,
USA
Tel: (+1 707) 459 55 63 Fax: (+1 707) 459 66 17
Vice President: Ted Mayfield
Sales & Marketing Manager: Walt Hess
Rail Products Manager: James J Johnson
Marketing Manager: Ross C Beck

Products: Macerator toilet/waste systems, air-assisted flush systems for rail vehicles, buses and locomotives; fuel gauges; thermo-electric refrigerators; air compressors.

UPDATED

Mitel Semiconductor

Mitel Semiconductor
Doddington Road, Lincoln LN6 3LF, UK
Tel: (+44 1522) 50 05 00 Fax: (+44 1522) 51 05 00
e-mail: richard.davis@gpsemi.com
Business Unit Manager, Power Semiconductor Division:
  P D Taylor
Sales/Marketing Manager, Power Semiconductor
  Division: A Faulkner
Export Manager, Power Semiconductor Division:
  S F Coley

Products: Power semiconductor devices: thyristors, diodes, transistors, IGBTs, gate turn-off thyristors, power modules, and air, oil, water and phase change cooling assemblies. These products may be used for onboard or trackside applications.

Contracts: Include Eurostar, TGV Nord, Sybic, Metro Interconnexion (RER), France; Hong Kong MTRC; London Underground Ltd's Jubilee line, Class 325 emus for Royal Mail, Networker Class 465 in the UK; Seoul Metro, South Korea; and locomotives for Taiwan.

UPDATED

Mitsubishi Electric

Mitsubishi Electric Corporation
2-3, Marunouchi 2-chome, Chiyoda-ku, Tokyo 100, Japan
Tel: (+81 3) 32 18 34 29   Fax: (+81 3) 32 18 28 95
(See main entry under Rail Vehicles and Traction Equipment)

Products: Traction motors for AC and DC, chopper controller, VVVF inverter control equipment, main transformers, main rectifiers, auxiliary power supplies (SIVs and MA sets), monitoring units, data transmission systems, ATO and ATP.

Contracts: A consortium of Mitsubishi and Hyundai has won an order from MTR Corporation, Hong Kong, to design, supply and commission 13 eight-car standard gauge trains fitted with ATO. The trains will operate at a speed of 80 km/h.

UPDATED

Motor Coils

Motor Coils Manufacturing Company
Two Gateway Center, 14th Floor, Pittsburgh, Pennsylvania 15222, USA
Tel: (+1 412) 201 11 01   Fax: (+1 412) 201 28 84
President: J Lynn Young

Products: Traction motors, alternators and all component parts including axle and pinion gears.

UPDATED

MTB

MTB Equipment Ltd
7-9 Barton Road, Water Eaton, Bletchley MK2 3HX, UK
Tel: (+44 1908) 37 95 21   Fax: (+44 1908) 27 06 04
Managing Director: J W Mainwaring
Sales Director: A D Berrington

Products: Seating, roller blinds, vehicle interior equipment.

VERIFIED

MTU

Motoren- und Turbinen-Union Friedrichshafen GmbH
D-88040 Friedrichshafen, Germany
Tel: (+49 7541) 900   Fax: (+49 7541) 90 22 47/90 39 18
Chairman: Dr Rolf A Hanssen
Senior Vice President, Operations:
   Dr Gerd-Michael Wolters
Director of Sales & Technology: Hermann Amrein

Products: Diesel engines for rail vehicles. MTU diesels are liquid-cooled, direct injection, four-stroke engines with turbocharging and intercooling.

Contracts: More than 500 Series 183 engines have been installed in DB dmus and railcars. Series 183 engines have also been installed in dmus and railcars in service with ÖBB, DSB, NSB and in Australia.

VERIFIED

Multipart

Multipart Bus Parts
Pilling Lane, Chorley PR7 3EL, UK
Tel: (+44 1257) 22 55 77   Fax: (+44 1257) 22 55 75
Managing Director: Chris Monks

Products: Fleetwatch Model 392 electronic trip recorder, which fits on to the rear wheel hub. A data recorder via a radio link automatically transfers mileage information and vehicle number as the vehicle enters the depot.
   Low-cost catalytic converter which does not rely on precious metals.

VERIFIED

MZT Hepos

MZT Hepos AD
Pero Nakov bb, 91000 Skopje, Macedonia
Tel: (+389 91) 61 27 22
Fax: (+389 91) 52 20 32/52 17 94
Managing Director: S Bostov
Sales Director: Goran Joksimovic
Marketing Director: D Popović

Products: Complete pneumatic and brake systems for locomotives, passenger and freight vehicles; brake equipment (UIC approved) including pneumatic, electropneumatic, hydropneumatic systems and electronic components; driver's brake valves, distributors, disc brakes and tread brake actuators, brake cylinders, slack adjusters, load brake valves, auxiliary pneumatic equipment, end cocks, hoses and coupling heads, air dryers, brake panels, windscreen washers, wheelslide protection device, diagnostic and test stands.

UPDATED

Nelson

J T Nelson Company Inc
1733 Research Drive, Louisville, Kentucky 40299, USA
Tel: (+1 502) 493 01 05   Fax: (+1 502) 491 43 95
e-mail: info@jtnelson.com
www: www.jtnelson.com
General Manager and Chief Operating Officer:
   Davis Bremner
Director, Sales & Marketing: Susan Storms Mingus

Products: Windows and glazing systems.

UPDATED

New York Air Brake

New York Air Brake Corporation
A Unit of Knorr Brake
Starbuck Avenue, Watertown, New York 13601, USA
Tel: (+1 315) 786 55 94   Fax: (+1 315) 786 56 75
General Manager, Transit Marketing: Kenneth E Towns

Products: Hydraulic and pneumatic friction brake systems and controls for rail transit applications, including microprocessor brake controls and slip/slide systems, air compressors, master controllers, hydraulic power units, disc brakes, and tread brakes.

VERIFIED

Nuti

Roberto Nuti SpA
Via Artigianato 3, I-40064 Ozzano Emilia, Italy
Tel: (+39 051) 79 96 41   Fax: (+39 051) 79 88 78
Commercial Director: Massimo Nuti

Products: SABO shock-absorbers.

VERIFIED

Otaco Seating

Otaco Seating Co Ltd
PO Box 2310, Harvie Settlement Road, Orillia, Ontario
Canada L3V 6S2
Tel: (+1 705) 325 70 52   Fax: (+1 705) 325 70 73
Sales Manager: Dick Lauer

Products: Bus, metro, rapid transit and trolleybus
seating. After-market service parts on all Otaco and
American Seating (qv) models. Seating and securement
systems for special service vehicles.

NEW ENTRY

Oerlikon-Knorr

Oerlikon-Knorr Eisenbahntechnik AG
Mandachstrasse 50, CH-8155 Niederhasli, Switzerland
Tel: (+41 1) 852 31 11   Fax: (+41 1) 852 31 31
General Manager: M Wittwer
Sales Manager: J Gysi
Parent company: Knorr-Bremse Systeme (qv)

Products: Air brakes for automatic and direct systems,
distributors, electropneumatic, electrohydraulic and
pneumatic brake control valves, electronic anti-slip/slide
systems, automatic load brake devices and weighing
valves, screw compressors, air compressors, air dryers;
electromagnetic and permanent-magnet track brakes,
eddy current track brakes. Complete brake systems for
rail transit applications.

UPDATED

Oleo

Oleo International Ltd
Grovelands, Longford Road, Exhall, Coventry CV7 9NE,
UK
Tel: (+44 1203) 64 55 55   Fax (+44 1203) 64 57 77
e-mail: railsales@oleo.co.uk
Managing Director: R Elden
Sales & Marketing Director: R W Elliott
Technical Director: R C Page

Products: Hydraulic cushioning units for centre couplers,
designed for new vehicles or upgrading existing rolling
stock; anticlimbers, incorporating energy absorption, to
prevent over-riding on impact; collapsible struts for fitting
to the front of rail vehicles behind the obstacle deflector to
absorb impact and help prevent derailment caused by
track obstructions; hydraulic cushioning for fixed and
sliding friction end stops.

UPDATED

Parizzi

Elettromeccanica Parizzi SpA
Via Romani 10, I-20091 Bresso, Milan, Italy
Tel: (+39 02) 66 52 31   Fax: (+39 02) 614 04 08

Products: Synchronous motor drives; body tilt controls;
static converters; battery chargers; converters/inverters.

VERIFIED

Percy Lane

Percy Lane
Division of Heywood Williams Ltd
Lichfield Road, Tamworth B79 7TL, UK
Tel: (+44 1827) 638 21   Fax: (+44 1827) 31 01 59
Managing Director: D J Inglis
Deputy Managing Director: J C Smith
Sales & Marketing Director: R J Humphries

Products: Windows and glazed assemblies supplied
under the Beclawat name; windscreens, luggage rack
systems, detrainment and emergency escape equipment,
driver assault protection doors, aluminium fabrications.
Equipment supplied for metro cars, LRVs, buses,
coaches and minibuses.

Contracts: Include detrainment steps for London
Underground Piccadilly line cars; PBKATGV2N side
windows (for ALSTOM) and bodyside glazing for MP89
stock for Paris Metro.

UPDATED

Pilkington Rail Glazing

Pilkington Rail Glazing
Eckersall Road, Kings Norton, Birmingham B38 8SR, UK
Tel: (+44 121) 606 41 00   Fax: (+44 121) 606 41 91
Managing Director: P Molineux
Director, Sales & Marketing: R Harper

Assembly plant: Knowsley Road, Eccleston, St Helens
WA10 4QB

Products: Toughened and laminated glass for transit
vehicles.

VERIFIED

POLI

POLI Costruzione Materiali Trazione SpA
Via Fontanella 11, I-26010 Camisano, Cremona, Italy
Tel: (+39 0373) 27 01 26   Fax: (+39 0373) 72 90 97
e-mail: polibrakes@computech.it
Technical Export Sales Manager: Dott Giuseppe Vendite

Products: Braking equipment, including disc brakes, pad
holders, electromagnetic brakes, resilient wheels and
pumps.

UPDATED

Power Parts

Power Parts Co
1325 Pratt Boulevard, Elk Grove Village, Illinois 60007,
USA
Tel: (+1 847) 952 89 00   Fax: (+1 847) 952 91 80
President: Phil Brown
Vice President, Sales & Marketing: Martin Yoemans

Products: Locomotive, rapid transit and passenger car
replacement parts.

VERIFIED

Powernetics

Powernetics Ltd
Jason Works, Clarence Street, Loughborough LE11 1DX,
UK
Tel: (+44 1509) 21 41 53   Fax: (+44 1509) 26 24 60
President: Satish Chada
Financial Controller: A J Marples
Export Sales: Aran Chada
Sales Office/Marketing Manager: J A Goddard

Project Sales Manager: Nilesh Chouhan
Quality Assurance Manager: A J Reilly
Purchasing Manager: I W Dakin

Products: Specialist power supply equipment designer
and manufacturer; uninterruptable power supplies for rail
applications; static inverters/converters; static frequency
changers; switch mode power supplies; battery chargers;
DC-DC converters.

Contracts: With Railtrack, UK (DC-DC converters for
Stoneblower project); Adtranz (static converters);
Bombardier Prorail (static converters for London
Underground), Manchester Metrolink (UPS systems
for signalling and telecommunications); G T Rail
Maintenance (UPS systems for signalling); Amec Rail,
Amey Railways and Jarvis Facilities (battery chargers for
signalling) and Hong Kong Tramways (static inverters for
lighting, air conditioning, fans and similar equipment).

Developments: A new range of uninterruptable 2-10 kVA
power supplies for trackside and railborne applications is
available; new developments on static inverters for fan
systems within onboard train air conditioning units.

UPDATED

Proximeter

The Proximeter Co Ltd
16 Tiller Road, London E14 8PX, UK
Tel: (+44 171) 345 50 50   Fax: (+44 171) 345 50 51
Managing Director: Stephen J Franklin

Product: Proximity warning equipment for road vehicle
reversing systems including closed circuit television.

VERIFIED

Q'Straint

Q'Straint Inc
3085 Southwestern Blvd, Orchard Park, New York 14127,
USA
Tel: (+1 716) 675 22 22   Fax: (+1 716) 675 22 70
President: Jean Girardin
General Manager: Jim Reaume

UK subsidiary
Q'Straint Ltd
10 Wilson House, John Wilson Business Park, Thanet
Way, Whitstable CT5 3QT
Tel: (+44 1227) 77 30 35   Fax: (+44 1227) 77 00 35
Manager: Michael Simmonds

Products: Wheelchair and occupant restraint systems for
buses and rail rolling stock.
   A low-profile high-efficiency floor fastening restrains the
individual with a lap belt attached to the rear wheelchair
fasteners and a shoulder belt that fastens to the vehicle
side.
   A variant of the wheelchair and occupant restraint
system is available for operators who do not want to fit
floor pockets. It allows installation on vehicles fitted with
tracking.

VERIFIED

Raychem

Raychem Limited
Faraday Road, Dorcan, Swindon SN3 5HH, UK
Tel: (+44 1793) 52 81 71   Fax: (+44 1793) 57 25 16
Public Relations Manager, Europe: Neil Madle

Products: Low fire hazard cable and harness
components; temperature and condensation control for
sensitive electronic displays, ticket-issuing equipment
and passenger vehicles; multiplex databus systems.
   Lightweight wire and cable meeting low fire hazard
criteria. Zerohal 100 wire offers a range of reduced fire

hazard properties while retaining good mechanical performance and chemical resistance. The low fire hazard range of products has been expanded with the TMS-ZH-SCE family of heat-shrinkable cable markers.

Contracts: Zerohal 100 wire from Raychem has recently been utilised on a number of major rail and mass transit projects around the world – recent among them the New Jersey Transit Hudson Bergen line, Talent in Germany, the Bruxelles Metro, the Seoul Metro, as well as on several other major rolling stock projects in Europe and Asia.

UPDATED

Rica Seats

Riihimäen Metallikaluste Oy
Käpälämäenkatu 10, FIN-11710 Riihimäki, Finland
Tel: (+358 19) 72 26 61   Fax: (+358 19) 72 26 62
Managing Director: Aatos Hämäläinen
Export Manager: Arto Varanki

Products: Seating for rail vehicles.

VERIFIED

Robert Wagner

Robert Wagner
PO Box 1604, D-42477 Radevormwald, Germany
Tel: (+49 2195) 70 04/70 05   Fax: (+49 2195) 10 19
Managing Director: Reinhold Wagner

Products: Hinges for doors, window locks and mechanisms, water valves and associated equipment, interior fittings for rail vehicles.

VERIFIED

Rose Bearings

Rose Bearings Ltd
Doddington Road, Lincoln LN6 3RA, UK
Tel: (+44 1522) 50 09 33   Fax (+44 1522) 50 09 75
Managing Director: R P Chapman
Industry Specialist, Transportation: P Hogarth

Products: Self-aligning and special bearings including couplers, suspension and door operating mechanisms, complete assemblies and linkages.

VERIFIED

Roues et Trains Montes

Roues et Trains Montes, RTM SA
A subsidiary of Usinor-Sacilor
Quai Greiner, porte 2, B-4100 Seraing, Belgium
Tel: (+32 4) 338 83 00   Fax: (+32 4) 338 82 29
Managing Director: R Konat
Sales Manager: P Marchettini

Products: Wheelsets, loose wheels (monobloc and tyred), loose axles; rewheeling and overhaul of wheelsets.

VERIFIED

Ruspa

Ruspa Srl
Via Christoforo Colombo 2, I-10070 Robassomero, Italy
Tel: (+39 011) 924 10 16/11 40/10 46
Fax: (+39 011) 924 11 06
President: R Ruspa
General Manager: M Tamietti
Chief of Sales Department: R Ruspa

Products: Interior styling equipment, including magazine nets, ashtrays, handles, glass holders, food trays, lighting, and stainless steel wheel covers; plastic seats for urban vehicles.

VERIFIED

Sabre

Sabre Rail Services Ltd
Grindon Way, Heighington Lane Business Park, Newton Aycliffe DL5 6SH, UK
Tel: (+44 1325) 30 05 05   Fax: (+44 1325) 30 04 85
Managing Director: David A Thompson
Technical Sales Manager: E M Burnside

Products: Remanufacture of hydraulic dampers for rail rolling stock, also brake cylinders, slack adjusters, valves and current collection equipment.

VERIFIED

SAB WABCO

SAB WABCO
Roskildevagen 1B, PO Box 193, SE-201 21 Malmo, Sweden
Tel: (+46 40) 35 04 60   Fax: (+46 40) 30 38 03
President: Alf Göransson
Senior Vice President, Finance Administration:
  Rolf Lundahl
Senior Vice President, Marketing: Lars Blecko
Senior Vice President, Business Development Manager:
  Nils Lennart Nilsson

Subsidiaries
SAB WABCO AB, Sweden
SAB WABCO International AB, Sweden
SAB WABCO SA, France
SAB WABCO NV, Belgium
SAB Iberica SA, SAB WABCO SA, Spain
SAB WABCO BV, Netherlands
SAB WABCO Davies & Metcalfe Ltd, UK (qv)
SAB WABCO SpA, Italy
SAB WABCO do Brasil SA, Brazil
SAB WABCO Pty Ltd, Australia
SAB WABCO D&M Engineering Ltd, Australia
SAB WABCO KP GmbH, Germany
Gutehoffnungshutte Radsatz GmbH, Germany
SAB WABCO BSI Verkehrstechnik GmbH, Germany
SAB WABCO sro, Czech Republic
SAB WABCO Korea Ltd, South Korea
SAB WABCO India Ltd, India

Associated company
FACTO AG, Switzerland

Products: Braking systems for locomotives, passenger and freight vehicles, including LRVs and guided vehicles with rubber tyres; UIC-approved automatic airbrakes to the requirements of most railway administrations; electropneumatic, electrohydraulic, electromechanical and all-electric brake systems; vacuum and combined brake systems; air supply equipment, reciprocating and screw compressors, air treatment devices and accessories; airbrake control devices; automatic slack adjusters, variable load devices; friction brake devices, tread brakes, brake discs, calliper assemblies, disc brake actuators with spring, hydraulic or mechanically operated parking; friction materials; electromagnetic track brakes; UIC approved.
  Automatic door systems; sliding door systems (external and internal); plug sliding door systems; swing-plug door systems. All available in single or double leaf, electropneumatic or electric. Automatic retracting and fixed steps.
  Wheel products: solid wheels, wheelsets, resilient and low-noise wheels, running gear.
  Microprocessor-controlled wheelslide protection devices, anti-slip and speed controls; automatic test equipment for brake controls; automatic computer-controlled systems for marshalling yards; transit car coupling systems.

Contracts: Dmus and emus: brake systems and brake equipment for vehicles in Australia, France, Germany, Hungary, Italy, Netherlands, Spain, Sweden, Taiwan and United Kingdom.

LRV/Trams: electrohydraulic brake systems to Cologne, Strasbourg, Grenoble and Val-de-Seine; electro-mechanical system to Hungary and Czech Republic; electrohydraulic brake systems, wheels and door systems for Hungary and Czech Republic; wheels for Darmstadt, Nuremburg, Vienna; wheels and door systems for Manila; and door systems for The Hague.

Metros: electropneumatic brake systems for the Paris, Rome, Santiago and Teheran metros; electropneumatic brake systems for Stockholm metro.

UPDATED

SAB WABCO Davies & Metcalfe

SAB WABCO Davies & Metcalfe Ltd
Thermal Road, Bromborough L62 4TR, UK
Tel: (+44 151) 473 02 60   Fax: (+44 151) 473 02 72
Managing Director: L C Snowdon
Technical Manager: D Horsley
Business Managers, Aftermarket: M T Tamroni,
  J D Summers

Parent company: CARDO BSI Rail AB, Malmo, Sweden

Products: Electronic, pneumatic and electropneumatic brake control systems; air compressors, air dryers, electronic overspeed protection equipment, automatic couplers, wheel and axle-mounted disc brakes and pads, brake rigging regulators, brake cylinders, track brakes, tread brake units, wheelslip detection and correction equipment, point setting mechanism.

UPDATED

SAFT

SAFT
Advanced and Industrial Battery Group
156 Avenue de Metz, F-93239 Romainville, France
Tel: (+33 1) 49 15 36 00   Fax: (+33 1) 49 16 34 00
Commercial and Marketing Manager: Fred-Erik Hapiak

Products: Nickel-cadmium batteries.

Contracts: Include supply of units for NYCTA, Hong Kong and Stockholm.

NEW ENTRY

Sanivac

Sanivac Vakuumtechnik GmbH
Hafenstrasse 32a, D-22880 Wedel, Germany
Tel: (+49 4103) 916 80   Fax: (+49 4103) 91 68 90
Sales & Marketing: Ian F Goodwin

Products: Toilet compartments, vacuum toilets, retention tanks.

VERIFIED

Saydair Commercial Seating

Saydair Commercial Seating Pty Ltd
A wholly owned subsidiary of the Clifford Corporation Limited
Garden Drive, Tullamarine, Victoria 3043, Australia
Tel: (+61 3) 93 39 41 00   Fax: (+61 2) 93 39 14 60
General Manager: Chris Vevers

Products: Bus and coach seating, seats for rail and ferries, together with automatic bus doors and other components.

VERIFIED

SBF

SBF Spezialleuchten Wurzen GmbH
Badergraben 16, D-04808 Wurzen, Germany
Tel: (+49 3425) 92 01 81   Fax: (+49 3425) 92 01 78
Managing Director: Hans D Sehn
Sales Manager: Fritz Strobelt

Products: Light fittings for urban rail vehicles.

VERIFIED

Scharfenbergkupplung

Scharfenbergkupplung GmbH & Co KG
PO Box 411160, D-38233 Salzgitter, Germany
Tel: (+49 5341) 21 46 30   Fax: (+49 5341) 21 46 13
General Manager: W Weinhold
Sales Director: Christos Ramnialis
Technical Director: Reinhardt Friedow

Associate company
Radenton Scharfenberg Ltd
Unit 7, Silverdale Industrial Centre, Silverdale Road, Hayes UB3 3BP, UK
Tel: (+44 181) 561 21 31   Fax: (+44 181) 869 17 26

Products: Automatic multifunction couplers, semi-permanent couplers and drawgear for light rail, rapid transit, trams, metros, commuter rail systems, automated

guideway transit, mountain railways; electric couplers and transition couplers.

Contracts: Include automatic couplers for UK rolling stock (Adtranz and ALSTOM).

Developments: Radenton has introduced a new type of auto-coupler for the UK post-privatisation market. It is modular in concept and permits a range of interchangeable mechanical heads, electrical connections, energy absorption devices and other options to be fitted depending on the requirements of the train operator.

UPDATED

Products: Auxiliary converters, DC high-speed circuit breakers (HSCB), AC and DC power and auxiliary contactors, AC vacuum circuit breakers, disconnecting and changeover switches, earthing switches, single-arm pantographs, master controller, electronic on-train monitoring and recording systems (OTMR), speed indicators, pulse generators, radar systems and multifunctional display systems, wheel flange lubricators, automatic centre-couplings.

Complete system engineering, installation and setting up of modular control electronics and associated traction/auxiliary components.

UPDATED

Sguinzi Pietro

Sguinzi Pietro SpA
70 Via Marco Polo, I-20083 Gaggliano, Italy
Tel: (+39 02) 908 10 39   Fax: (+39 02) 908 13 97/410 27
President: Virginio Sguinzi
General Director: A Nicoli
Sales Director: Antonio Sguinzi

Products: Windows, hatches, folding doors and seating for buses.

VERIFIED

Sécheron

Sécheron Ltd
14 Avenue de Sécheron, CH-1211 Geneva 21, Switzerland
Tel: (+41 22) 739 41 11   Fax: (+41 22) 738 73 05
e-mail: info@secheron.com
www: http://www.secheron.com
Chief Executive Officer: Beth Krasna
Executive Vice President: Paul Bieri
Sales Manager: Jimmy Cuche
Marketing Manager: René Jenni

Subsidiary companies
CKD Sécheron spol sro, Prague, Czech Republic
Sécheron Hasler Praha spol sro, Czech Republic
Pixy AG, Baden, Switzerland

See also Electrification and Signalling sections

SEPSA

Sistemas Electrónicos de Potencia SA
Polig Indust La Estación, C/Albatross 7 y 9, E-28320 Pinto, Spain
Tel: (+34 91) 691 52 61   Fax: (+34 91) 691 39 77
President: Nicolas Fuster
General Manager: Felix Ramos
Commercial Director: Antonio Sosa
Technical Director: Carlos de la Viesca

Products: Static converters for rail and trolleybus applications (DC, AC, multivoltage); inverters, choppers, rectifiers and battery chargers; (featuring microprocessor control, and GTO/IGBT technologies).

VERIFIED

Sigma

Sigma Industries Pty Ltd
4 Bachell Avenue, Lidcombe, New South Wales 2141, Australia
Tel: (+61 2) 93 30 71 00   Fax: (+61 2) 93 30 71 99
Chair: Kevin Kirby
Deputy Chair: Roger Dane
Managing Director: Keith Allen
Export Manager: Geoff Rule

Subsidiary companies
Sigma Air Conditioning Inc
321 S Fairbank, Addison, Illinois 60101, USA

Air International Transit UK
Britannia House, Britannia Way, Britannia Industrial Park, Lichfield WS14 9UY, UK
Tel: (+44 1543) 41 61 81   Fax: (+44 1543) 41 81 21

Products: Air conditioning equipment for buses and rail vehicles; IFE body side door systems; Microphor mobile toilets; Purafil air filtration systems.

Converter and VVVF inverters; environmentally benign refrigerant systems using HFC.

UPDATED

SKF

SKF Industrial Division
SE-415 50 Gothenburg, Sweden
Tel: (+46 31) 37 14 32   Fax: (+46 31) 37 10 87
Director, Railway Division: Egon Ekdahl

Subsidiary
SKF GmbH
Gunnar-Wester-Strasse 12, D-97421 Schweinfurt, Germany
Tel: (+49 9721) 56 33 39   Fax: (+49 9721) 56 20 29

Products: Axleboxes for all types of rolling stock; spherical, cylindrical, taper journal roller bearings; double row taper bearing units with speed and temperature sensors; traction motor and transmission bearings; motor support housings and roller bearings; maintenance equipment and mounting/dismounting equipment.

UPDATED

SMC

SMC Transit International
Vincent Avenue, Crown Hill, Milton Keynes MK8 0AN, UK
Tel: (+44 1908) 56 87 91   Fax: (+44 1908) 56 18 12
Managing Director: Steve Bangs
General Manager: Laurence Seward

Products: Pneumatic and external door systems, including external pocketed, plug, sliding, bi-leaf folding, gangway and emergency doors. Door operating mechanisms; linear and rotary actuators; bonded and fabricated door leaves; electric door operating controls including microprocessor-controlled with TMS interface; door track and trolleys; obstacle detection and integral locking mechanisms. Components such as electropneumatic solenoid valves for auxiliary purposes including heating and ventilation systems.

Contracts: SMC Transit International has supplied door systems for the Putra light metro in Kuala Lumpur, Boston Redline; MTRC Hong Kong; Manchester Metrolink; Sokol high-speed line, Russia; Amtrak North East corridor.

UPDATED

Socar

Socar-Ics SpA
Strada Vecchia Orbassano 94, I-10040 Volvera, Italy
Tel: (+39 011) 990 66 66   Fax: (+39 011) 990 67 15
Managing Director: G Pignocchino
Sales Manager: A Cortese
Quality Assurance Manager: B Felettigh

Products: Glazing, including laminated windscreens.

VERIFIED

Specialty Bulb

Specialty Bulb Co Inc
80 Orville Drive, Bohemia, New York 1176-0231, USA
Tel: (+1 516) 589 33 93   Fax: (+1 516) 563 30 89
President: Judith Beja
Sales Manager: Edie Muldoon

Products: Replacement lightbulbs for rail and road vehicles; signal, marker indicator lamps, headlight and ditch light lamps.

UPDATED

Sportworks

Sportworks NW Inc
15500 Woodinville Redmond Road NE, Bldg C-600, Woodinville, Washington 98072, USA
Tel: (+1 425) 483 70 00   Fax: (+1 425) 488 90 01
e-mail: lisar@swnw.com
www: www.bicycleracks.com
Product Manager: Lisa Foley

Products: Front-mounted cycle rack for buses, able to carry two cycles per vehicle.

Contracts: Sportworks bike racks are used in more than 150 undertakings, totalling 14,000 racks on buses. The latest contract is from MTA Los Angeles for 1,400 racks.

UPDATED

Startmaster

Startmaster Air Starting Systems
6501 Barberton Avenue, Cleveland, Ohio 44102, USA
Tel: (+1 216) 281 78 10   Fax: (+1 216) 281 11 32
President: Theodore J Berger

Parent company: Maradyne Inc

Products: Air-assisted power steering; air starting systems for rail and bus applications; engine intake air precleaners; hydraulic fluid filtration; heaters and ventilating fans.

VERIFIED

Stewart & Stevenson

Stewart & Stevenson Services Inc
5840 Dahlia Street, PO Box 220, Commerce City, Colorado 80037, USA
Tel: (+1 303) 868 74 41   Fax: (+1 303) 287 49 36

Products: Wheelchair lifts for buses and coaches.

VERIFIED

Stone Ibérica

Stone Ibérica SA
Montalbán 7, E-28014 Madrid, Spain
Tel: (+34 91) 532 41 81   Fax: (+34 91) 522 76 97
e-mail: if@albatros.dobytec.es
General Director: Nicolás Fúster
Managing Director: Julio Rey
Marketing Director: Ignacio Fúster

Works: C/Gavilanes 16, Poligono Industrial La Estación, E-28320 Pinto-Madrid
Tel: (+34 91) 691 41 61   Fax: (+34 91) 691 09 97

Products: Air conditioning equipment, static converters for power supply of fluorescent lamps; speed regulators for synchronous motors; microprocessor controls.

UPDATED

Stone International

Stone International
Unit 9, Crossways Business Park, Dartford DA2 6QG, UK
Tel: (+44 1322) 28 93 23   Fax: (+44 1322) 28 92 82
Managing Director: Anthony J Walsh

Background: A member of the Vapor Group, Montreal, Canada.

Products: Air conditioning, heating, pressure ventilation and temperature control equipment, static inverters, battery chargers, alternators, DC motors.

VERIFIED

Stone Safety

Stone Safety Service Corporation
240 South Main Street, South Hackensack, New Jersey 07606, USA
Tel: (+1 201) 489 02 00   Fax: (+1 201) 489 93 62
General Manager: Vincent Mirandi
General Sales Manager: Douglas C Cavallo

Products: Air conditioning, heating and temperature controls for all rail rolling stock; static auxiliary power supplies; microprocessor controls; diagnostic equipment; 134 A conversion systems. Static inverters and associated static equipment, reversible heat pumps and microprocessor controls.

VERIFIED

Stone UK

Stone UK Limited
A member of Vapor Group of Westinghouse Air Brake Company
Crossways Business Park, Dartford DA2 6QG, UK
Tel: (+44 1322) 28 93 23   Fax: (+44 1322) 28 92 82
Managing Director: Anthony J Walsh
Commercial Manager: Lynne Smith
Sales & Marketing Director: Nigel Twort

Products: Air conditioning, heating and ventilation equipment; train lighting and temperature control equipment; auxiliary power generation equipment, including alternators, inverters and converters.

VERIFIED

Stork RMO

Stork RMO BV
PO Box 1250, NL-1000 BG Amsterdam, Netherlands
Tel: (+31 20) 523 37 00   Fax: (+31 20) 622 06 17
Managing Director: Ir R J A Kortink
Manager, Marketing and Sales: Ing J W Pijl
Manager, Product Development: Prof Ir C P Keizer

Products: Powered and trailer bogies for trains, metro cars and LRVs; automatic retractable interconnecting gangways for trainsets; radial powered and trailer bogies; overhaul of bogies and components.

Contracts: Stork RMO Flexy bogies are used for the newest trainsets on Netherlands Railways including the IRM and mDDM double-deck emus. Powered bogies have been supplied for LRVs in Amsterdam, Rotterdam, and Den Haag. Stork is also building the bogies for the Bombardier Eurorail cars that will run on the new Rotterdam metro.

UPDATED

Sumitomo

Sumitomo Metal Industries Ltd
1-1-3 Otemachi, Chiyoda-ku, Tokyo 100, Japan
Tel: (+81 3) 32 82 61 11   Fax: (+81 3) 32 82 67 64
General Manager, Sales: M Takeya
Manager, Railway Products & Equipment Sales: R Iino

Works: Osaka Steelworks, 5-1-109 Shimaya,
Konohana-Ku, Osaka 554

Products: Wheels, tyres, axles, wheelsets, bogies, air
springs, gear units, brake discs, automatic couplers,
draftgear, bogie rotating test stands.

Sumitomo has developed a bolsterless bogie with 40
per cent fewer components and weighing some 15 per
cent less than conventional designs. Better running
performance through curves is claimed. Based on this
experience, SMI has developed several new bogie
designs and test equipment. Included are a prototype
high-speed test bogie for JR Shinkansen trains, and bogie
rotational test equipment. Also developed linear induction
motors for the Osaka and Tokyo mini-metro systems.

Contracts: Numerous types of powered and trailing
bogies have been supplied to Japanese private railways
and metro systems. Sumitomo's market share of bogies
for Japanese private railways and metros is put at over
70 per cent.

UPDATED

SÜTRAK

SÜTRAK Transportkälte GmbH
Heinkelstrasse 5, D-71272 Renningen, Germany
Tel: (+49 7159) 92 32 06   Fax: (+49 7159) 63 62
Chairman: Dieter Weckerle
Manager, Climate Control, Buses: Hans-Peter Eckstein
Manager, Climate Control, Rail Vehicles: Andreas Hille

UK office
Sütrak UK Ltd
24-25 Saddleback Road, Westgate Industrial Estate,
Northampton NN5 5HL
Tel: (+44 1604) 58 14 68   Fax: (+44 1604) 75 81 32
Sales Director: Jeremy Smith

USA office
Sütrak Corporation
6899 East 49th Avenue, Commerce City, Colorado 80022
Tel: (+1 303) 287 27 00   Fax: (+1 303) 286 10 05

Products: Air conditioning equipment for rail vehicles,
people movers and buses; roof-mounted, integrated
modular and integrated compact systems, all available
with R134A refrigerant.

VERIFIED

Tamware

Oy Tamware AB
Yrittäjänkulma 5, FIN-33710 Tampere, Finland
Tel: (+358 3) 283 11 11   Fax: (+358 3) 283 15 00
Main works: Teollisuustie 6, FIN-66100 Maalahti
Factory Director: Bjarne Smeds
Export Manager: Urpo Kasurinen
Product Development Manager: Teuvo Rahikkala

Products: Doors for buses, trams, trains and coaches;
destination and route number displays.

UPDATED

Tecalemit

Tecalemit Systems Ltd
Estover Road, Plymouth PL6 7PS, UK
Tel: (+44 1752) 77 57 81   Fax: (+44 1752) 77 73 16
Marketing Manager: Dr David Higgs

Products: Interlube automatic chassis lubrication
systems.

VERIFIED

Teknoware

Teknoware Oy
Ilmarisentie 8, FIN-15200 Lahti, Finland
Tel: (+358 3) 88 30 20   Fax: (+358 3) 883 02 40
Export Manager, Overseas: Esa Melkko
Export Manager, Scandinavia, Benelux & France:
   Ari Valavaara

Joint venture company (in association with Lab Craft, UK)
Transport Lighting Company
Bilton Road, Waterhouse Lane, Chelmsford CM1 2UP, UK
Tel: (+44 1245) 35 98 88   Fax: (+44 1245) 49 07 24
Managing Director: Rodney Luscombe
Sales Manager: John Leek

Subsidiary company
Teknoware GmbH
Beethovenplatz 1-3, D-60325 Frankfurt/Main, Germany
Tel: (+49 69) 97 46 72 76   Fax: (+49 69) 97 46 71 00
Managing Director: Markus Alholm

Products: Inverters/ballasts and fluorescent lighting
systems for buses and rail vehicles; halogen converters
for rail applications, plus design service for special
requirements.

Contracts: Customers include Mercedes-Benz, MAN,
Kässbohrer, Van Hool, Volvo, ALSTOM and Adtranz.
Exports have been made to Germany, Switzerland,
Austria, Hungary, Czech Republic, Slovenia, Croatia,
Yugoslavia, Slovakia and Romania.

UPDATED

Temoinsa

Técnicas Modulares e Industriales SA
Poligono Industrial Congost, Avenida San Julián 100,
E-08400 Granollers, Spain
Tel: (+34 93) 846 68 35   Fax: (+34 93) 846 64 86
General Manager: José M Pedret
Deputy General Manager: Vincente Polo
Commercial Manager: Antonio Fábregas

Products: Design, manufacture and technical assistance
for fitting out of coach interiors with modular systems,
including air conditioning, vacuum toilet systems,
passenger information modular system, high-technology
composites, heating and ventilation systems.

Turnkey projects for complete interiors for new vehicles
and refurbishment.

Contracts: Customers include Copenhagen metro,
Metro Atlanta, Amtrak USA and Adtranz UK (60 toilet
modules for Connex).

UPDATED

Texstar

Texstar Inc
802 Avenue J East, Grand Prairie, Texas 75053-4036,
USA
Tel: (+1 214) 647 13 66   Fax: (+1 214) 641 28 00
Marketing Manager: Carl Becker

Products: Composites for rail and bus applications.

Thermo King

Thermo King Corporation
314 West 90th Street, Minneapolis, Minnesota 55420,
USA
Tel: (+1 612) 887 22 00   Fax: (+1 612) 887 25 29
Vice President, North America: P Donahue
Vice President, Europe, Africa, Middle East, India:
   P Veenboer
Vice President, Asia Pacific: Dick Pedtke
Vice President, South America: Tony Zabala
Global Product Manager, Bus & Light Rail HVAC:
   Mark Watson
International Product Manager: LeRoy Bottemiller
North America Product Manager: Steve Johnson

Products: Heating, ventilation and air conditioning for
buses and light rail vehicles. Range includes roof-
mounted and integral systems, front-mounted systems,
heating convection systems and small bus air
conditioning systems, backed up by global service
network.

Contracts: Supply of systems to Manila LRT. Also to
operators in Europe, North Africa, Middle East and India.
Main supplier of AC systems to North American
operators. New facility in China produces roof-mounted
units for the Asia-Pacific market.

VERIFIED

Tibram

Tibram AG
Aarestrasse 29, CH-3661 Uetendorf, Switzerland
Tel: (+41 33) 345 10 57   Fax: (+41 33) 345 59 57

Products: Earth contacts for locomotives, LRVs and
emus, rated at 400 to 1,000 A; glass fibre insulators; air
exchangers; parts for axle housings.

UPDATED

Time 24

Time 24 Ltd
Unit 69, Victoria Road, Burgess Hill RH15 9TR, UK
Tel: (+44 1444) 25 76 55   Fax: (+44 1444) 25 90 00
Sales Manager: Chris Young
Quality Assurance Manager: Robert Thomas
Production Director: Mark Willifer
Director: David Shore

Products: Traction and brake controllers; cable
assemblies, harnesses and looms.

VERIFIED

Timken

The Timken Company
Canton, Ohio 44706, USA

British Timken Division of The Timken Company
16 Quorn Way, Grafton Industrial Estate, Northampton
NN1 2PN, UK
Tel: (+44 1604) 62 70 15   Fax: (+44 1604) 63 64 54
General Manager, Rail: P C Vials

Products: Tapered roller bearings; AP and SP tapered
roller bearing cartridge units; complete axleboxes and
motor suspension units. Timken supplies tapered roller
bearings and ancillary equipment including
transmissions, axleboxes, traction motor suspension
units and other equipment such as cooling fans and
screw compressors. Also used extensively in bus
transmission and axle applications.

VERIFIED

Toshiba

Toshiba Corporation
Railway Projects Department
Toshiba Building, 1-Shibaura 1-chome, Minato-ku, Tokyo
105-800, Japan
Tel: (+81 3) 34 57 49 24   Fax: (+81 3) 54 44 94 22
(See main entry under Rail Vehicles and Traction
Equipment)

Products: Heating, ventilation and air conditioning
equipment; AC and DC electrification equipment.

UPDATED

Transintech

Transintech Ltd
PO Box 21, Derby Carriage Works, Litchurch Lane, Derby
DE24 8AP, UK
Tel: (+44 1332) 25 75 00   Fax: (+44 1332) 37 19 50
Commercial Director: Andrew Burrows

Background: Transintech was formed in 1995 following
the purchase from Adtranz (qv) of its Interiors Division.
Transintech has a marketing alliance with French
manufacturer Compin for seating, and with Compin and
MBM Technology for at-seat entertainment facilities.

Products: There are four groups: seats, interiors, cab and
electrical and specialised systems.
   The product range includes the Belton composite
crashworthy rail seat, lightweight saloon ceilings, toilet
modules and vehicle electrical cupboards/panels. The
Belton seat range is lightweight, with maximised
kneeroom and comfort. It is made from new reinforced
composite materials and was designed in association
with Compin for crashworthiness.

VERIFIED

Transmatic

Transmatic Inc
6145 Delfield Industrial Drive, Waterford, Michigan 48329,
USA
Tel: (+1 248) 623 25 00   Fax: (+1 248) 623 28 39
President: O K Dealey Jr
Vice President, Sales & Marketing: M T Hoffman
Vice President, Environmental Systems:
   D Scott McConnell

UK subsidiary
Transmatic Europe Ltd
B3 Hortonwood 10, Telford TF1 4ES, UK
Tel: (+44 1952) 60 83 83   Fax: (+44 1952) 67 76 93
Managing Director: Terry Calnon

Products: Interior lighting and advertising coving for
buses and urban transit vehicles; multipurpose lighting/
air conditioning duct modules; surface-mounted
fluorescent lighting; destination sign lighting; interior
cleaning systems for buses and rail vehicles.

VERIFIED

Transpec

Transpec Worldwide
7205 Setrling Ponds Court, Sterling Heights, Michigan
4831-2575, USA
Tel: (+1 810) 274 94 00   Fax: (+1 810) 274 94 40
President: Ronald C Lamparter
General Manager: James A Haigh
Director of Sales: Michael Martinez
International Sales: Robert A Peticca

Products: Combination roof ventilator and emergency
exits for buses and rail vehicles; crossing control and stop
arms.

Crossing control and stop arms are supplied for the
North American school bus community.

UPDATED

Transtechnik

Transtechnik GmbH
Ohmstrasse 1-3, D-83607 Holzkirchen, Germany
Tel: (+49 8024) 99 00   Fax: (+49 8024) 99 03 00
e-mail: info@transtechnik.com
www: www.transtechnik.com
Chair: Wilhelm Sterff
Managing Director: Robert Sterff
Manager, Marketing Communications:
   Tom Weber-Reichardt
Sales: Andreas Baerend
Technical & Engineering: Helmut Eisinger

UK Marketing Office
Transtechnik PSI
Chiltern House, High Street, Chalfont St Giles HP8 4QH,
UK
Tel: (+44 1494) 87 15 44   Fax: (+44 1494) 87 31 18
Marketing Manager: Ian Lavis

Italy Sales & Marketing Office
ITP (International Technical Products di Maurizio Favini &
Co) SA
Via Cilea 78, I-20151 Milan
Tel: (+39 02) 353 45 61   Fax: (+39 02) 353 45 61
Marketing Manager: Bruno Favini

Czech Republic Sales & Marketing Office
Robin Cochrane, Hotel Stirka, D, Ke Stirce 11, Prague
8/CS
Tel: (+42 2) 688 18 27   Fax: (+42 2) 688 67 36
Sales Manager: Robin Cochrane

France Sales & Marketing Office
Serge Colle, 11 rue des Vosges, F-57444 Reding
Tel: (+33 3) 87 03 59 19   Fax: (+33 3) 87 03 59 26
Sales Manager: Serge Colle

USA Sales & Marketing Office
Transrail Inc, 7100 W Camino Real Blvd, Suite 206, Boca
Raton, Florida 33433
Tel: (+1 561) 417 00 14   Fax: (+1 561) 417 06 05
e-mail: transrail@aol.com
Vice President: Gary Provenzano

Products: Auxiliary power converters for all rail vehicle
and trolleybus onboard services and special power
electronic applications.

Contracts: Converters have been supplied for: P2000
LRVs in Los Angeles (DC/AC-DC); Guangzhou metro cars
(DC/DC and DC/AC); København commuter cars (DC/
AC-DC); London Heathrow Express (AC/AC-DC); üstra
Hannover TW2000 cars (DC/AC-DC).

VERIFIED

Twiflex

Twiflex Limited
104 The Green, Twickenham TW2 5AQ, UK
Tel: (+44 181) 894 11 61   Fax: (+44 181) 894 60 56
Managing Director: J T Starbuck
Sales Director: J Cooksley

Parent company: Tomkins plc

Products: 'Layrub' flexible couplings and shafts; 'Laylink'
flexible couplings and shafts; 'Twiflex' disc brake
systems, automatic clutch couplings and flexiclutch
couplings.

VERIFIED

Twin Disc

Twin Disc International SA
54 Chausee de Namur, B-1400 Nivelles, Belgium
Tel: (+32 67) 88 72 58   Fax: (+32 67) 88 73 33

Products: Power transmission equipment for railway
applications including power-shift transmissions for
dmus, ranging from 210 up to 560 kW. These
hydrodynamic transmissions are provided with built-in
two, three or four speeds, torque converter, reverse
mechanism, integrated retarder and electronic controller.

Contracts: 17 units have been in operation for four years
in the Type 2600 Iarnrod Eireann dmus. A further 27 units
have been delivered for the IE railcars supplied to IE by
ALSTOM Spain, in 1998.

VERIFIED

Unicel

Unicel Corporation Transportation
Composites Division
1520 Industrial Avenue, Escondido, California 92029,
USA
Tel: (+1 619) 741 39 12   Fax: (+1 619) 741 88 32
Vice President: Michael Henderson
Sales Manager: Thomas F Ryan

Products: Lightweight composites and honeycomb
panels for passenger car interiors.

VERIFIED

UWE

UWE Verken AB
PO Box 5063, SE-600 05 Norrköping, Sweden
Tel: (+46 11) 13 44 25   Fax: (+46 11) 12 47 04

Products: Purmo range of bus and coach one- or two-
pipe convector heating systems.

VERIFIED

Vapor

Vapor
6420 West Howard Street, Niles, Illinois 60714, USA
Tel: (+1 847) 967 83 00   Fax: (+1 847) 965 98 70
Executive Vice President & General Manager: K N Nippes
Vice President, Sales & Marketing: W J Kleppinger
A Westinghouse Air Brake company

Associated companies
Vapor Canada Inc
10655 Henri Bourassa West, St Laurent, PQ H4S 1A1,
Canada
Tel: (+1 514) 335 42 00   Fax: (+1 514) 335 42 31

Vapor UK
28 Springdale Court, Mickleover, Derby DE3 5SW, UK
Tel: (+44 1332) 51 87 88   Fax: (+44 1332) 51 90 71

HP srl
Viale Regina Pacis 298, I-41049 Sassuolo (Modena), Italy
Tel: (+39 0536) 80 64 41   Fax: (+39 0536) 80 17 89

Products: Automatic door systems, accessibility devices,
relays and contactors for rail passenger cars and buses.

Contracts: Door equipment for 1,080 New York City
Transit R142 rail transit cars built by Bombardier and
Kawasaki, 100 cars for Atlanta built by Breda, and 216 T-1
cars for Toronto by Bombardier.
   Also, door systems for I34 C3 Commuter Cars for the
Long Island Railroad by Kawasaki, 45 LRVs for the New
Jersey Transit Hudson Bergen Project by Kinki Sharyo
and 23 LRVs for Salt Lake City by Siemens. Door systems
and accessibility devices for 100 LRVs for Boston by

Breda, 52 LRVs for Portland, Oregon by Siemens and 77 LRVs for San Francisco Muni by Breda. Bus door equipment and door systems to all major North American bus manufacturers for vehicles for North American public transport agencies.

UPDATED

VAW aluminium

VAW aluminium AG
Georg-von-Boeselager Str 25, D-53117 Bonn, Germany
Tel: (+49 228) 552 02   Fax: (+49 228) 552 22 68
Chair: Dr Helmut Burmester
Board Members: Dr Karl Heinz Dörner, Dr Dieter J Braun, Jürgen Hermans, Karl D Wobbe, Thomas Unger

UK subsidiary
VAW Motorcast Ltd
PO Box 159, Clarence Road, Leeds LS1 1QX, UK
Tel: (+44 113) 283 10 42   Fax: (+44 113) 283 10 67

Products: Metal production and fabrication including rolling and converting of aluminium; aluminium engine castings; flexible packaging; extruded products.

UPDATED

VBK

VBK Transport Interior AS
PO Box 98, N-3191 Horten, Norway
Tel: (+47 330) 737 00   Fax: (+47 330) 733 15
General Manager: Olav Fossgard

Products: Seating for rolling stock; interior equipment, including luggage racks and modules, crew compartment.

Contracts: Include refurbishment of 37 trams for Oslo Sporveier, including new seats.

VERIFIED

Veam

Veam, Division of Litton Systems Inc
100 New Wood Road, Watertown, Connecticut 06795, USA
Tel: (+1 860) 274 96 81   Fax: (+1 860) 274 49 63
General Manager: Peter Bialobrzeski

Products: Electrical, optical and pneumatic connectors for trainline, brake systems, air conditioning, speed sensing, communications, lighting, automatic coupling and traction motor applications.

UPDATED

Vogelsitze

Vogelsitze
Kleinsteinbacher Strasse 44, D-76228 Karlsruhe, Germany
Tel: (+49 721) 470 20   Fax: (+49 721) 470 21 70

Subsidiary company
Vis-Vogel Interieur Schienenfahrzeuge
Eisenbahnstr 3, D-06132 Halle/Ammendorf, Germany

Products: Seating.

VERIFIED

Voith

Voith Turbo GmbH & Co KG
Railway Components & Systems Division
PO Box 1930, D-89509 Heidenheim, Germany
Tel: (+49 7321) 370   Fax: (+49 7321) 37 70 00
Chairman of Rail Products: Hermann Bruns
General Manager, Turbo Transmissions: Karl Dahler
General Manager, Axle Drives: Klaus Brosius
General Manager, Service Centre: Karl Sing

Subsidiary companies
Japan, South Korea, Hong Kong, Australia, USA and major European countries

Products: Turbo transmissions for rail vehicles, axle drives, cooling units, cardan shafts; torsional vibration dampers.

Drive components for light rail vehicles and tramways: axle drives (bevel gearboxes and spur gearboxes); Voith Hydrolock limited-slip differentials.

Hydrolock: this is a hydrostatic limited-slip for modern single-wheel drives. It consists of an enclosed planetary gearbox driven by a spur or bevel gear stage, which allows independent rolling of the wheels without alteration of existing low-floor concepts in LRVs or trams. The drive is via only one motor. Hydrolock has the characteristics of a single-wheel motor drive, but with the advantages of a rigid wheelset. It is offered as an alternative to more complex separately controlled electric motors.

Contracts: Voith Turbo transmissions have been supplied for 27 trains for North Western Trains; turbo transmissions, retarders, cardan shafts and final drives are being supplied for the new X-TER fleet for SNCF. Hydrolock limited-slip differential has been developed for LRVs in Stuttgart.

UPDATED

WABCO

Westinghouse Air Brake Company
Passenger Transit Division
PO Box 11, Spartanburg, South Carolina 29304-0011,
USA
Tel: (+1 864) 433 59 00   Fax: (+1 864) 433 01 76

Products: Brake systems for rolling stock; couplers;
electronic control equipment; current collection systems,
overhead electrification equipment.

Contracts: Brake and coupler equipment has been
supplied for Los Angeles Green line cars; brake
equipment has been supplied for Mexico Line A; brake,
coupler and current collection equipment has been
supplied for NYCTA R142 and R142A rolling stock;
coupler equipment has been supplied for Portland LRVs.

Developments: Include the E+A air dryer for improved
drying capability; R-style magnet valves and a new-design
actuator.

UPDATED

Webasto

Webasto Thermosystems GmbH
Kraillinger Strasse 5, D-82131 Stockdorf, Germany
Tel: (+49 89) 85 79 40   Fax: (+49 89) 856 24 17
Managing Director: Michael Kempter

UK office
Webasto Thermosystems (UK) Ltd
White Rose Way, Doncaster Carr, Doncaster DN4 5JH,
UK
Tel: (+44 1302) 32 22 32   Fax: (+44 1302) 32 22 31
Managing Director: Roger Edwards

Products: Air conditioning, heaters; independent
combustion heaters for engine preheating and passenger
saloon heaters in rail and road vehicles; escape and
ventilation roof hatches for bus and coach applications
and bus doors.

UPDATED

Westinghouse Brakes

Westinghouse Brakes Limited
PO Box 74, Foundry Lane, Chippenham SN15 1HY, UK
Tel: (+44 1249) 44 20 00   Fax: (+44 1249) 65 50 40
General Manager: P R Johnson
Commercial Manager: R Bew
Head of Engineering: J Abbott
Head of Sales & Marketing: D Powell
Head of Projects: M O'Brien
Head of Finance: A Priestly
Head of Manufacturing: P Brittain
Business Development Manager, Brakes & Freight:
   C Blake
Business Development Manager, After Sales: T Park

A member of the BTR Rail Group and a subsidiary of
Westinghouse Brake and Signal Holdings Ltd

Products: Brake systems — air and vacuum brake
equipment, electropneumatic brake equipment with
digital (Westcode) or analogue control for metro and
commuter passenger vehicles. Equipment includes rotary
and reciprocating air compressors, air dryers, brake and
traction controllers, brake actuation equipment and
wheelslip control equipment.

A comprehensive aftersales service is available
providing equipment overhaul, repair and long-term
maintenance in addition to spare parts supply.

Contracts: Brake systems are currently being supplied
for Gatwick Express, South West Trains, LTS Rail,
Connex, Great Western Holdings, Singapore–Changi
extension, Class 66 and Class 67 locomotives (UK);
wheelslide equipment for London Underground Central
line trains.

UPDATED

Widney Transport Components

Widney Transport Components (Pty) Ltd
PO Box 124167, Alrode 1450, South Africa
Tel: (+27 11) 864 48 04   Fax: (+27 11) 908 18 56
Managing Director: S R Jennings
Export Marketing Director: P Pretorius
Technical Director: G Szabo
General Manager: P N Van den Biggelaar
Sales & Marketing Manager: Tiny Jansen

Products: Windows for passenger vehicles, including
sliding, hopper and double-glazed types; doors for
locomotives and passenger vehicles; locks and general
carriage fittings.

Contracts include the supply of hopper windows for
suburban rolling stock.

NEW ENTRY

Williamson

T & R Williamson Ltd
36 Stonebridgegate, Ripon HG4 1TP, UK
Tel: (+44 1765) 60 77 11   Fax: (+44 1765) 60 79 08
Managing Director: Abubakar A Sheibani
General Manager: R J Herod
Technical Service Manager: N Kershaw

Products: Specialist livery and protective coatings for all
types of urban transport vehicles, including anti-graffiti
and fire-retardant finishes.

VERIFIED

Woodhead

Woodhead Shock-Absorbers
Church Street, Ossett WF5 9DL, UK
Tel: (+44 1924) 27 35 21   Fax: (+44 1924) 27 61 67
Chairman: S Beyazit
Sales Manager: A C Kart

Products: Twin-tube hydraulic dampers for LRVs and
metro cars; door closing gear dampers.

VERIFIED

ŽDB

ŽDB AS
Wheelset Division
Bezručova 300, CZ-735 93 Bohumín, Czech Republic
Tel: (+420 69) 608 23 04   Fax: (+420 69) 608 28 05
President & General Manager: J Tomšej
Managing Director, Wheelset Division: R Bonček
Commercial Director, Wheelset Division: J Sedlák

Products: Wheelsets, with and without disc brakes,
monobloc technology, axles and tyres for LRVs.

Contracts: Products have been supplied to rolling stock
manufacturers in 35 countries.

UPDATED

ZF Hurth

ZF Hurth Bahntechnik GmbH
Adelheidstr 40, D-88046 Freidrichschafen, Germany
Tel: (+49 7541) 306 01   Fax: (+49 7541) 30 64 00

Products: Helical, hypoid and bevel gear axle drive units
for fully or partially suspended drives; input couplings,
axle gearboxes and flexible axle couplings for LRVs,
multiple-unit trains and locomotives; transmissions for
diesel railcars; special transmissions (including planetary
wheel hub drives) for low-floor vehicles; custom-designed
gears.

VERIFIED

ZF Padova

ZF Padova SpA
Via Penghe 48, I-35030 Caselle di Selvazzano Dentro,
Padua, Italy
Tel: (+39 049) 829 93 11   Fax: (+39 049) 829 95 50
Managing Director: Roland Heil

Background: ZF Padova was formerly Meccanica
Padana Monteverde (MPM).

Products: Special drive units. Calculation and design of
transmission to customers specifications with use of
computer programs (including FEA). Trials can be carried
out on recirculating power test rigs which automatically
simulate the actual duty cycles of the vehicle involved.

UPDATED

cornered rubber gaskets to facilitate speedy replacement, but they also now feature a matt black moulding along the top and bottom edges.

The skirt panels are now gently curved inwards helping reduce vulnerability to minor accident damage.

Inside, Alexander have made minor styling changes to improve the ambience of the vehicle.

A batch of 30 has been delivered to Arriva Group companies, with the first running in Leicester for Arriva Fox County. These will be followed by 40 for Stagecoach and then a further 30 for Arriva.

UPDATED

Alexander ALX200 buses on Dennis Dart SLF chassis in service with Grey-Green
1999/0043458

Alexander ALX500 low-floor double-deck three-axle bus body
1998/0011566

Alexander (Far East)

Walter Alexander (Far East) Pte Ltd
7500A Beach Road 14-322, The Plaza, Singapore 0719
Tel: (+65) 296 58 96   Fax: (+65) 296 66 42
Managing Director: Kenneth Ho

Products: Single- and double-deck bus bodies.

Range: Specialises in design and supply of aluminium body kits tailored for the Asian market. The kits are mainly acquired from the parent company but many parts are procured locally. The vehicles are derivatives of the Alexander (qv) single-deck and ALX400 double-deck buses.

The company can either assemble the kits or supervise assembly within specific territories and also provides an after-sales service for the region.

VERIFIED

Alexander (Far East) Royale two-door bodywork on three-axle Volvo Olympian of KMB Hong Kong
(Andrew Jarosz)
1999/0024992

Alusuisse Road & Rail

Alusuisse Road & Rail Ltd
Buckhauserstrasse 11, CH-8048 Zürich, Switzerland
Tel: (+41 1) 497 44 22   Fax: (+41 1) 497 45 85
Managing Director: Jürg Zehnder
Marketing & Sales: Giorgio Destefani
(See also entry under Rail Vehicles and Traction
Equipment)

Background: A subsidiary of Algroup (formerly Alusuisse-Lonza Group), which operates plants in 15 countries. Alusuisse Road & Rail is the engineering, marketing and sales organisation representing all the Group companies in the transport market.

Products: Development, design, stress calculation, prototyping, static strain gauge testing and fatigue testing of bus bodies including interiors and other components; supply of ready-to-assemble aluminium components for bus bodies such as aluminium and composite structures which can be bolted, screwed or bonded, for manufacture of low-floor buses, articulated vehicles, double-deck buses and coaches.

Contracts: Alusuisse Road & Rail Lts has entered into co-operation agreements with several bus manufacturers. Recent contracts include: Omnicity bus family (Scania); Cobus airport bus (Caetano/Hess); Cito midibus (Mercedes-Benz).

UPDATED

Cito low-floor midibus manufactured by Mercedes-Benz using Alusuisse hybrid technology   **1999**/0043459

Scania Omnicity manufactured using Alusuisse Road & Rail technology **1997**

AMO ZIL

AMO ZIL
23 Avtozavodskaja ul, 109280 Moscow, Russia
Tel: (+7 095) 275 33 28   Fax: (+7 095) 274 00 78
www: www.glasnet.ru/-crpzil
General Director: Valery Borisovitch Nosov
Chief Engineer: Nikolai Alekseevitch Kurochkin

Foreign trade firm
Director FTF ZiL Export: Andrey Anatolievich Zorya

Background: ZIL is one of Russia's largest truck manufacturers, though it is perhaps best known in western countries for its seven-seater limousines.

In 1996, the city of Moscow bought a 30 per cent stake in ZIL. Bus production has started in Uzbekistan and Kurgan on ZIL chassis.

Products: Truck chassis suitable for bus bodywork.
ZIL 5301: City truck chassis used in the Ikarus 18-seat minibus.
ZIL 54236A tractor: This has a Caterpillar 3116 diesel engine and is used for a high-capacity articulated unit, carrying 100 on urban and suburban routes.

UPDATED

Minibus conversion on AMO ZIL chassis
1998/0011574

Asco

Asco Coachwork
Blessington, Co Wicklow, Ireland
Tel: (+353 45) 86 53 05   Fax: (+353 45) 86 53 05

Products: Minibus, midibus and midicoach bodies.

Range
Asco: Minibus bodywork on Peugeot Boxer, Fiat Ducato, Citroën Relay/Jumper and Mercedes-Benz chassis and van conversions.

Also on LDV chassis to 16-seat public service vehicle specification. A luggage compartment is available for the conversion based on the Mercedes-Benz 408.

VERIFIED

Ashok

Ashok Leyland Limited
19 Rajaji Salai, Madras 600001, India
Tel: (+91 44) 58 91 41
Chair & Managing Director: R J Shahaney

Main works
Ennore, Madras 600057
Sipcot Industrial Complex, Hosur 635126, Tamil Nadu
MIDC Industrial Area, Gadegaon, Bhandara 441904,
    Maharashtra
Matsya Industrial Area, Alwar 301030, Rajasthan

Background: Ashok Motors was established in 1948 to assemble Austin cars and in 1950 acquired sole rights for assembly and distribution of Leyland commercial vehicles. Capacity was raised to 15,000 by 1982 and 37,000 per year in 1990, involving setting up three new plants on green field sites. Associated companies are

Ashok-Leyland CNG-powered bus with BEST Bombay   **1997**

Ashok-Leyland bus in Sri Lanka (David Hickham)
1998/0011575

Ennore Foundries Ltd and Lanka Ashok Leyland Limited, Sri Lanka (assembly operation). Ashok Leyland is jointly owned by Land Rover Leyland Industrial Holdings Ltd, which in turn is jointly owned by the Hindiza Group and Iveco. Iveco has a 37.5 per cent share. It is now controlled by the Hinduja Group and Iveco.

Products: Bus chassis including double-deck and prototype integral and articulated; engines.

Range
Viking: City bus seating up to 61, in left-hand drive and right-hand drive versions.
Titan: Double-deck bus with front engine (AL400 series), carrying 78, 43 seated on the upper deck, 25 on the lower. RHD only.
Integral: 52-seat service bus.
B16 Articulated: 15.3 m long, carrying 150, 82 seated. RHD only.

Chital: Short wheelbase minibus, seating 27, 7.13 m long and with Iveco 8040.05 engine driving through a five-speed synchromesh gearbox. LHD/RHD.
Cheetah: This is a single-deck service bus seating 57.
Ashok is building 27- and 59-seater city and intercity buses, powered by Iveco engines. Included is India's first CNG-powered city bus, a prototype of which entered service with BEST Bombay in 1997.

VERIFIED

Austral Pacific

Austral Pacific Group Limited
Head office: 75 Marigold Street, Revesby, New South Wales 2212, Australia
Tel: (+61 2) 97 73 03 01   Fax: (+61 2) 97 71 28 18

6-14 Wirraway Street, Tamworth, New South Wales 2340
Tel: (+61 2) 67 62 09 44   Fax: (+61 2) 67 62 19 86

356 Bilsen Road, Geebung, Queensland 4034
Tel: (+61 7) 32 65 05 55   Fax: (+61 7) 32 65 15 68

7 Brandwood Street, Royal Park, South Australia 5014
Tel: (+61 8) 82 40 91 00   Fax: (+61 8) 82 40 91 90

Garden Drive, Tullamarine, Victoria 3043
Tel: (+61 3) 93 39 41 00   Fax: (+61 3) 93 35 14 60

Associate company
TransPacific International Limited
A wholly owned subsidiary of the Clifford Corporation Limited
Unit A, 70 Riverside Road, Chipping Norton, New South Wales 2170, Australia

Tel: (+61 2) 97 55 51 40   Fax: (+61 2) 97 55 51 47
Chief Executive Officer: Gene Losew
General Manager: Robert Day

Background: Austral Pacific Group Ltd (APG) is a wholly owned subsidiary of the Australian publicly listed Clifford Corporation Ltd.
APG supplied approximately 50 per cent of the local bus and coach market and over 60 per cent of the fire fighting vehicle market. APG employs over 750 people including 22 design engineers.
TransPacific International Limited imports and distributes a range of chassis in Australia including Renault and Csepel. Full sales and after-market support is provided through a dealer network in each state.

Products: Bus and coach bodies including integral chassis, together with a range of fire fighting vehicles.

Range
City bus
APG *Citibus* offers bodies of composite corrosion-resistant materials with advanced styling and design on low-floor and ultra-low-floor chassis in body lengths of 8, 10 and 12 m. Designed to meet all Disability

Discrimination Act standards. Detachable quick-replacement side skirts minimise down time with minor accident damage.

Route bus/school bus/three star coach
The *Starliner* is sold in Australia mainly as a school bus and has a major share of that market. It also may be used as a route bus or three star coach. Built on chassis by most suppliers such as the Mercedes-Benz 1418, 1421 and 1630, Renault MRC, Csepel 1810, the Starliner is offered with seating up to 57.

Coach
The APG range of five star touring coaches are the *Aspire* two-axle and the *Majestic* three-axle bodies, both built on chassis by others, and the *Classic II* and *Classic III*, being two- and three-axle and manufactured mainly on APG's own integral chassis using mainly American engines. These vehicles have proved popular with long-distance coach operators. Equipped with reclining seats, video/TV and toilet washrooms.

UPDATED

Autobus

Autobus
Denby Way, Hellaby, Rotherham S66 8HR, UK
Tel: (+44 1709) 53 51 00   Fax: (+44 1709) 53 51 02
Managing Director: Colin Childs
Sales & Marketing Director: Alan White
Sales Manager: David McKinless
Financial Director: Michael Wrightson

Background: Autobus was acquired by Optare (qv) in 1996.

Products: Bus and coach bodies.

Range: Small buses and coaches, conversions on Mercedes-Benz Sprinter and various van models.
Nouvelle 2: This coach body is based on the Mercedes-Benz Vario chassis cowl. This updated body was introduced in 1997 and has a restyled front end, bonded glazing, and interior styling. It seats up to 33 and is available in luxury or executive versions.

Production: The number of Nouvelles in service is now approaching 200.

Contracts: The first Nouvelle 2 has been delivered to D & J Dickinson, Wrangle, Boston, following delivery of more than 100 Nouvelle 1 bodies since 1995.
Seven Mercedes-Benz 10-seat Sprinters were sent to a Reading operator for operation on a Eurodollar contract at London Heathrow airport and six 18-seat Nouvelles

Autobus Nouvelle 2 on Mercedes-Benz Vario chassis   *1999*/0043460

went to Europcar, Heathrow airport. Eight Nouvelle 33-seat buses have been delivered to Bebb Travel, Wales.
Further deliveries of the specially adapted Sprinter models for operation on the National Car Rental contract at Heathrow airport. Bebb Travel of Llantwit Fardre,

Wales, has placed an order for more 33-seat buses based on the Nouvelle 2. These were due to enter service in February 1999.

UPDATED

Autodromo

Carrozzeria Autodromo Modena Soc
Via Malavolti 18, I-41100 Modena, Italy
Tel: (+39 059) 25 03 60   Fax (+39 059) 25 00 88

Products: Bus and coach bodywork; trolleybuses.

Range
Bussotto: Carries up to 109 (25 seated, 84 standing);

integral construction. It is powered by the MAN D0826-LUH12 engine.
Other products include the *Pollicino* minibus on Iveco Daily chassis carrying up to 35 passengers with facilities

for the disabled, 12 m buses and 18 m articulated versions, and trolleybuses. A midibus, the *Alé*, has been introduced.

UPDATED

Three-door low-floor Autodromo Bussotto of ATAC Rome at Vatican City terminus (Andrew Jarosz)
1999/0024993

Autoradgona

Autoradgona Gornja Radgona n sol o
Proizvodno Transportno Podjetje
Ljutomerska 26, SI-69250 Gornja Radgona, Slovenia
Tel: (+386 9) 740 07/745 11/749 41
Foreign Trade Manager: Ivan Zvegla

Products: Minibus bodies.

VERIFIED

Autosan

Autosan SA
cka Fabryka Autobusów
ul Lipińskiego 109, PL-385-00 Sanok, Poland
Tel: (+48 137) 502 82/504 26
Fax: (+48 137) 504 30/504 00/504 29/501 95
Managing Director: Andrzej Krzanowski
Marketing Director: Roman Majewski
Technical Manager: Marek Zmarz

Background: Previously known as Sanocka Fabryka Autobusów (SFA Sanok), Autosan is one of two major bus

manufacturing companies in Poland. Autosan and Jelcz (qv) are now part of the Zasada Group, though the firms trade separately. Zasada is also the Mercedes-Benz dealer for Poland and Mercedes-Benz engines are increasingly being used by both manufacturers.

Products: Buses and coaches.

Range
Lider: This is a 10 m dual-purpose body with up to three doors and carries 70. It has Mercedes-Benz running units.
H9: This is Autosan's most popular bus for the Polish market. It is a rear-engined integral vehicle 10 m long.

H10: This is 11.2 m long and has an unladen weight of 10.5 tonnes. It carries 77 and has two or three doors.
H10-11: Two versions of the H10, for wheelchair passengers, one carrying 11 wheelchairs plus five seats and the other for two wheelchairs plus 33 seats. Both vehicles have wheelchair lifts.
The *H10-12* is a touring coach, 11.86 m long.
H6: Small city bus with 18 seats plus 14 standing, on various chassis with option of a Perkins engine.
The newer *A10-10* bus range has a lower floor height and more modern styling.

VERIFIED

Avtomontaža

Celovška c180, SL-1000 Ljubljana, Slovenia
Tel: (+386 61) 159 41 16   Fax: (+386 61) 55 25 69
e-mail: quality@am-bus.si
www: http://www.am.bus.si
Director: Lucijan Rejec

Background: Avtomontaža is the oldest and largest Slovenian bus body manufacturer, having been established in 1936. It was the biggest bus manufacturer in the former Yugoslavia, producing more than 30 per cent of the country's bus output and having a 50 per cent share of the export market. In the 1980s, more than 1,000 buses were produced but this figure has drastically declined following the break-up of Yugoslavia and the collapse of TAM, the main chassis supplier. The company employs 620 people.

Products: Bus and coach bodies, including articulated.

Range: Under arrangement with Volvo and Mercedes-Benz, Avtomontaža offers steel-framed bodywork for vehicles built by the two manufacturers, though other chassis can be bodied. Bodies available cover 11 and 12 m city bus, interurban and tourist coach (including high-floor) requirements, with various seating styles.

Production: Up to 600 bodies have been produced annually.

Avtomontaža bus body on Volvo B10B chassis

1998/0011577

Contracts: Buses have been exported to Egypt, Poland, Denmark, Dominican Republic, Saudi Arabia, Jordan, Oman, Syria, Gambia, Kuwait, Iraq, Sudan, Lebanon, Ethiopia, Libya, United Arab Emirates, Sweden, USA, Germany, Turkey, Russia, Iran, Austria, Greece and Slovakia.

UPDATED

Banbros

Banbros Ltd
PO Box 76511, Nairobi, Kenya
Tel: (+254 2) 54 10 11/55 88 36   Fax: (+254 2) 54 02 74
Managing Director: M S Bansal
General Manager: K Raj

Subsidiary company
Sarwan Singh Bansal Ltd
PO Box 72777, Nairobi

Products: Bus and coach bodywork, including city buses, express buses and coaches.

VERIFIED

Banbros bus body (Andrew Jarosz)
1997

Beijing

Beijing Motor & Public Transportation Corporation
44 Nanlishi Lu, Beijing, People's Republic of China

Background: Operator of extensive bus and trolleybus services in Beijing, a division of the company builds its own standard and articulated vehicles, and also supplies a number of other cities. Beijing designs are also built in other parts of China.

Products: Buses and trolleybuses.

Range
BD 562 trolleybus: The current BD 562 appears in two variants, with chopper control and conventional electrical equipment, and in standard two-axle and articulated lengths.

VERIFIED

Berkhof

Berkhof Jonckheere Group
PO Box 118, NL-8440 AC Heerenveen, Netherlands
Tel: (+31 513) 61 85 00   Fax: (+31 513) 62 97 89
Managing Director: P Govaert
Commercial Director, Netherlands: S Bruggeling
Commercial Director, Northern Europe: R van Gent
Manager, Purchase Department: H de Lang
Parent company: Berkhof Holding BV, Netherlands

Subsidiary companies
Berkhof Heerenveen, Netherlands
Berkhof Valkenswaard BV, Netherlands
Kusters Venlo, Netherlands
Postma Heerenveen, Netherlands
Jonckheere Bus & Coach, Belgium
Denolf & Depla, Belgium
Berkhof Jonckheere SA, France
Berkhof UK Ltd

Marketed in the UK by:
Berkhof UK Ltd, Coach Centre Unit B
Rutherford Road, Basingstoke RG24 8PB
Tel: (+44 1256) 47 53 00   Fax (+44 1256) 47 53 03

Background: The Berkhof Jonckheere Group comprises eight companies in the Netherlands, Belgium, UK and France.

Products: Integral buses and bus bodies, including low-floor, articulated and midibuses, manufactured in stainless steel. Roof, front, side and rear panelled in glass-fibre-reinforced plastic.

Range
Midi Junior: Available on MAN, Volvo or Dennis chassis, length 9 m, width 2.3 m. There are 38 seats.

Berkhof 2000NLF 12 m low-floor bus on Dennis Lance SLF on Canterbury Park & Ride service (Andrew Jarosz)
1999/0024988

Midi 2000SL: Available on MAN, Volvo or Dennis chassis, length 9 m, width 2.3 m. There are 38 seats. It has a different roof from the Junior.
Standard 2000NL: This is available on DAF, Dennis, MAN, and Volvo chassis, in lengths from 9 to 15 m and 18 m articulated (NLG).

2000NLF: This is a low-floor body available on DAF, Dennis and Volvo chassis, in lengths from 8 to 15 m and 18 m articulated.
2000NLE: This is a low-floor midibus body available on the Dennis SLF chassis. It is a basic bus designed to keep maintenance costs down.

Berkhof Premier low-floor 18 m articulated   *1997*

Berkhof ProCity midibus   *1998*/0011578

Berkhof Radial interurban dual-purpose coach
1998/0011579

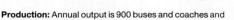

Berkhof low-floor concept bus   *1998*/0011581

Berkhof President airside bus   *1998*/0011580

Premier: This is an integral low-floor bus and is available from a midi up to 15 m in length. An 18 m articulated version and a 24 m double-articulated version are available. The body frame is of Cromweld 3CR12 stainless steel. It has a mid-mounted engine.

Premier SB250: This has the same specification as the Premier, but on DAF SB250 chassis.

Radial: Interurban and touring coach of 2.55 m width, available in various lengths and on various chassis.

Premier on LPG: Integral low-floor city bus, manufactured in stainless steel.

Production: Annual output is 900 buses and coaches and 600 minibuses.

Contracts: In 1997, 60 city buses were delivered to Brussels; 115 regional transport buses to SRWT Belgium; 55 city buses to Amsterdam; 14 regional buses for Luxembourg; 160 buses on DAF TB2175 chassis were delivered to Ethiopia; and 22 city buses to Copenhagen.

A trolleybus body has been jointly developed with Jonckheere for service in Arnhem. It has Traxis electric drive.

Developments: For the airport market a low-floor wide-body apron bus, *President,* has been developed.

The low-floor city midibus, the *ProCity,* was successfully introduced on the European market.

UPDATED

Berliet Maroc

Berliet Maroc
PO Box 2624, Ain Sebaa, Casablanca, Morocco
Tel: (+212 2) 73 32 90/73 21 07
Fax: (+212 2) 73 32 40/73 10 42
Director General: Omar Amraoui

Associated with Renault VI

Background: Assembly operations for vehicles supplied CKD by Renault Véhicules Industriels. The company is part-owned by Renault VI and partly by local private interests including investment and insurance companies.

Products: Bus chassis.

VERIFIED

Bharat

Bharat Heavy Electricals Ltd (BHEL)
Transportation Business Department
Lodhi Road, New Delhi 110003, India
Tel: (+91 755) 469 93 75/461 67 56/65 44
Fax: (+91 755) 462 94 23/461 77 49/07 79
General Manager, Transportation: R P Raghuwanshi
Additional General Manager: S P Bindra

Products: BHEL is a large electrical equipment manufacturer supplying the power plant and transport

industries (see Bharat entry in Rail Vehicles section). Its Electric Vehicle Division has developed battery-powered buses.

Range

Electravan: This is an 18-seat minibus having a maximum speed of 45 km/h and a cruising speed of 40 km/h. It has a range of 70 km on the level and has a 96 V 300 A/h lead acid battery assembly.

The Electravan has a separately excited 30 kW DC motor (20 hp).

Electrabus: This carries 40, 30 seated. It has a cruising

speed of 40 km/h and a range of 75 km. It has a 300 A/h 160 V lead acid battery pack and a 28 kW DC series-wound motor.

Production: 300 vehicles annually.

VERIFIED

Blue Bird

Blue Bird Corporation
PO Box 937, Fort Valley, Georgia 31030, USA
Tel: (+1 912) 757 71 00   Fax: (+1 912) 474 91 38
President & Chief Executive Officer: Paul Glaske
Vice President, Sales: Richard Maddox
Director, International Operations: Mark Welden

Assembly operations in Monterrey (Mexico), Venezuela and Saudi Arabia

Overseas associate
Canadian Blue Bird, Brantford, Ontario

Products: Buses and minibuses; bus bodywork (including kits for overseas assembly and mobile homes).

Range

Q-bus: This is for airport and city shuttle work and has a coach-type interior. It is powered by a rear-mounted Cummins 6BTA 5.9 litre diesel engine driving through Allison AT545 transmission.

CS Bus: Available as either forward or rear engine option, diesel or CNG. For light transit, commuter or activity vehicle operations, in lengths from 7.3 to 11.8 m.

TranShuttle: This bus has a flat floor and front-mounted engine.

VERIFIED

Blue Bird 8.8 m Q-Bus of Shamrock, Pontypridd, UK (Andrew Jarosz)   *1997*

Front-engined Bluebird CS bus of First Class, Florida (Andrew Jarosz)   *1999*/0024989

Blue Bird school bus of Richmond Transportation, USA (Andrew Jarosz)   *1998*/0016399

BMC Sanayi

BMC Sanayi ve Ticaret AS
Kemalpasa Caddesi 32, TR-35060 Izmir, Turkey
Tel: (+90 232) 479 18 70   Fax: (+90 232) 479 13 64
Managing Director/Vice Chairman: Mehmet Demirpence
Vice President: Muharrem Erkan
Vice President, Sales & Marketing: Turgut Cankiliç
Vice President, Technical: Hüsnü Ergeng

Background: BMC was established in 1964 to build
tractors, trucks, buses and vans under licence from the
former British Motor Corporation. It is now part of the
Turkish Cukurova Group, and has a licence agreement
with Cummins.

Products: Integral city buses.

Range
Belde 220-17: City bus with two or three doors, seating
between 36 and 43 passengers with many standing.
Levend 3.0GDM: Midibus, seating 14 or 17 plus driver.

Contracts: Include 192 city buses for Uzbekistan, 150
minibuses and four city buses for Azerbaijan, four city
buses for Ethiopia and 125 minibuses for Syria.

BMC Sanayi Belde 220-17 bus   *1999*/0043461

Developments: New projects for minibus, midibus and
city buses are under study.

UPDATED

BOVA

BOVA BV Autobusfabriek
PO Box 5, NL-5550 AA Valkenswaard, Netherlands
Tel: (+31 40) 208 46 11/47 38   Fax: (+31 40) 204 20 45
Managing Directors: W Van Doorne, M H Hendrikse

Background: BOVA first started building coaches in
1931. In 1969, it built its first integral coach and in 1983
announced the Futura, with its distinctive styling.

Products: Integral interurban, express and touring
coaches.

Range
Futura: Available in two heights and five lengths. Powered
by DAF, MAN or Cummins engines.
Futura FL: Dual-purpose vehicle for interurban and
express work, 12 and 15 m lengths. Powered by DAF or
Cummins (12 m version) engines.
Futura FH: Luxury coach, 10, 12, 13, 14 and 15 m options;
powered by DAF, MAN or Cummins engines.

Contracts: BOVA has completed a major order for the
Swedish bus company Göteborgs Spårvägar,
Gothenburg, with delivery of 10 15 m vehicles. The
Gothenburg company, which operates a fleet of
approximately 175 buses, chose the BOVA Futura FLD
15-340 Magnum with automatic gearbox for the
expansion of its fleet operations with express coaches.
Because of its length (15 m) this type of coach is
equipped with a smart trailing axle that automatically
becomes a steered third axle when driving forwards at
low speed or reversing. This prevents needless tyre wear
caused by scrubbing. At higher speeds the axle
automatically locks in the central position.

BOVA Futura FLD 15-340 Magnum for Göteborgs Spårväger   *1999*/0038776

Bovo Tours, Roelofarendsveen, Netherlands, has taken
delivery of six FHD 12-340 BOVA Futura coaches for use
on UK express coach operator National Express Eurolines
services, and the 100th three-axle Futura Magnum was
handed over to Etzelmüller Reisen, Fronhausen,
Germany. It is an FHD 15-430 and is 15 m long.

Developments: BOVA has received ISO 9001
certification and has also been presented with the Dutch
Conformity of Production.

BOVA has increased its production of vehicles by 20
per cent, from 10 to 12 coaches per week. In 1998, the
company made and sold a record number of 425
coaches. This is an increase of 12 per cent over 1997.

UPDATED

BredaMenarinibus

BredaMenarinibus SpA
Via San Donato 190, I-40127 Bologna, Italy
Tel: (+39 051) 637 21 11   Fax: (+39 051) 51 03 53

Parent company
Breda Costruzioni Ferroviarie SpA
Via Ciliegiole 110/b, I-51100 Pistoia, Italy
Tel: (+39 0573) 37 01   Fax: (+39 0573) 37 02 92
Chairman: Dr Gioacchino Gabbuti
General Director, Breda Group: Dr Ing Corrado Fici
General Manager: Ing Antonio Valenti
Technical Director: Ing Robert Golimbioschi

Background: BredaMenarinibus was created by Breda

BredaMenarinibus low-floor articulated city bus   *1996*

Costruzioni Ferroviarie following acquisition of the bus builder Menarini. Breda has plants in Bologna, Pistoia and Rome for manufacture of buses and trolleybuses for city, intercity and tourist operations.

Products: City buses, coaches and trolleybuses.

Range: Five low-floor city bus body lengths: 7.7, 9, 10.8, 12 and 18 m; coach, 12 m; trolleybus, 12 and 18 m.

Production: Annual capacity is 800 to 1,000.

Contracts: 50 12 m low-floor buses are being supplied to Rome, 90 9 m low-floor buses are being supplied to Naples and 20 articulated to Milan.

St Petersburg Municipal Transport Company is taking delivery of two BMB221 12 m buses for appraisal. The order also covers the supply of complete Breda buses and the incorporation of a company under the name Severnyj Avtobus SpA jointly with Breda and Zavod for

manufacture of buses in St Petersburg, using local components. The initial production volume is set at 1,000 vehicles in four years, rising to 500 vehicles a year.

Developments: A low-floor articulated trolleybus with a diesel auxiliary power unit has been developed.

VERIFIED

BUSiness

BUSiness BV
PO Box 410, NL-5500 AK Veldhoven, Netherlands
Tel: (+31 40) 55 44 33   Fax: (+31 40) 55 44 11
Director: O E P Veldhuizen

Works: De Run 4425, NL-5503 LS Veldhoven

Products: 12-seat minibus (13 standing) based on Peugeot Boxer chassis cowl. Also conversions on Mercedes, Ford, Iveco, Fiat and Citroën base vehicles.

The BUSiness 2002 body can be mounted on Citroën, Peugeot or Fiat chassis. It carries up to 25 and has a flat floor 320 mm above the road surface. The vehicle can kneel a further 50 mm.

VERIFIED

BUSiness 1001 minibus conversion
1996

Busscar

Busscar Ônibus SA
PO Box 477, Rua Paré 30, 89204-420 Joinville-Santa Catarina, Brazil
Tel: (+55 474) 35 11 33   Fax: (+55 474) 41 13 76
Sales Director: Roberto Palhano
Technical & Industrial Director: Antonio Camilo Policastro
Export Manager: Fábio Luis Nielson

Works: Rua Otto Pfuetzenreuter 1385, 89219-200 Joinville-Santa Catarina

Background: Founded in 1946 by Augusto Bruno and Eugenio Nielson, the company, then Carrocerias Nielson, started manufacture of wooden bus bodies and produced its first metal body in 1956.

Products: Bus and coach bodies.

Range
Urbanbus: Can be specified with three doors for city operation, seating 45 with up to 55 standing. For city use, it is mounted on Mercedes-Benz, Volvo, Scania, Volkswagen and Ford chassis. Framework, external panelling and flooring is in heavy-duty aluminium alloy.
Busscar: City bus and also for urban work on Ford, Volvo or Scania chassis.

UPDATED

Cable Car

Cable Car Concepts Inc
Dept B, PO Box 6500, Deltona, Florida 32728, USA
Tel: (+1 407) 860 03 33   Fax: (+1 407) 574 36 00
President: R B McFadden

Products: Mini trackless trolleys (replica tramcars), seating 21 to 32, and trolley trams (mini road trains) carrying up to 97.

VERIFIED

Cacciamali

Carrozerie Cacciamali
Via VI Novembre, I-25030 Mairano, Italy
Tel: (+39 030) 97 53 61   Fax: (+39 030) 97 52 26

Products: Buses up to 10 m, on Iveco Daily, A-series and other Iveco chassis.

The company is building bodywork on Iveco chassis from the DailyBus up to EuroRider. It has also developed a range of midibuses, of 6.0, 6.7, 8.9 and 10.36 m overall

lengths. All employ Iveco engines, of varying sizes, mounted in line in the offside rear corner.

VERIFIED

Caetano

Salvador Caetano Indústrias Metalúrgicas e Veículos de Transporte SARL
Estrada Nacional 222, Km 1, Oliveira do Douro, Apartado 51, P-4401 Vila Nova de Gaia Codex, Portugal
Tel: (+351 2) 782 07 53/19 04/16 04
Fax: (+351 2) 782 58 76
President: Salvador Caetano
Managing Director: J L Abreu Teixeira
Commercial Director: Manuel Amaral

UK subsidiaries
SC Coachbuilders Ltd
Hambledon Road, Waterlooville PO7 7UA, UK
Tel: (+44 1705) 25 82 11   Fax: (+44 1705) 25 56 11

Salvador Caetano (UK) Ltd
Mill Lane, Heather, Coalville LE67 2QE, UK
Tel: (+44 1530) 26 33 33   Fax: (+ 44 1530) 26 33 79
www: www.caetano.co.uk

Background: Salvador Caetano is one of Portugal's leading companies, with a wide range of interests mainly connected with the motor industry. The roots of the

company date back to 1946, when Salvador F Caetano started building wooden-framed coaches. The Caetano group of companies now employs over 2,200 people.

Activities include, other than coach building, manufacture of a variety of automotive products, assembly of Toyota light commercial vehicles and distribution of Toyota, BMW and MAN products throughout Portugal.

Salvador Caetano exported the first coach to the UK in 1967, and formed Salvador Caetano (UK) Ltd in 1984. The UK company moved to purpose-built premises in 1988 and extended these in 1993 with a new paint spray booth.

Salvador Caetano (UK) Ltd made two important purchases in 1998. The purchase of neighbouring Reliant Coaches Ltd gave the company an insight into the needs of a coach operator, while the formation of SC Coachbuilders Ltd in the factory previously occupied by UVG (Bus and Coach) Ltd has provided the company with the opportunity to manufacture bus and coach bodies in the UK for the first time.

Products: Buses and trolleybuses including articulated; bus and coach bodywork.

Range

Enigma: Coach on Volvo B10M, Dennis Javelin and MAN 11.220 chassis, Enigma is the flagship of the Caetano range. The standard specification is: length 12 m, width 2.55 m, height 3.4 m (Volvo and Dennis chassis), length 8.8 m, width 2.55 m, height 3.2 m (MAN chassis); all metal jig assembled structure conforming to ECE R66, front and rear styling panels in glass reinforced plastic, tinted double-glazed bonded side windows, Fainsa Gaudi moquette-trimmed reclining passenger seats with retractable seat belts (53 on Volvo and Dennis chassis, 35 on MAN chassis).
Cutlass: UK coach on Dennis Javelin chassis.
Optimo: Midi coach on Toyota Coaster chassis for UK and other markets.
Compass: Bus on Dennis Dart chassis for UK market. In addition to standard service bus applications, the Compass can be supplied to provide airport perimeter services, executive airside services, fire control command vehicles and mobility vehicles. It is 10.7 m in length, width 2.4 m, height 2.35 m. Also offered are 10 and 9.3 m lengths.
Interior features include moulded roof panels and decorative waist panels, sound insulation fitted in engine compartment, standard service type bus seating with tubular frames and top rail, foam filled and trimmed.
Integral city bus: While Caetano can offer integrally built city buses, requirements from the Portuguese market for diesel buses have largely been for body-on-chassis construction.

Trolleybus: Integral trolleybuses, both standard and articulated.

Contracts: Bus bodies have been exported to Peru and other countries in joint deals with Iveco. Caetano is assembling Duple (Metsec) (qv) kits on Dennis Dragon chassis for Hong Kong. It is also assembling Cobus airside buses, using Alusuisse construction.

Developments: The Optimo IV now has a wheelchair tail lift option.

SC Coachbuilders (owned by Salvador Caetano) has introduced the Compass bus and Cutlass coach, both built in the UK. The Compass design is based on the UVG Urban Star before UVG was bought out by Salvador Caetano and it has been substantially redesigned, though it retains its distinctive front end styling. It is mounted on a Dennis Dart chassis.

UPDATED

SC Coachbuilders Compass low-floor bus   *1999*/0043462

Caio

Companhia Americana Industrial de Onibus
Rodovia Marechal Rondon, km 252, Zona Industriel, CEP 18603-970, Botucatu, São Paulo, Brazil
Tel: (+55 14) 820 32 00   Fax: (+55 14) 821 30 75
Chairman: José Gildo Vendramini
Superintendent Director: Cláudio Regina

Subsidiary company
Cia Americana Industrial de Onibus do Norte, Jabotão

Background: Caio has a 15 per cent holding in Mercedes-Benz Omnibuses Mexico SA.

Products: Bus, trolleybus and minibus bodies, including articulated.

Range
Alpha: City bus body, 12.7 m long and air conditioned, with 47 seated and 30 standing, on Mercedes-Benz, Volkswagen, Agrale and Ford chassis. An articulated version seats 60.
Carolina V: This is an 8 m midibus seating up to 32 on Volkswagen and Mercedes-Benz chassis.

UPDATED

Camena

Inversiones Commerciales Camena SA
Avenida Industrial No 400, Lima, Peru
Tel: (+51 14) 52 27 12   Fax: (+51 14) 64 08 50
Executive President: Carlos Olguin
Finance & Administrative Manager: Luis Perez Bisrror

Products: Bus bodywork. Bodies are mounted on Volvo and Mitsubishi chassis.

VERIFIED

Camo

Camo-Indústria de Autocarros SA
Apartado 8, Canelas, P-4405 Valadares, Vila Nova de Gaia, Oporto, Portugal
Tel: (+351 2) 711 47 78/48 03/49 51
Fax: (+351 2) 711 49 51
General Manager: Manuel Leão E Seabra

Background: A subsidiary of Auto-Sueca set up with Volvo interests to mount bodies on Volvo chassis assembled locally.

Products: Bus and coach bodies. The latest vehicle is the U90 articulated bus, on Volvo B10MA three-axle chassis.

VERIFIED

Camo body on Volvo B7R chassis
1998/0011583

Capre

Carrocerias Preconstruidas SA
Fulton No 8, Tlalnepantla, Edo de Mexico CP 54030,
Mexico
Tel: (+52 5) 65 66 00/30 22   Fax: (+52 5) 65 33 04
General Director: J I Amaya
Planning Director: Mario Mugica

Commercial Director: Alfredo Notni
Technical Director: Ricardo Pous
Design Engineering Director: Julian Espino

Background: Capre was set up in 1954 in San Bartolo
Naucalpan to make buses.

Products: Bus and minibus bodies.

Range: Includes the *CD* and *Boxer,* both with Mercedes-
Benz engines, batches of which were delivered in 1991 to
Mexico City operator Ruta 100. Conventional bus bodies
on Dina/Navistar, Mercedes-Benz, Chrysler and Ford
chassis are produced.

VERIFIED

CARRUS Oy

CARRUS Oy
Fabianinkatu 9, FIN-00100 Helsinki, Finland
Tel: (+358 9) 82 58 41   Fax: (+358 9) 82 14 14
Managing Director: Harry Ström

Background: Volvo Buses acquired Carrus in 1997. The
company retains its original name. Carrus and Volvo have
set up a joint venture to build city buses in Poland using
the Carrus stainless steel system. It is based in Wrocław
next to the Volvo truck plant.

Products: Bus and coach bodies and special vehicles.
Annual production is around 550 bus bodies and 150
special vehicles. There are about 850 employees.

All bus and coach bodies are built on the Carrus
Stainless principle, with stainless steel for load-bearing
structures — framework and side panelling.

CARRUS Oy Ajokki
PO Box 15, FIN-33721 Tampere, Finland
Tel: (+358 3) 27 71 11   Fax: (+358 3) 277 12 77

Products: Intercity bus bodies, tourist coaches on Volvo,
Scania and Mercedes-Benz chassis.

CARRUS Oy Delta
PO Box 23, FIN-21421 Lieto, Finland
Tel: (+358 2) 87 17 11   Fax: (+358 2) 87 10 02

Products: Luxury tourist coach bodies on Scania, Volvo
and Mercedes-Benz chassis.

CARRUS Oy Wiima
PO Box 23, FIN-01531 Vantaa, Finland
Tel: (+358 9) 82 58 41   Fax: (+358 9) 82 14 14

Products: City and intercity bus bodies.

Carrus City U low-floor bus body on Volvo B10L chassis   *1996*

Range: Bodies with welded steel tube framework are
offered on various makes of chassis including articulated.
The *City-204* series covers low-floor and articulated
buses, which are built to withstand hard northern road
and climate conditions. The vehicles have double-glazed
side and rear windows, fresh-air defrosters and front
heating units for the driver. There is also roof channel
ventilation with heating radiators and recirculating heaters
for the passenger saloon.

City-204 bodies can have two or three single/double
doors and varying seating layouts.

Production: Annual capacity is over 200 bodies.

Contracts: City-204 buses have been supplied to a
number of Scandinavian operators, on Volvo and Scania
chassis.

VERIFIED

Castrosua

Carrocera Castrosua SA
Ctra. La Coruña, Km 59.5, E-15890 Boisaca, Santiago de
Compostela, Spain
Tel: (+34 981) 58 24 11   Fax: (+34 981) 58 24 69

Managing Director: José Manuel Castro Rodriguez
Sales Manager: José Manuel Conde Gonzales
Technical Manager: Antonio Barriero

Products: Bus and coach bodies.

Range
CS-40 City: This urban bus body is available in 9, 10, 12
and 18 m (articulated) versions carrying up to 180. It is
3.2 m high and can be based on many chassis.

A low-floor version of the CS-40 City bus, based on
MAN SL202F, Volvo B10B and B10BLE chassis and
Mercedes O405N and Iveco CityClass, is available, with
two or three doors.
Master Coach: This is an 11.96 m coach with a high
specification.
Junior GT: This is 7.6 m long on the Mercedes-Benz 814D
chassis and is to touring coach specification seating 22.

Contracts: Castrosua is a regular supplier of urban
vehicles to Madrid, Barcelona, Valencia, Sevilla and
Santiago de Compostela. Vehicles have also been
supplied to France, Benelux countries, Bucharest,
Romania and Greece.

Orders include 160 bodies on Iveco CityClass chassis
for EMT Madrid.

Developments: Castrosua has acquired the former Unica
factory at Villagarcia en Arosa and is building buses on
Scania low-floor chassis.

Castrosua CS-40 City bus in Bucharest, Romania   *1996*

UPDATED

Champion

Champion Motor Coach Inc
Commercial Vehicle Division
PO Box 158, Imlay City, Michigan 48444, USA
Tel: (+1 810) 724 64 74   Fax: (+1 810) 724 18 44
President: Garner Bailey
Vice President, Sales & Marketing: Duane Galbreath
Vice President, Operations: Warren Marsh
Director, Engineering: David Carter
Director, Quality Assurance: John Gustaf
Manager, Aftermarket Services: Dick Cutcher

Works: 331 Graham Road, Imlay City, Michigan 48444, USA

Products: Medium-size buses, seating 14 to 30.

Range
CTS: This is offered in seven floor plans and four lengths — 6, 7.3, 7.9 and 8.8 m. It is powered by Ford or Cummins engines driving through Ford or Allison gearboxes. Suspension is leaf spring, and a wheelchair lift can be provided. The vehicle seats 19 to 31.
Challenger: A medium-duty body series offering roomier interiors, 30 per cent larger windows and more aerodynamic styling than previous models. There are also deeper entrance steps, a larger destination screen and a revised cab. Challenger bodies come in 11 interior formats and seat from 13 to 29. Ford, GM and Navistar chassis are used for power trains.
Contender: This is a rear-engined bus capable of seating 35. A wheelchair lift can be fitted and it has a low step height.
Crusader: This seats up to 14 and is powered by a Ford diesel or petrol engine.
SoLo: This has a rear engine, low-floor no-step entrance and can kneel.

Contracts: Buses have been supplied to undertakings in Dallas, Seattle, San Antonio and Portland, New Jersey Transit, Prince George County, and Michigan DoT.

VERIFIED

Champion SoLo low-floor bus

1996

Champion CTS bus

1997

Chance

Chance Coach Inc
2188 N Ohio, Wichita, Kansas 67219, USA
Tel: (+1 316) 838 12 11   Fax: (+1 316) 838 77 44
President: Scott Culbertson
Vice President, Customer Service: Dick Carlon
Director, Market Development: Reba Malone

Works: 2811 N Ohio, Wichita

Products: Complete heavy-duty small buses and articulated modular vehicles; rubber-tyred replica vintage trams (streetcars).

Range
RT-52 bus: This heavy-duty chassis bus is now in operation with a number of US transit systems. It is 7.62 m long and is suitable for routes requiring seating capacity of 25. It has a fuel consumption of 2.5 km/litre; turning circle is 9.15 m. It seats 23, or 19 if two wheelchair positions are included. A wheelchair lift can be fitted.
American Heritage Streetcar: The RT-52 also forms the basis of this car, with a body in the style of a 19th century streetcar (tram), with brass fittings and mahogany woodwork. It seats up to 28 with 19 standing. The Chance transit chassis provides a 9.15 m turning circle for congested areas. A wheelchair lift can be provided. A high-capacity heating and air conditioning system is fitted, along with heavy-duty insulation. A natural-gas-powered version is available, with a Cummins B5.9-195G engine.
Articulated Modular Transit Vehicle (AMTV): Using the RT-52 as a power unit for up to two trailing modules, this

Chance RT-52 bus

1999/0043463

arrangement allows for a total of up to 85 passengers. The RT-52 module can be used on normal routes. One or two trailing modules, each seating 30, can be attached to the power module by the driver alone, providing peak passenger capacity. The trailing modules have four-wheel steering allowing tight cornering.

UPDATED

Chavdar

Chavdar United Bus Works
Botevgrad, 2140 Bulgaria
Tel: (+359 723) 20 63

Exports: Balkancarimpex
Boul Kliment Ohridski 48, 1040 Sofia
Tel: (+359 2) 655 01/75 33 01/77 82 01
Fax: (+359 2) 77 13 01

Director General: Alexander Tsokev
Advertising Manager: Mrs R Nikolova

Products: Buses. Engines. Chavdar bus production is

exported under the 'Balkancar' name. Also builds trolleybuses and offers interurban and luxury coaches in limited numbers.

Contracts: Include supply of buses to China.

UPDATED

Chavdar B-FCR trolleybus in Sofia, Bulgaria
(Norman Griffiths)
1999/0043464

Chinese bus manufacturers

Background: Information recently received on the bus manufacturing industry in China is not sufficiently complete to provide separate entries for the companies involved. They are grouped together here for easy reference.

AVIC

China National Aviation Industry Corporation

Background: Since 1983 has offered road vehicles through subsidiary companies, of which six build buses.

CHAIC – Changhe Aircraft Industrial Co
Products: Include the CH6350, CH6531,CH590, CH591 and CH6600 minibuses, built under licence from Suzuki.

Harbin Aircraft Manufacturing Corporation
Products: Include the Songhuajiang HFJ6350 minibus.

SAMC – Shaanxi Aircraft Manufacturing Corporation
Products: Include the SFJ1010X2 microbus built under licence from Suzuki and the SFJ6900 midibus and SFJ61220 12 m bus.

SAC – Shenyang Shenfi Automobile Manufacturing Corporation
Background: Has built motor vehicles since 1980.
Products: Include the Shenfi SFQ6880, SFQ6980, SFQ6981, SFQ6982, SFQ6984, SFQ6122 buses and, since 1994, the SFQ 6890 coach.

Yunma Aircraft Manufacturing Plant
Background: Founded in 1960.
Products: Include the Yunma YM6700, YM6970, YM6971 and YM6972 buses.
Production: About 1,000 vehicles annually.

Xian Aircraft Manufacturing Corporation
Products: Has been building Volvo B10M buses under licence since 1993.

BAIC

Beijing Automotive Industry (Group) Corporation

Background: Founded as a repair workshop in 1938, it has built bodies since 1949 and became Beijing Automobile Works in 1958. There are four companies in this group, of which two build buses.

BUAMMC – Beijing United Automobile & Motorcycle Manufacturing Corporation
Products: Include the BJ6450 microbus.

BLC – Beijing Light Bus Co
Background: Known as BLC since 1985, it started building bus bodies in 1995.
Products: Includes the BL6440 and BL6480 as well as the BJ6560, BJ6590 and BJ6600 buses.
   Since 1994 the BE22 and BE36 have been built under licence from Isuzu, which now has a 25 per cent shareholding in BLC.
Production: In 1994, was 6,311 vehicles.

China Space Automotive Industry Corporation

Background: Diversified into the automotive industry in 1980. Two of the three subsidiaries offer buses.

China Jiangnan Space Industry Group Corporation
Products: Include the Hangtian GHT6470 and GHT6490 microbuses.

Yunnan Coach Works
Products: Include the Kunming YM6560 and YM6600 microbuses.

DFM

Dongfeng (Eastwind) Motor Corporation

Background: Until 1992 this was known as Second Automobile Works and is China's leading manufacturer of commercial vehicles. There are 11 subsidiaries, of which eight build buses.

Liuzhou Automobile Factory
Background: Production started in 1969, mainly of trucks, but since 1988 buses have been built.
Products: Chenlong LZ6400 4 m minibus.

Yunnan Automobile Plant
Background: Started around 1970.
Products: Include the Dongfeng KM6890 and 10 m KM6990 bus.

Dong Feng Hangzhou Motor Corporation
Background: Was taken over by DFM in 1992.
Products: Include the Zhejiang DHZ6960 9.6 m and DHZ6970 9.7 m buses.

Ningbo Tourist Bus Plant
Products: Include the Beilungang NP6470 4.7 m, NP6582 5.82 m, NP6600 6 m and NP6740 7.4 m buses.

Shenzhen Dongfeng Auto Corporation
Products: Include the Dongfeng SE6910 9.1 m bus.

Zhengzhou Light Automobile Factory
Products: Dongfeng Asia ZQ6400 4 m, ZQ6560 5.6 m and ZQ6600 6 m buses.

Wuhan Wantong Motor Co
Products: Include the Wantong WT6471 microbus, a licence-built Hyundai H100 4.7 m minibus.

Wuhan Light Duty Automobile Corporation
Products: Include the WHQ6450 minibus.

FAW

China First Automobile Works (Group) Corporation

Background: Founded in 1953 and until 1992 known as First Auto Works, the group comprises 20 subsidiaries, of which four build buses.

Jilin Light Duty Factory
Products: Light vehicles built under licence from Suzuki, Japan, including the JL6320 3.2 m microbus and the Jiefang CA6440 4.4 m minibus.

Wuxi Auto Works
Background: Founded in 1959 and taken over by FAW in 1986.
Products: Currently produces only buses under the Taihu brand including the XQ6940 9.4 m, XQ6960 9.6 m, XQ6961 9.6 m and XQ6990 9.9 m buses.
Production: About 1,000 vehicles annually.

Harbin Light Vehicle Plant
Background: Taken over by FAW in 1993.
Products: Include the XG560 5.6 m bus.

Yanbian Highway Bus Works
Background: Founded around 1953 and absorbed by FAW in 1993.
Products: Include the ZY6700 7 m, ZY890 8.9 m, ZY6980 9.8 m and ZY6120 12 m buses.
Production: About 466 vehicles were produced in 1994.

Guangzhou Junda Automobile Enterprise Group

Background: Until 1992 was called Guangzhou Automobile & Agricultural Machinery Co. Two of the three subsidiaries offer buses.

Guangzhou Automobile Plant
Products: Guangzhou Dongfeng GZ650 and GZ655 buses have been built since the 1970s. Current production includes the GZ6890 and GZ6921 buses.

Guangzhou Bus Plant
Products: Offers buses under the Guangzhou trade mark; the range includes the GZK6700 7 m, GZK6944 9.4 m, GZ6972 9.7 m, GZK6100 10 m and GZK 6120 12 m buses.

Hubei Automobile Group Corporation

Background: Owns four subsidiaries, of which two build buses.

Hubei Special Purpose Vehicle Manufactory
Products: Light commercial vehicles under the Chufeng trademark, including the HQG6600 bus.

Hubei Tianfeng Automobile Company
Products: Include the Hubei Tianfeng SZG6660 bus, until 1994 known under the Suizhou name.

Jinbei Automobile Company

Background: Formerly known as Shenyang Auto Co, it owns two subsidiaries, one of which produces buses.

Shenyang Jinbei Bus Manufacturing Co
Products: Include the Toyota HiAce, built under the Jinbei SY6480 name, with 30 per cent Chinese content. Also offers the original Jinbei SY6472, SY6474 and SY6475 microbuses.
Production: 3,776 Toyota SY6480 vehicles were built in 1995.

NORINCO

China North Industries (Group) Corporation

Background: Armaments and rail vehicle manufacturer, but buses for the civil market have been offered since 1988, through two subsidiaries.

NVW — Beijing North Vehicle Works
Products: Since 1986 has assembled Neoplan buses marketed as the BFC6830 (8.3 m), BFCC120 (12 m) and double-deck BFC6120SD/2 (12 m).

Changan Automobile Ltd
Products: Builds the Suzuki SuperCarry microbus under licence as well as the SC1010X, SC1014X and SC6331 microbuses.

SAIC

Shanghai Automotive Industry Corporation

Background: Founded in 1957 and four of the five subsidiaries build buses.

Shanghai Huizhong Auto Manufacturing Corporation
Background: Founded in 1958 and builds trucks and buses.
Products: Include the SH6120 coach and SH6600 and SH6601 microbuses.

Shanghai Bus & Coach Plant (qv)

Shanghai Feiyi Automotive Manufacturing Co
Products: Include the Feiyi SF6971, SF6123, SF6123, SF6124 and SF6125 buses.
Production: About 1,000 vehicles annually.

Shanghai Huling Auto Works
Products: Include the HL6600, HL6601 and HL6602 buses.
Production: About 2,000 vehicles annually.

TAIC

Tianjin Automotive Industrial Corporation

Background: Founded in 1951 with the assembly of rugged-terrain vehicles. There are now three subsidiaries, of which two produce buses.

Tianjin Sanfeng Minibus Co
Background: Founded in 1950, the company produced its first minibus in 1965.
Products: Include the TJ6480B minibus, in production since 1988, and the newer TJ6481A.
Production: About 20,000 vehicles annually.

Tianjin Automobile Works
Products: The Diahatsu Hijet microbus has been produced under licence since 1984 under the Dafa TJ110 name. Other models include the TJ6320 and TJ6350.

YMC

Yuejin Motor (Group) Corporation

Background: Until 1995 this was known as the Nanjing Auto Works and was founded in 1947 as a repair workshop and parts manufacturer. Since 1958, Russian trucks have been built under licence. In 1985, an agreement was reached with Iveco which includes production of the Daily A30, A35, A40 and A45 minibuses. There are three subsidiaries.

Jiangsu Nushen Motor Corporation
Products: Microbuses, including the Nushen JB6430, JB6470 (based on the Toyota HiAce), JB6401, JB6570, JB6700 and NS2310.

Jiangsu Zilang Automobile Group
Products: Microbuses, include the Zilang NTT6482 (based on the Toyota HiAce), NTT6461 and NTT6462 as well as small NTT660 6 m and NTT6700 7 m buses.

Individual manufacturers

Annhui Huaihai Machinery Works
Products: Include the Feihu 1012X microbus built under licence from Suzuki.

Beijing General Bus Plant
Products: Include the BK6451 (Mitsubishi L300 body) ,BK6581 and BK6580 minibuses. Larger buses are built under the Jinghua name and include the BK6920 (9.2 m), BK6980 (9.8 m), BK6120 (12 m) and the articulated BK6170 17 m bus, designed for operation in Beijing.
Production: About 6,000 minibuses and 2,000 large buses annually.

Beijing Tiantan Bus Works
Products: Include the Tiantan BF5040X microbuses.

Beijing Traffic Bus Plant
Products: Include the Jintong BJK6900, BJK6970, BJK6973, BJK6100 and BJK6120 buses.
Production: About 1,000 vehicles annually.

Beijing Yanging Automobile Factory
Background: Founded in 1950.
Products: Include the Yanging YJ6401 and YJ6501 microbuses.

CBF — Changzhou Bus Factory
Background: In 1993, China Flxible Auto Co was established as a joint venture between CBF and the former Flxible Corporation, USA; 103 Flxible series B and C buses were built in the first year.

Products: Include the CJ6600, CJ6220, CJ6921, CJ6922, CJ6120 and CJ6151 buses.
Production: About 2,000 buses and 3,000 bus chassis were built in 1993.

Changsha General Bus Factory
Background: Founded in 1952 and now produces buses under the Sanxiang name.
Products: Include the CK6480, CK6560, CK6640, CK6892, CK6892-2, CK6960 and JT6120 buses.
Production: About 2,000 buses were produced in 1995.

Cityview Bus
Cityview Bus Installation Co Ltd
Guangzhou, Guangdong Province

Background: Cityview Bus Installation Co is a joint venture company.
Products: Single- and double-deck buses up to 12 m long built in aluminium alloy, including Eagle two-door rear-engine bus.

Cityview Eagle bus in Guangzhou   **1999**/0043465

Dadong Automobile Works
Background: China's second largest builder of big buses started production of trucks in 1958. Bus production started during the 1980s under the Huanghai name.
Products: Include the DD6620, DD6990, DD6111, DD6112, DD6113, DD6120 buses and DD6125 coach.
Production: About 4,500 buses and coaches annually.

Fuzhou Automobile Works
Background: Started building three-wheel vehicles in 1958.
Products: Since 1986 has included the FZ6490 bus built under licence from Isuzu.

Guangdong Sanxing Automobile Corporation
Background: Until 1972 known as the Zhanjiang Sanxing Motor Enterprises Corporation. Production of commercial vehicles started in 1970.
Products: Include the Sanxing SXZ6440 microbus, built under licence from Mitsubishi.

Hainan Auto Manufacturing Plant
Products: Since 1991 has built the HMC6440, HMC6450 and HMC6470 under Mazda licences.

Hefei Bus Factory
Products: Include HK6670, HK6911, HK6960, HK6962, HK6963, HK6111, HK6111, HK6121, JT6912, JT6100, JT6121 and JT6150 buses, built under the Heke name.

Hefei Feihe Auto Works
Products: Include the HFF6120 bus built under licence from Setra.

Hefei Jianghuai Automobile Manufactory
Products: Builds commercial vehicles under the Jianghuai name, including bus chassis.

Hunan Changsa Furung Automobile Manufacturing
Products: Include the Furung FR6600 bus.

Hunan Social Welfare Special Vehicle Factory

Products: Include the XL6580 microbus under the Xiangjing name.

Jiangsu Yizheng Automobile Works

Background: Founded in 1971.
Products: Include the Liming YQC6460NL and YQC6450 microbuses.

Liuzhou Minicar Factory

Background: Light commercial vehicles have been built since 1980.
Products: Based on an agreement with Mitsubishi, the Wulin LZ110 series was started in 1985, which included a microbus. Current production includes the LZW1010VH, LZW6320, LZW6370 and LZW6430 microbuses.

Qinling Automotive (qv)

Shijiazhuang Automobile Manufacturing Ltd

Background: Founded in 1946.
Products: Include the Zhengtian SQ6450, SQ6470, SQQ6440, SQQ6460 and SQQ6482 microbuses.

Songliao Automotive Company

Background: Founded in 1947.
Products: Include the SLQ6501 microbus.
Production: About 10,000 vehicles annually.

Wanshan Special Vehicle Works

Products: Include the WS6600, WS6600AZ, WS6482, WS6483 and WS6320 buses.
Production: About 10,000 vehicles annually.

Wuhan Bus Works

Background: Founded in 1958 with the production of three-wheel vehicles. In 1970, production of buses began under licence from Nanjing/GAZ.
Products: Include the WH6700, WH6910, WH6923, WH6960, WH6970 buses and, since 1994, the WH6980 9.8 m bus and WH6120 12 m coach.
Production: About 3,000 large buses annually.

Yangzhou General Bus Manufactory

Background: This is the biggest Chinese manufacturer of medium- and large-size buses.
Products: Include the Yangzhou Yanxing JS6701, JS6970, JS6971, JT6960, JT6970 and JT6120 buses. In 1995, an agreement was signed with Mercedes-Benz for the production of 10,000 chassis and 6,000 buses.
Production: About 5,500 vehicles were built in 1995.

Yangzi Auto General Plant

Products: Include YZK6650, YZK6780, YZK6100, YZK6111 and YZK6120 buses.
Production: About 1,000 buses annually.

Yunnan Lanjian Automobile Works

Background: Builds Isuzu vehicles under the Xinan-Isuzu name.
Products: Include the LJC6490 microbus.

UPDATED

Ciferal

Ciferal, Comércio Industria e Particioações S/A
Rua Pastor Manoel Avelino de Souza 2064, 25250-000 Xerém, Duque de Caxias, RJ, Brazil
Tel: (+55 21) 679 10 11   Fax: (+55 21) 679 10 32
Export Division, Tel: (+55 21) 679 17 24
President: Lélis Marcos Teixeira
Commercial Director: Gilson Mansur
Export Manager, South America & Caribbean:
    Hermando de Andrade
Export Manager, Middle East: Rose Manso

Background: The company expanded in 1992 to a new 300,000 m³ plant 50 km from its previous 40,000 m³ location in Rio de Janeiro. It now employs 800.

Products: Bus bodies.

Range: Aluminium-structured bus bodies for urban and suburban use. Short- and long-distance coaches built on Mercedes, Scania and Volvo chassis produced in Brazil. Also minibuses and airport buses.
Minibus: Carrying up to 27, on Mercedes-Benz LO814 and VW 8140-CO chassis. Two doors can be fitted.

Highway: 13.2 m long, 3.6 m high, for 50 passengers, built of aluminium and glass fibre, on Scania, Mercedes and Volvo chassis.
Articulated Urban: This is 18.2 m long, on Scania or Volvo chassis.
Urban: This is an urban bus on Mercedes, Scania, Volvo, Ford and VW chassis.

Production: 1,784 bodies were produced during 1997.

UPDATED

Citroën

SA Automobiles Citroën
62 Boulevard Victor-Hugo, F-92208 Neuilly-sur-Seine Cedex, France
Tel: (+33 1) 45 78 61 61   Fax: (+33 1) 47 48 51 09

Products: Minibuses and chassis.

Range: The front-wheel-drive *Jumper* van (named *Relay* in UK) is available with a choice of three diesel engines of 53, 64 and 77 kW (71, 86 and 103 hp). Payloads range from 1,165 to 1,605 kg.

The Citroën models are powered by a choice of PSA 1.9 or 2.5 litre diesel engines, naturally aspirated or turbocharged.

A small 1.9 litre diesel or turbo diesel passenger carrier, the *Jumpy Combi* (called the *Dispatch* in the UK) seats up to 9 and is 4.4 m long. Twin side load doors are standard.

A 17-seat minibus specially adapted for schools has seat belts, mobile phone and free signwriting.

VERIFIED

Citroën Jumper 35LH with BUSiness body
1998/0011584

Comil

Comil Carrocerias e Onibus Ltda
Rua Alberto Parenti 1382, Distrito Indl, CEP 99700-000 Erechim, RS, Brazil
Tel: (+55 543) 21 61 24   Fax: (+55 543) 213 31 41
President: Rovilio Mascarello
Sales Manager: Silvio A De Marchi
Export Manager: Luis Amaral

Background: Founded in 1985.

Products: Bus bodies.

Range
Galleggiante: 12 m express bus, with 13.2 m version available.
Versatile: 12.2 m interurban bus.

Doppio: Articulated urban bus in 16.8 and 18.1 m versions.
Micrao: 9 m midibus.
Svelto: Urban bus, seating up to 91.

Production: 959 units in 1997.

UPDATED

Contrac

Contrac GmbH
Max-Planck-Ring 43, D-65205 Wiesbaden, Germany
Tel: (+49 6122) 955 30   Fax: (+49 6122) 514 61
Managing Directors: Jürgen Kamps, Lothar Elbel

Subsidiary companies
Contrac Beijing, China
Contrac International (GB) Ltd

Products: Low-floor small buses and airport buses. Mechanical subassemblies are by NAW (qv) and bodywork is by Caetano (qv).

Range
Cobus 1000: This is a low-floor diesel airport bus, 6.535 m long and with an entrance height of 240 mm, when kneeling. The width is 1.94 m. There are no steps inside. Air conditioning can be fitted.

Cobus 3000: Low-floor airport bus, 14 m long, with six doors and 3 m wide. The entrance height, when kneeling, is 270 mm and it carries 140. It is of aluminium alloy construction.

VERIFIED

Csepel

Csepel Autógyár FA
PO Box 38, H-2311 Szigetszentmiklós, Hungary
Tel: (+36 24) 36 68 71   Fax: (+36 24) 36 73 10
Director: Antal Varga

Background: Csepel's main customer traditionally was Ikarus until the Russian market collapsed and Ikarus made its own underframes. Csepel has links with Cummins (qv).

Products: Bus chassis, including articulated. Trucks (8 to 10 tonnes).

Range

844: This is rear-engined and is 12 m long. It is available as a city bus or as a long-distance model. Power is from a Cummins C 8.3 litre engine, and suspension is air over-leaf.
856: This is powered by a Cummins L10 engine and is similar to the 844 chassis.
888.02: This is an articulated bus chassis, 17.5 m long, powered by a rear-mounted Cummins 8CTA driving through a ZF 4HP transmission with hydraulic retarder.
613.02B: This is a midibus type 7.2 m long, in coach or city bus specification. The chassis is rear engined.

VERIFIED   Csepel bus chassis with Ikarus body (Andrew Jarosz)   *1996*

Custom Coaches

Custom Coaches Sales Pty Ltd
PO Box 3, 34 Marian Street, Guildford, New South Wales 2161, Australia
Tel: (+61 2) 96 32 02 21   Fax: (+61 2) 96 32 16 53

NSW Sales Division: 31-39 Sturt Street, Smithfield, New South Wales 2161
Tel: (+61 2) 98 92 19 66   Fax: (+61 2) 96 32 74 48
Managing Director: J Violet
Chief Executive Officer: R Smith
Sales Manager: N Stott

Manufacturing plants: Smithfield, New South Wales, Preston, Victoria and Arundel, Queensland, Australia

Products: Bus and coach bodies.

Range

Mini: This is based on the Mercedes-Benz O812 and O814 chassis and seats from 27 to 33 passengers.

Custom Coaches Mini Series II body on Mercedes O814 chassis   *1997*

510 series: This is a one- or two-door bus body with curved windscreens, seating from 49 to 61 passengers, mounted on Volvo, Mercedes-Benz, Scania and other chassis.

516 series: This is a one- or two-door bus body with flat windscreens, seating from 49 to 61 passengers, mounted on Volvo, Mercedes-Benz, Scania and other chassis.
525 series: This is a one- or two-door narrow bus body with flat windscreens, seating from 37 to 51 passengers, mounted on Volvo, Scania and other chassis with reduced wheel track.
550 series: This is a low-floor bus body with wheelchair accessibility and has one or two doors, curved windscreens and seats from 37 to 53 passengers, mounted on Volvo, Mercedes-Benz, Scania and other chassis.
420 series: This is a coach-style body with curved windscreens, seating from 49 to 57 passengers, mounted on Volvo, Mercedes-Benz, Scania and other chassis.

Contracts: Low-floor city buses are being supplied to State Transit Authority of New South Wales for delivery early 1999.

UPDATED

Daewoo

Daewoo Motor Co Ltd
199, Changchon-dong, Puk-gu, Inchon, Republic of Korea
Tel: (+82 32) 520 21 14   Fax: (+82 32) 524 43 62
Managing Director: Jae Ho Kim

Seoul office
Daewoo Center, 541 Namdaemunno 5-ga, Chung-gu, Seoul
Tel: (+82 2) 776 40 31/40 35   Fax: (+82 2) 754 06 69

Products: Buses.

Range: Includes 12 m front-engine versions.

Contracts: Daewoo is supplying buses to several Asian markets and 19 Caravan and 30 Royale buses for the Indian market.

UPDATED

Daewoo intercity bus in Syria (Wilhelm Pflug)
1998/0011585

Daewoo Avia

Daewoo Avia s p
Beranových 140, CZ-193 03 Prague 9, Czech Republic
Tel: (+420 2) 859 02 40/07 40   Fax: (+420 2) 859 29 55
General Director: Kil-Su Chung

Background: A controlling interest in Avia was obtained by Daewoo (qv) in 1996 and the company was renamed Daewoo Avia.

Products: Light truck chassis suitable for bus bodywork, 6 to 7.5 tonnes and powered by 65/76 kW Euro-1, or 76/85 kW Euro-2 engines.

A 2.9 tonne light truck chassis is available as a minibus and is powered by a 51 kW engine.

Contracts: Chassis suitable for bus bodywork have been delivered to customers in Poland, Slovakia, Hungary, Romania, Ukraine and France.

Developments: Two new light truck chassis suitable for minibus bodywork, the A60 and A75, have been announced. They are developed from the AD100 truck chassis and have a GVW of 6 to 9 tonnes. Production was expected to start in April 1999.

VERIFIED

DAF Bus

DAF Bus International
PO Box 7122, NL-5605 JC Eindhoven, Netherlands
Tel: (+31 40) 250 05 00 Fax: (+31 40) 257 09 04
Managing Director: Hubert G. van Wees
Technical Director: Louis Spaninks

DAF Bus International products are sold in the UK through:
Arriva Bus & Coach, Lodge Garage, Whitehall Road West, Gomersal BD19 4BJ, UK
Tel: (+44 1274) 68 11 44 Fax: (+44 1274) 65 11 98
Managing Director: Bob McLeod

Background: In 1989, DAF NV transferred its bus and coach underframe manufacture and development to a new company, DAF Bus. DAF Bus International is now owned by a Dutch consortium, with a minority stake held by DAF Trucks (19 per cent). The latter company was acquired by US truck manufacturer Paccar in 1996 and that company has inherited the 19 per cent stake held by DAF Trucks.

The other main partners are the VDL Group of specialised companies in the metal and plastics industries (which owns 100 per cent of Berkhof Jonckheere (qv)), with a 51 per cent shareholding, and De Rooy Transport, a parts distribution and transport company, with 30 per cent.

DAF International BV is the Netherlands importer for DAB (see Scania-DAB).

Products: Bus and coach underframes, including articulated.

Range: Chassis are manufactured with front- and rear-mounted engines. DAF makes engines in variants for urban, interurban bus, and tourist coach operations. All engines now meet Euro-2 exhaust emission standards.
SB220: This city and interurban bus underframe is powered by a horizontally mounted 8.65 litre ATI Euro-2 engine, driving through a ZF or Voith automatic gearbox, with integral retarder. Air suspension is standard, as is encapsulation of the engine and gearbox to reduce noise and vibration. The SB220 has kneeling capability which enables it to be lowered by 100 mm. The SB220 is also available as a pusher articulated underframe and as a dual-purpose chassis, the SB225.

A low-entry version of the SB220, the SB220 Low Floor can take bodywork with a floor height of 320 mm. It has a new front-axle module and can be powered by the 8.65 litre LPG engine.

A version powered by liquefied petroleum gas (LPG) has multipoint LPG injection. DAF reports that this offers extra benefits when compared with the present generation of LPG engines.

The DAF LT160 LPG engine was announced in 1995 and has timed multipoint liquid LPG injection, designed to improve reliability. A three-way catalytic converter cuts nitrogen dioxide emissions to 0.7 g/kW h, which is below the proposed Euro-3 standard. It produces 50 per cent

less noise than a diesel engine. Costs are cited as 7 per cent lower than those for a diesel engine.
DB250: This low-floor chassis has been developed for double-deck city bus bodywork and has a 203 kW 8.66 litre Euro-2 low-emission RS200 DAF-ATI engine. It is transversely mounted at the rear and drives through a ZF or Voith gearbox.
SB3000 range: This is a rear-engined underframe for semi-integral bodywork. It is air suspended and various engine options are available, up to the 315 kW (430 hp) Euro-2 engine. This range of chassis is available with either an AVS electropneumatic eight-speed manual synchromesh gearbox or a five-speed automatic ZF5 HP600 gearbox, both of which have retarders. AVS preselect gearshift can be specified.
TB2100: A rugged front-engined chassis for export markets, with conventional leaf springing. The chassis uses the vertical DAF 8.25 litre engine developing 170 kW (230 hp).
SB2100: This is similar to the TB2100 chassis, but with a rear-mounted ATI engine developing 200 kW (272 hp).

All vehicles with a manual gearbox can be fitted with the new PGS (Precision Gear Shifting) gear shifting system.

Contracts: Dordrecht, Netherlands, has purchased the SB250, the new LPG public transport bus. Nijmegen, Netherlands, has purchased the diesel version. After extensive research, Brussels and Amsterdam have both chosen the SB250. The Walloon transport company TEC has purchased 115 SB220 low-floor vehicles to be used for services in the Belgian Ardennes.

Arriva Bus & Coach, UK, has placed the following orders with DAF Bus:

DAF Bus DB250LF low-floor double-deck in Arriva London livery   **1999**/0043472

It is supplying Eastbourne Buses, with 12 DB250RS double-decks with Optare Spectra low-height bodies; Arriva Yorkshire has taken delivery of 50 12 m DAF SB220GS low-floor single-decks to be fitted with Alexander's all-aluminium 2.55 m wide ALX300 body; 16 low-floor DAF DB250RS double-decks for Capital Logistics, London – six will have Optare Spectra bodies and 10 will have the first production examples of Plaxton's new 2.55 m wide President body; Harris Bus has returned to Arriva Bus & Coach for another two DAF DB250 double-decks with Plaxton Wigan Palatine II bodywork, built to LT Buses two-door specification.

New DAF DKDL engines, also supplied by Arriva Bus & Coach, have been installed in four Leyland Leopard single-decks operated by Blue Bus & Coach of Horwich, Bolton, UK.

Developments: The SB3000 range has been largely replaced by the SB4000.
SB250 underframe: DAF Bus has developed the SB250 for service bus use. It has a low floor of 340 mm along its entire length. This vehicle has three doors of equal width at the front, in the middle and at the rear. The SB250 is available in diesel or LPG versions. The engine is positioned vertically in a corner behind the rear axle.

PGS (Precision Gear Shifting) – PGS is a gearshift with three cables with no play or elasticity. The influence of temperature fluctuations on the required gear-shifting forces has been reduced to a minimum. PGS does not transmit any vibrations or noise from the gearbox. DAF Bus International has a worldwide patent for this system.

UPDATED

DAF Bus SB220 Berkhof-bodied LPG-powered bus   **1999**/0043471

DAF Bus SB250 low-floor underframe   **1999**/0043473

Daihatsu

Daihatsu Motor Co Ltd
1-1, Daihatsu-cho, Ikeda-shi, Osaka 563, Japan
Tel: (+81 6) 727 54 30 47 Fax: (+81 6) 727 53 68 80

Daihatsu UK Ltd
Poulton Close, Dover CT17 OHP
Tel: (+44 1304) 21 30 30 Fax: (+44 1304) 21 35 25

Hijet production for Europe:
Piaggio Veicoli Europei
Italy viale, R Piaggio 23, I-56025 Pontedera, Italy
Tel: (+39 0587) 27 25 48 Fax: (+39 0587) 29 09 06
Piaggio assembles the Daihatsu Hijet for the European market where, other than in the UK, it is known as the Porter. In the UK, the name Hijet is retained.

Products: Buses, midibuses and minibuses.

Range: Light truck designs are adapted for use as buses and midibuses.
Delta: Available either as a chassis cab or a van conversion.

The V119B-U 26-seater bus is 6.18 m long. It is powered by a 3.6 litre diesel engine.
Hijet: This is powered by the three-cylinder Otto 993 cc 29 kW engine. The standard version seats six. Since 1992, there has been an agreement with Italian

East Lancs Flyte body mounted on Scania L113 chassis supplied to Lakeland Coaches of Hurst Green, near Blackburn **1999**/0043480

Range

Spryte: Single-deck low-floor midibus or full-sized body using Alusuisse (qv) aluminium alloy construction. Seats 25 to 44.

Flyte: Single-deck bus body using Alusuisse construction method. Seats 45 to 53 and is mounted on mid- or rear-engine chassis.

Pyoneer: Double-deck conventional construction for mid- and rear-engine chassis, standard and low height, seats 72 to 86.

LoLyne: Double-deck Alusuisse construction low-floor available in low or standard height, 72 to 90 seats, suitable for leading makes of chassis.

Production: Capacity for 300 units in 1998.

Contracts: With UK operators Blue Bus, Bournemouth Transport, Brighton & Hove, Dawsonrentals, Delaine, Dunn-Line, Metrobus, Nottingham City Transport and Yorkshire Traction.

Outside the UK, buses have gone to Cityrama/Bridet (Paris), Les Cars Rouge (Paris), First Citybus (assembly of Duple Metsec kits, Hong Kong).

UPDATED

East Lancs Spryte body on Dennis Dart chassis supplied to Lincolnshire Road Car **1999**/0043478

East Lancs two-door 10.5 m Pyoneer body mounted on Volvo Olympian chassis supplied to Harris Bus Company of Grays, UK **1999**/0043481

ELBO

Hellenic Vehicle Industry SA
Industrial Area Sindos, GR-541-10 Thessalonika, Greece
Tel: (+30 31) 79 85 02   Fax: (+30 31) 79 84 26
Sales Manager: H Valetopoulos

Background: ELBO was founded in 1972 as Steyr Hellas SR to build trucks and tractors. In 1986, it became Hellenic Vehicle Industry.

Products: Buses, trucks, military vehicles.

ELBO C97.N4007 midibus on Neoplan chassis **1999**/0043482

Range

C98.405GN: This is an articulated bus on Mercedes-Benz O405GN chassis. It seats 46 with 116 standing. It is 18 m long and 2.5 m wide. It is powered by the Mercedes-Benz OM447hLA, driving through a ZF 4HP590 engine with hydraulic retarder. Air conditioning is fitted.

C97.N4007 Midi: This is based on the Neoplan N4007 and has 15 seats with 43 standing. It is 8.2 m long and 2.4 m wide. It is powered by a Mercedes-Benz OM366LA engine driving through a ZF 4HP500 auto transmission with retarder.

Contracts: ELBO has secured a major contract from HLPAP Athens for nearly 630 buses and 96 trolleybuses.

UPDATED

ELBO C98.405GN articulated bus on Mercedes-Benz chassis
1999/0043483

El Detalle

El Detalle
Argentina

Brazil assembly plant: El Detalle do Brazil, Automotores Ltda, Estrada Cavalhada 900, CEP 94190-230, Parque do Anjos, Gravatai, RS

Tel: (+55 51) 488 13 39/23 44   Fax: (+54 51) 345 17 66
President: Juan Carlos Surdo

Products: Bus chassis for urban, suburban and highway buses.

Range: The OA-101 is a two-door vehicle with engine ratings of 143, 157 and 298 kW, 4,200 to 5,700 kg and

wheelbase of 4.6, 5.17, 6.17 and 7.1 m.
OA-101/2/4: Chassis from 9.8 to 13.5 m, powered by Deutz 913 Series engines, with ZF steering, Eaton or Allison transmission, Rockwell-Braseixos front axles, Eaton rear axles and air suspension; CNG option being tested.

VERIFIED

El Dorado National

El Dorado National Co
304 Avenue B, Salina, Kansas 67401, USA
Tel: (+1 913) 827 10 33   Fax: (+1 913) 827 09 65

13900 Sycamore Way, Chino, California 91710, USA
Tel: (+1 909) 591 95 57   Fax: (+1 909) 591 52 85
President: Andy Imanse
Senior Vice President: Sheldon Walle
Director of Transit Sales: Gentry C Shaw
Parent company: Thor Industries

Background: El Dorado National was established in 1991 following the merger of El Dorado Bus and National Coach Corporation. El Dorado Bus started building buses in 1979 and National had been in business since 1975. El Dorado Bus was acquired by Thor Industries, manufacturer of recreational vehicles, in 1988.

Products: Small and mid-size buses.

Range

Aerotech: This is on the Ford E-350 chassis and seats up to 29; wheelchairs can be carried and perimeter seating fitted.
Aero-XT: Built on the Chevrolet GP cutaway chassis, this model can carry up to 29 without a third axle.
Escort RE: Rear engine bus, seating up to 33, 8.76 or 11.3 m long; can be supplied with one or two doors and perimeter seating can be fitted. It can be powered by CNG, diesel or propane engines, driving through an Allison automatic gearbox. Leaf springs or air suspension can be specified. A CNG version is available.
Escort RE-A: This version is designed for the tour and charter markets and has air suspension. It seats up to 41.
RE-29-E: This is an electric bus, called the Zero Emission Bus, 8.76 m long. It has a top speed of 77 km/h and a range of 112 km.

El Dorado National low-floor bus   *1997*

El Dorado MST bus   *1996*

Two-door El Dorado Transmark RE on Dash service, Los Angeles (Andrew Jarosz)   *1998*/0016407

Transmark-RE: This is a rear-engine coach seating up to 33 and can be adapted to carry disabled people.

MST: This is the Mid-Sized Transit on an Oshkosh front-engine bus chassis or on a Chevrolet chassis, seating up to 31.

Escort FE: This is designed to combine the comforts of a car with the reliability of a bus, bridging the gap between van conversions and coaches. It carries from 12 to 27 and is based on the Chevrolet P-30 chassis.

Aerolite: This is the smallest of the El Dorado family and is built on the single rear wheel Ford E350 chassis cowl (cutaway) and does not require a commercial driver's licence. It seats up to 14.

Elf: This is a no-step low-floor vehicle, based on the Ford E350 cab and controls. It seats up to 21 and there are positions for eight wheelchairs.

The *Li'l Elf* is a smaller version, also based on the Ford E350 cab and controls, seating up to 17 or carrying five wheelchairs. It has a no-step low floor.

VERIFIED

El Nasr

El Nasr Automotive Manufacturing Co
Wadi Hof, Helwan, Cairo, Egypt
Tel: (+20 2) 369 19 01/26 08
Fax: (+20 2) 369 26 12/54 25
General Manager, Information Centre:
  Kamel El-Shabrawy
Chair: Acc Ahmed Kamel Abdel-Salam
Managing Director: Eng Abdel-Meneim Khalifa
Commercial Director: Acc Mohamed El-Boushy
Technical Director: Eng Maamoun Abdel-Shafy

Products: Buses, minibuses, microbuses and coaches, including bodywork.

Range
Nasr High Deck: This is a tourist coach, powered by an Iveco 8210.02 diesel engine, driving through a ZF S6-80 six-speed manual gearbox. It is 12.1 m long, 3.57 m high and seats 55.
Nasr 96 Inter-City: This is an express bus, powered by a Deutz BF6M diesel engine, driving through a ZF S6-86 six-speed manual gearbox. It is 12 m long and seats 54.
Nasr Combi: Based on Iveco running units with the Iveco 8140.07 diesel engine driving through an Iveco five-speed gearbox. It seats up to 17 and weighs 3.5 tonnes. The internal height is 1.52 m and it is 2 m wide.
Nasr Minibus: Powered by Iveco 8040.05 diesel engine driving through a ZF 5.36 gearbox. Seats 29.

Contracts: Cairo Transport Authority has taken delivery of 25 Nasr 96 buses. Alexandria Transport Authority has taken 35 Nasr 96 buses and 50 Nasr Minibuses.

UPDATED

Nasr High Deck coach **1999**/0024987

Nasr Combi minibus **1998**/0011597

Nasr Minibus **1998**/0011598

ERF

ERF Limited
Sun Works, Sandbach CW11 9DN, UK
Tel: (+44 1270) 76 32 23   Fax: (+44 1270) 76 60 68
Managing Director: J W Bryant
Export Sales: C J Waggott

ERF South Africa (Pty) Ltd
PO Box 3944, 5 Clarke Street North, Alrode 1451, South Africa
Tel: (+27 11) 864 26 40   Fax: (+27 11) 864 71 31

Background: Canadian truck manufacturer Western Star, Canada, bought ERF in 1996. It also owns Orion Bus Industries (qv). Dorbyl Transport Products, South Africa, took a 70 per cent interest in ERF South Africa in 1996.

Products: Bus chassis.

Range: Though the UK parent company is primarily a truck builder, ERF in 1979 introduced a straight-framed bolted construction single-deck bus chassis with front-mounted engine. Since then mid- and front-engine units have been developed including a three-axle double-deck chassis.
Trailblazer (forward-engine): Intended for the rugged and arduous operating conditions found in southern Africa, the front-engine chassis with bolted ladder frame is available in wheelbases to suit 11 to 12.5 m maximum legal capacity single-deck bodies. There is a choice of the ADE 407 (Mercedes-derived) naturally aspirated engine coupled with Rockwell S160E rear axle or ADE 354T (Perkins six-cylinder 354T) turbocharged unit coupled with Rockwell R140 rear axle. The Gardner 6LXB is available for other markets.
Trailblazer 'Jumbo': A Trailblazer 'Jumbo' articulated 20 m bus chassis has also been developed to a legal load capacity of 185 passengers, with 86 seated. It is built to order with either the front or mid-engine standard Trailblazer front section with trailing rear axle.

VERIFIED

ERF Trailblazer with Kenya Bus at Nairobi bus station (Andrew Jarosz)
1997

Ernst Auwärter

Ernst Auwärter Karosserie- und Fahrzeugbau KG
Industriegebiet Kringstrasse 2, D-71144 Steinenbronn,
Germany
Tel: (+49 7157) 40 81   Fax: (+49 7157) 93 90
www: www.ernst-auwaerter.de
Managing Director: Ernst Auwärter
Marketing Director: Ingeborg Bahn
Technical Director: Jürgen Schöllhammer

Products: Mini and midibus bodies, also full-sized coach
bodywork.

Range: Primarily a luxury touring coach body builder,
Ernst Auwärter also produces a number of small bus and
coach bodies on chassis from Mercedes and
Volkswagen.
Teamstar City: 7.37 m city midibus on the Mercedes
O814 Vario and O815 chassis and is available in two
wheelbases, 4.25 and 4.8 m. It seats up to 29, with up to
seven standing.
Teamstar City Low-Floor: This is on the Mercedes-Benz
O815 Vario and has a full low floor with two doors. It has a
total capacity of 38, with up to 18 seated and up to 24
standing. It is available in two wheelbases, 4.25 and
4.8 m.
   The *Clubstar MAN Midibus* is on the new MAN 220 low-
floor chassis with a 169 kW rear engine and air
suspension, the 8.7 m version carrying 25 seated and 35
standing.
   The *Economy Mercedes O614* is converted to a small
7.1 m city bus, carrying up to 40 (20 seated).
Microstar: The Microstar 12-seat minibus, based on the
Volkswagen Caravelle, has 1.3 m wide doors and a step
floor height of 320 mm.
Microstar Multimax: A twin-axle version, based on the
Volkswagen T4 and seating 13 with 10 standing. It has a
low floor with no steps. The boarding step height is
320 mm.
Eurostar: This three-axle coach is based on the Mercedes-
Benz O404 and is 15 m long, seating 68. It is 3.75 m high.
Super Sprinter 412: This is based on the Mercedes-Benz
Sprinter and seats 20. There is capacity for four
wheelchairs. It has a large windscreen and electric-
powered door, and is 6.5 m long.

Production: 210 vehicles annually.

UPDATED

Ernst Auwärter Microstar Multimax low-floor urban minibus on VW T4 chassis   ***1999**/0043484*

Ernst Auwärter minicoach body on VW LT46 chassis   ***1999**/0043485*

EvoBus

EvoBus GmbH
Sitz Stuttgart, Amtsgericht Stuttgart, HRB-Nr D-17316,
Germany
Tel: (+49 711) 179 90 14   Fax: (+49 711) 179 91 02
www: www.evobus.com
Managing Director: Wolfgang Diez
Development Director: Bengt Hamsten
Commercial Director: Johann Graf
Evobus UK Managing Director: Hans Smits
Managing Director, Product Construction:
   Harold Landmann

Subsidiaries
EvoBus Austria GmbH, Salzburg
EvoBus Belgium SA, Brussels
EvoBus Bohemia sro, Prague
EvoBus Danmark, A/S, Ringsted

EvoBus France SAS, Paris
EvoBus Hellas SA, Thessalonika
EvoBus Ibérica SA, Sámano
EvoBus Italia SpA, Modena
EvoBus Nederland BV, Utrecht
EvoBus (Schweiz) AG, Zürich
EvoBus Sverige AB, Spånga
EvoBus (UK) Ltd, Coventry

Background: EvoBus GmbH was created by Daimler-
Benz in 1995 to encompass the European bus and coach
activities of both Mercedes-Benz and Setra. In the UK, the
merging of the coach and bus activities of Mercedes-Benz
UK and Setra was seen as the next logical step.
   EvoBus GmbH has five production plants: at Mannheim
and Ulm in Germany, Ligny in France, Istanbul in Turkey
and Samano in Spain. For product information see
Mercedes-Benz and Setra.

Developments: The UK bus and coach operations of
Mercedes-Benz and Setra have been combined to form
Evobus UK, based at Coventry where a new headquarters
and service centre has been built.
   The facilities at the £4 million site include a purpose-
built bus and coach workshop, able to accommodate
double-decks. It will be able to look after the full range of
Mercedes-Benz PCV products including the Vario, Vito,
Sprinter and Traveliner, as well as Setra coaches. In
addition to normal services, it will be able to carry out
body repairs, MoTs and more specialist repairs.
   In addition, there is a central parts warehouse which
combines spare parts services for both Mercedes-Benz
and Setra buses and coaches.

UPDATED

FAP-Famos

SP FAP Famos FFB-Komerc SA Beograd
PO Box 68, Francuska 61-65, 11001 Belgrade, Yugoslavia
Tel: (+381 11) 18 21 82   Fax: (+381 11) 63 69 61
President: Peter Drobnjak
General Manager: K Kijak
Export Manager: B Manojlovic
Sales Manager: Z Lucic

Factories
Chassis components and truck production: FAP, Priboj
Engines, gearboxes, clutches: Famos, Sarajevo

Buses and bus bodies: FAS 'Il Oktomvri', Skopje

Background: Links with Daimler-Benz have led to a
number of Mercedes coach models being licence-built
and German technology being adopted in other types
produced. The main FFB bus and coach production plant
is that of Fabrika ZA Autobusi in Skopje, Macedonia
(FAS), where integral vehicles are assembled from
Mercedes and FAP-Famos running units under the Sanos
name.

Products: Buses and coaches, including articulated

buses and trolleybuses. Bus and coach bodywork. CKD
kits.

Range
Sanos S115: The FAP-Sanos S115 12 m integral bus for
urban operations with pressed plywood seating for 25;
total capacity is 115. Provision is made for a seated
conductor at the rear. Wheelbase is 6.15 m, with air
suspension.
   Power is from a mid-mounted horizontal Mercedes
diesel engine.
S200ZG: The 18 m articulated version of the S115 has an

Ikarus 415 city buses on DAF chassis at Leeds airport (Andrew Jarosz) **1997**

including Russia. To counteract this, Ikarus has diversified into special bus production, tools and spare part manufacture for the automotive industry.

Ikarus has now split into two companies, Ikarus EAG (Special Coach Factory) being responsible solely for coaches and with separate shareholdings of 68 per cent by Ikarus and 32 per cent by Bayal, Turkey.

Gábor Széles bought Ikarus from ÁPV Rt, the state holding company, in 1998.

Products: Buses, coaches, minibuses, trolleybuses, railbuses, CKD kits.

Range

200 series: This bus was developed at the end of the 1960s, with 200,000 being sold by 1993. It is 9.5, 11 or 12 m long. The articulated version is 16.5 or 18 m long.
300 series: This is a luxury touring coach, either integral or body-on-chassis.
400 series: This is a city or urban bus, 11.5 m rigid or 18 m articulated, with a rear under-floor engine. A version is built on the DAF SB220LF chassis for the UK market.
405: This is a 7.3 m midibus for city work, powered by a Perkins Phaser engine, driving through a Voith Midimat gearbox.

Ikarus 415 citybus **1999**/0043488

Trolleybuses: Trolleybus versions of the 200 and 400 series are produced. A dual-mode bus, the 435TD has a diesel engine as well as electric propulsion.
411: This is a low-floor bus, with a floor height of 320 to 350 mm.

Production: Around 60 per cent of the annual production (1,807 in 1997) goes to Russia and Ukraine.

Contracts: The Indonesian government is taking 400 articulated buses, with final assembly being carried out locally.

Ikarus won the World Bank funded contract to supply 168 CKD versions of 283 articulated buses to Kurgan, Siberia. BKV Budapest bought 90 405 midibuses in 1995.

Other orders include 300 for Moscow and 200 for Volan, Hungary.

Developments: A low-floor articulated bus, the 417, was announced in 1995; it is 17.97 m long, 2.5 m wide and 2.8 m high. The total weight is 26.5 tonnes and it can carry 53 seated with 103 standing. The floor is flat throughout and the step height at all doors is 330 mm. There are no steps inside the vehicle.

It is powered by a Cummins C83-290 11 turbocharged engine, driving through a ZF 4HP590 gearbox. The articulation is by Hübner and the coachwork is in steel with anti-corrosion protection. A Webasto heater is provided and there are four roof vents/emergency exits. A Bode wheelchair lift can be fitted.

The 412 is a new low-floor 12 m bus carrying 92 (38 seated), and powered by a Mercedes-Benz OM447hLA Euro-2 engine.

UPDATED

Irizar

Irizar
E-20 216 Ormaiztegui, Guipuzcoa, Spain
Tel: (+34 943) 88 19 00   Fax: (+34 943) 88 91 01
Managing Director: Koldo Saratxaga
Part of Mondragon co-operative group

UK distributor: Scania Bus & Coach UK Ltd
Claylands Avenue, Worksop S81 7DJ
Tel: (+44 1909) 50 08 22   Fax: (+44 1909) 50 01 65
Managing Director: Don MacIntosh
Export Director: Jose Aizpuru

Products: Coach bodies.

Range
Century 1235: 12 m body with 3.5 m height, seating around 49, with washroom and air conditioning.
Century 1237: 12 m body with 3.7 m height, seating up to 57.
Intercentury: 12 m long, 3.2 m high, for intercity work, seating up to 57. It is on a MAN chassis and is for dual-purpose work.

Developments: Scania Bus & Coach has appointed two further body service and parts specialists. Flights Motor Services, Birmingham, and Scantruck Ltd, Stansted, join Buddens Commercial Services, southern England, to provide three centres in the UK.

UPDATED

Irizar Century body on Scania K113 three-axle chassis belonging to Applebys (Andrew Jarosz) **1997**

Isuzu

Isuzu Motors Limited
6-26-1 Minami-oi, Shinagawa-ku, Tokyo 140, Japan
Tel: (+81 3) 54 71 11 11   Fax: (+81 3) 54 71 10 90
President: Kazuhira Seki

Subsidiaries
In addition to those listed below, there are also subsidiaries in Indonesia, China, Egypt, Turkey and Australia

Isuzu Motors America Inc
46401 Commerce Centre Drive, Plymouth Township, Michigan 48170, USA
Tel: (+1 313) 455 75 95

Isuzu (China) Holding Co Ltd
No 1601 Beijing Fortune Building, 5 Dong San Huamg Bei-Lu, Chao Yang District, Beijing 10004, China
Tel: (+86 10) 65 01 48 30   Fax: (+86 10) 65 01 41 34

Malaysian Truck & Bus Sdn Bhd
Kawasan Perindustrian, Peramu Jaya, PO Box 3, 26607 Pekan, Pahang, Darul Makmur, Malaysia
Tel: (+60 9) 426 86 54   Fax: (+60 9) 426 98 70

Isuzu Motors Co (Thailand) Ltd
38 Poochao Saming Road, Samrong-Tai, Phra Pradeng,
Samutprakan 10130, Thailand
Tel: (+66 2) 394 25 41   Fax: (+66 2) 394 25 52

Products: Light and heavy-duty trucks and buses.
Engines, transmissions and other major chassis
components are built.

Range: Complete buses and chassis are offered in a
variety of configurations and lengths ranging from 7 to
12 m and seating 29 to 54. Isuzu-built diesel engines are
fitted.

Standard Isuzu buses have traditionally been designed
for rugged operating conditions with a heavy-duty ladder-
type frame, though more sophisticated integral city buses
are now in production.

MR series: Front engine and two variants, weighing
up to 7.2 and 8.5 tonnes. Choice of 6BD1 six-cylinder
5.79 litre or 6BG1 six-cylinder 6.5 litre engines. Seating up
to 33.

MT series: Front engine. Two versions, weighing 12.5 or
13.5 tonnes. Engine options as for MR series. Seating up
to 46.

LT series: Available with new 6HH1 six-cylinder 8.2 litre
engine in two gross vehicle weights, 13.5 and 14.5
tonnes. Seating capacity is up to 50.

CJR/CQR/CHR series: The CJR bus has a separate
chassis suited to a variety of bodywork for interurban and
tourist use. It is powered by the 6QA1/6RA1/6RB1 engine
and is for bodywork seating up to 54.

Gala GHD: Integral coach with kneeling facility, powered
by a rear-mounted 12PE1 450 kW diesel engine. Anti-lock
braking is provided; length is 11.99 m.

An emissions control system is based on a sensor
which stops the engine when it idles. When the
accelerator is depressed, the engine automatically starts
up. Isuzu reports a 10 per cent reduction in nitrogen oxide
emissions.

A permanent magnet retarder has been produced for
Isuzu buses.

Production: Isuzu has an annual output of 2,500 vehicles.

Contracts: About half the annual bus production is
exported. Markets supplied include South East Asia, the

Isuzu HiDecker **1996**

Isuzu Gala IV HD-9 sightseeing bus **1998**/0011608

Middle East and the Pacific region, with new markets
developing in South America through CKD assembly
operations in Colombia, Ecuador and Venezuela. CKD
kits of the integral buses in the range are supplied both
direct and for assembly through the worldwide

manufacturing operations of General Motors, and
versions with chassis are built clear of protuberances for
ease of installation of bodies locally.

UPDATED

Iveco

Iveco SpA Bus Division
Via Puglia 35, I-10156 Turin, Italy
Tel: (+39 011) 687 21 11   Fax: (+39 011) 273 47 59
General Manager: E Valente
Commercial Manager: V Lasalvia
Engineering Manager: M Boccenti

UK subsidiary
Iveco Bus
Iveco Ford House, Station Road, Watford WD1 1SR
Tel: (+44 1923) 24 64 00   Fax: (+44 1923) 22 63 46
Manager: Harry Chambers
Director, Light Vehicle Business Unit, UK:
Sandy Mathieson

Background: Iveco was formed in 1975 after an
agreement between Fiat SpA of Turin (with which three
vehicle manufacturers — OM, Lancia Veicoli Speciali and
Unic of France — had already joined forces) and Klöckner-
Humboldt-Deutz of Cologne (through Magirus-Deutz)
to merge their vehicle manufacturing operations.
Subsequently, KHD pulled out of the joint venture and
now the Iveco shareholding interest fully belongs to Fiat
SpA.

Iveco TurboCity-U articulated bus **1998**/0011642

In 1986 Iveco and Ford of Britain entered into a joint
venture, Iveco Ford Truck Ltd to market in the UK the
Cargo range and the complementary Iveco range of
vehicles.

In 1989 Iveco acquired the complete share capital of
Orlandi, the oldest bodybuilder in Italy, and the complete
share capital of Sicca, specialised producer of chassis for
buses and coaches.

In 1991 Iveco acquired 60 per cent share capital of the
Spanish Enasa-Pegaso Group and in 1994 bought the
remaining 40 per cent, thus consolidating its industrial
presence in the major European countries.

In addition to its 21 plants and 13 research centres in
Italy, France, Germany, UK and Spain, Iveco has 23
industrial collaborations, 14 licensees with shareholding
interests and nine licensees without shareholding
interests outside Europe. Iveco International Operations
works through its subsidiaries and industrial
manufacturing/assembly activities of buses and
chassis in China, Egypt, Ethiopia, India (Iveco owns 37.5
per cent of Ashok Leyland (qv)), Iran, Kenya, Libya,
Tunisia, Turkey, Venezuela and Vietnam. This activity is

Iveco Daily with Orlandi body **1998**/0011649

Iveco EuroMidi with Indcar body **1998**/0011646

Iveco CityClass CNG-powered   **1998**/0011643

Iveco Daily with Marshall body   **1998**/0011650

Iveco EuroClass HD   **1998**/0011645

based on supply of components and CKD sets from Iveco.

Products: Complete buses and coaches, chassis, chassis for articulated buses and trolleybuses, CKD kits. Low emission vehicles, zero emission vehicles (electric).

City range

DownTown: This is a low-floor urban bus 7 m long with front engine and a floor height of 330 mm (no step apart from initial step from road). It seats nine with 33 standing and has two doors.

The engine, complying with Euro-2, has a power of 76 kW (102 bhp); there is automatic transmission, independent suspension at front, single wheels at the rear, disc brakes and a wheelchair lift can be fitted.

CityClass: This has a low floor and is of integral construction. It is 10.8 or 12 m long and carries up to 113. There are 21 standard versions with two, three or four doors in city and suburban configuration. There are no steps at any door and the floor height is 330 mm (340 mm at the back). A kneeling mechanism lowers this to 250 mm. There is also now an articulated version.

It is powered by the Iveco 8360.41 turbocharged after-cooled water-cooled Euro-2 engine with either 164 kW or 210 kW output.

The wheelbase is 5.11 or 6.15 m and width is 2.5 m.

TurboCity 490E: This semi-integral welded steel rear-engined city bus is offered in 10.7, 12 and 18 m (articulated) lengths carrying up to 105, 115 and 165 passengers respectively in city and suburban versions. Power for both variants, the 490E.10.22 and 490E.12.22, is the same, coming from a 164 kW (220 hp) 8460.21 turbocharged Iveco Fiat water-cooled Euro-2 engine. The engine for the articulated version, the 490E.18.29, is the 8460.41, turbocharged and after-cooled, 214 kW (290 hp).

Wheelbases are 5.11, 6.15 and 5.3 + 6.63 m. The interior body floor height is 550 mm with two steps. The front section of the articulated version has a floor height of 330 mm with no step (apart from the one from the road).

Trolleybus Chassis: Chassis lengths of 10, 12 and 18 m (articulated) are available. Electrical equipment, motor and final drive are not fitted.

Rear engine chassis range

EuroRider: This is a multipurpose chassis 12 m long with a rear engine; chassis height is 700 mm. The engine is the Iveco 8460.41, complying with Euro-2. It has a mechanical or automatic gearbox. It is available with air suspension

for a normal body or for a high-deck body. It has disc brakes at the front and drum at the rear. ABS braking is fitted. It is available in 12 and 13 m lengths.

The EuroRider chassis is available in the UK for interurban bus or luxury coach bodies. Beulas (Spain) bodywork is offered for the coach version. The floor height can be as low as 650 mm at the entrance and complies with DPTAC-2 regulations. The rear-mounted engine complies with Euro-2 regulations. A Telma retarder is fitted and ZF power steering is standard. A network of 20 specialist dealers has been appointed for the EuroRider range.

EuroRider 391.12.29 This 12 m chassis is powered by the 9.5 litre Iveco 8460.41R engine mounted vertically in-line at the rear. The model is fitted as standard with the ZF S6-85 six-speed synchromesh gearbox. The ZF 5HP.600 automatic five-speed gearbox with integral retarder is available as an option. The EuroRider has full air suspension, with two air springs on the front axle and four on the rear axle.

AP 160: This is for export markets where rugged and less sophisticated bus chassis are required. It weighs 18 tonnes gross and comes in 11.3 and 12 m lengths for city and intercity service, equipped with a rear-mounted 8460.41 Euro-1 six-cylinder engine producing from 194 kW to 216 kW. The chassis is designed for high ground clearance and has reinforced ladder construction. Leaf suspension is standard though there is an air suspension option. Manual and automatic transmission is offered.

Midibuses

EuroMidi 80: Jointly developed by Iveco Bus and the AW Group with Indcar Maxim coachwork seating 29 passengers. It has a 5.9 litre direct injection six-cylinder turbocharged diesel engine mounted vertically at the

front, driving through a six-speed synchromesh gearbox to a single reduction rear axle. The EuroMidi 80 has disc brakes all round and an exhaust brake. ABS is fitted as standard on the EuroMidi chassis.

Minibuses

TurboDaily: This range includes the A 40.10 in 5.97 m length with the turbocharged 8140.27 Iveco engine and the A 45.10 and A 45.12 with a length of 6.86 m and respectively a turbocharged and turbo-intercooler engine. These models are available in service bus, private hire and touring versions. The touring version has Orlandi bodywork.

Chassis cowls for minibuses: The TurboDaily range is rounded off by the 49.10, 49.12 and 59.12 chassis cowls for bodywork, with turbo and turbo-intercooler engines, GVW from 4.7 to 6 tonnes, left- or right-hand drive, with wheelbases and dimensions for bodywork up to 7.5 m length.

DailyBus: A low-floor version of the 59.12 has been produced, bodied by Marshall, with a 650 mm floor height complying with the UK DPTAC-2 regulations for access. It is powered by the Sofim Euro-2 engine.

Daily 35.10 minibus, which has 15 seats including the driver; *DailyCoach 40.10,* with 15 passenger seats

DailyCoach 49.10, with 18 seats. All three Daily models have steel floors reinforced by box section steel to provide

Iveco battery-powered DailyBus with Camden Community Transport, London (Andrew Jarosz)
          1998/0016410

Marshall-bodied Iveco TurboDaily 59-12 of Home James, Southampton (Andrew Jarosz)   **1999**/0024991

Iveco low-floor CityClass bus of ATAC Rome at Piazza Venezia (Andrew Jarosz)   **1999**/0024990

secure anchorage for all the passenger seats. Similarly, the side walls are reinforced to provide secure side anchorage for the passenger seats. All seats are fitted with lap and diagonal belts. The new M2 Daily minibuses and DailyCoaches are built with a high roof as standard.

All three models are powered by the Iveco 2,798 cc engine. Each model is fitted as standard with a five-speed full synchromesh gearbox. All three models can be offered with the option of Iveco's new clutchless transmission. Known as Daily Free, this does away with the clutch pedal but retains the gear lever. Iveco's own tests have shown that drivers change gear up to 225 times an hour, or about 1,800 times a day, in urban conditions. The M2 Dailys are fitted with disc brakes all round. An indicator lamp on the dash warns when pad wear is approaching the time for renewal.

The Daily 35.10 minibus is only available as a complete vehicle. The DailyCoach 40.10 and DailyCoach 49.10 are available either complete from Iveco or as shells to be completed by subcontractors who meet the required standards.

Iveco Bus has worked with UK body builder Mellor Coachcraft (qv) to develop a new small coach, the *Opus*, on the DailyBus 59.12 chassis. The chassis comes with a 2.8 litre direct injection engine driving through a five-speed synchromesh gearbox with a specially low first gear for pulling away on steep inclines. Air suspension is available as an option on the rear axle. The 25-seat body is wider than panel van conversions, which allows four passenger seats across the coach, reached by a gangway with full headroom.

Zero and low emission vehicles

ElectricDaily: This retains the original structure, braking system and safety circuits of the TurboDaily range. It is powered by a 22 kW DC motor, supplied by lead acid batteries. It can reach a top speed of 55 km/h with a range of up to 60 km.

Altrobus: This system for 6 and 12 m buses is the outcome of a joint engineering project undertaken by Iveco and two research centres, Ansaldo Ricerche and Genova Ricerche. This system eliminates the range restrictions imposed by batteries thanks to an integrated system involving two energy sources (the battery plus a small, constant-speed internal combustion engine). The battery, which is kept charged by the generator, is independent, relative to time, of the vehicle drive requirements. It delivers peak power during acceleration and stores energy recovered during deceleration and braking.

Iveco is also carrying out a commercial programme based on CNG as a fuel for the CityClass. The new engine has been designed and tuned up for the best balance between efficiency and emission control.

Intercity range

EuroClass: This coach is available in two lengths: 10.6 and 12 m, normal and high-decker, and is of integral construction.

It is available in regular route and touring versions, from 45 to 57 seats. The engine is the Iveco 8460.41 complying with Euro-2, from 216 to 269 kW (290 to 375 bhp). It has a mechanical or automatic gearbox and the driveline is on a

subframe that can be quickly detached for heavy maintenance. McPherson independent suspension, air suspension and ABS electronic braking are standard. The steel frame is of Corten anti-corrosion alloy.

Air conditioning, video, cellular phone, kitchen, toilet and refrigerators are optional extras.

TopClass Orlandi: This is based on the EuroClass HD but is the most luxurious of the range. It is available in limited numbers, only for the Italian market at present and has 46 seats. It is 12 m long and is powered by the 8460.41 engine, developing 269 kW and has a manual transmission with automatic control.

Production: Total sales of chassis, buses and coaches over 4 tonnes in 1996 were 1,695 for the Italian market, 1,378 for European operators and 2,210 elsewhere.

Iveco holds 60 per cent of the Italian market and claims a 13 per cent share of the total European market. It has almost 3 per cent of the French market and 31 per cent of the mini/midi market in Germany. In France the EuroRider is being sold as a Car de Ligne vehicle for interurban and school work. Iveco reports an 11 per cent of market share in the UK in 1996.

Contracts: Assembly operations serve the important markets of China, Egypt, Ethiopia, Libya, Tunisia and Turkey, and there is a major midibus assembly operation in Iran. Other significant assembly arrangements have been made by Iveco with Mekong (Vietnam) and other export markets include Kenya and Venezuela. In India a joint venture has been established with Ashok Leyland (37.5 per cent Iveco) to develop local bus and truck production through the technical support of Iveco.

Leighton Buzzard-based Marshalls Coaches has taken delivery of eight Iveco EuroRider coaches from A W Group Leicester. The four EuroRider 391.12.35 and four 391.12.29 chassis will be used for commuter services, school contracts and tour. The four EuroRider 391.12.35 chassis have Beulas Stergo 49-seat coachwork and the four 391.12.29 chassis have Beulas Stergo 53-seat bodywork.

UPDATED

Iveco DownTown front-engined midibus   **1996**

Jelcz

Jelcz Automotive Works
Jelcz Laskowice, PL-552-21 Wroclaw, Poland
Tel: (+48 71) 380 61   Fax: (+48 71) 339 60
Exports: ul Lucka 11, Warsaw
Tel: (+48 22) 66 56 32 89
Export Manager: Ryszard Wrzesiński

Background: Buses are generally based on imported designs. Autosan (qv) and Jelcz are now part of the Zasada Group which holds an interest of 52 per cent in each, though each firm will continue to trade separately.

Zasada is also the Mercedes-Benz importer for Poland and Mercedes-Benz engines are increasingly being used by both manufacturers.

Products: Buses, trolleybus bodies.

Range

120M: Three-door 12 m city bus with rear engine. Flat windscreen, with styling similar to former Berliet models. A choice of engines includes the Polish Leyland 0.680 and the MAN DO826 LUH. The transmission is either four-speed manual (ZF licence) or automatic ZF 4HP500. A wheelchair lift can be fitted.

M121M: A low-floor bus based on the 120M.
T120: This is an intercity express coach seating 46 to 51. A bar, air conditioning and toilets can be fitted.

The integral 46-seater uses the CSRS-built ML 637-LIAZ turbocharged 257 hp engine.
M181MB: 18 m articulated bus with Mercedes-Benz engine and carrying up to 180.

Production: A total of 650, of which 404 were urban, were sold in Poland during 1996.

VERIFIED

Jonckheere

Jonckheere Bus & Coach NV
Schoolstraat 50, B-8800 Roeselare, Belgium
Tel: (+32 51) 23 26 11   Fax: (+32 51) 23 27 90
General Management: Tony Buyck, Pierre Pauwels
Technical Director: Pierre Pauwels
Commercial Director: Tony Buyck

Background: The coach-building activities of Jonckheere were taken over by Berkhof (qv) in 1995.

Range

Communo: This is a two-door city bus and the low-floor version, the Premier, has three doors, none with steps.
Transit: This is a city or intercity body, made of stainless steel. It is 11.6 m long and has two doors. The front and rear are GRP. The floor is low at the front and it can seat 39 plus about 45 standing.

It can be mounted on Scania L94, Volvo B10B and B10M chassis and on DAF SB220 chassis.
Auteuil: This is a 9 m midicoach, 3.3 m high, on MAN or Volvo chassis.

Jonckheere Pacific   **1999**/0043491

Mistral: This is a luxury coach. There are two versions, the Mistral 50 (3.5 m high) and the Mistral 70 (3.7 m high).
Modulo: Interurban coach.
Monaco: Double-deck coach.
Pacific: heavy-duty bus.

Contracts: Jonckheere secured a large order for STIB Brussels, an order for 24 articulated buses for De Lijn and a large order for a Bulgarian customer.

UPDATED

Jonckheere Premier delivered to
MVIB/STIB Brussels
1999/0043489

Jonckheere Transit bus
1999/0043490

Jubilee

Jubilee Coach Conversions
Woden Road South, Wednesbury WS10 0NQ, UK
Tel: (+44 121) 502 22 52   Fax: (+44 121) 502 22 58
Director: Michael Holland

Products: Bus and coach bodies.

Range: Bus and coach bodies are built on Ford, LDV, Mercedes-Benz, Mazda and Volkswagen running units. They include the Service-Master, a local bus body on Mercedes 609 chassis, seating up to 24. It has a wide folding door.
Pro-Tect: This has been produced with safety of schoolchildren in mind. It is based on the LDV 400 (qv) and has twin side-impact bars, heavy box section vertical pillar supports to strengthen normally weak window lines and a roof roll cage. Rear impact protection is provided by a single heavy vertical pillar in box section steel anchored from the chassis to the roof section roll cage. A third emergency escape route is provided through a US-imported roof hatch. Also from the USA are electroluminescent signs that work automatically in the dark or in an emergency. All seats have inertia lap and diagonal belts.

UPDATED

Kapena

Kapena SA
ul Grunwaldzka 12, PL-762-00 Slupsk, Poland
Tel: (+48 59) 43 88 71   Fax: (+48 59) 43 84 16

Products: Mini- and midibuses, including low-floor three- and two-door citybus and express bus.

UPDATED

Karosa

Karosa AS
PO Box 3, CZ-566 03 Vysoké Mýto, Czech Republic
Tel: (+420 468) 212 60/212 52/212 88
Fax: (+420 468) 213 86/213 39
www: www.karosa.cz
Managing Director: Stanislav Jankåu

Products: Single-deck buses, including articulated, and coaches.

Karosa C934 bus
1998/0011651

Range: Produced in association with Renault (qv), includes the *C934* for interurban use, powered by the Renault MIHR 62045 Euro-2 engine, driving through the Praga 5 P115 manual five-speed gearbox. It is 11.347 m long and 2.5 m wide, and seats 46 with 35 standing.

Other models include the *B931* three-door 12 m city bus and the *B941* articulated version.

The *LC936* express coach seats up to 49. It is 11.32 m long, 3.165 m high and is powered by a Renault MIHR 062045/A41 Euro-2 turbocharged engine.

Developments: As part of a joint development between parent company Renault VI and Karosa a multipurpose coach has been announced called Ares. It is a 12 m suburban feeder-route coach with 59 seats in a Renault-built body. Also launched is a 53 seat version of the Recreo school coach. Both are aimed at the growing suburban market and the driveline includes a Renault 224 kW (300 bhp) diesel engine and transmission by ZF. A 254 kW (340 bhp) Renault diesel is an option.

Total sales of Renault's bus and coach unit (including Karosa) were up 31.7 per cent in 1998, reaching 2,585 vehicles.

Karosa is now part of Iris.Bus.

UPDATED

Kowex

Kowex Fahrzeugtechnic GmbH
Industriegebiet, D-74232 Abstatt, Germany
Tel: (+49 7062) 54 90   Fax: (+49 7062) 95 49 29

Background: Kowex has re-entered the bus market after some years' absence.

Products: Buses and midibuses.

Range: The *Regio SL* is a midibus with 14 seats and room

for 25 standing. It is based on the Mercedes-Benz 814D and there are six different versions on offer.

A dual-purpose bus is available.

VERIFIED

Kusters

Carosserie Kusters Venlo BV
PO Box 38, NL-5900 AA Venlo, Netherlands
Tel: (+31 77) 51 70 45   Fax: (+31 77) 51 70 48
A member of the Berkhof/Jonckheere group

Background: Kusters has been in coachbuilding since 1920 and is now a member of the Berkhof/Jonckheere group.

Products: Mini and midibus bodies on Mercedes chassis seating up to 25.

VERIFIED

Kusters Speeder midibus on Mercedes-Benz Sprinter chassis
1996

Kutsenits

Kutsenits International
Siget 39-41 Industriegebiet, A-7053 Hornstein, Austria
Tel: (+43 2689) 221 60   Fax: (+43 2689) 22 16 10

Products: Small buses.

Range
City: These midibuses have a feature window at the front and the bodies are mounted on Volkswagen chassis.

Contracts: 20- and 37-passenger buses are being supplied on Volkswagen Transporter and L80 chassis through the Volkswagen dealer network in Germany.

A CNG-powered three-axle bus is available.

VERIFIED

Labh Singh Harnam Singh

Labh Singh Harnam Singh Ltd
PO Box 45569, Athi River Road Industrial Area, off Addis Ababa Road, Nairobi, Kenya
Tel: (+254 2) 54 06 36/7   Fax: (+254 2) 54 18 79
Managing Director: Gurmej S Sokhi

Products: Bus and coach bodywork.

Range: City bus bodies can be supplied on DAF front-engined chassis, seating around 30 with room for about 30 standing. The front door is behind the front axle, and the rear door is behind the rear axle. Bodies can also be supplied on ERF chassis.

Smaller bus bodies are supplied on Isuzu chassis, seating around 30, depending on specification, and bodies can also be supplied on truck chassis.

VERIFIED

Labh Singh 12 m body on ERF Trailblazer of Kenya Bus (Andrew Jarosz)   *1998*/0016411

available as an option. Seating capacities from 28 (7.7 m) to 33 (8.4 m) with up to 14 standees. Available in left- or right-hand drive.

Solo: Integral low-floor midibus range, introduced at the end of 1997 and entering full production early in 1998. The Solo is available in a choice of lengths, 8.5 or 9.2 m, with full-width body (2.5 m). Standard or fastflow doorway options.

Mercedes-Benz 900 Series engine with Allison AT545 automatic gearbox and Telma retarder. Normal entrance step height at 250 mm with optional kneeling to 180 mm. Seating capacities up to 33 (8.5 m) and up to 37 (9.2 m) with up to 26 standees. Available in left- or right-hand drive. The Solo has won the Millennium Products award by the UK Design Council.

Excel: Integral low-floor city bus range. Available in a choice of four lengths — 9.6, 10.0, 10.7 and 11.5 m — with full-width body (2.5 m). Cummins 6BT 119 kW (160 bhp) or 160 kW (215 bhp) engine with Allison B300R 'World Series' automatic transmission with integral retarder. A two-door version is also available and the vehicle can be supplied in either left- or right-hand drive. Normal entrance step height 320 mm, kneeling to 250 mm. Guide wheels can be fitted for kerb-guided operation.

Delta: City bus based on DAF SB220 underframe, 11.8 m long and 2.5 m wide, with Alusuisse alloy bodywork and available with either one, two or three doors. DAF 163 kW (218 bhp) six-cylinder turbocharged/intercooled engine and ZF four- or five-speed automatic transmission with integral retarder. Can be fitted with up to 53 seats with up to 24 standees. Normal entrance step height 320 mm, kneeling to 250 mm. Guide wheels can be fitted for kerb-guided bus operation.

Prisma: City bus based on Mercedes-Benz O405 underframe, 11.6 m long and 2.5 m wide, with Alusuisse alloy bodywork and available with either one or two doors. Mercedes-Benz 159 kW (213 bhp) six-cylinder turbocharged/intercooled engine and ZF four-speed automatic transmission with integral retarder. Can be fitted with up to 55 seats with up to 24 standees. Normal entrance step height 320 mm, kneeling to 250 mm. Guide wheels can be fitted for kerb-guided operation.

Spectra: Double-deck city bus based on DAF DB250 underframe, 10 m or 10.7 m long and 4.32 or 4.17 m high with 2.5 m body width, available with either one or two doors, with Alusuisse alloy bodywork. DAF RS 203 kW (272 bhp) six-cylinder turbocharged/intercooled engine and ZF or Voith four- or five-speed automatic transmission with integral retarder. Can be fitted with up to 80 seats plus standees. Normal entrance step height 320 mm kneeling to 250 mm.

Autobus Nouvelle 2: Midicoach based on Mercedes-Benz Vario chassis, 8.4 m long and 2.4 m wide. High-specification luxury coach capable of carrying up to 33 seated passengers (Luxury model) or up to 29 seats (Executive model). Mercedes-Benz 101 kW (136 bhp) turbocharged/intercooled engine with five-speed ZF synchromesh gearbox. Air-operated single-swing door and large luggage capacity.

Autobus Vario 24: Mini-coach conversion based on Mercedes-Benz Vario, 7.2 m long. Luxury specification mini-coach with capacity of up to 24 seated passengers. Mercedes-Benz 101 kW (136 bhp) turbocharged/intercooled engine with five-speed ZF synchromesh gearbox.

Autobus Sprinter 16: Mini-coach conversion based on Mercedes-Benz Sprinter, 6.5 m long. Luxury specification mini-coach with capacity of up to 16 seated passengers. Mercedes-Benz 76/91 kW (102/122 bhp) turbocharged/intercooled engine with five-speed overdrive synchromesh gearbox.

Optare Solera: Luxury touring coach based on Mercedes-Benz O1120L chassis, 9.2 m long and 2.5 m wide. Fitted with up to 35 high-backed reclining coach seats. Mercedes-Benz 157 kW (211 bhp) turbocharged/intercooled engine with six-speed synchromesh gearbox. Air-operated plug-type entrance door with large luggage compartment at rear plus side lockers. Options include double-glazing, air conditioning, video system, continental door, toilet and servery.

Bova Futura FLC/FHC: Integral executive coach range, 12 m long and 2.5 m wide with a choice of heights – 3.5 m (FHC) or 3.15 m (FLC). Seating up to 57 on luxury high-backed seats and each with very large luggage capacities.

Available through the Optare CoachSales Division with Cummins engine ZF five-speed automatic or six-speed manual transmission. Options include double-glazing, air conditioning, continental door, video equipment, toilet and servery.

Short wheelbase MetroRider of Warrington Borough Transport (Andrew Jarosz)　　**1999**/0024997

Optare Prisma of UK operator Black Prince in Leeds　　**1999**/0043950

Optare Spectra 76-seat low-floor bus in the livery of UK operator Wilts & Dorset Bus Company for service in Salisbury
1999/0043951

Optare Solera coach **1999**/0043953

One of two Optare low-floor Solos on Merseytravel subsidised routes in Liverpool (Andrew Jarosz)
1999/0043949

Optare International, Export Division

Offering access to Optare services and products worldwide. Complete vehicles, left- or right-hand drive, CKD kits, technology transfer and manufacturing licences are available on Optare's range of integral products.

Optare has designed buses for operation in Sri Lanka following a joint development to produce the *ColomboRider* with Ceymo Automotive (Pvt) Ltd. Optare's partners in the venture are the Sri Lankan insurance company, Ceylinco, and a Japanese trading house, the Itochu Group. The ColomboRider, capable of carrying 60 passengers, is based on a Chinese-built chassis from Chaoyong Diesel, Yangzhou.

The vehicle is 10 m long, has a welded-steel frame and combines features from the Optare MetroRider and Delta bodies.

Other international activities include sales in Malaysia, a joint venture in Malta, and a strategic alliance with Austral Pacific Group, part of the Clifford Corporation, in New Zealand and Australia.

UniTec AfterSales Division

Provides spare parts and service support for all Optare Group products, both domestic and overseas, together with a range of other buses and coaches. Technical documentation, accident damage repairs and vehicle maintenance at its new service centre. In-service problem solving and product training facilities. Customer support is available through the UniTec network of 26 dealers in the UK.

Production

Total group registrations for 1998 were set to reach around 550 vehicles in the UK. In the region of 3,000 MetroRiders had been delivered towards the end of 1998 mainly in the UK but increasing numbers are being exported to worldwide operators. In excess of 300 Solo vehicles had been ordered towards the end of 1998. Particular successes are evident in the integral vehicle sector, with Excel and Solo sales substantially exceeding expected demand. The AutoBus Nouvelle 2 has seen an increased level of interest following the introduction of the restyled model and the Optare Solera has almost doubled initial sales targets.

Buy by wire has been pioneered by Optare CoachSales, the newly formed organisation to sell all of Optare Group's coach products. It can be viewed on Optare's website (qv).

Contracts

Significant orders from Travel West Midlands, Trent Buses, Blackpool Transport, The Go-Ahead Group, Reading Buses and Wilts & Dorset Bus Company have been secured for 1998/1999. The current order book for the UK bus market now exceeds 400 vehicles.

UPDATED

Optare ColomboRider built in Sri Lanka for Far East market **1998**/0016424

Optare Excel low-floor bus on UK city Ipswich's Park & Ride service **1999**/0043955

Orion

Orion Bus Industries Ltd
350 Hazelhurst Road, Mississauga, Ontario L5J 2Z9, Canada
Tel: (+1 905) 403 11 11/78 32   Fax: (+1 905) 403 88 00
Chief Operating Officer: T J Peabody
Vice President, Marketing & Sales: Gordon A Nevison
Director, Corporate & Government Affairs:
   Louis H Parsons

American subsidiary
Base Road, RD-1, Oriskany, New York 13424, USA

Orion VI low-floor hybrid bus
1998/0011685

Orion II low-floor bus **1998**/0011686

Background: Established in 1995 when Western Star Truck Holdings of Kelowna, British Columbia, bought certain assets of Ontario Bus Industries Ltd and Bus Industries of America Inc.

Products: Single-deck complete buses and specialist vehicles powered by clean diesel, CNG or hybrid electric/diesel.

Range
Orion V: An integral heavy-duty vehicle in 9.1 m, 10.6 m and 12.2 m lengths tailored to transit bus, coach or airport shuttle requirements; width is 2.4 or 2.6 m.

The Orion transit bus versions for urban and suburban duties can seat up to 47 plus 34 standees. Axles are from Rockwell and basic power plant is the Detroit Diesel Series 50 205 kW (275 hp) engine with Allison B400R four-speed automatic transmission. Optional engines include the Detroit Diesel Series 40 and Cummins ISM and ISC series. Optional transmissions are available from ZF and Voith. Front suspension kneeling and wheelchair lift can be incorporated and air conditioning can be specified.
Orion CNG: A version of Orion V, powered by CNG.
Orion II: A small heavy-duty low-profile front-wheel-drive bus in 6.4 m and 7.6 m lengths and 2.4 m wide. It features a detachable 'power train module' with the engine, transmission, cooling system, front-wheel-drive assembly, suspension and steering all removable as a unit from the main body structure. The wheel bearings and brake system components on all four axles are interchangeable.

Orion V diesel bus **1998**/0011684

The design is intended for full transit operations, with easy access for disabled and wheelchair passengers by electric ramps. Engine options include the Cummins ISB 5.9 litre diesel engine with catalytic converter providing 131 kW (175 hp) and the Cummins ISB CNG version rated at 145 kW. Transmission is the Allison Automatic AT545.

Floor height throughout the passenger compartment is 305 mm. The front suspension kneeling feature is standard, with the floor height at the front reduced to 203 mm. An optional rear kneeling capability lowers the rear door to within 101 mm of the ground. Integral swing-out ramps are provided for both doors.

The 6.4 m version of the Orion II is designed to carry up to 18 ordinary seated passengers or seven wheelchairs, and the 7.6 m version will take 24 passengers or nine in wheelchairs.
Orion VI: Hybrid electric low-floor bus with either diesel or CNG power options. It has a step height of 353 mm and a very low floor with no steps from front to rear. An integral front ramp helps boarding by wheelchair passengers. It is

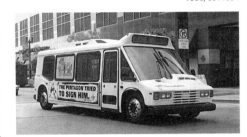

6.4 m Orion II of Long Beach Transit **1998**/0016425

diesel-powered. The electric version is powered by motors on the rear wheels.

CNG tanks for the Orion V, VI and II bus models are supplied by SCI. All buses are designed to have the tanks roof-mounted.

UPDATED

PAZ

Pavlovo Autobusnij Zavid
Pavlovsk, Russia
Exports: c/o Avtoexport
14 Volkhonka, 119902 Moscow
Tel: (+7 095) 202 85 35/83 37
Avtokron President: Boris Kaminsky

Background: PAZ is part of the Avtokron bus manufacturing group, Golizynow, Moscow, the country's largest bus manufacturer. Avtokron builds Mercedes vehicles under licence. Bus production started in 1950.

Products: Buses.

Range
PAZ-672V: The 7.15 m PAZ-672V 3.6 m wheelbase bus is 2.44 m wide and suited for narrow city streets and mountain roads. Observation windows can be fitted in the roof to suit the vehicle for tourist use. The bus can carry up to 46 with 24 seated, and has a V-8 four-stroke front-mounted petrol engine giving 85 kW (115 hp), with a mechanical four-speed gearbox.

Production: 8,681 vehicles were produced in 1997.

Contracts: PAZ minibuses are extensively used throughout the former Soviet Union for both urban bus and other collective transport duties. Examples are also operating in Havana, Cuba.

Developments: PAZ has developed larger buses to fill the space created by the collapse of Liaz, including the 4223 10 m and 5220 11.9 m models, with Cummins B and C-series engines respectively.

UPDATED

Peugeot

Automobiles Peugeot
PO Box 0116, 75 avenue de la Grande Armée, F-75761 Paris Cedex 16, France
Tel: (+33 1) 40 66 55 11   Fax: (+33 1) 45 62 70 20

Subsidiary company
Peugeot Motor Co PLC
PO Box 227, Coventry CV3 1LT, UK
Tel: (+44 1203) 88 40 00   Fax: (+44 1203) 88 40 01
LCV Product Marketing: George Coles

Peugeot Motor Co PLC is a subsidiary of PSA Group, France. The full range of minibuses are converted in the UK and marketed through the Peugeot dealer network.

Products: Mini- and midibus chassis, engines and gearboxes.

Peugeot Boxer minibus on bus service in Dobrich, Bulgaria (Norman Griffiths)
1999/0043960

Range

Chassis and chassis cabs from the Peugeot range of vans and light trucks, suitable as the basis of mini- and midibuses with specialist bodywork, are produced by Durisotti amongst others.

SEVEL (Société Européenne des Véhicules Légères), which builds the Ducato for Peugeot, also builds for Peugeot.

Boxer Minibus: Based on the short-wheelbase Peugeot Boxer, this model has a side opening door and seats 12 including driver. All forward-facing seats with three-point seat belts.

Available with 1.9 litre diesel engine. Power steering is standard.

UPDATED

Plaxton

Plaxton Coach & Bus
Subsidiary of Henlys plc
Eastfield, Scarborough YO11 3BY, UK
Tel: (+44 1723) 58 15 00   Fax: (+44 1723) 58 13 28
Managing Director: Neil Beresford
Sales & Marketing Director: David Quainton
Export Manager: Kevin Taylor
Sales Manager: Kevin Wood

Background: Plaxton's parent company Henlys acquired UK bodybuilder Northern Counties (now Plaxton Wigan) in 1995.

In a joint venture between Henlys UK and Volvo, Prévost (qv) was acquired in 1996 to enable Plaxton to penetrate the North American market. NovaBUS was added in 1997. Henlys will also acquire from Volvo a 35 per cent shareholding in MASA Mexico, after Volvo has restructured MASA. Volvo bought a 10 per cent share in Henlys in 1998.

Products: Coach and bus bodies.

Range

Pointer 2: Built on an aluminium frame and magnagrip riveted, the Pointer is available on chassis including the low-floor Dennis Dart SLF.

Seating capacities vary from 25 to 46, with space for 19 standing. Features for disabled (DPTAC in UK) include a 250 mm first entrance step and 1.28 m front door aperture.

Super Pointer Dart: Developed from the 11.3 m Dart SLF chassis jointly by Dennis and Plaxton. It is the largest bus possible without adopting full-size wheels and has a total seating capacity of 41 with up to 23 standing. Gasket or bonded glazing is available. The 24-seat capacity in the front flat-floor section is possible by retaining the standard Dart SLF wheels with low-profile tyres.

Beaver 2: This minibus body is on the air-suspension Mercedes-Benz Vario O814D chassis and has been styled by Ogle and built at Plaxton's Small Bus division at Anston, England. The standard door aperture is 930 mm with an optional 1,290 mm width. This body has lower entrance steps to meet UK DPTAC regulations. The first step is 250 mm high, followed by two 200 mm-high steps. The entrance width is 700 mm.

Premiere and *Excalibur:* These coach bodies have been designed to meet ECE R66 roll-over requirements.

The seating has been designed to meet ECE R80, ensuring passenger safety by setting standards of energy absorption. Inertia-reel seat belts and anchorages, where fitted, meet the loading requirements set by ECE R14.

Premiere and Excalibur are offered with a range of specifications and can be mounted on many chassis.

Prestige: Aluminium-construction low-floor single-deck urban bus body for the European market including the UK, seating 33 to 53 with 24 standing. Dual door can be specified. Available on Scania L113CRL, Dennis and Lance, Volvo B10M, B10B and B7 chassis.

First Eastern National Plaxton Super Pointer Dart on service in Colchester, UK   **1999**/0043957

Pointer 2 body on Dennis Dart SLF chassis belonging to Metroline Travel, London   **1999**/0043956

Bluebird Plaxton Beaver 2 body on Mercedes-Benz Vario chassis running on Manchester city centre service   **1999**/0043958

Prima B7R coach bodied by Plaxton and with Volvo chassis   **1998**/0011693

Developments: Setra models are now grouped into three classes, TopClass, ComfortClass and MultiClass. The last includes all interurban and low-floor models.

Setra has announced an extra-long low-floor bus designed for regional bus operation – the *S319NF*. The low-floor version follows on from the original S319UL. It has 55 seats (plus two folding seats in the pram/stroller area) and a total passenger-carrying capacity of 126.

Demand for the new model has come from Germany and other major European markets such as Scandinavia and Spain.

It has a rear-mounted Daimler-Benz OM447hLA turbocharged engine producing 220 kW (299 bhp) and is equipped with a catalytic converter and ZF Type 5HP590 automatic transmission. Despite its 14.47 m, the S319NF has a turning circle of 23.5 m, a front overhang of 2.6 m and features the Setra RAS rear-axle steering system.

UPDATED   *Setra S315NF low-floor bus*   **1996**

Shahab

Shahab Khodro
Iran

Background: This is Iran's second biggest bus builder, producing 1,500 buses annually.

Products: Assembles 11 m and 12 m touring coach chassis by Renault, Iveco and Mercedes-Benz.

Contracts: Bus bodies have been supplied to Ashgabat, Turkmenistan, on TAM chassis.

VERIFIED

Shanghai

Shanghai Bus & Coach Plant
535 Xiang Yang Road South, 200031 Shanghai, People's Republic of China
Tel: (+86 21) 437 00 25   Fax: (+86 21) 437 11 28
Director: Xie Cheng-Xiang
Chief Engineer: Xu Wang Xi

Background: This is one of China's biggest bus builders with an annual production of 4,000. It is a subsidiary of SAIC (see Chinese bus manufacturers). Bus body building started in 1945.

Model numbers are prefixed SK — S for Shanghai and K for Bus & Coach Plant.

Products: Buses and trolleybuses.

Range includes:
SK6601: Minibus, 6 m long.
SK6942: Midibus, 9.42 m long.
SK6972: Midibus, 9.72 m long.
SK6113: Bus, 11.3 m long.
SK6173: This is an articulated bus, 17.3 m long.
SK562: Articulated trolleybus.

VERIFIED   *Shanghai SK562 articulated trolleybus*   **1996**

Sitcar

Sitcar SpA
Via Copernico 41, I-41041 Casinale di Formigine, Modena, Italy
Tel: (+39 059) 57 33 63   Fax: (+39 059) 57 33 61
www: www.sitcar.com

General Director: Zanasi Guiseppe
Commercial Manager: Dr Rudolph Vallet

Products: Bus bodywork and van conversions.

UPDATED

Sitcar minibus based on Mercedes-Benz 412DF, seating 16
1998/0011726

Škoda

Škoda Ostrov sro
Dolní Žd'ár 43, CZ-363 29 Ostrov, Czech Republic
Tel: (+420 164) 61 21 45   Fax: (+420 164) 61 26 41
Managing Director: Jiří Juránek
Vice President, Commerce: Petr Kasenčák

Background: Škoda is a subsidiary of Škoda AS, Plzeň Concern which has, *inter alia*, a 43 per cent stake in Tatra, the Czech Republic's biggest heavy truck maker.

Products: Trolleybuses, including articulated, for 600/

700 V DC; diesel buses. Service and maintenance, implementation of complete systems.

Range
22Tr: Articulated low-floor trolleybus 17.8 m long and 2.5 m wide. The three-axle bus carries 140 with 40 seated. The floor height is 360 mm, 560 mm at the back. There is a 160 V auxiliary accumulator drive.
21Tr: Rigid version of 22Tr.

Škoda 21aB bus
1999/0043966

21Ab is a low-floor three-door diesel bus, similar to the 21Tr bus. It is powered by a MAN D0826LOH Euro-2 diesel engine.

14TrM: The 11.3 m long, 5.42 m wheelbase incorporates thyristor control for starting and braking. The stepless electric drive is designed to achieve a smooth start with constant acceleration until full power and the control system provides for smooth deceleration with the constant braking torque ranging from 60 km/h to 10 km/h and full stop by use of the air brake. A series four-pole traction motor is self-ventilating. Continuous rated output is 100 kW, current start limitation of 260 A or 320 A according to route characteristics, and rated speed 1,540 rev/min. The 14TrM has an alkaline storage battery to power 24 V circuits for lighting and control functions.

Total capacity can be up to 100. Top speed is 65 km/h.
15TrM: 17.7 m long, articulated, with turning circles meeting international regulations. Total passenger capacity is 153 (44 seats) producing a 10,300 kg payload for a kerb weight of 15,800 kg, though a maximum occupancy from the space available is put at 170. Two 100 kW motors power the middle and rear axles. An optional back-up battery pack for off-wire operation up to 2 km, on flat ground, can be supplied.

Škoda articulated 22Tr trolleybus   *1999*/0043967

Škoda 21Tr trolleybus   *1999*/0043968

Contracts: Dayton, USA, ordered 57 trolleybuses based on the 14Tr with final assembly by AAI of Baltimore. The vehicles are equipped with wheelchair lifts.

Forty trolleybuses have been supplied to Lithuania.

A joint venture between Škoda and Bharat (qv) has been set up for the production of trolleybuses. The city of Tirupati has ordered 120.

Trolleybuses are also being supplied to San Francisco, which is taking 220 14Tr and 30 15Tr models, as part of a joint venture with AAI and Škoda. Delivery started in 1998 and is expected to be complete by the end of 1999.

A tender for the World Bank has been made for the supply of 38 complete buses for a joint venture of Škoda and VMZ in Russia.

Another tender for the World Bank is for Latvia, for the supply of 26 14TrM buses and four 15TrM buses. A tender for the supply of five 14TrM buses direct from Škoda has been made.

Almaty, Kazakhstan, is taking 30 21Tr trolleybuses.

Developments: Include a low-floor trolleybus with AC drive, a bus on the chassis of a 14TrM trolleybus and an articulated bus designated 22Ab.

UPDATED

Spartan

Spartan Motors Inc
PO Box 440, 1000 Reynolds Road, Charlotte, Michigan 48813, USA
Tel: (+1 517) 543 64 00   Fax: (+1 517) 543 77 28
President: John Sztykiel
Director of Export & Specialty Sales: Edward Hendler
Director of Bus Sales: David Gruber

Background: Spartan is the equity holder in bus manufacturer Carpenter Manufacturing (qv) and owns three fire apparatus companies (Spartan Apparatus Group). Spartan Bus Australia imports a range of chassis for bodying in Australia and New Zealand.

Products: Custom designed and built chassis for buses, fire appliances, coaches, motor homes and specialist applications.

Range: Front- and rear-engined ladder-frame chassis in various formats. The chassis are available in various lengths with a range of GVWs, and feature air brakes, leaf spring or air suspension and diesel or natural gas power; automatic transmissions.

The Spartan single-deck chassis is being imported from the USA for bodying by East Lancs (qv). It is powered by a rear-mounted Cummins B-series engine driving through an Allison MTB643 gearbox. Suspension is full air and the brakes are S-cam drum.

Two- and three-axle coach chassis for semi-integral or bolt-on bodywork have been introduced. A CNG-powered bus chassis is now available. Chassis for electric or diesel replica trolley car operation are now offered.

UPDATED

Spartan three-axle chassis with coach bodywork
1998/0011729

East Lancs bodied Spartan chassis with Yorkshire Traction, UK (Andrew Jarosz)   *1999*/0024996

Spijkstaal

Spijkstaal Elektro BV
PO Box 9, NL-3200 AA Spijkenisse, Netherlands
Tel: (+31 101) 61 22 66   Fax: (+31 101) 62 39 58
Managing Director: Ing W Heijboer

Works: Zilstraat 9, 3201 CX Spijkenisse

Products: Electric vehicles.

Range
Ecobus: This seats 32 passengers. It has a range of 70 km
and a battery change takes 3 min. It is 6.7 m long, 2 m
wide and 2.6 m high. Empty weight, including batteries, is
4.3 tonnes and the floor height is 340 mm. The motor is
rated at 25 kW at 96 V. The battery pack is 96 V, 376 Ah.
Caravelle: This is a microbus version, based on a
Volkswagen van, seating 8, and has nickel-cadmium
batteries, a 60 kW motor and a top speed of 100 km/h.
Battery recharging takes one hour.

VERIFIED   *Spijkstaal low-floor electric Ecobus*   **1996**

STIA

Société Tunisienne des Industries Automobiles
Sousse, Tunisia

Background: Independent bus building by STIA started
using designs developed by Van Hool (qv) and previously
built under licence. Before independent production, Van
Hool had been a major supplier of bodywork in semi-
finished form for completion by STIA on locally
assembled Fiat chassis, having helped the company set
up bus manufacture to add to its Peugeot commercial
vehicle production line.

Renault VI (qv) has links with a number of overseas
commercial vehicle manufacturing and assembly
operations including STIA, which it helped establish in its
present form.

VERIFIED

SYNRI

SYNRI
Pyongyang, Democratic People's Republic of Korea

Background: Little information is available about bus
production in North Korea, but locally built midibuses and
trolleybuses are depicted in official photographs as being
produced at a factory somewhere near the city of
Pyongyang. The factory is believed to be part of the
national vehicle-building company SYNRI.

Products: Buses and trolleybuses.

VERIFIED

Tata

Tata Engineering & Locomotive Co Ltd (TELCO)
Bombay House 24, Homi Mody St, Fort, Bombay 400001,
India
Tel: (+91 22) 204 91 31   Fax: (+91 22) 204 54 74
Chairman: Ratan N Tata
Executive Director, Corporate Affairs: F K Kavarana
Executive Director, Automobiles: V M Raval
Executive Director, Construction Equipment: A S Rangan

Export Division
Block A, Shivsagar Estates, Dr Annie Besant Road, Worli,
Bombay 400018
Tel: (+91 22) 493 85 66   Fax: (+91 22) 495 03 76

Works: Jamshedpur, Lucknow and Poona

Assembly operation: Bangladesh

Background: The Tata Group is one of India's largest
industrial companies, with interests in iron and steel,
engineering, chemicals, commercial vehicles and other
areas. In terms of sales, Tata Engineering & Locomotive is
the largest company in the group and produced 150,000
medium, light, heavy and utility commercial passenger
vehicles in financial year 1997. It also manufactures
components and mining/earthmoving equipment.

Products: Buses and coaches; bus and coach chassis.

Left-hand-drive Tata two-door midibus   **1999**/0043976

Range: A variety of single-deck buses is produced in
rugged designs suited to conditions in the Indian
subcontinent and other developing countries. Vehicles
are available in left- and right-hand drive form, full forward
control, semi-forward control and semi-semi-forward
control, and with front and rear engines, and include
urban bus, coach and mid-sized vehicles.

Developments: Telco has collaborated with Cummins
Ltd, USA, to manufacture the Cummins range of engines
for buses and coaches. The expanding range of
Cummins-powered vehicles is now added to Telco's
range.

UPDATED

Tecnobus

Tecnobus
Loc. Mola dei Frati, I-03100 Frosinone, Italy
Tel: (+39 0775) 29 18 03   Fax: (+39 0775) 29 41 36
Managing Director: Ing Guiseppe Panza

Products: Gulliver battery electric minibus, 5 m in length and powered from a 72 V battery set. Range is 100 km on a single charge and the batteries can be replaced in three minutes. It carries 26 passengers (eight seated) and has a floor height of 330 mm.

Contracts: In the UK Tecnobuses are running in Liverpool and Bristol.

UPDATED

Gulliver battery electric minibus operated by Crosville on a supported route in Birkenhead, Merseyside, UK (Andrew Jarosz)
1999/0051917

Temsa

Temsa AS
Büyük Istanbul Otogari, TR-34200, Bayrampasa, Istanbul, Turkey
Tel: (+90 212) 658 26 60   Fax: (+90 212) 658 36 21
e-mail: steveaj@temsa.com.tr
Director: Haluk Dinçer
Export Manager: Steve Angel-Jones

Manufacturing facility: Adana, Turkey

Background: Temsa is part of the Sabanci Group. It is one of the largest manufacturers of coaches in Turkey, has a large share of the local Turkish market and has a sizeable export market. All Temsa products are based on Mitsubishi or MAN power trains. Temsa manufactures the chassis and bodies.

Products: Bus and coach chassis and bodies.

Range: Includes basic city 31-seat midibus and high-deck 46-seat coach with toilet and full accessories.

Developments: Future products will include a low-floor midibus for urban use.

NEW ENTRY

TFM

TFM Industries (Pty) Ltd
Bus and Coach Division
PO Box 8717, Centurion 0046, South Africa
Tel: (+27 11) 316 20 70   Fax: (+27 11) 316 32 00
e-mail: rayk@tfm.co.za
Managing Director: Ray Karshagen

Works: 6 Hammer Road, Clayville Ext 8, Gauteng 1665

Products: Bus and coach bodies.

Range
Pathfinder: Bus for urban and commuter use.
Explorer: Bus for urban or commuter use, exclusively designed for MAN front-engined chassis utilising F2000 truck cab components.
Apollo: Express/touring coach for front or rear-engine chassis available in semi-luxury to full luxury specification.

Contracts: Pathfinder buses have been supplied to Mozambique, Explorer buses to Durban Transport and Apollo coaches have been supplied to Mozambique and Zimbabwe.

Developments: To tap the South African bus market still further, MAN Nutzfahrzeuge has taken over the Bus and Coach division of TFM. The new MAN Bus and Coach is 100 per cent owed by MAN and production of up to 200 complete buses, mainly in the 12 m class, in a year is envisaged in the initial phase.

UPDATED

Thomas

Thomas Built Buses Inc
PO Box 2450, High Point, North Carolina 27261, USA
Tel: (+1 336) 889 48 71   Fax: (+1 336) 889 25 89
Vice President, Domestic Sales: Bob Price
Commercial Sales Manager: Curt Kiser

Bus manufacturing subsidiaries
Thomas Built Buses of Canada Ltd
PO Box 580, Woodstock, Ontario N4S 7Z5, Canada
Tel: (+1 519) 539 12 26   Fax: (+1 519) 539 14 97

Thomas Built Buses de Mexico SA de CV
Avenue A 100 Franc, Industrial Almacentro, Apodaca, NL CP Mexico
Tel: (+52 8) 369 39 69   Fax: (+52 8) 369 39 70

Products: Buses, bus bodies, bus chassis, including minibus.

Range: Though a producer of chassis and semi-integral vehicles, Thomas specialises in rugged bus bodies for school and developing countries' needs. Minibus bodywork is also offered. Options include air conditioning. Wheelchair lifts, air suspension and custom seating can be specified.

Thomas TL 960 rear-engine bus
1998/0011732

Thomas TL 960: Rear-engine coach or city bus, 2.4 m wide and with 1.98 m headroom. It seats 28 to 45 and engine options include the Caterpillar 3126 diesel, Cummins 6C or CNG versions. Allison World Series automatic transmission can be specified.

Developments: Freightliner, which is owned by Daimler-Benz, bought Thomas at the end of 1998.

UPDATED

Tomassini Style

Tomassini Style
Via dell'Industria 1, I-6065 Passignano sul Trasimeno, Italy
Tel: (+39 075) 82 92 45   Fax: (+39 075) 82 92 46

Background: The company was set up by Agenore Tomassini in 1964 and it moved to its present location in 1972.

Products: Urban buses and shuttle vehicles, including VIP minibus shuttles.

VERIFIED

Tomassini Style Urban minibus
1998/0011733

Toyota

Toyota Motor Corporation
1, Toyota-cho, Toyota-shi, Aichi Pref 471, Japan
International Public Affairs Division
No 4-18, Koraku 1-chome, Bunkyo-ku, Tokyo 112, Japan
Tel: (+81 3) 38 17 71 11   Fax: (+81 3) 38 17 90 17

Main minibus production plant: Honshu

Overseas minibus assembly operations: Indonesia, Malaysia, New Zealand, Trinidad, South Africa, Portugal

Toyota (GB) Ltd, The Quadrangle, Redhill RH1 1PX, England
Tel: (+44 1737) 78 53 20   Fax: (+44 1737) 76 08 70
Sales Director: S Prime

Toyota España SL, Madrid

Background: Toyota is a major car and light van builder and also produces purpose-designed minibus chassis and bodied vehicles.

Products: Mini- and midibuses.

Range
Coaster: The front-engined purpose-built Coaster midibus chassis has a 3.12 m wheelbase and is available in left-or right-hand drive format with a range of Toyota-built bodies up to 6.2 m overall length, or as a chassis for outside bodying. Seating can be provided for up to 26 in the standard model or for 22 in luxury versions, and in

Toyota Optimo IV chassis with 26-seat Caetano body

1998/0011734

high-capacity school bus and wheelchair lift-equipped models.
Optimo IV: This is a Caetano (qv) coach body on a Coaster chassis, seating up to 26. It has the Toyota 15B-FT four-cylinder turbocharged engine meeting Euro-2 regulations and producing 100 kW, driving through a five-speed manual gearbox.
New Hiace: Now has advanced styling and the engine has been moved forward but rear wheel drive is retained. It is 1.45 m longer (4.715 m), 110 mm wider (1.8 m) and 210 mm higher (1.95 m) than the previous short

wheelbase model. The 6/9 Van option seats eight plus driver.

Contracts: With minibus assembly operations in six countries and direct overseas sales, the vast majority of production is exported. Toyota minibuses are widely used for paratransit operations in Southeast Asia, Africa and the Caribbean, including Barbados, Trinidad and Jamaica.

VERIFIED

Trolza

Trollejbusny Zavod JSC
413105 Engels City, Saratov Region, Russia
Tel: (+7 845) 119 13 01   Fax: (+7 845) 116 39 45
Director General: Nikolaj Poluliakh
Sales Manager: Valerij Ageev
Technical Director: Alexander Plykin
General Designer: Sergey Kloutcharev

Background: This used to be the world's largest trolleybus manufacturer, formerly known as Uritsky. Production began in 1950 of the MTB-82, this being replaced in 1961 by the ZIU5, and in 1970 by the ZIU9, which was in production until 1992. Currently in production is the Trolza 52642, formerly the ZIU682G. Construction of articulated vehicles started in 1986.

Products: Trolleybuses, bodyshells.

Range
Trolza 52642: This is the principal model of the ZIU family. The body is of stainless steel construction, with steel sheet panelling. Traction equipment for all models comes from Dynamo (qv), Moscow. Power supply is taken at 550 V to 600 V supplying a DK-213 electric motor rated at 115 kW. Independent movement from a battery set of 12 providing 72 V and a capacity of 140 A/h is optional. These provide an off-wire capability of some 5 km at full power. Several interior layouts are available, with seating for up to 27 and a total capacity of 116. This trolleybus has chopper control.
Trolza 6205: This is a high-capacity articulated version of the 52642, of which over 600 are in service in Russian

Trolza 6020 passenger unit with AMO ZIL tractor

1996

cities. Total capacity is 166, with 46 seated. Power comes from a DK-211BM traction motor with thyristor control. A rheostatic-contactor-controlled version is available, along with a battery emergency supply.
Trolza 6206: Similar to the 6205 but has a low-floor body/chassis and different layout of electrical equipment. It has been developed jointly with Siemens (qv) and has five doors. It is being delivered to Moscow, St Petersburg and Saratov.
Trolza 6020: Passenger body, drawn by AMO ZIL B44210 tractor unit, carrying 100 on urban and suburban routes.

Contracts: Buses are operated by undertakings in Moscow, St Petersburg, Yekaterinburg, Tashkent, Varna, Samara, Volvograd, Almaty, Ashgabat, Mendoza and Budapest. Orders have come from Rostov, Saransk, Nizhny Novgorod and Saratov.

Production: Total annual output was around 2,600 but is now around 330.

VERIFIED

Trolza 6206 articulated trolleybus   1998/0011736

Trolza 52642 trolleybus   1998/0011735

Turtle Top

Turtle Top Inc
Terra Transit Division
67819 State Road 15, New Paris, Indiana 46553, USA
Tel: (+1 219) 831 43 40   Fax: (+1 219) 831 43 49
Vice President: Richard D Cripe
Operations Manager: Dan Daniels

Products: Mini- and midibus bodies.

Background: Turtle Top has been producing vehicles since 1962.

Range

Terra Transit Bus: This has seating capacity for 16 to 29, with a 736 mm wide entrance. Various floor layouts are available, from 12 seats plus two wheelchair passengers to 29 seats. Perimeter seating can also be specified. The 29-seat vehicle has a second rear axle, is 8.56 m long and is now available on a Chevrolet chassis.
Terra Transit II Van: Available on the Ford Supervan chassis in two versions — a disabled-transport model with single bus-style front door and a wheelchair door directly

Turtle Top Terra Transit Bus with wheelchair lift

1997

behind, and a shuttle bus with single or double leaf bus-style door. Up to 14 seats and four wheelchair spaces can be specified.
Econo Transporter: Minibus seating up to 15. Available as

luxury version, seating 9. Luggage compartment and air conditioning can be specified.

VERIFIED

Van Hool

Van Hool NV
Bernard Van Hoolstraat 58, B-2500 Lier-Koningshooikt, Belgium
Tel: (+32 3) 420 20 20   Fax: (+32 3) 482 30 68
Chairman: Alfons Van Hool
Sales Director: Paul Van Hool
Public Relations Manager: Yves Goffin

Background: Van Hool NV was founded in 1947 and is one of the largest independent manufacturers of integral buses and coaches in Western Europe. Over 1,500 buses and coaches are produced each year. Van Hool also builds semi-trailers, trailers and tank containers.

Products: Integral city and intercity buses (standard, midi, articulated, double articulated (three-section) and CNG/LPG/hybrid/trolleybuses). Integral coaches (conventional, high-deck, articulated and double-deck). Bus and coach bodies. Integral airport apron buses.

Range

100 per cent low-floor buses
Van Hool's 100 per cent low-floor concept, launched in 1991, is based on a mid-mounted engine fitted sideways and vertically between the axles, ensuring a stepless low floor throughout the entire vehicle length. This low floor, combined with large platforms, double doors and a boarding height of only 320 mm, gives easy access at all doors. The concept is available in five versions:
A300: 12 m long with three double doors. Maximum passenger capacity is 110 and various interior arrangements are possible.
A308: Two doors and 9.4 m long and carrying up to 63.
AG300: The articulated version of the low-floor A300, with four double doors. It is 17.98 m long and carries up to 160.

AGG300: The AGG300 is a double-articulated three-section bus 24 m long and works on the puller principle with side-mounted engine and driveline in the tractor part. It has five double doors. Maximum passenger capacity is 180.
A330: See Developments below.

This 100 per cent low-floor range is also available with alternative fuels and drive systems. The additional components such as gas tanks, traction batteries and

Van Hool AGG300 low-floor double-articulated bus

1999/0043981

power electronics, are integrated in the roof structure and do not compromise the low-floor concept.
Available are:
The CNG-powered *A300 CNG* (12 m), *A320 CNG* (12 m), *A308 CNG* (midibus) and *AG300 CNG* (articulated bus).
The LPG-powered *A300 LPG* (12 m), *A308 LPG* (midibus) and *AG300 LPG* (articulated bus).
The articulated trolleybus *AG300T*, available in two versions: one with a diesel auxiliary group and one dual-mode version. A 12 m trolleybus *A300T* is in production (see Developments).
The hybrid midibus *A308 HYB*, powered by either a set of batteries or a diesel generator, powering the electric motor or batteries. In this way, the bus can run without exhaust emissions on batteries only, when in the city centre. When outside, the diesel generator is switched on.

Low-floor buses
A320 retains the stepless floor, as in the A300, with a slightly sloping floor behind the second entrance. It has an offset rear-mounted underfloor engine. It has a large passenger capacity of 110, combined with a large number of seats. Available with two or three doors.
A360: A low-floor rear-mounted underfloor engine two-door bus with a low floor forward of the rear axle. The rear section is for seating and the vehicle is designed for urban and suburban transport.

Medium low-floor buses
A500: Launched in 1985, this was the predecessor of the A300. It is a 12 m city bus with a completely flat floor at 500 mm above ground and has three double doors. It carries up to 113.
A508: Based on the A500, this midibus is 8.94 m long, has two double doors and carries up to 70.

Van Hool A300 100 per cent low-floor bus

1999/0043987

Van Hool AG300T 100 per cent low-floor trolleybus

1999/0043991

Van Hool AG300 CNG articulated 100 per cent low-floor bus　*1999*/0043986

Van Hool A308HYB 100 per cent low-floor hybrid midibus　*1999*/0043989

AG700/AG500: Articulated bus based on the A500, 17.69 m long, and carrying up to 140.

A600: This is a city bus, with rear engine, 11.64 m long and carrying 112. It has two double doors.

Airport buses

The range includes apron buses up to 16.24 m long and 3.75 m wide, with up to six entrances and passenger capacities up to 200. Van Hool also offers crew coaches, shuttle buses and VIP coaches for airport use.

Coaches

The integral T9 coach range consists of the *T915 Alicron,* the high-deck *T915 Acron,* the 13.7 m *T917 Acron* and the double-deck 12 m *TD924 Astromega* and 13.7 m *TD927 Astromega.*

The EOS coach range includes the 12 m high-deck *EOS200,* the 12 m long and 3.40 m wide *EOS90,* the compact 9.5 m *EOS80,* the three-axle *EOS230* coach and the 13.5 m long three-axle *EOS233.*

Bodywork

Van Hool bodywork to the same design as its integral buses and coaches has been built on Volvo, Mercedes-Benz, Scania, DAF and other chassis.

For markets in Africa and the Middle East, Van Hool has developed a range of rugged bus bodywork to the needs of each customer.

Van Hool A320 low-floor bus　*1999*/0043990

Contracts: 1998 contracts in Belgium include: 18 A300, 10 A308, 45 A360, 71 and option for 10 A600/3 and 21 AG500 for the Flemish public transport company VVM; 12 AG300 for the Walloon public transport company SRWT; 30 A308 for the Brussels public transport company STIB.

For other markets, contracts include: 13 A300 for STRD Dijon (France), 20 AG300 for Bologna (Italy), 60 AG300 for Turin (Italy), 10 A308L for Titsa (Spain), 15 A320 CNG for Lausanne (Switzerland) and 96 trolleybuses for ILPAP Athens (Greece).

Developments: Recently developed vehicle types: *A330* 100 per cent low-floor city bus, 12m long, three doors, passenger capacity around 110, rear-mounted engine (left side); three-door version of the low-floor bus *A320* with 100 per cent low-floor; *A300T* 12 m trolleybus.

New A330 100 per cent low-floor city bus with rear-mounted engine　*1999*/0043985

UPDATED

Volgren

Volgren Australia
221-243 Hammond Road, Dandenong, 3175 Victoria, Australia
Tel: (+61 3) 791 42 55　Fax: (+61 3) 794 03 36

Products: Bus and coach bodies, including both articulated and 14.5 m units.

Range: Bodies are made in aluminium under the Carosserie Hess AG (qv) system of construction. They can be mounted on Scania, Volvo, Mercedes, MAN, Hino and Isuzu chassis.

The CR221 is for low-floor chassis, such as the Volvo B10BLE, though it can be mounted on the Volvo B10M chassis. A school bus variant is offered.

Developments: Volgren has produced a body on a low-entry chassis from Scania. The body is made entirely of aluminium, with a low floor at the front and large passenger capacity. The bus features a low floor all the way to the rear of the middle doorway. After a low step in the aisle at the middle door, the floor continues at a gentle

Volgren-bodied Mercedes-Benz bus　*1996*

incline towards the seats at the very rear. The body features large windows and is on the Scania's L94UB city bus chassis. It is equipped with Scania's 9 litre engine and a four-speed ZF automatic transmission. It is installed longitudinally and inclined at 60 degrees to keep the floor

at the rear of the bus as low as possible. The body is built on a frame of extruded aluminium profiles which are bolted together.

UPDATED

Volkswagen

Volkswagen AG
D-38436 Wolfsburg, Germany
Tel: (+49 5361) 90   Fax: (+49 5361) 92 82 82

Volkswagen TDI Combi nine-seater   **1996**

Subsidiary companies
Volkswagen do Brazil, (qv)
Volkswagen de Mexico SA de CV, Pueblo, Mexico
Volkswagen Nigeria
Volkswagen South Africa Pty Ltd

Products: Minibuses, and mini- and midibus chassis.

Range: The main minibuses currently produced from the VW German plants are the Transporter panel van-derived

Volkswagen LT with Q-Bus bodywork **1998**/0011748

minibus and the larger LT range of chassis and chassis cabs.

Transporter: This has front-wheel drive and is powered by a transverse-mounted diesel (1.9 or 2.4 litre) engine or 1.8, 2 or 2.5 litre petrol engine. It is available as a chassis cab or high-roof van and is in two lengths, 3.3 m or 2.9 m.

Transporter TDI has a direct injection petrol engine rated at 75 kW, five-speed gearbox and seats nine. Airbags can be fitted to all vehicles in the Transporter range.

Caravelle: This has the same new design as the Transporter and seats nine.

LT: The LT range was updated in 1996. It includes standard and high-roof options and weights are from 2.8 tonnes to 4.6 tonnes. The LT is based on the same platform and running units as the Mercedes-Benz Sprinter (qv). It has rear-wheel drive with a front-mounted engine, available in two petrol and two diesel variants. Power ratings up to 93 kW are offered.

Developments: A less powerful version of the Transporter TDI has been introduced alongside the existing model, rated at 65 kW. This has a direct injection charge-cooled Euro-2 diesel engine.

UPDATED

Volkswagen do Brasil

Volkswagen do Brasil SA
Rua Volkswagen 291, Jabaquara, CEP 04344-900, São Paulo, SP, Brazil
Tel: (+55 11) 55 82 50 82   Fax: (+55 11) 55 82 50 31
Parent company: Volkswagen AG, Germany

Products: Bus and minibus chassis.

Range
8.140 CO: 7.7 tonne GVW midibus chassis with MWM 100 kW engine.
16.210 CO: 16 tonne GVW front-engine chassis with MWM 154 kW engine. An articulated version is available.

Production: In 1997 production was 1,945.

UPDATED

Volvo

Volvo Bus Corporation
405 08 Gothenburg, Sweden
Tel: (+46 31) 66 80 00   Fax: (+46 31) 53 68 08
www: www.bus.volvo.se
President: Jan Engstrom
Executive Vice President: Hans Ramér
Vice President, Corporate Communications:
   Lennart Alverén
Tel: (+46 31) 66 64 52   Fax: (+46 31) 66 72 88

Directors, Business Regions
Nordic: Anders Galfvensjö
Tel: (+46 31) 66 86 80
UK and Eire: Michael Ball
Tel: (+44 1926) 41 45 50/40 17 73
Continental Europe: Ove Andersson
Tel: (+32 2) 663 30 01
North America: Roland Sundén
Tel: (+1 450) 974 01 11
South America: Oswaldo Schmitt
Tel: (+55 41) 317 81 97
Asia Pacific: Finn Adolfsson
Tel: (+852) 22 19 12 10
International: Thomas Appelbom
Tel: (+32 2) 663 30 02

Body building subsidiaries/associates
Säffle Karosseri AB, Sweden
Aabenraa Karrosseri A/S
Volvo Busse Deutschland GmbH, Germany
Merkavim Metal Works Ltd., Israel
Xian Silver Bus Corporation, China
Carrus Oy, Finland

Volvo 5000 complete bus   **1999**/0043978

Volvo B12 600 coach   **1998**/0011754

Volvo B7L chassis   **1999**/0043983

Major subsidiaries/associates
Volvo Bus Ltd, UK
Volvo do Brasil Veículos Ltda
Volvo del Peru
Prévost Car Inc, Canada including NovaBUS Corporation
Volvo Poland Sp zoo
Volvo Bussar Sverige AB, Sweden
Finbus SpA, Italy
Volvo Bus Asia Pacific Ltd, Hong Kong
Volvo East Asia (Pte) Ltd, VEA Bus, Singapore
Volvo Coach Sales (Loughborough) Ltd
Volvo India PVT Ltd
MASA, Mexico

Bus manufacturing plants: Borås, Sweden; Irvine, Scotland; Curitiba, Brazil; Wroclaw, Poland; Heilbronn, Germany; Xian, China; St. Eustache, St. Claire, Canada; Roswell, Schenectady, USA; Tampere, Turku, Finland; Vienna, Austria; Tel Aviv, Israel.

Bus chassis assembly plants also in Australia, Greece, Malaysia, Morocco, Peru, Portugal and Russia.

Background: Volvo Bus is one of the world's largest manufacturers of buses over 12 tonnes GVW, producing chassis and complete buses. Volvo Bus also advises on comprehensive city transport systems.

Product development, drive system manufacture and other technology-intensive activities are mainly in Sweden, Denmark, Germany, Austria and Poland, where city and express buses are also manufactured.

In Canada, Volvo's subsidiary Prévost Car Inc (qv) makes long-distance coaches and special buses for the North American market. NovaBUS, Canada, manufactures city buses mainly for the North American market. In Mexico, Volvo acts jointly together with the subsidiary MASA. Volvo has joint venture agreements with local partners in the People's Republic of China for the manufacture of complete buses. The company has a minority holding in the Israeli bus manufacturer, Merkavim, and also works with a number of independent body building companies worldwide.

The most important markets for Volvo Bus are in Europe, Latin America, North America and Southeast Asia.

Products: Volvo Bus Corporation – complete buses, bus and coach chassis, including articulated and double-deck. Chassis also available in CKD kits. Bodywork is produced for the Nordic market through Volvo's subsidiary Säffle Karosseri in Sweden and Aabenraa supplies the Danish market. For the German-speaking markets, Volvo Austria Buses is the outlet for buses, while the outlet for coaches is Volvo Busse Deutschland. Volvo Bus Ltd, UK, makes bus and coach chassis, including double-deck. Volvo Bus Poland is a newly opened plant making city and express buses.

Range
Complete buses
The *Volvo 5000* and *Volvo 7000* are two new city buses for intense city traffic. They are both low-floor with just one single step for boarding and exit, available either as two-axle or three-axle articulated models. The driver's compartment and the D7C engine are of new design.

The 7.3 litre engine is available in four different power ratings: 164, 187, 216 and 231 kW (215, 250, 290 and 310 hp). The buses meet Euro-2 legislation and are designed for a swift flow of passengers throughout the vehicle.

The Volvo 5000 has an extruded aluminium body and the Volvo 7000 is of mainly stainless steel construction.

Chassis
For 40 years, Volvo has mainly developed the mid-engine concept. In 1991, Volvo Bus launched a new generation of rear-engine bus and coach chassis – the Volvo B12, Volvo

Volvo B7R with Camo bodywork   **1998**/0011753

Volvo 7000 complete bus   **1999**/0043977

B10B and Volvo B6BLE. Volvo has now extended the range of products including the Volvo B10BLE, Volvo B7R and the newly introduced Volvo B7L. They have been built from components in the existing bus and truck programme.

B10M: This is the mid-engine chassis with low-emission engine rated at between 180 and 265 kW, based on a development of intercooler technology with twin cooling stages. The B10M meets Euro-2 emission standards and is available in left- and right-hand drive configurations. It has two manual synchromesh gearbox options as well as a range of automatic gearboxes. The radiator is on the nearside (RHD version) to allow for a thermostatically controlled hydraulically driven fan.

The Volvo eight-speed gearbox completes the Volvo driveline and the G8-EGS Easy Gear Shift has an electropneumatic gear change system which gives the driver a short car-type gear lever and a conventional gate with a very light change.

With a choice of several engine variants of the Volvo THD102 and DH10, plus several manual and automatic transmission options, the Volvo B10M can be adapted for use as a city or intercity bus or as a coach, both as normal two-axle (with or without a rear tandem axle) or articulated versions with a rear trailer. It can also be adapted for use as a double-deck bus. Short or long front overhang can be specified, depending on door size, and wheel-bases from 5 m up to 7 m. A tandem rear axle model is also available.

B10B: This rear-engined city bus chassis was launched in 1992 and is powered by a Volvo 10 litre horizontal engine.

B6BLE: A low-floor, easy-access 12.2 tonne, 10.5 m bus which, depending on configuration, can accommodate up to 60 passengers. It has been developed for both right- and left-hand drive applications for international markets. Independent front suspension is fitted, similar to that used on the Volvo B10BLE and Volvo's new-generation city bus, the B7L. This has boosted the gangway width between the front wheel arches by more than 100 mm, to nearly 900 mm, smoothing passenger flows and improving access for wheelchair users and parents with buggies.

B10M articulated: The articulated bus chassis based on the Volvo B10M features a steered or rigid third axle, Volvo G8-MGS and EGS manual gearboxes, several choices of automatic transmission and full air suspension. With a steered third axle the GVW is 27 tonnes, or 28.5 tonnes with a rigid third axle. THD102 and DH10 engines are can be specified.

B10BLE: This is a low-entrance model with independent front suspension and the driveline of the B10B.

B7L: This is designed for inner city traffic. The location of the engine at the left rear of the vehicle has enabled the entire floor to be made low and flat, affording passengers a single, convenient level of entry and exit through all doors. The model's new engine complies with Euro-2 emission control standard. Volvo B7L comes both as a two-axle city bus as well as a three-axle articulated version. The B7L can also take double-deck bodywork. There are four power ratings available on the 7.3 litre engine – 158, 184, 213 and 223 kWh.

Super Olympian: This is an updated version of the Olympian double-deck bus chassis. It is a low-floor city bus in a double-deck version aimed for the East Asian market. It is powered by the Volvo D10 rated at 210 kWh.

B12: This rear-engine coach chassis is powered by the Volvo D12A 12 litre engine with an output of 250-309 kW (340-420 hp). Turbocharger and intercooler are standard

and the torque is 1,850 Nm at 1,100-1,300 rev/min for the 309 kW engine. Equipped with electronic diesel control (EDC) it drives through a G8-EGS gearbox or an Allison 5B500 automatic gearbox.

There are three driving positions, the lowest allowing the passenger floor to extend above the driver within a total height of 3.7 m.

The Volvo B12 is also available as a three-axle version with a 6.1 m wheel-base. As the rear bogie axles are independently suspended, it has been possible to fit the gearbox between the wheels, closer to the driving axle. This results in a shorter rear overhang and improved weight distribution.

B7F: This front-engined chassis has a normal GVW of 16,000 kg with an optional heavy-duty version of 18,000 kg GVW, intended for operations with heavy loads and tough road conditions. Both are leaf sprung. The wheel-base variants are 5.5, 6.0 and 6.5 m. The engine is the Volvo D7 with an output of 169 to 210 kW. The air intake and the filters have a high position for good performance in flooded areas. The overhang permits the placing of a single door in front of the axle with an approach angle of a full 12°. A high degree of standardisation has been achieved by using many components in common with Volvo Truck.

B7R: This rear-engined chassis has a standard-height floor, designed for developing markets and niche sectors in established markets. It is suitable for city bus, intercity/urban/commuter and coach operation.

It is of bolted ladder frame chassis construction with a 6.3 m wheel-base. A lowered-front version is available for city bus operation. Full air suspension is fitted, based on that of the Volvo B10M at the front and FL7/10 truck at the rear. Leaf springs can be specified. S-cam brakes are specified all round. The engine, from the Volvo FL7 truck range, is the D7B six-cylinder rated at 193.96 kW (260 hp) and has mechanical fuel injection. The transmission can be either manual or auto with integral retarder. The manual version takes the Telma electric retarder.

CNG: A CNG bus based on the B10BLE chassis has gone into production, with roof-mounted gas tanks. The gas is stored at a pressure of 200 bar. The Volvo GH10A245 is designed to run on CNG and an oxidising catalytic converter cuts carbon monoxide (CO) and hydrocarbon (HC) emissions. A computer controls the air/fuel mix. Emissions of particles and oxides of nitrogen are put at one-third of those of the best diesel bus.

Bodywork
Bodywork for all the Volvo chassis is offered in conjunction with independent body builders, as well as Volvo subsidiaries.

Production: In 1998 a total of 8,928 units were produced. During 1998 the decision was made to concentrate parts of the European production in Volvo Poland Sp zoo. Volvo has also set up production in Omsk, Russia.

Contracts: Include 120 B7LAs for ETHEL Athens and 300 B7R AM-Bus for Saudi Arabia.

Developments
1996: Volvo Bus Corporation received the UN Corporate Best Practices Award for its part in the development of public transport in the cities of Curitiba, Brasil and Gothenburg, Sweden.
1997: In joint a venture between Henlys UK and Volvo,

Volvo bi-articulated bus, Curitiba   ***1998**/0011751*

Prévost was acquired by Volvo and Henlys to penetrate the North American market. NovaBUS (qv) was also acquired. Prévost is offering Volvo driveline components.

A rear-engined mid-sized high-floor chassis, the B7R, was introduced worldwide. Volvo acquired bus body builder, Carrus Oy, Finland.

1998: The Volvo 5000 and Volvo 7000 low-floor city buses were introduced, together with the chassis version, Volvo B7L. Production of city and intercity buses started in Omsk, Russia. Volvo acquired Mexico's second largest bus manufacturer MASA in 1998.

Volvo Truck Corporation has announced its intention to withdraw from truck building at its plant at Irvine in Ayrshire, UK, by July 2000. The announcement mirrors that in June 1998 by Volvo Bus Corporation of its intention to transfer bus assembly from Irvine to plants in Sweden and Poland. As a result, and based on current market forecasts, it is anticipated that both truck and bus assembly will cease at Irvine by July 2000, when the plant will close with the loss of 450 jobs.

UPDATED

Volvo Austria

Volvo Austria GmbH
Am Cooncorde Park 1/A1, A-2320 Wien-Schwechat, Austria
Tel: (+43 1) 70 12 80   Fax: (+43 1) 76 31 24
Directors of Marketing & Sales: Hans Schmid
   Harald Rumpel

Background: Formerly called Steyr Bus, the parent company is Volvo Bus Corporation, Sweden, which bought 75 per cent in 1990. A 61 per cent share in the Polish commercial vehicle manufacturer FS was acquired in 1995.

A controlling interest in Avia (qv) was acquired in 1996 by Daewoo (qv) and Steyr-Daimler-Puch, which is a separate company, and Daewoo bought 65 per cent of Steyr-Daimler-Puch in 1995.

Products: Bus bodies based on Volvo chassis and minibuses of own design.

Range

SS11 Transitbus: This city bus is on the Volvo B10B rear-engined chassis. Power is from the Volvo THD102KD, THD102KF, THD103KF, THD103KB or THD103KD diesel engines, encapsulated, and driving through ZF 4HP 500/590 or ZF 5HP 500/590 automatic gearboxes, each with integral retarder.

The body is integral, 11.7 m long, and is of welded steel. There are three doors on the standard version. There are seats for 36 and standing room for 56.

SL12: Intercity bus on Volvo B10B rear-engine chassis. It has the Volvo EGS (electropneumatic Easy Gear Shift) G7 box. The body is of similar construction to the SS11.

SG18MU articulated: An articulated version of the Transitbus on the Volvo B10M mid-engine chassis. The SG18MU, which has a length of 18 m and a width of 2.5 m, has seats for 48 and maximum standing room for 106.

City-bus: The smaller City-bus is aimed at the market for small buses for park-and-ride and dial-a-bus systems, special transport for the disabled and city-centre operations. It has a platform height of 300 mm, no steps or raised platforms and an internal height of more than 2 m. It has 15 seats and room for 15 standing. Wheelbase is 3.3 m, wheel track 1.72 m and overall length 5.8 m. Turning circle is 14 m.

UPDATED

Volvo Bus

Volvo Bus Ltd
Wedgnock Lane, Warwick CV34 5YA, England
Tel: (+44 1926) 40 17 77   Fax: (+44 1926) 40 74 07
Managing Director, Volvo Truck & Bus: Tommy Svensson
Managing Director: Mike Ball
Commercial Director: Steve Dewhurst
Coach Sales Manager: Don Johnston

Products: Single-deck and double-deck bus chassis.

Range

B7R: This is a standard-height chassis designed for developing markets and niche sectors in established markets. It is suitable for city bus, intercity/urban/commuter and coach operation.

In the UK it satisfies the requirements of the interurban sector and medium/heavyweight coach operation and is jointly marketed by Volvo and Plaxton (qv) as the Prima B7R.

It is of bolted ladder-frame chassis construction with a 6.3 m wheelbase. A lowered-front version is available for city bus operation. Full air suspension is fitted, based on that of the B10M at the front and FL7/10 truck at the rear. Leaf springs can be specified. S-cam brakes are specified all round. The engine, from the Volvo FL7 truck range, is the D7B six-cylinder rated at 193.96 kW (260 hp) and has mechanical fuel injection.

The transmission can be either ZF S6-85 manual or ZF 4HP500 auto with integral retarder. The manual version takes the Telma 191 electric retarder.

It is available through two major UK dealerships, Kirkby Coach & Bus and Volvo Coach Sales.

B10M: This mid-engine chassis has a Volvo underfloor power unit. It takes bus or coach bodywork and can carry up to 90 with a bus body. Gross vehicle weight is 19 tonnes. It is Volvo's most frequently purchased chassis.

B10M articulated: The articulated bus chassis based on the Volvo B10M features a steered or rigid third axle, Volvo G8-MGS and EGS manual gearboxes, several choices of automatic transmission and full air suspension. With a steered third axle the GVW is 27 tonnes, or 28.5 tonnes with a rigid third axle.

B7L: This is designed for inner city traffic. The location of the engine at the left rear of the vehicle has enabled the entire floor to be made low and flat, affording passengers a single, convenient level of entry and exit through all doors. The model's new engine complies with Euro-2 emission control standard. Volvo B7L comes both as a two-axle city bus and a three-axle articulated version. The B7L can also take double-deck bodywork. There are four power ratings available on the 7.3 litre engine – 158, 184, 213 and 223 kWh.

Super Olympian: An updated version of the Olympian double-deck bus chassis. It is a low-floor city bus in a double-deck version aimed for the East Asian market. It is powered by the Volvo D10 rated at 210 kWh.

B10BLE: A low-floor model combining the low-floor independent front suspension of the B10L and the

Volvo B10BLE low-floor bus chassis with Wright Floline bodywork on Star Bus route in Keighley, UK
***1999**/0043982*

Volvo/Plaxton Prima B7R   ***1998**/0011758*

driveline of the B10B. It is for operators who do not require the expense of a no-step/low-floor area to the rear saloon, as offered by the B10L. The floor at the front is 320 mm high, kneeling to 230 mm. The gangway width between wheel arches is 955 mm. The engine is mounted longitudinally as in the B10B.

Contracts: Volvo Bus has announced two orders from London operating companies. The first is for 46 Volvo B7L chassis for London Central, part of the Go-Ahead Group, and the second for French-owned London United, which has signed a deal for 45. The vehicles will enter service progressively with both companies during late 1999.

Both companies have chosen Alexander ALX400 bodywork for all vehicles in their respective orders.

The Isle of Wight's (UK) major bus operator, The Southern Vectis Omnibus Company Ltd (a subsidiary of Southern Vectis plc), has relaunched its 'Island Explorer' circular sightseeing route with a new livery and eight new Volvo Olympian double-decks.

Part of an order for 12, the eight Olympians are the first with Volvo engines to join Southern Vectis. They have Northern Counties (now Plaxton) Palatine 1 bodies with 70 semi-coach, high-back seats and they can also accommodate 17 standees. Seats in the upper saloon are arranged with groups of four seats facing each other.

Volvo and Plaxton have unveiled a semi-integral version of the B7R coach. The Plaxton Prima body has sufficient strength and rigidity to be integrated with the 3.25 m version of the chassis to offer the same 6.3 m overall wheelbase as its fixed chassis stablemate, yet increases luggage space by approximately 20 per cent.

The new semi-integral Prima B7R offers 55 reclining seats and a Volvo D7B engine driving through a ZF S6-85 six-speed manual gearbox. A Telma retarder is standard. A ZF automatic gearbox with integral retarder continues to be available as an option.

Developments: Volvo Bus has announced a midibus chassis, the *B6BLE*, a low-floor, easy-access 12.2 tonne, 10.5 m bus which, depending on configuration, can accommodate up to 60 passengers. Offering low cost of operation and a higher seated passenger capacity than the Volvo B6LE it replaces, the B6BLE complies with the Disabled Persons Transport Advisory Committee (DIPTAC) recommendations and has been developed for both right- and left-hand drive applications for international markets. Independent front suspension is fitted, similar to that used on the Volvo B10L, the Volvo B10BLE and Volvo's new-generation city bus, the B7L. This has boosted the gangway width between the front wheel arches by more than 100 mm, to nearly 900 mm, smoothing passenger flows and improving access for wheelchair users and parents with buggies.

Other changes at the front include a new chassis frame which significantly increases the low floor area. Similar in design to that of the Volvo B10L, the top of the frame is just 305 mm from the ground, 80 mm lower than the Volvo B6LE, with front end 'kneeling' comfortably bringing the bus to a 250 mm step height. The top of the frame is also totally flat, giving a lower gangway and facilitating body mounting.

On the suspension, electronic control supersedes air-operated valves to speed up response times and provide a more comfortable ride. The new control system also reduces air consumption. Packaging changes incorporated in the design of the Volvo B6BLE include a repositioning of the air tanks and a new swing-out battery tray located under the driver's seat. New radiator ducting has improved the serviceability of the cooling system. Developed jointly by Volvo Bus's design teams in Irvine and Gothenburg, and in close co-operation with UK body builder Robert Wright (qv), the Volvo B6BLE accepts a 2.5m width body and retains the driveline combination of its predecessor – the low-emission Volvo D6A 6 litre engine and 4/5 speed HP500 automatic gearbox. The rear axle has an uprated driving head.

Developed for world markets, the new Volvo B7L low-floor city bus family (see Volvo Bus Corporation) includes the successor to the Volvo Olympian 2-axle double-deck chassis. The Plaxton President (see Plaxton Wigan) double-deck body can be mounted on this chassis.

Volvo Olympian with 68-seat dual-door Northern Counties (Plaxton) bodywork with Stagecoach London
1999/0043980

It combines a transverse engine layout with a range of new features from the design of its single-deck cousin.

These include: a new 7.3 litre engine which meets Euro-2 emission standards and is rated at either 160 or 187 kW (215 or 250 bhp); a CRT (exhaust filter) or oxidising catalytic converter exhaust treatments as production options; new multiplex electrical system with PC-based diagnostics; new-generation automatic gearboxes from ZF and Voith (using multiplex communications); independent front suspension based on the Volvo B10L and B10BLE; and a new driver's compartment and instrument panel.

It retains the familiar transverse engine layout with a short rear overhang which maximises the low-floor space available in the saloon for passengers.

The main differences from the new Volvo B7L single-deck are at the rear end of the vehicle, but the chassis frame is identical from the front to as far back as the rear suspension, the new rear structure being combined with sole bars and a perimeter frame for body mounting/building.

The rear axle has the same 80° drive from the back of the gearbox, but has a right-hand input to suit the driveline layout.

Volvo Truck Corporation has announced its intention to withdraw from truck building at its plant at Irvine in Ayrshire, UK, by July 2000. The announcement mirrors that in June 1998 by Volvo Bus Corporation of its intention to transfer bus assembly from Irvine to plants in Sweden and Poland. As a result, and based on current market forecasts, it is anticipated that both truck and bus assembly will cease at Irvine by July 2000, when the plant will close with the loss of 450 jobs.

UPDATED

Volvo B10M with Northern Counties (Plaxton) body with Stagecoach, Kingston upon Hull
(Andrew Jarosz)
1999/0043992

Volvo do Brasil

Volvo do Brasil Veículos Ltda
Av Juscelino Kubitschek de Oliveira, 2600 CIC Curitiba,
CEP 81260-000 Paraná, Brazil
Tel: (+55 41) 271 81 11   Fax: (+55 41) 272 69 11
Commercial Director: Oswaldo Schmidt
A subsidiary of Volvo Bus Corporation

Background: Domestic production of buses by Volvo do
Brasil began in 1979 and is based on the urban bus
design previously built by the parent company in Sweden.

Products: Urban bus chassis, including articulated and
double-articulated.

Range

B58ECO: This is based on the B58 design built in Sweden
before the present B10M. The mid-engined chassis are
offered for standard urban (6.25 and 6 m wheelbase),
articulated and double-articulated (5.5 m wheelbase) and
three-axle bus applications. Power plant is the Volvo
THD102KJ, THD102KF and THD101KB turbocharged
engines equipped with intercooler, producing 165 kW,
182 kW and 210 kW respectively. Gearboxes are the
mechanical ZF S6-90 or fully automatic ZF 4HP500 and
Voith D863, both with retarder. The gearbox on the
double-articulated urban chassis is the ZF S6-90. The
vehicles are assembled with air/leaf suspension.
B10MECO: This is a new articulated urban bus chassis,
developed from the B10M coach chassis, equipped with
a Volvo THD102KF engine, ZF 4HP500 or Voith D863
automatic gearbox, with retarder, and full air suspension.
B10M: Introduced in 1986 in parallel with the B58, the
B10M long-distance chassis and a three-axle bus chassis
are powered by the turbocharged intercooler THD101KC
engine (228 kW), driving through a ZF S6-90 gearbox.

Production: In 1997 was 1,485, of which 920 were
domestic.

Developments

Guided buses: The first of the bi-articulated Volvo B10M
buses, 25 m long and with a capacity of up to 276
passengers, started operating in São Paulo at the
beginning of 1999. The city will be served by 20 Volvo

Volvo do Brasil B10MA high-platform bi-articulated bus at bus station in Curitiba (Bill Luke) **1999**/0043993

B10M bi-articulated buses featuring engines that conform
to Conama IV (Euro-2) emission requirements. The
vehicles are serving a 20 km system linking the outskirts
of São Paulo to the city centre, with a commuter rate of up
to 130,000 passengers a day in each direction.

São Paulo chose Volvo bi-articulated buses after a
series of exhaustive tests that started two years ago. The
results showed that in addition to high carrying capacity
and frequency – similar to that of the metro – the bi-
articulated bus system has an implementation cost which
is a fraction of that of a metro system.

With the use of Volvo bi-articulated buses, São Paulo
becomes the second city in Latin America to use this kind
of bus for urban passenger transportation. The first city
was Curitiba (qv), where 114 bi-articulated units have
been operating the transport system for over six years.
Volvo do Brazil constructed the buses. About 15 buses
per hour will travel the route in each direction.

Operating results and low implementation costs are
leading other cities in South America to study the use of
the bi-articulated system, such as Bogota, Buenos Aires
and Rio de Janeiro.

The bus interior features upholstered seats, rubber-

lined anti-slip flooring and doors on both sides of the bus.
The driver has a set of eight micro-cameras to enable
monitoring of boarding/alighting via the three right-hand
doors and the four left-hand doors. The cameras are also
used for monitoring manoeuvring.

The bi-articulated buses have Volvo B10M chassis
equipped with full air suspension, automatic gearbox,
ABS brakes, ASR anti-slip system, retarder and power
steering.

The new buses have been purchased by bus
companies Campo Belo of the Ruas Group, and Kuba
Viação Urbana Ltda of the Kuba Group.

The system started operating with eight buses. The
remaining 12 are now in the final stage of body building at
Marcopolo. By the end of the year, all 20 units will be in
operation.

The route that the vehicles will serve extends for
approximately 20 km, with main stops at Capelinha, Joao
Dias and Praça das Bandeiras. This route is also serviced
by another 160 articulated buses – 130 of which are
Volvos – and 116 standard buses.

The Volvo chassis will also be used in the electric-
powered bus system within the Fura-Fila project, an
initiative to integrate the bus into a controlled network
utilising a light-transit guidance system. This advanced
project will feature 25 m bi-articulated Volvo buses. The
major differences compared with the regular bi-
articulated bus are electric power and a kerb guidance
system where the vehicle is equipped with side wheels.
The first unit is now being run on a test track and the first
section is to be inaugurated in the middle of 2000.

A project structured around long electrically powered
vehicles for passenger transport in the São Paulo
metropolitan system features 10 Volvo articulated buses
purchased by bus company Metra. These buses have
been in service since July 1998. With these recent
innovations in its urban passenger transport system, São
Paulo now has the largest number of articulated buses in
Brazil, with a current fleet of 351 units, 240 of which are
Volvos. The Volvo buses are particularly suited for
articulated and bi-articulated configuration as they carry a
mid-mounted engine, leaving the passenger floor free for
any type of body and interior layout.

Bi-articulated bus on Volvo B10M chassis for São Paulo
1999/0043979

UPDATED

Volvo del Peru

Volvo del Peru SA
Casilla 815, Lima 100, Peru
Tel: (+51 14) 94 35 00

Works: Km 6.5 Central Highway, Lima
A subsidiary of Volvo Truck Corporation

Background: Volvo's Lima plant, opened in 1966,
assembles bus chassis from kits supplied from Sweden
and Brazil. There is about 40 per cent local content.

Products: Buses.

VERIFIED

Vozila

MPP Vozila doo
Ptujska c 184, SI-2000 Maribor, Slovenia
Tel: (+386 62) 45 01 00   Fax: (+386 62) 41 24 55

e-mail: marketing@MPP-VOZILA.SI
www: www.mpp-vozila.si

Background: MPP Vozila was established in 1996 though
production at this location dates back to 1946 when the

Vozila three-door city bus
1999/0043984

Dynamo

Dynamo Electrical Works
Moskva, Russia
Exports through:
V/O Sovelectro, 1/2 kor 1, ul Sadovaya-Spasskaya,
107078 Moscow, Russia
Tel: (+7 095) 208 28 37   Telex: 411003 SOEL

Products: Electric motors.

Range: Supplier of 550-600 V series wound DK-210 electric motors with bias winding for installation in trolleybuses produced by Trolza (qv).

VERIFIED

Firema Trasporti SpA

Ercole Marelli Trazione Unit
Viale Edison 110, I-20099 Sesto San Giovanni, Milan, Italy
Tel: (+39 02) 249 41   Fax: (+39 02) 248 35 08

(See main entry under Rail Vehicles and Traction Equipment)

Products: Trolleybus traction equipment.

UPDATED

Ganz Ansaldo

Ganz Ansaldo Electric Ltd
PO Box 63, Lövöház utca 39, H-1024 Budapest, Hungary
Tel: (+36 1) 375 33 22   Fax: (+36 1) 356 29 80

(See main entry under Rail Vehicles and Traction Equipment)

Products: Electrical traction equipment.

Contracts: In 1999 five low-floor IK412 trolleybuses, with IGBT chopper-controlled equipment and Ikarus bodywork, have been put into service in Tallin, Estonia.

UPDATED

GE Transportation Systems

GE Transportation Systems
2901 East Lake Road, Erie, Pennsylvania 16531, USA
Tel: (+1 814) 875 53 85   Fax: (+1 814) 875 31 54
www: www.ge.com/transportation
General Manager, Rail Passenger Group/Marketing, Sales & Service: Vivek M Joshi

Manager, Customer Support, Passenger Rail Group: Robert E Hall

Products: Electromechanical and solid state DC cam and AC inverter propulsion systems; phase-controlled AC/DC propulsion systems; auxiliary systems, including static converters and inverters.

Developments: A new venture, GE-Harris Railway Electronics, has been created by GE Transportation Systems Division and Harris Corporation, to manufacture and market electronic systems for transport authorities.

UPDATED

GM Hughes

GM Hughes Power Control Systems
3050 West Lomita Boulevard, PO Box 2923, Bldg 237, M/S 1455, Torrance, California 90509-2923, USA
Tel: (+1 310) 517 57 17   Fax: (+1 310) 517 57 27

Marketing Manager: Fred Silver

Products: Power electronics and AC induction motors for heavy vehicle drive systems and auxiliary systems such as air conditioning, power steering, DC to DC converters and battery charging. Power ratings vary from 1 to 240 kW.

Product trade marks are Dolphin Drive Systems and MagneCharge Systems.

VERIFIED

Kiepe

Kiepe Elektrik GmbH & Co KG
PO Box 130540, D-40555 Düsseldorf, Germany
Tel: (+49 211) 749 71   Fax: (+49 211) 749 73 00

e-mail: info@kiepe-elektrik.com
www: www.kiepe-elektrik.com
Chairman: T Weber
General Manager, Marketing & Sales: W Huober

Background: In Europe Kiepe is one of the leading manufacturers of trolleybus traction systems. Kiepe was established in 1906. Formerly a subsidiary of ACEC, the company became part of GEC Alsthom (now Alstom) in 1988 along with its Austrian subsidiary Kiepe Electric in Vienna. In 1993 Kiepe became a subsidiary of AEG Rail Systems and in 1996, following the merger of AEG and ABB, Kiepe became a member of the Schaltbau Group, Munich.

Products: Complete electrical and electronic equipment for trolleybuses rated 600/750 V DC.

Range: Three-phase IGBT AC (direct pulse inverter) and DC chopper power electronics controlled by microprocessor technology, with regenerative braking, built-in diagnosis interface, and roll-back inhibitors. Contactor bank or rotating pedal controllers give switched resistor control.

Contracts: Currently supplying three-phase equipment for: Arnhem, Netherlands; Bologna, Parma, Milan and Modena, Italy; Berne, Biel Montreux and Zurich, Switzerland; Lyon, France; Salzburg and Linz, Austria; Quito, Ecuador; Athens, Greece and Minsk, Belarus.

UPDATED

Artist's impression of Kiepe-equipped trolleybus in Athens
1999/0043943

Mitsubishi

Mitsubishi Electric Corporation
2-2-3 Marunouchi Chiyoda-ku, Tokyo, Japan
Tel: (+81 3) 32 18 34 29   Fax: (+81 3) 32 18 35 94
President: Takashi Kitoaka

Products: Electrical equipment for rail and road vehicles.

Contracts: 200 VVVF inverters using IGBT technology have been supplied for trolleybuses of STE Mexico.

VERIFIED

Siemens

Siemens Aktiengesellschaft
Transportation Systems Group (VT)
Mass Transit Rolling Stock Division (VT5)
PO Box 3240, D-91050 Erlangen, Germany
Tel: (+49 9131) 70   Fax: (+49 9131) 72 69 33

(See main entry under Rail Vehicles and Traction Equipment)

UK representative
Siemens Transportation Systems
Siemens House, Windmill Road, Sunbury on Thames TW16 7HS
Tel: (+44 1932) 75 29 73   Fax: (+44 1932) 75 29 79

Products: Propulsion and auxiliary equipment for trolleybuses and battery-operated buses; dual-mode propulsion systems.

A new propulsion system has been developed that brings down the total cost of a complete trolleybus to little more than 20 per cent above that of a conventional diesel bus. The unit is called ELFA — Electric Low-Floor Axle — and is drop-centre allowing a low floor. Two small lightweight traction motors are fitted in the drop section, driving through a reduction gear train.

The motor is rated at 105 kW, and is supplied with alternating current by two inverters. Each motor weighs 85 kg and is 425 mm in length, with a cross-section of 245 mm by 245 mm. Each inverter weighs 17 kg to 30 kg depending on specification and is around 500 mm long with a cross-section of about 200 mm by 153 mm. The width between the reduction units is 1,100 mm, allowing a gangway over the drop centre.

The motor and inverter are mass-produced for machine tools, industrial robots and battery vehicles so there are no development costs.

Contracts: Electrical equipment has been supplied for two-axle and articulated trolleybuses for several operators worldwide, including Geneva, Switzerland.

VERIFIED

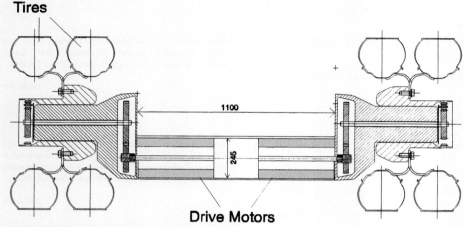

Siemens ELFA — electric low-floor axle for city buses   **1997**

Škoda

Škoda Ostrov Company Ltd
Dolní Žďár 43, CZ-36329 Ostrov, Czech Republic
Tel: (+420 164) 61 21 45   Fax: (+420 164) 61 26 41
General Manager: Jiří Juránek
Vice President, Commercial: Petr Kasenčák

Products: Trolleybuses, complete trolleybus systems, electrical units, including motors and solid-state control and power systems. (For complete trolleybuses see Buses section.)

Converters with IGBT modules are supplied for trolleybuses and trams.

Developments: Include a low-floor trolleybus with AC drive, a bus on the chassis of a 14TrM trolleybus and an articulated bus designated 22Ab.

UPDATED

Škoda Ostrov low-floor trolleybus   **1999**/0043942

Toshiba

Toshiba Corporation
Railway Projects Department
1-1, Shibaura 1-chome, Minato-ku, Tokyo 105-8001, Japan
Tel: (+81 3) 34 57 49 24   Fax: (+81 3) 54 44 94 22
President: Taizo Nishimuro
General Manager: Shigenori Yamakawa
Senior Manager, Railway Projects Dept: Shunji Uchino

Products: Electrical traction equipment for trolleybuses and electric battery buses.

Range: Has produced large varieties of electric and diesel-electric power systems for locomotives, railcars and trolleybuses. A fleet of 15 trolleybuses supplied for

operation at the Kurobe Dam by the Kansai Electric Power Co Ltd has Toshiba traction equipment with a one-hour rated output of 120 kW and maximum speed of 70 km/h.

In 1996 a fleet of eight similar trolleybuses was supplied to Kurobe Kanko Co Ltd for operation in the Tateyama Tunnel.

A prototype BT 900 series battery bus was operated in 1989 by the Nagoya City Transportation Authority, based on a Hino vehicle. It has seating capacity for 26, continuous rated output of 60 kW and a maximum speed of 60 km/h. Running distance without recharge is 170 km. A thyristor chopper control system with regenerative braking is incorporated. Battery voltage is 384 V DC.

UPDATED

Toshiba-powered trolleybus on the Kurobe Dam route

production since January 1996 and has 187 to 201 kW (250 to 270 hp) ratings.

L10: The 10 litre natural gas engine has a rating of 209 to 224 kW (280 to 300 hp).

M11: This has urban bus ratings of 209 kW (280 hp) and 246 kW (330 hp), and coach ratings of up to 336 kW (450 hp).

Developments: Cummins has developed joint ventures with Scania, Komatsu (Japan), Telco (Tata, India), Wartsila of Finland and China National Heavy-Duty Truck Corp. Its first joint venture was with Kirloskar of India around 1965.

A joint venture with Iveco called EEA (European Engine Alliance) was announced in 1996, for the design and manufacture of a new series of diesel engines.

A dual overhead cam diesel engine, the 15 litre Signature 600, has been unveiled. It develops 448 kW (600 hp).

VERIFIED

Cummins (UK)

Cummins Engine Co Ltd
50 Coombe Road, New Malden KT3 4Q1, UK
Tel: (+44 181) 700 69 00   Fax: (+44 181) 942 42 34
Vice President, European Automotive Business:
 Peter McDowell
Technical Director: Bob Scott
Public Relations: Peter Dorey
Rail Business: David Peters; David Moore

A subsidiary of Cummins Engine Company Inc (USA)
Production plants: Darlington and Daventry, UK
Reconditioning plant: Diesel ReCon, Cumbernauld, Scotland

Products: Diesel and natural gas engines.

Range: Cummins manufactures a wide range of engines in the UK for European passenger applications, covering the 97 to 335 kW power sector and certified to Euro-2 emission standards.

B series: The 5.9 litre six-cylinder B series engine has become Europe's most widely specified proprietary engine in the light and middleweight chassis range. The B series is available in Dennis and Optare passenger vehicles.

The B series is produced in naturally aspirated, turbocharged and turbo/aftercooled formats, covering the 97 to 134 kW sector.

C series: The 8.3 litre six-cylinder C series is available in power ratings covering the 112 to 198 kW (150 to 265 bhp) sector. Though a larger design, the C series uses the same advanced engineering techniques as the B. It is the power unit in both the Dennis Lance city bus chassis and Dennis Javelin coach (qv).

M series: M series models are light and compact in relation to their size and are suitable for use in double-deck buses and touring coaches. Reliability and durability have been increased through features such as steel-crowned articulated pistons. Service intervals between major overhauls have been increased to one million kilometres.

CNG/LNG: Natural gas versions of the six litre B series and 8.3 litre C series engines are offered. The CNG engines meet Euro-3 regulations. A CNG-powered bus, based on the Plaxton Pointer midibus body and Dennis Dart chassis, has been produced. Power for the new bus comes from a Cummins B series engine developed to run on CNG.

Light rail
The 10.8 litre M11E-R and M11-R engines (187 to 276 kW) have been specifically designed for light rail applications.

Cummins B series natural gas engine   *1996*

The M11E-R features the CELECT electronic fuel management control system for maximum fuel efficiency and power. CELECT also logs engine performance data to assist planned maintenance. The M11E-R meets Euro-2 emissions standards, the M11-R, with a stepped timing control fuel system, is designed to meet NRMM Tier 1 emissions requirements.

A remanufacturing service is offered by Diesel ReCon UK, a subsidiary of Cummins Engine Co. Instead of replacing a whole engine, operators can specify a short engine. This is a remanufactured unit which comprises the heart of the engine but minus application-specific components including fuel pump, turbocharger, compressor, manifold and plumbing arrangements. It is available for B, C and L10 series.

Cummins has developed joint ventures with Scania, Komatsu (Japan), Telco (Tata, India), Wartsila of Finland and China National Heavy-Duty Truck Corp.

A joint venture with Iveco was announced in 1996; called EEA (European Engine Alliance), it will design and manufacture a new series of diesel engines.

VERIFIED

Cummins M11 engine   *1996*

Dennis Dart bus with Plaxton body, powered by CNG conversion on Cummins B series engine   *1997*

Dana

Dana Corporation
Drivetrain Service Division
PO Box 321, Toldeo, Ohio 43697, USA
Tel: (+1 419) 866 39 00   Fax: (+1 419) 866 39 25
www: www.dana.com

UK subsidiary
Dana Ltd
Birch Road, Witton, Birmingham B6 7JR, UK
Tel: (+44 121) 344 44 77   Fax: (+44 121) 344 40 03

Products: Axles, including rigid drive, steer drive and dead steer types for light and heavy commercial trucks, four-wheel drive utility, buses and off-highway applications. Other products include brakes, ball joints, differentials and auxiliary gearboxes, overdrive units and drop forgings for automotive engineering.

Contracts: The first of 182 low-floor 12 m Dennis Trident three-axle double-deck chassis was delivered to KMB Hong Kong in 1998. Each bus has a low single-step entrance 325 mm off the ground and has a welded steel frame with Dana axles.

UPDATED

DDC

Detroit Diesel Corporation (DDC)
13400 Outer Drive, West Detroit, Michigan 48239-4001, USA
Tel: (+1 313) 592 52 92/51 12
Fax: (+1 313) 592 70 66/72 88
www: www.detroitdiesel.com
President: Chip McLure
Chairman: Roger Penske
Vice President, Bus and Coach Sales: Patrick J Scully

Products: Diesel and natural gas engines, for coach and bus.

Range
Series 50: This has a DDEC computerised fuel management system and is a four-cylinder 8.46 litre air-to-air intercooled design. Up to 235 kW (320 bhp).
Series 50G: A CNG (natural gas) engine, derived from the Series 50, up to 205 kW (275 bhp).

Series 60: Six cylinder four-stroke engine up to 373 kW (500 hp).

Developments: New fuel system has been introduced for the 50G series with full DDEC control.

UPDATED

Deutz

Deutz AG
Deutz-Mulheimer-Strasse 147-149, D-501057, Germany
Tel: (+49 221) 822 25 10   Fax: (+49 221) 822 25 29
www: www.deutz.de

Products: Air-cooled and water-cooled diesel engines including the 2013 series of commercial vehicle engines.

Contracts: As a result of a co-operation agreement with Volvo, Deutz has become Volvo's main supplier of small and mid-sized diesel engines.

NEW ENTRY

Eaton

Eaton Limited
Eaton House, Staines Road, Hounslow TW4 5DX, UK
Tel: (+44 181) 572 73 13   Fax: (+44 181) 572 59 96
Vice President, Truck Components Operations, Europe:
    Joaquin J Zuza

Parent company: Eaton Corporation

UK Transmissions
Aycliffe Plant, Walworth Road, Aycliffe Industrial Estate, Newton Aycliffe DL5 6BJ
Tel: (+44 1325) 30 03 33   Fax: (+44 1325) 31 92 89

Products: Truck driveline components.

Range: The main range of gearboxes is also known as Eaton Fuller and is for both bus and truck applications.

UPDATED

Gardner

L Gardner & Sons Ltd
Barton Hall, Hardy Street, Patricroft, Eccles, Manchester M30 7WA, UK
Tel: (+44 161) 789 22 01   Fax: (+44 161) 787 75 49
Managing Director: Stan Lawrenson
Engineering Director: Alan Hilton
Sales & Marketing Director: Gareth Williams

Background: The company was started by Lawrence Gardner in 1868 and began production of engines in 1891. It pioneered diesel engine development from 1918 onwards and the first diesel engine was installed on a bus in Britain in 1931.

The company is now fully accredited to ISO 9000 standards.

Products: Diesel engines for buses, coaches, trucks, marine and other applications.

Range: Engines from 21 kW (28 bhp) to 313 kW (420 bhp). With the exception of the 2LW engines, all models are in-line six-cylinder units, available in either vertical or horizontal form, with engine capacities including 10.45, 12.7 and 15.5 litre.
LG1200 Euro-2: This meets Euro-2 legislation without the need for electronics. It is available in four ratings — 164, 187, 208 and 224 kW (220, 250, 280 and 300 bhp).

It has a modification to the fuel injection equipment to retain the flat torque curve characteristics. The piston compression ratio is increased from 15:1 to 16:1, reducing NOx levels and improving cold-starting white smoke emissions and part-load hydrocarbon emissions.

Remanufactured engines
The Gardner remanufactured engine range was introduced in 1988, followed in 1991 by the Green environmentally friendly versions.

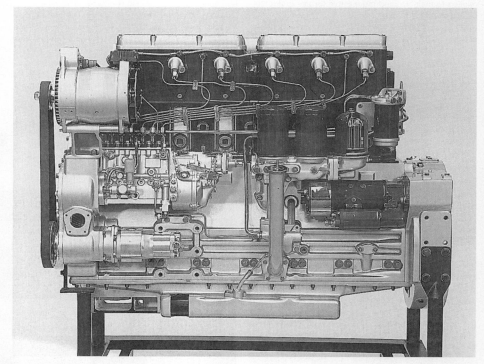

Gardner LG1200 engine which meets Euro-2 regulations

1996

Contracts: Gardner engines are available in bus and coach chassis supplied by a number of UK manufacturers including Volvo and Dennis Specialist Vehicles. The LG1200 series is in service in London, Manchester and Hong Kong, and Dennis is offering the LG1200 in its standard specification.

Africa is a popular market for Gardner-engined buses, with engines supplied to Malawi, Kenya and South Africa, on both ERF and Dennis chassis.

VERIFIED

SIGNALLING, COMMUNICATIONS AND TRAFFIC CONTROL EQUIPMENT

Company Listing by Country

AUSTRALIA
Philips Projects & Traffic Systems
Teknis

BELGIUM
SAIT-Devlonics

CANADA
Alpha Zaicon Technology
IRD
Mark IV
Primetech
Wardrop

CHINA, PEOPLE'S REPUBLIC
Casco Signal

CZECH REPUBLIC
Metra Blansko

DENMARK
ALSTOM
Focon
Infocom Systems

Finland
Mitron

FRANCE
Alcatel CGA
Alcatel Transport Automation
ALSTOM
CSEE Transport
Fels
Gorgy Timing
Lumiplan
Matra Transport
MDO
MS Relais
SLE
Steria
SYSECA

GERMANY
Adtranz
AEG Mobile Communication
Bosch
Dambach-Werke
Hanning & Kahl
Krauss-Maffei
Krueger
Lumino
Meister Electronic
Siemens
Transit Media
Trion
Visolux
Wandel & Goltermann

HUNGARY
Ganz Ansaldo

INDIA
Crompton Greaves

IRELAND
Data Display

ISRAEL
Ofek

ITALY
Aesys
AnsaldoBreda
Firema
Hitesys
Italtel Telesis
OTE
Sasib Railway
Solari
Sysco

JAPAN
Habuka
Hitachi
KE
Mitsubishi Electric
Nippon Signal

NETHERLANDS
Algemene Sein Industrie
Ansaldo Signal NV
Fokker Space
Nederland Haarlem
Peek
Simac

SPAIN
Sainco
SEPSA

SWEDEN
ATSS
Mobitec
PS Presentation System
Thoreb

SWITZERLAND
EBO
FP Displays
HPW
Moser-Baer
Motorola (Switzerland)
Omega Electronics
Sécheron

UK
Bosch
Data Display (UK)
Ferranti
GAI-Tronics DAC
ALSTOM
GEC-Marconi Aerospace
GEC-Marconi Defence Systems
Hanover Displays
Hoskyns
Howells
Jasmin Simtec
Minorplanet
Mirror Technology
Optech
Poletech
Racal Acoustics
Raychem
Redifon MEL
RSL
Sema
Siemens Traffic Controls
Siemens Transportation Systems
Techspan
Time 24
Transmitton
Vaughan Harmon Systems
Voice Perfect
Vultron
WCL
Westinghouse Signals

USA
American Loop
Amtech
Doron
EMX International
Globe
GRS
Harmon
Loronix
Motorola
Nu-Metrics
Orbital Sciences Corporation
Oval Window Audio
Postfield Systems
Quantum Sky
Rockwell
Siemens Transportation Systems
Talking Signs
Telephonics
Transit Control Systems
Union Switch & Signal
Vultron Incorporated

Classified Listing

ATC
Adtranz
Alcatel Transport Automation
ALSTOM
CS Transport
Firema Trasporti
Matra Transport
Sasib Railway
Siemens
Union Switch & Signal
Westinghouse Signals

ATO
Adtranz
ALSTOM
Firema Trasporti
Sasib Railway
Siemens
Westinghouse Signals

ATP
Adtranz
ALSTOM
ATSS
Firema Trasporti
Sasib Railway
SEPSA
Siemens
Westinghouse Signals

CLOCKS
Dambach-Werke
Gorgy Timing
Moser-Baer
Solari

CTC
Adtranz
Alcatel CGA
Alcatel Transport Automation
Algemene Sein Industrie
ALSTOM
Casco Signal
CSEE Transport
Firema Trasporti
Howells
Sainco
Sasib Railway
Teknis
Thoreb
Wardrop
Westinghouse Signals

GLOBAL POSITIONING SYSTEMS (GPS)
GRS
Hanover Displays
Infocom Systems
Italtel Telesis
Jasmin Simtech
Meister Electronic
Minorplanet
Orbital Sciences Corporation
Quantum Sky
Racal
Rockwell
Simac

PUBLIC ADDRESS
Adtranz
Alcatel CGA
American Loop
DAC
Firema Trasporti
Focon
Italtel Telesis
Jasmin Simtec
Meister Electronic

Moser-Baer
Optech
Oval Window Audio
SEPSA
Talking Signs
Telephonics
Thoreb
Transit Media
Transmitton
Voice Perfect
Wandel & Goltermann
WCL

RADIO COMMUNICATIONS SYSTEMS
Adtranz
AEG Mobile Communication
Alcatel CGA
Amtech
Bosch
DAC
GEC-Marconi
Harmon
Italtel Telesis
Jasmin Simtech
KE
Motorola
Motorola (Switzerland)
Nu-Metrics
OTE
Primetech
Redifon MEL
SAIT-Devlonics
Siemens
Siemens Transportation Systems
Simac
Telephonics
Transmitton
Vaughan Systems
Visolux
WCL
Westinghouse Signals

RADIO CONTROL
Adtranz
Alcatel CGA
Alcatel Transport Automation
ALSTOM
DSC Communications
Motorola
Visolux

SURVEILLANCE
Alpha Zaicon Technology
Italtel Telesis
Loronix
Mirror Technology
Optech
Primetech
Rockwell
Steria
Telephonics

SIMULATION SYSTEMS
Adtranz
Doron
Fokker Space
Hoskyns
Krauss-Maffei

TRAFFIC CONTROL
Adtranz
ALSTOM
AnsaldoBreda
Bosch
CSEE Transport
EMX International
Ganz Ansaldo

Hanning & Kahl
Hanover Displays
Harmon
Hitachi
Hitesys
HPW
IRD
Italtel Telesis
Moser-Baer
Nederland Haarlem
Nippon Signal
Nu-Metrics
Ofek
Peek
Philips Projects & Traffic Systems
Poletech
Rockwell
Sainco
SAIT-Devlonics
Sema
Siemens Traffic Controls
SLE
Solari
Steria
SYSECA
Vaughan Harmon Systems
Westinghouse Signals

VIGILANCE
Italtel Telesis
Loronix
Westinghouse Signals

VISUAL DISPLAYS
Adtranz
Aesys
DAC
Data Display
Focon
FP Displays
Globe
Gorgy Timing
Habuka
Hanover Displays
Harmon
Jasmin Simtech
Krueger
Lumino
Lumiplan
Mark IV
MDO
Meister Electronic
Metra Blansko
Mitron
Mobitec
MS Relais
Omega
Postfield Systems
PS Presentation System
Racal Acoustics
Redifon MEL
RSL
Sécheron
SEPSA
SLE
Solari
Sysco
SYSECA
Techspan
Thoreb
Transit Media
Transmitton
Trion
Vultron
Vultron Incorporated

Adtranz

DaimlerChrysler Railsystems
Signal Group
Holybrook House, 63 Castle Street, Reading RG1 7SN, UK
Tel: (+44 118) 952 48 00   Fax: (+44 118) 952 48 10
Product Unit Chief Executive, Signalling: P Nottrodt, NTC UK
(See main entry under Rail Vehicles and Traction Equipment)

Bangladesh: Kanta International Ltd, Signalling Agent for Bangladesh, 7/4 Aurangazeb Road, Dhaka 1207
Tel: (+88 2) 31 58 28   Fax: (+88 2) 81 33 72
Executive: G Ahmed

China: Adtranz Signal Ltd, 16 Bei 3-Zhong Lu, Tiexi District, 110025 Shenyang
Tel: (+86 24) 564 28 05   Fax: (+86 24) 564 28 08
Executive: Raymond Black

Denmark: DaimlerChrysler Railsystems (Signal) AS, PO Box 1509, DK-2650 Hvidovre
Tel: (+45 36) 39 01 00   Fax (+45 31) 49 57 50
Executive: Jrgen Green-Pedersen

Finland: DaimlerChrysler Railsystems (Finland) OY, Signalling Division, Atomitie 5C, FIN-00371 Helsinki

Germany: DaimlerChrysler Railsystems (Signal) Germany GmbH, PO Box 2656, D-38012 Braunschweig
Tel: (+49 531) 22 40   Fax: (+49 531) 224 10 65
Executive: Karl Ulrich Dobler

India: DaimlerChrysler Railsystems (India) Ltd, Signalling Division, Race Course Circle, PO Box 284, Baroda 390 001

Italy: DaimlerChrysler Railsystems (Signalling Division), Via Campo Romano 59, I-00173 Rome
Tel: (+39 67) 257 21   Fax: (+39 67) 267 10 72
Executive: Franco Pietrini

Korea, Republic of: DaimlerChrysler Railsystems (Korea) Ltd, Signalling Dept, 143-42 Samsung-dong Kangnam-ku, Wonbang Bldg, 10th Floor, 135-090 Seoul

Norway: DaimlerChrysler Railsystems, Signalling Division, Stasjonsveien 1, N-2011 Stroemmen

Poland: Adtranz Zwus Signal Ltd, UL Modelarska 12, PL-401-42, Katowice
Tel: (+48 32) 104 22 50   Fax: (+48 32) 104 22 44
Executive: Henryk Hytry

DaimlerChrysler Railsystems, UL Hoza 63/65, PL-006-81 Warszawa
Tel: (+48 22) 624 47 07   Fax: (+48 22) 624 47 68
Executive: Jan Walaszkowski
Production plant in Zory

Spain: DaimlerChrysler Railsystems, San José Artesano No 12-14, Poligono Industrial de Alcobendas, E-28100 Alcobendas (Madrid)
Tel: (+34 1) 657 91 00   Fax: (+34 1) 657 92 13
Executive: Ismael Olea

Sweden: DaimlerChrysler Railsystems (Signal) AB, PO Box 42505, SE-126 16 Stockholm
Tel: (+46 8) 681 50 00   Fax (+46 8) 681 51 00
Executive: Lennart Dock

Thailand: DaimlerChrysler Railsystems (Korea) Ltd, 3354/16-19, 6th floor Manorom Building, Rama 4 Road, Klongton, Klongtoei, Bangkoj 10110
Tel: (+66 2) 82 90   Fax: (+66 2) 249 85 19
Executive: Hans-Olof Hofverberg

UK: Adtranz, Signal House, Letcombe Street, Reading RG11AX
Tel: (+44 118) 953 80 00   Fax: (+44 118) 953 80 09
Executive: Ray Haines

USA: DaimlerChrysler Railsystems (North America) Inc, 1501 Lebanon Church Road, Pittsburgh Pennsylvania 15236-1491

Background: Adtranz signal technology has been fully electronic since 1978. Up to 1997, 146 electronic signal boxes have been commissioned, 41 are in production; 235 operation guiding control systems are in service supervising 2,500 stations. Around 4,000 vehicles have been equipped with the transponder (Balise) ATP control and 110,000 transponders commissioned.

Products: Development, design, engineering, production, sales, installation, maintenance, after-sales service for signalling systems including Integrated Control Rooms, Traction Management Systems (TMS), passenger information and station automatic systems.

Electronic systems for safety applications, including wayside and onboard computers with software for interlocking, ATP and Automatic Train Operation (ATO), train/track communications, including cable and radio transmission, coded track circuits, loops and transponders with associated wayside and trainborne equipment.

Trackside components include point machines, barriers, signals and electromechanical interlocking systems.

Auxiliary equipment includes train detectors, interference monitoring, GPS-based positioning, speed measuring and health monitoring systems.

Contracts
Australia: A contract has been signed with Victoria Public Transport Corporation and ABB Signal, Australia, with Adtranz as partner, for the replacement of the traffic management system for the Melbourne suburban lines. The new system will replace one supplied by ABB in 1982. It will cover 215 stations and control 38,000 departures per day. Delivery was scheduled for 1999.
Brazil: Trensurb (Empresa de Trens Urbanos) de Porto Alegre in southern Brazil has a contract with Adtranz Brazil for the 6.5 km extension of a metro line between Sapucaia and Sao Leopoldo districts.
Germany: Upper Rhine Railway Company Ltd, a suburban and regional LRT system, has taken delivery of a new electronic interlocking system for the Weinheim—Handschuheim line. The system will control 13 km of track including six stations.
Iran: Metro Teheran is taking delivery of electronic interlockings, local control systems and ATP from Adtranz as subcontractor. The system will have two lines, 44 stations and 31 trains operating on 54 km of track. It is being commissioned in three stages, December 1998, June and October 1999.
Korea, Republic of: Pusan metro Line 2 is receiving a turnkey signalling system with electronic interlocking, onboard ATP, ATO, track circuits and colourlight signals. Included is the supply of radio-based communication equipment. Commissioning was planned for September 1998 and during 2001.

SL has also ordered a complete signalling system for the new light rail branch between Gullmarsplan and Alvik, to be commissioned in 1999 and 2000. The turnkey contract includes design, installation and commissioning and will comprise a control system, three electronic interlockings, ATC and trackside equipment. Also included in the contract is an ATC system for the Saltjöbanan light rail line.

Developments: Following government backing to Nottingham Express Transit (NET), a privately-financed light rapid transit system serving the Greater Nottingham area, commercial contracts for the tram system are now being finalised with the preferred contractor, Arrow Light Rail Limited. Adtranz Total Rail Systems, the lead member of Arrow Light Rail Limited, is also responsible for project management and supply of 15 trams, signalling, electrification and depot equipment. The trams will be supplied by Adtranz Rolling Stock division in Derby, and this is a further order for the Eurotram which is already operating in Strasbourg and is currently being supplied to Strasbourg Phase II, Milan and Oporto. Signalling and electrification equipment will be supplied and installed by Adtranz Signal based in Reading.
Latvia: Latvian Railways has ordered the Adtranz Ebilock 950 which will be the first electronic interlocking system to be used in Latvia. Initially it will be used for stations in the capital of Riga and Tornakalns across the river Daugava. Starting in the year 2000, electronic. Adtranz will supply local control and supervisory equipment as well as interlocking computers and route indicators. It will also supervise installation and operational start-up. The contract with Latvia also includes control equipment from Finland and route indicators from the United Kingdom.
Russia: Linda near Gorki and Kalashnikovo, 250 km northwest of Moscow are being equipped with Adtranz Ebilock 950.

UPDATED

AEG Mobile Communication

AEG Mobile Communication GmbH
Wilhelm-Runge-Strasse 11, D-89081, Ulm, Germany
Tel: (+49 731) 505 02   Fax: (+49 731) 505 18 00
Directors: Dr Rainer Lasch; Marko Ançer

Products: Train radio systems for long distance, shunting and maintenance (trunking radio) and metro applications.

NEW ENTRY

Aesys

Aesys
Via Artigiani 41, I-24060 Brusaporto, Italy
Tel: (+39 035) 68 30 00   Fax: (+39 035) 68 00 30
General Manager: Dr Marcello Biava
Assistant to General Manager: Giuseppe Biava

Products: Electronic bus destination signs; next stop announcements; information displays at bus stops; fuel delivery control systems; vehicle control systems; LED bus destination signs.

VERIFIED

Alcatel CGA

Alcatel CGA Transport
PO Box 57, F-91229 Bretigny/Orge Cedex, France
Tel: (+33 1) 69 88 52 00   Fax: (+33 1) 69 88 58 50
General Manager: Jean-Claude Hue
Commercial Manager: Gilles Denacé
Communication Manager: Patricia Huc

Products: Automatic vehicle monitoring systems for bus, trolleybus and tram/light rail; traffic light pre-emption; vehicle location; onboard and at-stop passenger information displays, scheduling and statistics; voice and data radio transmission.

UPDATED

Alcatel Transport Automation

54 Rue Boétie, Paris, France
Tel: (+33 1) 40 76 10 10   Fax: (+33 1) 40 76 59 07
www: www.alcatel.com
President: Jean-Piere Forestier
Vice Presidents: Friedrich Smaxwil, Gérard Guiho
Director, Marketing and Communication: Renaud Da

Background: Alactel employs 2,500 people and has offices in Argentina, Austria, Brazil, Canada, China, Denmark, France, Germany, Italy, Mexico, Netherlands, Portugal, Singapore, Spain, Switzerland, UK and USA.

Products: ATC; train routing and signalling; network management; field equipment including axle counters, point machines, detectors, warning systems and signal controls; integrated rail communications; fleet management; passenger information boards; traffic management and maintenance.

Contracts: Interlocking systems over all Europe; ATC (Seltrac® technology) for Docklands Light Rail, UK, KCRC West Rail, Hong Kong and Kennedy airport, USA; integrated rail communications for Cairo, Istanbul, Oslo Gardermobanen, Stockholm Arlanda line and Copenhagen; network train mangement centre for Hong Kong, Madrid and Hamburg; fleet mangement systems for buses in Bordeaux, Strasbourg and Berlin (expected to be installed 2000).

UPDATED

Algemene Sein Industrie

Algemene Sein Industrie BV
Moeder Teresalaan 100, NL-3527 WB Utrecht, Netherlands
Tel: (+31 30) 292 96 11   Fax: (+31 30) 294 76 21
General Manager: R O van Manen
Sales and Marketing Manager: H J van Adrichem

A company in the Sasib Railway Group

Products: Specialists in turnkey projects for signalling and telecommunications schemes; complete signalling and control equipment, and associated components; automatic train control; computer-controlled CTC and NX interlocking; track circuit equipment; coded track signal control; level crossing warning equipment; cab signals/speed control; automatic vehicle identification equipment.
Signalling projects can be undertaken on a consortium basis.

VERIFIED

Alpha Zaicon Technology

Alpha Zaicon Technology Inc
35 Weston Road, Toronto, Ontario, Canada M6N 3P1
Tel: (+1 416) 763 51 58   Fax: (+1 416) 762 10 54
e-mail: alpha@istar.ca

Works
110-7808 132nd Street, Surrey, British Colombia, Canada V3W 4N1
Tel: (+1 604) 20 70   Fax: (+1 604) 591 90 70

Products: PIES (Platform Intrusion Emergency Stop) system based on sensor panels linked to MID-5000 controllers which integrate directly with SCADA and ATC control systems.

NEW ENTRY

ALSTOM

Alstom Signaling
33 rue des Bateliers, PO Box 165, F-93404, Saint-Ouen, Cedex, France
Tel: (+33 1) 40 10 63 35   Fax: (+33 1) 40 10 61 00
Senior Vice President : Gérard Blanc
(See main entry under Rail Vehicles and Traction Equipment)

ALSTOM Signalisation France
address as above
Managing Director: Philippe Huchant

ALSTOM Signaling Ltd
Borehamwood Industrial Park, Rowley Lane, Borehamwood WD6 5PZ, UK
Tel: (+44 181) 953 99 22   Fax: (+44 181) 207 59 05
Managing Director: Charles Burch

ALSTOM Signaling Benelux
PO Box 4211, B-6000 Charleroi, Belgium
Tel: (+32 71) 44 54 11   Fax: (+32 71) 44 57 75
Managing Director: Dominique Hausman

ALSTOM Signaling Italy
Via di Corticella 87/89, I-40128 Bologna, Italy
Tel: (+39 051) 41 91   Fax: (+39 051) 419 14 36
Managing Director: Giuseppe Bonfigli

ALSTOM Signaling Telecommunication
Via dell Elettronica 17, I-37139 Verona, Italy

ALSTOM Signaling Transportation
Via Nazario Sauro 38, I-20099 Sesto S Giovanni (Milano), Italy

ALSTOM Signaling Research
Via Salvatore Mattarese 4, I-70124 Bari, Italy

ALSTOM Transporte Ltda
Av. Octaviano, Alves de Lima 1480, Casa Verde, 02501 000, São Paulo, Brazil
Tel: (+55 11) 855 62 00   Fax : (+55 11) 855 63 90
Managing Director: André Guyvarc'h

ALSTOM International Operations (address as for head office above)
Managing Director : Henry Bussery
Deputy Managing Director: Emilio Gallocchio

ALSTOM Signaling Inc
150 Sawgrass Driveee, PO Box 20600, Rochester, New York 14602-0600, USA
Tel: (+1 716) 783 22 09   Fax: (+1 716) 783 20 50
Managing Director: John Penney

ALSTOM Signarail Canada
9 Place de Commerce, Brossard, Quebec J4W 2V6, Canada
Tel: (+1 514) 465 52 66   Fax: (+1 514) 465 52 67
Managing Director : Guy Desnoyers

ALSTOM Signaling Iberica
Apolonio Morales 13A, E-28036 Madrid, Spain
Tel: (+34 91) 343 17 70   Fax: (+34 91) 350 99 95
Managing Director: Antonio Puyol Gomez

ALSTOM Signaling Hellas
6 Parnassou Street, GR-151 24 Marouissi, Greece
Tel: (+30 1) 614 31 87   Fax: (+30 1) 614 31 85; 6
Managing Director: John Korialos

ALSTOM Signaling Dedicom
Priorparken 530, DK-2605 Brøndby, Denmark
Tel: (+45 43) 43 84 00   Fax: (+45 43) 43 84 01
Managing Director: Reiner Vanmanen

ALSTOM Signaling Hungary
Lehel út 3/b 1 Floor, H-1062 Budapest, Hungary
Tel: (+36 1) 359 98 71   Fax: (+36 1) 351 98 70
Managing Director: Rita Agoston

ALSTOM Transportation Pty Ltd
Railway Signaling South Africa
PO Box 4583, Germiston South 1411, South Africa
Tel: (+27 11) 902 77 20   Fax: (+27 11) 902 90 20
Managing Director: Hugh Rickert

ALSTOM Signaling Egypt
Street 201, No 13 Maadi, Cairo, Egypt
Tel: (+20 2) 352 80 73   Fax: (+20 2) 355 06 39
Managing Director: Jean-Peirre Fourment

ALSTOM Hong Kong Transport
9/F New Kowloon Plaza, 38 Tai Kok Road, Hong Kong
Tel: (+852) 23 90 19 00   Fax: (+852) 23 90 19 01
Managing Director: Andy Hunter

Products: Integrated signalling and control systems for main line and urban transport networks, from conception through design and installation to full life support. Relay-based and solid-state interlocking, ERTMS (European Rail Traffic Management System), ATC, ATP, ATO and ATS, CTC; driverless systems; passenger information systems, train graph systems, computer-aided maintenance systems; marshalling yard automation; safety plug-in relays; automatic level crossing barriers; control panels and illuminated diagrams; electric point machines, microwave communications; colourlight signals; jointed and jointless track circuits.

Contracts: ALSTOM has been selected to start an extensive test programme of Communication Based Train Control (CBTC) core technologies on MTA New York city transit.
A contract has been awarded by the Land Authority of Singapore to design and supply a driverless system for the North East line of Singapore metro.
ALSTOM is supplying a signalling system for Caracas metro authority, CAMC, Line 4 for completion in 2002.
ALSTOM is involved in the ERTMS programme development (European Rail Traffic Management System). It has been awarded a test-track contract to investigate compatibility of existing onboard and trackside equipment in Italy and France.
An advanced signalling system for the UK west coast main line is being installed for completion in 2006. GT Railway Maintenance Ltd, a joint venture between ALSTOM and Tarmac Construction, has acquired the Control Infrastructure Maintenance Company (CIMCo). CIMCo is responsible for maintenance of Railtrack's signalling and electrification equipment in the Midlands, East Anglia, mid-Wales and the West Coast route between London and Carlisle.
An agreement to sell, distribute and install products of Canadian company Télécité in Europe, Asia, South America, Africa and Australia has been signed. Télécité specialises in the design and manufacture of LED rail passenger information systems, including train instrumentation, control and passenger information.

Developments: ALSTOM Signaling has been awarded quality approval status ISO 9001.

UPDATED

American Loop

American Loop Systems Inc
29 Silver Hill Road, Suite 100, Milford, Mississippi 01757, USA
Tel: (+1 508) 634 02 00   Fax: (+1 617) 666 52 28
Project Co-ordinator: Robert A Gilmore

Products: MobiLoop hearing assistance system for buses and rail vehicles to provide accessibility for people who are hard of hearing.

VERIFIED

Amtech

Amtech Corporation
17304 Preston Road, E100 Dallas, Texas 75252-5613, USA
Tel: (+1 214) 733 60 59   Fax: (+1 214) 733 66 19
President and Chief Executive Officer:
  G Russell Mortenson

Products: Radio communications systems; hardware and software; radio frequency identification (RFID) technology for trucks, rail vehicles and other transport equipment.

VERIFIED

AnsaldoBreda

Ansaldo Trasporti
Ansaldo Transporti SpA
425 Via Argine, I-80147 Naples, Italy
Tel: (+39 081) 24 31 11   Fax: (+39 081) 243 26 98
An Ansaldo Finnmeccanica company

Subsidiary company
Ansaldo Signal NV
This company controls the Ansaldo signalling companies Ansaldo Signalamento Ferroviario, Italy, CSEE Transport, France, AT Signal System, Sweden, Union Switch & Signal, USA and Union Switch & Signal Pty in Australia.

Products: Power signalling apparatus; electronic relay interlocking; electronic track circuiting and continuous cab signalling; microcomputer-based automatic train operation equipment; centralised traffic control; train describer and automatic line supervision systems; level crossing automation and traffic control systems. Ansaldo also provides computer design for signalling and electrification systems with advanced technology.

Contracts: Include a centralised traffic control system for SNCFT Tunisia between Tunis and Bordj Cedria; driverless system in Copenhagen; an automatic signalling system for New York CTA; Microlok II control system for the Nuneaton to Peterborough line for Railtrack plc; CTC and signalling systems for emu depot in Seremban, Malaysia; ATC system for urban and suburban railways in Tehran, Iran; CTC and ATC signalling systems for Lines B, C and D of Metropolitano de Lisboa, Portugal.

UPDATED

ATSS

AT Signal System AB
A subsidiary of Ansaldo Trasporti SpA
PO Box 8142, SE-163 08 Spånga, Sweden
Tel: (+46 8) 621 95 00   Fax: (+46 8) 621 14 24
e-mail: atss@atss.se
Managing Director: Roberto Bauducco

Background: Parent company Ansaldo Trasporti acquired ATSS in 1997.

Products: ATP systems, traffic control centres and general signalling equipment.

Contracts: ATP systems have been supplied to WAGR and HI Australia, Midland Metro UK, KTMB Malaysia, BV Sweden, SJ Sweden, NSB Norway, FS Italy, Öresund Link Denmark/Sweden and NJT USA. ATO and radio block systems have been supplied to LKAB Sweden and traffic control centres to BV Sweden.

VERIFIED

Bosch

Robert Bosch GmbH
Zitadellenweg 34, D-13578 Berlin, Germany
Tel: (+49 711) 81 10   Fax: (+49 711) 811 66 30

UK subsidiary
Bosch Telecom Ltd
PO Box 98, Broadwater Park, North Orbital Road, Denham UB9 5HJ
Tel: (+44 1895) 83 44 66   Fax: (+44 1895) 83 85 48

Products: Mobile radio communications, including radio transceivers, trunked radios and base stations; satellite systems; security techniques; traffic control techniques.
  Bosch has been involved in pioneer work on the digital PMR standard and the DISCO SR 440 has a digital/analogue dual function system with encryption.
  Range of trunked radios in the VHF and UHF bands; Dikos 210 digital communications system; Flexplex XMP1 combined PCM transmission and cross-connect system; intercom systems for platform and trackside operations.

VERIFIED

Casco Signal

Casco Signal Ltd
1150 Qiu jiang Lu, Shanghai 200071, People's Republic of China
Tel: (+86 21) 663 70 80   Fax: (+86 21) 663 92 23
President: Lu Delian

Products: Microcomputer-based CTC; DSS (dispatcher supervision system); marshalling yard control systems.

VERIFIED

Crompton Greaves

Crompton Greaves Ltd
Rail Projects Division
5G, Vandhna, 11 Tolstoy Marg, 110 001 New Delhi, India
Tel: (+91 11) 331 70 75/373 04 45
Fax: (+91 11) 331 70 75/332 43 60
Chairman & Managing Director: K K Nohria
Board Member & President: C P Dusad
Vice President, Rail Transportation: B Banerjee
Deputy General Manager, Rail Transportation:
  M P Singhal

Products: Signalling relays, point machines, axle counters, mosaic control and indication panels; route relay interlocking, solid state signalling; signal multiplexers.

VERIFIED

CSEE Transport

CSEE Transport
4 Avenue du Canada, PO Box 243, Les Utis, F-91944 Courtaboeuf, France
Tel: (+33 1) 69 29 65 65   Fax: (+33 1) 69 29 07 07
Chief Executive Officer: G Dubot
Vice President, Marketing & Sales: E Viollet
Vice President, Technology & Development: A Roche

Products: Control systems for urban and suburban railways.
  CTC systems; ATC; SACEM and SESAM and ATO systems; vital relays; hot axlebox and wheel detectors; odometer; electric point machines; electronic treadles; level crossing systems.

UPDATED

Dambach-Werke

Dambach-Werke GmbH
Adolf-Dambach Strasse, D-76571 Gaggenau, Germany
Tel: (+49 7225) 64 01   Fax: (+49 7225) 643 00

Products: Infra-red bus location system; clock systems.

VERIFIED

Data Display

Data Display Co Ltd
Deerpark Industrial Estate, Ennistymon, Co. Clare, Ireland
Tel: (+353 65) 712 42   Fax: (+353 65) 713 11
www: http://www.data-display.com
Marketing Manager: Conor McFadden

Subsidiary company
Data Display UK Ltd (qv)

Products: Design, manufacture, installation and service of LED electronic passenger information display systems.

Contracts: IGG Data Display is installing LED passenger information displays in the 12 new stations along the London Underground Jubilee Line Extension. The project consists of 92 platform displays and 37 ticket hall displays. The platform displays show two lines of ultra-bright yellow characters, 40 characters per line. The ticket hall displays show six lines of standard amber characters, 30 characters per line.
  The displays show passengers relevant travel information such as the destination of on-coming trains, warning messages, reminders to purchase tickets, and ticket prices.
  Past contracts successfully designed and installed by IGG Data Display include passenger information displays for London Underground Central Line and also front-of-train indicators.

Developments: Data Display's new radio pager-controlled information display is designed for those applications where connection of a display to a system using data cable is prohibitively expensive or impractical. With this radio pager display, Data Display can now install a cost-effective information display system at any location within pager network coverage.
  The new radio pager display offers two lines of up to 20 characters, 50 mm height, with multicolour characters. The display comes complete with attached radio pager Motorola J39 series or RS-232 data input for connection to a pager docking station. The contrast-enhancing front screen is anti-reflective. The character lines are separated to make readability easier. Customised software is also available. The displays offer the extra benefit of an audible alarm function.

UPDATED

Data Display UK

Data Display UK Ltd
3 The Meadows, Waterlooville PO7 7XX, UK
Tel: (+44 1705) 24 75 00   Fax: (+44 1705) 24 75 19
e-mail: datadisplay@dial.pipex.pipex.com
Managing Director: Alan Graham
Sales Manager: Ray Hodson
Director: Paul Neville

Background: Formerly IGG Systems, the company was acquired by Data Display (qv) in 1996.

Products: Approved supplier of visual communications equipment to British railway companies, road and airport applications and for bus stop, terminus and vehicle information displays.

Contracts: Include supply of display systems for Dublin Area Rapid Transit, London Underground Jubilee line and Buslink route signs in Bournemouth, UK. UK Highways Agency-approved.

Developments: A radio pager information display system has been introduced; a range of LED graphics and display systems is available.

UPDATED

Doron

Doron Precision Systems Inc
PO Box 400, Binghamton, New York 13902-0400, USA
Tel: (+1 607) 772 04 78   Fax: (+1 607) 772 67 60
Vice President and Chief Executive Officer:
   Karl J Hirshman

Products: Bus driver simulation systems; interactive L300VMT-Bus simulator.

VERIFIED

EBO

EBO AG
Zürichstrasse 103, CH-8134 Adliswil, Switzerland
Tel: (+41 1) 487 22 11   Fax: (+41 1) 487 22 77

Products: Cable management systems; halogen-free cable trays and ground ducts in grp; pultruded profiles for electric cabinets, ladders, grates and guard rails.

Contracts: Supplied equipment for DB rolling stock reconstruction, BVG Berlin, RER Paris and London Underground Ltd.

Developments: Include insulation systems for overhead lines, cable tray systems for suspension of heavy lighting units and non-conductive support systems.

VERIFIED

Fels

Fels SA
2 rue J M Jacquard, F-67400 Illkirch Graffenstaden, France
Tel: (+33 3) 88 67 10 60   Fax: (+33 3) 88 67 04 10

Products: Electrical contacts; special connectors.

VERIFIED

Ferranti

Ferranti Technologies Ltd
Cairo Mill, Waterhead, Oldham OL4 3JA, UK
Tel: (+44 161) 624 02 81   Fax: (+44 161) 624 52 44
e-mail: sales@ferranti-technologies.co.uk
www: www.ferranti-technologies.co.uk
Managing Director: T R Tuckley
Commercial Director: P Davies
Finance Director: F Brinksman
Operations Director: D J Platt
Sales and Marketing: Andrew Beesley

Products: Non-contact distance/velocity measurement (DMVD) for traction braking, signalling; auxiliary power conversion for ancillary systems; UKAS accredited environmental testing; stabilisation technology for tilt control.

Contracts: Ferranti Technologies has secured a contract from ALSTOM for supply of DVMD in support of an overseas refurbishment programme.

UPDATED

Firema Trasporti SpA

Ercole Marelli Trazione Unit
Viale Edison 110, I-20099 Sesto San Giovanni, Milano, Italy
Tel: (+39 02) 249 41   Fax: (+39 02) 248 35 08
(See main entry under Rail Vehicles and Traction Equipment)

Products: Complete signalling systems for tramway, light rail and metros; electronic remote-control and CTC systems; ATC, ATP, ATO and ATS; onboard computer; automatic voice announcement of next stop, public address for buses and trains.

VERIFIED

Focon

Focon Electronic Systems A/S
PO Box 269, Damvang, DK-6400 Sønderborg, Denmark
Tel: (+45) 73 42 25 00   Fax: (+45) 73 42 25 01
e-mail: focon@focon.dk
www: www.focon.com
Managing Director: Henrik Raunkjaer
Senior Manager, Sales: Niels-Henrik Hansen

Products: Audio-visual and communication systems for onboard applications, passenger entertainment systems, public address, alarm, crew communications and talk-back systems, automatic seat reservation systems. Video surveillance and full-colour graphic displays.

Contracts: Internal and external information displays, PA with digital voice announcer, passenger emergency talkback system, cab alarm system and crew communication have been supplied to ALSTOM for London Underground Jubilee Line trains, to Siemens for 112 Copenhagen S-Bane trains, for Penduloso trains in Lisbon, to SL Stockholm for tramcars and for Copenhagen Oresund Train Unit including GPS positioning, train radio communication and luggage racks.

UPDATED

Fokker Space

Fokker Space BV
PO Box 32070, NL-2303 DB Leiden, Netherlands
Tel: (+31 71) 524 50 00   Fax: (+31 71) 524 55 07
e-mail: info@fokkerspace.nl
Product Manager, Civil Simulators: Jos A Hoogstraten

Products: Driver training simulation systems. Includes a low-priced video system, combined with computer-generated images, available as full in-cab simulation system and also as software for computer.

The system is customised for each operator, who produces a video tape of the line for which training is required. This can then be added to with signals, traffic, emergency incidents and similar problems that the driver will be expected to deal with. A similar system is available which is based on a fully computer-generated image of the outside view.

An addition to the simulation system is a train commissioning/decommissioning training programme in which the driver is trained to carry out the necessary procedures and then tested on them (Vehicle Procedure Trainer). This may be combined with a stand-alone route trainer that provides an interactive environment for the student to quickly familiarise with routes, signalling systems and driving procedures.

UPDATED

FP Displays

FP Displays AG
PO Box 823, Zürich, Switzerland
Tel: (+41 1) 810 68 58   Fax: (+41 1) 810 81 36
Director: Andrew Murray

UK subsidiary
Park House, 10 Park St, Bristol BS1 5HX
Tel: (+44 117) 925 11 25   Fax: (+44 117) 922 55 03

Products: Dot matrix displays

Range: Electronic displays for bus destination displays, information displays for buses, railway stations and airports.

Contracts: Supplies major bus destination sign manufacturers in Europe.

Developments: A display is being developed combining light-reflecting displays with LED lighting.

VERIFIED

GAI-Tronics

Shobnall Street, Burton on Trent DE14 2HD, UK
Tel: (+44 1283) 50 05 00   Fax: (+44 1283) 50 04 00
e-mail: sales@gai-tronics.co.uk
www: www.gai-tronics.com
Managing Director: George Hopkin
Financial Director: Toby Balmer
Marketing Director: Don Borden
Systems Director: Paul Cooper
Sales Executive, Transport: Steven Dade
Manufacturing Director: Ralph Midgley

Products: Weather and vandal-resistant telephones and help points for rail and road applications including simple analogue, cellular and intelligent systems. Onboard train (metro, light and heavy rail) passenger communications.

Supplies distributed industrial PA and radio systems for road and rail builders, suitable for tunnelling applications; has supplied equipment for London's Jubilee line extension and the Channel Tunnel. Self-monitoring and reporting telephone (SMART) for its range of weather and vandal-resistant analogue telephones; simple diagnostics for onboard train communication systems.

Contracts: Held with Midland Metro for public address and crew communications systems; Heathrow Express onboard passenger communications; vandal and weatherproof telephones for Railtrack and London Underground; European Overnight Service onboard passenger communications; also PA system for refurbished Mk II and Mk III fleets for Virgin WCML, Midland Main Line, Anglia.

UPDATED

Ganz Ansaldo

Ganz Ansaldo Electric Ltd
Lövöház u 39, H-1024 Budapest, Hungary
Tel: (+36 1) 175 33 22   Fax: (+36 1) 156 29 89
President: Dr János Barabás
Managing Director: Ing Giuseppe Fittavolini
Commercial Director: Dr M Sauli

Products: Signalling and interlocking equipment; level crossing controls; colourlight signals; central traffic control system for metro and suburban lines; complete turnkey systems.

VERIFIED

GEC-Marconi Aerospace

GEC-Marconi Aerospace
Abbey Works, Titchfield, Fareham PO14 4QA, UK
Tel: (+44 1329) 85 30 00   Fax: (+44 1329) 85 37 97
www: www.marconicomms.com

Products: Monitoring and secure control systems.

UPDATED

Contracts: Orbital Sciences Corporation is supplying Virginia Railway Express commuter rail system with OrbTrac™-100 vehicle tracking and communications system on 14 trains and 19 station platforms throughout the company's system.

OrbTrac™-100 is a GPS system that provides customer information, vehicle tracking, digital cellular communications and timekeeping information.

VERIFIED

OTE

PO Box 402, Via Barsanti 8, I-50127 Firenze, Italy
Tel: (+39 055) 438 11   Fax: (+39 055) 438 13 21
President: Raffaele Esposito
Managing Director: Carlo Lastrucci
Sales Director: Luigi Papoff
Sales Director, ATC & Government Market:
   Aldo Pietro Paggi
Marketing and Product Definition Director:
   Mauro De Lauri

Parent company: Marconi Group

Products: OTE Elettra (standard TETRA system): Digital trunked mobile radio system complying with TETRA standard for bus, rail and other applications.

VERIFIED

Oval Window Audio

Oval Window Audio
33 Wildflower Court, Nederland, Colorado 80466, USA
Tel: (+1 303) 447 36 07   Fax: (+1 303) 447 36 07
Director of Research & Development: Norman Lederman

Products: Mobiloop hearing assistance system for buses and rail vehicles.

VERIFIED

Peek

Peek Traffic
PO Box 2542, NL-3800 GB Amersfoort, Netherlands
Tel: (+31 33) 454 17 77   Fax: (+31 33) 454 18 50
Managing Director: Ron Amsterdam

Products: VETAG (vehicle identification system); VECOM (vehicle communication), a two-way high-speed data communication system between vehicle and trackside; Transmation (Transport Automation), complete management information gathering and processing network.

Bus Tracker system for location of buses, improved fleet usage, improved management and better control.

Contracts: Automatic point switching systems have been provided for light rail networks, with in some cases automatic vehicle monitoring as well, in Den Haag, Amsterdam, Utrecht, Rotterdam, Wien, Graz, Turin, Genève, Philadelphia, Calgary, Boston, San Jose, San Francisco, Portland and San Diego; also in Denver, Rome, and 14 cities in eastern Germany.

Metro and commuter rail systems equipped include Den Haag (semi-metro), Bruxelles, Tyne & Wear, Chicago's Skokie Swift line and London Underground. Also involved in bus priority projects in 80 towns in the Netherlands, in Grenoble, Le Mans and Stockholm; and automatic control and management systems for compact bus/tram stations in Amsterdam, Lyon, Eindhoven and Zaandam.

Amsterdam's Amstelveen hybrid metro/tramway line is equipped with onboard timetable adherence system to ensure scheduled arrivals at critical traffic intersections. VECOM controls passenger information displays at stops and on board.

UPDATED

Philips Projects & Traffic Systems

Philips Projects & Traffic Systems
2 Greenhills Avenue, Moorebank, New South Wales, Australia
Tel: (+61 29) 612 54 99   Fax: (+61 29) 601 76 65
General Manager: Les Hill

A division of Philips Electronics Australia Ltd

Products: Integrated electronics solutions for infrastructure projects in the areas of communication, security, flow control, traffic management and environmental control. Also expertise on project financing, project management and life-cycle management. Applications include airports, railway stations, hospitals and traffic applications.

UPDATED

Poletech

Poletech Systems Ltd
Bowbridge Road, Newark NG24 4EQ, UK
Tel: (+44 1636) 61 14 26   Fax: (+44 1636) 61 21 21
e-mail: sales@poletech.co.uk
www: www.poletech.co.uk
Chairman: James R Lee
Managing Director: Dr A J Lawrenson

Products: Poletech pole mounting system allowing quick replacement of pole without civil works, also suitable for LRT systems; Flatpak cable access boxes.

Contracts: Poletech is supplying equipment for the Greenwich Millennium site interchange; the Poletech system is being used to support all lighting columns, traffic signals, pedestrian guard rail and signage during the refurbishment of London's bus stations.

UPDATED

Postfield Systems

Postfield Systems
Old Barn Lane, Kenley CR8 SAU, UK
Tel: (+44 181) 645 97 60
e-mail: carl.littlejohn@postfield.co.uk
www: www.postfield.co.uk
Directors: J F Coward; L E Hardy
Sales Contact: Carl Littlejohn

Products: Information displays

Contracts: A new customer information display system is being installed at Paddington station, London. The first phase of the project was due for completion at the end of October 1998. The Postfield Control System may be operated as a stand-alone system (as in Paddington) or alternatively may be operated in a networked environment.

NEW ENTRY

Primetech

Primetech Electronics Inc
275 Kesmark Street, Dollard des Ormeaux, Quebec H9B 3J1, Canada
Tel: (+1 514) 421 00 23   Fax: (+1 514) 421 12 41
Director of Marketing: Barry Simcoe

Products: Trainline multiplexing and radio-linked transmission; train monitoring systems; event logging; computerised diagnostics and maintenance; intelligent surveillance.

VERIFIED

PS Presentation System

PS Presentation System AB
PO Box 654, SE-581 07 Linköping, Sweden
Tel: (+46 13) 11 12 25   Fax: (+46 13) 13 07 47
Main Works: Hamngatan 9, Linköping
Managing Director: Mikael Hult
System Sales: Thomas Hult

Products: Passenger information public monitor presentation systems; TV monitors display information in colour. System also available with LCD, LED and electromagnetic flip-dot displays.

VERIFIED

Quantum Sky

Quantum Sky Inc
108W Chicago Blvd, Tecumseh, Michigan 49286, USA
Tel: (+1 517) 424 80 00   Fax: (+1 517) 424 83 00
www: http://www.qsky.com
Chief Operating Officer: Dr S George Schiro

Products: DataGuide™ GPS-based stop announcement system, precise to 1 cm; GPS vehicle location.

VERIFIED

Racal Acoustics

Racal Acoustics Ltd
Waverley Industrial Park, Hailsham Drive, Harrow HA1 4TR, UK
Tel: (+44 181) 427 77 27   Fax: (+44 181) 427 03 50
Managing Director: D L McDonald
Sales and Marketing Director: A Dent

Associated company
Racal Telecom
Phoenix House, Station Hill, Reading RG1 1NB, UK
Tel: (+44 118) 908 60 72   Fax: (+44 118) 908 66 15

Products: Include the RA705 weatherproof telephone for use by railways, power stations, local authorities, the armed services and by both heavy and light industrial areas which require reliable telephony in adverse conditions. A particular feature of the RA705 is the ease of installation and maintenance. The front panel telephone unit can be quickly detached from its housing by undoing tamper-resistant panel fastenings. Handsets and cordage can also be quickly replaced. Telephones can be wall, side of pole or top of pole mounted, either through the top and bottom cap fixing holes, or if extra security is required, directly through the rear of the casing. Four basic types of telephone are available in the range: full keypad DTMFILD, Central Battery (CB), Magneto (LB) and Autodialers with between one and six installer programmable numbers. A feature unique to the RA705 series is the optional line-powered illuminated panel.

Racal's RA706 Self Reporting telephone is suitable for use by railways and other areas which require reliable telephony in adverse conditions. At the time of installation, the telephones are manually programmed with their location numbers, (network number of the telephone and management station) and auto-dial number(s) if applicable. The telephone is commissioned by the installer invoking it to call the management system. Once this first connection is made, the management system automatically logs the telephone onto the system and installs its reporting functions. Thereafter, status reports from telephones are instigated, received and stored by the management station, and presented to the user automatically in near-realtime. Users can specify whether the information is to be presented on-screen or remotely via fax/printer links. Maintenance engineers can be alerted within seconds of a telephone failure report of location, type of phone and nature of fault. Corrective action can then be taken very quickly.

The Management Station consists of a standard PC, and a Line Interface Unit (LIU). The LIU allows the PC to interface into the public switched Telephone Network. The Line Interface Unit and the PC are linked via a standard RS-232 link. The Line Interface Unit has the capacity to accept up to 2,000 reports per 24 hours.

The data base allows for statistical analysis of usage and faults for each telephone and/or site location at any time. Reports from telephones are automatically logged, day and night, and the status of the complete system is also available.

The RA708 weatherproof telephone is fully contained within a cast aluminium weatherproof case. The handset is moulded in polyurethane and designed to withstand arduous use. The handset can be fitted with an armoured cord, if required, to provide additional resistance to vandalism or heavy industrial use. It can be wall mounted or side-of-pole mounted using the standard fittings supplied. If required a top of pole mount is available.

The RA711 vandal resistant telephone is based on a single sheet of stainless steel and provides hands-free, loudspeaking operation. Since there are no protruding parts to be damaged, these telephones offer high resistance to vandalism. A version incorporating full dial pad is made for applications where there is a requirement to dial other extensions. All versions include the facility for the provision of an external inductive loop for hearing-aid users, where this is required. The vandal resist telephone is suitable for security systems, shipboard communications, railways, underground transport, emergency applications in places like lifts, rail platforms and other outside buildings.

UPDATED

Raychem

Raychem Limited
Faraday Road, Dorcan, Swindon SN3 5HH, UK
Tel: (+44 1793) 52 81 71   Fax: (+44 1793) 57 25 16
Managing Director: David Ryan
Worldwide Rail Market Manager: Martin O'Brien
Public Relations Manager, Europe: Neil Madle

Products: Low-fire-hazard cable and harness components; multiplex databus systems; permanent identification systems; interconnection devices; freeze protection of contact rails, points and crossings, brake and diesel fuel lines; temperature and condensation control; HV and LV cable accessories.

Computerised marking with TMS System 90 equipment reduces time and effort spent on electrical installations for locomotives.

VERIFIED

Redifon MEL

Redifon MEL Limited
Newton Road, Crawley RH10 2TU, UK
Tel: (+44 1293) 51 88 55   Fax: (+44 1293) 41 64 00
e-mail: kenm@rmel.com
Transport Sales Manager: Ken McFarland

Products: Inductive loop track-to-train data transmission system, available in both one-way and two-way variants. This system can be used for correct side door enable (CDSE) and selective door control. Current and next station on-train information can also be provided. Applications requiring in-cab signalling and platform edge door control and synchronisation, can also be satisfied with these products. High-availability radio-based data transmission system for use in signalling applications.

Contracts: Development contract for a Train Protection Warning System (TPWS) for Railtrack PLC. Provision of track to train transmission systems for both the Jubilee line extension (JLE), and Northern line projects of London Underground. Supply of platform screen door synchronisation system for LRT II, in Kuala Lumpur. New competitively priced track to train vehicle identification system.

UPDATED

Rockwell

Rockwell Collins Inc
Collins Avionics and Communications Division
350 Collins Road, NE, Cedar Rapids, Iowa 52498, USA
Tel: (+1 319) 395 51 00   Fax: (+1 319) 295 47 77
e-mail: cacd@cacd.rockwell.com
www: www.cacd.rockwell.com
Director: Gregory W Tomsic

Subsidiary
Rockwell Collins (UK) Ltd
Suttons Business Park, Reading RG6 1LA, UK
Tel: (+44 118) 935 90 70   Fax: (+44 118) 935 14 56

Products: Electronic systems for surveillance and control of vehicles in traffic; advanced traffic management systems; passenger information systems.

UPDATED

RSL

Regional Services Ltd
Unit 3, Fullwood Close, Aldermans Green Industrial Estate, Coventry CV2 2SS, UK
Tel: (+44 1203) 61 81 89   Fax: (+44 1203) 62 22 46

Products: Video display units consisting of monitors, line receivers and digital video converters.

VERIFIED

Sainco

Sainco Trafico
Albarracín 21, E-28037 Madrid, Spain
Tel: (+34 91) 304 42 66   Fax: (+34 91) 327 02 17
General Manager: Joaquin Corodado
Marketing Manager: I del Barrio
Activity Manager: Martinez Jorcano

Products: CTC; advanced remote-control systems for traction power substations; communication systems.

VERIFIED

SAIT-Devlonics

SAIT-Devlonics
Member of the SAIT-RadioHolland Group
Chaussée de Ruisbroek 66, B-1180 Bruxelles, Belgium
Tel: (+32 2) 370 54 78   Fax: (+32 2) 376 68 73
Managing Director: S Verstraete

Products: Radiotelephony and data transmission systems; passenger information systems; radio transmission system developed for use in tunnels; modems, X25, ISDN.

UPDATED

Sasib Railway

Sasib Railway SpA
Via di Corticella 87-89, I-40128 Bologna, Italy
Tel: (+39 051) 419 11 11   Fax: (+39 051) 52 95 94
Chief Executive Officer and Managing Director:
   Giuseppe Bonfigli
(See ALSTOM SIGNALING in this section)

Signalling Division (address as above)
General Manager: Stefanino Amaroli
Sales Manager, Italy: Augusto Cei
Technical Manager: Rolando Bassignani

Telecommunications Division
Sales Manager, Export Division: P E Prina Mello
Technical Manager, Export Division: Adriano Ghetti

Other locations
Sasib Railway Ibérica SA
c/Estudiantes 5, E-28040 Madrid, Spain
Tel: (+34 91) 535 25 00   Fax: (+34 91) 554 99 53
General Manager: Antonio Pujol
Sales Manager: M Tolmos

Sasib Hellas SA
53 Solomou Street, GR-104 32 Athens, Greece
Tel: (+30 1) 523 86 25   Fax: (+30 1) 523 86 47
General Manager: John Korialos

Casco Signal Ltd (qv)
Algemene Sein Industrie bv (qv)
General Railway Signal Corporation (GRS) (qv)

Products: Design, supply, installation and commissioning of signalling, telecommunications and electrification systems.

Electronic and relay-based route control interlocking systems; steady and coded-current automatic block; continuous and intermittent cab signalling and speed control; CTC and train describer systems; ATP, ATO and ATS; electromechanical and electronic equipment for signalling installations such as track circuits; DC and AC safety relays; level crossing protection; mosaic-type control panels.

Telecommunications: computerised workstations; telephone operator installations; internal and portable telephones; single line control systems; CTC; passenger information systems; track-to-train and train-to-train communications via cellular and private UHF radio networks; fibre optics.

Contracts: Signalling systems for: railways in Lithuania, China, Denmark (Banestyrelsen), PKP Poland, CD Czech Republic and Banverket Sweden.

UPDATED

Sécheron

Sécheron Ltd
14 Avenue de Sécheron, CH-1211 Genève, Switzerland
Tel: (+41 22) 739 41 11   Fax: (+41 22) 738 73 05
e-mail: info@secheron.com
www: http://www.secheron.com
Chief Executive Officer: Beth Krasna
Executive Vice President: Paul Bieri
Sales Manager: Jimmy Cuche
Marketing Manager: René Jenni

Subsidiary companies
CKD Sécheron spol sro, Praha, Czech Republic
Sécheron Hasler Praha spol sro, Czech Republic
Pixy AG, Baden, Switzerland
(See also Electrification and Rail and Bus Components sections)

Products: Microprocessor-controlled On-Train Monitoring and Recording (OTMR) systems, speed and distance measuring systems, optical pulse generators for axle or gearbox mounting, modular cab display systems for ATC and ATP applications; compact LCD display systems including high-performance LCD displays based on PC architecture.

UPDATED

Sema

Sema Group Systems Ltd
Rail Control Systems
Lindsay House, 149 Farringdon Road, London EC1R 3AD, UK
Tel: (+44 171) 830 43 33   Fax: (+44 171) 278 05 74
Business Manager: W Parkman

Products: Design and supply of computer systems; electronic signalling; passenger information; ticketing software; traffic management planning; management information systems; transport consultancy.

VERIFIED

SEPSA

Sistemas Electrónicos de Potencia SA
Polig Indust La Estación, C/ Albatross 7 y 9, E-28320 Pinto
Madrid, Spain
Tel: (+34 91) 691 52 61   Fax: (+34 91) 691 39 77
President: Nicolas Fuster
General Manager: Felix Ramos
Commercial Director: Antonio Sosa
Technical Director: Carlos de la Viesca

Products: Public address systems; automatic station
announcer; internal and external displays (LED or dot-
matrix); monitoring/control systems for auxiliary and
traction equipment; crash event recorders; ATP systems.

VERIFIED

Siemens

Siemens AG
Transportation Systems Group
Signalling and Control Systems, Mass Transit
Ackerstrasse 22, D-38126 Braunschweig, Germany
Tel: (+49 226) 22 30   Fax: (+49 531) 226 22 30
President: Thomas Ganswindt
Vice President, Business Administration and Finance:
  Michael Duttenhofer

Subsidiary
HPW (Häni-Prolectron)(qv)

Joint venture
Matra Transport International (qv) is a joint venture of
Siemens Transportation Systems and the Lagadère
Group.

Products: ATC, ATP and ATO (up to fully automated
driverless train operation); interlockings (SICAS); signals;
detection of vehicles on track.
  AVM, AVL; onboard information systems; traffic light
pre-emption.
  Also   passenger   information   systems,
telecommunications/train radio and ticketing and fare
collection management systems; data communication
systems; fire detection and intrusion detection systems.

Contracts: Contracts have been received for ATC
systems for Stockholm, Zürich S-Bahn, Stuttgart
Stadtbahn, Bielefeld, Frankfurt, Mainz, München, Berlin
and Wien. Also SICAS interlockings for Köln, Guangzhou
and Bangkok.

Siemens Aktiengesellschaft
Transportation Systems Group (VT)
Berlin Production Centre
PO Box 9002 20, Elsenstrasse 87-96, D-12414 Berlin,
Germany
Tel: (+49 30) 38 65 19 86   Fax: (+49 30) 386 51 11
Managing Director: Dr R Bänsch

Products: Intelligent displays, auto-ID systems, radar
sensors, cab driver panels, master switches, LED and
filament lamps for signals, relays, control equipment
cabinets and boxes, heating systems, plastic cable ducts.

UPDATED

Siemens Traffic Controls

Siemens Traffic Controls Ltd
Sopers Lane, Poole BH17 7ER, UK
Tel: (+44 1202) 78 20 00   Fax (+44 1202) 78 24 35
Managing Director: David Carter
Marketing Manager: Colin Baker

Products: Road traffic controllers (junction and
pedestrian); urban traffic control systems (fixed time and
adaptive – SCOOT), control office equipment, data
transmission and field equipment; motorway control and
communications systems; bus priority and information
systems.

Contracts: SCOOT systems have been installed in the
UK, North America, China and the Middle East;
expressway emergency telephone systems in China and
Brazil; variable message text signs in the UK and Brazil.

Developments: New products recently developed
include a new traffic controller (ST800), a four-channel
urban loop detector (ST4R), and a type-approved OMCU/
MOVA unit.

UPDATED

Siemens Transportation Systems Inc

Siemens Transportation Systems Inc
Headquarters and Mainline Infrastructure Division, 186
Wood Avenue South, Iselin, New Jersey 08830, USA
Tel: (+1 732) 205 22 00   Fax: (+1 732) 603 73 79
President and Chief Executive Officer: J Morrison

Products: Signalling, safety and management control
systems for mass transport systems and main line
railways.

UPDATED

Siemens Transportation Systems

Siemens Transportation Systems Ltd
Sopers Lane, Poole BHI7 7ER, UK
Tel: (+44 1202) 78 20 67   Fax: (+44 1202) 78 28 38
Managing Director: K Tutton
General Manager: A J Rose

Products: Radio systems have been developed covering
a range of analogue and digital technologies, each
system specifically designed to meet the railway
environment. The basic radio infrastructure utilises
standard systems such as MPT1327 analogue trunked,
TETRA digital trunked and GSM digital cellular.
Customised mobile racks support speech and data
communication with interfaces to a range of train
functions. These include train control, positive train
identification and train location (transponder or GPS). In
the control room a local area network links the radio
switch to dispatcher and maintenance terminals with
customer specific functionality.
  Onboard products include the RailVision television
systems, providing rail operators with an integrated
passenger information and entertainment system offering
the generation of additional revenue through advertising.

UPDATED

Simac

Simac Systems BV
PO Box 340, NL-5500 AH Veldhoven, Netherlands
Tel: (+31 40) 258 28 59   Fax: (+31 40) 258 22 60
Managing Director: Bert Duursma

Subsidiary company
Simac Technig Ltd
Leyland DAF Buildings, Eastern Bypass, Thame OX9 3FB,
UK

Products: Fleet management and vehicle location using
Inmarsat-C GPS (global positioning system); fuel
management; cellular radio, all making use of LOGIQ
onboard computer systems.

VERIFIED

SLE

SLE
A Mark IV Industries Company
Avenue Emmanuel Pontremoli, Nice La Plaine 1, Building
F4, F-06200 Nice, France
Tel: (+33 4) 92 29 60 30   Fax: (+33 4) 92 29 60 31
Managing Director: Beat Tanner
Export Manager: Didier Moraldo
Project Managers: Eric Marquet, Eric Laurence

Products: Onboard and stationary passenger information
systems; Videobus bus stop and Infobus onboard
information display; Busmatic automatic traffic light
priority system; computer-aided dispatching; automatic
vehicle location and monitoring.
  AIDA is an improved fleet management and passenger
information system comprising vehicle location,
computerised dispatching, and video/audio passenger
information.

Contracts: Has supplied systems to transport
undertakings in Helsinki, Nice, Orvieto and Terni (Italy).
The Countdown bus-stop passenger information system
demonstrated on London Transport's bus route 18 was
supplied by SLE and has been expanded to 350 sites.
Other passenger information systems are in operation in
Chambery and Cannes, France; Cayenne, French
Guyana; and Monaco.

VERIFIED

Solari

Solari Di Udine SpA
29 Via Gino Pieri, I-33100 Udine, Italy
Tel: (+39 0432) 49 71   Fax: (+39 0432) 48 01 60
President: Massimo Paniccia
Vice President: Arduino Paniccia

Products: Information display and traffic control systems;
clock systems; attendance recording systems; access
control; data collection systems; parking meter.

Contracts: Include indicators for Hamburg Hochbahn
and for New York (Jamaica, Grand Central and Newark).

UPDATED

Steria

Steria Group
12 rue Paul Dautier, F-78142 Vélizy PO Box 57, France
Tel: (+33 1) 34 88 60 00   Fax: (+33 1) 34 88 62 62
President: Michel Gautier
Executive Vice Presidents: Jean-Claude Narconti,
  Eric Hayat
Sales Manager: Eric Hayat

Products: Traffic regulation and monitoring systems,
road pricing and supervisory systems, railway supervisory
and monitoring systems; passenger information systems,
data   processing,   management   control,   training
simulators and programmes, computer-aided diagnosis,
traffic simulation; ticketing systems.

VERIFIED

Sysco

Sysco Srl
Via Monti Sibillini 10, I-00141 Rome, Italy
Tel: (+39 081) 881 25   Fax: (+39 081) 860 06
e-mail: sysco@mbox.vol.it
www: www.vol.it/syscoinfo
General Manager: Vincenzo Manzini
Director of Marketing: Bruno Angius

Products: Information display systems and peripherals,
including split-flap boards, vacuum fluorescent displays
and LCDs.

Contracts: Refitting of the control system of Rome Terminus station.

VERIFIED

SYSECA

SYSECA
Member of Thomson-CSF Company
66-68 avenue Pierre Brossolette, F-92247 Malakoff Cedex, France
Tel: (+33 1) 41 48 15 11   Fax: (+33 1) 41 48 16 91
www: http://www.syseca.thomson-csf.com
Director of Transport Department: Vincent Quentin
Marketing and Sales Manager, Transport:
 R Jourdan

UK office
Syseca Ltd, Southmoor House, Southmoor Road, Wythenshawe, Manchester M23 9SY
Tel: (+44 161) 946 10 01   Fax: (+44 161) 946 70 00

Products: Centralised control systems for metro, light and heavy rail applications, including traffic supervision, and regulation and public information display systems; SCADA systems; computer-aided operating systems for bus networks.

Contracts: Systems in use in: Atlanta, Baltimore, Bilbao, Caracas, Chicago, Hong Kong, Lille, London, Los Angeles, Marseille, Mexico City, Montreal, New York, Paris, Rio de Janeiro, Santiago de Chile, Singapore, Taipei, and Washington. Bus systems are in use in 10 French cities.

UPDATED

Talking Signs

Talking Signs Inc
812 North Boulevard, Baton Rouge, Louisiana 70802, USA
Tel: (+1 504) 344 28 12   Fax: (+1 504) 344 28 11
President: C Ward Bond
Vice President, Operations: David Steed

Products: Infra-red remote sign technology for labelling and location for visually impaired people. For use on buses to identify approaching stops, bus stops and for use in stations. Infra-red audible pedestrian signals and signs.

Developments: Infra-red bus destination signs have been introduced jointly with Luminator for visually-impaired people.

UPDATED

Techspan

Techspan Systems plc
Church Lane, Chalfont St Peter SL9 9RF, UK
Tel: (+44 1753) 88 99 11   Fax: (+44 1753) 88 74 96
Managing Director: Edward Terris
Finance Manager: Richard Nolan
Sales Manager: Russell Hartwell
Contracts Manager: John Wintle

Part of the Jarvis group of companies

Products: Design, supply, installation and maintenance of customer information and driver information systems including plasma and CRT monitors, transflective LCD boards, LED displays, bespoke control systems and software solutions.

Contracts: Supply and maintenance of CIS (customer information systems) for Eurostar and Railtrack. Design

and supply of DIS (driver information systems) for Highways Agency, UK. Supply, installation and maintenance of information systems for British Airports Authority including Heathrow and Stansted.

Developments: RTAP Decoder for Highways Agency, UK; range of plasma displays for CIS; rugged enclosures for railway station displays.

UPDATED

Teknis

Teknis Electronics Pty Ltd
Angas Mews, 75A Angas Street, Adelaide, South Australia 5000, Australia
Tel: (+61 8) 223 54 11   Fax: (+61 8) 223 54 99
Managing Director: K Bladon

Products: Electronic control systems, communications technology, SCADA systems, level crossing control, warning system for track workers.
 Electronic Flagman, work gang protection system; Safecross, level crossing warning device; DDU, train driver's display for in-cab signalling and train orders; WIM (wheel impact monitoring) used for detecting and identifying wheel flats or damaged wheels causing impact on track structure; Telemetry, for CTC and microwave systems.

UPDATED

Telephonics

Telephonics Corporation
815 Broad Hollow Road, Farmingdale, New York 11735, USA
Tel: (+1 516) 549 60 62   Fax: (+1 516) 549 60 18
Vice President, Business Development: Philip J Greco
Manager, Business Development: Norbert Trokki

Products: Integrated digital communications systems for rail vehicles, encompassing public address, passenger/crew intercom, automated announcements, radio communications. Other products include: train line multiplexers, integrated wayside communication, event recording, passenger coach monitoring, passenger coach network controllers, passenger entertainment, and CCTV surveillance.

Contracts: Train line multiplexer, network controller and vehicle communication systems for MTA New York R142 subway cars; vehicle communication, radio network and CCTV door observation for SEPTA Philadelphia; vehicle communication for MBTA Boston; vehicle communication, health monitoring and vehicle CCTV for Hudson Bergen LRVs; integrated wayside communication for Newark APM; vehicle communication and passenger entertainment for Caltrans.

UPDATED

Thoreb

Thoreb AB
Gruvgatan 37, SE-421 30 Västra Frölanda, Sweden
Tel: (+46 31) 49 69 10   Fax: (+46 31) 47 39 85
Managing Director: Thore Brynielsson
Marketing Manager: Magnus Johansson

Products: Automatic vehicle location, passenger counting, data communication, passenger information displays and communication systems for public transport vehicles.

VERIFIED

Transit Control Systems

Transit Control Systems
1145 North Ocean Circle, Anaheim, California 92806, USA
President: Peter J Anello
Vice President, Marketing and Contracts: J C Collins
Chief Engineer: J Kiel

Products: Operator's command and control consoles, head-end control logic, monitoring and communication equipment, and air-conditioning systems with microprocessor controls, manual controllers, microprocessor controls and diagnostic equipment for rapid transit vehicles.

Contracts: Supply of control panels for trolleybuses in the USA; supply of operator's consoles, controls and communications and diagnostic monitoring equipment for BART San Francisco, Los Angeles Red line, and Muni San Francisco; also air-conditioning equipment with microprocessor controls for MBTA Boston Red line cars. Overhaul HVAC system and new microprocessor controls for WMATA Washington Rohr cars.

UPDATED

Transit Media

Transit Media GmbH
Nobelstrasse 22, D-76275 Ettlingen, Germany
Tel: (+49 7243) 76 17 50   Fax: (+49 7243) 761 75 18
Managing Director: Robert W Huber

Products: Twin Vision LED/Flipdot destination sign systems; LED-based interior route indicators with automatic next-stop indication; one-line LED and LCD-based interior next-stop indicators; digital voice announcers.

Contracts: 350 units have been supplied for Saudi Arabia and 250 units for Turkey.

Developments: LED in combination with bi-stable elements as a display

UPDATED

Transmitton

Transmitton Limited
Smisby Road, Ashby-de-la-Zouch LE6 5UG, UK
Tel: (+44 1530) 41 59 41   Fax: (+44 1530) 41 42 24
Managing Director: David Moore
Sales and Marketing Director: Philip Stockdale

Products: Supervisory control and data acquisition (SCADA) systems for power supply applications; central master control systems for signalling, passenger information and CCTV installations; data logging, point-to-point and inter-trip telemetry systems.

VERIFIED

Trion

Trion Präzisionselektronic GmbH & Co
Voltastrasse 5, D-13355 Berlin, Germany
Tel: (+49 30) 46 40 70   Fax: (+49 30) 46 40 72 50
e-mail: server@trion.de
Managing Director: Sami Tabbara
Marketing Manager: Manfred Hildebrandt

Products: In-cab computerised diagnostic display units for LRVs and metro cars; passenger information systems.

Contracts: Latest contracts include supply of equipment for Berlin metro, Stockholm metro, people mover systems in Norway, Berlin S-Bahn and tram systems in Berlin, Mainz, Halle, Zwickau, Jena, Cherzow (Poland), USA and Japan.

VERIFIED

Union Switch & Signal

Union Switch & Signal Inc
1000 Technology Drive, Pittsburgh, Pennsylvania 15219-3120, USA
Tel: (+1 412) 688 24 59   Fax: (+1 412) 688 23 99
President and Chief Executive Officer: Gary Ryker
Vice President, Systems Operation: Michael Grossman
Director, Railway Sales: Gregor Rudge
Director, Transit Sales: Jon Oldfield
An Ansaldo Signal company

Products: Design and manufacture of signalling and train control systems for passenger, freight, high-speed and mass transit railways including: vehicle-mounted signalling, positioning and monitoring systems; marshalling yard components and management systems; automation and integration technologies for dedicated and multimodal traffic management.

Contracts: Include installation of CTC at Boden for Banverket, Sweden; two computer-controlled marshalling yards at Xuzhou, People's Republic of China; computer control system for Cervignano marshalling yard, Italy; microprocessor-based coded track circuit system with cab signalling for Hamersly Iron Ore Railway, Australia; integrated multimodal operations control centre for MBTA, USA; lineside and central control system for high-capacity driverless LRT operation for Green Line, Los Angeles, USA; communications and control system and operations control centre for Portland, USA; and microprocessor-based cab signalling systems and lineside and central train control for Lines 3, 4, 5, 7 and 8 of the Seoul Metro, South Korea.

VERIFIED

Vaughan Harmon Systems

Vaughan Harmon Systems Limited
The Maltings, Hoe Lane, Ware SG12 9LR, UK
Tel: (+44 1920) 44 33 00   Fax: (+44 1920) 46 07 02
Managing Director: A St Johnston
Deputy Managing Director: C H Porter
Signalling Technical Sales Manager: J M Warriner

Background: Vaughan Systems was acquired by Harmon Industries Inc in 1996 and has become Vaughan Harmon Systems Ltd.

Products: Information and control systems for main line and for urban transport systems, including network timetabling, train reporting, staff and management information, TDM remote control, panel multiplexers, large and small train describers, signalling control centres, and passenger information systems.

Electronic solid-state signalling interlockings and level crossing systems, track circuits, cab signalling systems and hot axle box detectors.

Train describers and signal control systems are available with colour or monochrome VDU maps, main panel LED displays and facilities for train reporting and enquiry. The Vaughan Harmon small train describer is available for low-cost small installations, typically 50 berths with either digital or serial interfaces to the interlocking. Automatic code insertion and route setting facilities are available from stored timetable or that received via a network from a central facility.

Train reporting systems are of two types, those providing automatic train reporting with enquiry facilities, or automatic reporting by exception. The latter uses the timetable as the basis on which the exception reports are prepared.

Area timetable systems have been installed connected to networks. These enable timetables to be made available to all the components forming part of the transport control and information system. These include automatic train reporting by exception, automatic code

insertion, passenger information systems, local and area staff information systems.

The Vaughan Harmon modular signalling control system (MCS) is capable of expansion into a fully integrated railway control system including traction power, telecommunications and track-to-train radio.

An MCS has been installed as a pilot project in Eastbourne for Railtrack. MCS has been developed following earlier work by Vaughan Harmon providing signalling control systems for the Leicester area for British Rail in the mid 80s, and then Korea, Ianrod Eireann, Dublin and for the Post Office Railway, London.

Electronic interlocking system (VLHC) is a multi-purpose solid-state device for control of railway interlockings complete with interface to trackside equipment, with local or remote control. Along with level crossing controller (NXP-8) with advanced microprocessor-control system, it is being evaluated for possible use by Railtrack after successful implementation in North America.

UPDATED

Visolux

Visolux Elektronic GmbH
PO Box 610500, D-10928 Berlin, Germany
Tel: (+49 30) 61 67 20   Fax: (+49 30) 61 67 24 50

UK office
Visolux Ltd
28 Clifton Road, Cambridge CB1 4ZG, UK
Tel: (+44 1223) 24 20 20   Fax: (+44 1223) 41 10 63

Products: Light-beam switches; proximity switches; ultrasonic sensors; data transmission sensors; distance measuring devices; onboard and stationary PIR detectors.

VERIFIED

Voice Perfect

Voice Perfect
2a High Street, Edlesborough, Dunstable LU6 2HS, UK
Tel: (+44 1525) 22 25 55   Fax: (+44 1525) 22 22 55
Director: Nick Hallett
Technical Director: Rufus Potter

Technical Department
Ghigham Road, London N17 6NF
Tel: (+44 181) 493 84 84

Products: Voice announcer and speech transference equipment.

The Voice Perfect PC-Discrete Customer Address System (PC-DCAS) plays announcements, digitised for storage on the PC's hard disk.

The discrete speech transference system, Talk-2, enhances communication between customer and cashier where thick security glass intervenes.

Contracts: London Underground is using touchscreen and PC-DCAS technology on Piccadilly, Metropolitan, Victoria and Northern Lines.

Talk-2 is being installed on the Jubilee Line extension in all ticket office windows and also on the Bakerloo and Central Lines.

Developments: Include enhancements to both PC-DCAS and Talk-2 systems.

UPDATED

Vultron

Vultron International Ltd
City Park Industrial Estate, Gelderd Road, Leeds LS12 6DR, UK
Tel: (+44 113) 263 03 23   Fax: (+44 113) 279 41 27
e-mail: vultronuk@aol.com

www: www.vultron.co.uk
Managing Director: J H Moorhouse
Project Manager: Paul Kiley

Products: Passenger information display systems, including 'Clearsign' Liquid Crystal Displays (LCDs), now available with transflective display technology, Digi-Dot electromechanical reflective disc displays now with Diamond Grade reflective film, high-intensity LEDs, talking signs and plasma panels.

Contracts: Recent contracts include large LED departures/arrivals display boards for Edinburgh Waverley, Scotland, an information system for Leeds bus station; supply of an on-board bus information system for ATAC Rome on 500 buses.

Developments: Vultron has announced the Ventriloquist, a new talking sign system, that translates visual information in airports, bus and rail stations into speech. It receives data communications from the host system in exactly the same way as an electronic sign and converts it into speech using true text to speech conversion software. The talking sign can then be activated using a device such as a contactless sensor, a contactless smart card or an infra-red device. Talking Signs are being supplied to West Yorkshire Passenger Transport Executive (Leeds city bus station).

UPDATED

Vultron Incorporated

Vultron Incorporated
2600 Bond Street, Rochester Hills, Michigan 48309, USA
Tel: (+1 248) 853 22 00   Fax: (+1 248) 853 75 71
e-mail: vultron@ix.netcom.com
www: www.vultron.com
President: Jessie Swinea
Sales and Marketing Manager: Eric Pearson

Products: Variable and changeable message signs, passenger terminal information display systems, on-board vehicle destination signs, voice annunciation systems and commercial variable message signs.

Vultron manufactures variable message signs using the following technologies: LCD, LED, Flip-Dot, Hybrid LED Flip-Dot, Hybrid Fibre Optic Flip-Dot, Fibre Optic.

Developments: A new generation of onboard dot-matrix bus destination signs has been announced, which meet both the UK DiPTAC and US ADA requirements. Signs are available in reflective dot matrix as well as Liquid Crystal (LCD). Reflective dot matrix signs use highly reflective film, improving visibility by 95 per cent, enhanced by either concealed fluorescent lighting or by LED lighting. Manual or automated voice annunciation systems are available.

Vultron has also developed a line of highway VMS signs designed for use in intelligent transportation systems applications. Highway VMS signs are available in walk-in cabinet and front service designs, in full matrix, line matrix, and character matrix designs. These signs are available in Fibre-Dot, LED, LCD, and the super-efficient LED-Dot technology - which uses less than one third of the electrical power of a comparable Fibre-Dot or LED sign. Also new is the Vultron-AEG Transflective Liquid Crystal Display. These displays offer better uniformity than older transmissive displays, and enable these displays to function efficiently in outdoor applications.

NEW ENTRY

Wandel & Goltermann

Wandel & Goltermann Kommunikationstechnik GmbH
PO Box 1262, D-72795 Eningen uA, Germany
Tel: (+49 7121) 86 16 16   Fax: (+49 7121) 86 13 33
e-mail: info@wago.de
www: www.wg.com
Managing Director: Fariborz Khavand
Director, Public Transportation Systems:
   Karl-Heinz Bahnmüller
Director, Public Safety Systems: Alex Treffers
A member of the Schaltbau Group

Products: Onboard computers, next-stop displays, digital announcement equipment, public address systems with integrated passenger alarm intercom for buses and trains.

Contracts: Include supply of equipment for Netherlands Railways, Berlin S-Bahn and München transport; also for low-floor trams in Düsseldorf and München.

UPDATED

Wardrop

Wardrop Engineering Inc
Suite 600, 6725 Airport Road, Mississauga, Ontario, Canada L4V 1V2
Tel: (+1 905) 673 37 88   Fax: (+1 905) 673 80 07
Chief Executive Officer and General Manager: Ernie Card
Principal Manager, Software: Henry A Martin
Project Manager: Steven Gallant

Products: PC-based CTC and passenger counting systems (see Revenue Collection Equipment section).

VERIFIED

WCL

Westinghouse Cubic Ltd
177 Nutfield Road, Merstham RH1 3HH, UK
Tel: (+44 1737) 64 49 21   Fax: (+44 1737) 64 36 93
Managing Director: John Lincoln
General Manager: Steve Harris
Operations Director: Nigel Bryant
Director, Strategic Operations: Peter Ellwood

Products: CCTV, public address, passenger information, passenger assistance and radio systems.

Contracts: Equipment has been supplied for London Underground's Jubilee line extension and for LU tunnel lighting and power installations.

VERIFIED

Westinghouse Signals

Westinghouse Signals Limited
A BTR Rail Company
PO Box 79, Pew Hill, Chippenham SN15 1JD, UK
Tel: (+44 1249) 44 14 41   Fax: (+44 1249) 65 23 22
Managing Director: J A Cotton
Deputy Managing Director and Infrastructure Maintenance: K Burrage
Product Group Director: D Pickering
Technical Director: F Montes
Contracts Director, Mass Transit: C M W Harding
Director, Main Line Systems: A C Howker
Sales and Marketing Director: J E Clark
Finance Director: G Campion

Associated companies
Westinghouse Brake and Signal Co (Australia) Ltd
Dimetronic SA (Spain)
Safetran Systems Corporation (USA)

Products: Signals, point machines, track circuits (jointless and jointed), safety relays, electronic interlockings and safety processors, control panels and VDU displays, workstations, data transmission systems; automatic train control (ATC) incorporating automatic train protection (ATP), automatic train operation (ATO), and automatic train supervision (ATS); relay interlocking; solid state interlocking (SSI); train-to-signalbox radio, centralised traffic control (CTC), electronic control centres; passenger information systems; train describers and traction power telecontrol; train management systems.

Westrace is a second-generation safety processor developed by Westinghouse Signals and its three associated signalling companies to satisfy a range of safety applications which range from simple wayside interlockings to complete CTC. The equipment can provide trainborne safety processing for ATP systems, can be configured as a solid-state highway crossing controller, or can simply provide safe data transmission.

The control and monitoring system (CMS) for train management provides: communication between intelligent subsystems (brakes, traction and so on); transmission of information between train subsystems and the operator; access to built-in diagnostic data of intelligent subsystems; transmission of information to trackside; diagnosis and recording of train faults; implementation of trainwide control functions; and integration of non-intelligent subsystems via intelligent I/O interface modules. The maintenance support system (MSS) complements CMS, providing depot-based facilities which receive downloaded data from the CMS, gathering use and trend data for planned and preventative maintenance, thereby achieving higher fleet utilisation.

Westronic System Two is a modular microprocessor-based data handling and transmission system that can be configured to suit an expanding range of railway applications, including CTC, train description, passenger information, traction power telecontrol, station plant supervision, panel processing and supervision of train radio systems.

TBS is a transmission-based signalling system which provides flexibility in both main line and metro applications. The system can be overlaid on existing signalling allowing minimal disruption to operations during installation. TBS provides greater capacity, better regulation and improved traffic management; it supports bidirectional working and provides ATP and ATO facilities.

UPDATED

In the past, you travelled with AES Prodata ...

In the future, continue your journey with ERG Transit Systems

As **AES Prodata** we pioneered the use of magnetic stripe cards and contactless smart cards as the payment media in mass transit systems. We have more than 200 installations on five continents handling 8.3 billion passenger transactions per year. Together with our parent company, the ERG Group, we have won major contracts such as the Hong Kong integrated transit system and prestigious awards such as the 1998 Sesames Award for Best Smart Card Application. To consolidate our strong link with the ERG Group, we have changed our name to ERG Transit Systems.

The **ERG Group** with its alliance partner, Motorola, recently won contracts to supply Automated Fare Collection (AFC) systems to the cities of Berlin and Singapore, with strong potential to win more contracts in other cities in the near future.

By combining the ERG Group's expertise in e-purse schemes with AES Prodata's extensive knowledge of the mass transit market, ERG Transit Systems is the ideal partner to help you meet the AFC challanges of the future.

ERG Transit Systems will continue to be a world leader in the provision of integrated AFC systems. Whether you are a single bus operator or a major regional transit authority carrying millions of passengers, ERG Transit Systems provides you with the opportunity to maximise your commercial potential.

ERG

TRANSIT SYSTEMS

Delivering the future of fare collection

For further information, please contact:

ERG Transit Systems (Africa, Europe, South America)
Tel : +32 2 722 89 11 • Fax : +32 2 720 87 94 • info@ergtransit.be

ERG Transit Systems (North America)
Tel : +1 905 890 2794 • Fax : +1 905 890 4590 • info@ergtransit-na.com

ERG Transit Systems (Asia, Australia, NZ)
Tel : +61 8 9273 1100 • Fax : +61 8 9344 3686 • info@ergtransit.com.au

www.ergtransit.com

REVENUE COLLECTION EQUIPMENT

Company Listing by Country

AUSTRALIA
Abberfield Technology
ERG

BELGIUM
Automatic Systems
ERG (AES Prodata)

CANADA
Cegelec
Microtronix
Wardrop

CROATIA
SKALA

DENMARK
Scanpoint

FINLAND
Buscom

FRANCE
Alcatel CGA Transport
Ascom Monétel
Dassault AT
Klein
Schlumberger
Steria

GERMANY
Adtranz
Atron Electronic

FD
Giesecke & Devrient
Höft & Wessel
Krauth
Scheidt & Bachmann
Siemens Transportation Systems

ITALY
EIS Elettronica
Elektrene
Firema Trasporti
Italtel Telesis
Mael
Mecstar
Mobile Data Processing
Tecnotel
Tecnotour-Eltec
Unnebo Italdis

JAPAN
Nippon Signal
OMRON
Sanyo Electric
Toshiba

KOREA, REPUBLIC OF
Intec

SPAIN
Indra

SWEDEN
Cambist

SWITZERLAND
Ascom
Fahel
Kaba Gilgen AG
Mars Electronics
Sadamel

UK
Almex
Booth
Burall Infocard
Magnordata
Newbury Data
Scan Coin
Thorn
Time 24
Transmo
Wayfarer
WCL

USA
Agent
BZA
CTS
Denominator
Diamond
DocuSystems Inc
GFI Genfare
Globe
Main
Mars Electronics
Roger Williams Mint
Standard Change-Makers

Classified Listing

ACCESS CONTROL
Alcatel CGA Transport
Ascom Monétel
Automatic Systems
Cegelec
Dassault AT
ERG
Firema Trasporti
Indra
Intec
Kaba Gilgen AG
Klein
Scheidt & Bachmann
Toshiba
Unnebo Italdis
Wayfarer
WCL

BOOKING OFFICE MACHINES
CHANGE MACHINES
Abberfield Technology
Adtranz
Agent
Ascom Monétel
Cambist
Elektrene
ERG
Giesecke & Devrient
GFI Genfare
Indra
Nippon Signal
Sanyo Electric
Scan Coin
Scheidt & Bachmann
Standard Change-Makers
Tecnotour-Eltec
Toshiba
Wayfarer
WCL

COMPLETE AFC SYSTEMS
Ascom
Ascom Monétel
Atron Electronic
CTS

Dassault AT
ERG
Firema Trasporti
Intec
OMRON
Tecnotel
Tecnotour-Eltec
Thorn
Transmo
Wayfarer
WCL

FAREBOXES
CTS
Diamond
ERG
GFI Genfare
Main

ONBOARD MACHINES
Alcatel CGA Transport
Ascom Monétel
Elektrene
ERG
Mael
Mobile Data Processing
Newbury Data
Sadamel
Scanpoint
Scheidt & Bachmann
SKALA
Tecnotel
Tecnotour-Eltec
Wayfarer

PORTABLE
Almex
Atron Electronic
BZA
Diamond
ERG
Mael
Newbury Data
Sadamel
Scanpoint

Thorn
Wayfarer

SMARTCARD SYSTEMS
Adtranz
Almex
Ascom Monétel
Atron Electronic
Buscom
BZA
CTS
Dassault AT
ERG
GFI Genfare
Höft & Wessel
Indra
Intec
Krauth
OMRON
Scanpoint
Scheidt & Bachmann
Schlumberger
Siemens Transportation Systems
Transmo
Wayfarer
WCL

STAND-ALONE MACHINES
Agent
Almex
Ascom Monétel
Elektrene
ERG
Indra
Italtel Telesis
Wayfarer

TICKET/TOKEN/CARD SUPPLIER
Booth
Burall Infocard
Buscom
DocuSystems Inc
FD
Globe
Magnordata

Mecstar
Roger Williams Mint
Scanpoint
Steria
Time 24
Transmo

VALIDATORS/CANCELLERS/COUNTERS
Abberfield Technology
Adtranz

Alcatel CGA Transport
Ascom
Ascom Monétel
Cegelec
Denominator
Elektrene
ERG
GFI Genfare
Giesecke & Devrient
Italtel Telesis

Klein
Mars Electronics
Microtronix
OMRON
Scanpoint
SKALA
Tecnotour-Eltec
Thorn
Toshiba
Wayfarer

Abberfield Technology

Abberfield Technology Pty Ltd
32 Cross Street, Brookvale, New South Wales 2100, Australia
Tel: (+61 2) 99 39 28 44   Fax: (+61 2) 99 38 34 62
Managing Director: John M Colyer

UK office
Abberfield (Europe) Ltd
4 Andover Street, Sheffield S3 9EG, UK
Tel: (+44 114) 272 71 08   Fax: (+44 114) 272 71 08
UK Manager: Dennis Sutherland

Products: Ticket vending machines and ticket validators; ticketing systems for all modes of transport. Note and coin-to-coin change machines.

VERIFIED

Adtranz

DaimlerChrysler Railsystems
PO Box 13127, D-13601 Berlin, Germany
Tel: (+49 303) 83 20   Fax: (+49 303) 832 20 00
(See main entry under Rail Vehicles and Traction Equipment)

Products: Ticket printers, systems for issuing tickets and producing accounting sales data, electronic payment and smartcards, automatic ticket vending machines, ticket cancellers.

Range: Microprocessor-controlled electronic print and record units (AFR200) for stationary and mobile operations. The AFAB system for issuing tickets and accounting sales data, comprising electronic print and record units, memory modules and depot units. The automatic ticket vending machine AFA400 is designed for installation on vehicles or at stations; it is microprocessor-based and can take paper currency as well as five types of coins. A recycling unit can pay out change. Microprocessor-controlled cancellers assembled from modular components. The machines offer remote control of up to 20 cancellers by time division multiplex via two or four control wires or an IBIS-bus.
  The ACT 400 is a smartcard terminal, designed for contact or proximity cards. ANDY is a hand-held ticket printer for paper tickets with an option for electronic payment with smartcards.

UPDATED

Agent

Agent Systems Inc
2015 Midway Road, Suite 111, Dallas, Texas 75006, USA
Tel: (+1 214) 774 04 00   Fax: (+1 214) 392 73 01
President: Brian G Walters
Marketing Manager: Bruce W Davies

Products: Automatic fare collection systems.

Range: Computer control systems for fare collection; debit/credit card-only ticket vending machines; represents Scheidt & Bachmann (qv) in North American market for ticket vending machines and fare gate products.

VERIFIED

Alcatel CGA

Alcatel CGA Transport
PO Box 57, F-91229 Bretigny/Orge Cedex, France
Tel: (+33 1) 69 88 52 00   Fax: (+33 1) 69 88 58 50
www: www.alcatel.com
General Manager: Jean-Claude Hue
Commercial Manager: Gilles Denancé
Communication Manager: Patricia Huc

Part of Alcatel Transport Automation

Products: Automatic fare collection for metros and buses using magnetic tickets or contactless smartcards incorporating gates, validators, ticket machines and similar equipment; fleet management and passenger information systems.

Contracts: Include bus ticketing systems in Las Palmas; AFC systems in France, Hong Kong, Chile, Taiwan and Malaysia, Venezuela, Brazil, Egypt, ticketing systems for Philippines (Manila LRTA); contactless fare collection system for Singapore (in service 2000).

UPDATED

Almex

Almex Division - Metric Group Ltd
Metric House, Love Lane, Cirencester GL7 1YG, UK
Tel: (+44 1285) 65 14 41   Fax: (+44 1285) 65 06 33
e-mail: Ashley@almex.demon.co.uk
Managing Director: Simon Armstrong
International Sales and Marketing Manager: Kevin Aspin
Sales Team: Ashley Bailey, Alistair Aitken, Alan Foulis

Subsidiaries in: Germany, USA

Products: Ticketing and revenue control systems including software packages for computer-aided management, revenue and marketing information.

Range: Ticketing systems for the small operator to large multimodal operations; ticketing issuing products, magnetic card handling devices; smart card systems. Each Almex system is configured to the requirements of the customer with back-up, technical advice and life support.

UPDATED

Ascom

Ascom Autelca SA AG
Vendomation Division
Worbstrasse 201, CH-3073 Gümligen-Berne, Switzerland
Tel: (+41 31) 999 61 11   Fax: (+41 31) 999 64 05
Head of Vendomation Division: Roland Greuter
Head of Strategic Marketing: Christian Schmid
Head of Sales: Leo Muff
Head of Product Section: Heinz Loosli

Associated company
Ascom Systec AG
Freiburgstrasse 581, D-3172 Niederwangen, Germany
Tel: (+49 31) 980 71 11   Fax: (+49 31) 980 71 59
Area Sales Manager: Laurence Hug

Products: Ticket vending machines, validators, emergency call and information systems, communication systems, automatic fare collection systems and equipment.

Range: Automatic ticket vending machines, agent-operated ticket printers, and information systems. The range of vending machines includes equipment for mobile applications. Microprocessor and PC controlled, they can interface with a central computer for data capture and auditing.
  Vending machines can be equipped to accept coins, notes, debit/credit cards and contactless/magnetic cards.
  The range is complemented by the products of Ascom Monétel SA (qv) (ticketing systems) and Ascom Zeag Ltd (park-and-ride systems), both part of the Ascom group.

VERIFIED

Ascom Monétel

Ascom Monétel SA
Rue Claude Chappe, F-07503 Guilherand-Granges, France
Tel: (+33 4) 75 81 41 41   Fax: (+33 4) 75 81 42 00
Managing Director: Antoine Faure
Transport Revenue Systems Director: Eric Jean
Sales and Marketing Manager: Dominique Trouche

Products: Automatic fare collection systems for rail, metro, urban and inter city applications, including ticket vending machines, access control equipment, booking office machines, driver control units and validators, magnetic and contactless smartcard technologies.

Range: Computer-Assisted Ticketing System (CATS) uses magnetic cards or smart cards and the system can rapidly collect operating data. The CATS uses the Proxibus range of products.
  The Proxibus range is designed for automated fare collection and management in buses, metros, trains and trams and includes ticket machines, access control equipment, booking office machines and card reader/decoders.

Contracts: Systems are in operation in over 200 cities including Paris, Lyon, Marseille, Lille, Toulouse as well as cities in Australia, Spain, UK, Ireland, South Korea, Mexico, USA, Colombia, Portugal, Switzerland, Brazil and Malaysia.

UPDATED

Atron Electronic

Atron Electronic GmbH
Landsberger Strasse 509, D-81241 München, Germany
Tel: (+49 8121) 50 71   Fax: (+49 8121) 403 33
www: http://www.atron.de

Products: Smartcard terminals; AFC systems; stationary and mobile ticket machines.

VERIFIED

Automatic Systems

Automatic Systems SA
Avenue Mercator 5, B-1300 Wavre, Belgium
Tel: (+32 10) 23 02 11   Fax: (+32 10) 23 02 02
Managing Director: Yves Le Clercq
General Manager: Michel Coenraets
Export Manager: Michel Meli
Marketing Development Manager: Daniel Wautrecht

Products: Passenger entry-control gates and tripod turnstiles; high-speed two-way access gate; full-height high-security turnstiles; automatic swinging gates to control one-way traffic; two-way swinging gates for disabled use; PNG gate to handle high passenger flows at unmanned access points; automatic ticket vending machines. Anti-fraud exit door.

VERIFIED

Booth

Henry Booth & Co
Stockholm Road, Sutton Fields, Hull HU7 0XY, UK
Tel: (+44 1482) 82 63 43   Fax: (+44 1482) 82 41 45
e-mail: matt—goodley@henrybooth.co.uk
www: www.henrybooth.co.uk
Managing Director: Andrew Lindsey
Sales and Marketing Director: Mike Shanley
Sales Manager: Derek Skelton

Products: Magnetic stripe, thermal and paper tickets to suit various applications including Adverticket, tickets with advertising on the back.

VERIFIED

Burall InfoCard

Burall InfoCard Ltd
Cromwell Road, Wisbech PE14 0SN, UK
Tel: (+44 1945) 46 81 00   Fax: (+44 1945) 46 70 95
Managing Director: R J Duddin
Sales and Marketing Director: M G Moorey

Products: Low- and high-coercivity magnetic stripe cards, tickets and tokens, in plain and thermal paper, card, laminate and plastic; pre-encoding is a speciality.

Developments: Include contactless chip cards, high-frequency, proximity cards to the Philips Mifare® standard; card personalisation and numbering.

UPDATED

Buscom

Buscom Oy
Teknologiantie 7, FIN-90570 Oulu, Finland
Tel: (+358 8) 551 43 66   Fax: (+358 8) 551 47 66
e-mail: veli.heikkinen@polar.fi
www: www.buscom.fi
Managing Director: Veli Heikkinen
Marketing Director: Erkki Kunnari

Products: Automatic fare collection systems; ticket vending machine for mobile and booking office use; card reading device; non-contact farecard; smartcards; electronic payment systems.

Range: The Proximity non-contact farecard is a smartcard which can be read at 100 mm distance to give rapid vehicle boarding times.

UPDATED

BZA

BZA
Suite 230, 8466 North Lockwood Ridge, Sarasota, Florida 34243, USA
Tel: (+1 941) 351 67 97   Fax: (+1 941) 351 95 12

Products: Stored-value smartcards, mobile ticket-vending unit, smartcard loading terminals, smartcard reader.

VERIFIED

Cambist

Cambist AB
Stockholmsvägen 59, PO Box 204, SE-761 23 Norrtälje, Sweden
Tel: (+46 176) 172 45   Fax: (+46 176) 139 51
Managing Director: Rolf Upman

Products: Coin change dispensers, cash tables, conductor's bags, ticket punches.

VERIFIED

Cegelec

Cegelec/BG Automatec
5845 Couture Boulevard, St-Leonard, Quebec H1P 1A8, Canada
Tel: (+1 514) 329 39 12   Fax: (+1 514) 329 39 11
e-mail: info@bg-automatec.com
President: Pierre Ranger
Marketing Manager: Jean-Claude Debaque

Products: Ticket vending machines; access control equipment; slide-through ticket readers.

Range: Equipment includes multipassage magnetic ticket turnstiles; magnetic coding of paper tickets for mass production of up to 1,000 million a year and a slide-through credit card-size ticket reader.

VERIFIED

CTS

Cubic Transportation Systems
Member of the Cubic Corporation family of companies
5650 Kearny Mesa Road, San Diego, California 92111, USA
Tel: (+1 619) 268 31 00   Fax: (+1 619) 292 99 87
www: www.cubic.com
Chairman: Raymond L deKozan
President and Chief Executive Officer: John Lincoln
Senior Vice President, Business Development:
   Stephen O Shewmaker
Vice President, Business Development/Proposals:
   John Hughes

Associated companies/locations
CTS-Merstham (UK)
CTS-Wells (UK)
CTS-Scanpoint A/S (Denmark)
CTS-Far East Limited (Hong Kong)
CTS Australia Pty Ltd (Australia)
CTS-Tullahoma (USA)
CTS-Chicago (USA)
CTS-Washington DC (USA)
CTS-New York (USA)
CTS-Bay Area (USA)

Products: Electronic ticketing and automatic fare collection systems, including magnetic and contactless smart card systems for advanced fare collection applications.

Range: CTS provides turnkey systems integration solutions, as well as maintenance operations, in automatic fare collection systems for rail, bus, parking and intermodal applications, using magnetic ticketing and contactless smart card technology. CTS system installations include AFC components and subsystems (for example, ticket vendors, add-fare machines, entry/exit gates, data acquisition, analysis and storage systems and central clearinghouse computer systems).

Contracts: CTS's AFC systems have been installed in London, New York, Chicago, Washington DC, Hong Kong, Singapore, Kuala Lumpur, Seoul, Sydney, Miami, Atlanta and Guangzhou (China). Future installations include Bangkok, Vancouver (British Columbia), and Shanghai. In 1998, a contract was awarded to the TranSys consortium in which CTS is a major shareholder for the London Transport Prestige project, LT's comprehensive upgrade of ticketing and revenue collection systems for both bus and rail. CTS won the contract for the London Underground's first AFC system in 1978.

UPDATED

Dassault AT

Dassault Automatismes et Télécommunications
9 rue Elsa Triolet, ZI Les Gâtines, F-78370 Plaisir, France
Tel: (+33 1) 30 81 30 30   Fax: (+33 1) 30 55 19 31
Chairman and Chief Executive Officer: Jean-Paul Vautrey
Executive Vice President: Daniel Pelletier
Director, Transport Department: Jean-Pierre Fournier

Subsidiary companies
Dassault AT of America, Atlanta, USA
ICS (Información, Control y Señalización), Madrid, Spain
Erulec, France

Products: Automatic fare collection systems; contactless systems; ticket vending machines; ATB printers, readers and gates. ATB gates for boarding; point of sales ticketing.

Range: Access control gates; self-service ticket vending machines; ticket office machines (magnetic or non-magnetic).

Contracts: With Greater Cairo, Calcutta, Paris, Madrid and Caracas metros, New York and Los Angeles. Also, Eurostar boarding systems.
   The first of a new series of self-service ticket vending machines has been installed by Dassault for RATP Paris. The machines can read bank cards, are weatherproof and are resistant to vandals. Dassault has supplied ticket machines to RATP for the past 20 years.

UPDATED

Denominator

The Denominator Company Inc
Main Street, Woodbury, Connecticut 06798, USA
Tel: (+1 203) 263 32 10   Fax: (+1 203) 263 53 51
General Manager: Thomas C Clark

Products: Ridership classification counters.

Range: Counters up to 12 tiers high and 24 units wide for recording numbers of passengers not otherwise registered through a ticket machine. The counters are provided with a mounting bracket for installation on to a farebox, ticket machine tray or elsewhere. Key tops can be provided in distinctive colours to speed counting.
   Typical ridership classifications are: regular fares, handicap fares, senior citizens, student fares, transfer fares and zone fares.

VERIFIED

Diamond

Diamond Manufacturing Inc
2330 Burlington, North Kansas City, Missouri 64116, USA
Tel: (+1 816) 421 83 63   Fax: (+1 816) 421 47 35
President: Dick Cull

Products: Non-registering fareboxes; low-cost debit card system.

VERIFIED

DocuSystems Inc

DocuSystems Inc
8700 Waukegan Rd, Morton Grove, Illinois 60053, USA
Tel: (+1 847) 583 76 07   Fax: (+1 847) 583 12 47
e-mail: vheaton@docusysinc.com
Vice President, Sales and Marketing: Vincent J Heaton

International office
Tring Business Park, Upper Icknield Way, Tring HP23 4JX, UK
Tel: (+44 1442) 82 40 11   Fax: (+44 1442) 82 85 31
Director of Sales: A Heseltine

Products: Magnetically striped and bar coded tickets and cards, and other security printed products, on paper and plastic.

UPDATED

EIS Elettronica

EIS Elettronica Ingegneria Spa
Via G V Bona 85, I-00156 Roma, Italy
Tel: (+39 06) 41 59 11   Fax: (+39 06) 41 59 14 00

Products: Automatic ticket machines; counter ticketing systems; automatic information systems; counter information systems.

VERIFIED

Elektrene

Elektrene SpA
Via Giuseppe Meda 28, I-20141 Milano, Italy
Tel: (+39 02) 89 51 12 43 Fax: (+39 02) 89 50 03 98
Managing Director: Antonio Calace

Products: Onboard validators, booking office machines (ticket vending machines and office machines), stand-alone vending machines.

VERIFIED

ERG

ERG Transit Systems
247-249 Balcatta Road, Balcatta, Western Australia 6021, Australia
Tel: (+61 8) 92 73 11 00 Fax: (+61 8) 93 44 36 86
Chief Executive Officer: P J Fogarty
Managing Director: Chris Ring
General Manager: Stephen Waterhouse
Marketing Manager: John Farrer

AES Prodata
Leuvensesteenweg 540, bus 2, B-1930 Zaventem, Belgium
Tel: (+32 2) 722 89 11 Fax: (+32 2) 720 87 94
General Manager, Marketing: Torben Nielsen

Background: ERG Transit Systems (previously AES Prodata) has experience in the design, manufacture and project management of AFC systems. The company offers a turnkey approach to the supply and installation of components for a complete AFC system.

Products: Fare collection systems based on magnetic tickets, contact and contactless smartcards and hybrid smartcards; for bus, tram, ferry, rail and light rail.

Range: Includes advanced onboard ticket issuing, card validation and inspection; ticket vending machines, point-of-sale terminals; on-station equipment such as barriers and validators; hardware and software for data communication, storage and handling; depot station and central clearing house computer systems.

The P2000 is a portable ticket issuer/verifier used by SNCB; the TP4000, a driver console combining contactless smartcard technology with a paper ticket printer; and the V3000, the first validator capable of reading hybrid smartcards.

Contracts: In the space of three months, ERG Transit Systems has been awarded eight new contracts with Australian and New Zealand private bus operators for smartcard technology.

ERG Transit Systems, through its UK subsidiary, has completed the first phase of a multimillion dollar contract to supply and install a new fare collection system for the Stagecoach UK bus fleet. The first phase of the Stagecoach contract involved 620 buses and five depots for Stagecoach Manchester's operations. ERG manufactured and supplied the TP4000 ticketing machines and TRACS depot computer systems.

Developments: The latest model, the TP4000 ticketing machine, incorporates both paper tickets and contactless smartcard technology, giving bus operators and passengers flexibility in the transition to contactless smartcards.

ERG Transit Systems has won a contract from Metrovias for an AFC system for Buenos Aires, Argentina. An integrated AFC system, based on magnetic card technology, will serve the metro network of five lines and 66 stations. ERG will supply 420 turnstiles with integrated magnetic stripe card readers. The system is expected to be operational by August 1999 and can be upgraded to smartcard technology when required.

GO Transit, Toronto, Canada, has selected ERG Transit Systems to design and supply an AFC system for commuter bus and train operations. A pilot project to demonstrate the smartcard system is being installed on the Richmond Hill Line before full network implementation. The system will use Motorola smartcards

and readers and is the first in which Motorola and ERG have worked closely together.

ERG has secured a research and development grant from the Australian Commonwealth Government's Industry Research and Development board for development of its smartcard system. It was originally developed for Hong Kong and in 1998 won the Sesames Award for best smartcard application at Cartes 98 in Paris.

UPDATED

FD

Fleischhauer Datenträger und service GmbH & Co KG
Kohlenstrasse 51, D-44795 Bochum, Germany
Tel: (+49 234) 944 40 Fax: (+49 234) 944 41 09
e-mail: direct@FleischauerDatentraeger.de
www: http://www.FleischhauerDatentraeger.de
Managing Directors: Dr Claus Bressmer
 Friedrich von Buchwaldt

Products: Magnetic stripe tickets, smartcards and contactless chip cards; prepaid value cards; tokens; barcode labels.

UPDATED

Firema Trasporti SpA

Ercole Marelli Trazione Unit
Viale Edison 110, I-20099 Sesto San Giovanni, Milano, Italy
Tel: (+39 02) 249 41 Fax: (+39 02) 248 35 08
(See main entry under Rail Vehicles and Traction Equipment)

Products: Automatic fare collection systems with magnetic or contactless smartcards; passenger gates, ticket vending machines, fare adjustment machines, computerised management and system control.

Contracts: Supply of AFC for Line B of the Roma metro.

VERIFIED

GFI Genfare

GFI Genfare
A unit of General Signal Corporation
751 Pratt Boulevard, Elk Grove Village, Illinois 60007, USA
Tel: (+1 847) 593 88 55 Fax: (+1 847) 593 18 24
President: James A Pacelli
Vice President, Sales and Marketing: Kim R Green

Products: Fare collection equipment, including AFC systems, electronic registering fareboxes, electronic fare gates for underground railways; magnetic and smartcard processing systems; passenger controls; ticket/token vending machines; data collection and reporting systems; automated stop announcement systems.

Contracts: In the USA, GFI equipment is in use in 200 cities and more than 40,000 electronic registering fareboxes are in service with major bus undertakings. GFI has supplied fare collection equipment to undertakings in Atlanta, Boston, Chicago, Cincinnati, Cleveland, Columbus, Dallas, Denver, Detroit, Kansas City, Los Angeles, Louisville, Memphis, Miami, Milwaukee, Minneapolis, Montreal, New Jersey, New Orleans, New York, Philadelphia, Pittsburgh, St Louis, Toronto, Canada and Washington DC.

VERIFIED

Giesecke & Devrient

Giesecke & Devrient GmbH
Unternehmensbereich
PO Box 70 07 03, D-81307 Munich, Germany
Tel: (+49 89) 41 19 44 55   Fax: (+49 89) 41 19 45 20
Director: H Nattmann

Products: Cash and bank note handling machines.

NEW ENTRY

Globe

Globe Ticket and Label Company
3435 Empire Boulevard SW, Atlanta, Georgia 30354, USA
Tel: (+1 404) 762 97 11   Fax: (+1 404) 762 92 60
Marketing Manager: Colette Acuff

Products: Tickets, press or computer printed, ticket books, boarding passes; magnetic tickets.

VERIFIED

Höft & Wessel

Höft & Wessel GmbH
Rotenburger Strasse 21, D-30659 Hannover, Germany
Tel: (+49 511) 610 20   Fax: (+49 511) 610 24 11
www: www.hoeft-wessel.de
Managing Directors: Michael Höft, Rolf Wessel
Marketing Communications Manager: Nicole Funck

Products: Vending machines and portable data entry units.

Range: The HW9096 is a portable terminal for use by staff in trains and buses. It accepts cashless payment means.

The H4290/95 is a fixed vending machine with a touch-screen or keys, payment with or without cash.

The HW4220 is a cashless smartcard vending machine, able to act also as an information terminal.

HW4560 proximity card reader is a smartcard read/write system, designed for reading and writing smartcards.

The H4225 mobile mini-ticket pillar is a mobile vending machine for use in vehicles and accepts electronic cards.

The HW4240 information pillar is a fixed information terminal and is operated with electronic cards and operated by means of a touch-sensitive screen.

The HW4510 ferry unit is a portable ticket sales unit for outdoor use and can take cashless payment means.

The HW4581 inspector unit is a portable device for checking electronic tickets.

HW Agent is management software for personnel and terminals, sales records and submission of cash data from electronic cards.

Contracts: Include 3,500 ticket machines for DB AG and 500 for ÜSTRA Hannover. DB AG has placed a follow-up order for 5,500 mobile terminal units.

UPDATED

Indra

Indra
C/La Granja, 84 Pol. Industrial, Alcobendas, E-28108 Madrid, Spain
Tel: (+34 91) 396 73 00   Fax: (+34 91) 396 73 33
e-mail: transport@alc.indra.es
Commercial Manager: Miguel Ángel Tapia
Export Manager: Alberto Calvo

Products: Access control equipment for ISO and Edmonson machines; automatic barriers, gates and turnstiles; automatic ticket machines (ISO and Edmonson) with thermal and conventional printing; ticket office machines (ISO and Edmonson) with thermal and conventional printing; magnetic and contactless

smartcard technology; credit card prepayment systems; computerised management and system control; urban, intercity and multimodal software applications; passenger control and flow regulation.

Indra supplies a range of radiocommunication systems for railway communications including radio networks, centres and dispatching applications. The systems support different type of services including voice, data and SCADA applications.

Contracts: Railway transportation and management systems for: RENFE suburban railways in Madrid, Barcelona, Bilbao, Valencia and Málaga; FGC Barcelona; FGV Valencia, Euskotren Bilbao; Trenes de Buenos Aires; Tren de la Costa Buenos Aires; Metro Santiago de Chile; Madrid, Barcelona and Bilbao metro and buses access control.

Radio communications systems have been supplied to RENFE, Spain and TBA Buenos Aires.

UPDATED

Intec

Intec Ltd
#192, Pang Yi-Dong, Song-Pa-ku, Seoul 138-040, South Korea
Tel: (+82 2) 34 34 40 00   Fax: (+82 2) 34 34 41 70
President: Yong-Nam Hong

Products: Ticket machines; access control cards; smartcard machines; AFC systems for rail and bus applications.

Developments: New validator, recharger, card-issuing machines have been introduced; a premium point card system for buses has been introduced.

UPDATED

Italtel Telesis

Italtel Telesis SpA
Piazzale Zavattari 12, I-20149 Milano, Italy
Tel: (+39 02) 43 88 20 14   Fax: (+39 02) 43 88 29 20
Managing Director and Chief Executive Officer:
    Alberto Nicoletti Altimari
Marketing and Sales Director: Gian Primo Monaci
Technical Director: Vittorio Formenti

Subsidiary
TLC.S (Automatic Fare Collection Equipment), Via Pacinotti 30, I-30135 Verona, Italy

Products: Validators; automatic fare collection equipment; ticket vending machines.

Contracts: Italtel is providing 50 ticket vending machines for Midland Metro Birmingham, UK.

VERIFIED

Kaba Gilgen

Kaba Gilgen AG
Freiburgstrasse   34,   CH-3150   Schwarzenburg, Switzerland
Tel: (+41 31) 734 41 11   Fax: (+41 31) 734 44 75
Sales Director: Konrad Zweifel
Project Director, Platform Screen Doors:
    Hans Krähenbühl

Products: Platform screen door systems, access control systems, automatic pedestrian doors.

Contracts: Recent contracts include platform screen door systems for metro and rapid transit projects in Hong Kong, Lille, New York and Toulouse.

NEW ENTRY

Klein

Etablissements George Klein
221 avenue Président Wilson, F-93218 Saint-Denis Cedex, France
Tel: (+33 1) 49 17 87 40   Fax: (+33 1) 42 43 99 93

Products: Ticket gates

Contracts: Gates have been installed in Rio de Janeiro, São Paulo, Santiago de Chile, Cairo, Calcutta, Montréal, Baltimore, Mexico City, Paris, Marseilles, Stockholm, Madrid, Napoli, Seoul, Pusan, Taipei, Hong Kong and Kuala Lumpur.

Developments: A new range of user-friendly AFC gates has been introduced.

VERIFIED

Krauth

Prof A Krauth Apparatebau GmbH & Co KG
PO Box 1334, D-69403 Eberbach, Germany
Tel: (+49 6271) 80 50   Fax: (+49 6271) 805 39

Products: Automatic ticket machines, fare collection machines, pay tables, manual and automatic coin dispensers, Ibis board computer, ticket printers, cashless fare collection, electronic vehicle location, passenger counting systems, traffic detection at traffic lights.

VERIFIED

Mael

Tecnost-Mael SpA
Vicolo Antoniniano 13, I-00153 Roma, Italy
Tel: (+39 06) 70 19 01   Fax: (+39 06) 700 27 11
Managing Director: Dr G Cisilotto
Marketing Director: F Olearo

Products: Automatic ticket issuing machines and associated equipment for self-service and onboard applications.

Range: The Mael 400 is a portable ticket issuing machine for bus and rail applications, while the Mael 400T is for magnetic and smartcard operation. The M402 is a self-service system with different payment methods — notes, coins, credit/debit cards.

VERIFIED

Magnadata International

A subsidiary of DocuSystems Inc (qv)
Norfolk Street, Boston PE21 6AF, UK
Tel: (+44 1205) 31 00 31   Fax: (+44 1205) 31 26 12
Managing Director: M A L Ward
Sales and Marketing Manager: P R Johnson

Products: Speciality/security printers of magnetic-based paper and plastic tickets and related documents. Services include magnetic precoding, bar coding, personalisation, security appliques, special packaging, global distribution.

Contracts: Tickets and related products have been supplied to New York City Transit, CTA Chicago, BART San Francisco, MTA Baltimore, Metro Houston, STCUM Montreal, London Underground, London Transport, MTRC Hong Kong, City rail, Sydney and highways in Malaysia and USA.

UPDATED

Main

Main Fare Box Co
Division of the Euclid Products Co Inc
3625 Lost Nation Road, Willoughby, Ohio 44094, USA
Tel: (+1 442) 942 73 10   Fax: (+1 442) 942 41 84
President: Bruce T Finke
Sales Director: Beth McCarty

Products: Mechanical, non-registering fareboxes; custom fare collection equipment.

Developments: The model P95 mechanical non-registering portable farebox on wheels has been designed to fit in the width of a turnstile.

UPDATED

Mars Electronics

Mars Electronics International
Geneva Branch
PO Box 2650, CH-1211 Geneva 2, Switzerland
Tel: (+41 22) 884 05 05   Fax: (+41 22) 884 05 04
Industry Manager: Reinhard Banasch
Marketing Manager: Serge Guillod
Business Development Manager: F Maurice Reber
Area Sales Manager: Ruedi Lüthi

US company
Mars Electronics International
1301 Wilson Drive, West Chester, Pennsylvania 19380, USA
Tel: (+1 610) 430 25 00   Fax: (+1 610) 430 27 94

UK company
Mars Electronics International
Eskdale Road, Winnersh Triangle, Wokingham RG41 5AQ
Tel: (+44 118) 969 77 00   Fax: (+44 118) 944 64 12
www: www.meiglobal.com

Products: Bank note validators produced under the trademark Sodeco® Cash Management Systems for incorporation into ticket vending machines.

Range: The new range of compact Sodeco® BNA5 is now completed and the machines can accept from four to 60 banknotes inserted in all four directions.
The BNA52/54 is a validator with an escrow facility for up to 15 notes, a stacker and a security cashbox with a capacity of up to 1,000 notes (with an option for up to 2,000 notes).
The BNA51/54 is a validator with a stacker and is compatible with the cashboxes already described. The BNA50 is a banknote validator only with an optional stainless-steel drawer box with a capacity between 100 and 400 banknotes.
All Mars products offer security against counterfeit notes and fraudulent manipulation, low jam rate, easy servicing and maintenance, robust construction for outside environments and optional Windows® NT/95 environment for networking TVM. The money collection is simple to operate with the principle of cash-box exchange and the protection of money is secured with electronic means as well as locks and keys. Mars also offers Cashflow® change-giving and coin mechanisms. Mars has achieved ISO9001 certification.

Contracts: Banknote validators have been supplied for ticket vending machines at Long Island Rail Road, Metro North New York, MTA Baltimore, WMATA Washington, Los Angeles Blue line, BC Transit Vancouver, SRA Cityrail Sydney, Berlin metro, KCRC/MTRC Hong Kong, SBB Switzerland, British train-operating companies; KTM Malaysia STIB; NYCTA; San Diego Trolley.

UPDATED

Mecstar

Mecstar SrL
Via Honduras 15, I-00040 Pomezia, Italy
Tel: (+39 06) 910 55 88   Fax: (+39 06) 910 55 98

Products: Magnetic tickets and cards.
VERIFIED

Microtronix Vehicle Technologies

955 Green Valley Road, London, Ontario N6N 1E4, Canada
Tel: (+1 519) 649 49 00   Fax: (+1 519) 649 03 55
e-mail: mvt@microtronix.ca
www: mvt.microtronix.ca
President: Mark Lowenstine
Marketing Manager: Karl Morgenroth

Products: Infra-red transceivers; automatic passenger counting doors; treadle switch sensors; infra-red zone sensors; optical passenger sensors and system integration.

UPDATED

Mobile Data Processing

Mobile Data Processing
Viale Regione Veneto 26, I-35127 Padova, Italy
Tel: (+39 049) 806 98 11   Fax: (+39 049) 806 98 43
e-mail: 4pmob@iperv.it
www: http://www.campiello.it/4p
Managing Director: Silvano Mansutti

USA office
7400 Oxford Avenue, Philadelphia, Pennsylvania 19111-3095

Products: Hand-held computer with card reader for outdoor operations.

VERIFIED

Newbury Data

Newbury Data Recording Ltd
Premier Park, Road One Industrial Estate, Winsford CW7 3PT, UK
Tel: (+44 1606) 59 34 24   Fax: (+44 1606) 55 83 83

Products: Flexfare modular revenue collection and on-bus information system; printer/peripheral terminals. Hand-held portable ticket reader called Flexstore.

VERIFIED

Nippon Signal

Nippon Signal Co Ltd
3-1 Marunouchi, 3-chome, Chiyoda-ku, Tokyo, Japan
Tel: (+81 3) 32 87 46 21   Fax: (+81 3) 32 87 46 46
President: O Miyaji

Products: Automatic fare collection systems, ticket vending machines, change-giving machines, monitoring equipment.

Range: Passenger gates, ticket issuing machines, fare adjusting machines, season ticket issuing machines and centralised monitoring equipment.

VERIFIED

OMRON

OMRON Corporation
Public Information & Transfer Systems Division HQ
4-10 Tranomon 3-chome, Minato-ku, Tokyo 105, Japan
Tel: (+81 3) 34 36 72 64   Fax: (+81 3) 34 36 70 56
General Manager, International Business Promotion Department: Takuo Iwakata

Products: Complete automatic fare collection systems, including ticket issuing machines, barrier equipment, validators/cancellers, and fare adjustment machines.
A contactless smartcard ticket has been developed for opening automatic gates. Lithium batteries are not used — the card has an induction system for its power supply.

Contracts: Supply of systems for Taipei MRT Phase II, Manila LRT3.

Developments: Include a new gate which can process two tickets for connecting two lines simultaneously.

UPDATED

Roger Williams Mint

Roger Williams Mint
PO Box 2350, Attleboro, Massachusetts 02703, USA
Tel: (+1 508) 226 33 10   Fax: (+1 508) 226 20 33
General Manager: Sheila Dellacona

Works address
79 Walton Street, Attleboro, Massachusetts 02703

Products: Fare tokens.

VERIFIED

Sadamel

Sadamel SA
Rue du Collège 73, CH-2300 La Chaux-de-Fonds, Switzerland
Tel: (+41 32) 968 07 70   Fax: (+41 32) 968 08 85
e-mail: sadamel@sadamel.ch
www: www.sadamel.ch
Sales Manager: Werner Frei

Products: Automatic ticket machines including sales and cancelling systems for onboard or platform locations, and automatic machines with microprocessor and electronic data processing.

Range: Stationary automatic vending machine Type 1512 accepts coins, notes, credit cards and tokens, and prints on plain paper or magnetically encoded stock. A microprocessor provides rapid accounting and statistical analysis.
Microprocessor-controlled Type 1588i rotary coin recycling system, for storage of up to six different coins and 120 of each type.
The Sadapplic system is based on a touchscreen, with processor-compatible MS DOS. In three versions — portable with printer, desk-mounted and onboard.

Developments: Sagatest data handling software and computer integrated operating system for Sadamel ticket vending machines. Interfaces for machines of different makes to customer's data base.

UPDATED

Sanyo Electric

Sanyo Electric Works Ltd
2-4-1 Kamitsuchii, Gifu 502, Japan
Tel: (+81 582) 33 78 11   Fax: (+81 582) 94 83 90

Products: Ticket issuing machines, data collection and revenue counting equipment.

VERIFIED

Scan Coin

Scan Coin-Omser (UK) Ltd
Dutch House, 110 Broadway, Salford Quays, Salford M5 2UW, UK
Tel: (+44 161) 873 79 49   Fax: (+44 161) 873 79 43
e-mail: sales@scancoin.co.uk
Managing Director: Jeffrey G Carr
Sales Executive: Ray Rees
Area Sales Manager for North East UK: Alison Clark

Products: Note changers, coin sachet packing systems, cash deposit points and coin sorters. The Super 7 note changer accepts up to eight international denominations and around 9,000 coins can be stored in the machine.
The Scan Coin 4,000 value sorter sorts up to 16 coin types at 4,000 coins a minute.

Developments: Scan Coin-Omser has introduced the CDP Euro which has a capability to handle up to 64 coin types in 17 sorting locations.
The new Scan Coin CDP3 cash deposit system features fault logging facilities as standard. The system imposes a simple but effective routine on all drivers. Before being allowed to deposit cash they must respond to questions on the CDP's display. Drivers confirm their own ID number and the number of the vehicle they have been operating. They must then confirm that any vehicle defects have been reported. A short software utility interrogates the CDP's log files and produces a simple report showing driver and vehicle number together with vehicle defect status.
The SC20 and SC22 coin sorting machines use electronic sensing technology. These microsorters are for sites that are processing lower volumes of coin.

UPDATED

Scanpoint

Scanpoint Technology A/S
Vibeholms Allé 22, DK-2605 Brøndby, Denmark
Tel: (+45 43) 43 39 99   Fax: (+45 43) 43 34 88
Managing Director: Yuris Nora
Marketing Manager: Kirsten Joensen

Products: Automatic fare collection systems.

Range: Onboard stationary and portable fare collection computers with automatic calculation of fares and validation in accordance with fare and route descriptions loaded into the computer. Automatic card readers, keyboard card readers, portable verifiers; portable or stationary data collection units for PC interface.
Various card technologies, including smartcards, magnetically encoded hard plastic cards, contactless smartcards, thin paper magnetic stripe cards and thermal printed tickets; technology for creation of combination cards with, for example, season ticket characteristics for some routes and stored-value for others, or multipurpose cards compatible with bank credit cards. Card-reader modules for non-transport applications, for example, telephones and automatic vending equipment, complementing the public transport card range and enabling creation of complete city card payment systems activated by a common card.

VERIFIED

Scheidt & Bachmann

Scheidt & Bachmann GmbH
Breite Strasse 132, D-41238 Mönchengladbach, Germany
Tel: (+49 2166) 26 60   Fax: (+49 2166) 26 66 99
Marketing Managers, Fare Collection Systems Division:
   Herr Poos/M Feiter

USA subsidiary
Scheidt & Bachmann USA Inc
1 North Avenue, Burlington, Massachusetts 01803
Tel: (+1 617) 272 16 64   Fax: (+1 617) 272 16 54

Products: Automatic fare collection systems.

Range: Automatic ticket vending machines including issuing systems for paper and magnetic tickets, with upgrade and replacement functions for magnetic tickets; devices for processing of smartcards; devices for payment with coins, bank notes and credit/debit cards; machines with colour displays, colour screens, keyboards and touch panels; fare computer, data recording for sales and transaction data; online/offline interfacing of central host-computers.
Fare gates including magnetic ticket processing modules with printing facilities; gate mechanisms; fare computer; various types of displays and online monitoring system.
Electronic ticket issuing machines for onboard and ticket office applications, including printing facility.
Fare collection equipment can be adjusted for use with any type of tariff structure including proof-of-purchase systems, zone or destination-oriented systems.

Contracts: Some 4,000 Scheidt & Bachmann ticket vending machines are in use in Germany on DB stations, and with over 60 German city transport undertakings, including Dortmund, which alone has some 500 S & B installations. Vending machines are installed in Denmark and the Netherlands, and North American customers include Bi-State Development Agency, St Louis; BART and CalTrans, San Francisco; Long Island Rail Road and Metro-North, New York; MTA Baltimore; and MTDB San Diego. DB AG has ordered another 3,500 machines and Metro North have settled new orders.

UPDATED

Schlumberger

Schlumberger Test & Transactions
50 Avenue Jean Jaurés, PO Box 62004, F-92542 Montrouge, France
Tel: (+33 1) 47 46 66 67   Fax: (+33 1) 47 46 67 82
General Manager: Gerard Leger

Subsidiaries
USA
825-B Greenbrier Circle, Chesapeake, Virginia 23320
Tel: (+1 804) 366 44 00   Fax: (+1 757) 523
General Manager : Carlos Lazalde

Asia
Block 12, Lorong Bakar Batu #07-07, Singapore 348745
Tel: (+65 746) 63 44   Fax: (+65 742) 64 84
General Manager: Goh Hock

Products: Automatic ticketing systems including ticket-vending machines, point-of-sale terminals, magnetic printers, smartcard readers/encoders, smartcards for transport use, management systems.

Range: Customised ticketing solutions for urban and inter-urban transport networks (bus, metro, tram, railways).

Contracts: Schlumberger has provided SNCF with 2,500 ticket-vending machines of different types installed throughout the entire railway network, DSB with 165 centralised simple cost-effective machines and SNCB with 150 rapid ticket dispensers. Schlumberger has also equipped the London South-east Tramlink operation with 80 ticket-vending machines and Nottinghamshire County Council with 70,000 contactless smartcards for bus users. Schlumberger is also refurbishing Paris underground, bus and regional express (RER) kiosks and RATP Paris is taking delivery of 900 advanced ticket sales terminals.

UPDATED

Siemens Transportation Systems

Siemens Transportation Systems
AFC Systems
Elsenstrasse 87-96, D-12435 Berlin, Germany
Tel: (+49 30) 38 65 13 21   Fax: (+49 30) 36 85 10 32
Contact: J M Janssen

Subsidiary
Siemens Nederland NV
Prinses Beatrixlaan 26, NL-2500 BB
Den Haag, Netherlands
Tel: (+31 70) 333 33 33   Fax (+31 70) 333 29 17

Products: Fare collection systems based on contact and contactless smartcards and data processing equipment; hybrid smartcard systems.

VERIFIED

SKALA

SKALA Technologies doo
Polj B Hanzekovića 45, 41000 Zagreb, Croatia
Tel: (+385 1) 33 07 55   Fax: (+385 1) 33 07 55
e-mail: karolj.skala@public.srce.hr
President: Dr K Skala
Sales Manager: R Skala
Technical Manager: F Halasz

Products: Hand-held ticket issuing systems for buses; ticket cancelling machines; data collection and evaluation; onboard microcomputers; multimedia point and information systems.
Ticketing, measuring and data acquisition; onboard microcomputers; data uploads and PC evaluation.

VERIFIED

Standard Change-Makers

Standard Change-Makers Inc
PO Box 36550, Indianapolis, Indiana 46236, USA
Tel: (+1 317) 899 69 66   Fax: (+1 317) 899 69 77
Vice President, Operations: James McNutt Jr
Chief Engineer: James Heidelberger
National Sales Manager: Barry O'Brien

Products: Fare collection equipment for US, Mexican and Canadian currency.

Range: Bill/note changers to provide correct change for use in other fare collection equipment, bill/coin-operated ticket dispensers for the issue of pre-encoded tickets and bill/coin-operated token or change dispensers. System 500 note acceptor accepts notes in four denominations and will separate into stacks by denomination. Complete machines will accept notes and give change in coins, tokens or passes. Also parking lot access system which accepts coins and notes.

VERIFIED

Steria

Steria Group
PO Box 57, F-78142 Vélizy P057, France
Tel: (+33 1) 34 88 60 00   Fax: (+33 1) 34 88 62 62
President: Michel Gautier
Executive Vice Presidents: Jean-Claude Narconti
   Eric Hayat
Sales Manager: Eric Hayat

Products: Ticketing systems.

VERIFIED

Tecnotel

Tecnotel Srl
Via Lazio 25, I-40069 Zola Predosa (BO), Italy
Tel: (+39 051) 75 97 14   Fax: (+39 051) 75 89 75
e-mail: tecnodir@tin.it
Managing Director: Bruno Piazzi
General Director: Antonio De Sicot

Marketing Director: Giorgio Giorgi
Commercial Director: Paolo Cecchetti
Technical Director: Davide Boschini
Research & Development Director: Gianfranco di Medio

Products: Electronic toll and revenue collection systems; portable ticket-issuing machines; magnetic cards; smart cards.

UPDATED

Tecnotour-Eltec

Tecnotour-Eltec SpA
A member of the Olivetti-Tecnost Group
Via T Tasso 19, I-25080 Molinetto di Mazzano, Italy
Tel: (+39 030) 212 11 11   Fax: (+39 030) 262 96 31
Managing Director: P Menegaldo

Products: Complete automatic fare collection systems; ticket vending machines for onboard and stationary applications; booking office machines; ticket cancelling machines; proximity detectors.

Contracts: Has supplied Italian Railways (FS) and many public and private transit companies. Has installed TVMs and ticket cancelling machines for Lisboa metro; supply of 350 ticket vending machines to ATAC Roma.

UPDATED

Thorn

Thorn Transit Systems International Ltd
Wookey Hole Road, Wells BA5 1AA, UK
Tel: (+44 1749) 67 02 22   Fax: (+44 1749) 67 93 63
Managing Director: J Slater
Sales and Marketing Director: K Thorpe
Technical Director: L Adams
Operations Director: B R Harris
European Marketing Manager: J O'Donnell
Marketing Manager, Asia: S Wright
Business Development Manager: D Croker

Background: In 1997, Thorn Transit Systems International became part of the Cubic Automatic Revenue Collection Group which owns WCL (qv) and Scanpoint (qv).

Products: Complete fare collection systems for urban transit systems and intermodal applications, including central computer systems, secure software, station monitoring systems, ticket vending machines, bus and rail validators, portable and desktop ticket machines, magnetic validator assemblies, automatic gates (flap and tripod) and proximity card systems.

VERIFIED

Time 24

Time 24 Ltd
Unit 69, Victoria Road, Burgess Hill RH15 9TR, UK
Tel: (+44 1444) 25 76 55   Fax: (+44 1444) 25 90 00
Sales Manager: Chris Young
Quality Assurance Manager: Robert Thomas
Production Director: Mark Willifer
Director: David Shore

Products: Ticketing systems, including technology for platform purchase of tickets and checking routes.

VERIFIED

Toshiba

Toshiba Corporation
International Operations - Information and Communication Systems and Industrial Plant Division
1-1 Shibaura, 1-chome, Minato-ku, Tokyo 105-8001, Japan
Tel: (+81 3) 34 57 25 45   Fax: (+81 3) 54 44 92 63

Products: Automatic fare and toll collection systems based on customised units from a basic range.

Range: Includes automatic gates, ticket vending machines, season ticket issuing machines, fare adjustment machines, multifunction booking office equipment and passenger-operated season ticket renewal machines. Manual and high-speed ticket issuing machines are also produced. A central processing system can also be installed by the company as the heart of an automatic fare collection system. Consisting of a mini-computer and peripheral equipment, the system is connected in an online mode to the fare collection equipment of each station. Data is collected on sales, number of passengers and maintenance needs, and the system then analyses and edits the statistics.
Automatic gates check tickets and allow through only passengers with valid tickets. The equipment is available as an entry gate, exit gate or reversible gate with flap-door type barriers. Automatic ticket vending machines accept coins and notes and have a change-giving facility. The thermally printed ticket is issued within 3 seconds of the passenger pressing the fare button.
The season ticket issuing machine, installed at the booking office window, is operated by pushing buttons to specify the departure station, arrival station, transfer station, duration of validity and discount rate and inserting an application form filled in by the passenger. Fare calculation is done automatically. The passenger's signature and age are transcribed onto the ticket from the application form.
When a passenger has ridden past his destination or changed route, the fare adjustment machine reads the inserted ticket and adjusts the fare accordingly. The passenger then inserts coins or a bank note into the machine and a new ticket, plus change if required, is returned.

Contracts: Automatic fare collection systems have been supplied in Japan to JR, Osaka Municipal Transportation Bureau, Nagoya Municipal Transportation Bureau, Sapporo Municipal Transportation Bureau, Transportation Bureau of Tokyo Metropolitan Government and many private railways such as the Hankyu Corporation.

UPDATED

Transmo

Transmo Ltd
Unit 1, The Maltings, Green Drift, Royston SG8 5DY, UK
Tel: (+44 1763) 26 32 29   Fax: (+44 1763) 26 34 49
Managing Director: John Batten

Products: Stored value smartcards for use on or off passenger carrying vehicles.

Contracts: In Hertfordshire a smartcard system was started in 1997. The Hertfordshire scheme combines stored-value smartcard technology with a contactless concessionary fare pass.

VERIFIED

Unnebo Italdis

Unnebo Italdis SpA
Via A, Votta 15, I-38015 Lavis, Italy
Tel: (+39 0461) 24 03 57   Fax: (+39 0461) 24 65 23
e-mail: info@italdis.com
www: www.gunneboitaldis.com
President and Managing Director: Marco Detassis
International Sales Manager: Leo M Detassis

Products: Automatic barriers, gates and full-height turnstiles for access control.

Range: Includes Hidden-Gate motorised sliding panel; Pass-O-Mat Duplex double swing gate passageway; Hercules tripod turnstile; security swing doors.

Contracts: Supply of equipment to Milano metro, Catania LRT, Italy; Lima metro, Peru; Portuguese Railways in Lisbon, Paris Metro, Hong Kong mass transit system.

UPDATED

Wardrop

Wardrop Engineering Inc
Suite 600, 6725 Airport Road, Mississauga, Ontario, Canada L4V 1V2
Tel: (+1 905) 673 37 88   Fax: (+1 905) 673 80 07
Project Manager: Steven Gallant

Products: Automatic passenger counting system (in association with Microtronix (qv)).

VERIFIED

Wayfarer

Wayfarer Transit Systems Limited
A Meggitt plc company
10 Willis Way, Fleets Industrial Estate, Poole BH15 3SS, UK
Tel: (+44 1202) 67 06 71   Fax: (+44 1202) 67 08 87
Managing Director: Dr Paul Middleton
Sales and Marketing Director: Peter Cheeseman

USA office
1170 McLester Street, Unit 4, Elizabeth, New Jersey
Tel: (+1 908) 354 45 42   Fax: (+1 908) 354 46 65

Products: Automatic fare collection and associated peripheral systems and software for road and rail transport.

Range: Automatic ticket issuing and fare collection systems including magnetic card validators, contact and contactless (proximity) smartcard processors, point-of-sale systems, passenger counting and vehicle location systems, on-vehicle terminals and portable ticket issuing systems, ticket verification systems, Ibis interface, ISO standard compatibility, data analysis and management information software.

Contracts: In the UK over 80 per cent of bus operators are cited by Wayfarer as using its equipment. Through local agents and distributors, Wayfarer has installed systems in Argentina, Australia, Chile, Germany, Ireland, Israel, Italy, the Lebanon, Malaysia, Netherlands, New Zealand, Norway, Portugal, South Africa, Spain, Sweden and the USA.
The first Wayfarer contact smartcard system was installed in Auckland, New Zealand, in 1991, with over 10,000 smartcards in daily use. Wayfarer also have several contactless smartcard systems in use, the largest being in Southport, UK, which was installed in 1994. There are now over 10,000 cards in daily use.

VERIFIED

WCL

WCL Ltd
177 Nutfield Road, Merstham RH1 3HH, UK
Tel: (+44 1737) 64 49 21   Fax: (+44 1737) 64 36 93
Derwent House, Kendal Avenue, London W3 0XA, UK
Tel: (+44 181) 992 80 70   (+44 181) 992 80 72
Managing Director: John Lincoln
Marketing Director: Peter Ellwood

Products: Automatic fare collection systems, passenger-operated ticket machines, booking office ticket machines, automatic passenger gates; and computerised management and audit control.

Provides turnkey ARC systems, from cash accepting and ticket issuing devices to computer hardware and software, communications networks, installation, lifetime maintenance and support. Magnetically encoded ticket systems provide management information and control. Detailed accountability and a full audit trail aid fraud prevention. Operating information can be made available to management in real time. Also smartcard technology — the Go Card is a ticketing concept where a contactless smartcard ticket replaces traditional magnetically encoded tickets. The system can be applied to stored value, period or concession ticketing.

Contracts: Has equipped all London Underground stations with passenger-operated and booking office ticket machines, automatic gates, station computers, control units and printers linked to central computer systems.

VERIFIED

VEHICLE MAINTENANCE EQUIPMENT AND SERVICES

Company Listing by Country

CANADA
Bombardier Transportation
Proceco

FRANCE
ALSTOM
Chemirail
De Dietrich Ferroviaire
Nord Productique
SEFAC

GERMANY
Adtranz
Hegenscheidt-MFD
HYWEMA
JAB
Neuero
Pfaff-silberblau
Windhoff

ITALY
CESPA
Ravaglioli

NETHERLANDS
RB Haarlem

SPAIN
INME

SWITZERLAND
Nencki
Von Roll BETEC

UK
ALSTOM
BWI Dawson
Chassijet
Mechan

REW
Smith Bros & Webb
Somers
Technorizon
Upright UK
Valematic
Wilcomatic

USA
Advantage
CAM
Containment Corporation
Hanna-Sheerman
InterClean
LWS
Marmac
N/S
Rotary Lift
SSI
Whiting

Classified Listing

CLEANING SYSTEMS FOR TUNNELS ETC
Hanna-Sheerman
InterClean
LWS
SEFAC
SSI

ELECTRIC MOTOR AND OTHER EQUIPMENT
CESPA

FLEET MAINTENANCE
Adtranz
ALSTOM
Bombardier Transportation
RB Haarlem

LIFTS & LIFTING EQUIPMENT
Advantage
CESPA
HYWEMA
INME
JAB
Marmac
Mechan
Nencki
Neuero
Pfaff-silberblau

Ravaglioli
Rotary Lift
SEFAC
Somers
Whiting
Windhoff

TOWER/MAINTENANCE VEHICLES
Nencki
Upright UK
Windhoff

TYRE FITTING/SEPARATING MACHINES
Ravaglioli

WASHERS AND WASHING EQUIPMENT FOR VEHICLES
Chemirail
BWI Dawson
Chassijet
Chemirail
Hanna-Sheerman
InterClean
LWS
N/S
Proceco
Smith Bros & Webb

SSI
Technorizon
Valematic
Whiting
Wilcomatic

WHEELSET MAINTENANCE
Hegenscheidt-MFD
Von Roll BETEC
Neuero
Nord Productique
Proceco

WORKSHOP EQUIPMENT
ALSTOM
BWI Dawson
CAM
CESPA
Containment Corporation
De Dietrich Ferroviaire
Mechan
Neuero
Nord Productique
SEFAC
Upright UK
Windhoff

Adtranz

DaimlerChrysler Railsystems
PO Box 130127, D-13601 Berlin, Germany
Tel: (+49 303) 83 20   Fax: (+49 303) 832 20 00
(See main entry under Rail Vehicles and Traction
Equipment)

Products: Component testing, fleet maintenance, field
service contracts including extended warranties.

UPDATED

Advantage

Advantage Lift Systems Inc
6359 Nancy Ridge Drive, San Diego, California 92121,
USA
Tel: (+1 619) 453 28 41   Fax: (+1 619) 453 09 27
Chief Executive Officer: Clayton N Carley
President: Robert Fletcher

Products: Workshop lifting systems for buses; wheel
dollies; in-ground lift; permanently mounted and portable
lifts.

VERIFIED

ALSTOM

ALSTOM Train Services
PO Box 248, Leigh Road, Washwood Heath, Birmingham
B8 2YF, UK
Tel: (+44 121) 695 36 00   Fax: (+44 121) 327 56 31

The Train Services HELPDESK offers a single point of
contact for technical advice worldwide

Technical assistance enquiry line:
e-mail: service.techelp@transport.alstom.com
Fax: (+44 1772) 55 38 84

For general enquiries, a single point of contact in four
languages:

English
Train Services
ALSTOM
Channel Way, Preston PR1 8XL, UK
Tel: (+44 1772) 55 33 03   Fax: (+44 1772) 55 37 96
e-mail: service.mkting@transport.alstom.com

French
Transport Service
ALSTOM
48 rue Albert Dhalenne, F-93482 Saint-Ouen Cedex,
France
Tel: (+33 1) 41 66 91 32   Fax: (+33 1) 41 66 87 98
e-mail: service.mkting@ transport.alstom.com

ALSTOM DDF
PO Box 35, F-67891 Niederbronn, France
Tel: (+33 3) 88 80 25 00

Spanish
Transport Service
ALSTOM Transporte SA
Paseo de la Castellana 257, E-28046 Madrid, Spain
Tel: (+34 91) 334 57 14   Fax: (+34 91) 334 57 21
e-mail: service.mkting@ transport.alstom.com

German
Transport Service
ALSTOM
PO Box 41 11 60, D-38233, Salzgitter, Germany
Tel: (+49 5341) 21 42 08   Fax: (+49 5341) 21 76 34
e-mail: service.mkting@ transport.alstom.com

Services: ALSTOM offers a range of after-sales services
catering for operator's needs to support existing in-house
capabilities or to completely out-source service and
maintenance. It also provides a modernisation and
renovation proficiency to extend product life and enhance
performance.

Caters for operator and maintenance provider needs
for rolling stock, equipment, signalling and locomotives:
Service, parts and repairs;
Renovation: returning to original specifications;
Modernisation and upgrade solutions: new technology
for older applications;
Technical and consultancy support including the newly
launched HELPDESK;
Contracted services;
Depot maintenance, depot management and system
maintenance.
ALSTOM also provides, through ALSTOM DDF,
automatic underfloor haulage systems for rail vehicle
washing installations, underfloor wheel lathes and
workshops.

UPDATED

Bombardier Transportation

Bombardier Transportation
1101 Parent Street, Saint-Bruno, Quebec, Canada
J3V 6E6
Tel: (+1 514) 441 20 20   Fax: (+1 514) 441 15 15
www: http://www.transportation.bombardier.com
See main entry under Bombardier Transportation in Rail
Vehicles and Traction Equipment

Services: Operation and maintenance (O&M)
programme for passenger rail vehicles and transit
systems.
O&M services supplied by Bombardier date back to the
early 1980s and Bombardier offers planning, structuring
and training services.

Contracts: Bombardier Transportation has been
awarded a three-year maintenace contract by the Board
of Directors of the Southern California Regional Rail
Authority (SCRRA), which includes the maintenance of
SCRRA's commuter rail fleet of 31 locomotives and 119
Bombardier bilevel commuter coaches. The SCRRA
governs Metrolink commuter rail service, a 640 km
network that runs throughout the five-county area
surrounding Greater Los Angeles. Bombardier carries out
the work at the Metrolink Taylor Yard maintenance facility
in Los Angeles.
In 1998 The Board of Commissioners of the Port
Authority of New York and New Jersey selected the
AirRail Transit Consortium, led by Skanska USA and
Bombardier Transportation, for the design, construction,
operation and maintenance of the New York JFK
International Airport Automated Light Rail System. Under
the Design-Build-Operate-Maintain (DBOM) approach,
the consortium is responsible for the turnkey design and
construction of the driverless light rail system, as well as
for its operation for a period of up to 15 years. The system
consists of 14 km (8.4 miles) of predominantly elevated,
double-track guideway with 10 stations and 32 vehicles.
Since 1996 Bombardier has been carrying out
locomotive and coach maintenance service under a six-
year contract with GO Transit in Toronto, Canada.
Services include supplying management, labour and
materials; managing train movements in the yard; and
maintaining over 300 Bombardier-built bilevels and 40
General Motors F59PH locomotives. The GO Willowbrook
maintenance facility can accommodate an entire 10-car
trainset with two locomotives.
In 1996 the Croydon Tramlink concession in the United
Kingdom was awarded to Tramtrack Croydon, a
consortium with Bombardier as a key member. The
concession will run for 99 years and the consortium will
design, build, operate, maintain and finance the 28 km
system, which is due to open at the end of 1999.
Bombardier was awarded the contract to manufacture 24
trams for Croydon and will also be responsible for
maintaining the vehicles.
In 1992 Bombardier supplied 21 bilevel coaches to Tri-
Rail Commuter Rail in Florida, and operated and
maintained the system, including five locomotives, from
1989 to 1992. Bombardier's maintenance procedures
and practices at Tri-Rail established many of its present
maintenance standards and are still used by Tri-Rail
today.
From 1985 to 1991 Bombardier supplied maintenance
services for the Vancouver SkyTrain. The maintenance
approach involved assembly of a core staff of highly
skilled employees equipped with the training, tools,

equipment and spare parts necessary to work effectively.
The staff performed all preventive and corrective
maintenance on those elements of the system critical to
meeting the demands of the daily operating schedule.

NEW ENTRY

BWI Dawson

BWI Dawson
Fieldhead Lane, Drighlington BD11 1JL, UK
Tel: (+44 113) 285 40 19   Fax: (+44 113) 285 40 20
Managing Director: Dennis Tallon
Project Enginer: K Dews/Ken Dews

Products: Train washing plant for light rail, underground
and main line stock, including brushing systems for sides,
roofs, fronts, rears and skirts; water recycling,
neutralisation and air knife blowers.

Contracts: Include washing plant for Sweden, UK and the
Philippines. Equipment has been supplied to Railtrack,
UK, and LTA Singapore.

UPDATED

CAM

CAM Industries Inc
215 Philadelphia Street, Hanover, Pennsylvania 17331,
USA
Tel: (+1 717) 637 59 88   Fax: (+1 717) 637 93 29
President: C A McGough Jr

Products: Complete equipment for electric traction
motor repair workshops including undercutters, handling
equipment, test equipment and universal armature
machines.

Contracts: SEPTA Philadelphia, LIRR New York and CTA
Chicago.

VERIFIED

CESPA

CESPA
Costruzioni Elettromeccaniche Spavone
Via Luigi Volpicella 145, I-80147 Napoli, Italy
Tel: (+39 081) 752 48 63   Fax: (+39 081) 559 05 61
e-mail: cespanet@mbox.volt.it
www: www.pagine gialle.it/cespa-01
Technical Director: Massimo Spavone
Managing Director & General Manager: Luigi Spavone

Products: Repair and workshop machinery; lifting
equipment; workshop bogies for supporting vehicles;
mobile lifting jacks for rail and bus applications; testing
platforms for bogies; elevated platforms for access to
vehicles; rain testing plants; electric motor maintenance
equipment.

Contracts: With Ansaldo Trasporti, Adtranz, Breda, Fiat
Ferroviaria, Firema and Italian Railways.

Developments: Underfloor lifts for bogies and wheelset
mounting equipment have been introduced.

UPDATED

Chassijet

Chassijet Ltd
Unit 6, Cape Road Industrial Estate, Cattell Road,
Warwick CV34 4JN, UK
Tel: (+44 1926) 49 59 00   Fax: (+44 1926) 49 79 00
Sales Manager: Chris Gray

Products: Vehicle washing systems, chassis cleaning equipment.

VERIFIED

Chemirail

Chemirail
Ets Roger Brillié, 25 rue de la Victoire, F-93150 Le Blanc-Mesnil, France
Tel: (+33 1) 48 14 27 50   Fax: (+33 1) 48 67 30 18
Director: J N Vassilopoulos

Products: Rollover brush washing machines for rail vehicles.

VERIFIED

Containment Corporation

Containment Corporation
10889 Portal Drive, Los Alamitos, California 90720, USA
Tel: (+1 714) 821 67 50   Fax: (+1 714) 821 99 49
Sales Director: Larry H Macofsky

Associate company
ChemFree
8 Meca Way, Norcross, Georgia 30093, USA
Tel: (+1 770) 564 55 80   Fax: (+1 770) 564 55 33

Products: Environment-friendly cleaning system for oiled parts, using microbial reclamation system.

VERIFIED

De Dietrich Ferroviaire

De Dietrich Ferroviaire
PO Box 35, F-67891 Niederbronn, France
Tel: (+33 3) 88 80 25 00   Fax: (+33 3) 88 80 25 12
President : Didier Genty
Sales Manager : Jean-François Pietom

See ALSTOM entry in this section

Products: Automatic underfloor haulage systems for rail vehicle washing installations, underfloor wheel lathes and workshops.

UPDATED

Hanna-Sheerman

Hanna-Sheerman International Inc
2000 Hanna Drive, Portland, Oregon 97222, USA
Tel: (+1 503) 659 03 61   Fax: (+1 503) 659 06 31
General Manager: Daniel C Hanna Jr

Products: Automatic vehicle washing systems, vacuum cleaning systems, water reclamation systems, under carriage wash systems.

VERIFIED

Hegenscheidt-MFD

Hegenscheidt-MFD GmbH
PO Box 1408, D-41804 Erkelenz, Germany
Tel: (+49 2431) 860   Fax: (+49 2431) 864 70
General Manager: Dr rer nat K-P Schwarz
Parent company: Vossloh Rail Systems GmbH (see Track Equipment section)

Subsidiaries
Hegenscheidt Corp, Troy, Michigan, USA
Hegenscheidt Australia, Melbourne
Hegenscheidt Liaison Office, Delhi, India

Products: Machinery and equipment for wheelset maintenance, comprising above-floor and underfloor wheel lathes; wheel presses; tyre separating devices; inductive tyre heaters; spring ring closing machines; rerailing equipment.

VERIFIED

HYWEMA

HYWEMA Lifting Equipment (GmbH & Co)
Wuppertaler Strasse 134-148, D-42653 Solingen, Germany
Tel: (+49 212) 257 70   Fax: (+49 212) 257 71 00
General Manager: D Paul

Products: Mobile universal vehicle lifts for rigid (20,000 kg capacity) and articulated (30,000 kg) buses; maintenance and repair of washing facilities.

Contracts: Recent contracts include supply to Volkswagen AG, ZF, Mercedes-Benz Spain, Evobus, Voith Iberica, Neoplan Poland, VRS Cologne, Auwärter KG, Koblenz transport authority and Mercedes-Benz Stuttgart.

VERIFIED

INME

INME
Alameda de Urquijo 87, E-48013 Bilbao, Spain
Tel: (+34 94) 442 04 48   Fax: (+34 94) 442 12 21
Marketing Manager: Pablo Diez
Engineering Manager: Jesus Ferro

Products: Mobile lifting columns, bogie platforms, overhead cranes, workshop haulage systems.

VERIFIED

InterClean

InterClean Equipment Inc
3918 Varsity Drive, Ann Arbor, Michigan 48108, USA
Tel: (+1 313) 975 29 67   Fax: (+1 313) 975 24 13
e-mail: sales@mail.interclean.com
President: Mia Lamminen
Vice President: Pasi Kaipainen

Products: Range of high-pressure automatic vehicle washing systems; also touchless bus wash, rail vehicle and locomotive cleaning systems.

UPDATED

JAB

J A Becker & Söhne Maschinenfabrik
PO Box 1151, D-74148 Neckarsulm, Germany
Tel: (+49 7132) 36 70   Fax: (+49 7132) 36 72 89

Products: Multiple ram electrically driven heavy-duty lifts with telescopic or standard rams.

VERIFIED

LWS

LWS Inc
3918 Varsity Drive, Ann Arbor, Michigan 48108, USA
Tel: (+1 313) 975 29 66   Fax: (+1 313) 975 16 46
President: Mia Lamminen

Products: Drive-through bus and train wash equipment; locomotive washing systems; bus and train wash equipment; interior cleaning systems; touchless bus and train wash systems; consulting and engineering services for all specialised cleaning applications.

Contracts: Has supplied over 400 bus and rail wash systems in North America.

VERIFIED

Marmac

The Marmac Company
PO Box 157, Xenia, Ohio 45385, USA
Tel: (+1 937) 372 80 93   Fax: (+1 937) 372 71 01
Executive Vice President: Sharon M Walthall
Vice President, Operations: Gary D Walthall

Products: Heavy-duty lifting equipment for vehicle servicing.

Contracts: Supplied lifting equipment to MBTA Boston.

VERIFIED

Mechan

Mechan Ltd
Thorncliffe Park, Chapeltown, Sheffield S35 4PH, UK
Tel: (+44 114) 257 05 63   Fax: (+44 114) 245 11 24
e-mail: admin@mechan.co.uk
Managing Director: A G Hague
Engineering Director: G L Cofield
Sales Director: O D Snell

Products: Rail vehicle jacks, turntables (for wheel sets, bogies and complete vehicles), bogie presses, bogie drops, traversers, rail vehicle lifting beams, under-car handling equipment, accommodation bogies, swing-jib cranes.
Mechan Micro-Link microprocessor control systems are used for the control, monitoring and synchronisation of rail vehicle jacks. The system allows the jacks to be linked by only two control wires for complete sets of jacks and can be fitted to new equipment or fitted to existing sets of jacks.
Weighing equipment can also be fitted to rail jacking systems.

VERIFIED

Nencki

Nencki AG
CH-4900 Langenthal, Switzerland
Tel: (+41 62) 922 76 76   Fax: (+41 62) 922 29 31
Managing Director: S Käppeli
Sales Manager: A Gerber

Products: Bogie and axle drop tables, lifting tables, scissor platforms and lifting jacks; hydraulic platforms for overhead line inspection; track maintenance equipment.
Self-propelled flat rail vehicle with telescopic boom-type working platform; computer-controlled horizontal rail bending presses for workshop use.

VERIFIED

Neuero

Neuero Technology GmbH
Bismarckstrasse 4-8, D-49324 Melle, Germany
Tel: (+49 5422) 60 70   Fax: (+49 5422) 21 04
Managing Director: Dipl Ing Bernhard Uhlen
Sales Director: Dipl Ing Heinrich Wöstefeld

Products: Lifting jacks, underfloor lift systems, bogie lift stands, lifting trucks and tables, dismantling devices for wheelsets and bogies, mobile handling equipment, turntables and maintenance platforms, lifting and turning devices, auxiliary bogies, bogie replacement systems, planning and commissioning of complete workshops, stress measuring devices, shock-absorber test bench, weighbridges, bogie assembly and test bench, test bench for cylinder and flexicoil springs; air cushion transport systems for manufacturers of wagons and locomotives.

Contracts: Supply of workshop equipment including track and rail bridges for DB Hannover and DB Erfurt, Germany. Underfloor lifting plants for DSB Denmark; underfloor lifting plants and bogie drop for DB AG Cologne, Germany; lifting platforms guided by induction loops for SNCB Belgium; underfloor bogie hoists for locomotive bogies for SNCB Belgium; bogie assembly and test bench for Adtranz Germany.

New developments: Planning and design of complete workshops for railways, metros, trains, light rail.

UPDATED

Nord Productique

Nord Productique
Le Val sur Sambre, PO Box 102, F-56920 Aulnoye Aymeries, France
Tel: (+33 3) 27 66 45 33   Fax: (+33 3) 27 66 60 88

Products: Underfloor wheel lathes; wheel grinding machines; above-floor portal-type wheel lathe; vertical boring machine.

VERIFIED

N/S

N/S Vehicle Wash Systems
235 West Florence Avenue, Inglewood, California 90301, USA
Tel: (+1 310) 412 70 74   Fax: (+1 310 673 02 76
e-mail: nstransit@aol.com
Vice President, Marketing: Thomas G Ennis
Advertising Manager: Keith Caggiano
Sales Representatives: Brent Feldman/Kevin Sudano/Jimmy Castro

Products: Wash systems for rail, light rail, small vehicle and bus applications, with water recovery systems; vacuum systems; high-pressure cleaning systems.

Contracts: Include equipment for NYCTA New York; SEPTA Philadelphia, OCTA Los Angeles; LAMTA Green Line, Los Angeles; Tren Urbano; Disney World, Florida.

UPDATED

Pfaff-silberblau

Pfaff-silberblau Hebezeugfabrik GmbH & Co
PO Box 102233, D-86012 Augsburg, Germany
Tel: (+49 821) 780 15 31   Fax: (+49 821) 780 12 05
e-mail: contact@pfaff-silberblau.de
www: www.pfaff-silberblau.de
Directors: Dr H Pfaff, S Pfaff
Sales Manager: Peter Zeller

Works
Derching, Äussere Industriestrasse 18, D-86316 Friedberg

Subsidiaries
Pfaff-silberblau, South Africa (Pty) Ltd
PO Box 1999, RSA Honeydew 2040, South Africa
Tel: (+27 11) 791 06 37   Fax: (+27 11) 792 35 73

Pfaff-silberblau, Romania
Str Turda 127 Bl2, Ap 172, ROM-Bucharest
Tel: (+40 1) 666 70 47   Fax: (+40 1) 666 70 47

Pfaff-silberblau, France SARL
Levage-Manutenton 215, rue Henri Barbusse, F-95100 Argenteuil
Tel: (+33 1) 34 34 60 50   Fax: (+33 1) 34 34 00 63

Pfaff-silberblau, Hungary Kft
Dözsa György Str 84, 222 Vecsés
Tel: (+36 29) 35 64 33   Fax: (+36 29) 35 64 34

Products: Include lifting equipment for rail vehicles, lifting jacks up to 35 tonnes; cranes, electrical and manual hoists; bogie-lifting installations; bogie handling units; drop tables; forklift trucks; scissor lifting tables, hydraulic equipment.

Contracts: Underfloor lifting systems have been supplied to Metropolitano de Lisboa, TTC Toronto, Metro Athens, Queensland Rail Australia, Vekehrsbetriebe Augsburg, ZWM Mannheim.
   Mobile lifting jacks to DB, SBB, Hyundai and RBA Augsburg.

UPDATED

Proceco

Proceco Industrial Machinery Ltd
7300 Tellier Street, Montreal, Canada H1N 3T7
Tel: (+1 514) 254 84 94   Fax: (+1 514) 254 81 84
Manager, Rail & Transit Products: John Runeckles
Subsidiary offices in USA and Germany

Products: Washing and drying equipment for wheelsets, traction motors, diesel engines, bogies, bearings, diesel engine components, axles and air brake components.

VERIFIED

Ravaglioli

Ravaglioli SpA
Via I Maggio 3, I-40044 Pontecchio Marconi, Italy
Tel: (+39 051) 84 63 48   Fax: (+39 051) 84 63 49
Subsidiary companies in France, Germany and USA

Products: Lifting equipment for rail and road vehicles, including mobile column lifts, scissor lifts, four-post lifts; tyre changers; wheel balancers; cranes; presses; lathes; brake testing equipment, underground piston lifts, wheel alignment systems.

Products: Lifting equipment has been supplied to transport undertakings in Paris, Singapore, Vancouver and Hong Kong.

VERIFIED

RB Haarlem

RB Haarlem, PO Box 1008, NL-2001 BA Utrecht, Netherlands
Tel: (+31 23) 516 13 46   Fax: (+31 23) 516 16 16
Communication & Market Research: Maaike Lemmers

Background: RB Haarlem is a business unit of NS Materieel BV.

Services: Overhaul, refurbishment, maintenance and damage repair of rolling stock including automatic couplers, wheelset and bogie overhaul, modern paint facilities.

Contracts: Contracts include all maintenance, modernisation, conversion and refurbishment of passenger rolling stock for NS Reizigers, refurbishment of bogies for DSB Denmark and repair of tramcars for RE Rotterdam.

UPDATED

REW

REW (Acton) Ltd
130 Bollo Lane, Acton W3 8BZ, UK
Tel: (+44 171) 918 66 66   Fax: (+44 171) 918 65 99
e-mail: douse@r-e-w.co.uk
Commercial Manager: Michael Douse

Products: Overhaul and repair of motors, compressors, alternators, door motors, safety interlocks, traction control equipment and generators; wheelset maintenance; wet-sand blasting; relay and associated signalling equipment maintenance; repair/refurbishment of seats; maintenance of CCTV, passenger information systems and associated electronic equipment; supply of master-clock systems.

Contracts: Maintenance work was solely for London Underground Ltd, but is now offered to any interested company.

VERIFIED

Rotary Lift

Rotary Lift
2700 Lanier Drive, Madison, Indiana 47250, USA
Tel: (+1 812) 273 16 22   Fax: (+1 812) 273 65 02
Vice President: Tom Phillips
Managing Director (Europe): Carlo Zenone
Tel: (+44 1322) 22 33 23   Fax: (+44 1322) 22 24 54
Parent company: Dover Industries

Products: Vehicle lifting equipment for maintenance and repairs; lifting capacities 2,727 to 45,454 kg (6,000 to 100,000 lb).

VERIFIED

SEFAC

Société d'Estampage et de Forge Ardennes Champagne
1 rue Andre Compain, F-08800 Montherme, France
Tel: (+33 3) 24 53 01 82   Fax: (+33 3) 24 53 20 24
Railway Marketing Manager: Vincent Jolliot
Railway Engineering Manager: E Letellier

Subsidiary companies
SEFAC Lift & Equipment Corporation
7175 Oakland Mills Road, Columbia, Maryland 21046, USA
Tel: (+1 410) 964 08 06   Fax: (+1 410) 964 08 77
Manager: Richard Kergen

SEFAC SA
Camino de Rejas, Nave 10, E-28820 Coslada, Spain
Tel: (+34 91) 672 36 12   Fax: (+34 91) 672 33 96
Manager: R Serrano

Products: Mobile lifts, jacks, bogie lifts, cleaning systems, depot/garage equipment for railways, metro, LRT and bus applications; dust removal systems.

VERIFIED

Smith Bros & Webb

Smith Bros & Webb Limited
Britannia House, Arden Forest Industrial Estate, Alcester B49 6EX, UK
Tel: (+44 1789) 40 00 96   Fax: (+44 1789) 40 02 31
Managing Director: K H Harrison

Products: Automatic washers for rail and road vehicles.

Contracts: Recent contracts include cleaning systems for Lisbon metro (2); Kowloon—Canton Railway, Hong Kong; Croydon Tramlink; and major refurbishment for Railtrack machines.
   Bus wash systems have been supplied to First Bus, Hong Kong, Ulsterbus, Travel West Midlands, CentreWest London, Essex Buses and Eastern Counties.

UPDATED

Somers

Somers Vehicle Lifts Ltd
15 Forge Trading Estate, Mucklow Hill, Halesowen B62 8TR, UK
Tel: (+44 121) 585 27 00   Fax: (+44 121) 501 14 58
Chairman: Robert Perkins
Director/General Manager: Tim Jackson

Products: Mobile vehicle lifts, scissors lift tables and support stands, including a range of lightweight mobile lifts designed for minibuses and other smaller vehicles.

Developments: A new lift, the SVL2000e, incorporates a fault-finding capability as part of the electronic control system and displays information of the fault, and the remedy, on a display screen.

UPDATED

SSI

SSI Corporation
1650 Bonhill Road, Mississauga, Ontario L5T 1C8, Canada
Tel: (+1 905) 795 92 74   Fax: (+1 905) 795 13 50
President: Seymour Techner

Products: Modular train and bus washing systems; vehicle interior vacuum cleaning systems; dryers.

VERIFIED

Technorizon

Technorizon Systems (UK) Ltd
54 Angel Hill, Sutton SM1 3EW, UK
Tel: (+44 181) 641 22 29   Fax: (+44 181) 644 11 51
Chairman: Des Cockerill

Products: Vehicle washing systems.

VERIFIED

Upright UK

Upright UK Ltd
Access House, Halesfield 17, Telford TF7 4PW, UK
Tel: (+44 1952) 68 52 00   Fax: (+44 1952) 68 52 05
e-mail: access@upright.co.uk
Managing Director: Frank Huish
Finance Director: Tony Jennings

Products: Range of access equipment such as aluminium towers and power platforms. Other products include scissors lifts, articulated booms, personnel lifts, Spandeck walkway and Span 400 towers.

UPDATED

Valematic

Valematic
Elles House, 4B Invincible Road, Farnborough GU14 7QU, UK
Tel: (+44 1252) 36 28 00   Fax: (+44 1252) 37 36 95
Chairman: Bob Chase
Managing Director: Noel Harasyn
Sales & Marketing Director: Robert Scott

Products: Jetwash®, Istobal, Celcato cleaning systems for buses and coaches. Equipment is supplied with water reclamation facilities.

UPDATED

Von Roll BETEC

Von Roll BETEC Ltd
Allmendstrasse 86, CH-3602 Thun, Switzerland
Tel: (+41 33) 228 20 20   Fax: (+41 33) 228 21 75
Managing Director: Peter Schildknecht
Marketing Manager: Marc Bickel

Background: Von Roll BETEC took over the production and aftersales support of underfloor wheelset profiling machines from Kellenberger in 1998.

Products: Underfloor wheel grinding and turning systems; wheelset measuring systems.

UPDATED

Whiting

Whiting Corporation
15700 Lathrop Avenue, Harvey, Illinois 60426-9006, USA
Tel: (+1 888) WHITING   Fax: (+1 708) 210 50 30
Vice President, Marketing & Sales: C J Skorpinski
Manager, Product Systems: M N Milligan
Manager, Product Applications: R S Koziel

Products: Drop tables, locomotive and car body supports, turntable equipment, transfer tables, portable electric jacks and overhead bridge cranes.

Contracts: Include equipment for Amtrak, Metra Chicago, Union Pacific, Burlington Northern, WMATA Washington and SEPTA Philadelphia.

UPDATED

Wilcomatic

Wilcomatic Ltd
123 Beddington Lane, Croydon CR9 4NX, UK
Tel: (+44 181) 684 99 00
Fax: (+44 181) 684 04 89/683 20 70
e-mail: sales@wilcomatic.co.uk
Sales Manager: Paul Golunski

Products: Vehicle washing equipment (drive-through two- and four-brush machines); under-chassis washers; water reclamation units to suit various site conditions, selection of hot/cold pressure washing equipment, own range of washing chemicals.

UPDATED

Windhoff

Windhoff AG
PO Box 1963, D-48409 Rheine, Germany
Tel: (+49 5971) 580   Fax: (+49 5971) 582 09
President: Dipl-Ing Heinz Lörfing
Export Manager: Dipl-Ing Helmut Pühs

Products: Heavy-duty lighting installation for vehicle servicing; lifting jacks; bogie exchange installations; axle and bogie lifts; traversers; turntables; multipurpose track maintenance machines; overhead line inspection and maintenance vehicles; special rail cranes; crib ballast removers; underground vehicles; catenary inspection vehicles.

Contracts: Windhoff's contracts have included supply of equipment for SBB Zürich, NSB Olso, KCRC Hong Kong, SL Stockholm and Ports & Railway Authority, Tel Aviv.

VERIFIED

Cembre

Cembre SpA
Via Serenissima 9, I-25135 Brescia, Italy
Tel: (+39 030) 369 21   Fax: (+39 030) 336 57 66

UK office
Cembre Ltd, Fairview Industrial Estate, Kingsbury Road,
Curdworth, Sutton Coldfield B76 9EE
Tel: (+44 1675) 47 04 40   Fax: (+44 1675) 47 02 20

Products: Petrol-powered and electric portable rail drill.
A drill for wooden sleepers is available; also the
Railtrack-approved rail web cable connection system.

VERIFIED

Chipman Rail

Chipman Rail plc
The Goods Yard, Horsham RH12 2NR, UK
Tel: (+44 1403) 26 03 41   Fax: (+44 1403) 26 47 99
Managing Director: Brian Ollier

Products: On-track weed control, off-track scrub
clearance, lead-jetting, traction gel application, weed
chemicals and equipment; drain clearing.

Contracts: Leaf clearance programme for Railtrack UK.
The project follows development of a dedicated leaf
jetting train. The train comprises a leaf blasting coach,
four water tank wagons and two locomotives and is
employed over much of Railtrack South's permanent way
which is affected by leaf falls each autumn.
    The leaf clearance unit travels at a constant speed of
32 km/h. Its leading water jet softens up the leaves, which
are then broken up and removed by the second jet. The
sandite — a sand/gel composite — is then applied, and the
resulting residue jet-washed off. The process ensures
effective track adhesion for train wheels even in difficult
weather conditions.

VERIFIED

Cogifer

Compagnie Générale d'Installations Ferroviaires
40 quai de l'Ecluse, F-78290 Croissy sur Seine, France
Tel: (+33 1) 34 80 45 00   Fax: (+33 1) 34 80 03 31
e-mail: contact@cogifer.fr
www: www.cogifer.com
Chairman: Régis Bello
Chief Executive Officer and Cogifer Industry Department
    General Manager: C Schwartz
Chairman, Cogifer TF: Henri Dehé
General Manager, Cogifer Signalling: Jean-Louis Wagner
Business Development Manager:
    Marc-Antoine de Dietrich

Specialised departments
Cogifer Industries (points and crossings)
Cogifer Signalling (signalling and catenary)

Subsidiary
Cogifer TF (laying and renewal of tracks for urban
transport)

Products: Supply, installation and maintenance of track,
points and crossings for metro, tramway and light rail
systems; electric switching and detecting equipment.

Contracts: Metro installations have been supplied to
Paris, Lyons, Marseilles, Lille, Orly, Toulouse and Rennes
in France; to Brussels, Manchester, Lisbon and Bilbao in
the rest of Europe; to Mexico City, Caracas, Santiago,
Cairo, Hong Kong, Monterrey, Chicago, Jackson and
Taipei in the rest of the world.
    Tramway/LRT installations have been supplied to
Paris, Grenoble, Lyons, Marseilles, Lille, Montpellier,
Nantes, Rouen, St Etienne and Strasbourg in France; to
Amsterdam, Oporto, Ostrava, Basle, Lausanne, Ghent,
Prague, Helsinki, Milan, Rome, Kosice, Rotterdam, Plzen
and many other European cities; to San Francisco, Los

Angeles, San Diego, Seattle and other cities in USA and
the rest of the world.

UPDATED

Contitech

Contitech Transportbandsysteme GmbH
Clouth Cologne Plant
Niehler Strasse 102-116, D-50733 Cologne, Germany
Tel: (+49 221) 777 36 24   Fax: (+49 221) 777 37 00
Managing Directors: Dr Richard Sohnemann
    Norbert Martin
Manager, International Marketing & Sales:
    Michael Kottmann
Research & Development Managers: Alexander Repczuk
    Dr Wilhelm Engst

Australia and Asia representative
Delkor Pty Ltd, PO Box 176, St Peters, New South Wales
2044, Australia
Tel: (+61 2) 95 50 51 11   Fax: (+61 2) 95 50 56 25

Portugal representative
Tradegal Lda, Av Visconde Valmor 69–5°, Andar, P-1050
Lisbon
Tel: (+351 1) 795 90 82/90 89   Fax: (+351 1) 795 90 97

Norway representative
Ragnar Lund A/S, Nedre Rommen 5c, N-0988 Oslo
Tel: (+47 2221) 80 80   Fax: (+47 2221) 80 81

USA/Canada representative
ATP (Advanced Track Products) Inc, PO Box 92,
Mattituck, New York 11952
Tel: (+1 516) 298 57 99   Fax: (+1 516) 298 57 89

Products: Sub-ballast mats for vibration control;
protective mats (Clouth-ASM®) for waterproof coatings of
bridges and structures; rolling rubber springs (Clouth
Rollfeder®) for primary and secondary suspension for rail
vehicles; resilient track fastenings; elastomeric bridge
bearings; mass-spring systems; Clouth Oil-Ex®
elastomeric mat to absorb liquid hydrocarbons, such as
oil, lubricants of low viscosity, motor fuels and organic
solvents.

Developments: A new high-resilience cost-effective rail
fastener for vibration control is the Clouth Alternative 1,
Type 065. It is designed for Pandrol and Vossloh
fastening clips and for axleloads to 250 kN and high-
speed lines, up to a maximum of 250 km/h.

UPDATED

Crompton Greaves

Crompton Greaves Limited
Rail Projects Division
Vandhna, 11 Tolstoy Marg, New Delhi 110001, India
Tel: (+91 11) 331 70 75/373 04 45
Fax: (+91 11) 331 70 75/332 43 60
Managing Director: K K Nohria
Board Member and President: C P Dusad
Vice President, Rail Transportation: B Banerjee
Deputy General Manager, Rail Transportation:
    M P Singhal

Products: Tower wagons.

Contracts: A four-wheel-powered tower wagon has been
supplied to the Indian Railway Board.

UPDATED

CXT

CXT Incorporated
PO Box 14918, Spokane, Washington 99214, USA
Tel: (+1 509) 924 63 00   Fax: (+1 509) 927 02 99
e-mail: CXT@IEWAY.com

President & Chief Executive Officer: John G White
Vice President & Chief Financial Officer: Russ Skrypchuk

Works
2420 N Sullivan Road, Spokane, WA 99216

Products: Prestressed concrete sleepers for track and
turnouts; prefabricated buildings and precast concrete
grade crossing panels.
    CXT has developed geometric design capabilities for
turnout layouts; for track, with a facility for gauge
widening; for tangent sleeper development, and for
standard track sleepers.

Contracts: Concrete sleepers supplied to the Calgary
LRT, MTA Baltimore, Vancouver, Utah, Los Angeles, New
Jersey, Denver, Portland and Southern California
Regional Rail Authority, UP, BNSF and many other heavy-
haul railways.

UPDATED

Edilon

Edilon BV
Nijverheidsweg 23, NL-2031 CN, Haarlem, Netherlands
Tel: (+31 23) 531 95 19   Fax: (+31 23) 531 07 51
Managing Director: R Vogelaar
Technical Director: A Aalberts

Products: Resilient track fastening and support systems;
embedded rail system using Edilon Corkelast compound;
adhesives.

Contracts: Have been held with Valencia Tramway, South
Yorkshire Supertram and Madrid metro.

VERIFIED

Elektro-Thermit

Elektro-Thermit Dienstleistungs GmbH
PO Box 101043, D-45010 Essen, Germany
Tel: (+49 201) 173 23 71   Fax: (+49 201) 173 19 03
Director: J H Wirtz

Services: Carries out electric build-up welding of rails and
crossings, build-up and reprofiling of rails with side-wear,
both grooved and flat-bottom section. Also improvement
of rail properties by submerged arc welding: anti-
corrugation welding, system RIFLEX; anti-wear welding,
system FTEKA 5; anti-noise welding. Joint welding of
head-hardened rails; head-hardening of rail for *insitu*
insulating joints.

Contracts: With urban transport systems in Germany
including Augsburg, Berlin, Frankfurt, Karlsruhe, Munich,
Stuttgart; with systems in the Netherlands including
Amsterdam, The Hague, Rotterdam; and in France in
Grenoble, Strasbourg, Montpellier, Orléans and others.

UPDATED

Eliatis

Eliatis sarl
Pré-Boissieux, F-38430 Moirans, France
Tel: (+33 4) 76 35 64 55   Fax: (+33 4) 76 35 64 53
Managing Directors: Jean Luc Perrin, Olivier Gallifet

Products: Aspirail road-rail unit for vacuum cleaning
roadway and tram rails, including leaf removal. Can be
fitted on to existing vehicles. Speed of operation is
25 km/h. Optional Total Road-Rail system for use on all
surfaces including asphalt, ballast, sand and grass.

VERIFIED

EWEM

EWEM AG
Thundorferstrasse 58, CH-8500 Frauenfeld, Switzerland
Tel: (+41 52) 375 20 00 Fax: (+41 52) 375 20 11
Director: A A G van Hees

Production sites: in Brazil, Indonesia, Thailand

Products: DE/Deenik elastic rail fastenings, fishplates, pads, insulators, baseplates, shoulders.

VERIFIED

Fassetta

Fassette mécanique
36 Bd de la Gare, F-13713 La Penne S/Huveaune Cedex, France
Tel: (+33 4) 91 87 70 30 Fax: (+33 4) 91 87 70 39
Managing Director: F Fassetta

Products: Gantries for switch and tracklaying rail positioning machines; machines for stressing operations; standard and special lorries; rail drills; abrasive rail saws; sleeper drills; rail derusting and grinding equipment; timber sleeper manufacture and machining plants.

VERIFIED

First Engineering

First Engineering
7th Floor, Buchanan House, 58 Port Dundas Road, Glasgow G4 0HG, UK
Tel: (+44 141) 335 30 05; 28 42
Fax: (+44 141) 335 36 08; 21 88
Managing Director: Tony Smith
Commercial Director: John Cowie

Products: Project management for infrastructure management, construction/projects and facilities management.

Developments: First Engineering is offering the new Plasser & Theurer APT500L road-rail mobile flashbutt welder for welding, track joint removal and track upgrading.

UPDATED

Gamble

Gamble
Nowhurst Lane, Broadbridge Heath, Horsham RH12 3PL, UK
Tel: (+44 1403) 21 01 21 Fax: (+44 1403) 26 36 89

Products: Road-rail equipment including ballast broom attachment for lines with third rail, crane with various attachments including dipper arms, tool hangers, notched bucket and concrete breaker; road-rail access platform.

VERIFIED

Getzner Werkstoffe

Getzner Werkstoffe GesmbH
Herrenau 5, A-6706 Bludenz-Buers, Austria
Tel: (+43 5552) 63 31 00 Fax: (+43 5552) 668 64
e-mail: verkauf@getzner.at
www: www.getzner.at/werkstoffe
Managing Director: R Pfefferkorn
Sales Director: P Burtscher

Associated company
Getzner Werkstoffe GmbH
Nördliche Münchner Strasse 27a, D-82031 Grünwald, Germany
Tel: (+49 89) 693 50 00 Fax: (+49 89) 69 35 00 11

Products: Sylomer® and Sylodyn® elastomers for track construction; ballast mats for metro, light rail and main line track; elastic bearings for track slabs; resilient baseplate pads and resilient rail pads.

UPDATED

Grant Lyon Eagre

Grant Lyon Eagre Limited
Hebden Road, Scunthorpe DN15 8XX, UK
Tel: (+44 1724) 86 21 31 Fax: (+44 1724) 29 52 43
Chairman: A V L Williams
General Manager: Dr T J Bessell
Works Manager: S Flower
Part of the British Steel Railway Group

Products: Design and manufacture of switches, crossings and special track components including expansion switches, buffer stops and insulated joints for urban rail systems. Prefabrication and installation of track layouts and junctions.

VERIFIED

GrantRail

GrantRail Ltd
Scotter Road, Scunthorpe DN15 8EF, UK
Tel: (+44 1724) 29 52 00 Fax: (+44 1724) 29 52 20
e-mail: 101775,332@compuserve.com
Trackwork Manager: Ray Rogers
Marketing & Business Development: Graeme Ferguson

Background: British Steel and Royal Volker Stevin formed GrantRail as a jointly owned company. It has been formed from the tracklaying division of British Steel subsidiary, Grant Lyon Eagre Ltd (qv), and Royal Volker Stevin's railway engineering company Railbouw (UK) Ltd.

Products: Construction, renewal and maintenance of LRT, metro, underground and heavy rail systems.
Complete systems are offered for LRT projects, covering planning, supply of rail and installation.

Contracts: Major customers include Railtrack UK, London Underground and Midland Metro.

VERIFIED

Hanning & Kahl

Hanning & Kahl GmbH & Co
Rudolph Diesel Strasse 6, D-33818 Oerlinghausen, Germany
PO Box 1342, D-33806 Oerlinghausen, Germany
Tel: (+49 5202) 70 76 00 Fax: (+49 5202) 70 76 29
e-mail: HANNING-KAHL@t-online.de
General Manager: Eckart Dümmer
Divisional Manager: Wolfgang Helas

Products: Points mechanisms for all gauges and types of rail with magnetic, motor or electrohydraulic drive; manual point setting mechanisms; point mechanism for grooved rail with mechanical double interlocking and tongue detector.

Contracts: Has supplied extensively to European tram and light rail networks, including HTM The Hague, WVB Vienna, TPG Geneva, GS Gothenburg, GVB Graz, ATM Turin, Manchester Metrolink and Sheffield Supertram, and also to other undertakings including KCRC Hong Kong, Birmingham, Croydon, ATAC Rome, RET

Rotterdam, Warsaw, Posen, Krakau, Tallin, Bucharest, Konya, Zurich.

UPDATED

Holland

Holland Company LP
1000 Holland Drive, Crete, Illinois 60417, USA
Tel: (+1 708) 672 23 00 Fax: (+1 708) 672 01 19
President: Philip C Moeller
Vice President, Sales/Wagon Components: L F O'Kray
Vice President, Rail Welding: R Madderom
International Sales Manager: Eugene Parker

Products: Hollube wear eliminators; air hose supports; flash-butt rail welding equipment; rail pullers; base grinders. Sales and contracting of electric flash-butt welding equipment; rail/road mobile welders; portable welding plant and related equipment. Super-Puller for in-track closure and repair welding, which, in addition to aligning the weld, prevents the flash-butt weld from distortion by track forces during the cooling cycle, and allows the operator to adjust the neutral laying temperature of the rail. Also K-355H welder head, designed for lower maintenance.
The MobileWelder is a road-rail unit which makes flash-butt welds in-track.
Track analysis using Holland's TrackStar® testing vehicle.

UPDATED

Infra Safety Services

Infra Safety Services
PO Box 1075, NL-3300 BB Dordrecht, Netherlands
Tel: (+31 78) 654 06 55 Fax: (+31 78) 651 44 21
Director: C J de Graaff
General Manager: J F A M Weijtmans

Products: Track safety systems including a total package for securing the work area. The company draws up and executes safety plans, and develops high-standard systems such as ARW 5/2 and Minimel 90 or PWA.

VERIFIED

Infundo

Infundo GbR
Pasteurstrasse 7, D-80999 Munich, Germany
Tel: (+49 89) 81 32 04 22 Fax: (+49 89) 81 32 04 23

Key Account Manager: Dipl Ing Günther Schnellbögl

Products: Infundo flexible rail system designed for light rail through to high-speed use. The system has been developed by Leonhard Weiss GmbH & Co, Goppingen (Germany) together with their partner Edilon BV, Haarlem, Netherlands. The main use of Infundo non-ballast track is for suburban traffic, including light railways, tramways, underground and suburban railways as well as European high-speed trains. It is also ideal for crossings, bridges and tunnels. For example, the system has been installed in the crossover section of the Channel Tunnel.

NEW ENTRY

Interep

Interep SA
Rue de L'Industrie, F-43110 Aurec/Loire, France
Tel: (+33 4) 77 35 20 21 Fax: (+33 4) 77 35 26 17
e-mail: interep@anais.aurecvideo.fr
Managing Director: Daniel Boffy
Sales & Marketing Manager: Philippe Charbonnier

Research & Development Manager:
Jean-Philippe Montagnon
Financial Manager: Patrice Cusin
Technical Manager: Marcel Boyer

Products: Microcellular rubber foams to reduce vibrations, for use as a ballast mat or under the sleeper for conventional ballasted tracks (marketed under the name Caoutchouc Mousse); also pad under block or baseplate for non-ballasted tracks.

Contracts: Microcellular rubber pads for non-ballasted tracks have been supplied to Bilbao, Spain, RATP Paris (Eole and Méteor) and Athens, Greece.

Developments: A microcellular rubber mat with advanced damping properties, Type 43-45, is suitable for metro systems. An in-house dynamic test machine for controls and simulation has been developed.

UPDATED

John Kelly (Lasers)

John Kelly (Lasers) Ltd
Broombank Road, Chesterfield S41 9QJ, UK
Tel: (+44 1246) 26 16 16   Fax: (+44 1246) 26 16 73

Products: Laser machine control for ballast cleaners, tampers, dynamic track stabilisers and crawler tilt dozers.

VERIFIED

Kaufmann

A Kaufmann AG
Railway Technology
Pilatusstrasse 2, CH-6300 Zug, Switzerland
Tel: (+41 41) 711 67 00   Fax: (+41 41) 855 17 04
Manager: Alois Kaufmann-Von Dach

Products: Contact clamps, electrodes, earthing equipment, fastenings and other track accessories and components.

UPDATED

KLDLABS

KLDLABS Inc
300 Broadway, Huntington Station, New York 11746, USA
Tel: (+1 516) 549 42 22   Fax: (+1 516) 351 71 90
President: Steven A Magnus

Products: Orian rail inspection, measurement and analysis systems.

VERIFIED

Kloos Railway Systems

Kloos Railway Systems BV
PO Box 3, NL-2690 AA Kinderdijk, Netherlands
Tel: (+31 78) 691 40 00   Fax: (+31 78) 691 45 42
Managing Director: J van Houwelingen

Works
West-Kinderdijk 24, 2953 XW Alblasserdam, Netherlands

Products: Design, development and construction of standard and custom-built materials for main line, metro and light rail systems; complete turnouts, crossings, expansion joints; specialised constructions.

Contracts: Turnouts and other equipment have been supplied to Angola, Brazil, Colombia, Egypt, Germany,

Ghana, Greece, Hong Kong, Indonesia, Iran, Netherlands, Portugal, Sudan, Singapore and Turkey.

VERIFIED

Lindapter

Lindapter International
Lindsay House, Brackenbeck Road, Bradford BD7 2NF, UK
Tel: (+44 1274) 52 14 44   Fax: (+44 1274) 52 11 30
e-mail: lindapter@dial.pipex.com
Managing Director: G R Browning
Sales Office Manager: Steve Christie
Export Sales Manager: Malcolm Eastwood
Technical Support Manager: M Knight
Marketing Manager: N A Tilsley

Products: Holdfast adjustable rail clips: the Soft clip holds rails in precise alignment while the Hard clip prevents vertical rail movement. A Spring clip also caters for rail wave while holding the rail down. A Type BR clip suits flat-bottom or bridge rails up to an 8° slope. The Temporary Support System supports and insulates running rails while essential repair work is being carried out.

Contracts: Include Manchester Piccadilly station re-roofing, Greenwich station transport interchange (connections in roof structure), London Underground Limited re-railing project.

Developments: A Type AF high-friction clamp has been introduced.

UPDATED

Matisa

Matisa Matériel Industriel SA
PO Box 58, CH-1023 Crissier, Switzerland
Tel: (+41 21) 631 21 11   Fax: (+41 21) 631 21 68
General Manager: R von Schack
Sales Director: Y Caffari
Technical Director: J Ganz

Products: Track construction, monitoring and maintenance machinery.

Range: Includes the M2000 multipurpose self-propelled track-measuring vehicle for recording track geometry, rail profile, corrugation, catenary position and other parameters.

VERIFIED

Mourgeon Industrie

Mourgeon Industrie et Engineering SA
15 rue Gay Lussac, Zone Industrielle, F-94438 Chennevières S/M, France
Tel: (+33 1) 45 94 20 20   Fax: (+33 1) 45 94 46 08

Products: Tamping tines reinforced with carbide; road-rail hydraulic excavator accessories; sleeper bale for handling up to 11 sleepers at a time; tamping attachment with which track is tamped, lined and levelled without use of tamping machine.

UPDATED

Newag

Newag GmbH & Co KG
Ripshorster Strasse Tor 73, D-46117 Oberhausen, Germany
Tel: (+49 208) 865 03 22   Fax: (+49 208) 865 03 20
e-mail: info@newag.de

Managing Director: C Kohl
Technical Director: W Kern
Sales Director: G Halfmann

Products: Track maintenance machines and equipment; tracklaying trains; catenary maintenance vehicles and equipment.

UPDATED

Ortec

Ortec GmbH
Mühlenweg 25, D-51588 Nümbrecht, Germany
Tel: (+49 2293) 910 40   Fax: (+49 2293) 91 04 31
Managing Director: Hermann J Ortwein

Products: Light rail installations, including resilient fixings/embedding, fastenings, rail coating material to reduce wheel noise and wear on bends; track landscaping with special plants between rails to reduce noise.

VERIFIED

Pandrol

Pandrol Rail Fastenings Ltd
63 Station Road, Addlestone KT15 2AR, UK
Tel: (+44 1932) 83 45 00   Fax: (+44 1932) 85 08 58
Managing Director: G M Lodge
Chief Operating Officer: J Beal-Preston

Products: Design and manufacture of track fastening systems and associated installation equipment; resilient rail pads; Vortok Coils (qv).

Developments: Work continues in the field of dynamic behaviour of track to understand fully the influence upon the total track structure of each of its components. Particular reference is being made to the generation of noise and vibration. The company has developed a range of new fastenings for specific applications including the Pandrol Fastclip®, a low-maintenance captive switch-on/switch-off rail fastening system, Pandrol VIPA® and the Vanguard®, a revolutionary rail fixation designed to reduce low-frequency vibration.

UPDATED

Pandrol Jackson

Pandrol Jackson Inc
200 South Jackson Road, Ludington, Michigan 49431, USA
Tel: (+1 616) 843 34 31   Fax: (+1 616) 843 48 30
President & Chief Executive Officer: A Zaydel
Executive Vice President, Chief Financial Officer & Administration: R J Orrow
Senior Vice President, Contracted Services/Marketing & International Sales: F Brady
Vice President, Sales & Service: J Reilly
Vice President, Engineering/Manufacturing, Rail Flaw Detection: M Havira
Vice President, Engineering: B Bradshaw
Vice President Operations: J Radowski
Vice President, Manufacturing: R Nash
Director, Pandrol Jackson Ltd: L Hawkes

Works
Pandrol Jackson Ultrasonic Manufacture
28 Eagle Road, Danbury, Connecticut 06810, USA
Tel: (+1 203) 778 68 11   Fax: (+1 203) 778 86 70

Pandrol Jackson Contract Services
PO Box 309, 1 Clark Street, E Syracuse, New York 13057, USA
Tel: (+1 315) 437 25 47   Fax: (+1 315) 463 01 80

Products: Design and manufacture of track maintenance machines, including production grinders, points (switch)

and crossing grinders, tamping machines and sleeper changers; ultrasonic equipment, including rail flaw detection cars; contract services for measurement of rail corrugation, and for main line production and points (switch) and crossings grinding.

Developments: A stoneblowing machine has been developed that will extend the time between track maintenance schedules. This new method is used as an alternative to conventional tamping. It restores the track's vertical and horizontal alignment by injecting ballast under the sleepers to achieve corrections to within 1.0 mm accuracy without disturbing ballast foundation.

UPDATED

Partner Jonsered

Partner Jonsered Power Products UK
Oldends Lane, Stonehouse GL10 3SY, UK
Tel: (+44 1453) 82 03 05/06   Fax: (+44 1453) 97 15 77
Marketing Manager: Shirley Pitts

Products: Hand-held power tools for rail maintenance/installation.

VERIFIED

Percevaut

Percevaut
14 avenue de la Plage, F-94340 Joinville-le-Pont, Paris, France
Tel: (+33 1) 43 97 62 80   Fax: (+33 1) 48 89 14 26

Products: Tunnel fan jets; exhaust gas scrubber; rail cleaner vehicle.

VERIFIED

Permaquip

Permaquip
Giltway, Giltbrook, Nottingham NG16 2GQ, UK
Tel: (+44 115) 938 70 00   Fax: (+44 115) 938 70 01
Director & General Manager: Tony Withers

Products: Tools, plant and vehicles for maintenance and construction of track including specialist plant and road/rail access vehicles. The Link Trolley expandable trolley system can be used in confined systems and transported up and down escalators.

Developments: A road/rail Land Rover with access unit has an integral boom offset system that allows access above the wire area.

UPDATED

Pfleiderer

Pfleiderer Verkehrstechnik GmbH & Co KG
Ingolstädter Strasse 51, D-92318 Neumarkt, Germany
Tel: (+49 9181) 280   Fax: (+49 9181) 284 19

Products: Sleepers and fastenings for heavy and light rail applications including ADT system consisting of a load-bearing asphalt layer with directly mounted sleepers, bi-block sleepers on concrete track and ADT-G green track for urban use.

Contracts: Include supply of trackbed/sleepers for Berlin S-Bahn.

NEW ENTRY

Phoenix

Phoenix AG
PO Box 900854, D-21048 Hamburg, Germany
Tel: (+49 40) 766 71/76 67 26 53
Fax: (+49 40) 76 67 22 11/29 24
President: Konrad Ellegast
Vice Presidents: Dr B Meister, H J Zwarg
Sales Manager: J Eggers

UK subsidiary
Phoenix (GB) Ltd
Timothy's Bridge Road, Stratford-upon-Avon CV37 9NQ, UK
Tel: (+44 1789) 20 50 90   Fax: (+44 1789) 29 86 38

Products: Range of elastomeric products for tracklaying; rail fastenings, sub-ballast matting, rail seatings, noise absorbers, grooved rail and flangeway sealing sections.

VERIFIED

Plasser & Theurer

Plasser & Theurer, Export von Bahnbaumaschinen GmbH
Johannesgasse 3, A-1010 Vienna, Austria
Tel: (+43 1) 51 57 20   Fax: (+43 1) 513 18 01

Main works: Pummererstrasse 5, 4021 Linz/Donau, Austria

Subsidiaries: Worldwide including Australia, Brazil, Canada, Denmark, France, Germany, Hong Kong, India, Italy, Japan, Mexico, Poland, South Africa, Spain, UK, USA

UK subsidiary
Plasser & Theurer International Sales (UK) Ltd
St Andrews House, St Mary's Walk, Maidenhead SL6 1QZ
Tel: (+44 1628) 78 86 48   Fax: (+44 1628) 77 04 28

Products: Tracklaying and maintenance machinery; levelling, lifting, lining and tamping machines; ballast distributing, profiling and cleaning machines; material conveyor and hopper units; rail and track points renewal machines; rail rectification, grinding and welding machines; vacuum scraper excavators; catenary maintenance and inspection cars; track geometry measuring cars; permanent way motor vehicles.

UPDATED

Rail Products & Fabrications

Rail Products & Fabrications
3422 1st Avenue South, Seattle, Washington 98134, USA
Tel: (+1 206) 622 01 25   Fax: (+1 206) 621 96 26
e-mail: railprod@aol.com

Products: Rail, points and crossings, special trackwork components.

VERIFIED

Relayfast

Relayfast
8th Floor, Buchanan House, 58 Port Dundas Road, Glasgow G4 0HG, UK
Tel: (+44 141) 335 26 68   Fax: (+44 141) 335 34 68
Business Development Director: Hugh Harvie
Marketing Manager: Rosalyn Dunn

Subsidiary company
Western Track Renewals Co Ltd

Products: Track renewals, LRT installations; track maintenance; on-track machine maintenance; on-track machine hire.

VERIFIED

RMC

RMC Concrete Products Ltd
St Helen Auckland, Bishop Auckland DL14 9AJ, UK
Tel: (+44 1388) 60 39 61   Fax: (+44 1388) 45 00 56
Operations Manager: Nick Gainsford
Sales Manager: James Tristram

Works
Aston Church Road, Saltley, Birmingham B8 1QF
Tel: (+44 121) 327 08 44   Fax: (+44 121) 327 75 45

Products: Pretensioned concrete sleepers and associated track materials for third-rail electrification, main line track, twin-block for main line track.

Contracts: Half of the annual requirement of concrete sleepers by Railtrack is supplied by RMC Concrete.

VERIFIED

Robel

Robel GmbH & Co
PO Box 2320, D-83391 Munich, Germany
Tel: (+49 86) 865 44 67 10   Fax: (+49 86) 86 54 46 71 45
Managing Director: B Ströbl

Works
Klebingerstrasse 19, 83395 Munich, Germany

Products: Track maintenance machinery and equipment; power wrenches; drilling machines; rail grinding machines; rail loading and transporting units; rail lifting equipment; track lifting and slewing machines; powered gangers' trolleys and trailers; small transport trolleys; road-rail excavators and switch laying units.

UPDATED

Rotamag

Rotamag
Rail Division
PO Box 206, Sheffield S9 5YX, UK
Tel: (+44 114) 291 10 20   Fax: (+44 114) 261 81 86
Managing Director: Mike Bryan
Divisional Director: D Learad

Products: Rail drilling and cutting systems; lighting systems; rail bonding systems; mobile boring machine; rail cutters.

Contracts: Railtrack; London Underground; Glasgow Underground, SNCB, SJ.

Developments: A 48 V battery-powered rail drill and base plate drilling machine range is now available. Base-plate twin-head rail-drilling machine.

UPDATED

Sateba

Sateba
262 boulevard Saint-Germain, F-75007 Paris, France
Tel: (+33 1) 40 62 26 00   Fax: (+33 1) 40 62 26 01
e-mail: sateba.paris@wanadoo.fr
Chief Executive Manager: Claude Cazenave
Deputy General Manager: D Valles

Products: Design and manufacture of Vagneux system of concrete sleepers, and prestressed concrete sleepers for turnouts; design and commissioning of sleeper manufacturing plants. Also technical studies, assistance and staff training.

UPDATED

Schwihag

Schwihag Gesellschaft für Eisenbahnoberbau mbH
Lebernstrasse 3, CH-8274 Tägerwilen, Switzerland
Tel: (+41 71) 669 22 30 Fax: (+41 71) 669 22 31/24 72
Managing Director, Technical: Dipl-Ing Armin Heim
Managing Director, Commercial:
  Dipl-Betriebswirt Karl-Heinz Schwiede

Products: Rail anchoring systems for pointwork, point operating systems, permanent way equipment including chair plates and check rail plates.

VERIFIED

Semperit

Semperit Technische Produkte GmbH
Triester Bundesstrasse 26, A-2632 Wimpassing, Austria
Tel: (+43 2630) 31 00 Fax: (+43 2630) 31 05 38
Divisional Managers: Ing Manfred Faustmann, Peter Horn

Products: Rubber and plastic track items, including rail pads, elastic sleeper supports and plastic fastenings. Elastomer profiles, including track trough sealing sections.

VERIFIED

Serco Railtest Ltd

Rtc Business Park, London Road, Derby DE24 8UP, UK
Tel: (+44 1332) 26 26 26 Fax: (+44 1332) 26 46 08
e-mail: serco.railtest@ems.rail.co.uk
General Managers
  Management Services: Andy Wishart
  Support Services: Neil Andrew
  Testing Services: Lee Bartholomew

Services: Condition monitoring of track and infrastructure components. Gauging and measuring structures. Route gauge clearance services. Testing, development, approval and introduction into service of new and modified vehicles. Monitoring of track geometry, condition and overhead alignment. Train operations and planning including Old Dalby Test Track, UK. NAMAS accredited maintenance, calibration and instrumentation laboratory, non-destructive testing and metallurgy.

UPDATED

Sika

Sika Ltd
Watchmead, Welwyn Garden City AL7 1BQ, UK
Tel: (+44 1707) 39 44 44 Fax: (+44 1707) 32 91 29
Managing Director: Bent Baggersgaard
Market Manager, Civil Engineering: Richard Barton

Products: SikaRail KC330 resilient rail fixing system is a combination of a tough, elastic reaction-curing binder and compressible fillers that absorb vibration, reduce noise and is available in a variety of grades to ensure suitability with differing load-bearing requirements. Materials are available for both base-plates and embedded rails. Sika is also able to provide admixture designs for high-specification concrete mixes, jointing systems, mortars and grouts, adhesives and bonding agents, waterproofing, corrosion inhibitors, concrete repair and protective coatings for concrete and steel including industrial flooring.

Contracts: Base-plate bedding material for direct fixation system used in 1997 for Heathrow Express, UK. Track fixation at Paddington station, London, and the cross-over known as SODS (Semi Outside Double Slip) at the Heathrow terminals. 1998 ongoing: London Underground Ltd, Track Replacement Project.

Developments: SikaRail KC340 resilient rail fixing system – a combination of a tough, elastic, reaction-curing binder and compressible fillers that absorb vibration, reduce noise and is especially suitable for embedded rails even in damp conditions.

UPDATED

Skelton

H J Skelton & Co Ltd
9 The Broadway, Thatcham RG19 3JA, UK
Tel: (+44 1635) 86 52 56 Fax: (+44 1635) 86 57 10
e-mail: hjskelton@compuserve.com
Director: Jeremy Smith

Products: Rawie sliding friction buffer stops to suit a range of applications. Range includes high-speed buffer stops to stop trains at up to 56 km/h and also for low-floor LRVs.
  Contec switch machines and track wiring systems. Range of rails, points, crossings and special trackwork.

Contracts: Supply of Rawie sliding buffer stops for Heathrow Express and Paddington station.

UPDATED

Skelton

H J Skelton (Canada) Ltd
165 Oxford Street E, London, Ontario N6A 1T4, Canada
Tel: (+1 519) 679 91 80
Fax: (+1 519) 679 01 93/434 47 87
General Manager: Peter Fraser
Sales Director: Geoffrey Richey

Associated company
TKL Rail, Australia

Products: Supplier of a wide variety of track components, special trackwork, sliding rail expansion joints, switch machines, sliding rail buffer stops, Icosit polyurethane/cork grout for undersealing grooved rail and injected pads for direct fixation. Specialises in LRT in-street applications, also railway rail (both T and grooved), crane rails and turnouts. High-speed buffer stops/bumping posts, to stop trains at up to 56 km/h.

Contracts: Five-year supply contract for TTC Toronto for all-manganese frogs, crossings and points for tram tracks; special trackwork for Calgary LRT; Icosit polyurethane grout for Tri-Met Portland, Memphis and Salt Lake City; screw spikes and washers for CN Rail and CP.

VERIFIED

SPEFAKA

Spezialfahrzeugaufbau und Kabeltechnik GmbH
Verlängerte Apoldaer Strasse 18, D-06116 Halle, Germany
Tel: (+49 345) 560 22 65/22 65
Fax: (+49 345) 560 81 61
General Manager: G Hofmann

Products: Road-rail vehicles from 3 to 25 tonnes for installation and maintenance of catenary infrastructures for urban and interurban railway; railcars (light, medium and heavy) with hydrostatic drive, adjustable for varying track gauges; hydraulic platforms; rail cleaners; high-pressure cleaning apparatus; ballast cleaning; rerailing equipment; road-rail trailers with cable and wire drums/reels or as motive power.

VERIFIED

Speno

Speno International SA
PO Box 16, 26 Parc Château-Banquet, CH-1211 Geneva 21, Switzerland
Tel: (+41 22) 906 46 00 Fax: (+41 22) 906 46 01
Managing Director: J J Méroz
Deputy General Manager: Jim Cooper
Marketing Manager: D Arvet-Thouvet
Technical Manager: J P Jaeggi
Production Manager: W Schöch
Maintenance Manager: G Ferioli

Works
Via Banchina Molini, Porto Marghera, Italy

Subsidiaries
Nippon Speno KK, Tokyo
Speno Rail Maintenance (Australia) Pty Ltd, Belmont, Western Australia

Products: In-track rail grinders, ultrasonic rail flaw detection vehicles, rail longitudinal and cross-profile measuring systems.
RR8M: Compact 'green grinder' specially designed for urban networks. In addition to the grinding dust collection system and the catalytic cleaning of exhaust gas, it features sound-proofing. Maximum travelling speed 80 kph, recommended grinding speed 4 to 6 km/h. Minimum radius when grinding 60 m. Maximum length 17.6 m, total weight in working conditions 37 tonnes. The machine complies with UIC and Japanese safety and environmental protection standards.
Mini 8M: Smaller rail grinding machine in the Speno range. All the functions of a grinding train for work in an urban environment are in one self-contained powered railcar: rail rectification units, rail reprofiling units, collection of grinding dust and rail corrugation measuring trolley. For networks with different gauges, the machine can be easily converted and, if needed, transported on a lorry.
RR16M: Self-propelled grinder unit capable of a maximum speed of 90 km/h in either direction. Complies with UIC and Japanese safety and environmental protection standards. Recommended grinding speed is 4 to 6 km/h. Minimum radius when grinding is 60 m and standard grinding angles are 70 inward to 30 degrees outward. Unit dimensions are 21 m length, 2.4 m wide with a maximum height of 3.4 m. Total weight unladen/loaded 52/56 tonnes. This grinder incorporates a dust collection system for better environmental protection in urban districts, tunnels and metros.
RR24MC: Similar to the RR 16 grinder, but with a length of 43 m, width 2.4 m and maximum height of 3.4 m. Total weight unladen/loaded 114/119 tonnes. Also includes a dust collection system as well as exhaust gas cleaning device.
HRR12M: This has a rapid on/off track capability which can operate on both Vignole and grooved rail to standard and metre gauges.

Contracts: Service and supply contracts with major urban, state and mining railways.

UPDATED

Spie Batignolles

Spie Batignolles
Departement Voies Ferrees, Parc Saint Christophe, F-95861 Cergy Pontoise, France
Tel: (+33 1) 34 22 50 02 Fax: (+33 1) 34 22 62 80

Products: Underground track installation; LRT installations; workshop installations.

VERIFIED

Tarmac Precast Concrete

Tarmac Precast Concrete Ltd
Tallington, Stamford PE9 4RL, UK
Tel: (+44 1778) 38 10 00 Fax: (+44 1778) 34 80 41
Managing Director: P R Strong

Technical Director: H P J Taylor
Commercial Director: N D Claxton
Commercial Manager, Rail: A B Moore
Parent company: Tarmac Heavy Building Materials UK Ltd

Background: In 1996 Tarmac Precast Concrete took over Costain Dow Mac.

Products: Prestressed concrete sleepers; Bomac level crossings; switch and crossing bearers; tunnel linings; tunnel track solutions; arch bridge units; prestressed concrete bridge beams; full design service. Crossing bearers and tunnel track systems, with particular emphasis on noise and vibration reduction and street track systems.
　　Technical support packages are offered worldwide.

Contracts: Supplying 40,000 T610 monobloc sleepers to Croydon Tramlink, London, and 12,000 EF36 monobloc sleepers for the Richmond to Gunnersby section, London.

Developments: F43 monobloc sleeper.

UPDATED

Tensol Rail

Tensol Rail SA
Bureau de vente, Case Postale, CH-3001 Bern, Switzerland
Tel: (+41 31) 308 53 59　Fax: (+41 31) 302 55 04
Marketing Director: Theo Geissbühler
Part of the Von Roll Group

Products: Rack and other rail installations.

VERIFIED

Thermit Welding

Thermit Welding (GB) Ltd
87 Ferry Lane, Rainham RM13 9YH, UK
Tel: (+44 1708) 52 26 26　Fax: (+44 1708) 55 38 06
Managing Director: A J Key

Products: Aluminothermic rail welding equipment and consumables; insulated rail joints.

Contracts: Include Ankara metro, Manchester Metrolink and South Yorkshire Supertram.

VERIFIED

Tiefenbach

Tiefenbach GmbH
Nierenhofer Strasse 68, D-45257 Essen, Germany
Tel: (+49 201) 486 30　Fax: (+49 201) 486 31 58
Technical Field Service Manager: Achim Weirather

Products: Microcomputer-controlled electrically operated point motors; level crossing systems; cable haulage systems.

VERIFIED

Tiflex

Tiflex Limited
Member of the James Walker Group
Hipley Street, Old Woking GU22 9LL, UK
Tel: (+44 1483) 75 77 57
Fax: (+44 1483) 75 53 74/75 77 15
Managing Director: Patrick V Stiles
Director & Trackelast Product Manager: Hugh M Kenyon

Director: Hugh T Rogers
Trackelast Product Manager: Steve C Barlow

Works
Treburgie Water, Liskeard PL14 4NB

Products: Rail pads; baseplate pads, undersleeper pads, ballast mats, floating slab track bearings and other anti-vibration track support materials.

Contracts: Trackelast resilient track support materials have been used extensively on the Hong Kong Mass Transit, Tuen Mun tramway, Rotterdam, Madrid, Barcelona, Milan, London and Paris metros and the London Docklands Light Railway; also tramways in The Hague, Gothenburg and Utrecht, and on British suburban lines. Rail pads have been supplied for London Underground's Jubilee line extension; track support bearings have been supplied for the Tsing Ma bridge, Hong Kong.

UPDATED

TSO

Travaux du Sud-Ouest SA
Chemin du Corps de Garde, PO Box 8, F-77501 Chelles Cedex, France
Tel: (+33 1) 64 72 72 00　Fax: (+33 1) 64 26 30 23
President: Emmanuèle Perron
Export Manager: Claude Petit

Products: Turnout-laying cranes and equipment; track construction and maintenance for main line and metro systems; ballast mats for ballasted track in tunnel; aluminothermic and flash-butt welding.

VERIFIED

VAE

VAE Aktiengesellschaft
Rotenturmstrasse 5-9, A-1010 Vienna, Austria
Tel: (+43 1) 53 11 80　Fax: (+43 1) 53 11 82 22
Presidents: Dr Mohamed Kaddura/Josef Mülner

Works
Alpinestrasse 1, A-8350 Zeltweg, Austria

Subsidiary companies: In Australia, Canada, USA, Hungary, Spain, UK, Latvia and Lithuania, South Africa, Germany, Romania and Bulgaria.

Products: Turnouts and crossings, frogs and switches, ballastless track system with plastic sleepers, fastening materials, turnout monitoring system VAE Roadmaster 2000, hot-box detectors; non-contact monitoring system for tongues.

UPDATED

Vortok

Vortok International
63 Station Road, Addlestone KT15 2AR, UK
Tel: (+44 1932) 82 88 12　Fax: (+44 1932) 82 86 91
Managing Director: J R Byles
Technical Director: P Shrubshall

Works
6-7 Haxter Close, Belliver Industrial Estate, Roborough, Plymouth PL6 7DD

Subsidiary
Multiclip Company Ltd

Products: Suppliers of products for the repair and rehabilitation of timber sleepers. These include Vortok Coil for loose screws; temporary sign board supports; track circuit maintenance solutions such as Trackguard

insulator and IBJ Trimmer system; adjustable check block spacers for switches and crossings.
　　Distributors of the non-destructive stress-free rail temperature measuring system Verse®.

Contracts: Supplier to most European railway companies.

UPDATED

Vossloh Rail Systems

Vossloh Rail Systems GmbH
PO Box 1860, D-58778 Werdohl, Germany
Tel: (+49 2102) 49 04 90　Fax: (+49 2102) 49 04 94
Managing Directors: Ulrich Rieger
Sales Manager: F G Heisler
Technical Sales: Ing Dirk Vorderbrück
Regional Sales Manager: J Spors (Overseas Business Office, Düsseldorf)

Works
Vosslohstrasse 4, 58791 Werdohl

Products: Elastic rail fastening systems for concrete, wooden and steel sleepers on ballasted and slab tracks, direct-fixing fasteners, sleeper anchors, systems for sleeper rehabilitation, systems for noise reduction and vibration damping, rail web cushioning.

Contracts: Has supplied equipment for the BTS project in Bagkok as well as for the two new lines of Taipei's DORTS system. Has also signed a contract for the supply of rail fasteners for Croydon Tramlink, London.

UPDATED

WALO

Walo Bertshinger AG
Road Construction Department, PO Box 7534, CH-8023 Zürich, Switzerland
Tel: (+41 1) 745 23 11　Fax: (+41 1) 740 31 40
Director: Sandro Contratto

Product: Trackbed construction using precast concrete.

VERIFIED

Western-Cullen-Hayes

Western-Cullen-Hayes Inc
2700 West 36th Place, Chicago, Illinois 60632-1617, USA
Tel: (+1 773) 254 96 00　Fax: (+1 773) 254 11 10
e-mail: wch@wch.com
www: www.wch.com
President: R L McDaniel
Vice President, Marketing: George S Sokulski
Customer Services Manager: William M Crain

Products: Rail safety signals and accessories, gate arms, rail crossing signals, industrial crossing warning systems, flashing light signals: incandescent and LED, bells: AC/DC and electronic, points lamps, and targets, bumping posts: fixed, sliding and hydraulic, wheel stops, chocks, switch point guards, programmable yard points machine, track drills, rail benders, rail tongs, journal and hydraulic jacks, derails: sliding, hinged and portable and accessories, derail operators: ELDO, Delectric and solar-powered, blue flags, wagon rerailers, locomotive revolving lights and warning bells, and other custom-designed equipment for railroad, transit and industrial applications.

Developments: Western-Cullen-Hayes 3590 Series, Model 10 level crossing barrier.

UPDATED

bring the Long Island Rail Road commuter service to Grand Central Terminal (GCT) on the east side of New York City.

UPDATED

BERGER/ABAM Engineers Inc

Suite 300, 33301 Ninth Avenue South, Federal Way, Washington 98003-6395, USA
Tel: (+1 206) 431 23 00   Fax: (+1 206) 431 22 50

Capability: Planning, environmental documentation, civil and structural engineering; site analysis, corridor selection, impact studies, alignment and alternative studies, aerial structure design, condition surveys, seismic assessment and design; repair/modernisation.

Projects: Include the State Route 509 urban interchange; design of the 7.5 km concrete structure for the J Paul Getty Museum, Los Angeles, and design checker for transit system structures, Bangkok.

UPDATED

The Louis Berger Group

PO Box 270, 100 Halsted Street, East Orange, New Jersey 07019, USA
Tel: (+1 973) 678 19 60   Fax: (+1 973) 672 42 84
Chair: Dr Louis Berger
President: Derrish M Wolff
Established: 1953
Staff: 2,850 in 83 offices

Capability: Engineers, economists, scientists and planners.

Projects: Include assignments in New York, Providence, Boston, Chicago, Las Vegas, Vancouver, Jakarta, Medan and Surabaya, Bangkok, Manila, Kuala Lumpur, Jaipur, Buenos Aries, Quito, Lima, Kaohsiung, Ankara, Istanbul, Izmir, Seoul, Pusan, Abidjan, Durban, Dakar, Lagos, Addis Ababa and Maputo.
For New York City, Boston, Vancouver and CTA Chicago, Louis Berger Group has provided a variety of services for major improvements including new stations, rail and rolling stock improvements. Other projects include the proposed LRT line serving John F Kennedy airport.

VERIFIED

Bestgroup Srl

Via Garibaldi 5, I-10048 Vinovo (TO), Italy
Tel: (+39 011) 580 89 50   Fax: (+39 011) 580 82 91
Electrotechnology Engineer: Gennaro Sardonico
Electronic Engineers: Pietro Losito/Cristina P Lopez

Capability: Process support: consultancy and software development. Product support: mechanical and electronic design, technical documentation and training courses.

VERIFIED

Bharat Heavy Electricals Ltd

Transportation Business Department
Lodhi Road, New Delhi 110003, India
Tel: (+91 11) 462 77 18   Fax: (+91 11) 462 94 23
Additional General Manager: S C Chopra

Capability: System planning; system engineering; feasibility studies; turnkey execution; project management.

Projects: BHEL has undertaken system and feasibility studies for various urban transport projects in cities in India, including Madras, Delhi, Srinagar, Trivandrum, Calcutta, Bombay and Nasik.

VERIFIED

BMT Reliability Consultants Limited

12 Little Park Farm Road, Fareham PO15 5SU, UK
Tel: (+44 1489) 88 52 52   Fax: (+44 1489) 88 50 38
e-mail: messages.bmtrcl.com
www: www.bmtrcl.com
Transportation and Safety Business Development Manager: Michael Starling

Capability: The company works with firms in the rail industry to assist in reducing risk and improving the reliability, safety and through-life economics of their products. Recent contracts include the supply of a life-cycle cost (LCC) model to Fiat Ferroviaria for integrating and interpreting design information from component suppliers, and all aspects of reliability and safety analysis for Heathrow Express. The company also runs related training programmes.

NEW ENTRY

Booz, Allen & Hamilton

Transportation Consulting Division
523 West Sixth Street, Suite 650, Los Angeles, California 90014, USA
Tel: (+1 213) 620 19 00   Fax: (+1 213) 622 24 64
Managing Partner: G Leslie Elliott
European office: 7 Savoy Court, Strand, London WC2R 0EZ, UK
Tel: (+44 171) 393 33 33   Fax: (+44 171) 393 33 05
Senior Associates: Adrian Foster,
   Carolyn Hayward-Williams, Chris Kinchin-Smith

Capability: Management consulting to railway companies, including strategy and strategic simulation, restructuring and business process re-engineering, privatisation, market surveys, pricing, mergers and acquisitions, asset management planning, and operations and maintenance planning. Technology consulting to railway organisations, including transport planning, engineering analyses, specification and commissioning of signalling systems and rolling stock, system integration, system safety analysis and certification.

Projects: Include Netherlands high-speed rail, Croydon Tramlink, Attiko Metro, Channel Tunnel Rail Link, St. Louis Metrolink, Bay Area Rapid Transit, Los Angeles Metro Rail, Hudson-Bergen Light Rail, San Francisco Municipal Railway, and State Rail Authority of New South Wales.

UPDATED

Bovis Construction Group

Bovis House, Northolt Road, Harrow HA2 0EE, UK
Tel: (+44 181) 422 34 88   Fax: (+44 181) 423 43 56
Chairman: Sir Frank Lampl
Managing Director, Bovis Europe: John Anderson
Executive Director, Consultancy: John McCloy
Executive Director, Commercial: Tony Ring
Business Development Director: Mike Temple
Divisional Director, Railways: Doug Chalmers

Principal subsidiary companies
Bovis Construction Ltd, UK
Bovis International Ltd (East), UK
Bovis International Ltd (West), UK
Bovis Asia Pacific
Bovis Inc, USA

Capability: Railway project management, consultancy and construction management services on main line, suburban or LRT projects. Feasibility assessment through preconstruction strategic planning to construction completion.

Projects: Include route resignalling and modernisation projects, structures renewals, Heathrow Express station developments at Paddington London, Dublin light rail project, LRT BOT projects in Sydney and Auckland, the new Kuala Lumpur central station, modernisation of Grand Central Terminal in New York, Newark International Airport monorail system and the urban railway project in San Juan, Puerto Rico.

UPDATED

Colin Buchanan and Partners

59 Queens Gardens, London W2 3AF, UK
Tel: (+44 171) 258 37 99   Fax: (+44 171) 258 02 99
Directors: Malcolm Buchanan, Michael Mogridge, Nicholas Bursey, Christopher Pyatt, Neil Parkyn, Malcolm Roberts
Offices in Edinburgh, Bristol and Manchester
Established: 1964
Professional staff: 65

Capability: Services connected with planning, land use, urban development, transport planning, highway design, parking strategy, computer software, market research, public transport provision, total safety management, specialist surveys and economics.

VERIFIED

CAM Industries Inc

Peerless Tool Division
215 Philadelphia Street, PO Box 227, Hanover, Pennsylvania 17331, USA
Tel: (+1 717) 637 59 88   Fax: (+1 717) 637 93 29
President/Director: Charles A McGough

Capability: Engineering consulting services connected with planning and equipping electrical departments in transport workshops and depots.

VERIFIED

Cambridge Systematics, Inc

150 Cambridge Park Drive, Suite 4000, Cambridge, Massachusetts 02140, USA
Tel: (+1 617) 354 01 67   Fax: (+1 617) 354 15 42
www: www.camsys.com
President: Dr Lance A Neumann
Travel Forecasting/Market Research: Thomas F Rossi (Principal)
   Dr Moshe Ben-Akiva (Senior Principal)
Transportation Planning/Policy Analysis: Arlee T Reno (Senior Vice President)
   Robert A Lepore, PE (Senior Vice President), Michael Heurta (Principal)
Commercial Vehicle/ITS: Lance R Grencebak (Senior Vice President);
   Bradford Wright (Senior Associate)
   Carol G Colman (Principal)
   Dr Vassili Alexiadis (Principal)
Economic/Investment Planning: Laurie L Hussey (Principal)
   Christopher Wornum (Senior Associate)
   John G Kaliski (Senior Associate)
Air Quality/Conformity: John H Suhrbier (Principal)
   Dr William R Loudon (Principal)
Intermodal Freight Planning: Marc R Cutler (Vice President);
   Michael P Huerta (Principal)

Public Transport Service and Policy Planning:
    Robert G Stanley (Principal)
    Laurie L Hussey (Principal)
Established: 1972
Professional staff: 130

Capability: Analytical techniques are applied in many areas including transportation planning and management; intelligent transportation systems; information technology; asset management; commercial vehicle operations products, services, and support; travel demand forecasting and modeling; and market research. More specialised work includes new technology assessments, congestion management/air quality planning, traffic and transport planning, multimodal planning, growth management, decision support, and geographic information systems (GIS).

Projects: Work has been undertaken for many federal, state, and local agencies in the United States, Europe, Asia, and other countries, as well as for private clients. Cambridge Systematics recently was awarded a contract to provide technical support to the USA Department of Transportation (DoT), Federal Highway Administration's (FHWA) Office of Environment and Planning in the areas of funding, planning, infrastructure management, and environmental provisions.
    Other recent work includes:
The Pontis bridge management system used by 46 licensed agencies, including 37 US state DoTs, Hungary, Kuwait, and Manitoba.
National infrastructure management systems for USA, Finland, Hungary, Israel, Sweden, and Switzerland.
Public transport-related studies for Puerto Rico, Mexico, the Republic of the Congo, Rhode Island, New Jersey and Oregon.
Statewide planning projects in Oregon, Washington, New Hampshire, Maine, and Wisconsin, USA.
Town centre transport management studies in Boston, San Antonio, Atlanta, and Los Angeles.
Transport and economic development studies in London, Osaka, Taiwan, Amsterdam, Scotland, and several USA cities.
Transport air quality analyses for Mexico City, the USA Environmental Protection Agency (EPA), the World Bank, and the government of Finland.

UPDATED

Capoco Design

Stone Cross House, Chickgrove, Salisbury SP3 6NA, UK
Tel:(+44 1722) 71 67 22   Fax: (+44 1722) 71 62 26
Director: Alan Ponsford

Capability: Design of buses and coaches in addition to other vehicles; midibus development.

Projects: Has been involved in the development and design of the Dennis Dart, Plaxton bodywork, Optare midibuses including Excel and Solo. Capoco records 86 per cent of registrations of midibuses as having Capoco involvement.
    Capoco has also worked on full-size single-deck buses, luxury coaches, double-deck buses and robust truck and bus designs for African, Asian and South American clients.

NEW ENTRY

Centro Studi Traffico

Via Cesare Correnti 21, I-20123 Milan, Italy
Tel: (+39 02) 837 65 89/58 10 72 71
Fax: (+39 02) 5810 4317
President: Pietro Gelmini
Directors: Massimo Percudani, Enzo Porcu, Angelo Rota
Established: 1978

Capability: Urban traffic planning, including traffic management and traffic control, bus priority and parking. Transport planning and new technology studies with technical, economical and environmental analysis. Surveys of traffic, public transport, parking and pedestrian mobility.

Environmental impact analysis, including noise and atmospheric pollution, and computer simulation. Also, computer modelling for traffic planning and for public transport companies. Training.

VERIFIED

Charles River Associates Incorporated

John Hancock Tower, 200 Clarendon Street, Boston, Massachusetts 02116-5092, USA
Tel: (+1 617) 425 30 00   Fax: (+1 617) 425 31 32
President: James C Burrows
Vice Presidents: John E Parsons, Daniel Brand
    Michael Kemp, George C Eads
Director of Transportation Projects: Daniel Brand
Senior Associates: Thomas E Panody, Mark Kiefer, Shomik Mehndiratta, Christopher L Cavanagh, Harry Keates
Offices in Boston, Washington DC, Los Angeles, Toronto and Palo Alto California
Established: 1965
Staff: 200

Capability: All aspects of transport planning and evaluation, including ridership and revenue forecasting, capital investment planning and budgeting, major investment studies, financing and pricing, management and operations planning, and market research. Specialist work is undertaken in travel demand and revenue forecasting for new systems, project and programme evaluation including ITS, travel surveys, transport economics, urban planning and computer applications.

Projects: Include the initial and subsequent capital programmes for upgrading the New York City metro, bus, and commuter rail systems, and the Chicago RTA's long-range capital plan. Has also undertaken high-speed ground transport studies in several intercity corridors, both North American and overseas, and various highway toll studies.
    CRA's policy analysis work has included developing analytical tools and studying the impact of federal policies on the transit industry. Comprehensive fare policy studies have been undertaken for several transit agencies.
    For the US DoT, has provided information for formulation of federal policy concerning major capital investments, privatisation, and productivity improvements. Benefits and costs attributed to new starts, extensions, modernisation projects and vehicle purchase programmes have been examined.
    Work has also been undertaken to evaluate existing and proposed ground access modes to a number of airports. Has also examined air quality regulations and impact of alternative fuels.

UPDATED

CIE Consult

Grattan Bridge House, 3 Upper Ormond Quay, Dublin 7, Ireland
Tel: (+353 1) 703 47 01   Fax: (+353 1) 703 47 25
e-mail: info@cie.ie
General Manager: Barry Collins
Manager, International Business: Michael Barry
Training Executive: Stephen Clohessy

Capability: CIE Consult draws on the expertise of CIE group companies Iarnrod Eireann (the Irish state rail network), Bus Atha Cliath (the Dublin city bus operator), and Bus Eireann (operator of all other bus services) to provide consultancy services in all aspects of public transport management, particularly restructuring and commercial orientation operations and staff training; civil and mechanical engineering; signalling and telecommunications.

Projects: Recent urban transport work includes:
Romania: Bucharest urban transport study.
Kirghizia: urban transport sector study.
Latvia: public transport master plan project.
Mongolia: urban transport components of the World Bank's transport rehabilitation project.

Uzbekistan: urban passenger transport study.
Other recent projects include:
Georgia: rail privatisation study.
Lithuania: transition management support project for Lithuanian Railways.
Zimbabwe: commissioning of NRZ infrastructure.

UPDATED

The Corradino Group

200 South 5th Street, Suite 300N, Louisville, Kentucky 40202, USA
Tel: (+1 502) 587 72 21   Fax: (+1 502) 587 26 36
Managing Principal: Joseph C Corradino
Established: 1971

Capability: Civil engineering, design and construction management; systems and management planning; transport and environmental engineering; land use and urban design; urban planning, environmental assessment and transport modelling.

VERIFIED

Cre'active Design

22 New Street, Leamington Spa CV31 1HP, UK
Tel: (+44 1926) 83 31 13   Fax: (+44 1926) 83 27 88
Executives: Neil Bates, Tony Hume

Capability: Designers, rolling stock engineers and ergonomists providing planning and development skills from feasibility studies through to implementation, in industrial design, ergonomics, three-dimensional computer simulation, rolling stock design, tender specification and project management. Services include concept studies, design schemes, production of specifications and finalised design details, computer simulations, full-size mock-ups, prototypes and user trials.

UPDATED

Daniel, Mann, Johnson & Mendenhall

3250 Wilshire Boulevard, Los Angeles, California 90010, USA
Tel: (+1 213) 381 36 63   Fax: (+1 213) 380 51 26
Director of Transport: Gerald W Seelman
Established: 1946
Staff: 1,200

Capability: Planning, design, engineering and construction management services for all facets of transport. In urban transport, activities range from feasibility studies to design and project management.

VERIFIED

DAVE Transportation Services Inc

26111 Antonio Parkway, Rancho Santa Margarita, California 92688, USA
Tel: (+1 714) 888 32 83   Fax: (+1 714) 888 89 90
President: James L Pierson
Vice President & Chief Financial Officer: C Marty Powell
Vice President, Strategic Development: Thomas J Higgins
Vice President, Corporate Development:
    Timothy B Colins
Vice President, Administration: Laverne David
Vice President, Financial Planning: John K Miller
Vice President, Operations, Eastern Division:
    Mark D Wells
Vice President, Operations, Western Division:
    John R Helm
Established: 1969
Staff: 3,000

Capability: Contract management and operations of fixed-route, shuttle and demand-responsive services. Maintenance training and consulting including bus route inspections. Transport management and paratransit brokerage programme administration. Transport planning and consulting.

VERIFIED

DCA Design International Ltd

19 Church Street, Warwick CV34 4AB, UK
Tel: (+44 1926) 49 94 61   Fax: (+44 1926) 40 11 34
Managing Director: Michael Groves
Established: 1958
Staff: 40

Capability: Design consultancy specialising in visual and ergonomic design, and component engineering. Services include exterior styling, interior design, engineering and electronic design, graphic design, model and full-size mock-up making, human factors, production drawing, three-dimensional computer modelling, visualisation and animation, and market research; ISO 9001.

Projects: Responsible for the visual design of London Underground's 1990 Central line stock, and for design of the Tangara double-deck trains in New South Wales. Visual and ergonomic aspects of the proposed Class 341 CrossRail and Class 371 Thameslink 2000 trains have also been undertaken, including full-size mock-ups; more recent work on buses for London and new designs of single- and double-deck trains for European countries.

UPDATED

DE-Consult

Deutsche Eisenbahn-Consulting GmbH
A subsidiary of German Railway (DB AG) and Deutsche Bank AG
Reinhardtstrasse 18, D-10117 Berlin, Germany
Tel: (+49 30) 634 30   Fax: (+49 30) 63 43 10 10
International Transportation and Railway Services
Oskar-Sommer-Strasse 15, D-60596 Frankfurt am Main
Tel: (+49 69) 631 92 20   Fax: (+49 69) 631 93 56
e-mail: info@de-consult.de
www: http://www.de-consult.de
Board of Managing Directors
    Chair: Dr Hermann Lenke
    Dipl-Kfm Gerd Wiederwald
Head of Business Unit: Werner Kellner
Regional Directors
    Americas: Karl Grossmann
    Europe (West): Eckhard Galdiks
    India: Juergen Jansky
    China, Korea, Vietnam: Ralf Fickenscher
    Europe (East), Russia: Peter Kulke
    Africa: Dr Emile Muvunyi
    South East Asia, Australia, Middle East: Arne Gooss
    Thailand, Taiwan: Bernhard Kraft
Established: 1966
Staff: 1,200

Capability: Range of advisory services from project identification, planning and evaluation, preliminary and detailed design to supervision of construction; permanent way, rolling stock and workshops, signalling and telecommunications; management consulting, operations planning, transport economics and marketing, manpower development and training.

Projects
Thailand: Bangkok Transit System.
Malaysia: Express rail link to Kuala Lumpur international airport.
China: Shanghai metro Line 2.
India: Selection of a mass rapid transit system for the city of Mumbai (Bombay).
Greece: Athens metro.
Netherlands: Amsterdam metro, Noord-Zuidlijn line.
Germany: Karlsruhe and region - dual-system LRT.

Brazil: Study on Rio de Janeiro-São Paulo-Campinas corridor.
Germany: Northern section of Berlin Inner Ring, Berlin urban railway city circle and operations concept for Berlin S-Bahn; urban railway Dresden and Leipzig.

UPDATED

Design Research Unit

The Old School, Exton Street, London SE1 8UE, UK
Tel: (+44 171) 633 97 11   Fax: (+44 171) 261 03 33
e-mail: info@dru.co.uk
Directors: Hugh Crawford, Irvin Morris, Maurice Green, Chris Ellingham
Established: 1943
Staff: 30

Capability: Station planning, architecture, interior design, graphic design and building condition surveys.

Projects: Architectural and planning work has been undertaken for many transport authorities including new lines and stations in Hong Kong and Bangkok, and improvements to Victoria station, London.

UPDATED

Design Triangle

The Maltings, Burwell, Cambridge CB5 0HB, UK
Tel: (+44 1638) 74 30 70   Fax: (+44 1638) 74 34 93
e-mail: mail@designtriangle.demon.co.uk
Partners: Siep Wijsenbeek, Andrew Crawshaw,
    Andrew Clark

Associated company
Peter Bayly Design, Melbourne, Australia

Capability: Design Triangle is an independent team of industrial designers, engineers and ergonomists. The integrated service encompasses styling, engineering design and ergonomics for operators and manufacturers of public transport and specialist vehicles; industrial design for manufacturers of transport-related products; and design management consultancy for operators.
    Other facilities offered include textile design, colour forecasting and trend analysis, finite element stress analysis, CAD draughting and 3D CAD modelling and visualisation, computer animation, virtual reality, ergonomic modelling (SAMMIE), full-size and scale modelling and prototype build.

Projects: Volvo C32 bus front end exterior facelift for Marshall SPV; modular bus ceiling system, including lighting, ducting and lockers for Lydney Products/TVI. Range of emergency roof hatches from concept to prototype for Happich, and midibus design and engineering for UVG. Urban bus seat range for Emsta and interurban bus seat range for Esteban, both from concepts to prototypes. Design and development of coach seat recline mechanism for Mercedes; engineering development including prototype subassembly design, manufacture and testing for Setra (Kässbohrer). Most recent work includes a brand identity programme for Cambridgeshire County Council bus services and concepts for Evobus.

UPDATED

Dorsch Consult Ingenieurgesellschaft mbH

PO Box 210243, D-80672 Munich, Germany
Tel: (+49 89) 579 70   Fax: (+49 89) 570 48 67
e-mail: ehm@dorsch.e
www: http://www.dorsch.de
President: Dipl-Ing Helmut Dorsch
Transport Division Manager: Dipl-Ing Michael Ehmsen

Capability: Transport master plans, analyses and forecasts, traffic management, traffic infrastructure studies, institution building, company organisation studies, research activities.

VERIFIED

Doxiadis Associates SA

487 Messogion Avenue, Agia Paraskevi, 15343 Athens, Greece
Tel: (+30 1) 601 68 60   Fax: (+30 1) 601 68 75
e-mail: doxiadis@techlink.gr
Managing Director: Constantine Maniotes
Vice President, Business Development:
    Anastasios C Antonopoulos
Vice President, Transportation and Traffic Planning:
    Emmanuel Constantas
Established: 1951
Staff: Transportation division 45

Capability: Transport planning and engineering design, traffic management, analysis and design, urban planning, project management, highway engineering, construction supervision and maintenance. Also participates in study teams for preparation of comprehensive development, regional and urban plans.

Projects: Include a Planning Transportation Study for Patras, Greece, involving environmental impact assessments, roadside interviews and speed surveys; inventory and operation of the road network and private transport in Attica, Greece. The Attica project provides the basic inputs to the transport study initiated by Attiko Metro SA to develop the metro and ensure its efficient integration with other modes in the greater Athens metropolitan area.

UPDATED

Duchscherer Oberst Design, PC

737 Delaware Avenue, Buffalo, New York 14209-2298, USA
Tel: (+1 716) 882 01 00   Fax: (+1 716) 873 27 60
President: David C Duchscherer
Marketing Manager: Rae L Duchscherer
Established: 1951
Staff: 47

Capability: Architectural, civil and structural engineering services; experienced in planning, design and construction of bus maintenance, garaging and administration facilities, multimodal facilities and rapid transit stations.

VERIFIED

Thomas K Dyer Inc

1762 Massachusetts Avenue, Lexington, Massachusetts 02173, USA
Tel: (+1 617) 862 20 75   Fax: (+1 617) 861 77 66
President: Charles L O'Reilly Jr
Vice Presidents: Glenn E Hartsoe
    David C Wuestmann
    Robert E Sutton
Established: 1964
Staff: 72
Other offices: New York, Philadelphia, Dallas, Chicago, St Louis

Capability: Planning and design engineering services in track, signal and train control systems; communications; AC and DC traction power and catenary; operations planning and related facilities; construction management and inspection services.

VERIFIED

Dynamics Research Corporation

60 Frontage Road, Andover, Massachusetts 01810, USA
Tel: (+1 508) 475 90 90   Fax: (+1 508) 475 21 57
President: Albert Rand
Manager, Transportation Programmes: Andrew S Millen
Marketing Manager, Transportation: Peter H Keller
Established: 1955

Capability: The Systems Division of DRC offers general capabilities in systems engineering, co-ordinating, analysing and applying technology to achieve cost-effective operational performance of transit systems. Components include computers, sensors, decision support aids and communications devices. Design, development and implementation of integrated models and databases are used to assess manpower, skill levels and training requirements for design, operation and maintenance of transit systems.

VERIFIED

Marcial Echenique & Partners Ltd

49-51 High Street, Trumpington, Cambridge CB2 2HZ, UK
Tel: (+44 1223) 84 07 04   Fax: (+44 1223) 84 03 84
www: www.meap.co.uk
Managing Director: Ian Williams
Executive Directors: Lynn Devereaux
    Prof Marcial Echenique
Non-Executive Directors: Jose Luis Burgos
    Prof David Newbery
    Richard Stibbs
Established: 1978

Capability: Integrated land use and transport planning covering infrastructure investment; road pricing/demand management, public transport fares and services, traffic generation, urban and regional regeneration; economic evaluation of transport policies; custom software for computer modelling; urban design and development feasibility studies.

Projects: ME&P has been commissioned by the Government Office for London (GOL) to update the APRIL (Assessment of Pricing Roads In London) model of road pricing and congestion charging in London. GOL is reviewing the effectiveness of the tools for assessing congestion charging and parking taxation within London in the run-up to the creation of the Greater London Authority. The APRIL model was originally developed for the Department of Transport in 1992/3 by ME&P as part of the London Congestion Charging study. The main objective of the study was to produce a fully operational, strategic model capable of evaluating alternative road pricing proposals within the Greater London area. The model was successfully used to test a large number of charging scenarios. The new commission involves updating the data on which the model operates from 1991 to 1996, and converting it so that it can be run on Windows®-based software. The revised model will be made compatible with the results from the Department's LTTS91 model. The project was due to be completed in February 1999.
An EC-funded study, led by ME&P, aims to produce an action plan for road travel reduction in Europe. The project, known as START (Development of Strategies Designed to Avoid the Need for Road Travel) will begin with a candid look at road travel reduction strategies and their implications for society. For example, teleworking could reduce the numbers of people driving to work, but would it lead to greater social isolation and a new set of problems? Would charging for the use of roads be seen as an infringement of individual liberties? The project will cover urban and regional road travel and will look at the relationship between land use planning policy and the need for travel. Information will be collected from existing travel surveys along with evidence from case studies and outputs from computer transport models. Attitude surveys will be used to help understand public perceptions and the likely response to transport policy changes. START has been commissioned by the Transport Directorate off the European Commission. ME&P will head an international

consortium of companies, including another British group Ecotec Research and Consulting Ltd, and firms from Italy, Spain and Finland.

UPDATED

Economic Studies Group

A division of the High Point Rendel plc Group
61 Southwark Street, London SE1 1SA, UK
Tel: (+44 171) 928 42 22   Fax: (+44 171) 928 55 66
Compuserve: 101533,3677
Director: Jeff Ody
Established: 1969

Capability: Economic and financial evaluation of transport and infrastructure systems, leisure and tourism projects and land use planning. Expertise includes institutional, regulatory and tariff studies; infrastructure planning; highways and road maintenance; port planning and operations; shipyard and shipping studies; rail and air transport studies; urban and regional planning; and industrial development and energy projects.

UPDATED

EcoPlan International

Transport Research Group
10 rue Joseph Bara, F-75006 Paris, France
Tel: (+33 1) 43 26 13 23   Fax: (+33 1) 43 26 07 46
Videoconferencing/whiteboarding: +33 1 44 41 63 40
www: http://www.ihc-commons.org
Managing Director: Francis E K Britton
Established: 1966
Staff: 5, plus international specialists in Transport, Energy communications, environment, sustainable development work, Access, and Athena East/West Science & Technology Network

Associate company:
Leber Ingeneria, Bilbao, Spain

Capability: Research, planning and education policy advisory services.

VERIFIED

Edwards and Kelcey Inc

299 Madison Avenue, PO Box 1936, Morristown, New Jersey 07962, USA
Tel: (+1 973) 267 05 55   Fax: (+1 973) 267 35 55
Chairman & CEO: Ronald A Wiss
Established: 1946
Staff: 550

Capability: Environmental, planning, design and construction services for railways, mass transit, highways, airports and ports. Urban transport services include: terminals and stations, railways and metros, tunnels, maintenance shops and yards, track, catenary support structures, bridges, and parking. Other services include alternatives analysis and transport planning, patronage forecasting, ridership surveys, urban freight movement, traffic control systems, traffic impacts, circulation studies, route and corridor selection, busways, cycleways and pedestrianways.

VERIFIED

Electrowatt Engineering Ltd

Bellerivestrasse 36, PO Box, CH-8034 Zürich, Switzerland
Tel: (+41 1) 385 33 22   Fax: (+41 1) 385 24 25
President: Dr Rudolph Bösch
Head of Transportation: Dr Rolf Bergmaier
Head of Infrastructure Division: Jonathan Schmieder

Regional offices: Germany, Eastern Europe, UK, Middle East, Asia, Latin America

Capability: Feasibility studies, modelling and data processing; economic assessment, planning, detailed design and engineering including preparation of tender documents, bid evaluation, inspection of manufacturing and construction supervision in the fields of system engineering, civil and electromechanical engineering and transport economy.

Projects: Include general consultancy work for two transit systems in Bangkok and for an LRT system in Kuala Lumpur, a masterplan study in Kunming, and a power supply study in India; and general consultancy work for the Cairo metro and the metro in Medellin.

UPDATED

The Engineering Link

Trent House, The Railway Technical Centre, London Road, Derby DE24 8UP, UK
Tel: (+44 1332) 26 34 48   Fax: (+44 1332) 26 21 04
e-mail: bpl@the-engineering-link.co.uk
www: www.the-engineering-link.co.uk
Managing Director: Tony Butler
Engineering Contracts & Projects Director:
    Martin Gibbard
Sales Director: David Barney
Engineering Resources Director: Martin Hayhoe
Finance Director: Chris Wright

Capability: Transport engineering consultancy service covering management of major projects and modifications, new build procurement, refurbishment and product improvement, electrical and mechanical engineering damage repair management, product/maintenance support, problem solving/expert opinion, risk assessment, audits, depot equipment procurement, feasibility studies, documentation, reliability engineering, data analysis and climatic testing, design validation, implementation and running of rapid transit systems.

UPDATED

ENOTRAC AG

PO Box 23, CH-3661 Uetendorf, Switzerland
Tel: (+41 33) 345 62 22   Fax: (+41 33) 345 62 25
e-mail: heim.voegeli@enotrac.com
www: www.enotrac.com
Executive: Heinz Voegeli

ENOTRAC UK Ltd
6th Floor, Times House, Throwley Way, Sutton SM1 4AF, UK
Tel: (+44 181) 770 35 01   Fax: (+44 181) 770 35 02
Executive: Dr Ziad S Mouneimne
e-mail: ziad.mouneimne@enotrac.com

Capability: ENOTRAC provides consulting services covering systems engineering, feasibility studies, planning, technology evaluation, tender preparation and evaluation, asset replacement strategy, equipment specification, procurement support, software development, field tests, quality assurance, reliability and safety assessments, signalling compatibility studies and operational procedures.
For rolling stock, the services encompass performance evaluation, energy consumption, comparative assessment of traction equipment, rehabilitation and maintenance management.
For maintenance management, ENOTRAC provides Tractivity — a complete computer-based system for vehicle fleet maintenance. The service includes the analysis of operational requirements, software implementation and training.
Power supply services include rating of equipment (substations, catenary), optimum substation spacing, reinforcement requirements, short-circuit calculations and protection, earthing, step and touch voltages, and energy, active and reactive power requirements and magnetic field computation. Optimised design is

achieved by a powerful software suite developed in-house for multitrain simulation of complex AC- and DC-supplied networks.

UPDATED

ESRC Transport Studies Unit

University College London, Gower Street, London, WC1E 6BT, UK
Tel: (+44 171) 391 15 86   Fax: (+44 171) 391 15 86
e-mail: rea@transport.ucl.ac.uk
Principals: Professors Phil Goodwin/Richard Allsop

Capability: The University of London Centre for Transport Studies brings together the transport expertise of the civil engineering departments at the Imperial College of Science, Technology and Medicine (ICSTM) and University College London (UCL), as well as relevant expertise from colleagues elsewhere in the two colleges and the University. The centre includes, at UCL, the ESRC Transport Studies Unit, and at ICSTM, the Railway Technology Strategy Centre.

The centre comprises 12 full-time academic staff and more than 60 research and administrative staff and research students. Members of the centre are drawn from a wide variety of academic and professional backgrounds and the centre has extensive links with other academic, professional and commercial organisations both in the UK and overseas.

NEW ENTRY

ETC Transport Consultants GmbH

Am Karlsbad 11, D-10785 Berlin, Germany
Tel: (+49 30) 254 65 0   Fax: (+49 30) 254 651 01
Managing Directors: Rainer Obst
    Dipl-Ing Ralph D Kabisch
Key consultants: Dipl-Ing Götz Klingbeil
    Dipl-Ing Hasko Theis
    Dipl-Ing Erich Kratky
Established: 1967 as a division of Berliner Verkehrs Betriebe (BVG) and founded as an independent company jointly by BVG and BC Berlin Consult in 1974. It was renamed ETC in 1995 after having merged with its subsidiary Ingenieurgesellschaft Verkehr Berlin GmbH (IVB)
Permanent staff: 120, with assistance from BVG and specialists if necessary.

Capability: Feasibility studies and network planning, traffic and transport engineering, preliminary and detailed design (structural, mechanical, signalling, electrical and safety), management and financial studies, operational planning, training and start-up operation, project management of turnkey projects, management information systems (MIS).

Projects
Chile: study of developments and optimisation of regional rail passenger transport in the Santiago de Chile region.
Germany: traffic forecasts and network planning, LRT and regional network studies; development of MIS and marketing concepts for transport co-operatives Rhein-Main and Halle/Leipzig; cost information system for DB; S-Bahn Berlin – planning, design, project management including reconstruction of the S-Bahn section between Berlin, Schonholz and Hennigsdorf; improvement of the Fürstenwalde—Beeskow railway section, preliminary and detailed design of workshops in Berlin.
Greece: training programmes and preliminary and detailed design of workshops for Athens.
PR China: setting up of a training centre for metro personnel including a training simulator; training programmes; advisory services for the introduction of metro and LRT systems; preliminary and detailed design of workshops in Shanghai; metro network studies in Shanghai and Quingdao.
Malaysia: advisory services for the introduction of metro and LRT systems in Kuala Lumpur.

Vietnam: traffic forecast, financial and economic evaluation for rolling stock modernisation.

UPDATED

W A Fairhurst & Partners

11 Woodside Terrace, Glasgow G3 7XQ, UK
Tel: (+44 141) 332 87 54   Fax: (+44 141) 332 50 83
Senior Partners: K Smith and N McNeill
Established: 1902
Staff: 350

Capability: Transport and environmental planning, structural and civil engineering design, and construction management.

Projects: Shop Mobility Centre, Broad Walk, Bristol; Safer Routes to School strategy, Bristol; Legible City Project, Bristol.

UPDATED

FFG Fahrzeugwerkstätten Falkenried GmbH

A subsidiary of Hamburger Hochbahn AG
Falkenried 7-19, D-20251 Hamburg, Germany
Tel: (+49 40) 42 10 30   Fax: (+49 40) 42 10 33 03
General Manager, Technical: Klaus Behrmann
General Manager, Commercial/Financial:
    Wolfgang Graudenz
Established: 1968

Capability: FFG was established as a subsidiary of Hamburger Hochbahn AG and specialises in bus technology and maintenance. FFG offers service for vehicle fleets as well as development and production of special vehicles. FFG provides service facilities for bus and tram stop facility systems, automatic vending machines, escalators and lifts and makes motor vehicle parts.

VERIFIED

First Engineering Ltd

Floor 7, Buchanan House, 58 Port Dundas Road, Glasgow G4 0HG, UK
Tel: (+44 141) 335 30 05   Fax: (+44 141) 335 30 06
Managing Director: Tony Smith
Commercial Director: John Cowie

Background: Formerly known as Scotland Infrastructure Maintenance Co, First Engineering was one of the British Rail Infrastructure Services Units sold off as part of the British Rail privatisation. The company was sold in 1996 to a management buyout team known as TrackAction.

Capability: Railway infrastructure and civil engineering consultancy.

NEW ENTRY

Fluor Daniel Inc

3333 Michelson Drive, Irvine, California 92730, USA
Tel: (+1 714) 975 71 00   Fax: (+1 714) 975 52 71
General Manager: Matthew C Stennes

Capability: Transport planning, engineering and design, programme management, construction management, systems and technology advice and equipment procurement for all types of rapid transit and commuter rail.

VERIFIED

Sir Alexander Gibb & Partners Ltd

Earley House, London Road, Earley, Reading RG6 1BL, UK
Tel: (+44 1734) 63 50 00   Fax: (+44 1734) 49 10 54
Chairman: Jim Dawson
Managing Director: Chris Green
Company Vice Chair: Jim G F Dawson
Group Chair: Tony J W King
Planning & Transportation Division Director: Nigel Ash
Offices in 30 countries
Staff: 1,600

Capability: Railway planning and design; demand forecasting, economic and financial appraisals; station planning; building, bridge and tunnel design; geotechnical studies; environmental assessment, management and land use planning; architecture and building services; town planning and urban renewal. Provides full range of services from conception to commissioning, operating and maintenance, including project and construction management, feasibility and pre-investment studies, site investigation surveys and models, project planning and detailed design, tender documentation and evaluation, contract administration and measurement, supervision of construction, operations planning, procurement, technical assistance and training, parliamentary procedures and public consultations.

VERIFIED

Giro Inc

75 Port Royal East Street, Suite 500, Montréal, Canada H3L 3T1
Tel: (+1 514) 383 04 04   Fax: (+1 514) 383 49 71
e-mail: info@giro.ca
www: www.giro.uk
President: Jean-Yves Blais
Vice Presidents: Jean-Marc Rousseau, Nigel Hamer
Marketing Assistant: Lyne Gauthier

Capability: Software for transport authorities, including vehicle and crew scheduling, passenger information and automated scheduling for demand-responsive transport.

UPDATED

Goudappel Coffeng BV

PO Box 161, NL-7400 AD Deventer, Netherlands
Tel: (+31 5700) 61 81 22   Fax: (+31 570) 61 29 42
President: R A Steenbergen
Established: 1963
Staff: 110

Capability: Feasibility studies for public transport systems; design of infrastructure and network planning; tailor-made computer programs are offered covering demand forecasting, modal split development, mobility growth and operational optimisation. A growing need for reliable management information has resulted in the development of the OMNIBUS program. This software allows network variables to be calculated and analysed as they affect passengers and costs. The program can also process data for routeing, stops, service frequency, schedules and transfers. The program PROVO optimises service levels in relation to passenger numbers, passenger-km or costs.

UPDATED

GRA Inc

115 West Avenue, Suite 201, Jenkintown, Pennsylvania 19046, USA
Tel: (+1 215) 884 75 00   Fax: (+1 215) 884 13 85
e-mail: gramail@gra-inc.com
www: http://www.gra-inc.com

President: Frank Berardino
Executive Vice Presidents: Richard Golaszewski
John J Grocki, Chris Frankel
Established: 1972
Staff: 20

Capability: Consulting services in operations, valuation, economics, planning and financing of rail transport and other modes, including cost-benefit analysis, economic impact analysis and modelling, fleet planning and valuation, operations planning, pricing and cost analysis, regulatory impact analysis, privatisation studies, environmental studies and expert witness testimony.

Projects
USA: Analysis of commuter rail line; economic impact study of proposed new rail line; equipment specification and selection; transportation planning; airport privatisation, air services development studies; regulatory impact studies and computer modelling.

VERIFIED

Haas Consult

Ingenieur Consult Haas & Partner GmbH
PO Box 2467, D-30023 Hannover, Germany
Tel: (+49 511) 911 70   Fax: (+49 511) 911 72 99
e-mail: post@haasconsult.de
www: www.haasconsult.de
Managing Director: Dipl-Ing Otmar Haas
Established: 1976
Staff: 965
Offices: Berlin, Bremen, Chemnitz, Dresden, Düsseldorf, Halle, Hamburg, Hannover, Karlsruhe, Leipzig, Munich, Rostock
Beijing, Baborone (Botswana), Hanoi, Islamabad, Jakarta (Indonesia), Prague (Czech Republic), Pretoria (South Africa).

Capability: Planning and design of computerised operational control systems, passenger information systems and project management; co-operation and association between undertakings, tariff measures, advertising policy; cost-benefit analysis, cost and utilisation models, performance evaluation; conceptual planning and design of facilities such as maintenance and storage depots, central bus stations, park-and-ride, guideways; fundamental research and system development; construction supervision; development of turnkey projects.

UPDATED

Hague Consulting Group bv

Surinamestraat 4, NL-2585 GJ The Hague, Netherlands
Tel: (+31 70) 346 94 26   Fax: (+31 70) 346 44 20
Managing Director: Hugh Gunn
Directors: Moshe Ben-Akiva, Andrew Daly, Eric Kroes
Subsidiary offices in France and UK

Capability: Specialises in provision of long-range and short-term demand forecasts for travel-related facilities, including private vehicles, road and rail capacity and local public transport.

VERIFIED

Halcrow Fox

Vineyard House, 44 Brook Green, London W6 7BY, UK
Tel: (+44 171) 602 78 72   Fax: (+44 171) 603 00 95
Managing Director: Peter N Daly
Staff: 200
Offices in: Kuala Lumpur, Hong Kong, Indonesia, Philippines

Associated companies
Sir William Halcrow & Partners Ltd (qv)
Halcrow Transmark (qv)

Capability: Consultancy services in transport, development and environmental planning, and economics; the firm can also call upon the specialised engineering and development resources of its associated company Sir William Halcrow & Partners, and the railway operations, management and training skills of sister company Halcrow Transmark.

Experience includes transport modelling — patronage and revenue forecasting, pedestrian congestion, station evacuation modelling; operational and institutional studies — operating and efficiency audits, management strategies, operating cost estimation, competition policy advice, fares and pricing strategy; market research and analysis — stated and revealed preference analysis, survey design and implementation; financial and economic studies — funding strategies, assessment of development gain, privatisation studies, preparation of BOT tenders, economic evaluation; environmental analysis; advanced transport telematics.

VERIFIED

Halcrow Transmark

Vineyard House, 44 Brook Green, London W6 7BY, UK
Tel: (+44 181) 970 18 00   Fax: (+44 181) 970 18 11
Chairman: P S Coventry
Managing Director: R Hoad
Director of Finance & Services: K Lockwood
Director, Operations & Safety: T Worrall
Technical Director, Transit Systems: J Baggs
Technical Director, S&T: R Wyatt
Regional Director, Europe & Africa: J Meara
Regional Director, UK: A Carlyle
Established: 1969
Staff: 240 permanent, 200 contract

Associated companies
Sir William Halcrow & Partners Ltd (civil engineering)
Halcrow Fox (transportation planning)
Halcrow Gilbert Associates (M&E engineering)

Capability: Feasibility studies, evaluation of alternative technologies and the development of package designs for metro and LRT systems; alignment design for on-street and fully segregated operation, rolling stock, power supplies, signalling, communications, overhead equipment, station equipment, fare collection, trackwork, workshops and depots; costing of construction, operation and maintenance; project management and training.

Projects
Manchester Metrolink: Phase 1 project management; Phase 2 project management and specification of rolling stock, signalling, communications and fare collection.
Cairo metro: project management of civil engineering and contractual matters including technical investigations; analysis of contractual matters and advice.
Sydney: project management for the design and construction of LRT system.
Kuala Lumpur Line 1: system integration, E&M and rolling stock.
Kuala Lumpur Line 2: specialist input on rolling stock and structures.
Dublin LRT: technical advisor to Irish government and EU project monitoring group.
Copenhagen metro: development of specifications for signalling, communications, SCADA, power supplies and permanent way.
Hong Kong tramways: electrical safety and training.

VERIFIED

Sir William Halcrow & Partners Ltd

Vineyard House, 44 Brook Green, London W6 7BY, UK
Tel: (+44 171) 602 72 82   Fax: (+44 171) 603 00 95
Transportation Directors: D S Pollock (Chair)
D S Kennedy, R N Craig, P Jenkin, A J Runacres,
R J Buckby, G P Gittoes, B J Whelan, P S Coventry
Established: 1868
Staff: 2,234

UK associate firms
Halcrow Fox (transport planning) (qv)
Halcrow Transmark (railway planning and engineering)
Halcrow Gilbert Associates (M&E works)

Capability: Feasibility studies, design, contract supervision and project management for all urban and interurban heavy and light rail transport civil engineering projects; specialises in tunnelling, underground works, station planning and bridges. Initial planning and financial appraisals often carried out within the Halcrow Rail Group of Sir William Halcrow, Halcrow Fox and Halcrow Transmark (formerly British Rail's consulting arm), which has the capability for advanced railway planning, railway services and revenue forecasting, as well as operational advice and planning.

Projects
Jubilee line extension, London: planning, route selection, detailed design for contracts 105 and 107 which include the tunnel from London Bridge to Canary Wharf and Bermondsey station.
CrossRail, London: work on two detailed design contracts for London's CrossRail project continues.
Docklands Light Rail, London: asset surveys for the Lewisham extension.
Liverpool Loop and Link line: feasibility study and recommendations for overcoming drainage problems in existing underground stations and tunnels caused by rising groundwater levels.
Woolwich rail tunnel, London: feasibility study for a railway river crossing and stations to confirm scheme viability.
Kings Cross underground works, London: preliminary designs and project studies for Parliamentary Bill and design development. Detailed design of London Underground interchange and accessways.
Kuala Lumpur, Malaysia: management and design of second LRT line.
Manila, Philippines: detailed design of Line 1 capacity extension.
Hong Kong: design of tunnelled sections of the MTR to the airport and East Lantau.
Lisbon, Portugal: design of bored tunnels for the southern extension of the metro.
Metrolink, Manchester, UK: project management assistance for extension to Salford Quays.
Copenhagen, Denmark: studies for a light metro and light rail system.

VERIFIED

Delon Hampton & Associates

800 K Street NW, North Lobby, Suite 720, Washington, DC 20001, USA
Tel: (+1 202) 898 19 99   Fax: (+1 202) 371 20 73
Chairman & Chief Executive Officer: Delon Hampton
President & Chief Operating Officer: Elijah Rogers
Executive Vice President: John M Zimmer
Established: 1973
Staff: 125

Capability: Engineering and architectural consulting and design services, including highway, railway, tunnel and related projects.

VERIFIED

Frederic R Harris Inc

The Atlantic Building, 260 South Broad Street, Suite 720, Philadelphia, Pennsylvania 19102, USA
Tel: (+1 215) 735 08 32   Fax: (+1 215) 735 0883
Founded: 1927
Staff: 1,300

Capability: Planning, design, construction management and operations for land and marine transport, energy and environmental projects.

VERIFIED

Harza Engineering Co

Sears Tower, 233 South Wacker Drive, Chicago, Illinois 60606-6392, USA
Tel: (+1 312) 831 30 00   Fax: (+1 312) 831 39 99
e-mail: info@harza.com
www: http://www.harza.com
Head of Business Development: Edward F Carter

Capability: Design and engineering studies and services during construction for tunnels, bridges and highways and for light rapid transit projects.

Projects: Include design engineer urban collector four-lane highway Route 83, including bridge over river and structural engineer for statewide bridge rehabilitation project.

UPDATED

Charles Haswell & Partners Ltd

99 Great Russell Street, London WC1B 3LA, UK
Tel: (+44 171) 580 24 12   Fax: (+44 171) 631 46 02
Managing Director: C M Nunn

Capability: Project management, feasibility and engineering studies for heavy and light rail systems, specification, tender preparation, bid evaluation and design and construction supervision, particularly tunnelling, with geotechnical services.

UPDATED

Hatch Mott MacDonald

6140 Stoneridge Mall Road, Suite 250, Pleasanton California 94588, USA
Tel: (+1 510) 469 80 10   Fax: (+1 510) 469 80 11
President & Chief Executive Officer: Gordon A Smith
Chief Operating Officer & Director, Western Operations: Peter Wickens
Vice President & Director, Eastern Operations: Jan J Feberwee

Canada office
2655 North Sheridan Way, Suite 130, Mississauga, Ontario L5K 2P8

Capability: Multidiscipline engineering consulting services, project and construction management, planning and architectural services for rail and transport systems, highways and bridges, ports and harbours, and airports. Services include: planning, route selection, environmental assessment and third party co-ordination; civil engineering, including alignment, trackwork, structures, bridges and elevated guideways; tunnels in soft ground or rock, including planning, safety; building services; systems engineering including signalling, telecommunications, traction power and distribution, tunnel ventilation; programme and project management; and construction management.

UPDATED

HDR Engineering Inc

8404 Indian Hills Drive, Omaha, Nebraska 68114-4049, USA
Tel: (+1 800) 366 44 11   Fax: (+1 402) 399 12 38
National Director, Transportation: James Shuttle
Established: 1939

Capability: Professional services for design of roads, bridges, airports, railways and urban transit systems; also carries out planning and design, inspection and project management.

VERIFIED

Hoskyns Group plc

Hoskyns House, 77-79 Cross Street, Sale M33 1HF, UK
London office: Hoskyns House, 130 Shaftesbury Avenue, London W1V 8HH
Tel: (+44 171) 434 21 71   Fax: (+44 171) 437 62 33
Director, Transport Sector: Mike Fill
Product Manager: Martyn Lewis

Capability: Supplier of computer services, offering a wide range of solutions and expertise to transport operators; incident reporting systems, privatisation advice, technical architecture reviews, education and training.

VERIFIED

Hyder Consulting Ltd

Plymouth House, Plymouth Road, Penarth, Cardiff CF64 3YF, UK
Tel: (+44 1222) 70 43 21   Fax: (+44 1222) 70 97 93
Divisional Director: M Renfrew

Associate company
Acer Consultants (Far East) Ltd
3/F Somerset House, Taikoo Place, 979 King's Road, Quarry Bay, Hong Kong
Tel: (+852) 29 11 22 33   Fax: (+852) 28 05 50 28
Key Contact: Kenneth Lau

Overseas offices
Germany, Cyprus, Spain, Ireland, Turkey, Australia, Egypt, Bahrain, Kuwait, Qatar, Saudi Arabia, United Arab Emirates, Pakistan, Malaysia, Singapore, Thailand, USA and Taiwan

Capability: Management and advisory services including: economic and financial appraisal, operations and research management, tariff negotiation, public transportation planning, traffic modelling and forecasting, operations audits and productivity enhancements, technical audits and quality audits, maintenance management, environmental impact assessment, safety and reliability audits, training and certification, value engineering, problem solving and troubleshooting.

Project planning and design including: design management, concept design and system selection, feasibility studies, outline designs and specifications for legislative approval, preparation of applications for grants (or other funding) as admissable, operations and system planning, alignment and permanent way engineering, civil and structural engineering, station planning, electrical and mechanical engineering, signalling and control systems engineering, rolling stock, freight terminal and depot design.

Project implementation including: preparation of contract documents, preparation of specifications, tender invitations and adjudication, project management and cost control, supervision and quality control of construction contracts, monitoring and quality control of procurement contracts, testing and commissioning, training and certification, operations and maintenance management.

Areas of activity include main line, regional and suburban railway services; metros and urban transit systems including light rail and people movers; heavy-haul freight, general merchandise, unitised loads, bimodal and intermodal technologies.

VERIFIED

ICB

Ingenieur-Consult Verkehrstechnik GmbH
Rudower Chaussee 4, Haus 8, D-12489 Berlin, Germany
Tel: (+49 30) 670 59 90   Fax: (+49 30) 67 05 99 11
e-mail: icb-gmbh.berlin@t-online.de
Managers: Dipl Ing Rainer Patzig, Dipl Ing Thomas Just
Hamburg office: Teilfeld 5, 20459 Hamburg
Tel: (+49 30) 374 93 40   Fax: (+49 30) 374 26 23

Capability: Railway and transport engineering including planning and implementation of railway projects; taking

over building supervision from railway organisations; tender preparation; traffic development planning; project co-ordination.

VERIFIED

ICF Kaiser Engineers, Inc

9300 Lee Highway, Fairfax, Virginia 22031-1207, USA
Tel:(+1 703) 934 36 00   Fax:(+1 703) 934 97 40
President & Chief Operating Officer: Keith Price
Chief Executive: James O Edwards
President, Engineering & Construction Group: Richard Leupen
Senior Vice President, Transit Programmes: John Bergerson
Established: 1914
Staff: 7,500
Other offices: Atlanta, Baltimore, Boston, Chicago, Hong Kong, Houston, Istanbul, Lisbon, London, Los Angeles, Manila, Miami, Moscow, New York, Oakland, Orlando, Perth, Pittsburgh, Rio de Janeiro, Seattle, Sydney

Capability: Mass transit and rail feasibility studies, development, design, engineering, project management and construction services.

The company also provides specialised services in the areas of safety and system assurance, automated guideway transit, buses, LRT, metros, underground structures ventilation analysis, systems engineering and integration, quality assurance, security planning for mass transit, as well as a range of environmental services from assessments to full corrective actions.

UPDATED

IDPO

Industrial Design Planning Office, Philippe Neerman & Co NV SA
Beverlaai 73, B-8500 Kortrijk, Belgium
Tel: (+32 56) 22 56 60   Fax: (+32 56) 22 85 84

Capability: Design of rolling stock; network system design.

VERIFIED

Ilium Associates Inc

600 108th Avenue NE, Suite 660, Bellevue, Washington 98004, USA
Tel: (+1 206) 646 65 25   Fax: (+1 206) 646 65 22
President: Carolyn Perez Andersen
Vice President: Robert M Prowda
Established: 1972

Capability: Consumer research and analysis; preparation of marketing strategies and plans; graphic design of signage systems; corporate identities, including vehicle graphics and uniforms; brochures, posters and map design.

VERIFIED

InfoMill Ltd

Lynton Mill House, Lynton Street, Derby DE22 3RW, UK
Tel: (+44 1332) 29 35 19   Fax: (+44 1332) 29 68 45
Managing Director: Jonathan Ralphs
Sales and Marketing Director: Holger Levey

Capability: InfoMill provides specialist information management consultancy services aimed at providing solutions to information generation, management and other information systems. These services are specifically designed to generate cost savings and operational efficiency improvements. InfoMill achieves this by ensuring that the engineering information required for the operating, maintenance and spare parts activities is properly organised and can be accessed quickly and efficiently through the use of electronic information retrieval tools.

Projects: Include specialist systems for spare part identification, control and retrieval using Intranet and Internet; design and development of a computerised maintenance planning system for Midland Mainline, UK; update and modifications of maintenance manuals for Brush traction, for the Euro Shuttle and for battery-powered locomotives; and consultancy for Railtrack (UK) to help select computer modelling software used to generate precise timing information and power requirements of the entire UK rail infrastructure.

NEW ENTRY

Italferr SpA

Via Marsala 53, I-00185 Rome, Italy
Tel: (+39 06) 497 51   Fax: (+39 06) 49 75 24 37
Chief Executive Officer: Livio Vido
Vice Chairman: Carlo Ianniello
Operations General Manager: Pier Ugo Simone
Technical General Manager: Massimo Palliccia
Commercial & Marketing Director: Gaetano Piepoli
Established: 1984

Capability: The consultancy subsidiary of Italian Railways (FS) offers expertise in metro and other guided transit systems, as well as high-speed and conventional main line railways.

Projects: Is responsible for revamping the urban nodes of Turin, Milan, Genoa, Venice, Bologna, Rome, Palermo, Bari and Naples in conjunction with the development of the Italian high-speed rail system.
   Other projects include a feasibility study for an integrated transit system in Roma; study and design for a rapid transit system connecting Rimini with San Marino; feasibility study, design and assistance during construction of the Lima metro; detailed design of the Perugia S Anna—Perugia Fontivegge rapid transit system; detailed design of the Saronno—Malpensa airport section of FNME Milan; study for a mass transit system for San Salvador.

UPDATED

Jakes Associates, Inc

Jakes Plaza, 1940 The Alameda, Suite 200, San Jose, California 95126-1427, USA
Tel: (+1 408) 249 72 00   Fax: (+1 408) 249 72 96
e-mail: JAI9330@aol.com
www: www.jakesassociates.com
President: Andrew S Jakes
Project Development Director: David Mori

Capability: Consulting in transport technologies, including rail, automated guideway transit and bus systems; procurement and project management; specification development and design review; feasibility and engineering studies; maintenance analyses; business development services.

Projects
Las Vegas: development of two monorail systems.
Washington: personal rapid transit system for Seatac City.
Big Bear, California: mountain railway.
Sacramento, California: strategic plan for city-ride bus system.
Indianapolis: city centre transit system (privately funded).

UPDATED

Japan Railway Technical Service (JARTS)

Taiyokan Building, 27-8 Hongo 2-chome, Bunkyo-ku, Tokyo 100, Japan
Tel: (+81 3) 56 84 31 71/31 79
Fax: (+81 3) 56 84 31 70/31 80
President: Hiroshi Okada
Executive Vice Presidents: Sadaaki Kuroda
   Naofumi Takashige, Masao Tari
Established: 1965
Staff: 50

Capability: Studies, surveys, design, planning specifications, preparation of contract documents, and project control and supervision of railway, metro, monorail and advanced guided transit; construction of new lines; modernisation and improvement of track; electrification; dieselisation; modernisation of rolling stock; installation of ATC, CTC, seat reservation systems, vending machines and automatic departure indicators.

UPDATED

J D Franz Research

1804 Tribute Road, Suite K, Sacramento, California 95815-4313, USA
Tel: (+1 916) 646 55 95   Fax: (+1 916) 646 48 39
e-mail: jdfranz@earthlink.net
President: Jennifer D Franz

Capability: Consultancy in public opinion, public policy and market research.

UPDATED

JHK & Associates

A SAIC company
1900 North Beauregard St, Suite 300, Alexandria, Virginia 22311, USA
Tel: (+1 703) 820 54 55   Fax: (+1 703) 820 79 70
Chief Executive Officer: Jack L Kay
Established: 1971
Staff: 300

Capability: Systems engineering, traffic engineering, and transit planning; traffic control systems; traffic design; transport research; modelling; parking; roadway lighting; environmental analysis.

VERIFIED

Jürgen Rauch

Helene-Weber-Allee 15, D-80637 Munich, Germany
Tel: (+49 89) 157 68 66   Fax: (+49 89) 157 24 73
Managing Director: Dr Ing Jürgen Rauch

Capability: Design of rail, light rail and bus stations, integration of lines and stations into urban environment. Consulting and planning for line and station feasibility studies, structures and materials; studies and engineering for innovative structures. Planning of station passenger guide systems, lighting and automatic train systems.

Projects: Recent work has been carried out in south and east Germany and in northern Spain which includes studies, planning and realisation management for improving station architecture, and on integrating commercial units into rail stations; patents pending for a new development in managing systems and passenger information and guidance through public transport stations using both electronic aids and design of architecture; psychological studies for difficult situations especially in underground metro stations; vehicle parking in cities as it relates to urban transport systems; design of new stations; innovative transport systems; participation

UPDATED

in the development of new systems for noise protection shielding along passenger railway lines; strategic consultancy for city authorities and consultant to several manufacturers in the public transport industry.

UPDATED

Kennedy & Donkin Ltd

A Parsons Brinckerhoff company
Westbrook Mills, Godalming GU7 2AZ, UK
Tel: (+44 1483) 42 59 00   Fax: (+44 1483) 42 51 36
Managing Director: John R Springate
Business Development Director: David O'Hagan
Transportation Director: Robert A Gray
Offices in 10 countries

Capability: Project management, feasibility studies, system design, multidiscipline engineering, safety and risk management and environmental services. The staff includes project managers, engineers, economists, operators and planners with a wide range of experience in the planning, design, operation and management of railways, LRT and metro systems. Expertise includes signalling, electrification, rolling stock, power supply, station services and railway operations; civil and structural services covering infrastructure and permanent way, stations, offices and depots; design and supervision of construction, geotechnical and environmental engineering.

Projects
Hong Kong: design, approval and installation supervision of automatic train protection and bidirectional operation for KCRC Hong Kong. Systemwide power supply and distribution review of Hong Kong MTR.
Thailand, Bangkok: specification, tender evaluation and contract supervision for the elevated metro developed by the Bangkok Transit System Public Company Ltd. Design of tunnel ventilation and E&M systems for the Bangkok MRTA.
Bulgaria: EC PHARE assisted technical assistance for railway restructuring and procurement of improvements.
UK projects include: light rail — Manchester Metrolink; Salford Quays Extension; Midland Metro Line 1; Croydon Tramlink track design; Hampshire LRT preliminary design. Railtrack—Euston remodelling; West Coast main line train control system, signalling, electrification, switch and crossings and forward track renewals; Dorset coast resignalling; South West Infrastructure Signalling Strategy (SWISS); Lincoln to Sleaford, Nuneaton to Peterborough, Dartford and Felixstowe remodelling.
London Underground Ltd — engineering adviser for public/private partnership; agent to Secretary of State for the Jubilee line extension; Central and Northern line modernisation; safety and risk management.

UPDATED

KPMG Peat Marwick LLP

2001 M Street NW, Washington, DC 20036-3310, USA
Tel: (+1 703) 442 00 30   Fax: (+1 703) 556 01 95
Practice Director for Transportation Consulting Services:
   Raymond H Ellis
Marketing Director: Amy Orringer

UK office
8 Salisbury Square, London EC4Y 8BB
Tel: (+44 171) 311 10 00   Fax: (+44 171) 311 33 11
Principal: Robert A Allison

Established: 1896
Staff: 79,000 in 1,100 offices in 812 cities in 142 countries

Capability: Financial planning and management; innovative financing; public/private partnerships; project planning; ridership traffic and revenue forecasting; management improvement services; information technology; human resources and assurances.

Projects: Current or recent clients include MTA New York City Transit, MTA Long Island Rail Road, MTA Metro North Railroad, Port Authority of New York & New Jersey,

RTA Chicago, CTA Chicago, MBTA Boston, New Jersey Transit, SEPTA Philadelphia, LAMTA Los Angeles, WMATA Washington, MTA Houston, METRO Seattle, DART Dallas, RTD Denver, GCRTA Cleveland, MDTA Miami, LYNX Orlando, Tri-Met Portland, City and County of Honolulu, COTA Columbus, SMART Detroit, TARC Louisville and TRT Norfolk.

Other clients include the Federal Transit Administration (FTA) and Federal Highway Administration (FHWA) of the US Department of Administration, Amtrak's strategic business units, Northeast Corridor, Amtrak West and the departments of transportation of more than 40 states; and over 200 local governments.

UPDATED

Kvaerner John Brown Engineers & Constructors Ltd

20 Eastbourne Terrace, London W2 6LE, UK
Tel: (+44 171) 262 80 80   Fax: (+44 171) 402 07 02
Vice President, Transportation: Andy Doherty
Offices: Bangalore, Bombay, Brisbane, Essen, Houston, Johannesburg, Maastrict, Melbourne, Montreuil, Perth, Sydney, Vancouver, Singapore, Paris, Baku, Moscow and Zoetermeer

Capability: Feasibility studies; procurement; project finance; project management, railway safety analysis; railway infrastructure.

VERIFIED

Laser Rail

Jessop House, 39 Smedley Street East, Matlock DE4 3FQ, UK
Tel: (+44 1629) 76 07 50   Fax: (+44 1629) 76 07 51
Managing Director: David Johnson
Director: Alison B Johnson

Capability: Structure gauging software, track design analysis, track gauging training/certification.

VERIFIED

Lea + Elliott Inc

1009 West Randol Mill, Arlington, Texas 76012, USA
Tel: (+1 817) 261 14 46   Fax: (+1 817) 861 32 96
www: www.LeaElliott.com
Principal: Jack Norton
Established: 1973
Staff: 80

Capability: Transportation system planning, analysis and design, as well as system procurement. Experience in automated people movers, metro, LRT, buses, monorails, cable-propelled and magnetic levitation systems.

Specialises in planning control systems, cost estimation, market analysis, microprocessor hardware and software design, multimodal transport planning, operations and maintenance, project management and oversight, propulsion systems, safety analysis, simulations, technical assessment, vehicle design and valuation.

Projects: Include independent engineering consultancy for MTA New York; safety review for MUNI San Francisco; Newark airport monorail; San Francisco Airport AirTrain; Seattle Metro dual-power bus procurement; Kuala Lumpur airport track transit scheme.

UPDATED

Light Rail Transit Consultants GmbH

Fritz-Vomfelde-Strasse 6, D-40547 Dusseldorf, Germany
Tel: (+49 211) 523 05 40   Fax: (+49 211) 523 05 61
e-mail: LRTC.Duesseldorf@t-online.de
www: www.lrtc.com/www.lrtc.de
Managing Director: Dr Ing Helmut Gerndt
Chairman of Board of Directors: Dr Hermann Lenke

Capability: Planning, design and realisation (including support of operation and maintenance) of urban public transport systems. LRTC is working with proven experts in the fields of engineering, construction and operational management, representing urban transport expertise.

Projects: During the last five years, LRTC has been active in a number of light rail-based projects in Europan cities and other parts of the world. These include Dusseldorf, Dresden, Leipzig, Hannover and Hamburg (Germany); The Hague (Netherlands); Sheffield and Manchester (UK); Kuala Lumpur (Malaysia); Jerusalem and Haifa (Israel); and Ankara (Turkey).

NEW ENTRY

Listavia International Consultants Ltd

13 Woodmancourt, Godalming GU7 2BT, UK
Tel: (+44 1483) 42 89 32   Fax: (+44 1483) 42 89 32
e-mail: listavia-international@BTInternet.com
www: www.btinternet.com/~Listavia
Principals: Warren S Lister, G T Lister
Established: 1970

Capability: Feasibility studies, route surveys, tender evaluation, contract administration, detailed design of innovative city and airport transport systems.

Moving walkways: Listavia has introduced low-profile moving walkways which are installed by placing them on top of existing floors. Floor pits and trenches are eliminated. Extensions can be added at will and the walkways can be extended or relocated quickly and easily. The new Listavia range includes single-path and twin-path trackways up to 150 m long, with moving handrails on both sides as standard. The tread surface is 150 mm above the existing floor. Walk-on Walk-off (WOWO) technology — single moving handrail versions are included in the new range, enabling passengers to join and leave the trackway anywhere along its length, in such locations as railway platforms, hospital corridors, exhibition centres, airport, bus and marine terminals and air-bridges. The walkways can be used on gradients and on the level in both indoor and outdoor applications.

UPDATED

LS Transit Systems Inc

1515 Broad Street, Bloomfield, New Jersey 07003, USA
Tel: (+1 973) 893 60 00   Fax: (+1 973) 893 31
e-mail: jjones@systrausa.com
www: www.systrausa.com
President: Albrecht P Engel
Vice Presidents: Dennis Fordham, David Thurston, S Feinsod, Ruby Siegel
Assistant Vice President, Marketing:
Judith Jones-Grinvalds

Capability: Includes planning, design, construction and operations consulting services for rail, LRT and bus applications; expertise includes advice on stations, maintenance facilities, yards, trackwork, signalling, communications, traction power, vehicles and control centres.

Projects: Include design and construction support services for the Newark International Airport railway station and northeast corridor connection; planning and design of new services and improvements for MBTA commuter rail system in Boston, Massachusetts; an advanced high-density interlocking system (HDIS) for the

Newark—New York line; study into improvements to transport links to lower Manhattan (the Lower Manhattan Access Alternatives Study).

UPDATED

LTK Engineering Services

Member of the Klauder Group
Two Valley Square, Suite 300, 512 Township Line Road, Blue Bell, Pennsylvania 19422, USA
Tel: (+1 215) 542 07 00   Fax: (+1 215) 542 76 76
www: www.ltk.com
Vice President: George N Dorshimer
Vice Presidents: F H Landell, J S Gustafson, F W Frandsen, T B Furmaniak
Director, Business Development: David H Oglevee
Established: 1921
Staff: 155

Capability: Planning, engineering and design for urban transport, including passenger rail vehicles, communications and signalling systems, traction power systems, fare collection systems and rail vehicle maintenance facilities.

Projects: Portland Tri-Met: Systems Engineer for Banfield, Westside and Hillsboro extensions.
Amtrak: rail vehicle engineering services for Northeast Corridor High Speed Rail Programme.
New York City Transit: rail vehicle engineering services for R142, R142A and R143 programs.
Seattle ST Link: Systems Engineer for the new light rail system.
Long Island Rail Road: rail vehicle engineering services for M-7 emu programme.
New Jersey Transit: engineering services for the Comet II overhaul.
Tren Urbano: engineering services for new rapid transit car fleet.
Los Angeles County MTA: rail vehicle engineering services for the LA Red, Blue, Green and Standard cars.
Sacramento RT: engineering services for LRV1 and LRV3 programmes.
Dallas Area Rapid Transit: engineering services for two LRV programmes.
Boston MBTA: engineering services for the Green line routes 7 and 8, Red line No 3, Blue line No 4, and Orange line No 12 cars.
Philadelphia: engineering services for SEPTA's M4 rapid transit car procurement.
Washington, DC: engineering services for WMATA's original 766-car fleet.

UPDATED

Maunsell Ltd

Maunsell House, 160 Croydon Road, Beckenham BR3 4DE, UK
Tel: (+44 181) 663 65 65   Fax: (+44 181) 663 67 23
Managing Director: Peter R Head
UK offices: Manchester, Birmingham, Cardiff, Norwich, Edinburgh, St Albans, Sheffield, Witham

Capability: Road and rail urban transport systems; planning, design, procurement and implementation management of fixed infrastructure transport systems including road, rail and all forms of public transport. Microprocessor and communication technology for control of transport and related networks.

Projects: Kowloon-Canton Railway Corporation Westrail Projects DD210, DD600 and D8350; Kowloon-Canton Railway Corporation Eastrail extensions: Tai Wai to Ma ON Shan and Hung Hom to Tsim Sha Tsui. Hong Kong MTRC East Kowloon Line and North Island Feasibility Studies. Second Railway Development Study Hong Kong.
Sydney—Canberra high-speed rail line; London Underground Line corporate track alliance programme; LUL Northern line track survey and gauging works (Wriggle).
Bangkok Mass Rapid Transit; Copenhagen Mini Metro Phases 1, 2A, 2B, 3 and 4; Nottingham Express Transit

(light rail); City of Edinburgh Rapid Transit (tender design — guided bus); Merseyside Rapid Transit (electronic guided bus); Medway Bridge advance strengthening and repair; Jubilee Line Extension — design from Green Park to Waterloo; Jubilee Line Extension Contract 103 — Southwark station and running tunnels.

UPDATED

McCormick Rankin Corporation

2655 North Sheridan Way, Mississauga, Ontario, Canada, L5K 2P8
Tel: (+1 905) 823 85 00   Fax: (+1 905) 823 85 03
e-mail: mrc@mrc.ca
www: www.mrc.ca
Chief Executive Officer: Bob Nairn
President: John Sutherns
Vice President: Ian Willams
Busways: John Bonsall (President MR International)
LRT/Heavy Rail: Dennis R Callan
Established: 1957
Staff: 220
Other offices: Ottawa, Kitchener and Brisbane, Australia

Subsidiary companies
MR International (Transit)
MR Pty Ltd (Brisbane)
Ecoplans Ltd (Environmental)

Capability: Includes system planning studies, feasibility studies, environmental assessments, operational studies, project management, structural rehabilitation, detailed design and construction management for busways, LRT, commuter rail and heavy rail systems.

Projects: Completed the Environmental Assessment for Toronto Transit Commission's (TTC's) proposed 13 km Yonge—University—Spadina Subway Loop, the design of the new Bayview station on TTC's new Sheppard Subway and the Sheppard metro box structure over the Don River. Recently involved in planning and design (with Michael Baker) on the Pittsburgh Airport Busway. Operational review, planning and preliminary design (with Serco) for the Northshore Busway in Auckland, New Zealand. Planning and preliminary design for several busways in Brisbane, Australia. Designed seven stations on the Ottawa Transitway as well as much of the Transitway guideway. Completed a preliminary study for expansion of the GO commuter rail corridor to provide access to Toronto international airport.

NEW ENTRY

Metro Consulting Ltd

Livingstone House, 11 Carteret Street, London SW1H 9DL, UK
Tel: (+44 171) 222 25 26   Fax: (+44 171) 222 25 27
Managing Director: W A E Bray
Development Director: Ron Taylor
General Manager, Sales & Marketing: Harvey Robinson

Subsidiary company
Metro Project Services Ltd

Capability: Management services, railway engineering, safety assessment, asset management and information, graphic design, including training, signalling communications, station control and infrastructure management.

VERIFIED

MHA

Michael Hamlyn Associates Ltd
Savant House, St Andrews Road, East Haddon, Northampton NN6 8DE, UK
Tel: (+44 1604) 77 04 85   Fax: (+44 1604) 77 08 85

e-mail: mha@compuserve.com
www: www.ourworld.compuserve.com/homepages/mha/
Managing Director: M J Hamlyn
Offices also in Reading, Derby, Glasgow, London and Hong Kong

Capability: A multidisciplinary rail and transport consultancy, with a broad range of engineering expertise in systems, safety critical systems, signalling, control, communications and rolling stock. Feasibility studies, design development, testing and maintenance support. Preparation of safety cases, quantified risk analysis, reliability studies and requirements analyses. Independent audit and review.

NEW ENTRY

Mott MacDonald

St Anne House, Wellesley Road, Croydon CR9 2UL, UK
Tel: (+44 181) 774 20 00   Fax: (+44 181) 681 57 06
Senior Directors: M O Blackburn, T J Thirlwall, P M Chesworth, R B Fox, J D Gadd CE (non-executive), A Knight (non-executive)
Company Secretary: P C Gregory
Offices in: Australia, Cyprus, Guyana, Kazakhstan, Namibia, Philippines, Syria, Bangladesh, Belarus, Bulgaria, Cambodia, Canada, China, Czech Republic, Egypt, Ghana, Greece, Hong Kong, India, Indonesia, Ireland, Jamaica, Japan, Korea, Laos, Lesotho, Malaysia, Mozambique, Nepal, New Zealand, Nigeria, Oman, Pakistan, Portugal, Qatar, Romania, Saudi Arabia, Singapore, Sri Lanka, Taiwan, Tanzania, Thailand, Trinidad, Turkey, Uganda, United Arab Emirates, USA, Uzbekistan
Established: 1902

Capability: Planning, design and implementation of urban public transport systems; comprehensive service in transport planning, civil and structural engineering, and mechanical and electrical engineering; traffic engineering and highway planning; tunnel and station ventilation; train control, signalling and communications; studies of electromagnetic compatibility and safety from traction interference; rolling stock and traction power supply performance; rolling stock procurement advice.

Projects
London Docklands Light Railway: safety studies; rolling stock door modifications; power supply assessments; independent technical audit of signalling upgrade and resignalling.
London Underground: ventilation and smoke control studies; Morden station remodelling, new track layout, study of existing formation and drainage, detailed structural survey; Jubilee line extension settlement studies, design of new London Bridge station, monitoring of Westminster station complex.
Bangkok metro: joint venture with De Leuw Cather and Thai companies.
Channel Tunnel Rail Link: in a joint venture with Ralph M Parsons and Gibb, Mott MacDonald is the Secretary of State's Project Representative.
Hollywood, USA: management of construction of the Los Angeles Metro Red line extensions.
Birkenhead, UK: feasibility study into extension of heritage tramway.
Taipei metro: joint venture with China Engineering Consultants to supply technical support for signalling, power supplies, safety and reliability.
Liverpool: feasibility study for conversion of Wapping and Waterloo disued rail tunnels for use as road.
North Wales: feasibility studies into signalling rationalisation for the North Wales line.
Railtrack: level crossing feasibility studies in the Midlands; abolition of signal boxes in the North West; outline design, site management and project control for the new Robin Hood passenger line from Nottingham; station regeneration.
West Coast Main Line: systemwide feasibility studies and preliminary design works in the northwest and Scotland.
Singapore metro: preparing design-and-build contract documentation.
Jakarta North-South Integrated Toll Road & LRT Project: transport planning and conceptual design for the light rail transit component of the project.

Heathrow Express: management of station maintenance.
Belfast—Lisburn track relay project: design, project management, site investigation and supervision.
Budapest metro: preliminary design of Line 4.
Connex South Eastern and Connex South Central, UK: customer information systems technical audit covering 350 stations.

UPDATED

Mouchel Consulting Ltd

West Hall, Parvis Road, West Byfleet KT14 6EZ, UK
Tel: (+44 1932) 33 77 00   Fax: (+44 1932) 35 61 22
e-mail: info@mouchel.com
www: www.mouchel.com
Chairman: Colin Coulson
Managing Director: Jim Harding
Directors, Transportation: James Measures, Keith Jackson, Malcolm Taylor, Richard Upton
Staff: 1,300

Capability: Expertise in advanced engineering design and project management, business financial and assessment management consultancy, outsourcing services including externalisation of professional public services.

UPDATED

MTR Corporation

Operating Railway Consultancy Services, MTR Tower, Telford Plaza, Kowloon Bay, Hong Kong
Tel: (+852) 29 93 38 66/23 17/21 11
Fax: (+852) 29 93 77 74
e-mail: odm@mtrcop.com
General Manager, Consultancy Services: William R Donald
Operations Development Manager: John R Gretton

Capability: MTR offers consultancy services to the railway industry in operating management, engineering management and maintenance fields. Based on its experience gained over 25 years, in building and operating MTRC's urban rail system and Airport Express line, assistance can be given in planning, financing, feasibility studies, safety management, asset management, design reviews, revenue and fare collection, operating planning and timetabling, documentation, trial running, training, and in overseas inspections prior to shipping of plant and equipment.

Projects: Recent projects have included management development and training programmes for Guangzhou metro, advice on ATC replacement for Singapore MRT, peer review of signalling systems for New York Transit Authority, AFC system reviews for Shanghai metro, advice and signalling works for London Underground and assistance with tender bids for various metro projects in Thailand, Singapore and China.

NEW ENTRY

Multisystems Inc

10 Fawcett Street, Cambridge, Massachusetts 02138, USA
Tel: (+1 617) 864 58 10   Fax: (+1 617) 864 35 21
President: John P Attanucci
Vice Presidents: Keith W Forstall, Karla Karash
Established: 1966
Staff: 411

Subsidiary companies
Access Transportation Systems Inc, Pittsburgh
Transportation Management Services Inc, Fairfax, Virginia

Capability: Management consulting and software products firm founded by faculty members of the

Department of Civil Engineering of Massachusetts Institute of Technology. Through its Planning & Policy Analysis Group the firm consults in the areas of transport information systems and management. Services include management and operations analysis, transit and paratransit planning, fare policy analysis, transport modelling and forecasting, market research and evaluation, and design of management information systems. Management and brokerage of paratransit systems is undertaken through a subsidiary, Transportation Management Services Inc. The Information Technology Group provides software systems for paratransit scheduling, fleet maintenance and parts inventory, Geographic Information Systems (GIS), ridership data collection and analysis, service planning, customer information and bid processing, dispatch control and timekeeping.

VERIFIED

MVA

MVA House, Victoria Way, Woking GU21 1DD, UK
Tel: (+44 1483) 72 80 51   Fax: (+44 1483) 75 52 07
e-mail: mail@mva.co.uk
www: http//www.mva-group.com
Joint Managing Directors: Fred Brown, Michael Roberts
Board Directors: Denvil Coombe, John Spiers, Christopher Queree, Martin G Richards
Other Directors: Martin Bach, John Baggaley, Mike Brewer, Geoff Copley, Martin Dix, Clive Gilliam, Peter Hague, Eileen Hill, John Kershaw, Ian Johnson, Andrew Last, Miles Logie, Steve Lowe, Hugh Munro, John Segal, Andrew Skinner, Mike Slinn, John Wicks, Steve Williamson, Tim Wood
Established: 1968
Staff: 396

Capability: International consultancy specialising in transport planning, research and related information facilities and operating from offices in Belfast, Edinburgh, London, Manchester, Woking, Paris, Beijing, Hong Kong, Daha, Manila and Kuala Lumpur. MVA advises on all stages, from strategy to implementation, in partnership with central and local government, transport operators and private-sector interests worldwide. MVA also offers a number of leading software products.

MVA's transport planning covers land use and integrated transport studies; air, rail, bus and car modes; passenger and freight movements, road and rail infrastructure schemes. MVA helps improve the performance of existing public transport systems, plan future provision and provide economic and financial appraisal of investment proposals and service provision for bus and rail operators and scheme promoters.

Advanced research and modelling techniques are applied to all modes of transport as well as to the evaluation of major policy issues. TRIPS is MVA's suite of programs for highway and public transport planning. MVA's START model provides a rapid assessment of transport options under different economic land-use scenarios, while TRAM evaluates the effects of parking and other car restraint on the demand for travel. MVA also develops traffic engineering and intelligent transport solutions for environmental traffic management, traffic calming and transport impact assessment.

Projects: Within the last year MVA has advised on a public transport priority corridor for London Transport; road charging systems in the UK; public transport accessibility and interchange facilities in Western Europe; urban traffic controls in Dalian, China; passenger demand and integrated ticketing for public transport in Singapore; transport planning for Sydney, Australia, for the 2000 Olympic Games; urban public transport in Uzbekistan; the Vietnam Urban Transport Management study, Hong Kong's West Rail scheme; and a number of projects related to surface access to Hong Kong's new airport, Chek Lap Kok, including demand forecasting for road- and rail-based transport and a pricing model for MTRC Hong Kong.

UPDATED

MVA Asia

3rd Floor, East Town Building, 41 Lockhart Road, Wanchai, Hong Kong
Tel: (+852) 25 29 70 37   Fax: (+852) 25 27 84 90
Managing Director: Fred N Brown
Directors: Martin Richards, Mick Roberts, Hugh Neffendort, Terry Bowker
Established: 1978 as part of MVA, 1989 as MVA Asia
Staff: 70

Associated companies
MVA (qv)
MVA Systematica

Capability: Consultancy services in the fields of transport, traffic and planning studies for road, rail, ferry and air travel; economic and financial appraisal; demand forecasting; highway planning and appraisal; project development and management. The firm has a strong social and market research capability, including marketing consultancy and public consultation studies. Offers computer-aided route and service planning, vehicle and crew scheduling, and advises on fare collection systems. Other services include traffic engineering, design and implementation; traffic surveillance and control.

MVA Asia, supported by MVA Systematica, distributes and supports Trips and MicroTrips, a comprehensive and portable transport planning suite installed at over 300 locations worldwide. MVA is also international marketing agent for the UK DoT software traffic engineering programs Transyt, Trafficq and Contram. MVA has exclusive rights in the UK and Hong Kong for the VIPS computer-aided public transport planning package.

VERIFIED

NEA Transport Research & Training

Polakweg 13, PO Box 1969, NL-2280 DZ Rijswijk, Netherlands
Tel: (+31 70) 398 83 88   Fax: (+31 70) 395 41 86
Managing Director: Dr Henk den Harder
Director, Training & Education: Menno M Menist
Director, International Acquisition: Evert J Visser
Director, General Research Transport Economics: Pieter B D Hilferink
Director, Research Transport Sector: Ad Rosenbrand

Capability: NEA specialises in research, consultancy and training services in the field of transport, traffic and logistics, with experience in training, development of course material and case studies, training needs.

Projects: Include an EC study on public service obligations; efficiency and effectiveness of public transport; national study of revenue allocation in local and regional transport; studies on tariffs, subsidies and ticketing.

UPDATED

NEL

East Kilbride, Glasgow G75 0QU, UK
Tel: (+44 1355) 22 02 22   Fax: (+44 1355) 27 29 99
e-mail: info@nel.co.uk
Managing Director: W Paton

Capability: Transport engineering technology; turnkey project management; design simulation; testing; training; technology transfer; free technical advisory service, covering environmental engineering, legislation, emission reduction, fuel systems, cooling techniques, rail vehicles.

VERIFIED

New Markets Ltd

Theocsbury House, 18-20 Barton Street, Tewkesbury GL20 5PP, UK
Tel: (+44 1684) 29 15 44   Fax: (+44 1684) 29 15 45
Principal: Ted Elwes

Capability: Representation of worldwide companies in European rail industry; materials procurement and subcontracting services; new product development and technology licensing; vendor appraisals, sourcing projects.

Projects: Markets to European customers, including Krauss-Maffei, MOB and Adtranz.

New Markets has been involved in several supply initiatives with the Birmingham Chamber of Commerce. These include co-ordinating the How to supply to the SNCF project and the organisation of a DB AG suppliers day with 120 suppliers. The company has also developed the partnership between Railcare ad PFA Germany in the Phoenix rebodying project based on the Puma concept in Germany.

UPDATED

Norconsult International AS

PO Box 626, N-1301 Sandvika, Norway
Tel:(+47 675) 710 00   Fax:(+47 675) 495 90
Manager, Transportation Planning: Nils H Jørol

Capability: Transport planning and feasibility studies, bus and rail service planning, highway and traffic engineering.

VERIFIED

Ogle Design Ltd

Birds Hill, Letchworth SG6 1JA, UK
Tel: (+44 1462) 68 26 61   Fax: (+44 1462) 67 48 14
e-mail: ogle@dial.pipex.com
Design Director: Tom Kaven
Design Manager: Michael Phillips
Sales: Andrew Barlow

Capability: Product development service including design, human factors, engineering full-size/scale/ interior modelling and prototyping with 40 years experience. Activity areas include bus, coach and rail vehicle design. Uses Alias, Unigraphics, Varimetrix and AutoCAD; accredited to ISO 9001.

UPDATED

OGM

Rue Belliard 205 bte 1, B-1040 Brussels, Belgium
Tel:(+32 2) 231 02 35   Fax:(+32 2) 230 39 05
General Manager: Yves Mathieu

Capability: Liaison between authorities and operators, tendering procedures, citizen charters, network assessment, total quality strategy.

VERIFIED

Oscar Faber

Marlborough House, Upper Marlborough Road, St Albans AL1 3UT, UK
Tel: (+44 181) 784 57 84   Fax: (+44 181) 784 57 00
Managing Director: John Vincent
Staff: 150 (Transportation Division)

Capability: Services in the engineering and planning aspects of moving people and freight — estimation of travel demand, identification and design of infrastructure requirements, identification and development of operation requirements of transport facilities, management and institutional arrangements, economic and financial analysis, environmental impact analysis, traffic systems management, and design of traffic control systems including advanced transport telematics. Research into intelligent transport systems and road safety.

Projects: Include the Aberdeen sustainable transport study to identify an integrated transport system for the city; guidance for local authorities and education authorities on school travel plans; work for the Highways Agency to promote road-to-rail transfer for freight and passenger traffic; identifying optimal solutions to enhance rail access to Heathrow airport; rebuilding Manchester city centre to give greater priority to pedestrians, cyclists, trains and buses.

UPDATED

Owen Williams Consulting Engineers

3 Duchess Place, Hagley Road, Birmingham B16 8NH, UK
Tel: (+44 121) 456 15 68   Fax: (+44 121) 456 17 57
Chief Executive: R O M Williams
Business Development Director: Keith Crowley
Founded: 1919

Associated companies
Owen Wiliams Railways
Owen Williams Design and Property Services

Capability: Railways and light rail; transport studies and economic assessments; highway and bridge engineering; highway maintenance management; bus priority; impact studies; park-and-ride studies; feasibility and privatisation studies; railway alignments and bridges; structure design. Traffic control and communications; ground engineering.

UPDATED

Pacific Consultants

7-5, Sekido 1-chome, Tama-shi, Tokyo 206, Japan
Tel: (+81 423) 72 01 11   Fax: (+81 423) 72 63 60
President: Tamio Araki
Executive Vice Presidents: Minoru Shibuya, Toru Ohta
Executive Managing Directors: Makoto Tanaka, Tetsuya Shiraishi
Managing Directors: Itaru Mae, Shota Morita
Established: 1951
Staff: 1,622

Capability: Master planning, feasibility studies, engineering design, construction supervision and project management; particular expertise in railway design.

Projects: Track rehabilitation project III, State Railway of Thailand.
Railway rehabilitation project, Chile.
Train operation control system, Jabotabek Railway Project, for Directorate General of Land Transport and Inland Waterways, Indonesia.
Railway Transportation Rehabilitation Project, Mongolia, for Mongolian Railway, Ministry of Trade & Industry.

VERIFIED

Pallavan Transport Consultancy Services Limited

A wholly owned company of the government of Tamilnadu
MN Office Complex (2d floor), 5 Greams Road, Chennai 600 006, Tamilnadu, India
Tel: (+91 44) 827 78 51/63 95/06 19
Fax: (+91 44) 823 78 76

Managing Director: Dr A Panneerselvam
Senior Consultant, Traffic & Transportation: R Krishnamurthy
Senior Consultant, Systems: G Marthandan
Established: 1984
Staff: 23

Capability: Consultancy services; undertakes projects and renders technical and managerial assistance in all facets of public transit and highway engineering. PTCS has the support of 20 sister transport corporations operating a fleet of 16,000 buses and the Institute of Road Transport (Research Institute) in the state of Tamilnadu. It also provides system design and software development.

Projects
Tamilnadu: preparation of traffic operational and management plans for Dindigul, Tituchengode, Dharmapuri and Mayiladuthurai. Consultancy for improvements to Christopher bus terminal in Nagercoil and construction of new bus terminal in Tirunelveli. Techno-professional study for motor vehicles maintenance department – a strategic plan to revamp functions.
Chennai: route rationalisation study for Metropolitan Transport Corporation Ltd, Chennai. Selection of suitable alignment and prefeasibility study of the same for the proposed Expressway between Chennai Harbour and Tambaram. Study on traffic improvements within Chennai Port Area.
Ahmedabad: Route rationalisation study for Ahmedabad Municipal Transport Services.

UPDATED

Parsons Brinckerhoff Inc

One Penn Plaza, 250 West 34th Street, New York, New York 10119-0061, USA
Tel: (+1 212) 465 50 00   Fax: (+1 212) 465 50 96
President: Thomas J O'Neil
Chair: Robert Prieto
Controller: Patrick D Sheridan
Technical Directors
   Transit Systems: W O Salter (Atlanta)
   Railway Engineering: Robert C VanderClute (Washington DC)
Transportation Planning: S Grava (New York), Greg Benz (New York), Michael Schneider (Orange, California)

Capability: Services in planning, design, architecture and construction management for all modes of urban transport.

Projects
Salt Lake City, USA: general engineering services for the design, construction and start-up of the Salt Lake LRT system.
Seattle, USA: General engineering consultant for facilities to the Regional Transit Authority for the implementation of the LRT component of the Sound Move Programme.
Orlando, USA: Civil engineering and design consultant to Lynx for implementation of the Central Florida Light Rail Transit system.

UPDATED

Parsons Transportation Group Inc

1133 15th Street, NW Washington, DC 20005, USA
Tel: (+1 202) 775 33 00   Fax: (+1 202) 775 34 22
President: Robert S O'Neil
A subsidiary of Parsons Corporation

Associated companies
De Leuw, Cather & Co
Steinman Boynton Gronquist & Birdstall
Barton-Aschman Associates Inc

Capability: Feasibility studies, engineering, design, procurement, construction, construction management and complete programme management of mass transit projects.

Projects
Washington DC: since 1966 has been general engineering consultant to Metrorail.
Kuala Lumpur, Malaysia: consulting engineer for LRT project.
Portugal: design of modification to suspension bridge to carry both road and rail.
London, UK: project representative for Department of Transport for development of Channel Tunnel Rail Link.
Manila, Philippines: managing partner of a joint venture for expansion of LRT system, including an additional line with 11 stations.
Bangkok, Thailand: preliminary design consultant for 20 km underground metro system with 20 stations.
New York, USA: structural investigation programme for whole transport system, employing electronic data collection to develop an asset management database for the underground railway system.
Los Angeles, USA: construction management of the initial Red line metro system.
Boston, USA: prime consultant for design of a modernised operations control centre for LRT and metro systems.
Newark International Airport, USA: construction management of ground access monorail linking urban rail network and Amtrak service.

VERIFIED

PB Power, Merz and McLellan Division

Amber Court, William Armstrong Drive, Newcastle Business Park, Newcastle upon Tyne NE4 7YQ, UK
Tel: (+44 191) 226 18 99   Fax: (+44 191) 226 11 04
Transportation Sill Centre Manager: Les J Brunton
Offices in: Australia, Indonesia, Chile, Hong Kong, Nigeria, Sudan, Singapore, Switzerland, United Arab Emirates, South Africa
Associates and agencies in: Argentina, Brazil, Canada, Chile, Czech Republic, Ethiopia, Jordan, Kuwait, Mexico, Peru, Saudi Arabia, Uruguay, USA, Venezuela
Established: 1899
Staff: 565

Background: Merz and McLellan merged with Parsons Brinckerhoff Inc (qv) in 1995.

Capability: System and engineering feasibility studies and specification of passenger vehicles, traction and control equipment, power supply and distribution (including overhead line), signalling, communications and SCADA systems, and fare collection equipment. Engineering and design of electrical and mechanical fixed ancillary systems, such as environmental control and building services in passenger, office and maintenance facilities, and auxiliary equipment including tunnel ventilation and pumping systems. Innspection and quality surveillance services at manufacturers' works and asset management services.

Projects: Current and recent projects include: Croydon Tramlink E&M design; Blackpool Tramway power infrastructure renewal; specialist electrical distribution advice to Railtrack; various Raltrack and London Underground resignalling schemes; Kowloon-Canton railway ATP design; inspection of Singapore MRT trains.

UPDATED

Peter Davidson Consultancy

105-109 Sumatra Road, London NW6 1PL, UK
Tel: (+44 171) 431 16 87   Fax: (+44 171) 435 93 69
e-mail: 100524.3645@compuserve.com
Managing Director: Peter W Davidson
Principal Transportation Planner: John M Brown

Capability: Specialist expertise in transport modelling, market research, railway planning and computer software for transport applications; computer-aided stated preference experimentation, disaggregate modelling techniques and geographical information systems using in-house software.

TAEGIS geographical information system designed for the transport planner. It facilitates network monitoring and planning of new infrastructure and services. TAEGIS includes over 20 custom-built data screens designed to interface directly with client's own databanks. Pol-Green is a new piece of software designed to develop and evaluate green travel plans. It directly interfaces with travel surveys to forecast modal switch and assists in the optimisation of transport measures aimed at reducing car dependency.

Projects: Research into the contribution of individual elements of a quality bus service to the overall perception of the service using stated preference techniques to identify passengers' willingness to pay for each element. Elements included low-floor buses, real-time information, friendly drivers, bus lanes and other similar criteria.

Research into perceptions of different forms of public transport for park-and-ride for Merseytravel, UK, including bus, road train, ultra light rail and LRT.

European research into strategic trip matrices for the Trans-European network.

UPDATED

PPK Environments & Infrastructure Pty Ltd

PPK House, 9 Blaxland Road, Rhodes, New South Wales 2138, Australia
Tel: (+61 2) 97 43 03 33   Fax: (+61 2) 97 36 15 68
e-mail: ppksyd@oze-mail.com.au
Chief Executive Officer: Denis White
Manager, Transport: Piers Brogan
Manager, International Business: Geoff Gore

Capability: Planning, engineering, and project management for heavy and light rail systems, integrated bus rapid transit (guided and unguided busways), public transport policy and transport interchange design, general highway and traffic modelling, airports and port facilities and bridges.
Licence held for TRANPLAN, from Urban Analysis Group to sell in most of southeast Asia and the Pacific. Also from T-Mode Corporation for exclusive distribution rights for T-Mode 12 in Australia and New Zealand.

Projects
Sydney: PPK is involved in a bus rapid transit concept for the Olympic Games in 2000.

UPDATED

Rail Consult

Rail Consult Gesellschaft für Verkehrsberatung mbH
Oskar-Jäger Strasse 50, D-50825 Cologne, Germany
Tel: (+49 221) 954 42 20   Fax: (+49 221) 95 44 22 99
General Manager: Dr Dietmar Berndt
Established: 1985
Staff: 60

Capability: Consulting services in systems, technical equipment, operation, organisation and EDP.
Supervision of construction of LRT systems and upgraded railway lines; analysis; safety engineering; telecommunications: power engineering.

UPDATED

Rail Transportation Systems

420 Lexington Avenue, Suite 450, New York 10170, New York, USA
Tel: (+1 212) 986 98 66   Fax: (+1 212) 986 98 55
e-mail: Dseidel@RTSnet.com
www: www.systrausa.com
President: Robert M Totillo
Director, Business Development: Debra Seidel

Capability: Engineering expertise in heavy and light rail applications, including train control, signalling, communications, catenary and trackwork, central control, SCADA, system assurance, systems integration and simulation.

VERIFIED

The Railway Consultancy Ltd

43a Palace Square, Crystal Palace, London SE19 2LT, UK
Tel: (+44 181) 653 10 97   Fax: (+44 181) 771 31 71
e-mail: 106351.377@compuserve.com
www: www.railcons.com
Managing Director: Dr Nigel G Harris
Director: David R McIntosh
Senior Analyst: Matthew Smith

Capability: Planning, economics and management for metros and railway systems; demand estimation; simulations; timetable preparation; contingency planning; transport policy and management advice; business planning; specification and design of IT systems to assist planning process; training courses on railway and transport planning issues.

Projects: Recent projects have included the economic assessment of different urban transport technologies for DETR, UK; database development for London Transport; fares policy advice for MTRC Hong Kong; demand estimation for a proposed station at Millhouses, for South Yorkshire PTE; industrial research for equipment suppliers. Has also completed a major study on the impacts of the privatisation of British Rail.
Carrying out a study, in association with Allot & Lomax, on transport aspects of a proposed new interchange at Allerton, designed to link Mersyrail's Northern Line with main line services, as well as providing a rail-head for Liverpool airport.
The GCOST® model for estimating the passenger demand, revenue and time-saving impact of new stations has been announced.

UPDATED

Raytheon Company

1001 Boston Post Road, Marlboro, Massachusetts 01752, USA
Tel: (+1 508) 490 24 48   Fax: (+1 508) 490 39 44
President & Chief Executive Officer: Benjamin D Redd
Vice President, Programme Manager, Rail:
   John C Johnston

Australia office
Raytheon International Inc Australia, Level 3, 40 Blackhall Street, Barton ACT 2600
Tel: (+61 2) 62 73 35 99   Fax: (+61 2) 62 73 36 99
Senior Country Manager: Ron Fisher

Capability: Engineering, design and construction services with special capabilities in signalling, communications and rail traction power. Services include planning, engineering design and construction for electrification, signalling, train control, communications, vehicle procurement and inspection, and operational control. The Transportation Infrastructure Group is responsible for all projects in railway and rail urban transport and in electrical power transmission and distribution.

UPDATED

RITES

Rail India Technical & Economic Services Ltd
A Government of India enterprise
New Delhi House, 27 Barakhamba Road, New Delhi 110001, India
Tel: (+91 11) 331 56 92/62 53
Fax: (+91 11) 331 52 86/373 01 30

Managing Director: B Singal
Group General Manager, Urban Transport:
   A K Chakravarty
Established: 1974
Staff: 1,900

Capability: Traffic surveys, urban transport planning, feasibility studies, tender designs, construction and contract management, project monitoring, modelling of transport demand, traffic engineering; system design; computer-aided analysis, traffic management proposals; bus system rationalisation, urban development, urban planning.

Projects: Current work includes general consultancy for Delhi Mass Rapid Transport System, preparation of detailed project report for Patel Nagar to Barwala corridor as a part of the Delhi MRTS, detailed engineering designs and tender document preparation for seven flyovers in Delhi, study on identification of rail projects for commuter traffic in national capital region and Delhi; high-capacity mass transit study for Poona; high-capacity mass transit system for Lucknow, Kanpur and Lucknow—Kanpur corridor.
Comprehensive traffic and transport study for Howrah; integrated multimodal public transport plan for Calcutta; comprehensive traffic and transport study for Amritsar and Jalandhar cities; survey of fifth and sixth lines for Bombay urban rail system; rationalisation of route network and timetable preparation for Delhi Bus System; revitalisation of Calcutta State Transport Corporation in the 9th five-year plan; techno-economic feasibility study of circular rail from Princep Ghat to Majerhat-Calcutta; short-term traffic engineering and management measures for urban areas of Siliguri and Jalpaiguri.

UPDATED

Ross Silcock Ltd

Old Brewery Court, 156 Sandyford Road, Newcastle upon Tyne NE2 1XG, UK
Tel: (+44 191) 261 81 01   Fax: (+44 191) 261 83 40
Managing Director: David Silcock
Principals: Mike Goodge, Alan Ross, John Barrell
   Chris Robson

London office
28 Mortimer Street, London W1N 7RA
Tel: (+44 171) 323 07 89   (+44 171) 323 02 26

Capability: Traffic and road safety engineering, traffic calming, safety audits, traffic and development impact studies, public transport studies, professional development and training, monitoring and evaluation.

UPDATED

Rummel, Klepper & Kahl

81 Mosher Street, Baltimore, Maryland 21217, USA
Tel: (+1 410) 728 29 00   Fax: (+1 410) 728 29 92
Partners responsible for transit: William K Hellmann
   David W Wallace
Established: 1923
Staff: 260

Capability: Civil engineering, including transport, and highway engineering. In rail transit provides preliminary engineering for line and station location, access and parking and complete final design services.

VERIFIED

ScanRail Consult

Soelvgade 40 E 3, DK-1349 Copenhagen, Denmark
Tel: (+45 33) 14 04 00 ext 155555   Fax: (+45 33) 32 30 84
Chairman of the Board: Erik Elsborg
Director: Preben Olesen

Capability: ScanRail Consult is an independent organisation within the Danish National Railway Agency. With approximately 500 engineers, planners, strategic business consultants, architects and assistants, ScanRail Consult covers a wide range of strategic planning, transport management and mechanical expertise related to railway systems.

ScanRail Consult is actively taking part in international research and development within its competence areas. Furthermore, ScanRail Consult assists the European Commission, UIC and ERRI in the development of European codes and standards for railway systems.

VERIFIED

Scott Wilson Railways

Western House, 1 Holbrook Way, Swindon SN1 1BY, UK
Tel: (+44 1793) 51 57 42   Fax: (+44 1793) 51 58 46
e-mail: peter.crane@swrail.com
www: www.swrail.com
Part of the Scott Wilson Kirkpatrick group
Staff: 185

Capability: Transport and environmental planning for passenger and freight railways, light and heavy; permanent way engineering, signalling developments and design, electrification, civil and structural engineering, electrical and mechanical engineering, environmental and transport planning studies, project management, construction management, supervision, land surveying, communications, safety and operations.

Projects
UK: Heathrow Express Rail Link, Thameslink 2000, West Coast route modernisation; Channel Tunnel rail link; West Anglia route modernisation, Docklands Light Railway, London.
Russia: regeneration of Russian railways, St Petersburg high-speed railway.
Australia: fourth generation train, Sydney.
Denmark: infrastructure quality analysis.
Thailand: intermodal freight study and Rayong to Trat feasibility study.
Malaysia: Kuala Lumpur express rail link.

UPDATED

SEMA Group Belgium

Rue de Stalle 96, B-1180 Brussels, Belgium
Tel: (+32 2) 33 35 511   Fax: (+32 2) 333 55 22
President: Michel Theys
Other offices: France, UK, Spain, Netherlands, Germany, Singapore, Switzerland, Sweden
Established: 1960 as Sobemap SA

Capability: Strategic planning for public and private transport systems; network reorganisation; feasibility studies; traffic management; administrative restructuring; application of new technology; computer modelling; surveys; environmental studies; land use and town planning; marketing studies.

VERIFIED

Semaly SA

Public Transport Consultants
25 Cours Emile Zola, F-69625 Villeurbanne, France
Tel: (+33 4) 72 69 60 60   Fax: (+33 4) 78 89 68 57
Manager: Hervé Chaine
Established: 1968

Capability: Semaly undertakes financial and economic studies, feasibility studies, preliminary and detail design work, construction management, operational management and training.

UPDATED

Serco Raildata

Dovedale House, rtc Business Park, London Road, Derby DE24 8UP, UK
Tel: (+44 1332) 26 35 84   Fax: (+44 1332) 26 24 38
e-mail: serco.raildata@ems.rail.co.uk
Business Manager: Ian Whiting
Sales Manager: Paul Jacobs

Background: Serco Raildata is a division of Serco Railtest.

Capabilities: Database management services, parts cataloguing, document, drawing and parts data management, data packaging, electronic delivery systems, archiving services.

NEW ENTRY

Sheffield Design & Property

2-10 Carbrook Hall Road, Sheffield S9 2DB, UK
Tel: (+44 114) 273 60 01   Fax: (+44 114) 273 61 82
Head of Service: I Stubbs

Background: Previously known as DBS Consultancy.

Capability: Design of viaducts and bridges in city centres; site survey, feasibility design, site supervision and operational work on LRT/quality public transport corridors/tram and bus priority (traffic management and signal priority systems, including AVL and enforcement systems)/highway schemes. Recent work includes LRT and ULRT CAD-based swept path analysis, design of traffic management, signals, highway arrangements and structures.

Also road safety schemes, surveys, quantity surveying; drainage engineering; architecture; project management, building services and refurbishment. Advice on LRT implementation, especially signalling.

Projects: Supertram, Sheffield, including design of bow-arch bridge and six-span viaduct; design of traffic signals, including priority systems, and traffic management; feasibility design of new tram stops and priority and safety improvement measures. Also advice and training on implementation issues of LRT including swept path analysis and tram priority measures. Priority measures in South Yorkshire.

UPDATED

Siemens

Siemens Aktiengesellschaft
PO Box 65, Elsenstrasse 87-96, D-12435 Berlin, Germany
Tel: (+49 30) 38 65 14 38   Fax: (+49 30) 38 65 12 75
Division Executive Management
   Technical: R van Ark
   Commercial: K Neubeck

Capability: Project management, installation/commissioning, training, service and maintenance of complete railway systems on a turnkey basis, including manufacture and supply of signalling and control systems, fare collection, telecommunications, electrification and rolling stock. Also planning, design and construction of both electrical and civil works.

VERIFIED

SMM Société du Métro de Marseille

44 avenue Alexandre Dumas, F-13272 Marseille cedex 8, France
Tel: (+33 4) 91 23 25 25   Fax: (+33 4) 91 23 25 00
General Manager: Michel Croc
Deputy General Manager: Jacques Tribout
Technical Director: Guy Lavergne

Capability: SMM is the public company which designs the metro and light rail systems in Marseille. It can offer project engineering capability in transport and communications; design and operation of advanced transit systems; infrastructure design; network reconfiguration studies; design and construction management.

VERIFIED

Socialdata

Institut für Verkehrs- und Infrastrukturforschung GmbH
Postfach 701629, D-81375 Munich, Germany
Tel: (+49 89) 710 81   Fax: (+49 89) 71 64 20
Managing Director: Werner Brög
Established: 1979 (predecessors 1972)
Staff: 28

Capability: Preparation of information and options for marketing and planning; surveys, forecasting and modelling for public and private transport use; cycle, pedestrian and parking studies; urban and interurban transport; price effect and tariff modelling; study of the effect of new technology and energy restrictions.

VERIFIED

Sogelerg Ingénierie snc

25 Rue du Pont des Halles, Chevilly-Larue, F-94666 Rungis, France
Tel: (+33 1) 45 60 12 34   Fax: (+33 1) 46 86 09 86
Chairman & Chief Executive Officer: L J Companyo
Chief Executive Officer: J Gaillard
Deputy General Manager: Denis Laroche
Vice President, Transport: Gerard Cartier
Vice President, Business Development:
   Patrick Yann Dartout

Capability: Feasibility studies, planning, engineering, basic and detailed design, procurement and construction management, programme management of urban transport systems.

VERIFIED

Southdowns Environmental Consultants

Suite A3, 16 Station St, Lewes, East Sussex BN7 2DB, UK
Tel: (+44 1273) 48 81 86   Fax: (+44 1273) 48 81 87
e-mail: secl@tcp.co.uk
www: http://www.tcp.co.uk/secl
Director: Patrick Williams

Capability: Assessment of environmental noise and vibrational impacts from railways. Mitigation of constructional and operational impacts. Technical support for liaison and consultation with public, local and other government bodies.

VERIFIED

Southern Vectis plc

Nelson Road, Newport PO30 1RD, UK
Tel: (+44 1983) 52 24 56   Fax: (+44 1983) 52 49 61
Managing Director: Stuart Linn

Capability: Drawing on the company's bus and coach experience, its consultancy section offers expertise in commercial, management, marketing and ticketing aspects of bus and tramway operation, including network design/assessment and commercial franchising.

Projects: The successful joint venture with Kalisz, Poland, has celebrated four years and is now joined by one with

Chelm, near the Ukrainian border. Other work has included Moldova and France.

The group's public transport database and access system, Xephos, successfully trialled in South Wales, drives the nationally backed Great Britain Bus Timetable, other printed material and the national multimode user-pays telephone enquiry service, Travel Call.

UPDATED

Spear Technologies Inc

One Market, Steuart Tower, Suite 700, San Francisco, California 94105, USA
Tel: (+1 415) 836 00 90   Fax: (+1 415) 836 80 99
www: www.speartechnologies.com

Transpolis Building, Postbox 2030, NL-2130 GE Hoofddorp, The Netherlands
Tel: (+31 23) 568 33 01   Fax: (+31 23) 568 57 01
Vice President, Marketing: Ken Voss
Director, International Sales: Bruce E Padula

Products: Spear 2000 software family for maintenance and materials management for both rolling stock and transport infrastructure, including: Work Manager, Materials Manager, Procurement Manager and Image Manager. Client component is a PC system capable of running Windows 95® or 98 or Windows NT® operating systems.

NEW ENTRY

Steer Davies Gleave

28-32 Upper Ground, London SE1 9PD, UK
Tel: (+44 171) 919 85 00   Fax: (+44 171) 827 98 50
www: www.sdg.co.uk
Managing Director: James Steer
Directors: Peter Twelftree, Charles Russell, Brian Martin,
   Luis Willumsen, Fred Beltrandi
Company Secretary: Don Nutt
Press & General Enquiries: Jo Hicks
Other offices: Leeds, Madrid, Santiago
Established: 1978

Capability: Transport planning and policy; demand modelling and forecasting; business strategy and marketing; feasibility, design and implementation; private and corporate finance; market research; traffic management and parking; environmental assessment; policy research; public consultation and training. Experience covers bus, light rail, metro, people mover, suburban rail, taxi, community transport and waterbus/ferry modes.

Projects: Include public transport strategy studies in Liverpool, London, Rome and Dublin.
   Responsible for LRT, guided bus, metro and suburban rail studies in Portsmouth, Manchester, Merseyside, Leeds, Tyne & Wear and Dublin.
   Demand and feasibility study of an extension of the Caracas metro to Los Teques.
   Demand and preliminary design of the Transmilenio quality bus corridor in Bogota.
   Feasibility study for several guided bus corridors in Santiago de Chile.
   Public transport plans for Granada and the Madrid region.
   Business strategy and plan for quality bus systems in Naples and Brescia in Italy.
   Implementation plan for new integrated ticketing system based on contactless smartcard technology for the cities of Bologna, Modena and Ferrara in Italy.
   Design and implementation for passenger information system for the public transport system of Rome in Italy.

UPDATED

Stirling Metro-Rail

Stirling House, 44 Richmond House, Kingston-upon-Thames KT2 5EE, UK
Tel: (+44 181) 549 37 20   Fax: (+44 181) 549 37 43
Director: Don Clarke
Director: Graham Jones
Group Marketing Manager: Patricia Holgate
Safety & Quality Manager: Rick Boughton
Recruitment Manager: Mark Downey

Associated company
Atlas Stirling Rail BV

Capability: Recruitment, training and contracting services to the heavy rail, mass transit and light rail industries. ISO 9002, Railtrack, SNCB, NS and London Underground approved.

UPDATED

Stratec SA

Boulevard Reyers 156, B-1040 Brussels, Belgium
Tel: (+32 2) 735 09 95   Fax: (+32 2) 735 49 17
e-mail: stratec@stratec.be
Managing Director: Hugues Duchateau
Directors: Françoise Boon, Luc Dens, Claude Rochez,
   Alain Counet, Sylvie Gayda
Commercial Manager: Hugues Duchateau
Founded: 1984
Staff: 25

Capability: Transport planning and engineering; regional and urban development planning; environmental management; public service management; business strategy; travel demand management programmes.

UPDATED

Strategies Unlimited

201 San Antonio Circle, Suite 205, Mountain View, California 94040, USA
Tel: (+1 650) 941 34 38   Fax: (+1 650) 941 51 20
e-mail: info@strategies-u.com
www: www.strategies-u.com
Principal: George Bechtel

Capability: ITS systems, such as route guidance, collision warning, vehicle location and information provision.

Projects: A study on collision warning for vehicles including buses has been carried out. The collision warning system has been installed on the Greyhound fleet of 7,500 buses in the USA.

UPDATED

STV Group Inc

205 West Welsh Drive, Douglassville, Pennsylvania 19518, USA
Tel: (+1 610) 385 82 00   Fax: (+1 610) 385 85 01
Chairman & Chief Executive Officer: Michael Haratunian
President & Chief Operating Officer:
   Dominick M Servedio
Offices in: New York, Baltimore, Chicago, Los Angeles and other US cities.
Established: 1968
Staff: 20 locations

Subsidiaries
STV Incorporated
STV Environmental
STV Construction Services
STV International
STV Architects
STV/Silver & Ziskind

Capability: Engineering, architectural, planning,

environmental and construction management services. The group is involved in planning and design of urban transport systems.

Projects: Programme and construction management in joint venture for the St Louis MetroLink LRT extension, USA.
   Construction management in joint venture for Blue line Pasadena extension for Los Angeles County MTA; modernisation of CTA Chicago's Skokie shops; consulting services for procurement of Long Island Rail Road's 114 cars and 23 AC-powered locomotives.
   Engineering services for bridges, stations, utilities and track on NJ Transit Hudson—Bergen LRT system.
   Maintenance shops, trackwork, bridges and construction services for Amtrak Northeast corridor and Florida Overland Express high-speed rail systems.
   Work on DART Dallas LRT system.
   Design engineering and construction inspection for light rail line linking New York City to JFK airport.

UPDATED

Sundberg-Ferar Inc

4359 Pineview Drive, Walled Lake, Michigan 48390-4129, USA
Tel: (+1 248) 360 38 00   Fax: (+1 248) 360 69 00
e-mail: indesign@sundbergf.com
www: http://www.sundbergf.com
President: Curt J Bailey
Vice Presidents: Jeff DeBoer, Mark Bonner
Established: 1934
Branch office: Minneapolis, USA
General Manager: Ken Parker

Capability: Product development firm specialising in light rail, metro and commuter cars.

Projects: Exterior design for new-generation underground car, MTA New York; has made designs for BART San Francisco; WMATA Washington; New Haven commuter area; Chicago commuter area; LIRR (double-deck commuter car); Baltimore metro; Rio de Janeiro metro, Brazil; MARTA Atlanta; Miami metro and Los Angeles; and completed a design for the DART system for Dallas. Redesigned metro car interiors for BART San Francisco.
   Computer visualisation of double-deck passenger car for Long Island Rail Road.

VERIFIED

SwedeRail

Klarabergsviadukten 78, SE-10550 Stockholm, Sweden
Tel: (+46 8) 762 37 81   Fax: (+46 8) 10 62 43
President: Bernt Andersson
Senior Vice President: Bo Marklund
Vice President: Sunit Ray
Managers: Robert Hallenborg, Björn Andersson,
   Jan Gullbrandsen

Capability: The transport consultancy of Swedish State Railways offers technical and management services from initial planning through to project implementation; feasibility studies; design, supervision, maintenance and operation; environment preservation; economics and business management; personnel training.

VERIFIED

Systra

5 avenue du Coq, F-75009 Paris, France
Tel: (+33 1) 40 16 61 00   Fax: (+33 1) 40 16 61 04
e-mail: systra@systra.com
www: www.systra.com
Chairman: Pierre Fa
President: Thierry Ossent
Vice President, Commercial: Jean-Christophe Hugonnard

Vice President, Engineering: Michel Leboeuf
Vice President, Projects: Serge Dassonville
Staff: 1,000

Subsidiaries
SOTEC Ingénierie, France
TPP, France
MEXISTRA, Mexico
SOFRECAD Chile
SFCM, China
Systra, Philippines.

Systra Group associated companies
Canarail, Canada
Systra SpA, Italy
Systra USA (LSTS-RTS)
MVA Group Ltd, UK, France, Hong Kong, Malaysia

Capability: Systra offers urban and regional transport consultancy services ranging from project identification to system operation.

Capability covers technical, economic and financial feasibility studies; economic and financial analyses, multi-disciplinary preliminary and detailed design, contract preparation, construction management, system commissioning, operations and maintenance services. Systra is a subsidiary of SNCF and RATP Paris.

Projects: Technical and economic feasibility studies: LRT system in Salvador de Bahia (Brazil); Alexandria regional metro (Egypt); Mulhouse tram project (France); preliminary studies for the Tel Aviv metro (Israel); urban projects for Rome (Italy); rail link, Taipei airport (Taiwan); transport planning for Maracabo and Merida (Venezuela). Design and construction: Metro Line 2 (VAL) Lille, Bordeaux LRT network; Orleans LRT Line 1 (France); Sentral station, Kuala Lumpur (Malaysia); Mexico City metro Line B; London/Channel Tunnel high-speed link project, founding associate of London & Continental Railways Ltd, member of the engineering consortium and leader for the systemwide design and procurement (UK). Operation and maintenance: General consultant for the start-up of the Guangzhou metro (China); commissioning of the Cairo metro system (Egypt); quality control of Line B equipment (Mexico City); supervision of operation for the Manila LRT III (Philippines); overhaul of rolling stock for Caracas metro (Venezuela).

UPDATED

TAMS Consultants, Inc

The TAMS Building, 655 Third Avenue, New York, New York 10017, USA
Tel: (+1 212) 867 17 77   Fax: (+1 212) 697 63 54
President: Anthony R Dolcimascolo
Principals responsible for transit: Frank A Baragona, Kenneth F Standig
Established: 1942
Staff: 420 in 19 offices (USA and international)

Capability: Architectural and engineering planning and design for railway, bus and rail transit facilities, including stations, tunnels, structures, maintenance shops and related facilities.

Projects: Provides engineering and design services for miscellaneous construction projects throughout the city of New York. Alarm/detection system for new Coliseum bus station, Bronx, New York; provides design services for the interior of a rail control centre for NYCT metro system.

Include rehabilitation of East New York Bus Garage; expansion of Jamaica Yard workshops and storage areas for NYCTA; modifications to the PATH station at Pavonia; rehabilitation of eight stations for Metro-North; planning and design for restoration of Hoboken terminal passenger facilities; designs to incorporate provision for access by the disabled to 14 NJT stations and six commuter rail stations for Connecticut DoT and Metro-North.

UPDATED

TAS Partnership Ltd

Britannic House, 1a Chapel Street, Preston PR1 8BU, UK
Tel: (+44 1772) 20 49 88   Fax: (+44 1772) 56 20 70
Managing Director: Peter Huntley

Capability: Passenger transport research; funding mechanisms; demand evaluation and business case development.

Projects: Include patronage evaluation with Croydon Tramlink; bidder support for Nottingham LRT; operational and strategic plans for Edinburgh CERT; accessibility arrangements for London Transport Buses; bidder support for Bristol City light rail; operating plan for Oxford Guided Bus project; guided bus study for Birmingham northeast corridor.

UPDATED

TecnEcon Ltd

Glen House, 125 Old Brompton Road, London SW7 3RP, UK
Tel: (+44 171) 373 77 55   Fax: (+44 171) 370 33 28
Managing Director: Jeff Ody
Established: 1985
Middle East Regional Office:
PO Box 52750, Dubai, United Arab Emirates

Capability: Multimodal urban transport planning specialists in modelling and operational studies, economic and financial appraisal; market research into public transport attitudes and product development in relation to real-time passenger information systems; technical assistance and policy advice to international lending agencies, governments and transport operators. Advice on public transport franchising and private finance for transport infrastructure projects.

VERIFIED

Thorburn Colquhoun

Transportation Division, 200 Harpur Centre, Horn Lane, Bedford MK40 1TS, UK
Tel: (+44 1234) 34 96 41   Fax: (+44 1234) 21 62 68
Director: C J Darling
Associate Directors: A Wakeman, K Holloway, R Pollock, D J Bennison, M Horsfall
Offices in: Ireland, Angola, Guinea, Ghana, Kuwait, Russia, Zambia, Cyprus, Poland
Established: 1994
Staff: 451

Capability: Consultancy services in transport policy, planning, economics, engineering, operations, management, training and research. Thorburn Colquhoun Transportation provides transport services for the whole company.

Work includes bus and rail system planning, minibus and paratransit studies, service costing, policy studies and information systems. Also highway appraisal, transport facilities design, transport planning, economics, bus priority, parking and urban traffic control.

Projects: Traffic management studies, review of corridor options for rail, rail and bus patronage studies, parking and urban traffic control, bus priority systems, park-and-ride studies, transport monitoring, traffic safety schemes.

Urban transport projects in the UK and other countries, due-diligence audit of PFI transport projects, international freight and communications studies. Regional planning studies in Botswana, Malawi, Portugal, Tanzania, Uganda and Zimbabwe.

UK National interurban speed survey, inner central and outer London speed surveys, Corporation of London speed surveys. Bus priority studies in several towns and cities. Safer routes to school studies for the UK Highways Agency. Traffic Management in the Evening and numerous other research projects for the UK DETR.

UPDATED

Tilney Lumsden Shane Ltd

5 Heathmans Road, London SW6 4TJ, UK
Tel: (+44 171) 731 69 46   Fax: (+44 171) 736 33 56
Director: Marvin Shane

Capability: Creative design and management consultancy in environmental and interior design for vehicles and buildings.

VERIFIED

Transcorp

1a Lonsdale Square, Islington, London N1 1EN, UK
Tel: (+44 171) 466 44 33   Fax: (+44 171) 700 05 97
e-mail: tcorp@fmgroup.co.uk
Principals: Peter Trickett, David Cowler

Capability: Feasibility and concept studies, exterior design, interior design, corporate design, computer simulation, tender assessment, product specification.

VERIFIED

Transmetrics Inc

4010 Moorpark Avenue, Suite 112, San Jose, California 95117, USA
Tel: (+1 408) 984 77 94   Fax: (+1 408) 244 82 50
President: Jack Ybarra
Vice President: Denis Pu
Vice President: Frank Addiego

Capability: Consultants in engineering, planning and construction management of railways, highways and airports.

VERIFIED

TransPlan

Transport & Planning Research Network
45 Beatrice Road, Thorpe Hamlet, Norwich NR1 4BB, UK
Tel: (+44 1603) 66 73 14   Fax: (+44 1603) 66 73 14
Director: Chris Wood

Capability: Environmental transport and planning consultancy specialising in sustainability.

VERIFIED

Transportation Management Solutions

PO Box 15174, Glasgow G4 9LW, UK
Tel: (+44 141) 332 47 33   Fax: (+44 141) 400 29 33
e-mail: tramsol@aol.com
Principals: Dave Holladay, Josephine Nevoh

Capability: Transport management solutions (Intermodal & TDM).

Projects: Include studies and application of bike/public transport issues including fitting cycle-carrying facilities on buses in UK and on secure storage/locker systems for bus and train passengers.

TMS is working to get the Sportsworks rack approved for use in the UK and other EU countries.

UPDATED

Transport Resources International

The Old Granary, Main Street, Ashby St Ledgers, Rugby CV23 8UN, UK
Tel: (+44 1788) 891 37   Fax: (+44 1788) 89 14 59
Partners: Janet Jack, Doug Jack
Established 1986

Capability: Market and product research and strategies; company acquisition and disposal; confidential commercial projects; bus fleet evaluations; UK/EC legislation and its effect on the bus industry; legal/commercial terms, documents and agreements; press and public relations; market analysis and statistical data; market databases, regularly updated; product liability legislation and its implications.

Projects: Regular clients include internationally known commercial vehicle manufacturers, bodybuilders and component suppliers.

UPDATED

TransTeC

TransTeC Beteiligungs-und Managementgesellschaft mbH
Lister Strasse 15, D-30163 Hannover, Germany
Tel: (+49 511) 399 50   Fax: (+49 511) 39 95 12 99
e-mail: ttc@transtech-hannover.de
Managing Directors: Bernd Kosiek, Hans-Heinrich Tonne, Ulrich Lüdtke
Established: 1986
Staff: 350

Branch offices
Berlin, Hamburg, Utrecht, Netherlands

Associated companies
TransTeC Bauplanungs- und Management-gesellschaft Hannover mbH
TransTeC Transport und Technologie Consult Hannover GmbH
TransTeC Intertraffic TTI Systems GmbH, Hannover
TransTeC America Inc, Chicago, USA
TransTeC Amsterdam BV, Amsterdam, Netherlands

Background: Once established as the consulting subsidiary of Üstra Hannoversche Vekehrsbetriebe AG, the TransTeC group comprises 18 national and international companies, providing a comprehensive spectrum of services in the public transport sector.

Capability: Transport planning, market research, business strategy, economic and financial studies, traffic management, infrastructure design and implementation, procurement supervision of construction, turnkey systems, project management, communication systems, transport operation and management staff training, software systems for planning, monitoring and operating public transport. Ability to integrate practical experience with operation of metro, LRT and bus systems.

Projects
Hannover: design and implementation of light rail extensions for Expo 2000 including integrated traffic management system and workshop/depot for 144 vehicles.
Hamburg: Preliminary design for new Hamburg light rail link to airport.
Wolfsburg: technical and legal assistance and design of the VW Wolfsburg people mover.
Copenhagen: procurement for the vehicle design for the metro project.
Utrecht: comprehensive engineering services for new town development (Leidsche Rijn) and the public/traffic systems.
Philadelphia: timetable information system.
   Vehicle scheduling and duty rostering systems for more than 100 transport operators; computer-aided dispatch/AVL for more than 30 transport operators.

UPDATED

Transurb Consult

Rue Ravenstein 60, Bte 18, B-1000 Brussels, Belgium
Tel: (+32 2) 548 53 11   Fax: (+32 2) 513 94 19
Chief Executive: Erik Vandenbroele
Established: 1973

Subsidiaries
TUC Rail and Technirail Belgium
Transurb Argentina
Transurb Gabon
Transurb Malaysia

Capability: Draws on the operating, engineering and planning skills of Belgium's public transport operators. It offers planning, feasibility and preliminary design studies, and detailed engineering and construction management of projects as well as operational advice, management training and technical assistance in day-to-day operations of all modes of mass transport.
   Privatisation and restructuring of mass transport networks, ranging from advice to shareholding.

UPDATED

Transurb Inc

85 Saint Catherine St West, Montreal H2X 3P4, Canada
Tel: (+1 514) 871 01 78   Fax: (+1 514) 397 97 50
President: Pierre Asselin
Vice President, Transportation: Michel Larocune

Capability: Undertakes services from initial studies to project management, including demand and traffic surveys, geological inspection, civil engineering design, railway design, procurement and construction management.
Projects: : Transurb has completed a feasibility study for multiple usage of railway infrastructure – rail and bus services.

UPDATED

Transys Projects Ltd

2 Priestley Wharf, Holt Street, Aston Science Park, Birmingham B7 4BN, UK
Tel: (+44 121) 359 77 77   Fax: (+44 121) 359 18 11
e-mail: transys@dial.pipex.com
Managing Director: Jeremy J Ashley
Marketing and Sales Director: Peter C Johnson
Engineering Director: Karl J Barras

Associate company
Traxis BV, Netherlands (qv Rail Vehicles and Traction Equipment section)

Background: Transys Projects Ltd (formerly known as Holec Ridderkerk UK Ltd), is a member of the Dutch Royal Begemann group.

Capability: Multidisciplined engineering consultancy and project management organisation, covering all aspects of passenger rail vehicles and their related support services. This covers mass transit vehicles, LRVs and tramcars, as well as main line dmus, emus, and pass coaches. Particularly specialising in UK Railtrack Group Standards, Safety Cases and vehicle acceptance.
   Certified to BS EN ISO 9001 with 'Link-Up' accreditation in eight relevant areas.
   Also Registered Corporate Supplier to London Underground Ltd for consultancy in Rolling Stock Engineering.
   Specific capabilities include:
Design Engineering
Design of complete rail vehicles or discrete areas
Concept to production drawings/schedules
Bodyshells, underframes, cabs, interiors
Assembly, component and system design
Mockups, modular design
Engineering Services
Optimise design to obtain requisite certification
FEA, classical calculations, kinematics, coupler movements

Specification and management of structural testing
Tender/tender response documents and purchase specifications
Electrical and Mechanical Systems, Engineering and Integration
Ability to project engineer a complete range of equipments, systems and services through design, testing and validation.
   — vehicle mechanical equipment, systems, including diesel drivelines
   — electrical/electronic systems including control and traction
   — material choice, fire safety and testing
   — vehicle performance, simulation on specified routes
   — vehicle acceptance and safety case issues
   — fault finding, trouble shooting
Project Support
   — provide project management and planning
   — select/monitor subcontractors and/or product performance
   — vehicle maintenance, efficiency and reliability improvement
   — developing technical literature and support information
   — product support group undertakes modification and upgrade work.

Projects: Class 323 emu with a three-phase 25 kV 50 Hz AC regenerative traction package; Glasgow Underground trailer cars. Numerous consultancy, design and bid support projects mainly in the UK and Europe, together with maintenance support activities.

NEW ENTRY

Robert L Trillo

The Homestead, Broadlands, Brockenhurst SO42 7SX, UK
Tel: (+44 1590) 62 22 20   Fax: (+44 1590) 62 22 20
Principal: Eur Ing Robert L Trillo

Capability: Consultancy and design work on all forms of waterborne transport, including hovercraft: investment feasibility studies and project appraisal for development financing; market studies for new forms of marine craft, with special emphasis on environmentally acceptable high-speed craft for urban transport; conceptual and preliminary design of craft.

VERIFIED

TTK

TransportTechnologie-Consult Karlsruhe GmbH
Gerwigstrasse 53, D-76131 Karlsruhe, Germany
Tel: (+49 721) 62 50 30   Fax: (+49 721) 625 03 33
Director: Dr-Ing Udo Sparmann
Deputy Directors: Dipl-Ing Axel Kühn
   Dipl-Ing Rainer Schneider

Background: TransportTechnologie-Consult Karlsruhe GmbH (TTK) is a subsidiary of the Albtal-Verkehrs-Gesellschaft mbH, Karlsruhe (AVG) and of the PTV Group, Karlsruhe. Both companies hold a 50 per cent share in TTK.
   AVG is a private public transport organisation for the surrounding region of the city of Karlsruhe and shares its board of directors with VBK, the tram operators of Karlsruhe and KVV, the Passenger Transport Authority. Karlsruhe is well known as the first joint running track, where trams and main line trains share the same track.
   The PTV group was founded in 1979 and has expanded to a group of six companies employing more than 160 people. The PTV group covers traffic and transport planning, and supplies transport planning software.
   In 1996 TTK started a permanent co-operation agreement (mainly for projects in English speaking countries) with AEA Technology Rail, Derby, (former BR Research), DRU-Lovejoy, London, GB and PTV System Software and Consulting GmbH, Karlsruhe. It goes under the name Transport Solutions.

Capability: By working in close collaboration with the

public transport services of Karlsruhe it is possible to combine theoretical ideas and practical experience giving maximum benefit to clients. TTK's capabilities include: feasibility studies, operational concepts, design, joint running, airport access, vehicle development, cost-benefit analysis, tariff structure, research, local public transport planning and assistance.

Projects: Germany: Alzey (1998) – local public transport plan; Baden airport (1997) – design, joint running, airport access, cost-benefit analyses; Bergstrasse (1996) – local public transport plan; Braunschweig (1998) – feasibility study, design; Calw (1998) – demand analyses; Stuttgart (1998) – design; Trier (1997) – design); Donnersberg (1998) – local public transport plan; Ettlingen (1998) – design; Freiburg (1997) – assistance; Germersheim (1998) – local public transport plan; Hagen (1997) – feasibility study, operational concept, design, joint running; Hamm (1997) – feasibility study, operational concept, design, joint running; Heidelberg (1997) – design, assistance; Heilbronn (1996) – feasibility study, assistance, design, operational concept; Heidelberg (1998) – design; Hildesheim (1998) – assistance; Ingelheim (1998) – tariff structure; Kaiserslautern (1998) – tariff structure; Karlsruhe (1998) – design, research; Kassel (1997) – operational concept, vehicle development, joint running, cost-benefit analyses, design, assistance; Krefeld (1996) – feasibility study, operational concept; Ladenburg (1998) – feasibility study; Kiel (1997) – feasibility study, operational concept); Ludwigsburg (1998) – feasibility study; Luxembourg (1998) – design; Mainz (1998) – tariff structure; Mannheim (1998) – tariff structure; Munich (1998) – feasibility study; Weinsberg (1997) – design, assistance and Worms (1998) – local public transport plan).

Brisbane, Australia, (1998) – assistance; Bristol, UK (1997) – joint running, operational concept, design, vehicle development; Glasgow, Scotland (1997) – feasibility study, operational concept, joint running, airport access; Grenoble (1998) – assistance; Heerlen, Netherlands (1996) – feasibility study, cost-benefit analyses; Kent, UK, 1996 (feasibility study, assistance, joint running); Ljubljana, Slovenia (1997) – feasibility study, joint running, operational concept; Luxembourg (1997) – feasibility study, design; Mulhouse, France (1997) – feasibility study; Nancy, France (1998) – local public transport plan; Nantes, France (1998) – assistance, joint running; Oslo, Norway (1996) feasibility study, vehicle development, joint running, assistance; Salzburg, Austria (1996) – operational concept, cost-benefit analyses, joint running; St Etienne, France (1998) – assistance; Strasbourg, France (1998) – assistance.

UPDATED

The Urban Analysis Group Inc

50 Oak Court, Suite 110, Danville, California 94526-4048, USA
Tel: (+1 510) 838 13 63   Fax: (+1 510) 838 13 72

Capability: Offers URBAN/SYS, a comprehensive integrated set of urban planning and related software tools including the following:
TRANPLAN: a set of integrated programs for the transport planning process. It encompasses the four-step travel demand model of trip generation, trip distribution, modal choice and trip assignment for both highway and public transport systems. The public transport software uses coding and analysis techniques similar to the US DoT's Urban Transport Planning System (UTPS).
NIS (Network Information System): this is a flexible, interactive, graphics editor for displaying and maintaining spatial data, including highway and transit network descriptions, and area (polygon) boundary and attribute data. Networks and related attributes can be graphically displayed using colours, patterns, annotation and bandwidths. Networks can be interactively updated.
TPMENU (TranPlan MENU): this is a menu shell that combines TRANPLAN functions, NIS and supplementary software. The menu system can be modified, modelling procedures updated and new programs incorporated by editing text configuration files.
DBC (DataBase Capable): this offers a simple means of

combining URBAN/SYS travel demand forecasting software with other software applications, including air emission models and GISs, by accessing a shared database. The DBC environment extends the capabilities of URBAN/SYS and provides access to supplemental data for URBAN/SYS processing.

VERIFIED

Urban Initiatives

35 Heddon Street, London W1R 7LL, UK
Tel: (+44 171) 287 36 44   Fax: (+44 171) 287 94 89
e-mail: @urbaninitiatives.co.uk
Partners: C Whife, K Campbell
Associate Directors: J E Lloyd, J Caulton
Associates: J Dales, J Dryden, A Gibbins, M Rawlinson, A Reeves
Founded: 1989

Capability: Planning and design consultancy specialising in urban planning and design; transport planning and traffic engineering; infrastructure planning and environmental assessment; development planning and economics.

Projects: These include:
London Underground: validation of station planning guidelines; appraisal of station designs for CrossRail and East London line, development of central London station strategy for proposed Chelsea–Hackney line; and computer modelling of stations across London.
Railtrack: development opportunities and pedestrian links around London Bridge station; development of scheme options for bus interchange at Cardiff station; survey of Thameslink passengers (with OPRAF) for Thameslink 2000 project; analysis of pedestrian movements in Liverpool Street station, London.
Centro, Birmingham: preparation of design guidelines for Line 2 of the LRT system.
LT Planning: creation of database on trip information for London rail network; assessment of local access arrangements for Jubilee line extension; projection of demand at Paddington station, London, for next 15 years.
Westminster City Council: feasibility studies for LRT line between Waterloo and Kings Cross, and advisers on rail planning and traffic impacts.
Various train operating companies: analysis of trip data for appraisal of new schemes.
Greater Manchester PTE: proposals for regeneration of Piccadilly station and surrounding area.
Vauxhall Interchange Study for Vauxhall Regeneration Company, looking at improvement options for the underground and rail stations situated in a major traffic gyratory scheme.

UPDATED

Uvaterv Engineering Consultants Ltd

PO Box 453/421, H-1537 Budapest 114, Hungary
Tel: (+36 1) 204 29 67   Fax: (+36 1) 204 29 69
e-mail: uvaterv@mail.datanet.hu
President-Director General: Gyula Bretz
Deputy Director General: Dr Lászlo Karsay
Division Director, Transportation Infrastructure: Frigyes Kavácsházy
Division Director, Bridges, Structures: Zsolt Kavács
Director, Metro and Architecture: Gábor Soós
Established: 1948

Capability: Engineering and general consultancy services for rail, metro and road systems; network planning, architectural design, structural and electrical engineering, signalling systems, traffic management.

Projects: Construction of Budapest's 17 km Line 4, postponed on cost grounds in 1995, was approved in August 1997. The first section (7.3 km, 10 stations) will link Etele Square and Baross Square, with connections

for Line 2 and 3, and crossing the River Danube. Uvaterv has directed the first phase of the project as well as a feasibility study for section 1. As a member of the consortium of Fomterv Rt and Mott MacDonald (UK), Uvaterv is taking part in the railway authorisation design documentation.

UPDATED

Vectra

Europa House, 310 Europa Boulevard, Westbrook, Warrington WA5 5YQ, UK
Tel: (+44 1925) 44 46 48   Fax: (+44 1925) 44 47 01
Principal: Stefano Scannali
A wholly owned subsidiary of Amey plc
Offices in: Aberdeen, Scotland; Bristol, England; Leiden, Netherlands; Kuala Lumpur, Malaysia

Capability: Engineering mechanics and design, safety and reliability.

VERIFIED

Harry Weese Associates

10 West Hubbard Street, Chicago, Illinois 60610, USA
Tel: (+1 312) 467 70 30   Fax: (+1 312) 467 70 51
Principals: John Corley, David Munson
Established: 1947
Staff: 45

Capability: Architectural consultant to urban transport authorities, offering specific services for station and facilities design, multimodal facilities design, landscaping and urban design.

Projects
Washington DC: work has included design of 86 stations on the Washington metro.
Chicago: Adams/Wabash station renovation and Midway Airport station design; Metra passenger terminal renovation and restoration.
Hamilton: commuter station design.
Toronto: consultant to the TTC's rail expansion programme and section design architect for York city centre station.
Other projects in USA: design of 20 Miami metro stations, 10 Los Angeles Red line stations, and 14 Buffalo LRT stations.
The company was architect for rehabilitation of Washington Union station, and was part of the team that produced the master plan for redevelopment of New York's Grand Central terminal.

VERIFIED

Wilbur Smith Associates

PO Box 92, 1301 Gervais Street, NationsBank Tower, Columbia, South Carolina 29201, USA
Tel: (+1 803) 758 45 00   Fax: (+1 803) 251 20 64
Chair & President: Robert A Hubbard
Senior Vice President, International: J W Bonniville
Senior Vice President, Transport Planning & Economics: R V Zuelsdorf
Vice Presidents: G Schneider, Stephen W Schar, William T Stone
Offices in: Bangkok, Hong Kong, London, Beijing, Guatemala City, Harare and other cities worldwide
Established: 1952
Staff: 650 in 30 offices

Capability: Transport planning, engineering and economic consultancy services including multimodal system planning, and planning and design of light rail, heavy rail and people mover systems, as well as bus transit operations analysis, including HOV intelligent transport systems and park-and-ride. Services include urban transport modelling, ridership forecasts, feasibility studies, alternative alignment studies, traffic and environmental impact analysis, traffic control, preliminary engineering, final design plans and contract documents, field supervision and construction engineering and inspection. Services also include industrial design, signage and graphics, and related visual communications systems, and interior space planning.

Projects

San Diego: WSA was selected for a congestion pricing demonstration project in 1996, involving a demonstration programme on an existing high-occupancy vehicle (HOV) lane.

USA: the Tampa Bay commuter rail feasibility study; BART Oakland Airport connecting link, California; Eureka rail corridor feasibility, Phase II study; Denver air train study; Bayshore corridor system planning, California; Florida rail system plan; Washington state rail study.

Thailand: high-speed train study.

Hong Kong: Ma On Shan railway study.

Jamaica: road-based projects transport sector study.

Malaysia: project management for elevated personal rapid transit system to serve central Kuala Lumpur and a proposed major linear city.

Singapore: Sentosa transport plan.

Bangkok Transit Master Plan; BART Access Strategy Study; Richmond, Virginia, multimodal terminal study; Chicago personal rapid transit ridership study; rail consolidation studies, California.

Hong Kong: electronic road pricing, in association with Hyder Consulting, UK (qv). Assessment of practicality, need, cost effectiveness, public acceptance and practicality.

VERIFIED

Vehicle-km: (1990/91) 5.1 million
(1991/92) 5.1 million
(1992/93) 5.1 million

Current situation: Operates 250 buses on services in Chiba city and prefecture, also a 39.1 km railway elsewhere in Chiba prefecture.

Chiba Chuo Bus

Chiba Chuo Bus
2-27-4 Nagasu, Chuo-ku, Chiba-shi 260-0854
Tel: (+81 472) 24 37 71

Bus
Passenger journeys: (1990/91) 12.3 million
(1991/92) 12.6 million
(1992/93) 11.8 million

Vehicle-km: 4 million
(1991/92) 4.1 million
(1992/93) 4.1 million

Current situation: This Keisei Group company operates 95 buses on services in Chiba; also owns 57 coaches.

UPDATED

FRANKFURT

RMV

Rhein-Main-Verkehrsverbund GmbH (RMV)
Alte Bleiche 5, D-65719 Hofheim am Taunus
Tel: (+49 61) 92 29 40 Fax: (+49 61) 92 29 49 40

Director: Volker Sparmann
Deputy Director: Hansjorg Rohrich
Managers
  Controlling: Herbert Jack
  Traffic Planning: Gerhard Stanek

Marketing: Siegfried Ziller
Production: Helmut Achenbach

UPDATED

HAMBURG

HVV

Tel: (+49 40) 325 77 50

UPDATED

HONG KONG/ GUANGZHOU

Developments: Stagecoach Holdings plc has acquired Citybus, one of the leading bus operators, providing both franchised and non-franchised services. The company operates 1,187 buses and has an estimated 63 per cent share of the Hong Kong island bus market.

UPDATED

Guangzhou metro train in depot (S H Lai)
1999/0058314

Double-deck sightseeing bus in Shenzhen, Guandong, on border of Hong Kong with China (Vic Davey)
1999/0058312

KWANGJU

Population: 1.3 million
Public transport: Bus services provided by private companies. Metro under construction.

Bus
Current situation: Nine companies run 965 buses over a network of 75 routes.

Metro
Current situation: In 1996 construction started of the 20.1 km line from Yongsandong in the south through the city centre to Ock Dong in the west. Completion is expected in 2004. A second line is expected be built from Song Am (southwest) to Mun Hack-Dong (northeast) intersecting the first line near city hall (13.7 km).

NEW ENTRY

LONDON

Developments: Sir Malcolm Bates has been appointed Executive Chairman of London Transport.

UPDATED

LYONS

Developments: SYTRAL Lyons, has ordered 67 Renault trolleybuses with an option for a further 60. The buses are second-generation passenger vehicles with a very low step height, flat floor and integral hub motors. Offered as standard or articulated vehicles, the Renault trolleybuses incorporate some of the advanced technologies from the Renault Civis integrated transport system. The first deliveries are due in Lyons by the end of 2000.

UPDATED

MARSEILLE

RTM
Bus and trolleybus
Passenger journeys: (1995) Bus 85.4 million, trolleybus 6.6 million
(1996) Bus 72.1 million, trolleybus 5.9 million
(1997) Bus 71 million, trolleybus 5.4 million
Vehicle-km: (1995) Bus 21.6 million, trolleybus 0.8 million
(1996) Bus 19.7 million, trolleybus 0.6 million
(1997) Bus 20.8 million, trolleybus 0.6 million

Number of routes: Bus 72, trolleybus 3, including 13 night
Route length: Bus 578 km, trolleybus 19 km
On priority right-of-way: 24.1 km

Fleet: 541 buses
Fleet: 47 trolleybuses, all Berliet ER100
In peak service: 460
Average age of fleet: 9.4 years

Metro
Type of operation: Rubber-tyred full metro, initial route opened 1978; two lines

Passenger boardings: (1994) 53.8 million
(1997) 49.5 million
Car-km: (1995) 9.1 million
(1997) 8.7 million

Tramway
Type of operation: Conventional tramway

Passenger journeys: (1995) 4.6 million
(1997) 3.5 million
Car-km: (1995) 0.5 million
(1997) 0.6 million

Current situation: A 3 km tram line (Route 68) with 14 stops links Noailles Line 2 metro station with St Pierre; 3 minute peak service.

UPDATED

PARIS

RATP LRV on Line T2 at Issy Val-de-Seine station
(Ken Harris)
1999/0058311

PYONGYANG

Metro and tram operation
The North Korean capital now operates two metro lines which started in 1973. Supply of power is provided by a thirdrail. The fleet comprises 48 cars of domestic manufacture by Kim Jong Tage factory in Pyongyang, which are coupled into train formations. Train frequency ranges between 5 and 7 minutes or just 2 minutes during peak hours.

In 1991 the first standard-gauge tram line 1 opened between Mangyongdae and Songsin with 20 route-km. Another two tram routes, 2 and 3, followed in 1992-94, bringing the total tram route-km to some 50.

Operation is provided by 45 Type KT8D5-K articulated trams and 129 Type T6B5-K trams, all built by ČKD Tatra, Czech Republic. Another 60 four-axle trams are running, built by Shenfeng Works in China. They are based on ČKD's Type KT4.

In 1995 a 1,000 mm tram line was built in the north-eastern suburb of the capital, stretching 3.5 km from Samhyng metro station to Kumsusan. The line is reported to be used exclusively for visitors to the Kim Ir Sen Mausoleum at Kumsusan. The fleet comprises 18 Type SWS/MFO trams purchased from Basle, Switzerland, and some four-axle trailers originally built by SIG, Switzerland.

UPDATED

LOS ANGELES

Torrance Transit

City of Torrance Transit System
20500 Madrona Avenue, Torrance, California 90503
Tel: (+1 310) 781 69 24   Fax: (+1 310) 618 62 29
City Manager: LeRoy J Jackson
General Manager: Tom Whittle
Staff: 104

Passenger journeys: (1990/91) 3.3 million
(1992/93) 3.4 million
(1996/97) 4.6 million

Number of routes: 9

Route length: 336 km
Fleet: 53 buses
Average age of fleet: 6.5 years
In peak service: 6.5 years

Most intensive service: 15 min
Fares collected on board: 95 per cent
Fare collection: Electronic farebox and smartcard reader
Fare structure: Two zones
Operating costs financed by: 80 per cent Federal and 20 per cent local funds
Average peak hour speed: 19.8 km/h

Current situation: Serves Torrance, Redondo Beach, the airport, Lomita, Long Beach, Carson, portions of Gardena and the city of Los Angeles adjacent to Torrance with nine lines, two of which extend to downtown Los Angeles and another to the Long Beach transit mall for light rail connection to LA. Fleet of 56 buses. Also supervises Municipal Area Express — two commuter routes linking South Bay with El Segundo, operated under contract with a fleet of 50 buses.

UPDATED

TAEGU

Population: 2.7 million
Public transport: Bus services provided by private companies. First section of metro opened in late 1997.

Bus

Current situation: 32 companies run 1,576 buses over a network of 84 routes.

Metro

Type of operation: Full metro, first section opened in November 1997.

Gauge: 1,435 mm
Electrification: 1,500 V DC, overhead

Rolling stock: 36 six-car trains (Hanjin/Siemens)

Developments: An 11.4 km section of Line 1 between Wall-Bae and Daegu was opened in 1997. Completion of the whole 27.6 km line was expected in summer 1998 and two branch lines by 2002.

Line 1 connects two major residential developments in the east and west with the city centre. Interchange facilities with KNR are provided at the main railway station, which is to the east of the business area.

Construction of Line 2 from Dasa to Kosan (29 km) was started in 1996 and is expected to be completed in 2002. By 2020 six more lines are expected to be built with a total length of 146 km.

NEW ENTRY

MANUFACTURERS

RAIL VEHICLES AND TRACTION EQUIPMENT

Adtranz

DaimlerChrysler Railsystems
Group Holding Headquarters
Saatwinkler Damm 43, D-13627/PO Box 130127,
D-13601 Berlin, Germany
Tel: (+49 303) 83 20   Fax: (+49 303) 832 20 00

Group Executive Board
President and Chief Executive Officer (CEO):
   Rolf Eckrodt
Executive Vice President (EVP), Business Segment
   Marketing & Service: Bert Van Dijk
EVP Business Segment, Mass Transit (MT):
   Christer Bådholm
EVP, Main Line Business Segment (ML):
   Jürgen Lochman
EVP, Systems & Components Business Segment (SC):
   Joachim Gaissert
EVP & Chief Technical Officer (CTO): Åke Wennberg
Chief Financial Officer (CFO): Rainer Schmückle
EVP, Team for Integration of the Organisation by end
   1999: Heinz Cronimund
President Marketing Services Product Unit (PU)
   Customer Support: Chris Sheppard
EVP, Transition Support: Ruben Ornstein

European Liaison Office
Rue Froissart 123-133, Bte 29, B-1040 Brussels, Belgium
Tel: (+32 2) 233 11 61   Fax: (+32 2) 233 11 62

Senior Vice President (SVP), Delegate to EU, UNIFE:
   Klaus Milz

Corporate staff officers and SVPs
CEO's office: U Rudolph, M Sefer, E Gartner
Corporate Communications: H Tjan
Group Marketing: Peter Albexon
Human Resources: Ian Butler
Legal Affairs: D Raepple
Representation, Public Affairs: Klaus Milz

Business Segments and Product Units
Chief Executives of PUs and Presidents of National
Transportation Companies (NTCs)
Customer Support: C Sheppard, NTC UK
Fixed Installations: M Leger, NTC Germany

Mass Transit
Innovia People Movers: R Betler, NTC North America
Incentro LRVs: Anders Larsson, NTC Germany
Movia metro vehicles: Andrew Lezala, NTC UK
TRS Total Rail Systems: K Rands, NTC UK

Main Line (ML)
Itino Commuter & Regional Trains: Michael Daum, NTC
   Germany
Crusaris Inter-City, Inter-Regional & High-Speed Trains:
   John Vinberg, NTC Sweden
Octeon & Blue Tiger Locomotives: Beat Müller, NTC
   Switzerland

Signalling: Peter Nottrodt, NTC UK

Systems & Components (S&C)
Bogies: Jürgen Fleischer, NTC Germany
Bodyshells: Phil Huston, NTC Germany
Converters: H Strasser, NTC Switzerland
Drives: Olof Persson, NTC Austria
Train Control & Communication: Par Astrom, NTC
   Sweden

Contracts: The Adtranz and Evans Deakin joint venture, Walkers-Adtranz Pty Ltd has been awarded a contract for 12 electric railcars in Brisbane. The Adtranz-designed vehicles will be built at the Evans Deakin's Walkers and Adtranz factories in Maryborough, Queensland, with the electric propulsion and control equipment from Adtranz in Sweden. A private consortium, Airtrain Citilink Ltd will build, own and operate the link which will serve Brisbane airport's domestic and international terminals. Trains will run every 15 minutes to the city and through to the Gold Coast every 30 minutes. The new vehicles will be similar to Queensland Rail's Intercity Multiple Units and will incorporate IGBT technology. The contract is due for completion in 2002. Adtranz Australia is part of the Brisbane Light Rail Consortium set to reintroduce trams into Queensland.

UPDATED

AnsaldoBreda

Ansaldo Trasporti SpA
Via Argine 425, I-80147 Naples, Italy
Tel: (+39 081) 24 31 11   Fax: (+39 081) 243 26 98
Chair: Luciano Cravarolo
Vice Chairman: Rodolfo De Dominicis
Chief Executive Officer: Luigi Roth
Directors
   Systems: Claudio Artusi
   Turnkey Vehicles & Power Supply: Fausto Cutuli

Subsidiary companies
Ansaldo Signal NV, Netherlands (controls Ansaldo
   Segnalamento Ferroviario, Italy)

Background: The transfer was completed in 1997 of Breda Costruzione Ferroviarie and Bredamenarinibus to the Finmeccanica Group, forming a conglomerate made up of Ansaldo and Breda. The companies in the signalling sector merged into Ansaldo Signal NV (AT Signal System, AT Signalling, CSEE Transport, Ansaldo Segnalamento Ferroviario, Union Switch & Signal).

Products: Electric propulsion equipment; AC and DC traction motors; electronic converters and controls; auxiliary apparatus.

Contracts: A turnkey contract has been signed for a 15 km automated LRT system in Copenhagen with 15 stops. The line links Norreport in the centre with Orestaden and Lergravsparken. The rolling stock fleet will consist of 19 driverless vehicles with IGBT inverter control.
   Four E86 metre-gauge emus have gone into service on the Trento–Malè line, Italy, with traction equipment by Ansaldo. AMT Genoa awarded Ansaldo a turnkey contract for the first section of its light rail system. The contract included electrification equipment, signalling and automation systems, as well as articulated LRVs with chopper control.

AnsaldoBreda LRV for Midland Metro Line 1, Birmingham   *1999*/0058310

Ansaldo was responsible for the electrical and other technical aspects of the Lima metro.
   In 1993 Ansaldo was awarded a turnkey contract, in association with Laing Civil Construction, for construction of Line 1 of the Midland Metro in Birmingham, UK. The consortium is called Altram and the contract for the 20 km route includes provision of 15 chopper-controlled LRVs, as well as the power supply, signalling and automation systems. Services are due to start in 1999.
   Ansaldo is also involved in the Manchester Metrolink extension.
   Oslo Sporveier has taken delivery of 17 articulated

LRVs with IGBT inverter drive. They have low floors and seat 96 with 122 standing; they are being built jointly by Ansaldo and Firema (qv). Each car is mounted on four bogies, each having two asynchronous traction motors; top speed is 80 km/h and floor height 350 mm. The cars are of the same type as those being supplied for Line 1 of the Midland Metro.
   NSB Norway has awarded Ansaldo a contract for the delivery of 36 emus for local traffic.

UPDATED

RAIL AND BUS COMPONENTS AND SUBASSEMBLIES

Fiberline

Fiberline Composites A/S
Nr Bjertvej 88, DK-6000 Kolding, Denmark
Tel: (+45 75) 56 53 33   Fax: (+45 75) 56 52 81
e-mail: fiberline@fiberline.com
www: www.fiberline.com
Sales Manager: Stig Krogh Pedersen

Products: Lightweight corrosion-resistant GRP profiles for rail vehicles.

Contracts: Include the supply of exterior panels for Talent dmus built by Bombardier Transportation for German Rail (DB AG).

NEW ENTRY

Fuji Electric

Fuji Electric Co Ltd
12-1 Yurakucho 1-chome, Chiyodaku, Tokyo 100, Japan
Tel: (+81 3) 32 11 71 11   Fax: (+81 3) 55 38 78 03
e-mail: info@fujielectric.co.jp
www: www.fujielectric.co.jp

Background: The Transportation & Defense Systems Division of Fuji Electric falls within the company's Systems Group.

Products: Linear motor-drive door systems for rail vehicles.

NEW ENTRY

Hodgson and Hodgson

Hodgson and Hodgson Group Ltd
Winnington Hall Mews, Northwich CW8 4DU, UK
Tel: (+44 1606) 765 93   Fax: (+44 1606) 743 15
Managing Director: G Balshaw-Jones
Operations Director: J Roberts
General Manager and Director – Acoustic: N Grundy
General Manager and Director – Thermal: P Rollinson
Export Sales Manager: E Fitzpatrick
Technical Manager: P Eade

Subsidiaries
Hodgson and Hodgson Ltd
Nevill Thompson Ltd
Ecomax Acoustics Ltd
Acoustic Design Ltd

Products: Thermal and acoustic services for bus and railway traction units, rolling stock and associated buildings. Consultancy, design, manufacture and supply of finished products or components, including just-in-time or 'kan ban' requirements.

Contracts: Recent projects have included Waterloo Eurostar Terminal (buildings), St. Petersburg Rail Terminal (buildings), Barrat Housing Project (railside development), Eurotram (complete vehicle), Europa Transrapid (complete vehicle), MTRC Hong Kong (complete vehicle), Arlanda Stockholm (complete vehicle), Juniper, Turbostar and Electrostar (rolling stock), Brush Engines (traction units), Hestair Duple and Plaxton (engine/exhaust jacketing), Eurotram (complete vehicle).

NEW ENTRY

HP

HP Srl
A Westinghouse Air Brake Company
Viale Regina Pacis 296, I-41049 Sassuolo, Modena, Italy
Tel: (+39 0536) 80 64 41   Fax: (+39 0536) 80 17 89
e-mail: hpdoors@sirnet.it
Managing Director: Luigi Camellini
Export Manager: Vinicio Mathis

Products: Sliding, slide-glide and plug doors for bus and rail vehicles, featuring infra-red sensitive edge and other passenger protection devices, body-end fireproof doors, both pneumatic and electric drive units with control electronics, mobile steps, bridgeplates and bus ramps.

Contracts: Recent orders include electric sliding plug doors for the Copenhagen automated metro, entrance doors, body-end fire doors and bridgeplates for bilevel commuter trains (TAF) for FS, all-electric slide-glide doors for citybuses, bus ramps, powered covers for couplers.

UPDATED

Kaba Gilgen

Kaba Gilgen AG
Freiburgstrasse 34, CH-3150 Schwarzenburg, Switzerland
Tel: (+41 31) 734 41 11   Fax: (+41 31) 734 44 75
Sales Director: Konrad Zweifel

Project Director, Platform Screen Doors:
  Hans Kráhenbühl

Products: Automatic train door systems synchronised with platform screen doors.

NEW ENTRY

Metra Blansko

Metra Blansko as
Hybešova 53, CZ-678 23 Blansko, Czech Republic
Tel: (+420 506) 49 41 15   Fax: (+420 506) 49 41 45
www: www.metra.cz

Products: On-train interior and exterior dot matrix and LED display systems.

Contracts: Include provision of information systems for Czech Railways Class 471 double-deck emu vehicles and for new metro cars for Prague.

NEW ENTRY

Nizhnedneprovsky

Nizhnedneprovsky Tube Rolling Plant
21 Stoletov St, Dnepropetrovsk 320060, Ukraine
Tel: (+380 0562) 20 73 01/20 73 90
Fax: (+380 0562) 27 16 43/23 05 45
Vice Director of Foreign Economic Relations:
  Dr Mikhail Staroseletsky
Head of Communications: Svetlana Chernikova

Background: Nizhnedneprovsky Tube Rolling Plant has been manufacturing wheels and tyres for over 60 years.

Products: Manufacture and supply of more than 50 sizes of wheels and tyres for emus, LRVs, metro cars, trainsets, locomotives and freight wagons. Steel for the wheels and tyres is produced in the company's open-hearth furnaces and is refined for resistance to fatigue and brittleness.

Contracts: Include supply of wheels and tyres to 36 countries including former CIS countries, Bangladesh, China, France, Germany, India, Italy and Tanzania.

NEW ENTRY

Nortrade

Nortrade srl, Railway Division, Cacciagrande, I-58040 Tirli (GR), Italy
Tel: (+39 0564) 94 42 03   Fax: (+39 0564) 94 41 13
e-mail: railway@nortrade.it
www: www.nortrade.it

Commercial Director: Marco Galleri

Products: Heating, ventilation and air conditioning systems and equipment for drivers' cabs and passenger vehicle interiors.

NEW ENTRY

Schindler Technik

Schindler Technik AG
CH-9423 Altenrhein, Switzerland
Tel: (+41 71) 858 43 53   Fax: (+41 71) 858 44 20
Product Manager, Components: Arthur Schläpter

Background: Schindler Technik AG remains within the Schindler Group following the 1998 acquisition by Adtranz of the company's Pratteln-based rail vehicle manufacturing division, Schindler Waggon AG.

Products: Seats, luggage racks, toilet modules and interior fittings for rail vehicles. Schindler Technik also produces complete interior modules of composite materials for the refurbishment of existing rail vehicles. See also Rail Vehicles and Traction Equipment section.

NEW ENTRY

Siemens SGP Verkehrstechnik GmbH

Bogie Division

Eggenburger Strasse 31, 8021 Graz, Austria
Tel: (+43 316) 59 46 05 11   Fax: (+43 316) 59 45 35 11
Director: Dipl Ing Hans M Schabert
Sales Manager: Dipl Ing Alf Windeck
Engineering Manager: Dipl Ing Hans Hoedl

Background: Since 1996 all bogie manufacturing activities within Siemens Transportation Group have been concentrated in the Bogie Division of Siemens SGP in Graz, Austria. Bogies formerly designed and manufactured by Duewag (qv) are now manufactured by Siemens SGP.

Products: Bogie development, design and construction for light rail, mass transit and main line rolling stock; motor and trailer bogies for both low-floor light rail applications (360 mm) and medium-height (550 mm); motor and trailer bogies for high-floor urban rail applications (1,000 mm); bogies for metro and suburban rail cars; single-axle bogies.

Siemens SGP also produces SF5000 bogies for metro trains, emus and dmus.

Contracts: The bogie division of Siemens SGP Verkehrstechnik has developed and delivered 432 motor and trailer SF2000 bogies for Taipei metro. The bogies have air suspension and disc brakes. A further 210 SF2000 motor and trailer bogies with resilient wheels have been delivered for the Bangkok rapid transit system. Delivered to Shanghai for Line 2 of the metro were 436 SF2100 motor and trailer bogies, and SF2100 bogies went to MTRC Hong Kong.

Other light rail contracts include delivery of bogies to undertakings in Erfurt, Bielefeld, Frankfurt, Dortmund, Halle, Dresden, Leipzig, Hannover, Tuen Mun (Hong Kong), Tunis, St Etienne and Salt Lake City.

Low-floor motor and trailer bogies have been modified to fit the narrow-gauge system of De Lijn, Belgium.

Production: 1,500 bogies were delivered in 1997/98.

Developments: A new bearing design has been incorporated into 128 metro motor SF2100 bogies for Tren Urbano, San Juan, Puerto Rico. The new bogies for Stuttgart's DT810 tramcars have been redesigned for parallel drives instead of longitudinal drive.

UPDATED

ZF

Friedrichshafen AG
D-88038 Friedrichshafen, Germany
Tel: (+49 7541) 770   Fax: (+49 7541) 77 29 48

Products: Helical, hypoid and bevel gear axle drive units for fully or partially suspended drives for rail vehicles; input couplings, axle gearboxes and flexible axle couplings for LRVs, multiple-unit trains and locomotives; transmissions for diesel railcars; special transmissions (including planetary wheel hub drives) for low-floor vehicles; custom-designed gears.

Developments: Complete drive lines for dmu applications; new low-floor concepts for LRVs; axle-mounted units for diesel/electric locomotives.

NEW ENTRY

BUSES - CHASSIS, INTEGRALS AND BODIES

Anadolu

Anadolu Otomotiv Sanayi ve Ticaret AS
Ankara Asfalti Uzeri, Kartal, TR-81412 Istanbul, Turkey

Products: Light commercial vehicles, including midibuses, built under licence from Isuzu. A 7 m midibus is offered seating between 22 and 27 passengers. The urban version can carry up to 41, including standees.

Contracts: Include exports to Poland.

NEW ENTRY

Ayats

Carrocerias Ayats SA
Portage Can Call, km 1, E-17401 Arbucies (Girona), Spain

Products: Integral buses and coaches, in co-operation with MAN

Range
AB 120: a 12 m urban bus for l00 passengers
Venus: an 8.4 m coach for 32 passengers
Atlas: a high-deck coach for 55 passengers
Bravo: a high-deck lounge coach for 60 passengers
Bravo 1: a double-deck coach for 74 passengers.

NEW ENTRY

Beulas

Beulas SA
C/Riera Xica s/n, E-17401 Arbucies (Girona), Spain

Products: *Stergo,* a 12 m coach on Eurorider chassis.

NEW ENTRY

DAF

DAF Bus SB220GSLF Plaxton-bodied LPG-powered bus (Andrew Jarosz)
***1999**/0058313*

Dennis

First example of the Dennis Mini Pointer Dart is with Springfield of Wigan (Andrew Jarosz)
***1999**/0058315*

Dörteller

Dörteller Otomotiv Sanay ve Ticaret AS
Ankara Yolu, Kastel Kavsayi No 17 pk 12, 16450 Kestel-Bursa, Turkey

Products: Bus and coach bodies, mainly on MAN chassis.

Range
7 m minibus on Isuzu chassis.
10.2 m midibus on MAN 11 230 HOCL chassis.
Prens: a 12 m high-deck coach.
Kral: a 12 m double-decker coach.

Contracts: Include export of buses to Gambia and coaches to Syria.

NEW ENTRY

EA KFB

EA Karosserie-und Fahrzeugbau Gera GmbH
Siemensstrasse 19, D-07546 Gera, Germany

Background: Associated with Ernst Auwärter of Steinenbronn

Products: Bodywork for mini- and midibuses.

Range: Includes *City Shuttle*, an urban microbus (5.5 m) based on the Sevel van (Fiat/PSA); *Sunny Boy City*, a 7.3 m midibus for 23 passengers, based on the IVECO Daily; *Sunny Boy*, a 6.9 m dual-purpose bus for 19 passengers based on the IVECO Daily 45.10; *Euroskate HD 210*, a 9.8 m coach for 34 passengers, based on the Volvo B6 chassis.

NEW ENTRY

Eurobus

Eurobus doo
Zeleni Trg 3, Zagreb, Croatia

Products: Bus and coach bodies.

Range: Includes the *AM117G*, an 11.6 m urban transit bus; *AV120L*, a 12 m interurban bus; *AV120*, a 12 m high-deck coach; and the *AV120D*, a double-deck coach on Volvo B12 chassis.

Contracts: Include supply of buses for ZET Zagreb on MAN chassis.

NEW ENTRY

Indcar

Industrial Carrocera Arbuciense SA
Poligono Industrial Torres Pujals 4, E-17401 Arbucies
(Girona), Spain

Products: Bodywork for mini- and midibuses.

Range: Includes the *Mago*, a 7.4 m urban minibus, seating 30, on Iveco 59.12 chassis and *Pive Car*, a dual-purpose bus, 6.9 or 7.2 m, seating 19 or 21 passengers on Iveco 45.10 chassis.

NEW ENTRY

Irizar

Developments: In 1998 major extensions were made to bring the manufacture into one factory. Further installations during 1999 are expected to raise capacity to 1,100 units a year. Irizar works exclusively with Scania in Austria, Belgium, France, Germany, Holland, Ireland, UK and the Nordic countries and during 1998 500 bodies were produced. It is supplying bodywork on several makes of chassis to the Spanish market and is active in over 30 markets. Joint ventures have been set up in Tianjin (China), Rabat (Morocco, with DAF importer) and with Ciao (Brazil). Irizar is also building on Spartan (USA) chassis and selling to Metrotrans, USA.

UPDATED

Macchi

Macchi Fratelli Carozzeri SpA
PO Box 255, Via 1 Maggio, I-21045 Gazzada-Schianno,
Varese, Italy
Tel: (+39 0332) 87 04 40   Fax: (+39 0332) 87 08 70
Part of the Socimi Group

Products: Bus bodies, mainly on Mercedes-Benz chassis.

Range: Includes the *URL 3*, a 12 m low-floor bus for 110 passengers and an articulated 18 m low-floor bus, carrying up to 116.

Production: In 1995 this was 72.

UPDATED

MAXIBUS

Metalbus Ind Metalurgica Ltda
Rua Vereador Dionisio Sandi, 251 B Santa Catarina-
Caxias do Sul - RS - Brazil 95030-760
Tel/Fax: (+55 54) 211 35 55

Products: Bus bodies.

Range
Micro: a midibus with up to 34 seats based on Mercedes-Benz 814 and other chassis.
Maxibus: an urban bus, length varying between 10.8 and 12 m according to chassis, available on Volvo B58, various Mercedes-Benz, Ford and Volkswagen chassis. Various interior layouts available.

NEW ENTRY

Obradors

Obradors/Fabus SA
Apartado Correos 443, E-08420 Manresa, Spain

Background: Founded in 1932.

Products: Bus and coach bodies.

Range: Includes the *22*, a 7 m bus seating 22 on MAN 8.153HOCL chassis; the *Prisma 28*, an 8 m bus on MAN 8.153HOCL chassis, seating 28; the *Prisma 35* 12 m bus, seating 55; and the *Prisma 77*, an 18 m articulated bus seating 77, on MAN chassis.

NEW ENTRY

Renault

Renault VI
40 rue Pasteur, PO Box 302, F-92156 Suresnes Cedex,
France
Tel: (+33 1) 40 99 71 11   Fax: (+33 1) 40 99 75 88
www: www.renault.com.

Chairman and Chief Executive: Patric Faure
Senior Executive Vice President: Odile Desforges

UPDATED

Temsa

Temsa AS
Büyk Istanbul Otogari, 34200
Bayrampasa, Istanbul, Turkey

Products: Bus and coach chassis and bodies.

Developments: The *Prestij* midibus has been announced. It is 7 m long and 2.22 m wide and seats up to 28. It is powered by a choice of Mitsubishi 4D34-2A direct injection or Mitsubishi 4D34-2AT4 turbocharged engine, driving through a five-speed manual transmission.

UPDATED

New Temsa Prestij midibus
1999/0058309

Trouillet

Trouillet Constructeur
Zone d'Active, F-01340 Attignatt, France

Background: Founded in 1988, took over production from Chardon, France.

Products: Bus bodywork.

Range: Includes the *Urbat 20*, a low-floor 5.6 m minibus seating 20, based on the Renault Master; the *Urbain*, a 7.1 m midibus, carrying 39; and the *Asturias*, a dual-purpose 7.5 m minicoach, seating 27, based on the Mercedes-Benz 814-1120.

NEW ENTRY

SIGNALLING, COMMUNICATIONS AND TRAFFIC CONTROL EQUIPMENT

Ikusi

Angel Iglesias SA
30 (Martutene), Apartado 1320, E-20080 San Sebastián, Spain
Tel:(+34 943) 45 08 00   Fax:(+34 943) 46 96 91

Products: Communications and information and help-point systems.
 Ikusi's Facility Management Unit has developed a new video interphone system, VIK-10, which started operating in the Catalonian region of Spain in 1998. It is a hands-free system which involves locating information posts next to ticket machines in stations, offering information and emergency help.

NEW ENTRY

CONSULTANCY AND CONTRACTING SERVICES

ScanRail Consult

Pilestraede 58, DK-1112 Copenhagen, Denmark
Tel. (+45) 33 76 50 05 ext 15555
Fax (+45) 33 76 50 61
Chairman of the Board: Erik Elsborg
Director: Preben Olesen

Capability: ScanRail Consult is an independent organisation within the Danish National Railway Agency with approximately 400 engineers, planners, strategic business consultants and architects. ScanRail Consult covers a wide range of strategic planning, transport management and mechanical expertise related to railway systems.
 Competence areas include: planning and design, supervision and rehabilitation, feasibility studies and cost/benefit analyses, construction management, project management, quality and environmental management, validation and safety assessment, management and training, business and management consultancy within transport and railways, consultancy services for restructuring and commercialisation of railways and transport related businesses.
 ScanRail Consult is actively taking part in international research and development within its competence areas. Furthermore, ScanRail Consult assists the European Commission, UIC and ERRI in the development of European codes and standards for railway systems.

Projects: Some of ScanRail Consult's current and recent projects are:
ERTMS: A project which will assess the viability of establishing a Traffic Management System on selected routes in the countries of central and eastern Europe.
European Commission: The elaboration of a Technology Whitebook for the future train and railways systems in Europe; participating in projects under the 4th Framework Programme and providing expert assistance under the 5th Framework Programme; and technical support to UIC and ERRI.
 ScanRail Consult is supplying consultancy services in the Nordic countries, eastern Europe and the Baltics. In Denmark all planning and engineering for the Danish National Railway Agency and the Danish Ministry of Transport is part of ScanRail Consult's total project portfolio. This includes building new and upgrading existing lines and construction of high-speed main lines.
 ScanRail Consult is also rendering consultancy services to the building of the Øresund Fixed Link (bridge and tunnel) between Denmark and Sweden. ScanRail Consult has played a significant role as consultant on the railway part of the Great Belt Link.

UPDATED

Index

Printed and bound in Great Britain by Butler & Tanner Ltd, Frome and London